Y0-BQN-829

Small Arms of the World

**THE BASIC MANUAL
OF
MILITARY SMALL ARMS**

SMALL ARMS OF THE WORLD

THE BASIC MANUAL OF MILITARY SMALL ARMS

American—Soviet—British—Czech—German

French—Belgian—Italian—Swiss—Japanese

and all other important nations

by

W. H. B. SMITH

Author of Book of Pistols and Revolvers; Book of Rifles; Walther Pistols; Mauser Rifles and Pistols; Mannlicher Rifles and Pistols; Gas, Air, and Spring Guns; etc.

and

JOSEPH E. SMITH

Army Materiel Command
United States Army

THE STACKPOLE COMPANY

Harrisburg, Pennsylvania

First Edition
First printing, December 1943
Second printing, January 1944

Second Edition, Revised
First printing, February 1944
Second printing, April 1944
Third printing, October 1944
Fourth printing, March 1945

Third Edition, Revised and enlarged
First printing, October 1945

Fourth Edition, Revised and enlarged
First printing, March 1948
Second printing, April 1949
Third printing, August 1951
Fourth printing, June 1952
Fifth printing, February 1953

Fifth Edition, Revised and enlarged
First printing, January 1955
Second printing, June 1955
Third printing, February 1957

Sixth Edition, Revised and enlarged
First printing, January 1960

Seventh Edition, Revised and enlarged
First printing, July 1962

Library of Congress Catalog Card Number: 62-18587

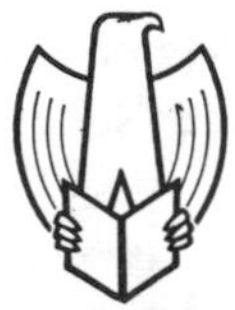

Printed in the United States of America
by
The Telegraph Press
Established 1831
Harrisburg, Pennsylvania

Author's Preface

Science knows neither nationalities nor boundaries. The power for peace we held from 1945 to 1950 because atomic bomb possession was ours alone has been dissipated by the developments in Russia since then. The monopoly is a monopoly no longer. And it is inevitable that within the next few years even the small nations will have evolved processes and plants to produce atomic and hydrogen weapons.

In the foreseeable future, only our capacity for immediate and massive retaliation can protect our Allies and ourselves from the hazards of the A-Bomb and the H-Bomb. Not to mention far worse horrors in the field of bacteriological warfare and other still nameless weapons of mass destruction; and the mechanical means to deliver them.

As science of this order advances, we find ourselves and the Soviets approaching a position of stalemate—a position we can only hope will lead toward some rational solution of the Free World's precarious state.

Under these circumstances, every potential aggressor hesitates at the thought of using the *ultimate* weapon. We saw it happen in World War II when the Germans even under Hitler held in check vast quantities of deadly gas because of well-justified fear of the retaliation its use would swiftly bring upon them.

And here, in the opinions of highly qualified observers who have discussed such matters with the author, lies an increasing necessity for concentrating more thought and attention on conventional armed strength, on *advanced* forms of conventional weapons and on the individuals who must use them.

From a manpower standpoint we cannot hope to match the might of the Soviets. In an era of atomic stalemate that fact can place us at a great psychological disadvantage. Unless we maintain the bulwark—the *conventional* armed might of all those whose borders adjoin areas of potential aggression, we can inevitably look for the Communist-inspired groups to seize by conventional arms and infiltration ever-increasing sections of freedom loving territory.

It follows, therefore, that we must keep abreast of world developments in the field of small arms even while we explore endlessly the fields of electronics, guided missiles and mass destructive instrumentalities.

History, if we may be trite for a moment, repeats itself quite as much in the field of firearms as in anything else. But methods do change. Processes change. Production methods change.

An instance may be found in the submachine gun—or machine pistol as it is commonly known abroad. As produced by the German, Bergmann, in 1918 it was a heavy, clumsy but highly efficient weapon of the truest simplicity. As produced in the United States in 1928 as the Thompson submachine gun it was still a highly efficient weapon —though not the miracle arm that publicity made it— though it then appeared as a costly, complicated piece of precision machinery. In 1938 it appeared as the equally deadly and efficient Schmeisser MP, designed now for relatively low-cost, high-speed manufacture. The British version, the incredibly cheap and simple British Sten, followed.

The Russian MP's from 1940 on developed their versions in the field of extremely low cost, yet reliable and deadly efficient "burp" guns. They extended the use of this weapon far beyond that of any of the Western powers, issuing it in huge numbers to replace pistols and even rifles at close quarters.

A glance at Part I (Historical) of this work will disclose, pictorially, proof that the Soviets have not only furnished such arms of their own manufacture to the forces of world aggression, but have also influenced design and manufacture in other countries not yet under their direct control.

In fact, the "burp" or "tommy" gun has become almost a symbol of Communist military advance. Where you find Communist violence breaking out anywhere in the world, there you find the low-cost submachine gun. Sometimes, as in Korea and Indo-China, it is the Russian-made product. Sometimes as in Guatemala it is from Russian controlled World War II captured equipment, or is the product of modern satellite factories. Always it is in evidence. And seldom indeed is it the product of American or Allied manufacture.

Part I of this work is an endeavor to compress the highlights of firearms history into a reasonably continuous outline. It must be emphasized that it is, however, merely an *outline*. Books can be—and many have been—written on any of hundreds of phases of arms or their development. The subject is well nigh inexhaustible. There is no section which the author personally could not have expanded into a book-size volume from his personal files; and except in the field of current and contemporary weapons he makes no pretense to particularly exhaustive knowledge.

Where parallels between the old and the new exist, an attempt has been made to indicate them. Where future potentials are to be found in past developments, an attempt similarly has been made to point them out.

Any designer, manufacturer, or military technician who studies not only the successes but also the apparent failures of past developers can save himself time, energy, and money in the field of modern arms development. By applying new methods to the already established principles, we as a nation can and should avoid repeating past mistakes or duplicating previous developments.

The larger portion of this book has to do with current weapons, or those of comparatively recent manufacture.

In dealing with these in Part II, the intent has been to simplify and digest all the facts while still retaining accuracy and technical value.

Wherever possible, accurate contemporary drawings and illustrations have been used. In many instances it has been necessary or advisable to produce original expensive art work and photographs to tell the story simply and accurately. In every instance the author has worked from actual examples of the arms dealt with.

It must be pointed out here that no firearms ever get into continued production in original forms. The simplest pistol or rifle will go through dozens to hundreds of modifications before the basic production pattern is set; and even then after field tests further modifications still will be made.

As a result, the author has sought at all times to use *representative* photographs, dimensions, and weights; while arms collectors and enthusiasts as a class tend to garner in related pieces which are exceptions to the rule. If the sights, or the barrel lengths, or the magazine capacities, etc., of individual arms do not check with the data in this work, this is the explanation for the variation. Such variations will be minor in all cases.

This work endeavors to present pictorially all items of design which have come to the attention of the author, with the hope that they will be of value and assistance to all those engaged in the design, development, production, and use of such arms in our common defense.

It is in this spirit that it is here presented.

This book is respectfully dedicated to the various branches of the Armed Forces of the United States and our Allies without whose cooperation its preparation would have been a far more arduous labor than it has been.

Individual manufacturers, collectors, engineers, and technicians both here and abroad who have been helpful in its preparation are too numerous and too widespread for individual mention; but I know they share with the author the hope that this work will be of value to our and their mutual security and defense.

Part I—even though presented only in fragmentary outline—represents data from thousands of reliable sources over the past quarter century of first-hand contact and observation. Here, however, more direct credit can be given since many of the valued and even hallowed mementoes it pictures could have been presented only with the fullest cooperation of the U.S. Signal Corps and its technicians and of the officials and employees of The United States Military Academy and its Museum at West Point.

W. H. B. Smith

New York, N. Y.
December 1, 1954

Preface to the Seventh Edition

Not too many years ago most of us read opinions, frequently expressed in the Sunday pictorial sections of newspapers, news magazines, and even some service journals, that the day of the foot soldier and small arms was nearly over. Some of these opinions intimated that the expenditure of ten cents on the development of or procurement of new small arms would be a flagrant waste of the tax payer's hard-earned money. Recent events in Southeast Asia, which unfortunately could occur in many other areas of the world, bear out the wisdom of those who turned a deaf ear to the siren song of saving the taxpayer's money by ignoring the development and manufacture of conventional weapons. No rational individual denies the necessity of the maintenance and further development of an overawing nuclear power; a necessary adjunct to that power is the maintenance of strong ground forces armed with the most modern conventional weapons, and small arms are the base upon which the larger conventional weapons systems are built. The infantry must hold or the artillery, armor, and support services are lost. I therefore do not consider this book to be in any sense the testament of a lost or dying art; rather it is intended to be a record of a basic, highly essential, and very much alive branch of the weapons family.

I have been in the weapons business long enough to learn that it is not wise to make any all-inclusive claims regarding the accuracy of all the data given in this book. There are multitudes upon multitudes of different variations of weapons. Just at that point when you believe you have learned all there is to know about a certain type of weapon, some bright young collector will come walking in with a specimen which proves that you don't really know as much as you thought you did. It is a somewhat shattering experience for a gun crank and it has happened to me more times than I would like to tell. I will say only this; considering the size and scope of this book, I believe it to be as accurate as is possible for a book of this type to be.

There are many points in relation to characteristics data which have to be considered when a high degree of accuracy is prerequisite. Most countries use the metric system of weights and measurements; these must be mathematically converted to render them in English measurements. Variations will appear which are the direct result of the number of decimal places used in working out a conversion. Variations in weights of weapons reported in different publications are common. There are two basic reasons for this situation: weights are frequently given, even in the manuals of various countries, which unfortunately do not make clear whether loaded or empty weight is meant, or whether the weight includes a sling and accessories, etc. The second factor applies to weapons with wooden stocks and fittings. These weapons will vary in weight between a humid climate and a dry one and even between a humid day and a dry day in the same area. Another area of confusion lies in muzzle velocity figures. There are actually two types of velocity figures for small arms, instrumental velocity and muzzle velocity; and yet, in characteristics charts published by governments, private concerns, and manufacturers, many times the figures reported as muzzle velocities are actually instrumental velocities. The instrumental velocity is always a shade lower than the true muzzle velocity, since it is taken at a point some distance from the muzzle (usually 53 feet or 78 feet). To obtain a muzzle velocity from an instrumental velocity some calculating must be done and there are various formulas for this purpose.

It is the intention of the Stackpole Company and myself to continually improve this book and to correct any errors of fact that it may contain. I am therefore most grateful to those readers of the Sixth Edition who found and pointed out an error in that work. I have tried to answer all correspondents personally. Unfortunately in some cases this has not been possible because of the press of work.

The opinions expressed in the revised sections of this book are my own. They are, for the most part, limited to pointing out what the advantages and/or disadvantages of a particular system might be; I have tried to be absolutely objective. My opinions do not represent the official opinion of the Department of the Army, the Army Materiel Command, or any other agency of the United States Government.

I would like to acknowledge the great help of various individuals and organizations who have assisted me in the preparation of this revision both directly and indirectly. The following individuals and organizations of the Army Materiel Command, have been of great assistance:

Lieutenant General John H. Hinrichs, USA Retired, former Chief of Ordnance; Lieutenant General August Schomburg, Dr. Fred H. Carten, Mr. Thomas E. Cosgrove, and Mr. A. C. Bonkemeyer, Lt. Col. Robert G. Blaylock, Mr. Calvin B. Low, Lt. Col. Robert A. Fuller, Mr. L. C. Burden, and Mr. Daniel McDevitt. Springfield

Armory and especially Mr. Herman H. Hawthorne, Mr. E. H. Harvey, Mr. E. Letourneau, Mr. O. H. Von Lossnitzer, and Mr. R. Colby. Very special thanks are due to Mr. Joseph Penton of the Ordnance Corps Technical Information Office; Tom Nelson, of Alexandria, Virginia; Ludwig Olson of the National Rifle Association; Mr. Burton D. Munhall and Mr. H. P. White of the H. P. White Laboratory in Scarboro, Maryland; and to my wife who assisted with sympathy and typing.

There are many people who have supplied data to me over the past several years which has been helpful in this revision. Outstanding among them are: Mr. J. J. Reen of McLean, Virginia; Col. G. B. Jarrett, Curator of the U.S. Army Ordnance Museum at Aberdeen Proving Ground; Mr. Karl Kempf, and Mr. Robert Faris, all of Aberdeen, Maryland; Mr. Philip E. Valentini of Washington, D. C.; Mr. Martin Hawkins of Arlington, Virginia; Mr. Richard Maguire of Detroit, Michigan; and Mr. Donald Bady of New York City.

The following arms manufacturers and arms dealers have been most helpful:

Fabrique Nationale of Herstal, Belgium
Dansk Industri Syndikat of Copenhagen, Denmark
Interarmco of Alexandria, Virginia
BSA Guns Ltd., of Shirley Solihull, Warwickshire, England.

JOSEPH E. SMITH

Vienna, Virginia
July 1962

CONTENTS

PART I. HISTORICAL

PART II. CURRENT WEAPONS

PART I

HISTORICAL

Chapter 1. Origins of Gunpowder and Firearms

GUNPOWDER

THE story of all modern projectile weapons begins, of course, with the first application of gunpowder as a projectile force. A study of all available source material shows definitely that in its obscure origins, gunpowder was known for a long time before it was used to hurl the earliest projectiles.

Who first discovered gunpowder—precisely when and where—under what conditions? No man can give a definite answer to any of those questions.

Ancient records have been mistranslated and quoted out of context to "prove" that the Chinese, for instance, used gunpowder before the time of Moses. These statements are commonly based on the Halhed translation of the Gentoo Code from the Sanskrit, a translation printed by the East India Company in 1776. Any scholarly analysis of the translation will show the twisting done by the translator to establish his case as for instance in the oft-quoted passage that "The Magistrate will not make war with any deceitful machine, or poisonous weapons, or with cannon or guns, or any kind of firearms." It is not until the 13th Century that we find anywhere in written records the use of terms which could reasonably be construed to mean "cannon," "guns," or "firearms."

It is possible to extract sentences from Plutarch's Life of Marcellus and also from Vitruvious to lead one to think that Archimedes was familiar with gunpowder, if the reader happens to be romantic rather than scientific. Valerius Flaccus can be quoted to show that the Brahmins tried to "reproduce thunder." In the Aeneid Virgil tells of a similar attempt by Salmoneous.

History is replete with proof that highly inflammable compounds were known and used in warfare from the earliest recorded times. Many such undoubtedly detonated at times or under given circumstances, just as gas and mine explosions occur today; and reports of such explosions undoubtedly account for most of the ambiguous statements which have been taken erroneously to mean an early knowledge of gunpowder itself.

If we explore the negative side of the matter, we find a tremendous body of evidence to show that gunpowder was neither known nor used before the 13th Century. "The Alexiad," the history of the Roman Emperor Alexius I, who reigned from 1081 to 1118, is a case in point. This work, written contemporaneously by the Emperor's daughter Anna, is accepted by qualified historians as perhaps the chief source of reliable data on the First Crusade and the Byzantine Empire. It lists numerous formulas for "Greek Fire." At no point, however, does it give any indication of a knowledge of gunpowder or any similar projectile or detonating substance. The unquestioned authority of "The Alexiad" completely disproves the efforts of some 19th Century French to establish that gunpowder was first carried to Europe by returning Crusaders who had learned of it from the Arabs.

Also high on the list of negative evidence is the extant report of the fabulous Ambassador Giovanni di Plan Carpin. This unusual man, whose very name is unknown to most historians, far outshone in real ability, knowledge, and experience the highly publicized Marco Polo. Carpin was a highly trained and seasoned soldier. He was thoroughly familiar with all the weapons of his period. In the year 1246 Pope Innocent IV commissioned him to travel to the Court of Genghis Khan, the Mongol conqueror, at Karakorum. The Great Khan was so impressed with Carpin that he permitted him to travel at will across the Mongol Empire. Carpin served as an observer with the Mongol armies in their campaigns against the Chinese, and he wrote in detail of the all but legendary siege of Kai-Fung Fu. Carpin's reports list systematically every type of weapon he saw. His accounts of the use of "balista," the artillery of the day, as well as of all varieties of slings and bows are classic. In dealing with varieties of Greek Fire, he told in detail of the assault and burning of cities by use of machines which hurled melted fat and tallow-loaded projectiles.

The first authenic manuscript known in which we find positive knowledge of gunpowder is the work originally ascribed to an unknown monk, Marcus Graecus. It is true that scholars can trace the original Greek manuscript to the year 846. However, the sections of this manuscript (Liber ignium ad comburendos bostes) which deal with Greek Fire and also with a *specific formula* for "ignis volans" (gunpowder) appear in Latin and were written not earlier than the middle of the 13th Century. Translations and comparisons of copies housed variously in museums at Paris, Munich, Nuremberg, and Oxford all help to establish this later date for the sections dealing with gunpowder. The "Liber ignium" gives 35 different formulas for gunpowder. It is noteworthy too in that it gives instructions for the manufacture of rockets. In passing it should be noted also that one formula specified "1 part quick sulphur, 2 parts willow charcoal, and 6 parts saltpeter"—a mixture which is actually too powerful for use in any known firearms of the 14th or even the 15th Centuries!

The next really positive references to gunpowder all

appear to derive directly or indirectly from the Graecus manuscript. One of these is an undated letter from a Spanish monk, Ferrarius, addressed to one "Anselm," and is in the Bodleian Library at Oxford. Another contemporaneous manuscript is the "Opus de mirbilibus mundi" credit to Bishop Albertus Magnus, (1193-1280). And finally, there is the classic Roger Bacon manuscript "Epistola de secretis operibus Artis et Naturae et de nullitate magiae" (Concerning the Marvelous Power of Art and Nature, and concerning the Nullity of Magic).

The Bacon manuscript was written in 1248 to the Bishop of Paris, William of Auvergne, and was in effect an answer by Bacon to charges that he was giving himself to the practice of magic and the black arts! This manuscript gave, for the first time that we know of, a description of the preparation of saltpeter, which is necessary to the production of refined gunpowder. His gunpowder formula of 7 parts of saltpeter, 5 of young hazelwood (or charcoal) and 5 of sulphur was long the military standard.

It should be noted, however, that Bacon makes no claim to having invented the mixture. In fact, he speaks of it as something then very well known, and talks of its use in fireworks. Moreover, while he suggests that an enemy might be "either blown up bodily or put to flight by the terror caused by the explosion," he seems to have had no awareness of the use of gunpowder for *firing projectiles*. No mention whatever is made of firearms as such.

There is no record of how or where Roger Bacon first learned of explosive mixtures. Since he spent some time in Spain, and since there are at the Escurial several ancient manuscripts dealing with chemical matters, it is possible he may have gathered something there. It is more likely, however, that the source was the Graecus manuscript, since even the most specific Escurial sources are vague by comparison with Bacon's own; while such celebrated Saracen sources as Nedj-id-din Hassan Abrammah show an awareness of the *ignition* factor of saltpeter but do not touch on its *explosive* use as Bacon did.

Passing mention must be made of the German monk Berthold Schwartz (or Bartholdus Niger) who in the past has often been credited with the invention of gunpowder at Freiberg. This monk lived from about 1310 to 1384. He was in fact one of the great experimenters of his time, and devoted great energy to the subject of casting cannons. From accounts and drawings of the period, it is evident that Schwartz was primarily an early-day precursor of the modern Krupps; and that his experimentation with explosives for use in cannon was responsible for the erroneous belief that he actually was the inventor of gunpowder. He opened a shop to cast bronze cannon at Venice late in life, and was condemned to death by the Senate of Venice when he insisted too volubly that he receive payment for work he had done on cannon designing.

Countless books have been written on the subject of the Origin of Gunpowder. Countless studies have been undertaken to prove or disprove them.

But when all the words have been read, when all the theories have been explored, when all the flights of conjecture and fancy have been weighed and all evidence analyzed and sifted, we come again always to the treatise of Roger Bacon, who himself disclaimed the invention. Nowhere else do we find an earlier unquestionable and incontrovertible statement on the subject: "Thus we may imitate thunder and lightning; for sulphur, nitre and charcoal, which by themselves produce no sensible effect, explode with great noise when closely confined and set on fire."

FIREARMS

Definition

Firearms may be defined as tubes used with a charge of gunpowder (or like explosive substance) to hurl projectiles. In their earliest forms as true projectile instruments, these hurled the same stone or metal balls, or variations of the spears and arrows, which were then in use for launching from bows, slings, ballistae and the like.

Flame Thowing Tubes

It is impossible to establish just when and where firearms as defined above were introduced. Tubes were used long before the advent of gunpowder to direct inflammable mixtures, much as the modern flame thrower does. "The Alexiad" specifies such use, for instance.

"Roman Candle" Tubes

The first use of gunpowder to launch objects without thought of penetration may well have been in the Far East. Both the Tartars and the Arabs are known to have made very early use of a variety of "Roman Candle" to start fires. These instruments were commonly hollow tubes of wood or bamboo. They were tightly wrapped around with hide or hemp or wire for strength. They were loaded from the muzzle with alternate charges of powder and an incendiary ball, often of tallow, though some seem to have been cloth saturated with crude petroleum. They were ignited at the muzzle, and as the fire worked around each ball it touched off the powder to launch the ball ahead. The German "Zeitschrift für historische Waffenkunde," a former learned society which

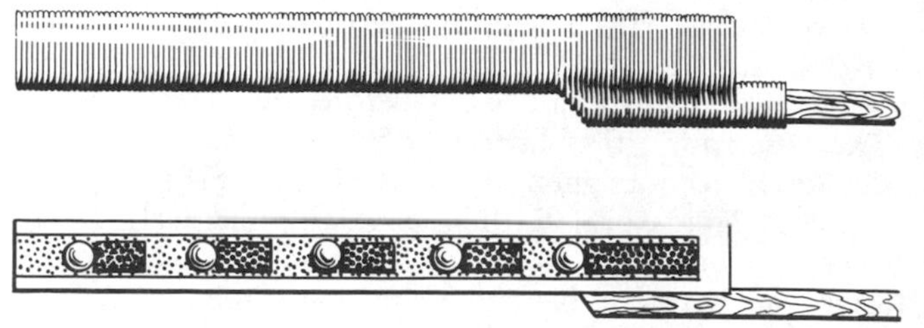

"Roman Candle" Tube. From a thirteenth century Saracen Manuscript.

went to great lengths to research ancient arms and armor, found mention in old Chinese annals authentically dated 1259 of this use of powder.

The Earliest Records

Early Saracen records have been translated to show that stone-throwing cannon were used in 1247 in the defense of Seville. However, the general evidence indicates that these were actually mechanically operated projectors—not gunpowder types.

German writers have made various claims that the town of Amberg had a cannon in the year 1301. This and similar claims have not been documented. The reports of many writers and researchers of the 19th Century indicating Flanders as the source of the origin of the first projectile gunpowder arms have been seriously questioned by later writers who had far better research facilities, notably Sir Charles Oman and Oscar Guttman.

The Manuscript of Walter de Millimete

The first contemporaneous illustration which can be fully authenticated showing an unquestionable gunpowder cannon is found in the Millimete Manuscript at Oxford. The illustrations on the manuscript show very fine illuminations of cannon. One vignette shows a soldier in armor firing a bottle shaped cannon at a fortress gate at close range. The gun itself is on a four-legged mount. From its muzzle projects a huge spear-like "bolt" of the pattern known as a "garrot" or "carreau" such as is shown in earlier illustrations dealing with mechanically launched projectors like the espringale. Smaller bolts of this type are shown at a later date being used in hand arms. Such "bolts" often had brass "feathers" to stabilize flight, patterned of course after the arrow, though many seem to have been used to impart rotation to the flying missile much in the manner that rifling does.

It must be noted that this manuscript is a dedicatory address Millimete gave to King Edward III upon accession to the throne in 1327. The text makes no mention whatever of the illustrated items. However, since we know that Edward III was among the earliest monarchs to employ cannon in battle, and since the authenticity of the manuscript is beyond question, the historical value is self evident.

Edward III

Shortly after he was crowned, Edward III led an army against the Scots. It is said that he had with him a group of cannoneers from Hainault, indicating that his guns came from Flanders. The weapons were apparently of the type shown in the Millimete manuscript, often spoken of as "pot-de-fer." Records of Ghent for the year 1313 indicate such weapons, while later records refer to their use at Metz in 1324. It is apparent therefore that Edward III used cannon, but did not develop them.

John Barbour's "The Metrical Life of Robert the Bruce" is the most often quoted source on this Scotch campaign, speaking of cannon as "crayks of war." The facts are in all probability accurate in general, though the careful historian must note that Barbour wrote late in life when he was Archdeacon of Aberdeen. He was only seven years old in 1327.

Many historians state that Edward III used two or three cannon at the battle of Crecy. This, too, may be true.

It is impossible to establish whether the hand gun or the artillery cannon was first used as a powder weapon. It is quite possible that the development may have been simultaneous. The construction and the loading and firing principles were the same for all types in the early stages of arms development. The ignition was the same.

In general the only source of recording knowledge in those days rested with the religious groups, more particularly with those in Europe, since few outside church circles could read or write. Moreover, as the era of record keeping developed early in the 14th Century, a new terminology built around the new weapons developed in various countries. The French records speak of "quenon" or "canon," for instance. The Lowlanders described them most often as "vogheleer." Among the Italians they were recorded as "bombardes." The German records still extant list them as "Büchsen."

There are very few firearms made during the early part of the 14th Century whose authenticity can be even vaguely established. However, art in the form of tap-

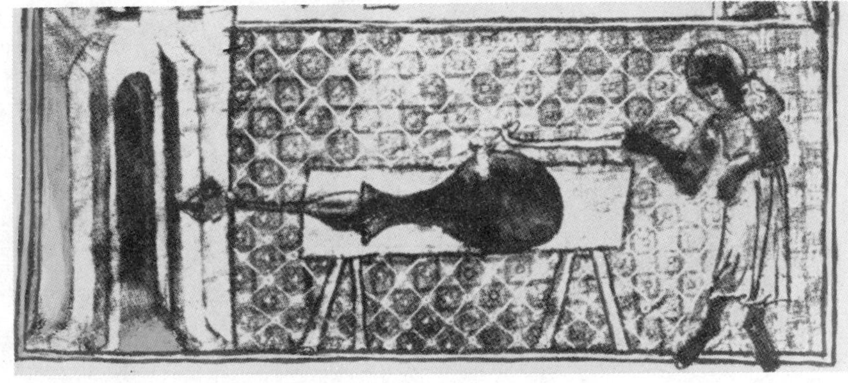

The oldest verifiable illustration of a weapon using gunpowder for hurling projectiles.
An illustration from the de Millimete Mss. executed in the year 1326 A.D.

estries, paintings, church frescoes and illustrative drawings was developed to a very high degree about this time, particularly in Italy and France. These art forms together with more detailed written records have enabled arms historians to correlate the terms in various countries, and thus to provide a pattern of continuity to show the development of firearms from this point on.

For the record, however, it must here be set forth that in the last century there were in existence in Italy two hand guns which historians of great ability believed to be the oldest then extant. The first of these was thoroughly discussed by German General Köhler in his comprehensive work on early arms "Entwicklung des Kriegswesens, etc." It was of bronze, ornamented with a Greek cross and oak leaves, bore the number 1322 (believed to indicate the date of manufacture) and the letters PPF. Köhler described it in his book published in 1887, though it had been described earlier (in 1847) by Count 'd' Arco who owned it at one time and also by the reliable Major Angelucci in his "Documenti inediti" published in Turin in 1869. This gun was stolen from the Monastery of St. Orsola at Mantua in 1849.

The second "sclopos" said to date from the early part of the 14th Century was a wrought iron piece having a very roughly finished barrel and shaft attachment which was understood to have been excavated from the ruins of ancient Monte Vermini castle in 1841. Assuming it to be genuine, this piece would date from at least 1341.

While these particular weapons are lost to historians, from this period on Italian records from unimpeachable sources verify the existence of their types; and from these records and those of other European countries we can establish a chronology of development accurate in every respect except that exact dates cannot also be provided. Some of these can be tied down to a given year, but in the main all but the official Annals and Chronicles can be assigned only to a period which may vary as much as 25 years. Of course, even in our own times it is often impossible to exceed that record on quite recent developments.

Chapter 2. Evolution of Firearms

PHASE I—THE CANNON LOCK

THE earliest firearms are classed as "Cannon Locks." These arms whether in the form of hand or artillery types were fired by holding a lighted coal or hot iron against powder placed over a touch hole at the rear of the barrel section. The flame flashed through the hole into the powder charge which had been loaded down the muzzle of the piece.

These were commonly made by casting brass, bronze, or similar alloy. Some were made of wrought iron. Many had straight bores, though others had clearly defined chambers. The hand types were usually attached to staffs or pikes. The heavier types used various forms of mounts ranging from cradles to carts.

Granulation was not known at this period. Gunpowder was actually a true powder. This required considerable wadding between charge and projectile to allow a build-up of gas pressure. The low saltpeter content of the mixtures also was a factor in slowing down combustion. The wads used were usually soft wood. Gas leakage around the wad naturally limited velocity and power.

The projectiles used are shown in profuse detail in many tapestries and manuscript illuminations. Balls of stone, iron, brass and even lead were used. Bolts—called variously "quarrels" and "garros a feu" were also employed. These bolts all developed from the crossbow types of missiles. They were made in a huge range of sizes for hand gun and siege gun work.

It is with these elementary firearms that our Chronology of Development begins.

When we remember that Italy was the best educated and most scientifically advanced country at this period, it is not strange that we find the best records in Italian archives. However, toward the middle of the century some authentic English records appear, most of the important ones indicating actual manufacture of the arms in the Lowlands (specifically Belgian areas which are still a source of export arms). French records at this period also become more specific and authoritative. Toward the close of the century the finest records of all become available as German manuscripts begin to chronicle the developments of that ever scientific and warlike Teuton mentality.

Early Italian Records

The most reliable sources of original material of the earliest days which the present author has been able to weed out of literally thousands of manuscripts, drawings, records and tapestries studied are as follows:

1324: *Archivo de Florence, reg. 23, De riformagioni, Page 65.* This record definitely establishes that various firearms were in general use in Florence at that time. It is obvious that the arms mentioned must have been in use for some time before this date, since such matters are not chronicled until well after all experimental stages have been passed.

1331: *Chronicles of Cividale.* This was an Italian town in Venezia. Its *Chronicon Extense* dated three years later also makes definite mention of hand guns (sclopetus).

1340: The famous artist Paolo del Maestro Neri began work in this year on a series of frescoes in a church near Sienna, Italy. The receipt signed by the artist upon receiving payment for completing the work is dated 1343. It is in the Library at Sienna today.

The Neri frescoes can still be seen, though they are

Cannon locks in military use. From the Italian Neri Frescoes dated 1343.

Wheel mounted cannon in siege. Defenders in tower are firing hand cannon locks. From Neri Frescoes.

Cannon lock drawing. From the English Burney Manuscript Number 169, Folio 127, dated 1469.

badly peeled. They are the most important records in the entire history of early firearms. These frescoes show clearly both land and naval warfare of the period. Besiegers are shown firing cannon against a castle in one panel. The defenders are shown using hand cannon and bows in defense.

The frescoes show guns of various types which are in all essentials identical with those shown in German manuscripts produced near the end of the 14th Century. By showing in the same panels the use of both siege and hand firearms, they establish historically that such developments were either parallel or very closely related.

1364: *Chronicles of Perugia.* These are important as showing the extent of firearms use at this period. They cite an order placed for "500 bombarde." The record shows that the specifications required that these hand arms must penetrate armor!

Early English Records

1347: Among the English records of early days only those of Thomas de Roldeston, Keeper of the King's Privy Wardrobe, are truly specific. He served during the period of Edward III. Items cover work on guns, purchase of gunpowder at 18 pence per pound, and substantial purchases of sulphur and saltpeter.

In other sources mention is made of the "ribauldequin" used by Edward III. This is one of the earliest types of multi-fire weapons which were the precursors of the machine gun. It consisted of several iron barrels arranged to fire simultaneously, and its earliest recorded use is in 1339.

1386: The first recorded use of the term "hand gun" is found in English records. The Chamberlain is recorded as having been sent three such by one Ralph Hutton.

Early German Records

The earliest true scientific approach to recording the progress of all firearms is found in German records. It is unlikely that the original gun as such was of German origin. There can be no question, however, that the most productive of the succeeding development work was done by them.

An instance in point is the *Codex Germanicus 600.* This is a manuscript in the Munich Museum. Some German authorities have dated it as far back as 1345. It is more likely that the date is that set by less prejudiced researchers—about 1390.

This manuscript translates "Directions for Preparation of Gunpowder. How to Load Guns and Discharge Them." It is extensive, detailed and scientific.

Many of the finest examples of German art, manuscript

Gun powder manufacture. From Codex Germanicus 600. Dated reliably 1390.

illumination, and tapestries dealing with early firearms were destroyed or looted during the period of the two World Wars in this century; so reference will be made here only generally to certain records which were unquestionably authenticated, or of which copies exist in accepted museums or libraries.

1389: The Vestaburg Inventory listed firearms, among them being "Handbüchsen" or hand firearms. Of course, this is again direct evidence that such arms were in use for a considerable time before the date of the Inventory, or at least had gone through the long experimental stages required in all scientific and mechanical developments.

1399: The *Tannenberger Büchse* is an actual hand gun excavated in 1849 at the site of a once powerful fortress. Vesta Tannenberg was a notorious robber stronghold in the late 14th Century. It was stormed in the year 1399 and every effort was made to destroy it utterly, quite as in the case of Carthage. For centuries tales about its very existence were considered legendary, so utterly was it obliterated.

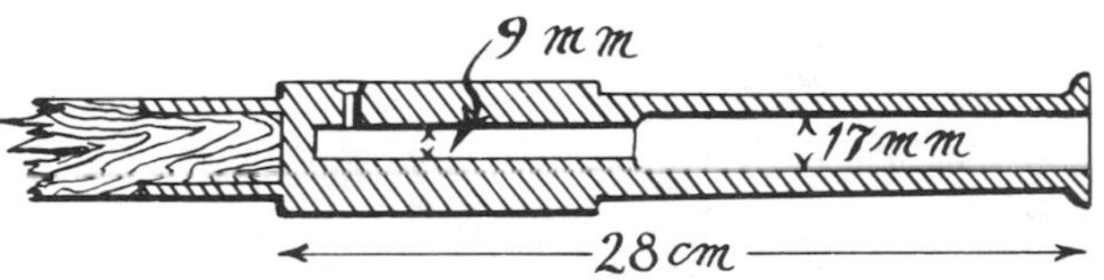

The Tannenberger Büchse in Section.

The gun itself is of cast bronze. Its design and construction is so superior to most authenticated arms of the period that scientists for a time related it to a much later date, but archeologists finally established the date satisfactorily.

Among other early German records meeting the qualifications given above may be mentioned the following: The *Gemeiner Regensburger Chronik*. Here is, for instance, an entry by a Ratisbon gunsmith delivering hand guns set in wood stocks, and weighing about 11 pounds each. In 1381 in the *Chronicles of Augsburg* are listed firearms purchased by the City Council to ward off expected attacks. *Chronicles of Nuremberg, Mohringen and Kaufbeuren* of this period all list firearms.

From 1396 to 1405 considerable research was recorded, notably the *Kriegsbuch Bellifortis* by Konrad Kyeser. This manuscript, Codex Ms. phil 63 at Göttingen

From contemporary fourteenth century drawings. Upper: Firing the cavalry Petronel cannon lock. Lower: Firing the infantry hand cannon.

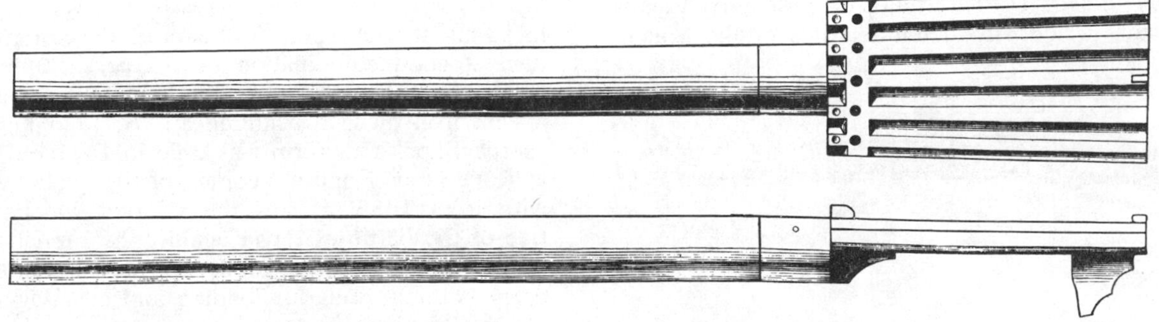

Upper: Five shot "Lade Büchse" with bronze barrels. Early German cannon lock. Lower: Early German Hakenbüchse for wall firing.

University covers in detail much of the transition period when the hand-fired "Cannon Lock" system was giving way to the next evolutionary step—the Matchlock.

This manuscript and others, *Codex 719 at Nuremberg* and *Codex 734 at Munich,* follows in detail the evolution of firearms at the time, particularly the shoulder-fired arms. Stocks are discussed in detail, and the one piece military stock is shown. Drilling methods were improved to provide tighter gas locks and better accuracy and range. Barrels, flash pans to protect the priming from wind and rain, recoil blocks—these and many other technical aspects are covered in detail.

The manuscripts and illuminations of this period show in great detail such items as multi-barrel guns which were the forerunner of the Gatling Guns. Two- and three-barreled arms are shown, both over-under and side-by-side types. There are guns to fire single balls. Others on the shotgun principle to fire a charge of shot. It is safe to say that every type of firearm in existence today was to some extent visualized and attempted in Germany in this period. The one thing that prevented great advances then was the lack of a suitable cartridge—a development which did not occur until five centuries later.

As the 14th Century drew to a close, primitive forms of a new firing mechanism began to appear, apparently developed in Burgundy. No advance in scientific method ever immediately wipes out the old methods, and so the Cannon Lock continued to be used far into the 15th Century. All early dates, therefore, must be taken as general except where otherwise specified with reference to new developments.

PHASE II—THE MATCHLOCK

Since the earliest times the ignition system in firearms has been called the "lock." The "Cannon Lock," as we have seen, required the shooter to touch a lighted coal or hot iron directly to the priming charge in order to fire.

The Matchlock was originally a very simple "C" shaped piece of metal pivoted to the side of the stock. It was split to grip a "slowmatch"—a cord generally made of hemp fiber treated with saltpeter and other chemicals to make it slow burning. It was commonly twisted and then held in shape by thread wrapped around it. The "match" burned at a rate of about 3 to 5 inches an hour.

This simple development revolutionized the use of firearms in its day. Up to the time of its introduction, sights were not used, since one hand had to be kept free to apply the burning coal. Field use under such conditions was all but impossible in hand arms. Only artillery was really practical.

With the Matchlock as initially introduced, the tip of the burning cord was held in the split iron holder, and could be pushed with the finger to bring the burning end into contact with the priming powder to fire the weapon. This made it possible to aim hand arms.

This revolutionary device was immediately seized upon by the soldiery of all nations, and development speedily brought it to its peak of possible perfection. The first positive record is found in the *Codex 3069 at Vienna* authentically dated 1411. Erlangen and also Vienna records of the period also detail features of the Matchlock; but it took some 50 years of development to produce a good combination of trigger, hammer and pan mechanism. The "C" form of holder was replaced with a bent iron piece resembling an "S," and known as the "serpentine." This form was used in 1471 by Edward IV at Ravenspur. English Yeomen of the Guard were armed with it in 1485. It was the weapon which turned the tide of the battle of Pavia against the French when used by the Spaniards. Swiss models of the era still in existence carry both ramrods for loading and cleaning needles for clearing the priming touch-hole.

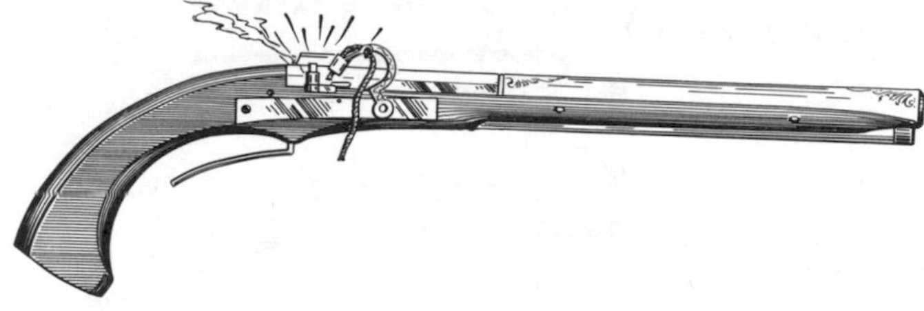

Original drawing from specimen early matchlock pistol. Showing ignition system.

From Codex Icon. 222, Munich. Harquebussier of Maximilian I with early matchlock.

The early developments of this lock included the addition of a sort of hammer spring. A button trigger was supplied. This feature of course speeded the ignition and made sighting still easier. At a later date the more formal trigger type was introduced.

The Merz Matchlock

Martin Merz was the most celebrated firearms authority of the time. A truly revolutionary form of the Matchlock was developed by him. It is shown in detail in the *Codex Germanicus 599* published in 1475.

This arm might have revolutionized warfare had its significance been grasped by the rulers of the day. It featured a lock plate covering a series of levers and springs which allowed use of a short sear. It brought the burning match forward away from the eye of the shooter, making aiming still easier. Like the Swiss matchlocks previously mentioned (which seem to have been developed from Merz' ideas) it carried both a cleaning needle and a ramrod. The importance of this latter item, which is meaningless to us in this day, cannot be overrated. It was not until 1698 that the iron ramrod below the barrel for ready field use in reloading was introduced. Prince Leopold I of Anhalt Dessau armed his forces with it. It was credited with playing a major part in providing the fire power which won the battle of Mollowitz in 1730! In addition to these other features, the Merz Matchlock had both front and rear sights, allowing a maximum of accurate aiming in those days when most arms did not have even a muzzle sight.

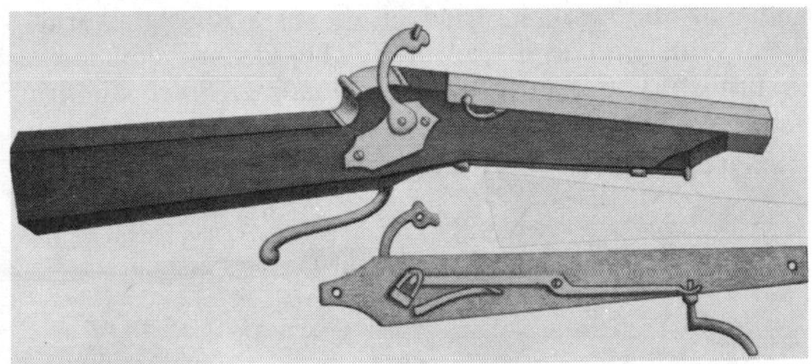

Merz matchlock and plate. From Codex Germanicus 599, published in 1475.

Had Merz been an unknown, the failure of the military to pick up his ideas would have been understandable; but in light of his standing it is one of the unsolved riddles of firearms history that they were so long overlooked.

Early use of matchlock in war. From Codex Germanicus 734.

Varieties of Matchlocks

The earliest form of the Matchlock, as we have seen, was merely a pivoted iron holder for the slowmatch which was pushed by the firer manually.

The Germans seem to have been the first to develop the next form already mentioned—the Button Lock. The cock or serpentine (equivalent to a hammer) was drawn back and held by a sear under spring pressure. Pushing a button released the cock and brought the lighted end of the match down on the priming. This was the standard military form used on all small arms until about 1520. It is shown in all the important arms research works of the time, such as the Arsenal Book of the Emperor Maximilian.

The next development was the most successful. It is used even to this day in some areas of Africa and Asia. This was the Pressure Lock. Cornelius Johnson, an English gunsmith, manufactured locks of this pattern as early as 1521 in the Tower of London, but available evidence again indicates the originals were probably German. This type in all its varieties consists essentially of a cock (equivalent of a hammer), a tumbler, sear, two flat springs and a hammer. Basically, it is the thumb-cocked "single action" system as shooters know it today. Pulling the trigger released the tumbler. It revolved 90 degrees to bring the match into contact with the priming.

The final form of the Matchlock was the "Snap Lock" which was in use in Europe in the 1570's and later. It was called by the Germans "light snapping lock" or in some forms "tinder lock." The names derived from the fact that instead of a long dangling slow match as in the regular Matchlock forms, this pattern held a small

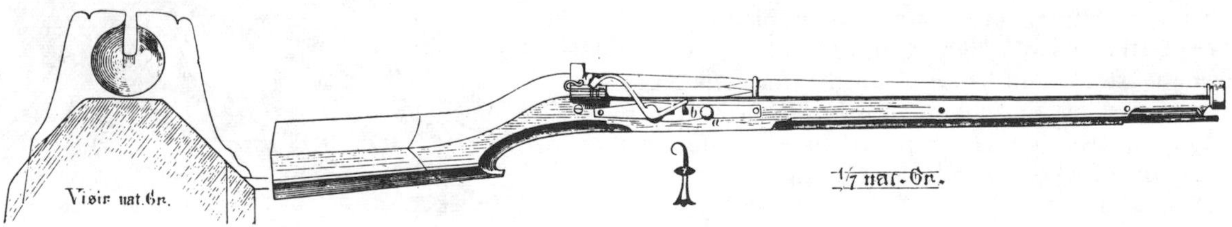

Early button lock with receiver sight and cleaning rod from Basle, 1500 A.D. Gun has a bronze barrel.

tube in the jaws of the cock. In this tube was a piece of tinder or a short section of match. The advantage (if any) was that the soldier did not expose himself by showing a light until he was ready to go into action, at which time he ignited the match or tinder. One of the disadvantages of the matchlock, of course, was that the enemy could see the men approaching with lighted slow-matches. Captain John Smith, of Pocahontas and tobacco fame at a later date, in early life fought the Turks as a mercenary in Europe. He tells of an instance where he frightened off a night attack by having a few soldiers carry lines between them with pieces of slowmatch burning at intervals of a yard. The enemy thought a huge force of Matchlock soldiers was approaching them. The snap lock was intended as an answer to this sort of maneuver. This form of lock was probably the forerunner of the Snaphaunce—the Flintlock arm of much later date.

Matchlock Arms

Most of the important principles of firearms which have since been developed were at least attempted in the Matchlock period. Rifling was introduced, for instance, though again no one can say precisely where or by whom. One manuscript at Leipzig dated 1498 gives an account of a system of cutting grooves in barrels as developed by Caspar Köllner of Vienna. The grooves were straight, as described, however. This would indicate that Köllner was interested primarily in rapid loading and easy cleaning, rather than in giving the bullet rotational flight to increase accuracy as is the purpose of true rifling. Rifling has also been ascribed to August Cotter who worked at Nuremberg from 1500 to about 1520. Again, this statement is not subject to proof. However, about this time twist rifling does appear. An Italian Inventory for the year 1476, for example, lists "firearm with spiral grooved barrels." At the British Woolwich Arsenal Museum are a group of arms and barrels most of which have spiral grooves, though a few are cut straight. Danish records indicate that the military use of the rifled barrel was introduced first in that country by Christian IV. He lived 1577 to 1648. It is noteworthy that one of these Danish rifles dated 1611 is still in the Woolwich Arsenal.

Yet another development of the Matchlock period was a very thorough use of sights. A manuscript at Erlangen University dated 1500 gives detailed descriptions. Some German documents indicate that shooting was done at 200 yards, a distance which would require both rifling and fairly good sight equipment.

The system of interchangeable barrels was also introduced at this early time. They are widely pictured in manuscripts of the early 16th Century. Some were dropped into the stock and secured at the forward end by a projection passing through a mortise. Others were secured by tang screws. These permitted use of different caliber barrels or of shot barrels at the option of the shooter much as ours do today.

Breechloaders were commonly attempted. Due to the lack of a good gas seal at the breech none were particularly successful, of course. Many of these operated on the lifting block principle used by our forces even at the beginning of the Spanish-American War in 1898—the basic difference being only that we had brass cartridge cases which would expand on firing and prevent gas from blasting back through the breech. The famous British breechloader made in 1866 to convert the muzzle loading Enfields of that day to cartridge breechloaders was developed by an American, Jacob Snider. The British paid him for it. Actually the conversion was almost a duplicate of one introduced in England by Henry VIII in 1537 except for the cartridge used. A sample of the 1537 conversion is in the Tower Museum!

"Chamber pieces" were also used. These were the forerunners of cartridges. They were commonly quite heavy and of steel. They were loaded with powder, wad and ball and were inserted at the breech of the arm—pistol, rifle and even repeater. The idea of course was to furnish a method of quick reloading. Since all firing

Examples of historical sources: Upper: German tapestry 1584 A.D. Lower: Drawing by von Solms 1550 to 1560.

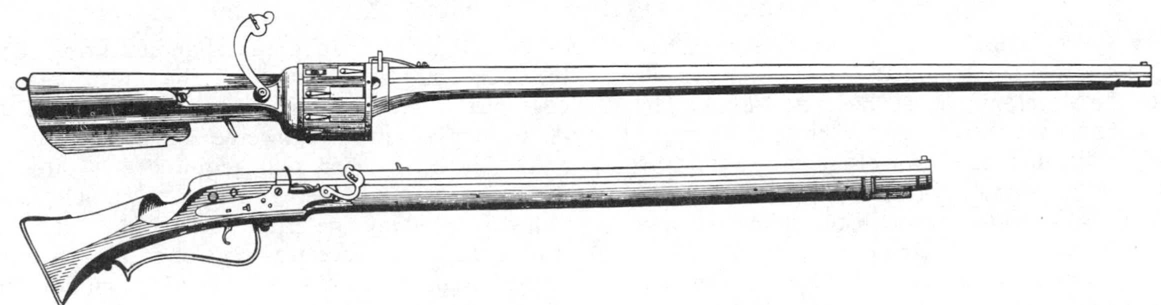

Early matchlock revolving Rifle and breech loader, German.

at that period depended upon use of flame or sparks, the ignition system also doomed the breechloading system of that day to failure. Every nation in Europe at that period did some work with breechloading and ample records are available to show how widespread was the recognition of the value of the system.

Repeating arms were also attempted. Many were cylinder arms much like the later Colt revolvers. Others had successive charges rammed down the same barrel, with the charges separated by heavy wads. Individual touch-holes on the side of the piece were primed and fired independently. However, as in the case of the Roman Candle, fire would get around the wads and fire successive charges. Often this would blow up the arm. In the face of this development work of the early 16th Century, it is interesting to find that during our own Civil War experimental rifles on this pattern were attempted. These were fired by percussion caps, but again they failed because of fire getting back past the protective wads.

Every type of multi-barrel gun of course was also tried. Records show clear drawings of two, three and four barrel guns arranged quite like our modern types. Others were built on the "pepperbox" principle used in America in the early 1800's, several barrels being grouped around a central axis.

Volley fire field guns—early forms of modern machine arms—were also common. Leonardo Da Vinci designed a wide variety of these. Some were designed to be breech-loaded. In general these were multi-barreled arms with barrels side by side. Only the lack of a satisfactory ignition system prevented the development of every arm we know today except our automatic designs.

With the arrival of the Hand Gun with Matchlock the infantry battalions became "the strength of battle." No more were the heavily armored knights the deciding factor in the field. In the history of England, Warwick actually brought about a revolution in military art when he introduced the Burgundian mercenaries at the second battle of St. Albans. It is true that in that engagement the Matchlock did little damage, a heavy rain handicapping the gunners by wetting their priming and their matches. But the start was made that day. The efficiency of the hand gun with all its drawbacks grew rapidly until by the time of Bannockburn the infantry became such a power that knights did not again engage in combat from horseback until the time of Henry VIII when the introduction of the Wheel-lock made shooting possible by mounted men.

The Knight so famed in history as the Flower of Chivalry, "without fear and above reproach" whose name, ironically enough, in our time is the trademark of a Belgian arms firm (H. Pieper)—the Chevalier Bayard—so feared and detested the new firearms that despite his knightly honor he summarily hanged every Spanish hand gun man who fell prisoner to him! Yet when it came his time to die, it was at the hand of a detested Spanish gunner who shot him from his steed.

Throughout the entire early history of firearms we find special interests and thc ultra-conservative—quite as in our own time—trying to discredit and to laugh off that which they most feared. In Fourquevaus' "Instructions for the Warres" translated from the French by Paul Ive in 1589 is the following passage: "The Harquebuse hath been invented within these few years, and is verie good—." He continues on to say that not many are yet expert in its use so that "in a skirmish wherein tenne thousand Harquebussados are shot, there dieth not so many as one man, for the Harquebusiers content themselves with making of a noyse, and so shoot at all adventure."

Quite a different sidelight however is that we find in the "Vitae Illustrorum Virorum" of Paulus Jovius, quoting Farbrizio Colonna who was with the great Captain Gonsalvo de Cordoba when the Spanish arquebus men were placed in shallow trenches to await the charge of the Flower of France on a bitter April day in 1503 at the bloody and decisive engagement of Cerignola: "Neither courage of the troops," he says, "nor the steadfastness of the general won the day; but a little ditch—and a parapet of earth—and the arquebus!"

Even in far off Asia Minor the arquebus was cancelling out the armor and the speed of the mounted man, as evidenced in contemporary illustrated manuscripts of the Persians dealing with the battle with the Turks at Tchaldrian on the 23rd of August, 1514, a manuscript still in existence at Oxford.

In the "Kriegswesen" of Max Jänns we find an inventory of Innsbruck for 1515 listing "469 best quality and 662 smaller arquebuses of brass; 1125 large and 665 small ones of iron;" still another index of the extent of arms development.

This then, was the picture when the Wheel-Lock, the next evolutionary step came.

PHASE III—THE WHEEL-LOCK

The military and sporting needs for an ignition system which would not depend on lighted match or live coals led directly to the development of the Wheel-Lock. The principle is simple. We use it today in our cigarette lighters. Spin a serrated steel wheel against a flint to give off a shower of sparks. The sparks ignite the priming powder to flash fire down through the touchhole into the powder charge in the firing chamber.

Again history is not clear on just when, where and by whom this system was invented. Various accounts of early historians credit Johann Kiefuss as inventing it at Nuremberg in 1517. Others cite the same inventor but place him in Vienna. In any event, an earlier form than the true Wheel-Lock existed in the form of the so-called "Mönchbüchse" of Dresden. This was a simple tube fitted with a rasp and piece of flint mounted near the priming hole. This of course was manually operated.

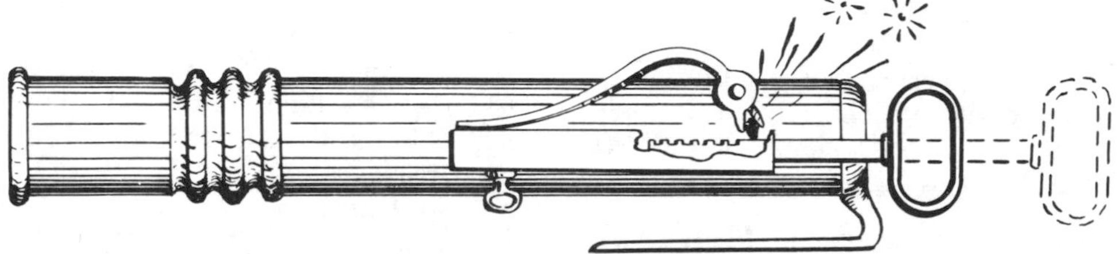

The Monchbüchse of Dresden, drawing from the original to show ignition principle.

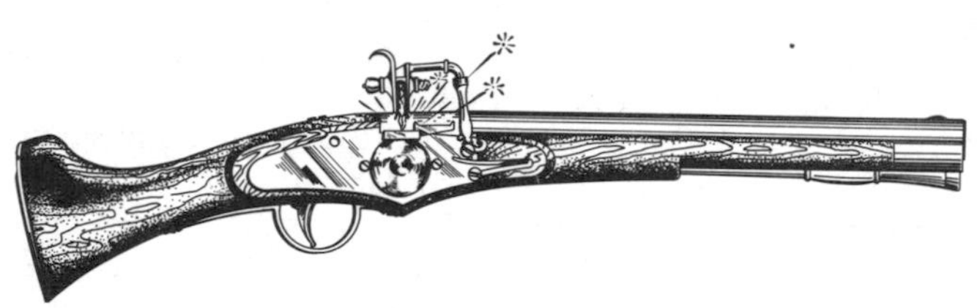

Original drawing of an early wheel-lock showing ignition principle.

The true Wheel-Lock principle involved use of a steel wheel with knurled or grooved edge mounted in a frame and connected with a chain and spring. The outer side of the wheel had a projection at its axis. A wrench fitted over this projection. It was used to wind the chain and compress the spring accordingly. The cock held a piece of flint or pyrites. In preparation for firing the head of the cock was pulled down until the flint rested against the edge of the wheel. Pulling the trigger released the wheel. As it spun around it showered down the firing sparks.

The heavy trigger pull required led directly to the development of the set-trigger pretty much as we use it today. By pushing one arm of the trigger when the weapon was cocked, the piece was pre-set so that a touch on the second trigger would fire it with a minimum of risk of shifting the pistol off the target.

Literally thousands of variations of the mechanism were developed. Such systems were expensive to make, and their use was generally confined to that of the wealthy and some of the military.

Again we find that the system was used in all European countries. Da Vinci described it in detail. Collardo writing in Italy in 1586 ascribed its development to the Germans. Henry the VIII used it in England.

Because of the firing system employed, much attention was now given to various types of safeties. There were trigger safeties, hammer and sear safeties, manual and automatic safeties. Every form of device now in use to prevent accidental firing in manually operated arms can be found, in at least elementary form, in the early Wheel-Locks.

Rifling also received increased attention because the firing system and the set-trigger and sight refinements permitted greater and greater accuracy. During this period experimental work was carried on covering use of every number of grooves from 2 to 34. Rate of twist of the rifling was also subject for experimentation. And even the shallow groove rifling currently being advertised as "micro-groove" was considered, some examples still existing in specimens at Woolwich and Zürich.

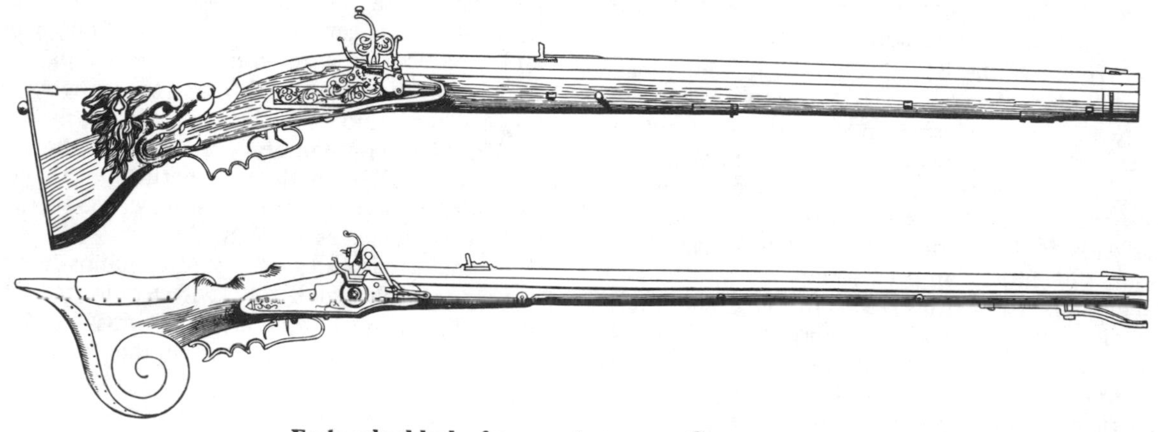

Early wheel-locks from contemporary German sources.

PHASE IV—THE SNAPHAUNCE

In place of the expensive wheel mechanism, there appeared about 1525 a simple form of mechanical fire striking lock called the Snaphaunce. It is really little more than an adaptation of the old Matchlock "light snapping lock" already described. In the jaws of the cock a piece of pyrites was fastened instead of a tinder or match holder. A steel point or anvil was provided near the touch-hole. Pulling the trigger released the cock. Its spring forced it ahead. The flint striking a glancing blow at the steel anvil showered sparks into the priming powder. Just as simple as that! Yet this was one of the great developments in the history of firearms.

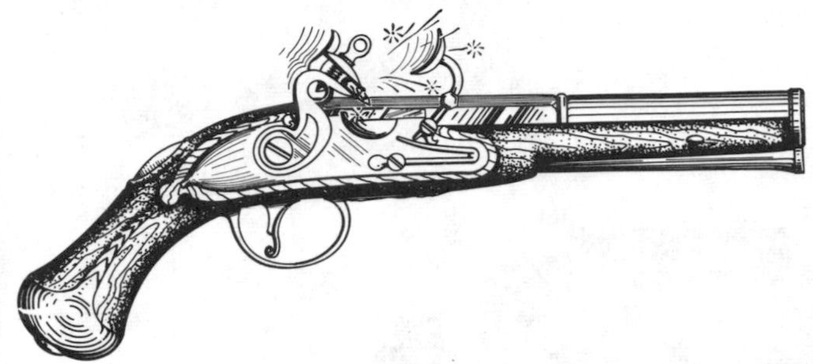

Original drawing from an early snaphaunce showing ignition principle.

Its name seems to have derived from the Dutch "schnapphan"—meaning snapcock. Some writers ascribe the name to the Dutch translation "chicken thieves." They theorize that it was developed by thieves who wished to poach for game without the tell-tale lighted match. The more probable explanation is that it merely indicated the snapping of the cock against the anvil to give sparks. Such derivations, of course, indicate Flemish origin for the system. However, it is referred to in many early German records as "der Spanische schnappschloss," and many authorities have claimed Spain as the place of origin. It was in general use throughout Europe not very long after the introduction of the Wheel-Lock, so that even France and Italy lay some claim to its invention.

In any event, the new system was recognized everywhere as a great forward step. Experimentation to improve it started promptly. However, it was a full 100 years before a perfected form of the system appeared to mark a still greater advance in firearms technology.

PHASE V—THE FLINTLOCK

The true Flintlock is basically the Snaphaunce as described plus a hinged steel right-angle pan cover hinged over the priming pan. As the cock falls the flint strikes this hinged piece (called the "batterie" or "frizzen"). The blow throws the hinged cover back, exposing the priming powder in the pan below. At the same time the flint scraping along the steel showers sparks down into the priming powder to fire the arm.

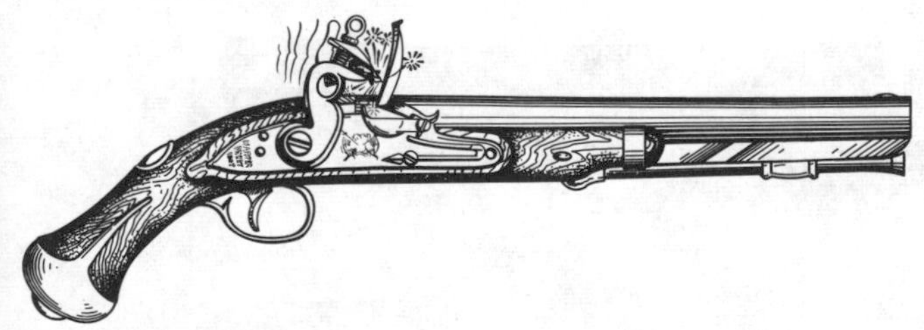

Original drawing of an early flintlock showing ignition principle.

This development is credited to the French. They successfully combined the principles of the Snaphaunce with a rather similar system known as the Spanish "Miquelet." Again we find that all European nations experimented with and finally adopted the system. It was officially adopted by the British in 1690. This arm was popularized in history and legend as "Brown Bess" from the color of its barrel plus the erroneous idea that it was adopted by Queen Elizabeth, a queen who had been dead 87 years at the time of its adoption! This anecdote gives some idea of the reliability of much that is popularly accepted in the story of firearms.

One model Flintlock manufactured by the French at Charleville was officially adopted by them in 1746 and with minor changes was the official pattern until 1842. A slight variant known as the 1763 Model was the basic arm of our forces under Washington during the Revolutionary War. Prussia, curiously, did not adopt the system until 1808.

The Flintlock in America

Very little is known about early firearms in America. We do know that the earliest settlers brought some Matchlocks; and one record of the Massachusetts Bay Company in 1628 shows the importation of Snaphaunces for their paid troops. Very little else is recorded of the earliest days, but it is certain that with the need for protection from Indians as well as for game shooting, considerable work must have been done by local gunsmiths.

The first scientific approach to arms making was done by the German settlers in Pennsylvania. They had a heritage of mechanical and gun skills to draw upon which the Puritan and Pilgrim settlers did not.

The German and Swiss settlers brought with them the finest arms of their countries. Generally these were large bore, heavy arms of general European pattern. The barrels were quite short as a rule. However, the gunmakers quickly realized the need for modifications required for American usage and changes came fast. Barrels were lengthened to provide better powder combustion and better sighting arrangements. Useless weight was removed by stock design. Full stocks of American maple and walnut were fashioned to protect the barrel in forest use. Calibers were changed in the interest of accuracy and range. By the year 1700 flourishing small gun businesses were producing gems of the art. In 1732 the noted Heinrich Brothers and Peter Leman and others were turning out the finest rifled arms available anywhere.

The early calibers averaged .54 but as time went on these were reduced for varying types of hunting so that the original balls weighing about half an ounce were greatly reduced in weight. Sights of a high order were provided on all these in various styles from bead to blade fronts and special notch rears.

But the biggest development of all was in speed of loading. The European types of the period required that the bullets be started down the barrel with a mallet, then punched down on top of the charge with a ramrod. The Pennsylvania gunmakers introduced the idea of wrapping the bullets in linen or buckskin patches which had been soaked in tallow. This system permitted easier and faster loading, and at the same time gave a degree of gas check hitherto unknown. This in turn gave better accuracy and longer range.

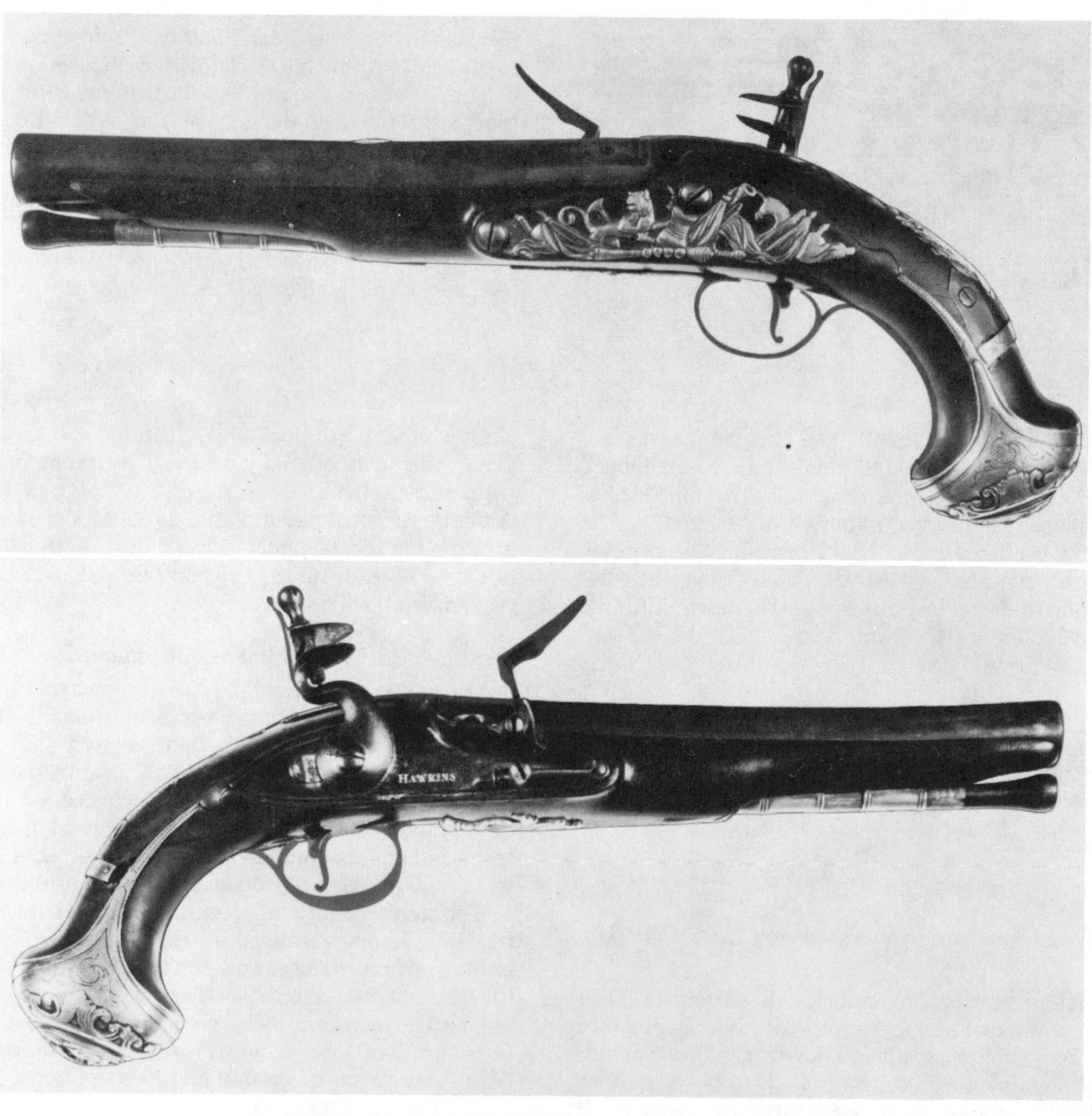

A Pair of George Washington's Pistols, Caliber .67.

These pistols were purchased at the sale of the effects of Batholomew Dandridge, Jr. in 1804. He was Washington's private secretary after the Revolution and it is believed the pistols were presented to him by our first President.

The lock plates of the pistols are signed "Hawkins" and their barrels bear the mark of R. Wilson, both London gunsmiths. Their silver inlay has British proof marks for 30th May 1748-30th May 1749, and the stocks are walnut. After passing through various hands they were acquired along with documents by Mr. Clendenin Ryan of New York who presented them to the West Point Museum where they now are.

These early rifles are famous as "Kentuckies," taking the name from the fact that the vast territory between the Cumberlands and the Mississippi River was then called Kentucky; and most of the settlers and hunters who ranged that area were outfitted in Pennsylvania. Tales of the accuracy of these rifles have been grossly overdone, of course. But the fact remains that they were the greatest precision arms of their day—and far ahead of any European designs for years to come.

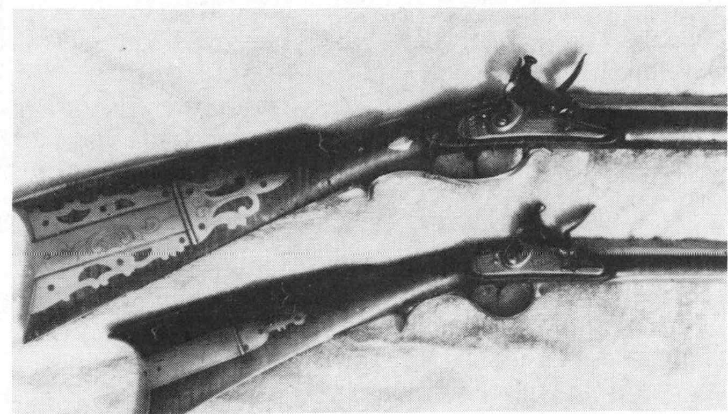

A representative American Kentucky flintlock rifle.

Our earliest official military arms are those of the Committee of Safety set up at the time of the Revolution. Committees in the 13 colonies authorized their adoption. The arms themselves were made by over 200 gunsmiths in Massachusetts, Rhode Island, Maryland and Pennsylvania. For the most part they were smooth bore muskets of Flintlock pattern. They weighed about 10 pounds average, calibers varying from .72 to .80.

The American Revolution compelled the military forces of the world to adopt rifled arms to replace the traditional smoothbores. In spite of all the European experimentation with rifling from the early days of the Matchlock, it was not until the American settlers armed with their highly accurate muzzle loading rifles had taken drastic toll of trained British troops that the British army accepted the value of rifling. British Captain Hanger was in command of one of the German Jäger Corps, trained riflemen employed by the British, in a desperate effort to counter the long range accuracy and fighting ability of the colonists. In his writings he expressed the greatest respect for both the deadliness and the manufacture of the American rifles.

Into the scene at this time came one of the most remarkable persons of that day, a British officer and gentleman whose name and fame are but little known, Major Patrick Ferguson, 2nd Battalion, 71st Regiment of Highlanders. Soldier, inventor, marksman extraordinary, inventor of the first breechloading rifle of English manufacture used in war by the British forces, Ferguson for one brief instant held the very life of the American Nation in his hands, when at Germantown on the field of battle General George Washington accompanied by a solitary French aide came under the sights of his rifle. Ferguson, one of the deadliest riflemen of his time, had been assigned to pick off the American General. When he saw him, he refused to believe that that casually dressed, fearless man who merely turned and stared at his call to identify himself could be the American Commander-in-Chief. On Ferguson's inability to realize that Washington could be so confident or reckless as to go about without pomp or bodyguard, on that one failure to grasp Washington's stature, the General's life was spared. Ferguson held his fire.

In British patent specification No. 1139 of the year 1776 we find the then Captain Ferguson's description of his breechloading flintlock. He does not claim the invention is new. He states that previous attempts of the sort have failed, that his is "an improvement in breechloading firearms."

The specification also sets forth an elevating rear sight. A single turn of the triggerguard lever drops the attached 3 to 12 thread vertical screw plug which passes through

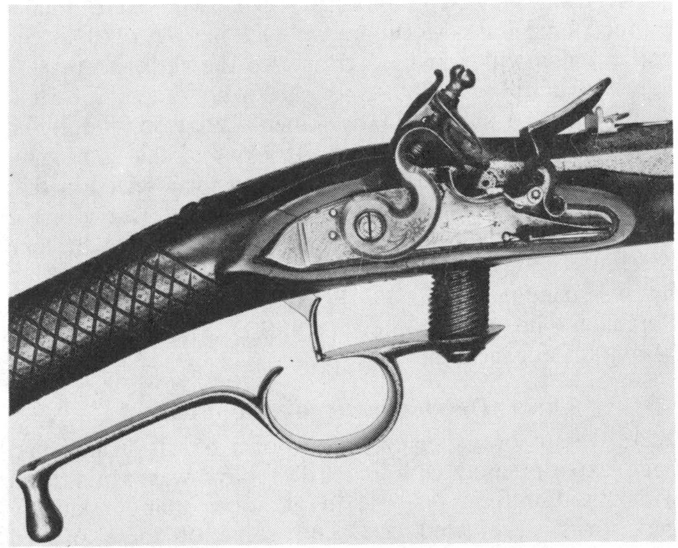

Ferguson rifle with action open ready for loading through breech.

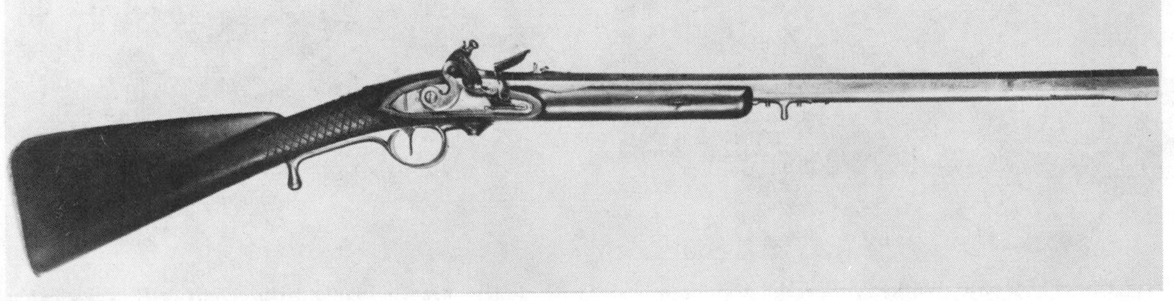

Ferguson breech loading flintlock rifle, very rare Officer's Model from the West Point collection.

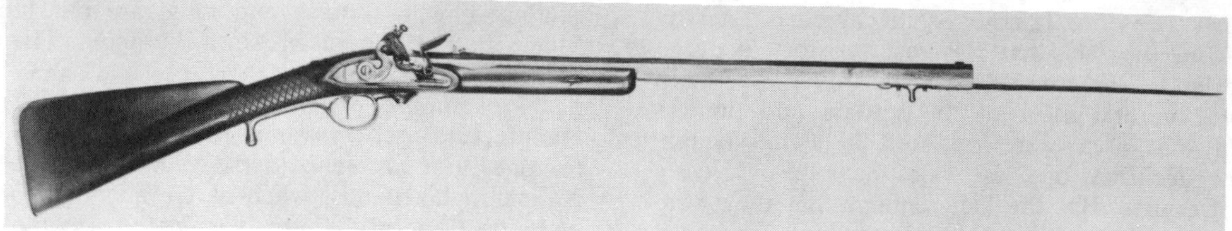

The De Peyster Ferguson with sliding bayonet extended.

the breech end of the barrel. As the quick-thread screw goes down, the ball is dropped into the chamber through the opening in the top of the breech, the powder poured in (or paper cartridge inserted) and the triggerguard swung back to elevate the breech plug. The pan is primed, the hammer cocked, and the weapon is ready.

A "History of the War in America between Great Britain and her Colonies" published in Dublin in 1785 says of Ferguson: "He was perhaps the best marksman living. . . . It has been reported that George Washington owed his life at the Battle of Germantown to the gentleman's total ignorance of his person, as he had him sufficiently within reach, and view during that action for the purpose." The story originally was told by Ferguson himself to a Tory, a member of the New York De Peyster family who joined with Ferguson in his mission of organizing in America those forces which sided with the British Army in its efforts to stamp out the Revolution.

Ferguson headed the Tory forces who were finally trapped on King's Mountain on October 7, 1780 in the battle which will ever be a tribute to the skill and marksmanship of those early Americans who fought for freedom. When a sniper finally killed Ferguson, the living Tories surrendered after some 400 out of the contingent of 1100 were casualties. The Ferguson rifles seized in that engagement were highly prized, but today we know of the existence of only three of them. Ironically enough, one specimen now in the Smithsonian Institute was donated by a descendant of the De Peyster who received it from Ferguson—he was somewhere else when the King's Mountain engagement took place.

Other Developments of the Flintlock

As was to be expected, every form of rifle which had been experimented with in earlier days was again tried with the Flintlock system. In addition, many relatively new ideas were tried out; and some of these proved successful at a later date when improved ignition was developed.

Of the earlier forms which were repeated as Flintlocks we find the familiar two- three- and four- and more barreled patterns. Again they were mounted side by side, over-under and around an axis in all conceivable arrangements.

Single barrel "repeaters" with several separated charges rammed down the single barrel were again tried. And of course they again failed. All the ingenuity of the inventors using sliding-rack arrangements for individual charge firing still could not get by the lack of a gas seal between the barrel charges; and firing one often set off the whole firing chain with disastrous effects to gun and shooter.

Breechloaders of a hundred types were tried. Again some were supplied with steel chambers which were individually loaded and which were inserted in the breech just as we do fixed cartridges today. Others were to be loaded directly from powder horn. Still others were to be loaded with the paper cartridges then becoming familiar, where the ball and powder were individually wrapped ready for shooting.

Special Italian models had devices attached to the cock which automatically primed the arm—when the devices worked! All previous forms of hinged blocks were used.

Among the newer designs, however, were breechblocks and also barrels hinged and operated by triggerguard levers. Some had barrels which slid forward or pivoted to the side when a lever was operated. Some of these patterns paved the way for the modern hinged shotgun.

Revolving barrel systems were again tried, as were revolving cylinder systems. Volley guns firing a number

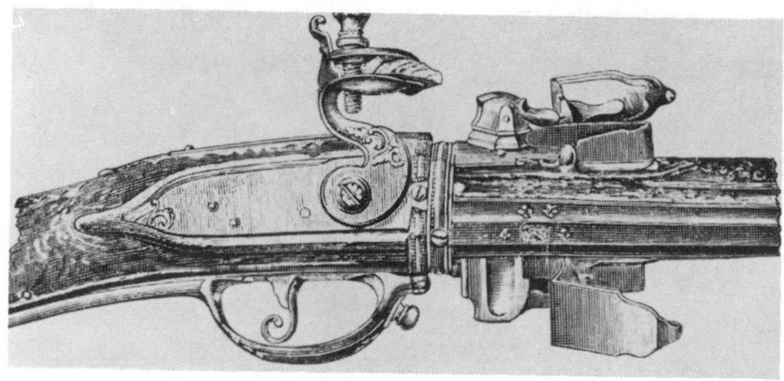

Italian "Over-Under" double flintlock. Barrels are hand rotated for firing. Gun in Birmingham Museum.

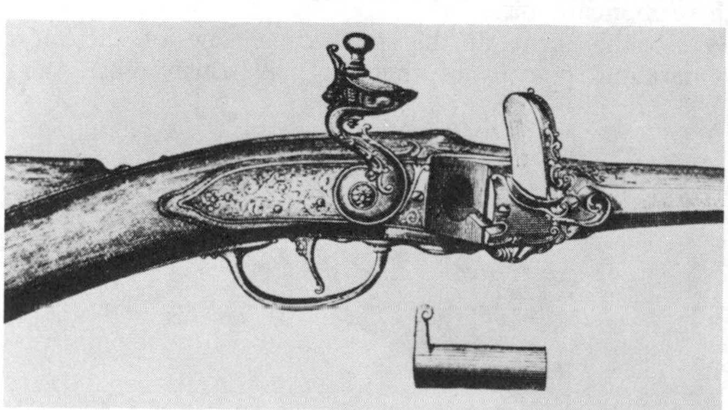

Italian breech loader with removable steel chamber "Chamber Piece." May 1694 A.D. by Aqua Fresca a-Borgia.

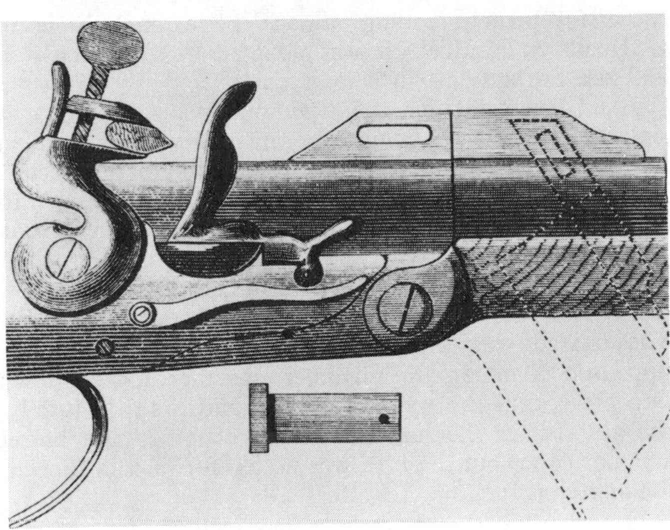

Early French flintlock breech loader with hinge barrel and steel "Chamber Piece" for loading. Cross bolt locked as in modern double shotguns.

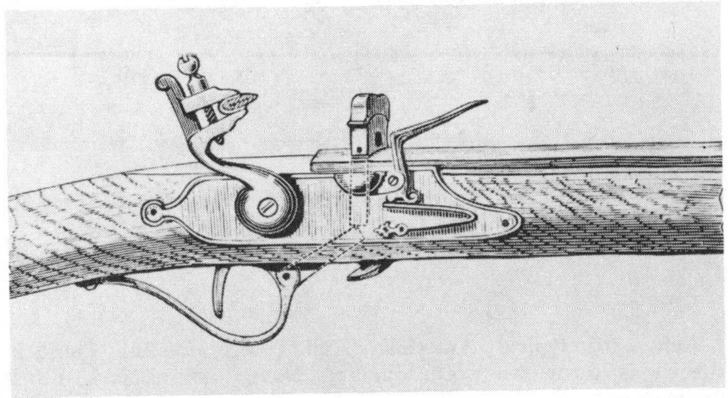

Early German Theiss flintlock breech loader. Lever operated. Block lock.

of barrels simultaneously and other multi-barreled types firing in rapid succession were again developed. And at least one unusual repeating type found its way to America. This was the fantastic "Cookson," an arm far ahead of its time.

The Cookson Repeating Flintlock

There is a tantalizing entry in Pepys Diary, written by the amazing Samuel at his house in Seething Lane on July 3, 1662, an entry never elaborated and one on which no other records or descriptions have ever been unearthed. It reads: "Dined with the officers of the Ordnance, where Sir Compton, Mr. O'Neile, and other great persons were. After dinner was brought to Sir W. Compton a gun to discharge seven times, the best of all devices that I ever saw and very serviceable and not a bauble; for it is much approved of and many made thereof."

What was this repeating gun? We do not know positively, but it may have been one of the "Cookson" guns, a specimen of which is now in the Smithsonian. It may have been a somewhat similar arm developed about that time by an unknown gunsmith in Vienna, samples of whose works are known. Or it may have been one of the guns made by a famous Italian gunmaker "Antonio Constantine"—the first repeating arm of which we have record which had a buttstock magazine (charge and priming powder chambers were loaded through the butt by raising the buttplate). In any event it belongs to the type called the "Cookson" because the outstanding specimen known to be in existence bears that name engraved on it.

While the name "Cookson" is English, this gun, bearing the date of 1586, is believed to be of the Lorenzo type designed late in the sixteenth century.

This arm was evidently brought to Maryland by early English colonists. It was one of the guns confiscated after a search for arms by the Provost Marshal in Baltimore in 1863 and remained in United States Government custody until the close of the Civil War. Unclaimed by 1867, it was then thrown in the scrap heap. Purchased by an individual for a small sum of money it was turned over to a gunsmith for checking. For the first time the unusual nature of the weapon was then realized.

Its front sight is like a Turkish crescent. The metal work is all heavily engraved with flags, drums, piles of cannon balls, cannon being fired, stacks of muskets, boarding pikes, and the like. On top of the barrel is stamped "John Cookson, Fecit." (Made by John Cookson.) This is a magazine flintlock gun of smooth bore. It fires spherical bullets weighing 260 grains and a charge of about 125 grains of black powder. The arm had a capacity of 10 rounds, with a magazine fitted into the lock carrying a similar number of priming charges. (Other known specimens have smaller magazines.)

There is a hinged flap on the left side of the receiver which is opened to permit bullets to be put into one compartment and powder into an adjoining one. Cylindrical passages lead from the compartments to the central chamber in the receiver in which is located a solid cylindrical block with its axis from right to left.

Early Italian magazine flintlock. Powder loads through butt. Lever loaded. Similar to Cookson.

This cylinder forms a recoil block. It has two radial cavities large enough to hold a ball and a charge respectively and is so located that when revolved the cavities will be opposite the passages from the magazines.

At this point the ball drops into the first cavity and the powder into the second. By turning the cylinder to the front the passages are closed and the ball and charge are brought in front of the rear part of the bore. (Since this is a gravity loader, the muzzle must be held down.) The bullet drops in and the block remains with the charge in line with the bore. The powder cavity, which has a diaphragm to prevent the bullet from dropping into it, is connected by a vent through the axis of the cylinder to the pan.

Turning the lever on the left side revolves the cylindrical breechblock and also cocks the hammer and closes the pan. The lock and trigger are of ordinary design; the sear, sear spring, and mainspring are the same as those used on the last models of flintlock guns. The highest mechanical skill is indicated in the manufacture of this weapon, the tolerances being astonishingly close.

This gun was far in advance of its time. Had it been provided with a wad to serve as a gas check, it might have established repeating rifles two hundred years earlier than their time.

Once the magazine is loaded with bullets and powder, no counting or measuring is necessary, as the charges are automatically measured and the loading is quite accurate.

With a magazine fully charged, 10 shots could be fired very nearly as rapidly as with the modern metallic cartridge repeater!

EARLY AMERICAN-MADE REPEATING RIFLES

The Jennings and the North

About the period of 1815 single-barreled arms were experimented with in America which were merely Flintlock versions of Emperor Maximilian's early repeaters, notably the "superimposed loading" system. In this dangerous system, already alluded to, a charge of powder and ball was rammed down the muzzle, a heavy wad pounded down, and then another load placed in on top of the wad. Some of these arms were provided with separate locks which would fire the charges in succession —the shooter fervently hoped!—starting from the one nearest the muzzle. Others like that of L. Jennings of New York (his later percussion rifle was one of the first reasonably successful repeating arms and was a fore-runner of the present Winchester line) were fitted with a sliding lock which was pushed forward on a track until it was opposite the first flash hole. It was moved progressively back as each charge was fired. A single trigger and one sear only were needed in this design. In 1824 and 1825 repeaters on this system were made by that master gunmaker Simeon North of Middletown, Connecticut. Sooner or later, of course, flame from charge one managed to bypass the wad and reach the other charges—a situation which speedily discouraged this system. Hope lives long in the human breast, however, and research is not utilized as it might be; and so in 1862 we find Springfield Armory experimenting with this superposed load system in the later percussion days under Lindsey's patents!

American Breechloading Flintlocks

The American Hall Rifle, patented in 1811 by Col. John H. Hall of North Yarmouth, Maine and William Thornton, is generally accepted as the first reasonably successful breech loading arm to be extensively used. Originally a Flintlock, it was adapted to the percussion and rim fire systems in a later day.

Hall developed his rifle without being aware that similar systems were being experimented with in Europe. His was the only one to achieve a measure of success. It had an outside hammer, of course, and was fitted with a special chamber pivoted at its rear and in a box receiver behind the barrel. Pushing down a short lever below the fore-end elevated the front end of this chamber, which had radial grooved locking blocks on either side. The charge was inserted into the front end of this tipped-up chamber, the chamber was then locked down into place, and the weapon primed and fired. Naturally, the gas seal at the juncture of the chamber and barrel was not good, but the arm was a step forward in breech-loading construction.

Typical American Hall rifle.

Action of typical American Hall breech loading flintlock. Breech is open ready for loading from forward end. Block snapped down to lock.

The Hall was officially adopted in 1816 as an experimental arm, and was used to a limited extent in the Seminole and the Mexican Wars, in .54 caliber. The arm went through a wide succession of improvements and changes in lockwork and caliber. The engrossing history of the Hall Rifles is still to be written, for while a vast amount of data concerning them has been printed in military and sporting records, the data has not yet been satisfactorily gathered together.

The one other American Flintlock Breechloader to receive official attention was the Jenks. Raising and pushing back a lever on top of the grip exposed the chamber for loading. (This arm is more commonly found as a percussion lock; but as a flintlock of .69 caliber was tested against the Hall.)

The Collier

Like so many later American inventors, Collier had to take his rifle, working on the principle of the common revolver, with a single barrel and a chambered revolving cylinder, to England to obtain any recognition. The original model of this smooth-bore arm of about .50 caliber was developed by Elisha H. Collier in Boston several years before he obtained his English patent (1818). Though later made in caplock and pillock, it was originally a Flintlock—it was invented just at the end of the flint era.

In the original Collier, a tube in the butt carried spare priming powder. Priming for about 10 charges was carried in a box which formed the frizzen. Each movement of the frizzen automatically dropped the correct amount of the priming in the flashhole.

A revolving cylinder with four, five or eight chambers was loaded from the muzzle end. These chambers were chamfered (cut back) at the muzzle. The cylinder was held forward by a spring which thrust the chamber in line with the barrel directly ahead and over the rear end of the barrel to form a reasonably tight gas seal. When the weapon was fired it was necessary to press a release stud to free the cylinder, which was then drawn back from its position over the barrel until it could be turned to bring the next chamber in line. The cylinder was then moved forward so that the end of the next chamber fitted over the barrel breech. The hammer or cock carrying the flint had to be thumb cocked for each shot.

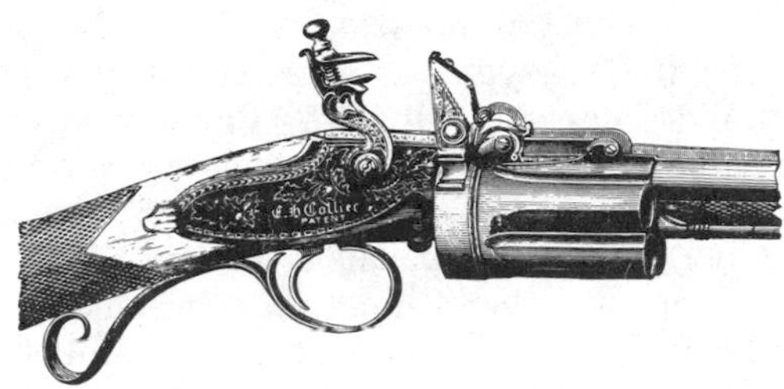

Collier flintlock action. This was made as a shotgun, rifle, and as a pistol.

The Close of the Flintlock Era

The flintlock marked the end of a period of purely mechanical changes to furnish ignition for firearms use.

From direct application of a lighted coal to the priming, development passed on as we have seen to the mechanical application of lighted slow match, then to the still mechanical system of showering sparks into the priming by wheel and by flint.

The next step, Percussion, brings us to the stage of chemistry where a new priming system of firing by detonation eliminates the need for direct fire or sparks.

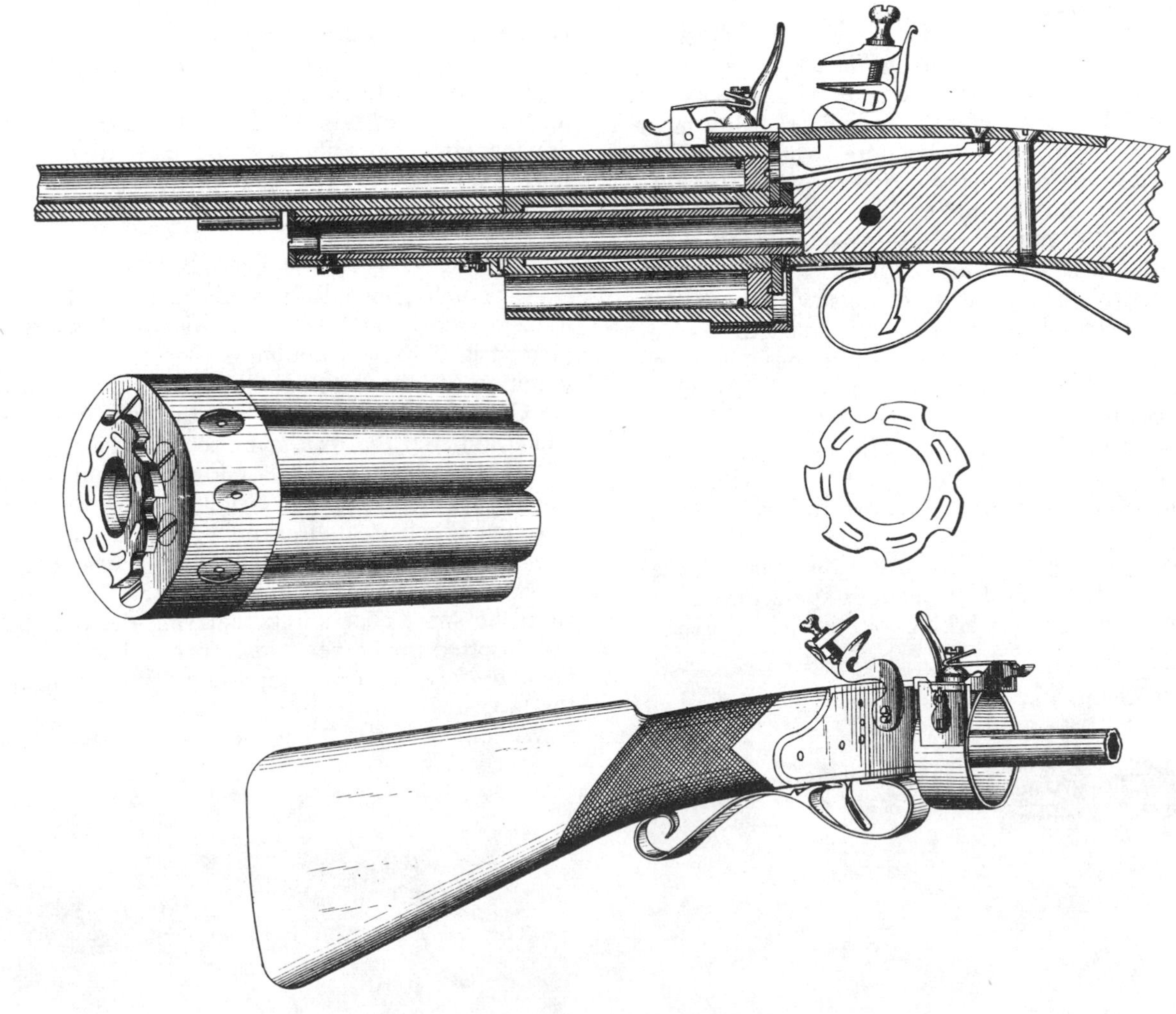

This weapon was designed by Artemus Wheeler in 1818 in America. Wheeler went to England a few years later at which time his design was incorporated by Collier.

PHASE VI—THE PERCUSSION LOCK

Percussion firing requires use of an explosive which will detonate when struck a sharp blow. Gunpowder of an early day could not be exploded this way, though certain types made today can be.

In its initial form priming powder was fulminate of mercury. A small quantity was placed in the gun pan over the touch-hole after the gunpowder charge, the wad and the bullet had been rammed down the muzzle. When the hammer fell it struck this fulminate and the crushing blow exploded it. Fire from the explosion passed down the touch-hole to set off the propelling charge of gunpowder below.

French scientists had recognized the existence of the principle as early as 1703, but no application of it was made until a Scottish minister, Rev. Alexander John Forsyth, began experimenting with it in 1793.

We will probably never know how old the discovery of detonation really is. We do know that Forsyth was definitely among the first to employ it. We also know that he worked the principle out himself without any knowledge that others were working along the same line at about the same period.

Let us at this point consider another documented instance of how a principle can be "lost" for centuries, this time in relation to percussion. In the astonishing diary of Samuel Pepys we find the following: "November 11, 1662. At noon to the coffee house, where, with Dr. Allen, some good discourse about Physics and Chymistry. And among other things I telling him what Dribble the German Doctor do offer of an instrument to sink ships; he tells me that which is more strange, that something made of gold, which they call in chymistry, Aurum Fulminans, a grain, I think he said, of this put into a silver spoon and fired will give a blow like a musquette and strike a hole through a silver spoon downwards without the least force upward."

No British records have yet been unearthed which give any further clue to this matter; but it is obvious that the principle of detonation lay fallow for well over a century at least.

Rev. Forsyth lived and died a Presbyterian minister in the village of Belhelvie. He spent his spare time hunting, repairing guns, and working on chemistry experiments. He himself made the first known gunlock to use detonating powder, and showed it to friends in 1805. He was induced by Lord Moira to travel to London where in the Tower he was given facilities for chemistry experimentation.

In 1812 Forsyth in partnership with James Watts, inventor of the steam engine, invented several types of Percussion Locks.

One curious sidelight on official thinking can be found in Forsyth's story. His friend Lord Moira was replaced by a politician who saw no sense in Forsyth's work; and in April of 1807 Forsyth was ordered out of the Tower. Three months later, on July 4th, Forsyth was granted a British patent for his invention, which was soon adopted by the British Army. Politics being politics, the Government did not make any payment to the minister until 23 years later, at which time they granted him 200 pounds. This niggardly treatment created much public furore, and an award of an additional 800 pounds was made in 1843. Unfortunately, Forsyth died three months before the grant was made.

Forsyth originally used the powder directly in the pan. However, he soon developed a system of "caps" by placing the powder between two pieces of paper. His next move was to make a roll of these "caps" to speed up the process of priming arms. These devices, of course, are the same basically as those used in toy cap pistols to this very day, but in their time they were the wonders of the firearms world.

Other Percussion Developments

A French gunsmith named Pauly used a paper fulminating device in 1808. It was fired when a needle pierced it. This was doubtless the forerunner of the ammunition of the Needle Gun later used effectively by the Germans, as well as of the American Volcanic system which initiated the true lever action repeating rifle.

In 1816 the famous London gun maker "Old Joe" Manton filed specification No. 3895 with the patent office covering the first attempt at a "tube lock."

Manton's true "tube lock," however, was not filed until 1818, under specification No. 4285. The name comes from the small copper tube carrying the fulminate which was inserted in the vent, its upper end resting against an anvil to form a lower support as the hammer crushed the tube to fire it.

William Westley Richards of Birmingham introduced

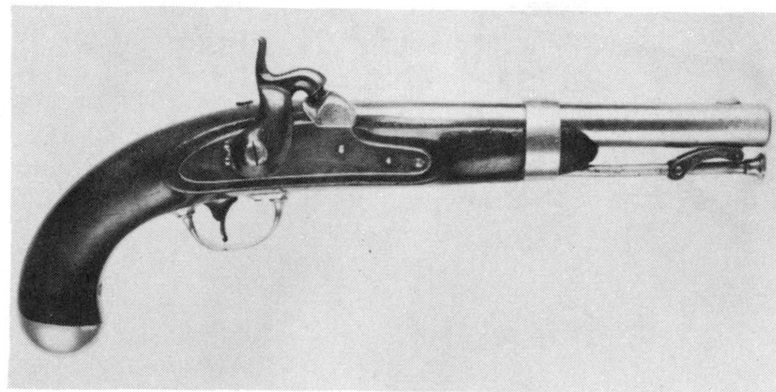

U. S. Army Aston muzzle-loading smooth bore percussion pistol. Caliber .54. Model of 1842. Representative percussion lock type.

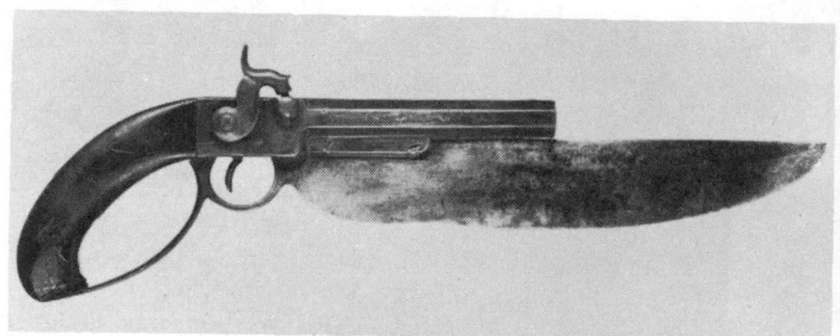

The famous U. S. Elgin Navy cutlass pistol, percussion type.

one of the most popular arms of the time in his "detonating gun" specification No. 4611 in 1821. This simple arm has a cock which strikes into the flash pan, which has a pivoted lid operated by a spring. As the hammer falls it forces against a point of a pivoted lever whose other end operates the pan cover. This arm could be primed with powdered fulminate, with paper caps, or with fulminate balls of pellets which were also called "pills." In America this was usually called the "pill lock."

We do not know positively who developed the copper cap to hold fulminate. This cap, of course, led eventually to modern cartridge development. The best evidence available indicates it was first produced by Joshua Shaw, an Englishman. He was working in Philadelphia, Pennsylvania when it first was brought to public notice in 1814.

Some British authorities ascribe the development to Joseph Egg, the noted gunmaker; and there is no question that he at least introduced it into England. A very wordy sportsman of the day, one Colonel Hawker, made some claim to having worked with Joe Manton in such an invention, but the facts are hazy at best. A large number of lesser lights also laid claim to it—after the fact, of course.

In 1824 the Berenger patent was granted covering percussion pellets fed from a magazine. A year later Joe Manton patented a revolving magazine primer. In 1834 Baron Heurteloup's continuous primer, a long tube of metal holding the fulminate which was fed forward and suitably cut by an edge on the hammer, was patented. Egg's self-acting primer magazine was introduced in 1836. In 1845 Dr. Edward Maynard was granted a U. S. patent for his "tape primer," consisting of priming pellets embedded in strips of paper or linen so they could be fed automatically as the hammer was cocked.

Rifling in the Percussion Era

While a brigade of the British 95th Regiment was armed with Baker Flintlock rifles in 1800, and at Waterloo the rifle brigade wiped out several brigades of French artillery, little military attention was given to rifling until 1838. The early British Baker had a rifling of one-quarter turn in the 30-inch barrel; the caliber was .615.

In the year 1789 one J. Wilkinson in English specification No. 1694 described a barrel rifled with two spiral grooves, the missiles to have belts or wings to fit the grooves. In 1836 a Board at Woolwich selected the two-groove Brunswick Rifle for service. The caliber was about .704, the rifling made one turn in 30 inches (the length of the barrel), and the bullet was a 555 grain belted ball, the ball corresponding to the width and depth of the grooves. (A few Lancaster rifles, two-grooved but firing conical balls with side ribs to fit the rifling, were issued during the Kaffir War from 1846 to 1852, the Lancaster being the first conical ball used in military service.) This form of rifling fouled up quickly, and its design was considered impractical, though in the metallic cartridge era it was again tried.

The Minié rifling next introduced had four grooves and fired a conical ball. As introduced in British service in

The Minié Ball.

1851 it was of .702 caliber. It too, proved unsatisfactory, though some were used in the Crimean war. It was replaced in 1853 by the first famous Enfield, a three-groove rifle of .577 caliber, with a pitch of one turn in 78 inches. This rifle was made in the Royal Small Arms Factory at Enfield which was equipped with special American-made machinery during this period.

Bullet Development

Since the bullet in a muzzle-loading rifle must be smaller than the bore to permit it to be rammed down effectively, much thought was given to a bullet which would enter easily but would then expand to fill the grooves and utilize the full force of the powder gases formed behind it. The problem was to design a ball which could be dropped down the barrel, then satisfactorily expanded. France did considerable experimentation on this problem. One of the first solutions was that of the Delvigne bullet. The powder rested in a chamber

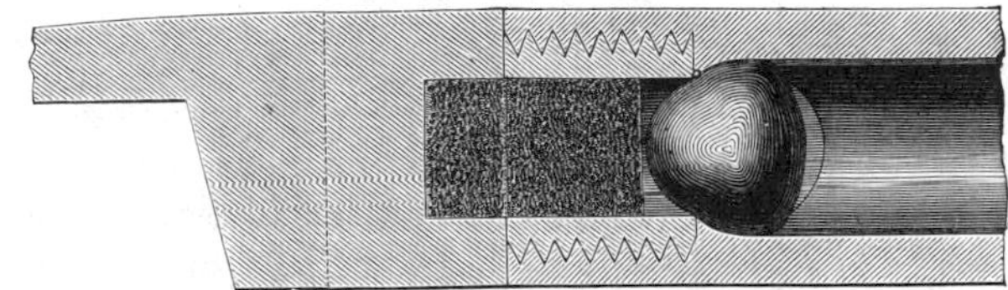

The Delvigne System.

smaller than the barrel bore. Thus the round ball, resting against the shoulders of the powder chamber, expanded when rammed down. Delvigne next introduced a hollow base bullet which was to be expanded by the exploding powder. The Thouvenin system, famous throughout Europe at the time, consisted of a stem, a sort of anvil projecting out of the breeching into the barrel. The gunpowder charge was distributed around this stem, while the cylindro-conical bullet dropped down the barrel after the powder, was pounded down until it expanded and took the rifling. This was famous as the system of the "carabine a tige"—or carbine with stem. This was followed by the famous Minié ball, designed by Captain Minié of the French Army, a conical ball with an iron cup in its base. The cup was thrust ahead and expanded the lead bullet against the rifling when fired.

Charles Claude Etienne Minié received 20,000 pounds from the British government for this little device,. just twelve years after W. Greener by his own story offered it to the British Army only to have it rejected as "useless and chimerical." Greener always insisted that Minié had learned of the bullet through seeing a French translation of an early Greener book; and after a series of suits the British Government finally paid Greener 1000 pounds.

However, since a Captain Norton suggested a similar idea 13 years before Greener, the facts in the case must always be in doubt.

In any event, the English version differed from the original French Minié. When in 1852 a new rifle was decided upon, the Pritchett bullet suggested by Metford (inventor of the Metford rifling) was used. First having only a hollow base, the bullet finally was made with a heavy plug fitted to the base, the whole being heavily lubricated, and was of .55 caliber to fit the .577 bore. These were the bullets which legend has it were a factor in the Indian Mutiny, the native soldiers because of caste distinctions refusing to bite off the ends of the paper cartridges which were heavily smeared with animal fat. As a result of this mutiny, which took two years to put down, the British Crown took over rule of India from the East India Company.

Because of poor manufacturing tolerances, in both bullets and arms, Joseph Whitworth, a pioneer in the field of scientific measurements, was called in to experiment. He suggested a hexagonal bullet and rifling; and while some experimental arms and ammunition were made, his ideas on these subjects were not employed.

The Minié ball played a tremendous role in American history. It was the ball generally used in all the muzzle loaders used by both the North and the South during our Civil War; it was responsible in very large measure for the catastrophic loss of life in that terrible conflict.

Percussion Breech Loading Firearms

The most successful of all percussion types, of course, were those using the well known "Percussion Cap." In this system the priming is held in a small hollow metal cup. The cap is placed over a projecting hollow nipple at the breech of the arm. The falling hammer crushes the metal cap to detonate the priming and fire the barrel charge.

As in all earlier developments, every conceivable type of single and multi-shot system was attempted using these caps. Also used were a wide variety of varying percussion systems, only a few of which can be described herein.

The most important feature from an arms development standpoint, however, was the intensive work on breechloading systems at this period. These mechanical experiments laid the direct groundwork for most modern arms and ammunition. And, as usual, most of them were the result of private development by individuals and manufacturing firms—not by government subsidized or controlled groups.

Indeed the conservatism of the military groups throughout the world was such that in 1859 in his noted book "Rifles and Rifle Practice" we find Lieut. C. M. Wilcox of the U. S. Army writing: "In Prussia part of the infantry is armed with the needle breechloading rifle; in Sweden and Norway the breechloader is partly introduced; and in France the Cent Guards are so armed. With the above exceptions, no breechloading rifles are in the hands of European troops . . . the future will determine whether or not the breechloading arm is to be more generally introduced into service, or to be abandoned."

While the Dreyse Needle Gun was adopted in Prussia in 1841, four years after its development, other government groups spent more time on telling what was wrong with it than on how to improve the principle.

Breech Loading Systems of the Era

At this period four systems of breech construction were in use, though literally hundreds of variations were attempted. First in importance was the BOLT SYSTEM. This was generally called the "slide system," and was introduced by Nicholas Dreyse in his Zündnadelgewehr or Needle Gun. When the bolt was withdrawn, a paper cartridge was inserted. A primer was attached to the base of the bullet, behind it was fastened the bag with the powder. A long needle inside the bolt functioned as the modern striker. When the trigger was pulled, the needle was driven ahead by its spring, its point passed

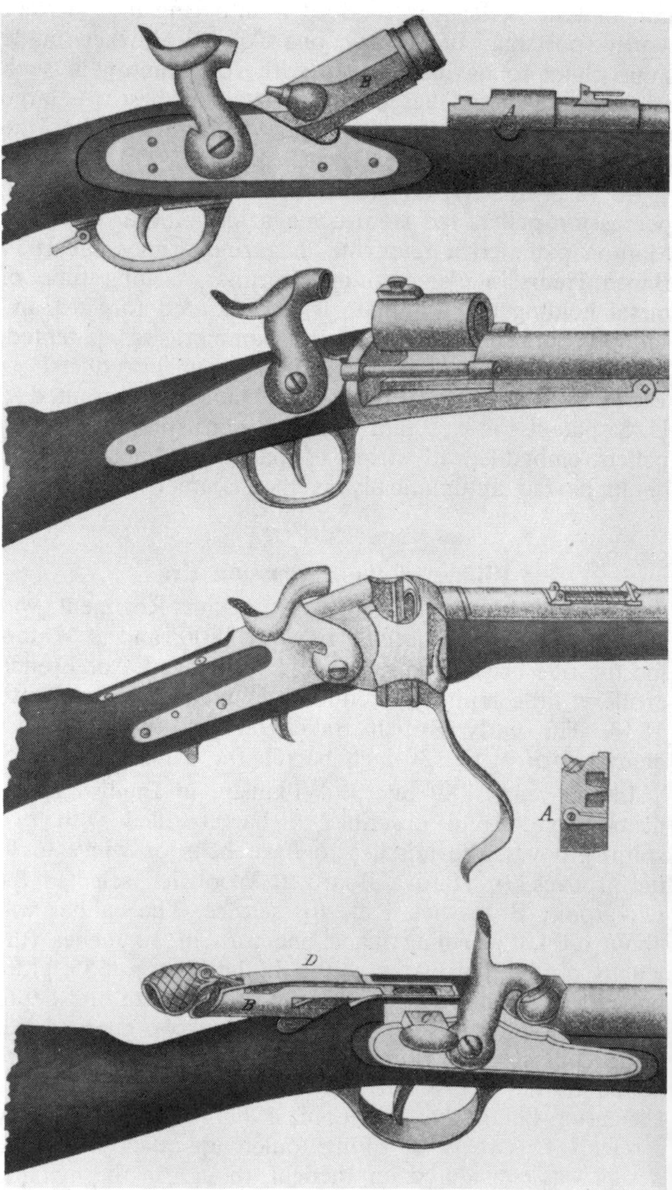

Representative specimens of percussion breech loaders. There were literally thousands of types, variations, alterations and conversions.

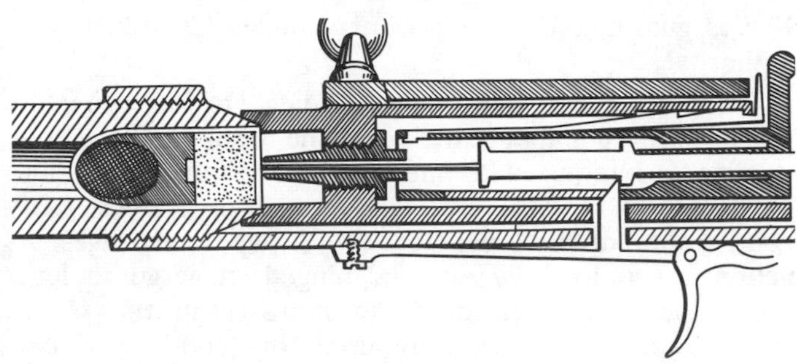

Original drawings showing Dreyse needle gun mechanism and cartridge.

through the powder and hit the primer ahead. The theory was that this placement of the primer would give more complete combustion of the charge. The tremendous importance of this invention, completely overlooked at the time, was the employment of the turn-bolt principle. With the coming of the metallic cartridges, it was to prove the simplest and perhaps the strongest breechloading system ever developed. In its early form, however, it could not seal the breech properly, with the paper cartridges used; and the needle corroded rapidly and was subject to breakage. There is one undated specimen of bolt pattern gun in Paris in the Musee d'Artillerie. So far as we know, however, the Dreyse is the first successful application to firearms of the simple system of the age-old turning bolt as used on doors.

In 1854 Charles W. Lancaster patented English specification No. 2089, a bolt action breechloader using a special paper cartridge fired by an ordinary lock and percussion cap placed over an outside nipple; but again the gas seal was not satisfactory.

As evidence of the fact that the true bolt principle was not grasped, we have the fact that the early American Greene carbine, an arm in which a forward trigger was pulled to unlock the barrel, permitting it to be twisted to the left and then slid forward for loading, was listed with the Dreyse as a "slide system." This quite unusual arm, invented by Col. J. Durrel Greene of the United States of America, was equipped with a Maynard tape primer. It is not to be confused with the later Greene oval-bored bolt action rifle tested by the United States Ordnance Board in 1872. In this later arm, a release button on the tang is pressed to free the bolt, which can then be turned up to the left and pulled back. A bullet—not a cartridge—is inserted in the breech. The bolt is pushed ahead past the normal turning point, thereby causing an auxiliary rod to force the bullet ahead in the chamber and seat it. The bolt is again withdrawn. A paper cartridge having another bullet at the rear is next inserted and the bolt pushed forward. Turning the bolt handle down revolves two front locking lugs into place—probably the first time this now universal front lug system was employed. Thus the rear bullet serves as a gas seal, and after firing, this rear bullet is forced ahead by the bolt to become the projectile for the next round! This arm has a ring-type hammer placed below the barrel. It is percussion cap fired.

The dropping block American Sharp's was classed together with the hinged frame early breechloaders of the Lefaucheux as "the Hinge System" by noted writers of this period. The other two classifications were listed as the "screw" or "trap-door" systems and the "revolver system" as used by Colt.

The Terry (1852) was a bolt action arm with two symmetrical lugs at the rear of the bolt. The Westley Richards, generally listed as "the best of the capping breechloaders," gained its reputation from the effectiveness of its gas seal and the felt wad cartridge used. This lifting hinged block arm was not mechanically in a class with the American Sharp's of the period, which marked the beginning of the long line of lever action dropping block systems.

In 1866 the French introduced the Chassepot, a rifle based on the Dreyse. The forward end of the bolt was fitted with the de Bang obturator of India rubber which expanded in the chamber behind the paper cartridge and was quite effective until hardened by the heat of firing. The Chassepot cartridge carried its primer in the head of the paper cartridge where the needle pierced and fired it.

Norwegian 1842 carbine. Percussion breech loading system.

The Norwegian military arm, 1842 model, had a chamber which was swung up for loading in the manner of the old American Hall. A side lever operated the block. The block had a nipple on its underside and was fired by an under hammer striking the cap on the nipple.

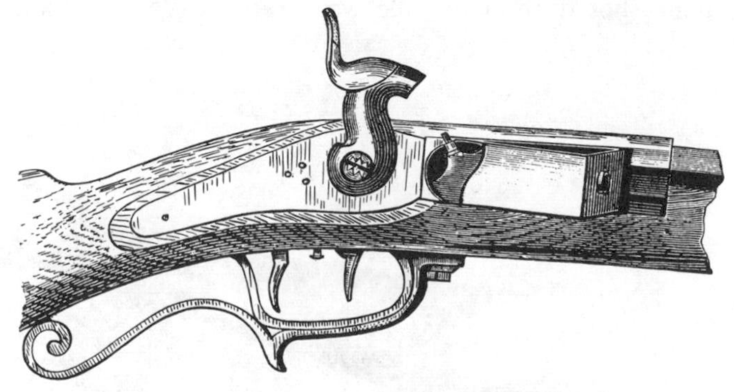

Swiss 1851 d'Abezz percussion breech loading system.

One unusual design was the Swiss d'Abezz in which turning a guard around the triggerguard withdrew the neck of the chamber block from the barrel, then swung the block on a pivot to the right so it could be loaded from its front end. This arm had the standard nipple and a side hammer.

AMERICAN PERCUSSION ARMS

The official U. S. muskets and rifles of the period are standard muzzle loading weapons adapted to the percussion system. The 1841 rifle, often erroneously called the "1842," used in hunting and in the Indian and Mexican Wars and even in the Civil War, was noted throughout the world for its accuracy. Variously known as the "Yerger"—a corruption of the old German Jäger, it is also known as the "Harper's Ferry Rifle" because many of them were made there and also as the "Mississippi." This arm used standard percussion caps. The new 1855 model employed the Maynard Tape Primer.

With the coming of the percussion system, many Kentucky Flintlocks were altered to pill locks, the pan being replaced by an iron bowl and the cock shaped to form a hammer with a projection which would hit down into the bowl to discharge the pill.

The Kentucky rifle now evolved into the "Plains Rifle" which played so important a part in American history. Gunsmiths such as Hawkins and Dimick in St. Louis adapted the Kentucky type to the needs of the settlers moving West, and the changes they originated caught on generally. The "Plains Rifle" weighed from 6.5 to 10.5 lbs. as a rule. The calibers ranged from .26 to .40. Barrels measured from 26 to 38 inches—occasionally longer. Set triggers were the general rule. Front bar locks were employed (the Forsyth system of having the lock mechanism behind the hammer was tried out but was not popular because it seriously weakened the stock, which in Plains service had to stand up under considerable punishment).

The Sharps Rifles

Christian Sharps patented in 1848 a mechanism which is unquestionably the most important American breechloader of this time. It introduced the principle of the successful "drop block" actions. When World War II began over forty actions of this pattern were still made in Europe for target and civilian use. Indeed a variety of the single shot drop-block rifle was used in 1953 by Indian Forces guarding Korean prisoners under United Nations authority!

Sharps designed it in cap-lock days. It was originally loaded with a paper cartridge. The design was merely modified as required to make it one of the great rifles of the early metallic cartridge era. It offered a fairly good sealing of the breech even with paper cartridges. Its action is simple. Lowering the hinged triggerguard lever drops the breechlock down in mortises in the frame. When paper cartridges were used, the end of the cartridge was automatically sheared off as the breech was closed by reversed triggerguard action. This allowed the percussion primer to flash directly into the charge and speeded up loading as well. Later a blade was added to the breechblock to give still better cutting of the cartridge. Some types were designed to be usable as muzzle loaders if the breech fouled too badly! These patterns had ramrods.

The Sharps rifle and carbine (the latter being merely a short rifle, of course) were widely used during the Civil War. When adapted to metallic cartridges, these arms were the famous buffalo guns of our early Western meat and buffalo-robe hunters. The arm passed through a tremendous range of alterations and modifications as time went on, none of which are important to this work and must therefore be passed over.

Other American Breechloaders

The first Joslyn carbine patented in 1855 had a ring above the small of the stock which when lifted raised the breechblock for loading. The Starr, of which over 25,000 were purchased during the Civil War, had a special two-piece breechblock, one part falling back to expose the breech. Literally hundreds of other types were produced experimentally or in some quantity.

Arms which require some passing mention are the Burnside, the Gallagher and the Maynard. The first, invented by Union General A. F. Burnside used a special brass cartridge of conical type. A hole at the rear permitted the cap to flash through into the charge; 55,567 of these rifles and 21,819,200 cartridges were made in

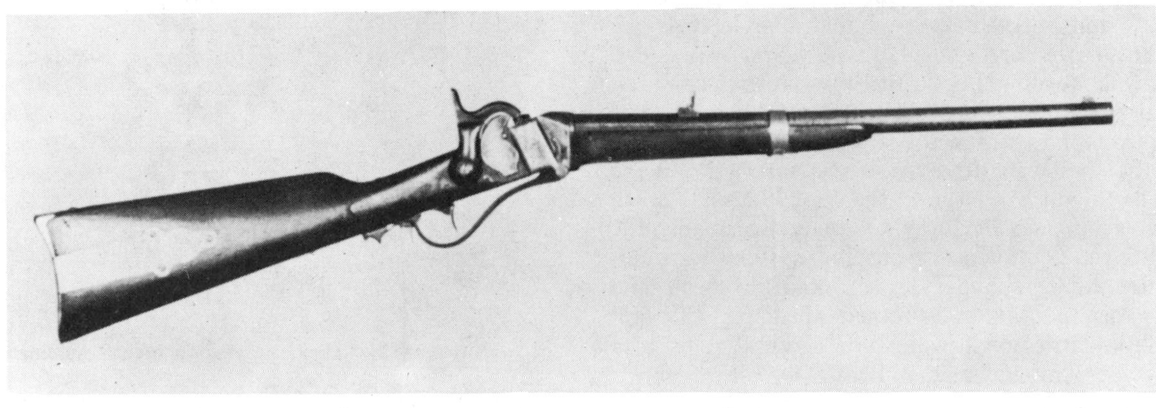

Typical American Sharps Carbine.

the original model. The Gallagher, invented by Mahlon J. Gallagher, had a triggerguard-lever operated breeching system which swung the barrel ahead and down for loading with a paper cartridge; 22,728 Gallagher rifles with 8,294,023 cartridges were purchased by the Government. The Maynard, like the Burnside and the Smith, approached being a transition arm; for while it was fired by percussion cap, it used a freak brass cartridge case. The case had a rimmed base with a hole in the center to permit the cap to flash through. The barrel was hinged down for loading by pushing the triggerguard lever. The Maynard mechanical system was later employed when true metallic cartridges were introduced. Its inventor was a Washington dentist. Earlier he had invented the common tape-primer or cap-roll as already mentioned.

Gilbert Smith's carbine is worthy of mention here, as records show that 30,062 were purchased by the Union Government during the Civil War, and the rifle was well received in Europe. It hinged at the breech somewhat in the manner of the common shotgun. The release mechanism was a small forward trigger within the triggerguard. It fired a freak India rubber cartridge with base perforated to permit a common cap to be used on a vent to fire the charge. Some were later altered to use the weird Crispin metallic cartridge. Over 13,000,000 Smith cartridges were produced during the Civil War.

REPEATING ARMS OF THE PERIOD

The United States inventors, spurred on by the need for improved firearms in the opening of the West as well as for war, repeated in this period every design heretofore experimented with to give many shots with a single loading and in some respects went far beyond anything ever done to that time.

Arms with two loads in the same barrel, as we have seen, were again tried. Legend has it that the Lindsay arm of this type made at Springfield Armory was designed by the inventor as a "surprise" weapon to be used against Indian tactics. The story goes that Lindsay's soldier brother was killed in an Indian attack when the red men charged his unit, drew their fire, and then overran them before they could load again. Lindsay's idea was to let the enemy see you fire an apparently single shot rifle, then be ready to give him the second "surprise" load as he charged. Most of the surprises in this system, however, usually came to the shooter, who was fortunate indeed when only one load went off at the first trigger pull.

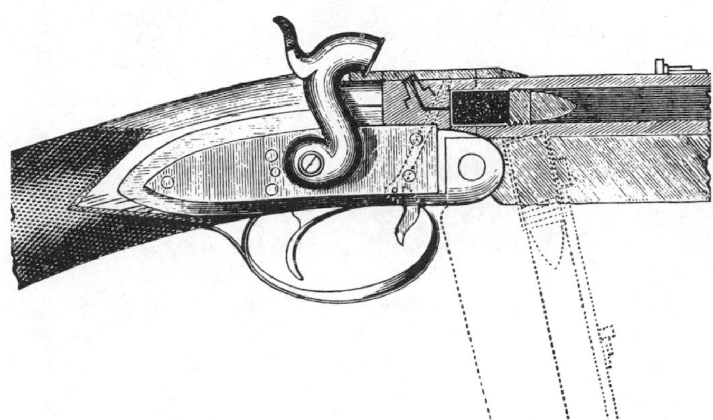

Action of Gilbert Smith's American carbine with hinged frame.

Multi-barreled rifles mounted like the conventional pepperbox also appeared, the barrels commonly being turned by hand to fire in succession from a single lock. The "Sweet" rifle was just one of this type.

"Harmonica" repeaters on the Jarré system were also made. One used by General Sam Houston and now in the Smithsonian has a rectangular feed block which is loaded from the forward end (there are five chambers), and is then inserted in the breech opening on the side. The chamber block, actuated by the hammer, slides across the breech horizontally, bringing each chamber successively in line for firing down the barrel. The "Kendall" of this system has an underhammer. When this is halfcocked, pressing the spring catch on the receiver permits the block to be slid across. John Browning's father made rifles of this type.

A weird collection of revolving cylinder types appeared, quite distinct from the familiar Colt type. These fell into two general classes. First was the "turret" type. The "Cochran" was of this design. The turret type cylinder on top of the receiver was loaded with paper cartridges thrust in from the muzzle openings. There were usually eight chambers. At all times when the arm was loaded, some chambers were pointing their bullets at the firer—and when fire flashed from a firing chamber to an adjoining one, anything could happen.

The "radial" type, to which the "Porter" belonged, operated on the common water-wheel principle, carrying the charges around in succession to line up with the bore as the triggerguard lever was operated. Again however the shooter had loaded chambers pointing right at him when firing, and again the ammunition in use could not be prevented from flashing to adjoining chambers.

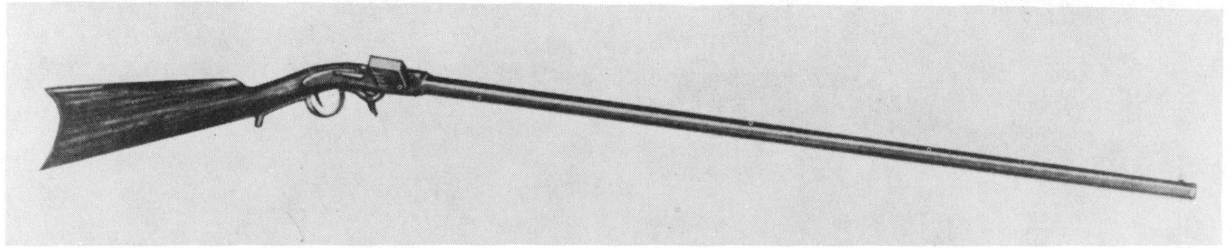

Harmonica percussion repeater made by Jonathan Browning, father of the great American arms wizard John M. Browning.

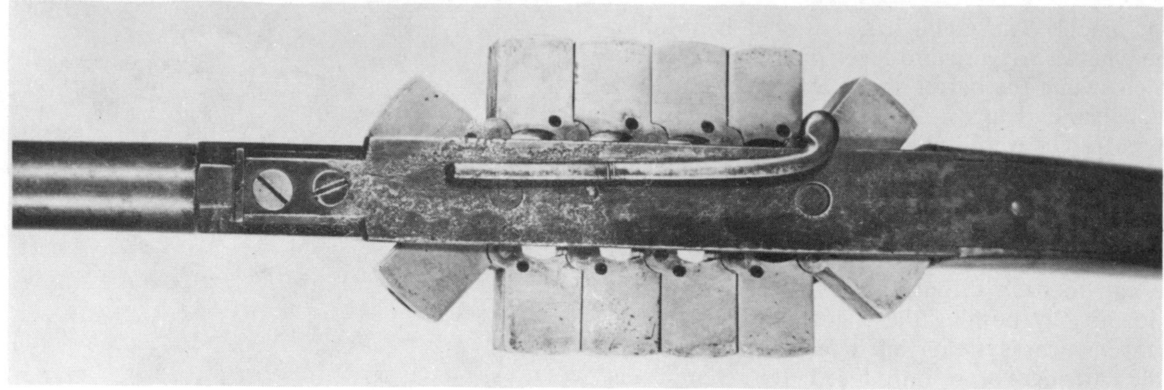

Bennett breech loading percussion rifle, caliber .40. Original inventor's model patented in 1838 by E. A. Bennett. The breech has twelve individual blocks which were fastened together and rotated horizontally instead of up and down as in the Colt and other revolvers and revolving rifles.

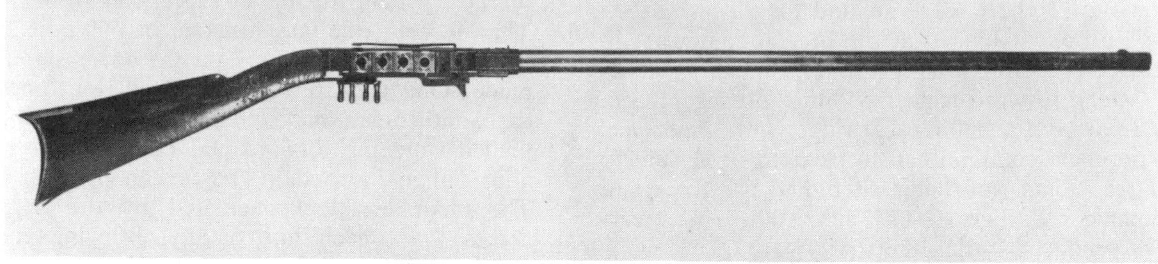

Overall view of Bennett rifle at West Point.

In 1852 North & Skinner issued a cylinder type resembling the older Collier, in which the cylinder was drawn back off the barrel breech and turned to slip the chamfered mouth of the next chamber over the barrel mouth for firing. Dr. Le Mat of New Orleans evolved this cylinder arm which was later made in pin-fire; and in the same year Alexander Hall also produced a cylinder rifle; while from Europe in this period came the Adams, the Deane and a host of others inspired by or frankly imitating the already famous Colt.

The Colt Repeating Rifle

While no arm without fixed ammunition has ever made a satisfactory breechloader or repeating arm, Sam Colt's first products came closest to doing so.

The first Colt Revolving Rifle—merely the Colt percussion revolver of the period with a shoulder stock and long barrel—was produced in 1836. Improvements were added in 1840, 1842 and 1855, and the arm was sold and used throughout the known world. The Colt Repeating Rifle Model 1855 with side hammer of Root patent is famous as being the first repeater bought and used by the U. S., though not many were used. These were .56 caliber arms with five-shot cylinders. In their day they were the wonder of the age, tales of their accuracy being told and re-told until they achieved the heights of the ridiculous. In Cleveland's "HINTS TO RIFLEMEN" published in 1864 we find them credited with accuracy at 680 yards! A more reliable yet still glowing account is that of Captain Hans Busk of the Victoria Rifles who in 1860 wrote his book "THE RIFLE AND HOW TO USE IT," the best work available on the military weapons of that period. He praised the Colt as being the best military arm produced up to that time.

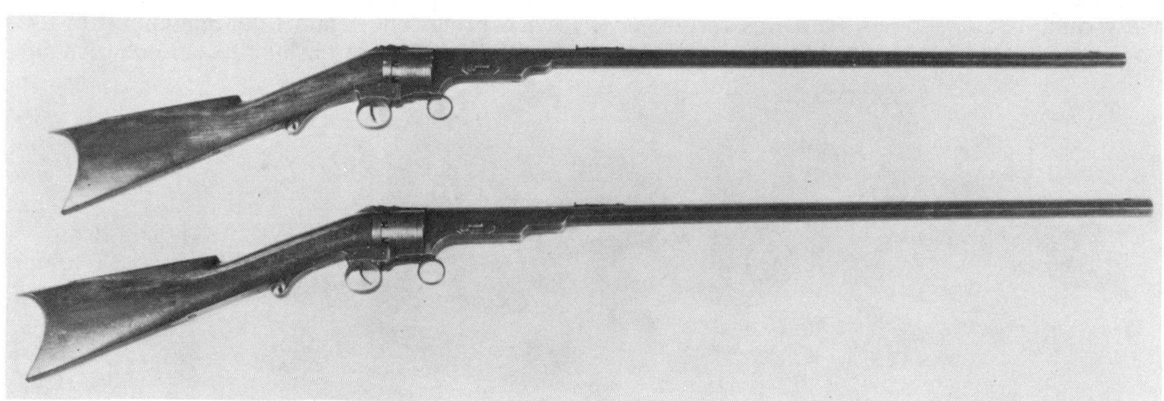

Representative Colt Revolving Percussion Rifles from the West Point Collection.

Repeating rifle with a revolving cylinder made by Jonathan Browning.

Captain Busk's account of the general accuracy and shooting ability of the English soldiers of the day may be gathered from the following extracts: "A patrolling party at the Cape," he says, "used 80,000 cartridges in 1851 to kill or disable 25 savages." This figures out about 3,200 rounds per man. By our modern standards this is most efficient! He tells us that "At the Crimea the French used 25,000,000 cartridges without stopping 25,000 Russians." Of the American rifleman he had high regard, quoting their record at Churubusco where they killed or wounded 800 Mexicans with an average cartridge expenditure of only 125 rounds!

In service use the Colt early received a bad reputation as a rifle. There was so much trouble encountered with the chamber being fired flashing to adjoining chambers that it was the practice of shooters to turn the attached rammer down, then to hold it for forward support. This way they escaped burns on the left hand and wrist from fire spitting at the barrel and chamber juncture or from multi-chamber firing. Even in metallic cartridge days the revolving cylinder system has never worked out satisfactorily in rifles, but it was a step in the evolution of the American rifle.

The Close of the Percussion Era

The percussion era in which a separate tape, pill, cap or priming charge was necessary, was now drawing to a close both here and abroad. Freak cartridges of all orders would still be tried, but all of importance would feature self-contained priming in some form. The popular, and more particularly the military, fear of cartridges containing their own ignition was waning. A period of transition was here. The metallic cartridge with its perfect breech seal was not yet to be fully accepted, but its arrival was foreshadowed in the freaks now to appear in a short passing phase.

PHASE VII—THE PERIOD OF TRANSITION

With the development of the percussion cap, inventors —particularly in England, France, and the United States —turned their energies to attempts to produce ammunition which would carry its own ignition, as well as arms to use such ammunition. The importance of the complete gas seal at the breech was not fully recognized until after thorough war tests had been made of the Dreyse Zündnadelgewehr.

Jean Samuel Pauly of Geneva invented a breechloader in Paris, working out the principle between 1808 and 1812. This was the first attempt at the needle gun, and the self-consuming cartridge was discharged when the needle pierced a paper detonating cap attached to the cartridge. Out of this first crude design Dreyse probably developed his famous needle gun, but that was not until some 30 years later.

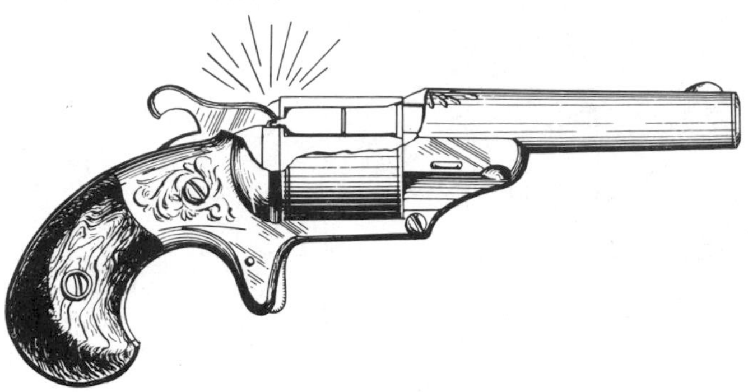

Moore Tit Fire. One of the scores of unsuccessful evolutionary metal cartridge types. This was an example of the American period of transition. Original drawing to show firing system.

Meanwhile in 1831 Augustus Demondion of Paris patented (No. 6137) an unusual rifle and cartridge. This rifle was manufactured by the noted gunsmith, Robert. It was a most important transition design as it marked the introduction of the system of the lifting breechblock hinged at the front. This was the forerunner of literally dozens of lifting block designs throughout the world.

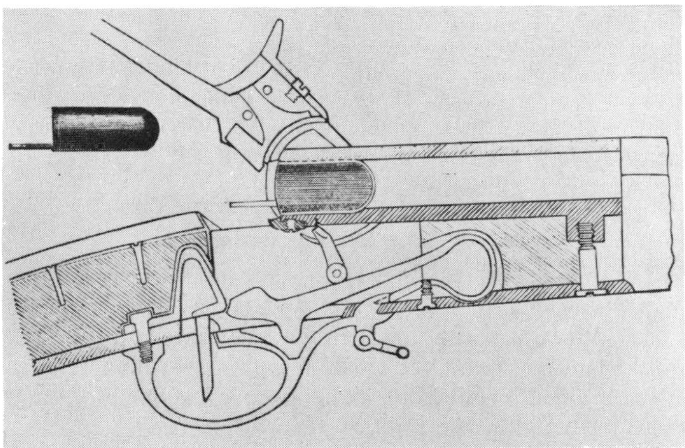

The French Demondion transitional breech loader.

The Demondion is also noteworthy as introducing a weird cartridge which later provided the germ of the idea for the successful pin-fire cartridge. This Demondion cartridge had a flat percussion tube in the shape of a tail projecting from the lower base of the cartridge. When the rifle was opened for loading, lifting the block with its lever automatically compressed a powerful mainspring below the breech. The cartridge was inserted with tail to the bottom. When the trigger was pulled, the flat mainspring snapped up and crushed the detonating tail against the underside of the breechblock. The cartridge case being self-consuming, no extractor was employed—but the breech was not fully sealed against gas escape. However, this design paved the way for the first true gas tight design which was to revolutionize arms manufacture.

At this point it might be well to consider Pauly's developments of 1814 and 1816, since they are generally confused with the inventions of more practical and successful designers. His English patent specification of 1814 (No. 3833) primarily concerns the discharge of black powder by heat generated through compressed air. The patent does not apply to later successful percussion systems. Since standard forms of black powder explode at temperatures around 600 degrees F., Pauly, Newmarch, and others developed experimental mechanisms to discharge the powder charge by obtaining such temperatures through piston arrangements which would produce detonation. A secondary part of this specification describes a hinged-lever breechloader of lifting block design.

Pauly's specification of 1816 is of historic interest, on the other hand, because it clearly recognizes and states the principle of effective breech sealing. It says, "A plug is so placed in the gun as to come between the charge of gunpowder and the movable breeching in all cases, and is formed of lead, copper, or such other ductile materials as will give way to the explosive force of the charge." Here clearly stated for the first time we find official record of the principle of the ductile expanding case which was to be introduced by other Frenchmen, Lefaucheux in 1836 and Houiller in 1847, though even those developments were foreshadowed by the introduction in 1835 of the French Flobert cap. This cap, however, was evolved directly from the familiar copper detonating cap; it did not use a propelling charge. The priming mixture itself was sufficient to drive the light, small gallery or "saloon" bullet out. The Flobert cap, which is practically our "BB" cap of today, was a cap evolution in theory and design, rather than a breech sealing cartridge.

For all practical purposes, the appearance in 1836 in France of the Lefaucheux paper cartridge with metal expanding base, cardboard body and projecting brass pin, marks the beginning of the true breech seal. Enthusiasts still argue as to whether this pin-fired cartridge or that of Houiller in 1847 marked the "true" pin-fire. The matter is entirely academic, since both have projecting pins which when hit by the hammer crush the detonator within the case head and fire the charge. In 1836 Lefaucheux introduced both this cartridge and a hinged-frame gun to handle it. This gun is essentially the grandfather of all our modern double barreled shotguns. The Lefaucheux system was not adapted to military needs, either in its early form using a non-sealing cartridge or its improved form with gas seal case.

Houiller's patents ranging from 1847 to 1850 touch on pin, rim and center fire ignitions; the outstanding feature of the specifications, however, being the use of full metal cases.

About 1854 the French "Mousquetoon des Cent Gardes" came into use. This strange arm used a cartridge of modified pin-fire type with a small pin projecting from its metal on the bottom to fire it, while a longer pin projected from the top to extract it. The breechblock was lowered to load the chamber. When the trigger was pulled the breechblock was driven up by the mainspring, and as it reached its top position a projection at the bottom of the block hit the pin and fired the cartridge!

This, then, was the general state of development in France when the Government adopted the Chassepot Rifle

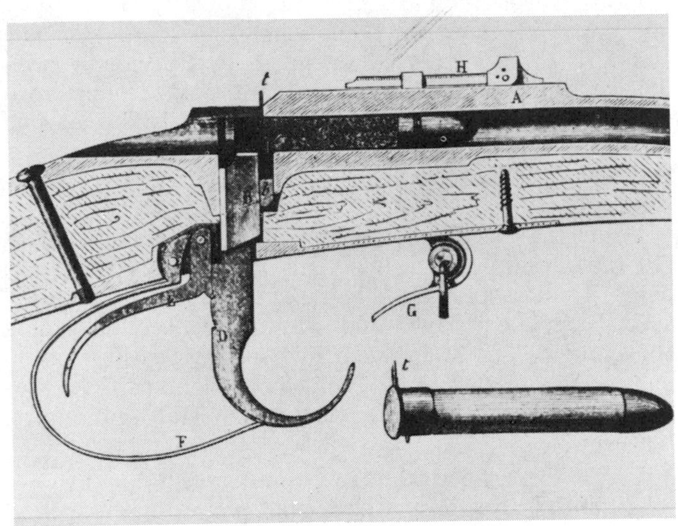

Action of the French Mousquetoon Des Cent Gardes.

already mentioned. It is said that Pauly offered his original needle gun to the great soldier Napoleon Bonaparte, who refused it. In the state of its development at that time, and considering the general conservatism of mankind whether dealing with breechloaders or atomic energy, that is not difficult to understand. By 1830 when Dreyse introduced his first needle gun many of the objections had been worked out. (As a matter of record, it must be pointed out that the gun and cartridge patented in England in 1831, No. 6196 by Moser were patented for Dreyse, English patent office regulations of the time making it wise to have patents handled by English agents.)

When the Dreyse was introduced into the Prussian service it was a "military secret" of the first order. Like most "military secrets" it was a secret only to those naive branches of the military who never seem to be aware of what has been done in their line—those naive branches with which every country is regularly afflicted, and which strangely enough seem to be nearly always in a position to make policy while submerging the real experts who are always present in any army.

And so it was that foreign observers of European powers watched with dread the success of the Dreyse gun in the Schleswig-Holstein war in 1864 and the Austrian War of 1866 where the Prussians again wrought terrible havoc by pitting this inefficient breechloader against the still more inefficient muzzle loaders of their enemies.

In far-off America by this time both the Spencer and the Henry repeating rifles with their metallic cartridges were in use. Breechloading arms of nineteen types were accepted even by the hidebound military and banking-type minds which worried about the heavy ammunition expenditure! These must be dealt with in subsequent chapters, but they require mention here because of their bearing on reactionary and pinch-penny psychologies which have cost so many nations so much throughout the course of history.

In his brilliant treatise, "The Past and Future of Artillery," the French ruler of that time, Napoleon III, wrote: "Inventions that are before their age remain useless until the stock of general knowledge comes up to their level. . . . Not only does routine scrupulously preserve, like some sacred deposit the errors of antiquity, but it actually opposes might and main, the most legitimate and the most evident improvements."

Perhaps, as some humorist would have it, the Emperor did not read his own book. Perhaps with the French Maginot-line mentality of an earlier day he was so obsessed with the terrible efficiency of the Germans that he could not conceive any other nation developing instruments of war superior to theirs. Whatever the cause, in the face of the great strides his own inventors had made, in the face of the ghastly efficiency of the metallic cartridge demonstrated in the tragic American Civil War, in the face of the ultra-conservative British War office testing some 50 systems for converting their old Enfield muzzle loaders to breechloaders and accepting the Snider with its gas-sealing cartridge—in the face of all these developments he adopted a modified needle gun! Oh, it was a great stride forward! It used an obturator of rubber to seal the breech more effectively than the German. (The rubber hardened and became worse than useless after a little firing; but that didn't turn up until later.) The cartridge was reduced to .434 caliber and fired a conical bullet of 380 grains to an extreme range of 1800 yards—but what of its actual efficiency? Consider what a contemporary writer says: "It is said that the Frenchmen spit on their cartridges, force their fingers into the breech action, and give every possible sign that after a few shots, the Chasse-

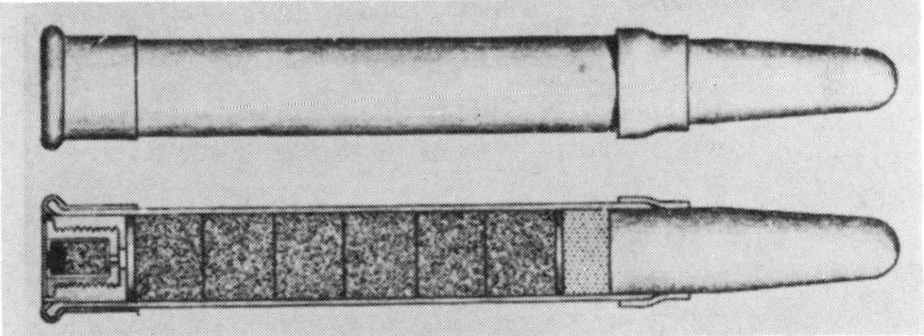

French Mitrailleuse cartridge and section.
(See "Montigny Mitrailleuse" on page 111.)

pot gets so foul they do not know how to treat it. There is a difficulty in getting the cartridge into the chamber when the rifle is foul; if force is used it becomes dangerous—the cartridge being soft, the percussion cap is compressed between the bullet and the point of the bolt, and has been known to explode in the act of loading, in many cases injuring the hand of the shooter." The rifling was given a left instead of a right twist to offset somewhat the bad trigger pull which tended to pull the muzzle to the right!

And what of the value of the long range cartridge? Apparently it wasn't very accurate beyond 100 yards in actual battle use. Yet the Chassepot was admittedly an improvement on the Dreyse. On the Prussian side, consider the report of our General Phil Sheridan who was an observer at the Meuse and Sedan in that fateful War of 1870: "The cavalry," he says, speaking of a charge of the French Hussars, "behaved most gallantly, were sheltered from fire till the last moment, were skilfully and bravely led, and the ground they charged over was not more than

400 yards; yet the result was their destruction as a military body without any effect whatever." The Prussian infantry in this engagement held the fire of their needle guns until the cavalry was within 150 yards, a case of disciplined men recognizing the limitations of their arms.

The Franco-Prussian War converted every nation to the idea of metallic cartridge breechloaders overnight—as time passes in military evolution, that is. In the United States the Dreyse had been imitated and sold by P. Klein in New York City, some 500 having been made by George Foster at Taunton, Mass. These were never popular however. In England, Needham, Sears, Schlesinger and others developed needle type arms, while in France the Comte de Chateauvillier patented a needle gun with a lock resembling the earlier Demondion. This Chateauvillier is interesting because it employed a form of toggle-joint lock which, like the American Jennings, pointed the way to the successful toggle-locking system of automatic days.

Of all these foreign transition arms only one form of the Needham warrants attention at this point. When one remembers that the original W. Greener was one of the greatest gun designers and writers of all time, his enthusiasm for the Needham Repeating Rifle can be explained away only on the ground of excessive British patriotism.

The fantastic English Needham repeating rifle and cartridge.

This weird specimen utilized a tube below the barrel for a magazine, plus a revolving cylinder. Special cartridges were used which were in two pieces, the base being rimless and tapering to the rear; a collared cap at the forward end fitting the exterior of the cap and projecting inside the case proper. When the percussion cap in the base of the cartridge was detonated, and the powder charge ignited, the collar about the case was supposed to drive ahead and expand to seal the joint between cylinder and barrel. When the magazine was loaded a spiral spring forced the cartridges back. Operating a finger lever triggerguard carried the cylinder through a one-quarter revolution, partly raised and then dropped the hammer to eject the fired case forward out of a chamber, lined up a chamber to receive a loaded cartridge, lined up the chamber with the barrel, and then cocked the hammer! Remember that metallic cartridge repeaters were as Greener puts it "flooding the market" at that time, then consider his appraisal: "This, the only English repeating rifle, is of novel construction; the idea, most happily conceived, combines the principles of the ejecting hammerless gun and the revolver with a tubular magazine gun. . . . The system is to be greatly commended. It is decidedly original, of sound principle, and unlike any of the numerous magazine arms now flooding the market." This closing remark referred to such arms as the Spencer, Winchester and Vetterli! The Needham, needless to say, was a complete failure.

While the Needham was the only one manufactured, several transition English designs in repeaters were patented. The Restall had a tube magazine below barrel, used special freak cartridges and was operated by a sliding triggerguard. The Maberly carried special cartridges in an endless chain device in the buttstock. None of the European transition arms are of fundamental importance, however.

American Transition Arms

American arms design during all phases of this period was the soundest in the world. Germany had the best military machine, France the best chemists and cartridge experimenters, England the best writers and public relations men. But the U.S.A. was most prolific in both design and manufacture of practical arms. The need for arms for frontier service, of course, had much to do with this.

The Germans were hampered psychologically by the fact that they were actually winning wars with the needle gun and had no time to consider change. The French were handicapped by their national psychology and by studying Prussia to the exclusion of all other countries. English inventors, faced with the fact that the War Office considered any cartridge with self-ignition dangerous and impracticable, and any breechloader as a useless expender of large quantities of ammunition, spent their energies on a hundred useless designs to make a more efficient cap-fired muzzle loader!

But in America there was a civilian hunting, sporting, and protective market to absorb really good designs. As a result, while every conceivable system of breech locking appeared, in every major instance the arm was fired by an elementary tube, cap or pill. No effort was wasted on the abortive groups of cartridges used in Europe which sought to combine the ignition with the charge, but without considering the necessity for an effective gas seal. In short, the American line of design, with only one truly notable exception, moved directly from percussion lock to metallic cartridge design.

The Jennings Repeating Rifle

Walter Hunt of New York City patented a lever operated "Volitional Repeater" in 1849, but it was an impractical weapon employing a special rocket-type cartridge with separately fed primer and was operated by two levers. Lewis Jennings improved on Hunt's basic idea.

The Jennings Rifle

Without question the Jennings was the most important firearms development of this era. Its system led directly to the transitional Volcanic which in its turn produced the rim fire metallic cartridge Henry rifle, which in turn became the first famous Winchester rifle.

The story of Windsor, Vermont, that great cradle of firearms development, manufacture and invention, has never been written. High among its achievements ranks the manufacture by Robbins and Lawrence of the first reasonably successful approach to the solution of the problem of the repeating rifle, the repeater of Lewis Jennings, patented Dec. 25, 1849. Pat. No. 6,973.

Some samples of the Jennings in collections have the Maynard tape primer. A tube below the barrel carries twenty conical bullets with hollow bases. The propelling charge is in the hollow bullet itself. The charges are loaded by gravity into the breech, no springs being used as in later cartridge types. The muzzle is raised to allow the bullets to slide back until the first one drops onto a carrier. This carrier is operated by a ratchet through the operation of a ring trigger. So far as we know, this is the first successful use of the familiar below-barrel magazine tube.

Much more important, however, is the breech locking system. This Jennings is the direct source of the mechanical principle of locking of some of the most successful of all automatic arms later produced. It was brought to a higher state of efficiency in its direct successor—the Volcanic pistol and rifle.

The Volcanic system of locking was modified in the Henry cartridge rifle and in the first rifle to bear the Winchester name. Hiram Maxim, one of the greatest arms inventors of all time, adapted the early Winchester rifle to an automatic loader by using a false butt plate and a system of springs. More important, however, he obtained from this pattern the idea for his later machine gun locking system.

This toggle-system of locking the breech was perfected by Maxim and used on the Maxim Machine Guns. With only slight modifications it became the locking system of the Vickers Machine Gun, the toggle being inverted.

Another inventor who drew on Jennings toggle-lock system was Hugo Borchardt. He was employed at Winchester for a time. He developed one of the earliest successful autoloading pistols. When he could not interest American makers in it, Borchardt took his design to Germany. It was manufactured there for a time. The Borchardt was developed into the world-famous Luger pistol—the toggle buckling up to unlock. Many experimental and a few successful recent machine guns use the principle, one being the Swiss Fürrer.

Historical Note on the Jennings

Jennings has received scant attention from firearms historians, though as we have seen he was one of the great pioneers of design. A note on the operation of his arms based on contemporary reports and drawings may therefore be of interest.

In a copy of the International Magazine published in 1852, one W. M. Ferris contributed a description of the Jennings rifle. A magazine on top of the breech was filled with percussion pills or priming powder, he says. A tubular magazine below the barrel was then loaded with hollow cartridges containing the propelling powder. These cartridges were merely bullets with cavities in them to hold the powder in the rear section. The magazine tube held 24 cartridges.

The forefinger of the firing hand was passed through the ring which formed the lever end below the receiver. The thumb was placed on the hammer. The muzzle of the rifle was then elevated sufficiently to let the cartridge nearest the breech slip by gravity onto the carrier. The lever was then pushed forward. Raising the hammer moved the breech pin back and raised the carrier, placing the cartridge in line with the barrel. Pulling the lever back forced the breech pin forward to push the cartridge into the firing chamber. This same motion took a percussion priming from the magazine by action of a special priming rack. This rack revolved the pinion forming the bottom of the magazine, and also threw up a toggle behind the breech pin securely locking it for the moment of discharge. An upward pressure of the finger within the ring released the hammer. The hammer pin struck the priming and flashed fire into the powder within the ball cavity. Releasing the finger pressure permitted the ring to take its normal rest position ready for the next shot.

Early reports give the tube capacity as 24 bullets and claim a rate of fire of twenty shots per minute.

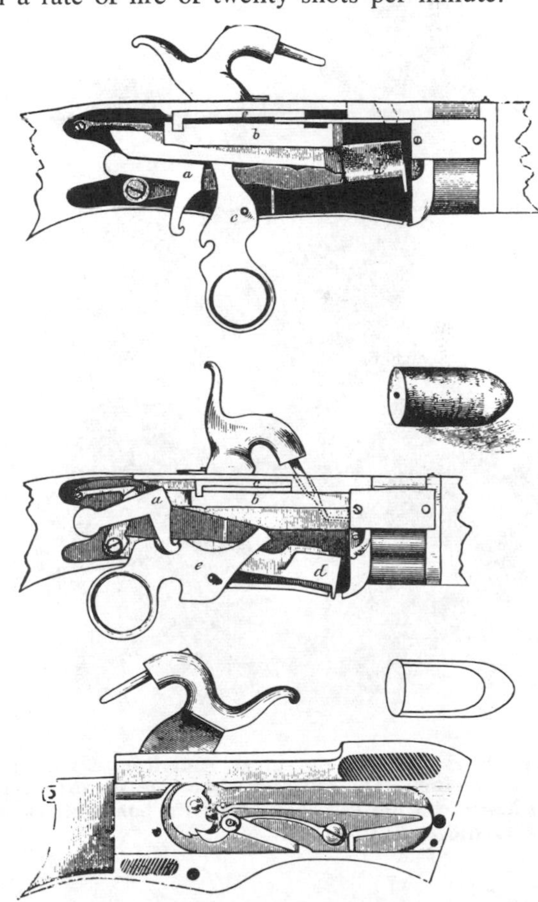

Action of Original Jennings Repeating Rifle.

Christian Buchel also of New York City patented a repeater also in 1849 intended to use a special paper-case cartridge resembling the needle type and operated by sliding the magazine tube. This, too, was an impractical arm.

The Jennings of the same year was actually manufactured as a repeater. Some are found in collections today as single shot arms, the gravity tubes having been dispensed with when found impractical under hard field conditions. Horace Smith improved the original patent with a reservoir for the percussion pills.

The Volcanic Rifle

However, the really important improvement in design came with the introduction of the positive double-toggle lock joint (pat. 10535) of Smith and Wesson filed on Feb. 14, 1854. Tyler Henry, an outstanding mechanic employed at the Robbins and Lawrence plant at Windsor, Vermont, had helped build the original Jennings. He was engaged to combine the Jennings and the Smith patents to produce the first Volcanic.

The Volcanic cartridge was new here, though several resembling it had been attempted in Europe. It consisted of a hollow base conical bullet having a charge of black powder in the hollow. The powder was kept in place by a cardboard disc which contained the primer. Since this cartridge had no gas seal, it was foredoomed to failure. This cartridge design in those days permitted only a low-power charge, and gas escape at the breech was impossible to prevent.

Originally introduced as the "Smith & Wesson" and manufactured at Norwich, Conn., in 1854 (both as a rifle and as a pistol), the arm was taken over by a corporation formed in July 1855 and renamed the "Volcanic." In 1856 the company moved to New Haven, and Smith and Wesson left to found their pistol company. When

B. Tyler Henry, one of the great American developers of arms and ammunition. The letter H appearing on the head of every Winchester rim fire cartridge case is in honor of his work in rim fire cartridge development.

Oliver P. Winchester, founder of the great arms and ammunition combine which today is part of the Olin-Mathieson Chemical Corporation.

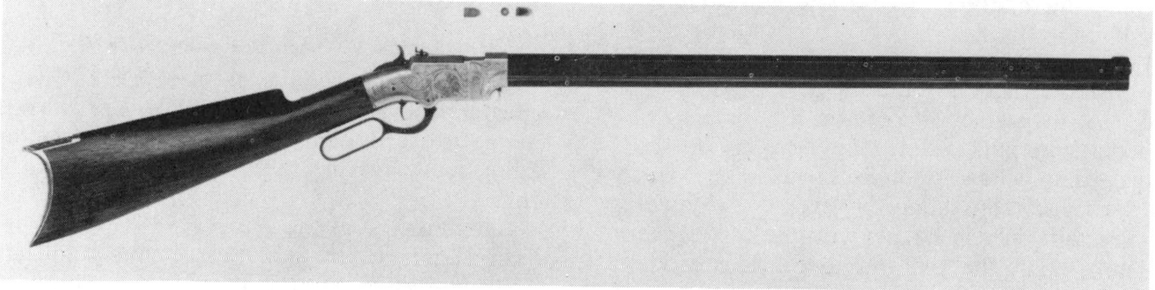

The original Volcanic Repeating Rifle from the Winchester Collection.

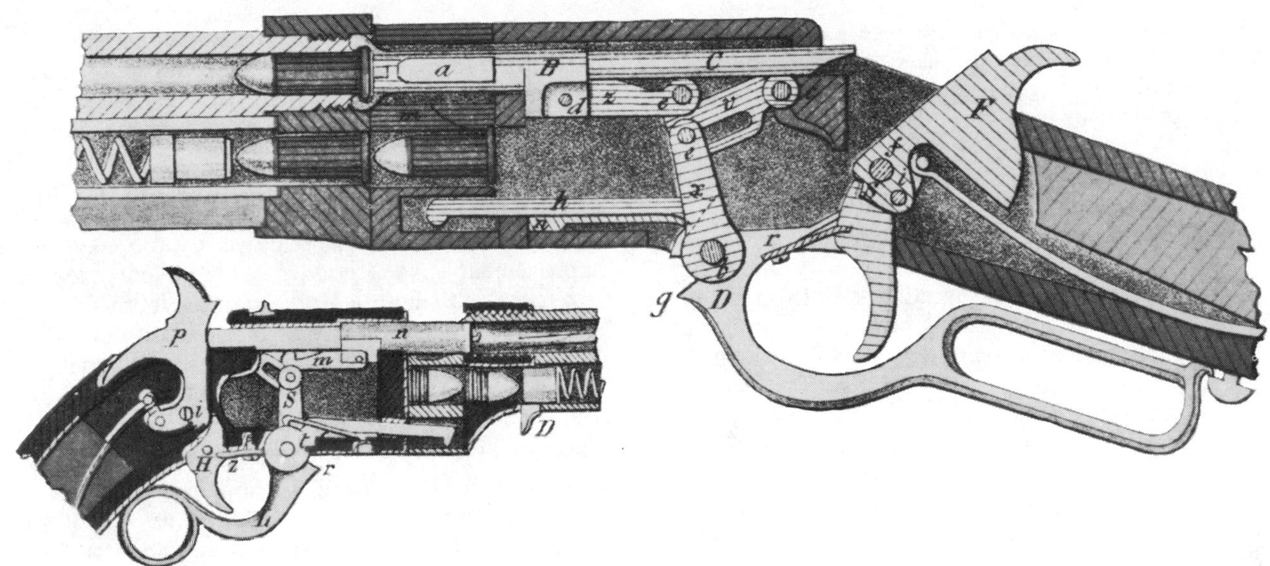

Contemporary drawings showing evolution from Volcanic (below) with its freak cartridge to Henry (above) with rim fire cartridge.

the company was thrown into bankruptcy in 1857, Oliver F. Winchester, one of the original stockholders, bought up the assets and formed the New Haven Arms Company.

Winchester at that time was neither the "successful manufacturer in the textile field" nor yet the "shirt manufacturer" that some have made him out. He was actually a prosperous haberdasher. True, he knew little about arms. But he had in him the native strains of shrewdness, foresight and courage which brought fame and fortune to so many New Englanders of the period. Oliver Winchester had to a supreme degree the characteristics which helped to mould America in those early days. Himself a tireless worker, he drove all those around him. He had the sound executive ability to hire and trust experts whose services he needed—a tremendous ability in itself; and he did not hesitate to back his judgment with his own cash—a characteristic that distinguished him from many of his critics.

In the October 9th issue for the year 1858 of "Frank Leslie's Illustrated Newspaper" is a long and glowing account of the Volcanic Repeating Rifle which has been the basis for hundreds of interesting if rather foolish stories about the arm. As the forerunner of the Winchester, the Volcanic is an epochal development. As a practical arm it was a distinguished failure.

Leslie's said: "It combines every quality requisite in such a weapon . . . thirty shots can be fired in less than one minute . . . the balls may be soaked in water with perfect impunity, and can be kept any length of time. They cannot be exploded by contact with flame. . . ."

"The squad of police sent down to Staten Island during the Quarantine riots," the article continues, "were armed with these weapons to the extent of some eighty or ninety rifles and forty pistols. We should judge that for police purposes and as cavalry carbines these Volcanic firearms can have no competitor, and the pistols are undoubtedly superior to anything yet produced. Their waterproof qualities render them especially desirable for the use of travellers and in the Navy."

The closing blurb, however, is an index to the reliability of much of the published literature of the time: "A Good Shot will hit a Quarter of a Dollar at Eighty Yards with one of the Navy pistols." Actually, of course, it is quite a problem to hit a flour barrel full of quarters—or full of anything else—at eighty yards with this cartridge. But the publicity sold weapons, helped to establish Oliver Winchester, and has been a great boon to writers ever since its original publication.

As a matter of further record, the Volcanic vanished from the American scene within two years of the publication of this glowing article! An actual machine rest test of a Volcanic with specially loaded cartridges (no original ones could be found which would fire) placed 5 shots just inside a 21-inch circle at 80 yards when fired from a practically unused collector's specimen.

With the coming of World War II, the Wheel of Design, like so many other things in history, completed a turn. Experiments conducted by the Japanese on Volcanic-like ammunition with the charge contained in a hollow in the ball, met with some success in properly sealed automatic cannon. In the United States freak cases with metal heads and weak plastic sides permitted us to develop the outstanding piece of portable artillery, the Recoilless Cannon—some of the powder gases escaping through the case walls to a Venturi tube where they blow back over the shoulder of the firer and counterbalance the recoil. In both the U. S. and Germany considerable headway was made on plastic cartridge cases; while some German developments in self-consuming cases used with modern breechlock designs met with a certain measure of success. . . . In short, the historical period of Firearms Transition repeated itself at its new place on the spiral of development; but for practical purposes, the metallic cartridge is still master of the ammunition world.

PHASE VIII—METALLIC CARTRIDGES

As we have seen, breechloaders were known even in the 14th Century. However, the successful breechloader became a possibility only when the first metallic cartridges containing both built-in ignition and expanding case were introduced.

Some soft metal cases were used in early European muzzleloaders. The rear end was removed and the case containing the powder and ball was rammed down the muzzle. Similar types were tried with the early American Maynard. In all such cases the ignition was from a separate cap. The metal case itself was blown out the barrel with the bullet. Such systems were devised solely to speed up muzzle loading.

The modern breechloader requires three things of its ammunition. First, it must be a "fixed" charge. That is to say, each must contain case, primer, propelling charge, and bullet. Second, it must have a ductile metal case which when fired will expand against the walls of the firearm chamber to prevent any gas blowing back along the sides of the case; and which will contract automatically after the gas pressure drops so that extraction will be easy. Third, its primer must have built-in a mechanical anvil in center fires or a folded head in rim fires which will allow the firing pin blow to crush and detonate the priming charge.

The varieties of such fixed ammunition must be discussed separately in the order of their development.

The Pin Fire Cartridge

The first successful breechloading cartridge was the Pin Fire.

Mention has already been made of Pauly's experiments in France on ammunition. He tried sealing the breech with ductile metal discs.

The honor of introducing the first truly successful breechloading cartridge and gun, however, belongs to Pauly's successor, E. Lefaucheux, a famous Parisian gunsmith. This was in 1836. Here again a certain qualification is necessary because of improvements made in the Lefaucheux case design by Houiller, another Frenchman, in 1847.

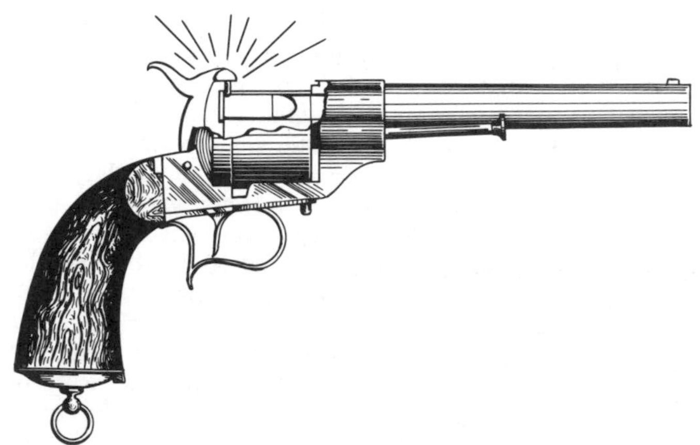

Pin fire principle—the Lefaucheux. Original drawing to show method of ignition.

The cartridges themselves are known as "Pin Fires." In its earliest form the Pin Fire introduced by Lefaucheux resembled a modern shot shell. It was a paper case which contained shot and powder. It was fitted with a metal head which contained the priming and which would expand as a gas seal at the instant of firing. A pin projected from the side of the case head and led down into the priming mixture. The gas seal was not too good. Houiller's improvement gave a good gas seal. Note must be made that seven years before Houllier's development yet another Parisian gunmaker, Bastin LePage, introduced a freak cartridge in which the copper cap and anvil projected from the base of the case. The design gave extraction trouble. It must not be confused with the successful Lefaucheux and Houiller developments.

Lefaucheux introduced his new cartridge and a hinged frame shotgun to use it in 1836. The gun itself is the parent of most of our common double barrel shotguns, though its breeching mechanism was crude and not too efficient.

In Pin Fire arms (rifles and revolvers and pistols as well as shotguns are made on the principle) a notch is provided in the arm itself to position the pin when the cartridge is chambered. As the hammer falls it drives the pin down into a reversed cap which is seated in a cup-shaped base within the case head, and which contains the priming mixture.

When Lefaucheux showed his double shotgun at the London Exhibition in 1851, the cartridges shown with it incorporated the Houiller improvements. All Pin Fires are very commonly referred to as "the Lefaucheux system," though Houiller played a considerable part in the ultimate design.

The Lefaucheux design was an instantaneous success in sporting use both as a cartridge and as a gun design. The military, understandably, did not rate the principle very highly. The hinged frame principle of breechloading, of course, is not suited to military needs, primarily because so much shooting and reloading must be done from prone positions where the drop-barrel system is impractical. Except as substitute standard arms purchased in times of stress where any arms available had to be used, this system has never been in official military use. The pin-fire cartridge principle was used in military service only on such freaks as the Cent Gards Musketoon (or "Treuille de Beaulieu" rifle, to give it its true name, which derives from the name of the French Artillery Captain who was responsible for its adoption); and the impractical rifle-shotgun combination of Dr. Alexandre Le Mat of New Orleans. This arm, having a revolving cylinder which fired through an upper rifle barrel while mounted on a lower shotgun barrel, was used by the Confederacy as a percussion arm. After the Civil War, the French and Belgian plants manufacturing it produced the weapon in pin-fire design.

The pin-fire system has been widely used in shotguns, revolvers and pistols in Europe, though very sparingly in rifles. These arms are of little interest and less importance to us in this study. The cartridge itself, whether of metal-and-cardboard shotgun type or of metallic pistol and rifle type, is also of little importance in the United States. No arms are made here for such cartridges.

However, the principle of the gas-tight cartridge, which completely revolutionized firearms design and the art of war, found its first successful expression and acceptance in the pin-fire; a fact which assures the system a high place in the history of arms and ammunition evolution.

Why the principle of the gas tight cartridge was not recognized by the military as it was by sporting gun manufacturers at that 1851 Exhibition is one of the mysteries of firearms. As late as 1866, as we have seen, the French adopted the impractical Chassepot needle cartridge. In 1867 the Russians adopted the Karl modification, also a bolt action needle system. In 1867 the Italians transformed their Carcano muzzle loaders to a bolt action needle system also!

And what about the United States Army? Well, we too, had observers and exhibitors at the London Exhibition in 1851. Yet at the outbreak of the Civil War the Union had on hand as arms for an infantry war some 530,000 muskets which were essentially only modified Revolutionary War design! They were fitted with rifled barrels and percussion locks, but were still muzzle loaders. In the initial year of that terrible War the Union armories turned out about 10,000 such muzzle loaders. In the second year production was stepped up to 200,000. In the next year the machine potential of the industrialized North swung into high gear and produced about 500,000 more. Still more muzzle loaders were purchased from abroad, ranging from some 428,000 Enfield .577's made in England to 60,000 Austrian tubelock alterations purchased from the Belgian firm of Herman Boker and Company. The North alone bought 726,705 European muzzle loaders in this period as shown by official War Department records.

When we add in any estimate for the arms of the Confederacy—the vast bulk of which were also muzzle loaders—it becomes apparent that in an advanced day of breechloading systems our own government was also caught short with muzzle loaders. The official Union tally lists 4,022,130 muzzle-loading muskets and 90,000.000 rounds of lead bullets issued during the War!

The inefficiency of the muzzle loader in battle conditions is highlighted in an official War Department report quoted by many writers from Napoleon III on: The Battle of Gettysburg occurred July 1, 2 and 3, 1863. Of 37,574 muskets salvaged from the field and sent to Washington for inspection, one musket had 23 rounds in the barrel; 6,000 had from 3 to 10 rounds each in the barrel; 12,000 had 2 rounds in the barrel; 6,000 had one load in the barrel. The remainder were unloaded. Allowing 13,574 fired and 6,000 correctly loaded, we get a very graphic picture of what happened under stress. Some men inserted paper cartridges incorrectly so the cap-fire couldn't reach the powder. Some tried to fire without caps. Others plugged the barrels in many ways. None of these things could occur with breechloaders, of course. Thus from one-third to one-half of the men engaged in this great battle on both sides are shown to have been practically useless as riflemen! And all because they used muzzle loaders!

The Rim Fire

The next successful stage was the development of the Rim Fire cartridge and arms to use it. In this design, still in common use in some calibers, the casehead has a projecting rim. The priming is spun into the space between the folds of this rim. Unlike the Pin Fire which must be deliberately positioned so that the hammer will hit the pin directly, the Rim Fire is loaded without positioning. The underside of the projection commonly rests on the face of the breech which thus serves as an anvil. When the firing hammer or pin hits the top rim of the case, it crushes the metal and detonates the priming.

Some of Houiller's French patents bear on a rim fire principle. So far as we know, however, he did nothing to develop the principle.

The noted French gunmaker Flobert took the common percussion cap of the time and re-shaped it to give it a rim. He loaded this with a small lead projectile. From 1835 to 1847 Flobert produced pistols and parlor rifles to use this ammunition. Note that such cartridges did not carry a projectile charge of powder. The priming fulminate itself generated enough power for the type of indoor (or "salon") shooting for which Flobert developed firearms. The present day "BB Cap" (meaning bulleted-breech cap) is almost identical with Flobert's cartridge.

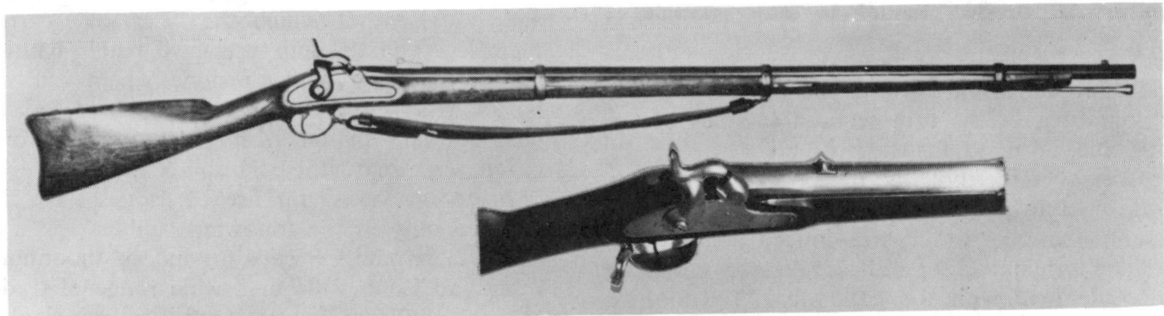

Typical representative American Civil War muzzle loader.

He too showed his arms and ammunition at the 1851 London Exhibition in the Crystal Palace.

There is no question that the first truly practical Rim Fire cartridge was the Smith & Wesson .22 produced in 1857. From his own research there is no question in the author's mind that the founders of the great Smith & Wesson Arms Company developed this cartridge directly from samples of Flobert's cap.

In 1851 Horace Smith, Daniel B. Wesson and B. Tyler Henry were all intimately associated with Robbins & Lawrence of Windsor, Vermont. This firm entered a series of rifles and interchangeable parts at the London Exhibition. Representatives of the firm secured samples of the Flobert caps and returned them to America.

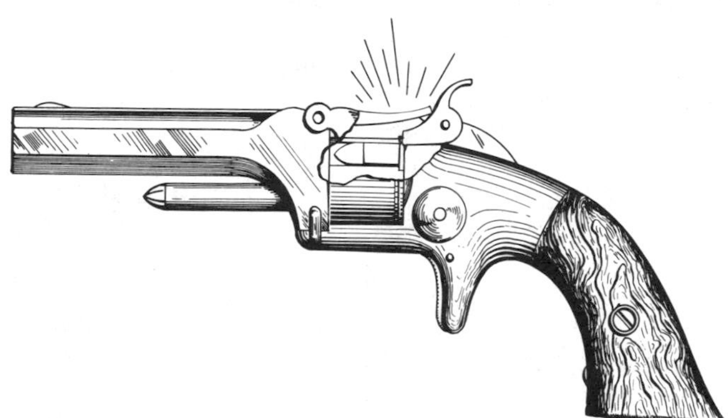

Rim fire principle—the first Smith & Wesson metallic cartridge revolver, caliber .22. Original drawing to show principle of ignition.

Smith & Wesson undertook the development of a low cost method of drawing the cartridge cases. This was their great contribution. And it was indeed a great one in its day. The original .22 Smith & Wesson cartridge is practically identical with the common .22 Rim Fire cartridge we know today.

B. Tyler Henry redesigned the old Volcanic rifle and chambered it for a rim fire cartridge of .44 caliber. The rifle patent was granted in 1860. It is noteworthy that Henry at no time ever laid claim to having designed the cartridge. However, Winchester, for whom he worked and later re-designed the .44 Henry to become the famous .44 Winchester of frontier days, stamped an "H" on the head of the copper cartridge case. To this day the tradition is maintained. Every Winchester-made Rim Fire cartridge case bears the letter "H" on its head.

The rim fire was the cartridge of the early successful American repeaters used during the Civil War to a limited extent: the rifles of Spencer, Ball and Henry. It was the cartridge of the early single shots, too: Peabodys, Remingtons, Ballards, later-day Sharps, of the Joslyns, converted Starrs, Cochrans, Whitneys, Millers, Needhams, Robert-Springfield conversions, Allen & Wheellocks, Ball & Williams—and of scores of others whose records may be found in the files of the Ordnance Corps.

In their time these rifles and carbines with the rim fire ammunition made history not only in America but throughout the world. In Europe the Peabodys and the Remingtons in particular were widely adopted by the military and were a big factor in foreign design. The rim fire cartridge itself was adopted for use in the Austrian Wänzl in 1867, the Albini-Braendlin made in England in 1867, the Belgian Terssen of 1868, the Swiss Vetterli repeater of 1869 and the Italian Vetterli-Vitali repeater of 1869.

The faults of the rim fire cartridge—the uneven distribution of priming around the rim, case weakness caused by rim crimping, and adaptability only to medium and low powered loads—has relegated this development to the obsolete in all except small bore, low powered designs.

While the earliest rim fire cartridge cases were of copper, later ones were made generally of gilding metal, 95% copper and 5% zinc. The use of mercuric priming made such a case necessary because the natural affinity of mercury for brass resulted in defective priming when attempts were made to use the rim fire system in the stronger brass cases.

With the development of non-mercuric priming in recent years, much rim fire ammunition has used strong brass cases, thereby allowing higher pressure in high speed ammunition. Steel cases, too, have become practicable as mechanics and metallurgy have developed.

Originally loaded with black powder, by 1905 these cartridges were also being loaded with a blend of black and smokeless of which the "Lesmok" cartridges were typical. While this mixture gave better ignition and accuracy, it left a heavy residue which fouled the small bore barrels rapidly. The common load today is smokeless powder, though some ammunition for ultra-precision work may still be Lesmok loaded.

In recent years rim fire cartridges have been manufactured only in the following calibers for United States use: .22 BB and CB caps for indoor shooting; .22 Short, Long and Long Rifle in a wide range of trademarks for plinking, gallery shooting and for precision small bore shooting; .22 magnum, .22 W.R.F. for target and small game; .22 Winchester Automatic and .22 Remington Autoloading for plinking and small game shooting; .25 Short Stevens and .25 Stevens and .32 Short and Long to meet the demands from large groups of owners of older weapons handling these cartridges; .41 Short to meet a large demand for cartridges for the long obsolete Derringer type pistols; and .41 Swiss to supply the cartridge demand from farm areas where huge numbers of obsolete Swiss Vetterli rifles, originally sold by Bannerman of New York City early in the century, are still in use.

The Center Fire

The development of the center fire cartridge permitted the design of the really high power firearm. In its common form it is the familiar rimmed or rimless case (though it may be semi-rimmed or belted also), in which the primer is an individual element seated in a depression in the center of the case head. This design is much more positive in its ignition than any rim fire can possibly be and it also lends itself to reloading which the crushed rim of the rim fire design does not.

Again the evolution of the design is such that it is not possible to ascribe it definitely to any one source. For all practical purposes, however, the French Pottet case patented in France in 1857 is the direct ancestor of all Center Fire cases. This design closely resembles our modern shotgun cartridge case, and its specifications are so clearly set forth in the patent that there is no question about its originality.

Many European writers in the past have credited the English gunmaker Charles Lancaster with the development. Actually the Lancaster case was merely an attempt to overcome the shortcomings of the earlier Pin Fire design. True, it was Center Fire in action. But it bears no such resemblance to the modern center fire, as does the Pottet. Lancaster's development was an expedient only. Pottet's development was a new principle of ignition.

The first widely used center fire cartridge case was patented in England in 1861. Patent is in the name of F. E. Schneider of Paris. This case was originally sold by the English gunmaker, G. H. Daw. In 1866 Daw sued W. T. Eley for making a similar cartridge. The suit was thrown out of court, and soon thereafter many varieties of center fire modifications were developed in England.

British observers of the Danish-German Wars were highly impressed with the field performance of the Dreyse Needle Breechloader. Based on their reports the Russel Committee was set up in 1864 in England to investigate the possibilities of breechloading systems. While the Henry and Spencer repeaters were already in use in the United States at the time, no thought was given by the English to such arms. Military thinking everywhere still favored the single shot. And hard economic facts also had to be faced—even as today.

The British tests not only covered rifle alteration and design. They also extended to ammunition; and in that connection historical note may be taken here of the Snider Rifle and its cartridges.

In answer to a Government advertisement in August of 1864, about fifty systems were offered to meet the requirements stipulated. Chief of these was that the system should be suitable for converting the Enfield muzzle loaders to breechloaders, and that proper ammunition should be available. This, it must be understood, was strictly an expedient. England realized her predicament in a breechloading infantry world at that time and sought a quick make-shift arm. Most of the systems presented were designed to utilize the available Enfield lockwork, naturally.

In 1867 a system offered by Jacob Snider, an American, was officially adopted. The conversion consisted of cutting away the breech of the arm to fit a breechblock hinged upon the right hand side of the barrel. A firing pin and spring were mounted in the breechblock. The original Enfield lockwork was employed. A spring catch locked the breechblock when in place. Turning the breechblock up on its hinge exposed the chamber for direct insertion of a cartridge. The block was then locked down into place, the hammer cocked and the trigger pulled. When the block was turned up on its hinge, it could then be pulled back a short distance, compressing a spring around the hinge pin. A "draw cartridge" or claw extractor was attached to the breechblock and the rearward pull drew the empty case out of the chamber. Turning the rifle over dropped the case out.

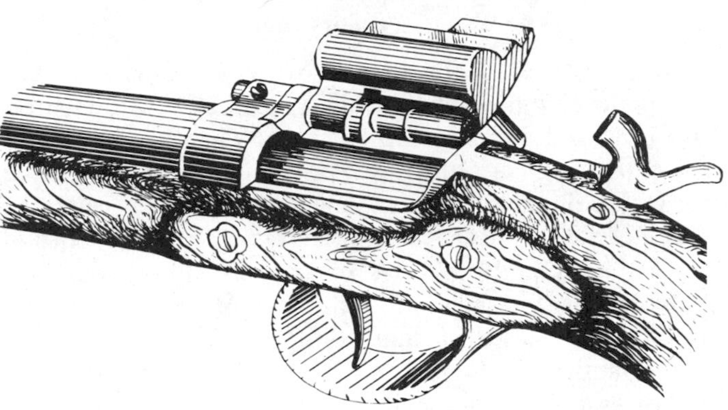

The Snider conversion mechanism. Original drawing to show rifle open ready for loading.

We have already noted the resemblance of this system to that of the old breechloaders of Henry VIII in the Tower. However, it is doubtful that Snider ever heard of those venerable relics. On the other hand, Snider may have gotten his inspiration from the little known American "Hubbell" caplock, patented by W. W. Hubbell (U. S. No. 3649) on July 1, 1844. This arm was well received in some military circles on the Continent. It was hinged to open from the right, and used a cartridge fired by an external cap. The principle of the Snider follows it very closely. Incidentally, U. S. officials rejected the Snider before it was offered in England.

The cartridge originally used in the Snider was not successful. This cartridge had a metal base, center fire priming, and a pasteboard body. The accuracy was poor. Colonel Boxer of the Royal Laboratory was assigned to iron out the cartridge troubles. He produced and patented an improved form of the original Pottet case. The walls of the famous Boxer cartridge were made of coiled brass, the bullet had a hollow taper at its base and a taper plug first of wood and later of clay to expand the bullet to fill the grooves, as well as a hollow in the front end which gave better weight distribution. With the new cartridge the accuracy exceeded that of the highly prized Enfield muzzle loader.

These conversions were known as "Snider-Enfield." They could be loaded and fired at a rate as high as 18 shots per minute and had a life as high as 70,000 rounds. For some years the Snider system was an official one in the Montenegrin, Serbian and Turkish armies. It was, however, merely a conversion introduced to re-arm the British infantry quickly and cheaply at a time when the new breechloaders were upsetting nations and vanquishing armies. It soon gave way to a rifle of entirely new design—again based on an American invention, the Martini-Henry. This arm was evolved directly from the already famous American Peabody, the original "falling block" breechlocking design.

The Boxer Primers and Cases

Colonel Boxer of the British Army was highly praised for the development of his coiled brass case with its iron base head and separate cap chamber. The introduction of that expanding case making a perfect gas seal started the trend of military change to center fire metallic cartridge breechloaders in Europe. In the United States sporting breechloaders and repeaters of superior design were already in use but handled rim fire cartridges. The cost of the Boxer cases of thin coiled brass was quite low. This doubtless had much to do with the fact that this type of case was continued in service by the British long after the superior American Berdan drawn brass case had been put into use. On the heels of the Egyptian campaign of 1885, however, complaints poured in at such a rate that, except for target use, the British replaced the Boxer coiled type with one of drawn brass. Today the Boxer case is obsolete, of course.

The Boxer primer, on the other hand, was such an outstanding achievement that today it is the almost universal primer form. This primer is merely a simple metal cup containing the priming mixture and having its own anvil (a pointed metal piece) crimped in so the point is imbedded in the priming. The single unit is retained in the pocket in the head of the cartridge case. The firing pin hitting the base of the primer drives it in against the point of the anvil. The friction ignites the priming which flashes through the vent in the case and in turn ignites the propellant.

This elementary device has been improved upon only to the extent of providing advanced priming mixtures and in improved primer-sealing and water-proofing. The mechanical principle itself remains the same.

American Case and Primer Designs—The Berdan

Most military cartridges made in the United States in the 1860 period were folded head types. The cases resembled the rim fire externally, though ignition was actually center fire. A priming cup was inserted down the mouth of the case. Indentations in the case just below the cup seat secured it in place. Priming was held in a dip at the center of the cup. Priming was crushed between this cup and the case head when the firing pin struck. The system was at once expensive and unsatisfactory. It was difficult to reload. Firing was very often uncertain. Still, this remained the generally used type in center fire until well into the 1880's.

In 1870 Colonel Hiram Berdan of the U. S. Ordnance Department developed a new primer to be used with a brass case he also designed. The case was a big advance technically, as was the system for rapid and low cost drawing of the brass which Berdan worked out.

The Berdan primer, though still widely used in Europe, is not made in the United States. It is inferior in many ways to the Boxer which, ironically enough, is the standard in this country and little used elsewhere.

The Berdan differs from the Boxer primer in that while it too retains the priming mixture, it lacks the integral anvil feature. In lieu of this important feature, the anvil is formed by part of the primer pocket in the case. Two small holes in the case allow the priming flash to reach the propelling charge. This style of primer was used in the United States only about 20 years.

The Boxer uses a comparatively large *single* flash hole. This is turns allows easy punching out of fired primers, so that cases using this primer are easy to reload. Also, in addition to being simpler to manufacture than the Berdan, the Boxer primer with its relatively large central hole allows use of higher intensity primers than the Berdan; and less set back and primer swelling is likely to be found.

Chapter 3. Single Shot Metallic Cartridge Arms and Lock Systems

THE single shot breechloader in practically all its varying forms has at one time or another been used as a rifle, pistol, and shotgun. Some are still made in each of these classifications. A somewhat detailed study of the origins and development of one covers the others for all practical purposes.

A modern single shot firearm is one in which the action must be opened manually at least for the first shot. The cartridge must be inserted manually into the chamber or onto a loading trough in the breech. The action must then be closed by hand.

The range of variations is tremendous. This work covers all the successful ones, but lack of space prevents inclusion of more than a fraction of the experimental ones with which the writer has come in contact.

This record of single shot arms is, of course, primarily intended for historical purposes. It may also serve another purpose—that of providing a ready reference work for designers and inventors who so often spend years of intense work on such matters only to find after the veil of developmental secrecy has been raised that their big "secret" has been the subject of much past experimentation.

In the course of business contact the author is constantly exposed to "secret developmental work" for which our government is paying on a cost-plus basis which is merely duplication of early experiments. This condition arises from lack of knowledge on the part of those placing contracts and those accepting them. Lack of research facilities accounts for some such wastage. This chapter, therefore, seeks to combine and simplify many of the basic elements of design; and to present them so they will be of practical value.

Some may question what value a single shot study, for instance, has in this day of machine weapons. The answer is simple. There is absolutely no element of locking principle or operating or firing principle used in the most modern automatic arms which is not reflected in single shot design; and these principles are constantly the subject of costly experimentation.

Even electrical ignition encountered in modern experiments in an endeavor to speed up fire rates was the subject of design studies in the 1880's! All the basic features of tomorrow's designs are to be found in yesterday's patterns. The creator of today may save himself time and energy by studying what the great men of the past did and did not succeed in accomplishing.

One more note must be made here on the reason for a single shot study. The history of the world was affected to a tremendous degree by the arms developments of America during the period of the 1860's and 70's. Few American histories have given more than passing notice to these. This record seeks to spread some little of this historical lore into popular channels—lore which heretofore has been largely confined to the arms enthusiast.

The Dropping Block Locking System

This is the earliest and one of the strongest and most successful of all breechlocking systems. Variants of it are in use today in both small arms and artillery. Christian Sharps, as we have seen, introduced the system during the percussion period. Its success with the metallic cartridge was immediate, of course, since it gave great breech strength and a perfect gas seal. Thousands of his early arms were converted to handle rim fire and center fire cartridges.

All dropping block systems in which the breechblock slides vertically (or nearly vertically) in mortises in the receiver walls are merely modifications of the Sharps. In the years between 1875 and 1880 this immensely strong single shot action was made by Sharps in heavy calibers and heavy weights for buffalo shooting. Professional hunters using telescopes frequently staked out and did

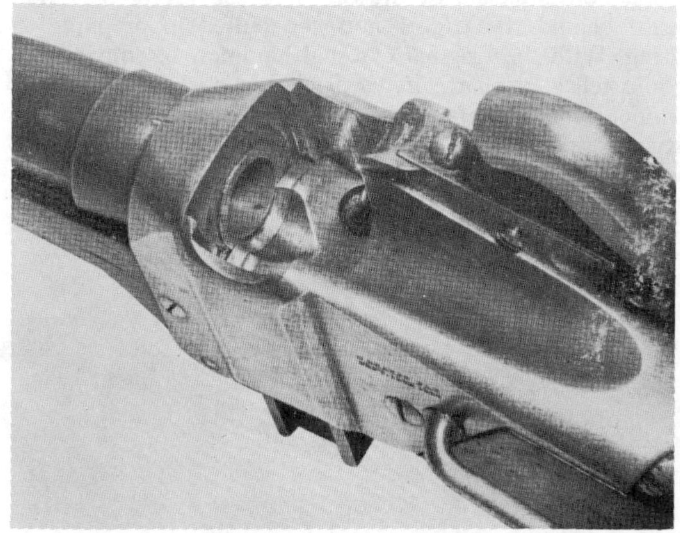

Typical Sharps carbine and action. Forerunner of the Browning-Winchester and other famous single shot rifle locks.

sniper shooting into herds at distances up to 1000 yards! These were the principal rifles which cleared the plains of big game. Indeed the very name "sharpshooter" derives from the astonishing accuracy and rapidity of fire the old percussion Sharps produced in the Civil War. Col. Hiram Berdan, later the designer of the Berdan primer and drawn brass case, led a regiment armed with Sharps which did much to save the Union Army from being wiped out in the battles in the Potomac Valley. Many of his troops were equipped with telescope Sharps rifles. "Berdan's Sharpshooters" have gone down in the annals of history for their deadly accuracy. The Union forces used nearly 100,000 Sharps' arms in the Civil War.

The Sharps in all calibers maintained their high accuracy ratings from the days when Christian Sharps himself dominated policy down to the closing days of the firm's history when the incredible P. T. Barnum, then Mayor of Bridgeport, Conn. joined with other businessmen to build a plant to transfer the Sharps manufacturing from Hartford to Bridgeport.

Rod and Gun for Sept. 30, 1876 carries an interesting account of the International Match of 1876 in which Sharps rifles captured the matches against 40 competitors using the arms of 6 manufacturers. In the following year the Sharps at the International Match averaged 420 points per man against 414 by the best competitor; while in the 1878 N.R.A. Fall Meeting at Creedmoor, Sharps took 12 out of 16 matches!

The original Sharps' design used the familiar external large hammer reminiscent of the military muzzle loaders of the day. In 1870 the Sharps-Borchardt modification was tested by U.S. Ordnance. This model concealed the hammer within the frame in what has become popularly known as the "hammerless" design. Actually there is a hammer in this model (though some other arms designs to be discussed later are truly hammerless). Drawing down the triggerguard lever lowers the breechblock, cocks the hammer and extracts and ejects the empty shell from the firing chamber. The safety is automatically applied as the action is closed by drawing back on the lever. A release behind the trigger must be pulled to prepare for firing. With the original external hammer, of course, one could tell at a glance if the arm were cocked. The 1878 Model of the Sharps-Borchardt was made in too many styles, weights and calibers for listing here. The action is still in great demand by cartridge experimenters and shooters as a basis for building special rifles.

In 1881 a French repeating rifle was built on the dropping block system. It was not considered a military success because a lever design does not lend itself to rapid fire when shooting prone, as so much military shooting is, in theory at least.

The Sharps was followed by a long line of fine variants, chief of which were the American Ballards, the Sims, and the line of Stevens "Ideals." Also using a rather minor modification of Sharps' principle was the original Winchester Single Shot .22 Rifle. This arm was developed by the late great John M. Browning. Its purchase and manufacture by Winchester started Browning on his career as the most prolific and successful of all small arms designers.

The basic design is still used by literally hundreds of small gunsmiths and gun plants in Europe today, though its use is confined in general to small bore, high priced, precision match rifles.

The Falling Block System

The next great original breechlocking system was that of Henry O. Peabody of Boston, Massachusetts. His basic patent was granted July 22, 1862.

The Peabody principle is that of hinging the breechblock at the rear and above the line of the barrel bore. It is unlocked by pulling the triggerguard lever down and forward. The front end of the block is drawn below the line of the chamber, permitting rapid loading. The first model used the familiar external military hammer of the day and was produced in .45 caliber rim fire. Its block system prevented action jamming by expanded case heads. It was a great advance over anything in the market at the time of its introduction.

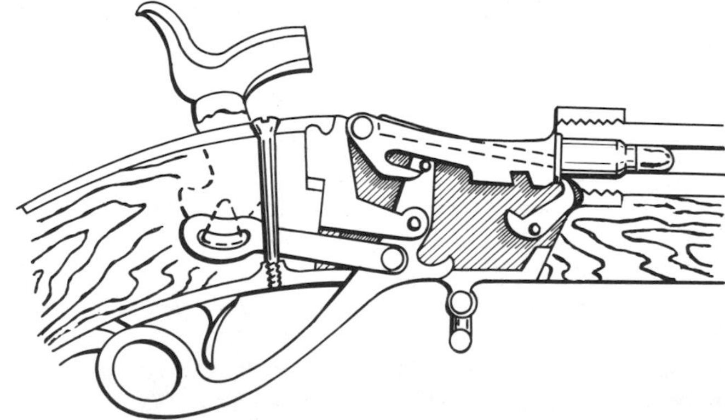

Peabody falling block mechanism. Original drawing to show principle of operation.

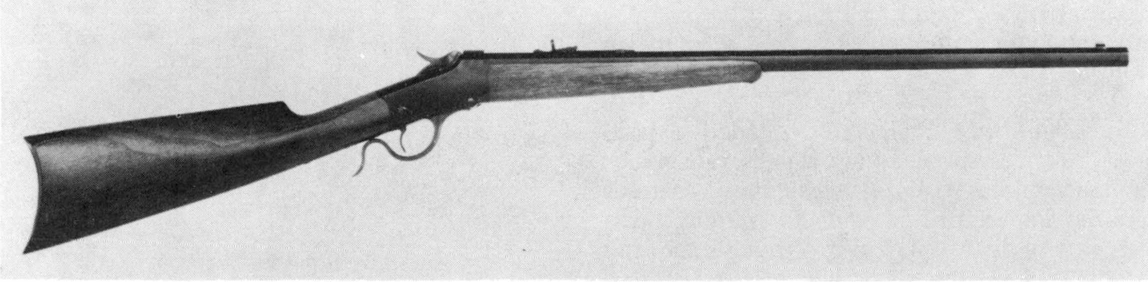

The famous Browning-developed Winchester single shot rifle.

This arm was tested at Watertown Arsenal in 1862. It is a commentary on U.S. governmental thinking of the day that while this superior metallic cartridge arm was available then, it was adopted only by some militia units. In Europe, however, its value was recognized almost from the first.

It was 1865 before the Examining Board at Springfield Armory got around to testing it seriously. Its performance alongside 64 competitors was so remarkable that it was recommended for purchase. The Civil War had ended by then and funds were not available for a changeover to a new model, however superior to the old.

Just as in the instance of Britain with her Snider conversion, American energies were turned to trying expedients to convert our enormous stock of muzzle loaders to breechloaders. This wasteful system still plagues every nation after a war. In the face of the most revolutionary advances, most efforts to completely modernize equipment fail because of the mistaken ideas of the uninitiated. In the determination to "save" money, both money and efficiency are invariably sacrificed by the winners.

It might be pointed out in this connection that the tremendous German equipment advances encountered in War II stemmed largely from the fact that as a defeated and disarmed country at the end of War I, Germany was able to start manufacture and design for War II equipment without the winner's psychological handicap. It can be stated here that when Germany rearms this time, her designs again will be superior because again she will start from scratch—using the best that experience has established, but developing the new without the hindrance of stocks on hand and old tools and plant equipment. History never changes.

Fortunately for the Peabody company, Canada in 1885 placed an order for 3000 new rifles, the caliber to be .50-60 rim fire (the ".50" indicated the caliber; the "60" indicated the powder charge in grains). Thus encouraged, the manufacturers turned to other world markets. In the next few years the Peabody was purchased by the military in such diverse areas as Austria, Bavaria, Denmark, France, Mexico, Roumania and Switzerland. In many of these countries the Peabodys played an important historical part; and in many others they influenced the target arms design to a point where some manufacture still persisted in the year 1962.

Switzerland, that staunch little nation of riflemen, recognized the potentialities of the Peabody. In 1867 Captain Michel of their Ordnance Corps came to Providence to supervise an order for 15,000 rifles in caliber .41 Rim Fire. Hard on the heels of this order came one from Denmark. Roumania bought 15,000 in Rim Fire and then another 10,000 in .45 Center Fire. Canada and Mexico totalled another 24,000. France, caught up in the War of 1870, managed to get delivery of 39,000 Peabodys to help reduce her military handicap, but had to take them in the .43 Spanish caliber. Austria and Bavaria both purchased and tested them. Reports on all hands spoke glowingly of their rapidity of fire—17 shots a minute aimed and 35 shots a minute off-hand being recorded in U.S. Government tests in 1866. As to accuracy, these arms were the marvels of their time. The Royal Danish Legation and Consulate General at New York reported to the manufacturers that a Royal Testing Commission reported "good hitting shots were obtained at 2400 feet." The Austrian Imperial Breech Loading Arms Commission reported fine accuracy at 600 yards. At 700 yards range (the practical maximum then, and not greatly exceeded today) the center of impact of the .43 caliber was 40.79 inches; the mean deviation only 23.6 inches.

The Swiss, unhampered by military dogmatism, turned the Peabody over to a master mechanic, Frederich von Martini of Frauenfeld, for modification. In the United States it was felt that a self-cocking army weapon was not practical. If it didn't have a huge outside hammer which had to be manually hauled back, it just wasn't a military arm. The Swiss had more confidence in the intelligence of their riflemen. Martini's first modification was an elementary leverage arrangement which automatically cocked the Peabody hammer as the action was opened. His next modification completely buried the name and fame of Peabody, the original designer. Martini dispensed entirely with the huge flintlock-days hammer and substituted an internal firing lock within the breechblock. The result was a pleasing design retaining the Peabody breech lock but which introduced the now famous Martini firing mechanism. This is operated by a lever to the rear of the triggerguard.

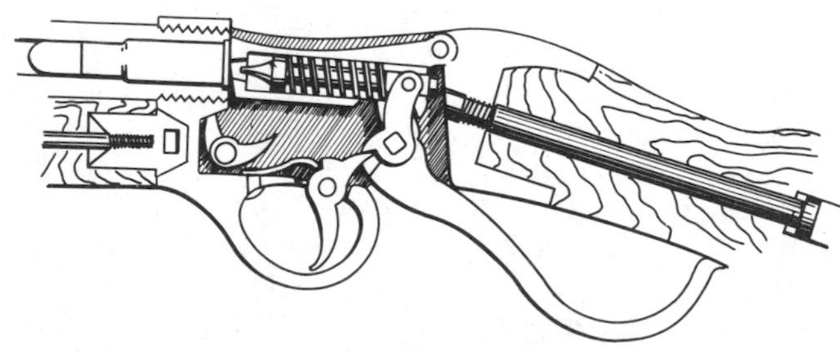

Martini-Henry mechanism. Original drawing to show variation and improvement over original Peabody system.

Martini submitted this design to England for tests. It was slightly modified at Enfield and fitted with a barrel rifled on the English Henry system. The Henry bore is polygonal. Lands are formed at the angles. They provide additional bearings for the projectile as it travels down the barrel. The resulting arm was named the "Martini-Henry." It was officially adopted in April 1871 as the British service rifle in caliber .45 using a Boxer rolled cartridge. During War II this rifle, altered to the current British caliber .303, was used by the Home Guard services in Britain. As a small bore precision rifle it is still made by the Birmingham Small Arms Company, in slightly modified form.

The Providence Tool Company made and delivered to the Ottoman Government 600,000 Peabody rifles in .45 caliber during the year 1873. The chamber was smaller for the Turkish cartridge than for the British.

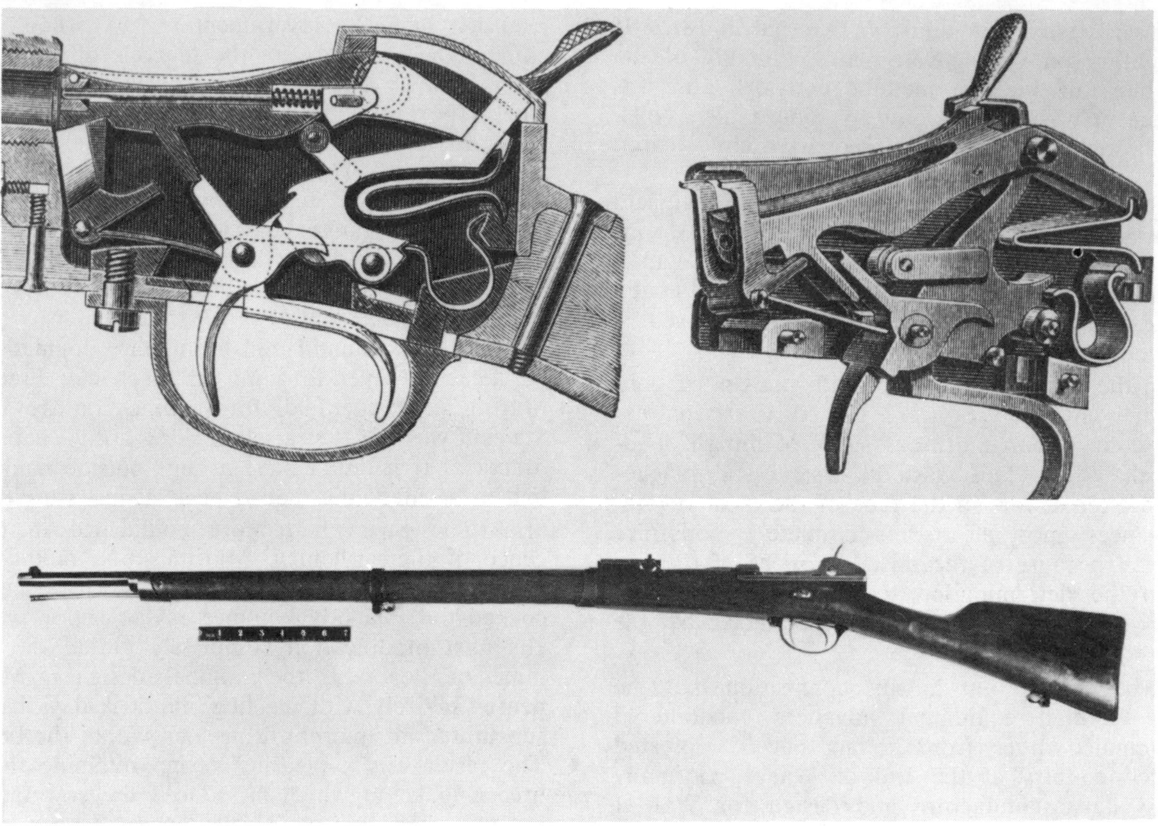

Upper: Bavarian lightning (Werder) lock. Left: Action closed ready to fire. Right: Action open ready to load. Lower: The Bavarian Werder Rifle. Caliber 11.15 mm.

These rifles are still encountered in the Balkans. They are clearly stamped "Peabody & Martini Patent. Man'f'd by Providence Tool Co., Prov. R.I. U.S.A." These have the Peabody breechblock and the Martini firing system, of course, but the firing system is somewhat modified from the original along the Enfield alteration line.

The British adopted their version under the name "Martini-Henry" and the name has tended to obscure Peabody's fame completely as years have gone by. Even in America this incorrect designation is the accepted one.

In Bavaria the Peabody lock was modified along quite different lines than in other places. Nevertheless, the basic "falling block" system was retained. The modification there was by J. L. Werder, noted director of a Nuremberg arms plant. He studied Peabody tests which a Bavarian Arms Commission had made over a period of a year, tests which proved very favorable except that they pointed up the military need for an arm which could be prone fired without shifting the position of the shooter's body. Werder accordingly modified the system to replace the under-lever release. In its place he used a special lever placed inside the triggerguard ahead of the firing trigger. This lever looks like a reversed trigger. It is forward of the firing finger position. The shooter pushes his firing finger ahead against this lever to unlock the arm. The lever releases a locking prop within the mechanism. This lowers the front face of the breechblock and exposes the chamber for loading. A cartridge is slid down the shaped slot in the face of the block and into the chamber with ease. On the right side of the arm there is a cocking piece shaped rather like an old time hammer. This is drawn back by the thumb of the firing hand. This action cocks the arm, and at the same time elevates the breechblock and locks it at its forward end. The rapidity of fire of this type of weapon, whether rifle or pistol, is astonishing when used by an experienced operator. A forward thrust of the firing finger opens the breech and expels the empty case. A cartridge is thrust down the concave face of the block into the breech with ease. A backward flip of the thumb of the firing hand locks and cocks the arm. Here again the breech locking system is but a variant of the Peabody. Again Henry Peabody received no credit. In passing it might be noted that the Werder "Bavarian Lightning" pistol and rifle were both used to some extent in Eastern Europe during World War I.

There are a score or more of other variants of the Peabody lock, usually combined with some modification of the Borchardt or Martini firing mechanism. Today's Belgian Francotte-Martini arms form one type. The British Martini is another. In England one still encounters old Swinburns, Stahls and Westley-Richards; while the Continent harbors any number of modifications made up by small gunmakers who appropriated Peabody's breechblock.

All but a few of the precision single shot rifles made in Europe and Britain in recent years fall in this general classification. In fact, the only commercially successful dropping block action which doesn't, and which can lay any claim to originality, is the German Aydt. The Aydt pivots its block below the line of the chamber.

Historically the principle of Peabody is also of interest as the breeching system of the early Spencer American repeating shotgun with which we will deal later. When Winchester introduced its first great "pump" shotgun invented by John M. Browning, the New York used military equipment firm of Francis Bannerman sued to restrain the manufacture. Bannerman had bought out the defunct Spencer firm for a song. The suit was lost by Bannerman, but it is strange that no one on either side seems to have recognized the derivation of the Spencer lock.

This then is a small part of the story of the Peabody lock. The Peabody-Martini lighted up the scene of history in a blaze of glory in the Russo-Turkish War of 1877-78, when in the course of a few hours of battle its use by the Turks slaughtered the Russians at long range as they approached en masse. And in that same encounter at Plevna the American name Winchester forged to the front in the world of military thought, completing the destruction the long range Peabody-Martini started on the fateful day. The Winchester repeater in the hands of the Turks completed the massacre at close range which the Peabody began at long range. The Winchester's terrific firepower that day sealed the doom of all military single shot rifles, though it was long before its lesson was effectively grasped in our own country. That story too belongs in another place in these pages, but first we must consider the remaining important single shot locking designs.

As to Peabody himself, in all the long history of firearms few inventors have played a greater part in shaping military events than did the invention of this obscure New Englander. It is a strange irony of circumstance that his name is so little known outside the circles of early cartridge collectors, while those of the men who utilized and modified his system have achieved world renown. It is unfortunate that we have little space here to devote to the man himself and his background; for like so many other Americans of his time, the products of his genius led to machine and manufacturing developments which started the United States on its way to the productive heights which made our nation great. The Peabody story deserves to be told in detail some day as a thrilling chapter in American business enterprise.

The Remington Rolling Block System

The rolling block action is still used to some extent in shotgun, pistol, and rifle types in Europe. The basic design principle is simple and can be made strong enough to handle about any conceivable load.

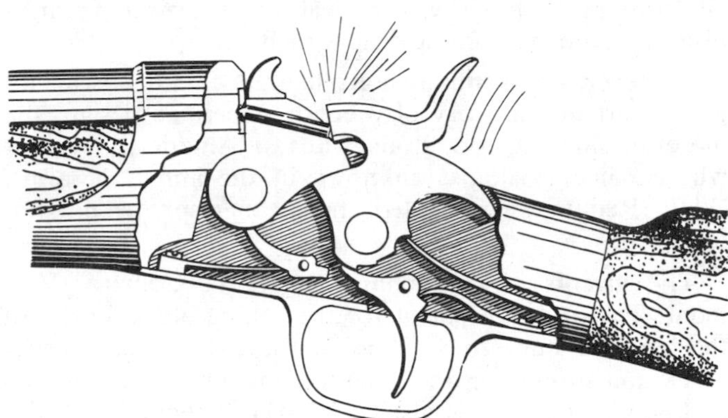

Remington rolling block system. Original drawing to show firing and breech locking mechanisms.

The mechanism for locking the breech consists of two parts. First is the breechblock itself. This is a heavy rolling member mounted in the receiver on an axis pin. It contains the firing pin in a hole in its center face; and is machined with a thumb-extension to allow it to be rolled back away from the breech when its locking support is withdrawn. The second unit is the firing hammer. It is a rotating member pivoted on its axis pin behind the breechblock. The lock is simplicity itself: The breechblock is spring-supported against the face of the breech when ready to fire; as the hammer falls when the trigger is pulled, a projecting under surface on the hammer rolls firmly into place below and behind the breechblock, supporting it immovably. This locking surface reaches its full support position before the striking surface on the hammer can mechanically reach the firing pin.

In its day this was the most widely-used army rifle lock design in the world. Its effective military life, like that of the Peabody, was short, however. It, too, came in during the Civil War when procurement officials had to concentrate on manufacturing the muzzle loaders we were tooled up to make, rather than many of the superior breechloaders which were new at the time, untested and untried. And it, like all other single shot rifles, became obsolete militarily on the day of the Russo-Turkish battle of Plevna.

The history of the Remington long arm has never been written. The story of Eliphalet Remington's hand-forged flintlock barrel, of his success as a maker of custom guns in the early days of the Republic, of the rise of the firm under Eliphalet Jr. and the manufacture of Harper's Ferry Rifles and Jenks Carbines during the Civil War,

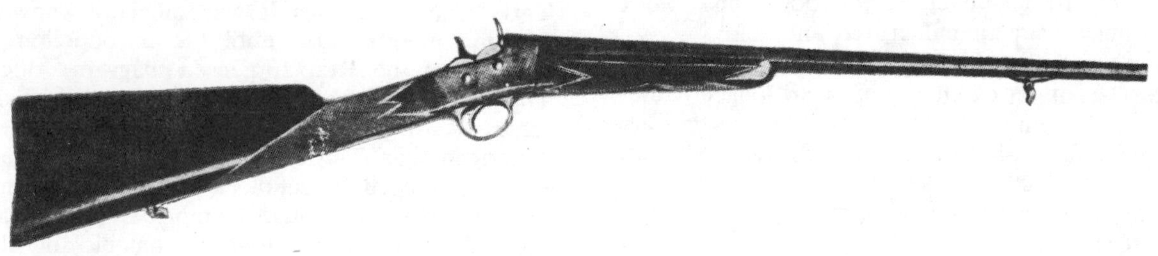

Typical Remington rolling block Carbine.

all form part of the vast canvas of American firearms history which we cannot deal with here.

However, the Remington Rolling Block Lock is an integral part of the story of modern American design, the more so since it, too, deals with an American inventor whose name is almost unknown in the annals of arms. While Remington marketed the mechanism, he did not invent it.

The inventor was Leonard Geiger of Colburn, Vermont. The first true patent for the rolling block lock with the hammer hung to the rear of the axis of the breechblock and supporting the block immovably is that granted to Leonard Geiger (U.S. No. 37501) January 27, 1863.

Joseph Rider's (or Ryder's) original patent clearly shows the hammer forward of the breechblock axis. The Remingtons purchased Rider's patent and also gave him a job in their Ilion, N. Y., factory. When Remington bought Geiger's patent, Rider and some other employees made minor changes which resulted in the original Remington "Split Breech" design, one of the simplest and strongest breech actions ever devised; and one ironically enough almost universally called the "Remington-Rider."

The "breechpiece" which closed against the head of the cartridge was combined with the extractor, while the hammer also was shaped to function as a breech bolt. The "breechpiece" in this first design was split to permit the firing pin in the hammer nose to strike through at the cartridge case head, resulting in a comparatively weak piece.

When the breechblock was made solid, being pierced only to receive a firing pin mounted within it, the design was an immediate military success. Cocking the hammer rolls the under locking surface out from its support of the breechblock. The breechblock is then pulled back by a projection on its right side to expose the chamber for loading. When the piece is closed, a flat spring holds it firmly against the head of the cartridge. When the trigger is pulled and the hammer falls, its shaped under-surface travels below and behind the breechpiece locking it firmly as the hammer hits the firing pin. This perfected design was completed in 1866, but production of the rifles did not get underway until the following year when the U.S. Navy ordered 12,000.

This rifle was adopted by Denmark in 1867, by Sweden and Norway in 1867, by Spain in 1871, by Egypt in 1870, by Argentina in 1879. It was also widely used in China, Austria, Italy and in several South American countries, and was the subject of military experimentation everywhere. In all, over 1,000,000 rolling block rifles and carbines were manufactured and sold!

The rolling block system was continued in low priced lines into the Twentieth Century but is no longer manufactured by Remington. Shotguns on this design are still made in Sweden, where the design is quite popular. A form of rolling block actuated by a triggerguard lever was made for some years, notably by Hopkins & Allen in America. The American "Buck" action lever repeater also used a form of rolling block.

For a time Remington manufactured, under the patent of Lewis L. Hepburn (Oct. 7, 1879), a dropping block action which is often erroneously referred to as a modification or "improvement" of the rolling block. This Remington-Hepburn as first issued had a right side lever operated by the thumb which through compound leverage unlocked the breechblock and lowered it in receiver mortises for loading. A later modification of this type, the Remington-Hepburn No. 3 Schuetzen Match Rifle, was operated by an under lever, the action being designed to thrust home a cartridge only partly inserted in the chamber as the block moved up and ahead.

Remington single shot rifles are currently manufactured only in modern bolt action designs.

The Whitney Arms Company of New Haven, Conn., submitted a rolling block action to our Ordnance Board of 1865. It was not accepted for service use. The system was patented by Captain T.T.S. Laidley (No. 54,743) and closely resembled the Remington, differing radically only in the shape of the extractor and in the way in which the hammer supported the breechpiece. This arm was not successful. (It is not to be confused with the later Whitney "Phoenix" line of rifles. In these the breechblock could be hinged up from the side when the hammer was half cocked. As in the case of the Snider and other side lifting breechblock actions, the Phoenix block, by passing across the head of the cartridge case instead of to its rear as in the rolling block, encountered extraction trouble if a primer blew out or a weak case was encountered.) Eli Whitney, founder of the original company, was one of the first arms manufacturers for our Government. He instituted interchangeability of parts in 1798. (The idea had been previously suggested in France, but nothing was done about it.) The cost proved prohibitive in those early days and the principle was temporarily abandoned.

Other American Single Shot Designs

While some other American designs were of importance in their day, none approach the original ones already described, and none are truly of American inception. At the U. S. Trials for Breech Loading Carbines held at Springfield Armory in 1865, there were 65 designs submitted. Five designs were selected for alteration of the muzzle loaders on hand—the same approach originally made by the British. The one finally selected was that then suggested by E. S. Allin, Master Armorer of Springfield Armory. After a score of modifications this became the official U. S. Rifle with which we armed all our Indian fighters, including Custer whose command was massacred because the Indians opposing him had repeating rifles. This "Cam Lock" as it was officially known was our first-line infantry arm until the introduction in limited quantity of the Krag-Jorgensen magazine rifle in 1892. This old black-powder Cam Lock was still in use by U.S. forces at the battle of San Juan Hill in the Spanish-American War. This arm is the familiar rifle (or carbine) with top hinged breechblock locked by a cam piece at the right rear. The huge hammer is pulled back to full cock, the cam latch pushed to unlock and then to lift the breechblock up. This action extracts the empty case

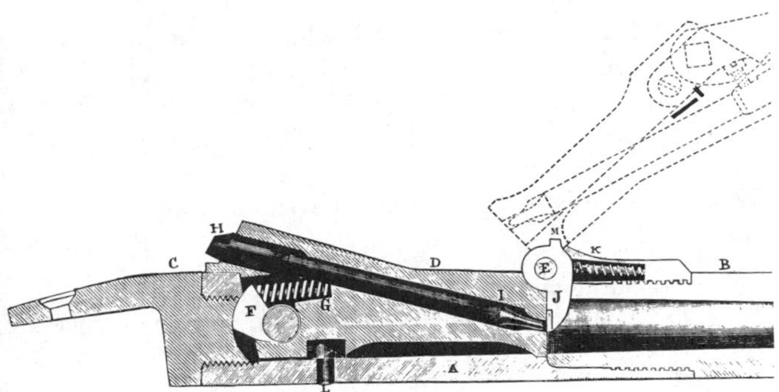

The U. S. cam lock mechanism.

and leaves the chamber exposed ready for loading. This form of action can be traced back to the French Demondion freak rifle of 1831; and its resemblance to a score of other foreign and American designs is too pronounced to escape notice. It, at least, served the purpose of arming our troops with cheap breechloaders; and we were fortunate that its first trial in war was against a foe so inferior in numbers that the quality of the weapon did not cost us too heavily in lives because of our conservatism and our penury.

General Berdan claimed the 1866 Springfield used his single-joint breechblock and he instituted suit. The suit dragged on long after his death, but in 1895 a judgment of $95,000 was finally allowed to his widow by the Government. The final form of this Single Shot was the 1888 Model, Cal. .45-70.

The Hinged Frame

Of all the other types developed, none has persisted but the hinged frame evolved from the Maynard, and that only to a minor degree. The Maynard, of course, was not the first hinged-frame rifle: that system was used in Italy as early as 1670; and was used with pin fire cartridges by Lefaucheux in France, as we have seen.

Stevens, Hamilton, Wesson, Wurfflein and others made low priced rifles on this system—a triggerguard or other lever being pushed to unlock the barrel from the standing breech and tilt it up for loading. In Europe this system is still widely used for high power game rifle design, though not for military purposes. In the United States its modified use is confined largely to shotguns and to target pistols.

Various Other Types

The sliding barrel design in which pressure on the triggerguard lever slides the barrel forward away from the standing breech for loading (as in the Sharps & Hankins); the side-swinging barrel of the Frank Wesson Pocket Rifle (he also made hinged frame types); the swingout breechblock of the Quackenbush; the Phoenix type of turn-out breech piece; and the Berdans were perhaps the outstanding designs. None have anything but historical importance today.

The Berdans are of interest because they were developed by General (Civil War Colonel) Hiram S. Berdan. Berdan resigned his commission in January, 1864, to undertake the construction of a new rifle. A test was made of one conversion, the cal. 58 Berdan, on November 12, 1864.

The Berdan I was a curious composite resembling the Albini block (swinging up on a forward hinge) and the Chassepot firing mechanism. A thumbpiece projected from the rear of the receiver and was drawn back to cock the arm. A spiral mainspring drove the locking bolt against the striker in the center of the breechblock, thereby assuring that the breechblock would be positively locked before the cartridge fired. In 1868-70 the Russians purchased 30,000 of the Berdan I pattern. The Russians developed an improved form, the Berdan II, using the Russian .42 cal. Center Fire cartridge. It was manufactured at Tula Arsenal in Russia. It has a circular thumbpiece at the rear of the bolt. This Russian cartridge is of military interest as it was the first center fire bottlenecked cartridge with outside Berdan primer. This development of course marks the beginning of the era of high-power small-bore rifles with great range and accuracy and relatively low trajectory.

When in 1872 a Board was established by Act of Congress to give further consideration to breech loading designs, 108 designs were submitted! It is noteworthy as an index of the way the United States had forged ahead on arms development at the time that only nine of the new designs were foreign. Since none of these types are of further evolutionary interest, they cannot be included in this work.

Noteworthy Historic and Freak American Designs

The Quackenbush Block System. This featured a breechblock pivoted below the chamber. The block was pushed to the right on its pivot to expose the cartridge chamber for loading and extraction. The striker was housed within the breechblock. A cocking handle on the

Berdan I, Russian rifle as made by Colt's for the Russian Czarist Government.

right side was drawn back to cock the arm. Gas sealing was not efficient. Nevertheless, the arm was so simple to manufacture that it was copied by European makers for export even in recent years. In general, its use has been confined to low power cartridges, since breech wear sets in rapidly.

The 1870 Joslyn-Tomes. In this design pulling back the hammer also retracted the breechblock and ejected the empty case. When a cartridge was placed in the receiver, the breechpiece was pushed forward against it forcing it into the chamber. Pulling the trigger fired the cartridge.

The Laidley-Chick. This design, a modification of the Remington Rolling Block, differed in the way the breechpiece was backed by the hammer. It had a three-click hammer and a safety. Legend has it that the name derived from the fact that the proud inventor, Captain Laidley, usually referred to it affectionately as "my chick."

The Jenks 1868. A top hammer when drawn back rotated and lowered a breechblock to expose the breech in this design, which was used in the Civil War.

The Cochran of 1865. This design is of interest as a modification of the Hall principle which was also attempted in Europe. Pushing down the triggerguard lever raises the front of the breechblock (which is pivoted at the rear as in the Hall). When a cartridge is inserted in the chamber, the lever draws the breechblock down to back it up. This arm has an external hammer and a firing pin in the breechblock. Cochran also invented the rather impractical revolving rifles already mentioned.

The Joslyn, 1862. Several types were made. Withdrawing a lock pin on the right permitted the breechblock to be turned to the left on a hinge. An inclined face on the block forced the cartridge home. This early design had a gas vent in the top of the block, a noteworthy item even today. Another unusual feature was a plane on the face of the block which acted to extract the cartridge. The Joslyn is of historical interest because 11,261 were bought by the North during the Civil War; and because the design was copied in Europe.

Miscellaneous. Other early metallic cartridge breechloaders of some importance included: The Ballard lever operated block rifle, 1509 bought by the Union in Civil War; Ball magazine rifle, 1002 purchased same period; Cosmopolitan (also called Union), 9342 purchased; Gallagher hinged frame, 22,728; Gibbs sliding and tilting barrel, 1052 delivered; Lindner, 892; Merril locked by a lifting top strap, 14,495; Smith hinged barrel, converted from special rubber cartridge to metallic design; Warner side swinging block with hand extractor, 4,001; and Wesson with barrel tilting when released by special trigger.

Multi-Barrel Rifles. Rifles with more than one barrel have never been well received in the United States. Their manufacture here has never been of military or commercial importance. When encountered they usually represent merely a shotgun action in double or treble design fitted with rifle barrels. Of course, there was a rash of such arms developed by individuals from time to time, but none were produced in quantity.

The one arm of the period which might merit attention is the G. R. Remington 3-barrel rifle. The breechlock was a modified rolling block, the block carrying 3 firing pins. Essentially this was a "volley gun," all 3 barrels firing simultaneously. The caliber was customarily .32 rim fire. These constituted a sort of long range shotgun.

Note: Important magazine rifles of the period will be considered later in this text. Several of the important developments of this order were started during the Civil War years.

It should be noted that the foregoing constitute but a very small fraction of the list of early American designs. It is the intent of the author to cover in this work only those designs which have either a direct evolutionary bearing or a historical bearing on later military arms design and use; or which contain design elements which have still not been completely exploited.

The Early Metallic Cartridge Rifle In Great Britain

Great Britain's contributions to small arms design, while great indeed in the development of the sporting double-barreled shotgun, have been particularly significant in the field of the rifle only in the evolution of rifling. Very little original rifle design has been done by the British; and even their modifications have not been particularly noteworthy.

The original machinery used at Enfield Armory was designed and manufactured in the United States, as Britain was not equipped with either facilities or designers to produce the required machine tools. In 1854 Lord Hardinge assigned Joseph Whitworth, a pioneer in the field of exact measurements in England, to experiment on the manufacture and design of rifle barrels. English gunsmiths and writers generally glossed over Whitworth's findings and recommendations as being merely a rehash of what was already known. Few realized that while Whitworth knew nothing about firearms, and was therefore ridiculed, he was a scientific observer whose findings couldn't be pushed airily aside by responsible authorities. Whitworth's rifle was not adopted. His recommendations for reduction in caliber were not given attention until some years later. However, his methods started the British in 1860 on a system of interchangeable parts, a mighty step forward in arms manufacture in a nation which had always prided itself on the indispensability of its hand fitting of parts.

The British Metford and The Enfield Rifling Systems

British developments in the field of rifling did much to advance the tempo of military small arms design in the United States and Europe. The Metford was the only really important rifling design for black powder loads. The Enfield rifling is the world standard form of rifling for smokeless powder cartridges. The Danish Krag and the Japanese Arisaka rifles still used in World War II the rifling designed by the noted British Consulting Engineer Metford in 1865.

The Lee Metford Mark I system had a bore diameter of .303 inches, land width of .023 inches, mean rifling depth of .0045 inches, and a left twist of 1 turn in 10 inches. There were 7 grooves. (The later Danish Krag uses 6 grooves, the Japanese rifle 4.)

Before the introduction of the Metford form, rifling generally was deep or polygonal. Used with black powder, the grooves fouled rapidly. The basic principle of the Metford rifling is very shallow grooving with grooves and lands slightly rounded. This system minimized both fouling and bullet and bore deformation to such a degree that it quickly outmoded all previous forms of rifling. The grooves being shaped to the segment of a circle, Metford is often called "segmental" rifling. The absence of sharp angles in the rifling provides a minimum hold for fouling.

Enfield rifling is today the form used in practically every military rifle made, with the exceptions already noted. Indeed, except for the very limited use in special rifle designs of the famous American Pope rifling and the modified English Lancaster oval-bore rifling used by the American Newton, it is in general use throughout the world in sporting rifles as well.

The Metford rifling was the perfect one for black powder use. But with the introduction of the new smokeless "cordite" propellant, the British found that erosion set in very fast, and the shallow Metford rifling washed out rapidly. (*Note:* With the new powders developed during and since the end of World War II, shallow rifling is again practicable. As this is written much experimentation is being conducted here and abroad in both military and sporting circles with so-called "micro-groove" rifling.)

British experimentation resulted in the Enfield form of rifling for smokeless powder use. The basic principle of this Enfield form is deeper grooves concentric with the bore, the grooves and lands both having square corners. As originally used by British forces, the Enfield rifling had a bore diameter of .303 inches, land width of .0956 inches, mean rifling depth of .0065 inches, and a twist of 1 turn to the left in 10 inches. It was rifled with 5 grooves. (In most military usage today 4 to 6 grooves are common. During World War II some barrels were rifled with only 2 grooves in the interest of economy and speed of manufacture; and for practical military use they are quite satisfactory.) Enfield rifling is commonly referred to as "concentric" rifling.

The British Martini-Henry Single Shot Rifle

We have already touched upon the early British conversions such as the Snider in our consideration of metallic ammunition development.

The Snider was merely a temporary expedient to permit rapid changeover to breechloading. In 1866 a Special Committee was convened to consider new breech loaders. About 120 different rifles and 49 types of cartridges were submitted to the Committee, representing domestic and foreign designs. All were rejected. In the following year the Committee sat to examine further into the matter. This time they separated the matters of caliber and barrel types from the action designs. Barrels submitted were tested with a Henry action. Actions submitted for tests were required to be adaptable for barrels meeting given requirements as to caliber, type of cartridge and so forth. Forty-five additional action designs were submitted which were also tested by these scientific methods. Bolt actions were glossed over because some early forms occasionally fired accidentally on the closing thrust of the bolt, a defect comparatively simple to overcome.

As a result of this detailed testing, the Committee decided on the Henry barrel using Boxer cartridges. The 480 grain bullets had waxed wads for lubrication. The action selected was the one developed by the Swiss, Frederich Martini, from the American Peabody. The arm was named "Martini-Henry." Tested in 1869 and 70, the arm was officially adopted in April, 1871. The caliber was .45.

A new Small Arms Committee, convened first in 1883, decided on lowering the caliber to .402, using a drawn brass cartridge case with a 380-grain bullet and 85 grains of black powder. This new design employed a modified form of Metford 7-groove rifling and the arm was designated the "Enfield-Martini." While many were made, they were not officially issued at the time. (In .303 caliber this type was used by Home Guards to some extent in World War II.)

By 1866 the Continental Powers had awakened to the value of the small bore rifle with smokeless powder, and Great Britain began experiments with the new rifle and cartridge designed in Switzerland by Col. Rubin.

Before passing on to a consideration of the British adoption of the Lee Magazine Rifle, we must pause to examine the few worthwhile single shot designs, since these designs marked practically the end of rifle design in England. Because of economic and geographical factors, there was neither need nor market for enough sporting rifles to warrant more than a passing interest in their development.

Consciously or not, the Small Arms Committee was unquestionably influenced by the success of the falling block locking system on the Continent when they set up the rules for tests. The design selected required that the cartridge be thrust fully home into the chamber before the action could be closed. In field use, when troops are under tension, such a system leads invariably to serious jamming of the rifle as the soldier tries to close the breech without fully chambering the round first. In addition, the extraction depended on a single pushing movement of the extractor which was insufficient to free swollen cases. As a military arm for use against the then modern armies, this design was a failure when it was adopted. However, in the hands of native troops for basically guerrilla fighting in Africa and Asia it still serves a purpose.

The Soper Single Shot

One of the most widely publicized rifles of its day was the British Soper. In 1866 the inventor offered an arm which was rejected as being too complicated. The day after the conclusion of the 1868 trials at which the Martini-Henry was accepted, the new Soper arrived—too late for entrance. British papers and magazines of the day tell remarkable stories of the rapidity of fire of this arm; some of the stories fail to stand up in the light of modern research. The arm had a side-hinged swinging breechblock on the general principle of the earlier American Joslyn. It was quite simple and efficient in design, an exceptionally fine feature being the fact that the hammer was low in the tang and when cocked, the opened breech could be cleaned from the rear. When the arm was fired, a thumb lever on the right side was pushed down. This cocked the internal hammer (whose upper end emerged through a hole in the tang when firing to hit the pin in the breechblock). This action also forced the striker back, raised the hinged block and ejected the empty case. The extractor worked off a lever operating from the hammer while being cocked, affording a form of primary extraction prior to the ejecting motion. In a rapid fire contest at Wimbledon in 1870 the Soper delivered 770 shots against 306 by a team of Sniders. However, in spite of tales of its "firing 60 times in one minute" as recorded in *The Field* in April, 1870, documented tests show it firing 68 shots in 2 minutes against 62 for the Martini-Henry—hardly a superiority to raise all the tales it did.

Other Interesting British Single Shot Designs

The Albini-Braendlin. This .60 caliber Rim Fire was a rifle designed by Colonel Albini of the Italian Army, manufactured in Birmingham, England, and actually used in Belgium. The Belgians used this system in 1867 to convert breechloaders. The action operated like the familiar American Springfield Single Shot: when the hammer was cocked the breechblock could be swung up over the barrel on its hinge. The design was a common one, in this case apparently stemming from the familiar percussion lock alteration patented by W. Mont Storm in 1857 in England, and extensively used in Europe, more particularly in Russia and England.

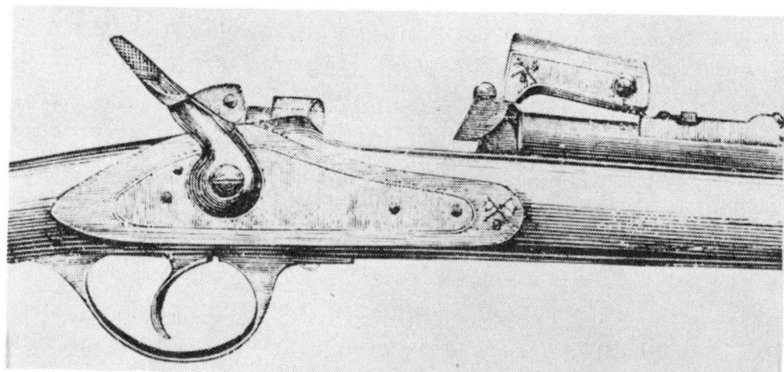

Albini-Braendlin rim fire, caliber 60.

The British Henry. This arm was a single shot made by the designer of the Henry barrel. At first it was little more than an imitation of the American Sharps dropping block. Using the general design of the American arm, Henry made the operating lever a separate lever mounted around the triggerguard. In later models he copied from the Martini system the idea of enclosing the firing mechanism in the breechblock itself and used a Martini-type extractor. This arm did have the good feature of having a block which dropped and exposed the barrel for cleaning from the breech end.

The Field. This arm was made in two lock designs. (1) The Field "sliding block" is a dropping block action operated by a thumb lever on the right side of the receiver. Pushing it forward acts through a system of levers to cock the hammer, lower the block and extract the case. The compound extractor system is unusually good for a block rifle. This arm very closely resembles our Hepburn. (2) The Field "hinge block" was merely another variant of the American Peabody, the block hinged at the rear falls at the front to expose the chamber when the lever is operated.

The Money-Walker. About 1868 this strange design appeared. In effect, it was the old Peabody idea again with a different opening system. While the block was hinged at the rear to drop at the front end to expose the chamber, the operating lever was a prolongation of the breechblock itself. It lay above the small of the stock. When lifted, it pivoted the block, dropping the front end. This design was copied on the Continent.

The Swinburn. This was a modified Peabody-Martini. It too, had a falling block hinged at the upper rear and operated by a lever below the small of the stock. Its "unusual" feature was to replace the spiral spring striker with an internal hammer and a V-spring. This arm also had an exposed right side lever to permit the hammer to be half-cocked and recocked. At this time spiral springs were in bad repute in England.

The Westley Richards. This arm was made in two designs. (1) The original Westley Richards "falling block" was on the Peabody pattern with an internal hammer and a block hinged at the upper rear. Operating a lever around the triggerguard cocked the hammer within the block and lowered the block. The extraction system was better than in most block types, being effected by direct powerful leverage. The hammer had the firing pin as part of its face. A V-mainspring was positioned below the cham-

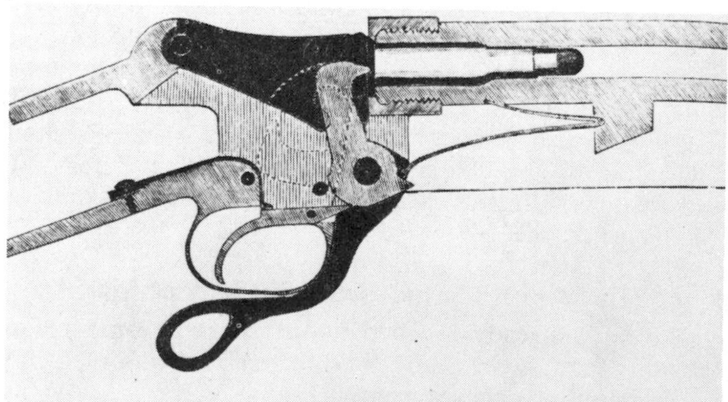

English Westley-Richards falling block system.

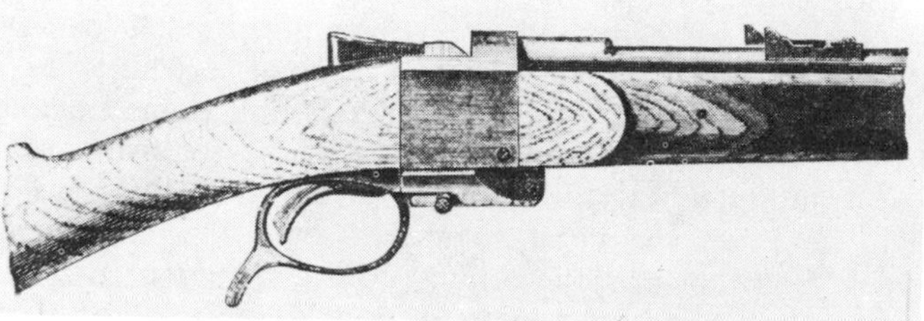

English Westley-Richards sliding block system.

ber. This was one of the simplest designs of this type, but had to be cleaned from the muzzle. (1a) A later model of this design used a horizontal striker operated by a V-spring behind it, making a much more compact action. (2) The Westley Richards "sliding block" was designed by two employees of the W-R firm named Anson and Deeley. These two designed the famous Anson & Deeley double barrel shotgun action, the best low-priced action of that pattern ever designed, and still the basis for most of the world's low-priced shotguns. Their military design, however, was not acceptable, coming as it did at the close of the single shot era in military usage. A vertical dropping block on the Sharps idea is lowered and raised by action of a triggerguard lever. The firing mechanism is concealed within the breechblock. As the block is lowered a tumbler is cocked and the extractor operated. One good feature of the action is that it is designed to permit cleaning the barrel from the breech end.

Modern British Single Shot Rifles

None are intended, of course, for military use. The B.S.A. and Vickers models are merely modifications of the old Martini-Henry action and are used generally for precision small-bore shooting. Birmingham Small Arms also makes a line of .22 single-shot bolt-action rifles on the order of the familiar American types.

Chapter 4. Early Metallic Cartridge Single Shots Throughout the World

EUROPEAN arms design differs radically in its approach from our own. The comparative results offer an interesting study in psychology and economic systems.

From the very beginning of rifle manufacture in America, the emphasis has been very largely centered on sporting arms to equip the individual pioneer, hunter, sportsman or target shooter. Except for the direct efforts of Springfield Armory as the prime designer for our armed forces, rifle development has been primarily in the interests of the free individual—the average citizen. From this fact stems the tremendous line of arms and ammunition types evolved in our country. While American arms played great roles in battles throughout the world, they were still primarily commercial sporting types used for more grim purposes. It is only since our involvement in World Wars I and II that specific manufacturing attention has been turned to military design as a practical necessity.

In Europe, on the other hand, practically all rifle design since the earliest times has settled around just one consideration—what type will kill the most men at the greatest distances. Hence, the sporting designs of European countries have been largely borrowed from successful American types, or have evolved from pure military weapons. Thus pump and semi-automatic arms of a non-military character sold abroad have been in practically every important instance either a product of the Belgium F.N. factory manufacturing weapons designed by our own John M. Browning, cheap Belgian or Spanish imitations of Winchester types originally designed by Browning, or Browning designs made under license in Germany. Only in target single-shots has any originality been shown.

As a natural outgrowth of a situation where military thought and fears constantly haunt the horizon, where few men are free to possess rifles except when the government hands them to them together with a uniform and a demand for subserviency, early European designers understandably had little to offer beyond modifications of types already known.

When we come to the period of military magazine and automatic arms the picture is quite different as we shall see in due course. But in the opening of the metallic cartridge era, little was developed beyond that which has already been discussed with one notable exception. That exception of course is the true turnbolt action which marked the opening of a new arms era throughout the world; and it is credited almost entirely to the German, Peter Paul Mauser.

Of all European nations only Switzerland and Turkey followed very closely the event of the American Civil War and kept well abreast of our developments. It was natural, of course, that the Swiss, a nation of riflemen, would see and understand the importance of the arrival of the breech-sealing metallic cartridge and the repeating rifle principles. On the other hand it is a distinct tribute to the Turkish leaders of the time that they, expecting a Russian War, should have had the progressiveness to see that the best European military minds were so blinded by European military might that they were not sufficiently attentive to the amazing arms development in America. The Turks, not having manufacturing facilities, turned to the United States first for Peabodys, then for Peabody-Martinis, then for Winchester repeaters; arms which they knew were not primarily military, but which would establish superiority until European military design woke up. The Swiss, after experimenting with the Peabody, focused attention on the development of a true military design—a bolt action, the Vetterli.

Since all modern military magazine rifles were evolved directly from the German Dreyse and the French Chassepot Needle Guns, the story of European design is essentially that of the bolt action. However, since the value of the bolt system was not fully recognized until after the Franco-Prussian War of 1870, a wide variety of other systems were tried before the metallic cartridge bolt action design was militarily perfected.

It is with those variants that we shall deal first because of their historical value.

Early European Single Shot Designs

The very earliest form, interestingly enough, was the French Flobert which appeared about 1845. It handled the first successful forerunner of the rim fire, the primed copper case and lead ball combination we know today

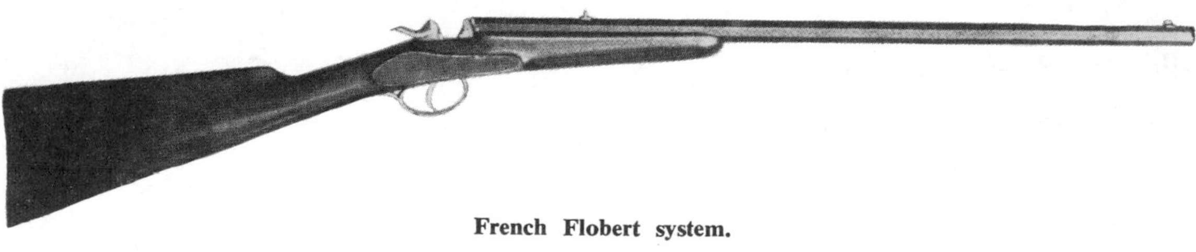

French Flobert system.

as the "BB" or bulleted-breech cap. In that original Flobert the thumb-actuated breechpiece was not backed up by a hammerlock as in our own Remington rolling block of later date. The French had the germ of one of the most successful locking systems later developed, but the military was too occupied with making a better needle gun to realize the prize within their reach. As has already been pointed out, Flobert's arms and ammunition were exhibited and listed as patented at the London Exhibition in 1851. Yet the French rifle of 1870 was a paper cartridge, needle fire!

According to Colonel Rudolf Schmidt of the Swiss Army, a noted authority writing first in 1877, the original Flobert action appeared in 1845. The Swiss experimented with rim fires at a very early date, probably about 1847, but the first practical and successful metallic rim fire was the American Smith & Wesson.

As early as 1865 the Swiss designers were experimenting with the Milbank-Amsler conversion. This system is like our later Springfield 1873. The hammer is cocked and the forward hinged breechblock turned up over the top of the barrel to expose the chamber. A perfected form of this design was adopted by the Swiss in 1867 and used until actually replaced by the bolt type Vetterli. (The Vetterli was officially adopted several years before it was actually put in service.)

In 1868 a strange design somewhat resembling the American Cochran of that period appeared in Belgium. Known as the "Reilly-Comblain," it had a side lever which served to elevate the front of the breechblock to give access to the chamber. Like the percussion American Hall, the breechblock was hinged at the rear. Since the R. C. was a metallic cartridge breechloader, the solid block was pierced only for the striker. The better known "Comblain," the dropping block design, did not appear until about 1870. It and the British-made Albini-Braendlin already described were in general Belgian use for some years, the Comblain being more generally used by the Civil Guards. Both of these last mentioned rifles in .43 caliber were actually used to some extent even in World War I! The Terssen of 1868 was still another hinged-block Belgian conversion on the order of the Albini and the American Springfield 1873. The Comblain drop-block model was adopted quite early by Brazil, Chile and Peru.

The Chabot of 1865 and the Austrian Wänzl of 1867 were also conversions based on the principle of the lifting hinge block.

The Swiss "Schmidt & Jung" rifle of 1865 was on the principle of the earlier American Joslyn, although one gathers from Col. Schmidt that he thought his breechblock hinging to the left was quite original.

In 1867 the original Remington rolling block swept over Europe. It is an interesting commentary on the business ability of the heads of the Remington concern at that time, that they were so well covered by patents—and by foreign representatives!—that no attempt was made to infringe on their basic system. Without exception every other American type was copied, modified or otherwise altered by foreign designers.

Hard on the heels of the introduction by Great Britain of the American Snider conversion came imitations, the Bonin, the Schneider and the widely used French "Tabatiere." Since the last named conversion had a breechblock hinged at one side to swing up from the other, it was promptly classed "Tabatiere" because of its resemblance to the cover of the then familiar French snuff box. This atrocity fired a Boxer-type cartridge of 12 gauge whose conical bullet was hollow from base nearly to point, the hollow being plugged with papier-mache to expand the bullet to take the grooves. The receiver of the British Snider was cut away to permit insertion of the breechblock, yet to leave plenty of breech metal behind it for the shooter's protection. The receiver of the Tabatiere on the other hand was cut away at the rear, making it easier to insert a cartridge and to clean the barrel. This weakened the breech, however. Defective cartridges made the design unsafe, and the French probably were just as well off that they entered the War of 1870 with needle guns. The Russian Krnka conversion of 1869 is another variant of the Snider, with all the defects of the Tabatiere. An iron breechblock was fitted into a bronze receiver well, and was hinged on the left. This Bohemian design automatically extracted the case as the breechblock being lifted acted on an extracting lever.

In 1867 Spain adopted the American Berdan lifting hinged block as a conversion unit for its muzzle loaders, and in the same year Russia adopted the striker-fired hinged block American "Berdan I" already described. (The Berdan II adopted in 1871 by Russia must not be confused with the Berdan-type lifting hinged block design. The name "Berdan II" generally used in Europe applied to the turning bolt action similar to that of the Mauser, and was made at the Russian Tula Arsenal.)

Russian Berdan I system ready for loading. This long obsolete rifle was made both in Russia and in the United States for Russia.

The Bavarian Werder, adopted in 1869, has already been described. This modification of the American Peabody was one of the noteworthy developments of its day, since it was not merely a conversion of an existing muzzle loader, but was actually an entirely new rifle.

In 1871 the Swiss "Kaestli," a striker-fired modification of the American Sharps dropping block system appeared. The French "Mesnier" dropping block (followed by a modified rolling block form which is little known) also appeared about this time.

The year 1874 saw the adoption by Greece of a modified dropping block rifle, the "Mylonas," which used a centrally hung hammer and was operated by a lever positioned ahead of the triggerguard.

In 1868 the Werndl rifle was introduced in Austria. This arm had a block hinged on the left to be turned up away from the breech when the hammer was cocked. A thumbpiece jutted out on the right side. This was the last single-shot rifle officially used by the Austrians.

The Belgian Martini-Francotte, a hammerless modification of the Peabody noteworthy because the entire lockwork unit can be removed without tools for cleaning, was later distributed by Greener, and is sometimes called the "Greener-Martini." This Francotte lock is still in extensive use on European single shot sporting rifles.

The early Krag-Petersson single-shot was also a modification of the Peabody system, the block being hinged at the rear to drop at the front for loading. This arm appeared in the early 1870's and was the basis for a later magazine rifle. About this time also appeared the French "Duprez," a hinged block operated by a side lever, a freak design of no particular importance, except that it illustrates the paucity of French design at that period.

In 1885 the last military design on the falling block principle appeared. This was the Guedes-Castro adopted by Portugal. The arm was made in 8mm caliber at the Steyr works in Austria. It was a direct modification of the British Martini-Henry and not, as it is often listed, a bolt locked rifle.

The only specimens of rolling block locks to appear at all in European design emerged after the passing of the value of the Remington system. In 1881 Nagant in Belgium brought out a hammer rifle with a rolling block lock operated by a lever below the triggerguard; and in the following year the Mesnier hammerless, its action operated by a triggerguard lever, made a brief appearance.

With this short survey of the outstanding modifications of American systems, we turn now to the bolt action military design which Europe pioneered and perfected; and then to the magazine arm, as it evolved.

Chapter 5. The Evolution of Military Bolt Actions

Bolt Actions in the United States

THE great part played by the United States in the use, evolution, and development of the early bolt action has been given little attention in the written histories of firearms. It is true that all modern bolt actions stem from the German Dreyse Needle Gun. It is also true that the direct descendant of that arm, the German Mauser, is the parent of most of its perfect forms.

However, American bolt-locking systems for metallic cartridges were manufactured and used first in our Civil War. The North issued 1001 Palmer carbines using .52 caliber Rim Fire cartridges. These arms were patented by William Palmer (41,017) December 22, 1863—a good four years earlier than the original Norris-Mauser. True, the two arms have a resemblance only in their method of opening and closing the breech, still the Palmer bolt breech locking design is a first evolutionary step. This carbine had screw threads at a rear section of the bolt which locked into corresponding receiver cuts when the bolt was pushed forward and the handle turned down. Since the Army at that time didn't consider a weapon a weapon unless it had a huge thumb cocking lock (or hammer) on the right side, Palmer provided one. The falling hammer hit the cartridge on the rim. This arm had a spring extractor on top of the bolt, an automatic ejector in the form of a pivoted lever in the side of the receiver, and had the receiver side cut away to make ejection positive. The Palmer, made by E. G. Lamson at Windsor, Vermont, was the source of design factors used in several later bolt actions in this country, though it seems to have been little known in Europe.

The first use of the bolt forward locking lug principle was, as we have seen, incorporated by Lt. Col. J. Durrel Green, U.S.A., in his percussion arm of 1857, though that principle was not used for metallic cartridges until the French (Lebel) introduced it, in 1886.

The first bolt action arm to use Center Fire cartridges, and also the first to have the firing pin directly propelled within the bolt, was the Ward-Burton Single Shot first patented Dec. 20, 1859 (No. 26,475 to Bethel Burton). Springfield Armory manufactured 313 carbines and 1000 rifles in caliber .50-70 C.F. and the arms were field tested in 1872 trials. Some were later made commercially in other calibers. The Ward-Burton bolt was unlocked in standard fashion by turning the bolt handle up. This disengaged lock threads at the rear of the bolt body from corresponding receiver cuts (as in the Palmer). The cartridge could be dropped into the magazine well, as in the best European modern single shot practice. Pushing the bolt home chambered the cartridge and cocked the piece. Ejection was automatic on retracting the bolt. This weapon was fitted with a special bolt lock which had to be released by the right thumb before the handle could be lifted, a device which could also be used as a safety. Soldiers long used to old side hammers soon gave the bolt design a bad name when they encountered accidental fire on bolt closing. The comparatively minor design changes necessary to overcome this defect were passed over at the time. (The British too were influenced against bolt actions because of possible accidental fire until Paul Mauser evolved his simple cam-cocking system.)

In 1872 Ward-Burton offered a rifle of this hammerless bolt design with a magazine tube below the barrel. It, too, was rejected by the Ordnance Board. This was the first American bolt action magazine rifle using the by then familiar Winchester magazine tube. Only the Swiss Vetterli and the Austrian Früwirth in this design were ahead of the Ward-Burton, both having appropriated the Winchester magazine idea before 1870 as a result of experiments with the Winchester 1866.

Also tested and rejected at the 1872 U. S. tests was a bolt action designed by G. Merrill, samples of which may be encountered with the stamp of the Brown Mfg. Co. of Newburyport, Massachusetts. This arm had an exposed hammer behind the bolt. When a right side lever was actuated to unlock the bolt and the action was opened, the bolt cocked and rode over the hammer. This system also appeared in later designs. The Merrill caliber was .58 C.F. Merrill alterations on Enfields bought from England during the Civil War (North and South each purchased some 400,000 of these muzzle loading Enfields!) were used by various state militia groups to some extent.

All told the Ordnance Board viewed 12 bolt action types in the 1872 tests out of a total of 108 designs—including 10 repeaters—but decided to retain a modified Springfield Single Shot, the 1873 Model, with its hinged block lock.

The 1878 Ordnance Board tested 29 rifles of magazine type. Eight were bolt actions. The Hotchkiss was officially adopted as our first official bolt-action magazine arm. The inventor, B. B. Hotchkiss, was an American. At the time he was living in France; and it was there that his model rifles were made. (We shall encounter Hotchkiss again under the history of Machine Guns.)

The Hotchkiss rifle came to the attention of Winchester

when it was shown at the Philadelphia Centennial Exposition in 1876. Arrangements were made for manufacture by Winchester. First U. S. patents were issued in 1860. Modifications of the rifle continued through 1878.

The magazine of the Hotchkiss rifle was a variant of the earlier Spencer, a spring-fed tube in the buttstock. New features were magazine cut-offs allowing the soldier to hold his magazine in reserve, and a good manual safety. Winchester supplied 2500 actions to the Navy and 1000 to the Army. Barrels and furniture were supplied by Springfield Armory, thus allowing utilization of Springfield single-shot bands, sights and bayonets in the interest of economy.

In 1882 Congress appropriated $50,000 to develop and test magazine rifle designs—the small sum being an indication of how hard it was in those days to convince people of the need for improved military arms in the United States.

The Lee Inventions

James Paris Lee was born in Scotland and educated in Canada. However, all his arms design work was done in the United States after he was granted citizenship here. He is another of the inventing genius group to whom due credit has never been extended.

The name "Lee" in firearms circles immediately conjures up the British Lee-Enfield and Lee-Metford rifles, the primary small arms of the British forces from 1888. Lee's development of those actions and of the straight pull Lee rifle are well known. His other achievements need some passing notice, however.

Lee patented in 1879 the arm known as the Lee U. S. Navy Rifle, caliber .45-70 Government. This rifle actually marked the introduction of the magazine system which revolutionized military rifle design—the centrally positioned box magazine in which cartridges are stored directly below the bolt. It seems simple today, but its development was a stroke of design genius at the time.

Lee further developed a magazine design which had been patented by three Englishmen; Walker, Money and Little in 1867. This box magazine overcame many of the troubles which had been encountered with tubular magazines.

But what of the inventor himself? James Lee was a man early dogged by troubles. In July, 1862, he patented a rim fire rifle, caliber .36 as first issued, which was manufactured by the Lee Arms Company, Milwaukee, Wisconsin. This was a single shot weapon with an exposed hammer. With the hammer at half-cock the barrel could be swung out to the right for loading, a barrel lug being provided for hand extraction. Lee lived at Stevens Point, Wisconsin, at the time, and it was there he worked out the patterns of many of his later designs. The Milwaukee plant was probably the only Middle Western works of any importance during the Civil War. Lee began manufacture on a War Department order for 1000 carbines early in 1865, having sunk most of his available capital in the Milwaukee plant. He placed an order with Remington at Ilion, N. Y., for the manufacture of the barrels. Assuming the Government order was for .44 Rim Fire Long, since the specifications did not state exactly, he found that the Ordnance Department had not so intended. The Government refused to accept his finished carbines. This unfortunate venture cost Lee his capital. The resulting suits were a further strain on Lee.

In 1874 Congress appropriated $10,000 for the manufacture and testing of a new Lee Single Shot—a curious design so impractical that one wonders if some conscious-stricken official was trying to make amends to Lee by providing the money to manufacture 134 of them. Having learned the lesson of tieing up his own money in governmental experimentation, this time Lee went to Springfield on salary to supervise manufacture. The arm was a failure and Lee turned his abilities to the design of a new bolt rifle and a new magazine.

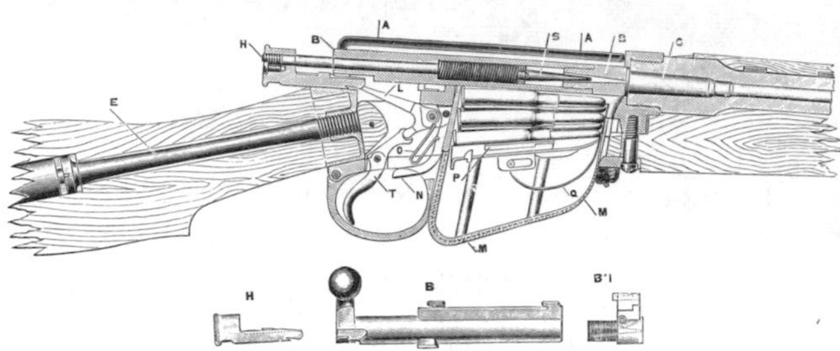

Mechanism of the Lee-Speed Magazine Rifle Mark II.

Lee submitted his Navy Magazine Rifle to the Equipment Board in July, 1879. He arranged for manufacture at Bridgeport by a new concern consisting of the group then operating as the Sharps Rifle Co. The group suddenly decided there was no money in the arms business and being unable to see enough future in it to warrant putting up more capital, turned the manufacture over to Remington at Ilion, N. Y. Lee went to work at Remington. Remington, which had been in danger of losing all its world markets now that magazine rifles were obviously here to stay, took a new lease on life. In the years that followed much of Remington's success was due to Lee and his designs. One of the men who sold Lee short by failing to back up his developments in the original Lee Arms Company was, curiously enough, old P. T. Barnum, a man whose business acumen in most matters was quite outstanding.

The 1879 Lee was designed without a cutoff. The magazine was intended to be removed from the action when the rifle was used as a single shot. Aside from the U. S. Navy caliber, the model was also made for use in China and in Spain in caliber .43 Spanish. It was a Civil Guards weapon for many years.

Lee was granted patents in England, Belgium and Russia. He sued both Mannlicher and Mauser for alleged infringements when they introduced their first box magazine rifles. Every student of design or invention, of course is aware of the phenomenon of "parallel development." When a need is recognized for any advance, geniuses in various areas seem to work out the same approach often in complete secrecy and without any way of physically knowing about other research in the field.

A study of the Mauser and Mannlicher records shows that such was the case with Lee and his magazines. The original work records of the German and the Austrian inventors show clearly that they were both experimenting with box designs before any word of Lee's magazine could have reached them. However, it is quite possible that both men benefited by later studies of the Lee work, and may have perfected their own types after seeing Lee's. It is a fact that the Lee was openly tested in both England and the United States well before the commercial introduction of the initial Mannlicher or Mauser box types.

In 1885 Great Britain tested the Lee action with the American Bethel-Burton side-feed magazine. By then, however, other European nations had beaten the British to the adoption of magazine rifles. Those in use at that time in France, Germany and Russia used tube magazines. Hence, as usual, the British authorities leaned towards the tube pattern also. Lee made further improvements on his box magazine. The British learned the Germans were concerned with a box design about this time. This again swayed official ideas. In 1887 the British tested both the Lee-Burton and Lee actions with Metford rifling in a new caliber .402. Meanwhile Switzerland had reduced its caliber, and after experiments with a Swiss Rubin of caliber 7.5mm, the British hit on the idea of combining the Lee bolt and magazine, the Metford rifling, and a new .303 cartridge originally using compressed black powder but later changed to a cordite load. (The change was made in 1892.) In December, 1888, the final form of the rifle was decided, the name Lee-Metford Magazine Rifle Mark I assigned, and Britain was now among the nations using magazine arms. The further story of these Lees must be told in the history of Great Britain, but this was the first of the series with which the British Tommies forged and protected the Empire from that day on. Meanwhile, the official U. S. arm was still the Single Shot Springfield cam lock!

Remington made the Lee as a Sporting Rifle in several calibers, following the design with the modified Remington-Lee Small Bore Military Rifle—an arm chambered for the 6mm U. S. Navy, the 7mm Mauser (30,000 of which were delivered to Cuba), the 7.65mm Mauser and the .30-40 U. S. Krag cartridges. Two thousand in the last caliber were used by the Michigan Militia, but the design was not adopted by the Federal Government.

In 1895 a Naval Board adopted the Lee Straight Pull in caliber 6mm (.236) the smallest military caliber ever

Navy Lee straight pull 1895 model. Caliber 6mm (.236).

adopted, although some as low as 5mm were experimented with abroad. Pulling the bolt straight back unlocked the arm, ejected the empty case and cocked the action. A forward thrust chambered a cartridge and locked the bolt. The locking design was decidedly original. Winchester was given a contract for manufacture and 10,000 were delivered. This was our first clip loaded official rifle. Though excellent in theory, the rifle did not work out well as a military design.

Other Early American Military Magazine Rifles

Many new American designs followed fast on the heels of the Lee 1879. For historical value, we shall here touch upon the outstanding ones.

Major W. R. Livermore and Captain A. H. Russell of the U. S. Ordnance Department made extensive researches into magazine construction about the same time that Lee introduced his noted magazines. What is often called the "Russell-Livermore" rifle, an arm which received considerable attention in European arms circles, is actually an altered Lee-Speed rifle fitted with a special feed case system. The case was a piece of bent sheet steel designed to carry enough cartridges to fill the magazine, permitting magazine loading with a single motion, the case being discarded after loading.

The "Russell" magazine rifle invented by the same A. H. Russell of Ft Union, N. M., was a different development, an unsuccessful straight-pull bolt action. The lock was ingenious. It consisted of a crosspiece within the bolt body of slightly greater diameter than the bolt, provided with cam-shaped wings extending into receiver seatings. The initial pull on the bolt acted to revolve the crosspiece out of locking engagement, and the continuing pull extracted and ejected the case. This arm was made with both a bottom magazine feed, Lee style, and a special side or lateral magazine.

In 1882 the Ordnance Board also recommended tests of a rifle offered by Gen. J. N. Reece, and known as the Chaffee-Reece. It had a tube magazine in the buttstock.

U. S. single shot black powder rifle, principal arm in Spanish-American War.

The loading point was a trap in the buttplate which could be opened only when the bolt was in open position. A magazine cut-off was provided. Setting a thumbpiece at half cock set the safety and locked the bolt. One thousand were ordered. They were the first U. S. magazine rifles made at Springfield Armory. Like the Hotchkiss, it was designed to take the old single shot sights, bayonet and fittings. It was soon discarded as too complicated and unreliable for field service.

The 1882 Board also arranged for testing of an improved Hotchkiss bolt action, the Model 1883. This arm was made by Winchester. It is of interest here only because its tests definitely decided U. S. design opinion against the buttstock-tube magazine for large cartridges. From that time on this tube system was confined to small bore arms. Winchester made the design as a sporting arm also.

The third design tested was the Lee Magazine Rifle 1882, usually called the Remington-Lee. While the arm could be used as a single-shot bolt-action without magazine, the 5-shot magazine itself actually constituted part of the rifle mechanism. As originally designed, several Lee magazines were intended to be issued to the soldier, who was to carry them loaded. They were costly to make and were not intended to be expendable. This magazine system was never favored by the U. S. military, and its later success was entirely in the sporting field where the individual owner is likely to be more careful of the fragile magazines than is the typical soldier. In passing it must be noted that with the coming of World War II, we designed our carbine to use detachable magazines; for by this time the manufacturing methods had improved, costs had been lowered, and the question of cost on the field of battle has now been subordinated to increased firepower such as is possible by rapidly replaceable magazines. Once again we see Lee's original ideas succeeding.

It is interesting to note in passing that the Lee was the first choice of the 1882 Board out of a total of 40 rifles submitted. These 40 represented the designs of only 13 inventors, however, and many models were merely modifications of a basic pattern. Of the remaining systems considered by the Board, only the Marlin Lever Action and the Remington-Keene Bolt Action were later produced commercially.

The Remington-Keene was a tube-under-barrel rifle originally patented by J. Keene in 1874. It had a cocking-piece shaped like a common hammer attached to the extreme end of the bolt. The Keene was tested by both Army and Navy in the Government .45 caliber, and is of interest as the only full rifle ever used by the U. S. Army with below-barrel-tube magazine, other types having been carbines. An outstanding feature of the design was that it could be magazine-loaded with bolt closed through the bottom of the action. The magazine was provided with a cut-off.

When the 1882 Board concluded its tests, the War Department settled back confident that the Springfield Single Shot was still the proper arm. Fortunately, we had no occasion to need an Army for a number of years. Meanwhile we were nearing the time when smokeless powder would be commonly used and a new design would be demanded.

The Krag-Jorgensen

By 1890 every important military group in the world was equipped with magazine rifles except the United States. Our Ordnance Board convened to consider magazine systems. Fifty-three systems were presented, both domestic and foreign arms. The Board eventually selected the Norwegian Krag-Jorgensen system around which to build our new rifle. It passed through five modifications before it was accepted officially. The adoption of this system is a sterling example in history of how important timing is in military decisions, and of how utterly inadequate theoretical tests may be. At a time when the simple Mauser bolt was already known, when the superior locking features of the dual front lug systems was evident, when the simplicity of both the Mauser and the Mannlicher types of clip loading devices had been field proved, we nevertheless adopted a bolt with a single locking lug and a cumbrous side box loader magazine which had to be loaded with single cartridges! A variety of clips were tried, but the Krag system did not allow a sensible clip to be developed. In all fairness it must be admitted that the Ordnance authorities in Great Britain and Germany seem to have been afflicted with the same virus as our own at that period. England had adopted the American Lee with its rear locking system, a system that from conservatism and from financial considerations they did not change over to any degree until the production of the FN after World War II, although experimentation was begun in 1913 and early 1914. Germany herself, meanwhile, had adopted the hodge-podge known as the "Commission, Mannlicher Loading System," the Gewehr 1888, flying in the face of Paul Mauser, her premier designer who at that time had a superior design in being. Austria adopted a Mannlicher with a wedge rear lock. Instead of selecting the best design the military all sought something different.

While smokeless powder had come into its own by 1892, making obsolete the single shot black powder rifle for first line military purposes, the flanged (rimmed) cartridge case was still in accepted use. For that matter,

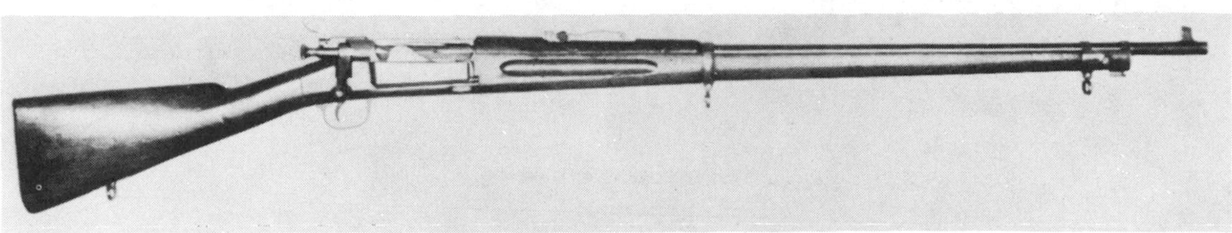

Representative Krag-Jorgensen rifle.

it still was used by both Great Britain and Russia in World War II, despite the superiority of the rimless.

However, by 1892 foreign use and practice had established the desirability of calibers of about .30 inches for maximum military efficiency. These facts doubtless influenced the development and adoption of the .30-40 Krag cartridge decided upon by our Ordnance authorities. The original 1892 rifle was not particularly satisfactory either as to accuracy or usage even with the cartridge of its time; but by 1896 Springfield Armory had remedied design and material defects to such a great degree that the Model 1898 (which mechanically differed only in minor details such as rear sights) established a record as one of the sturdiest rifles ever made. In all some 400,-000 were manufactured. The 1896-1898 models in general sporting use today are excellent arms in their class, reliable and accurate within the limits of the ballistics of the cartridge used, though they cannot of course compare with the Mauser action for strength.

The design could not be made strong enough to be used with the powerful Government loads later developed, a factor which many experts contended should have been considered at the time of the official adoption of the Krag. In any event, at the outbreak of the Spanish-American War only the Regular Army (which numbered only 27,000 total) was armed with Krags. State militia units had a variety of rifles of their own purchase, mostly single shot arms. As a result we actually entered the War of '98 armed chiefly with old .45-70 black powder arms.

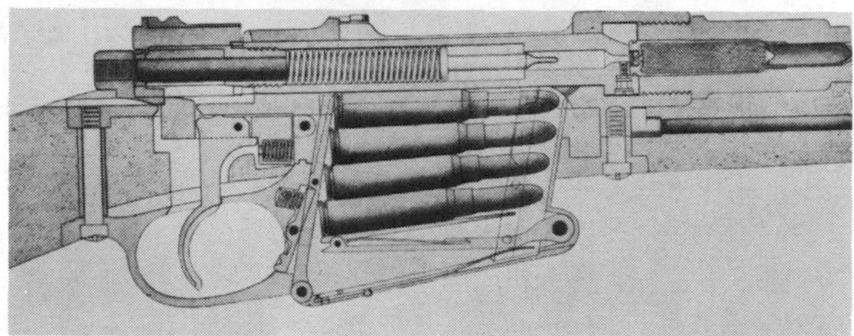

M-91 Mauser.

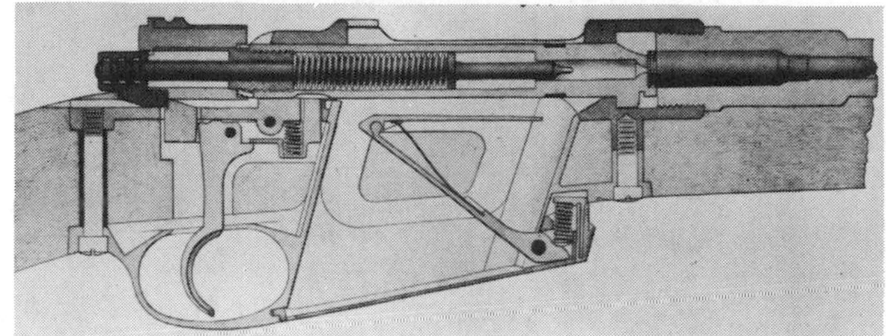

M-92 Mauser (also called M92/93).

The first of the new rifles was produced at Springfield Armory in 1900. It was chambered for a new .30 cartridge which was not very efficient. Actually it was little better than the Krag it replaced. An improved rifle was issued to our troops in 1904 and 1905 under the designation "Model 1903." From its point of design and manufacture it was popularly known as the "Springfield."

Spanish 7mm smokeless Mauser magazine rifle used by Spain in War of 1898.

Spain by this time had armed her Cuban forces with a variety of modern small arms. The principal one was the 7mm Mauser rimless made by Loewe, a precision cliploader. The Battle of San Juan Hill showed that the Krag just wasn't good enough—not to mention the single-shot Springfield. Our attack force of 15,000 was aided by Cuban insurgent groups. The garrison was only 700 men —but they had modern arms. The hill was taken, but not until some 1400 casualties were inflicted upon us!

The "Springfield"

The long series of U. S. Government bolt-action rifles listed as the Model 1903 and its modifications stem directly from the German Mauser. In 1900 and 1901 our Ordnance Department conducted intensive tests with captured German-made Spanish Mausers, and made studies of the new German Mauser designs then in use in Germany as the official "Gewehr 98."

The name has stuck through the years, even though the rifle has been made at other arsenal and manufacturing plants.

We paid Mauser $200,000 for manufacturing rights. The design was altered somewhat. A magazine cut-off was combined with the bolt release; a cocking piece was provided which could be pulled back for manual recocking in case of a misfire; and the excellent German one-piece firing pin was replaced with a two-piece design. Other minor alterations were made, resulting in probably the finest military bolt action produced. Its chamber support of the cartridge case is not as efficient as the German; but this is a technical factor which normally affects only individuals who dangerously overload used cartridge cases for experimental shooting.

The design and variations of the Springfield are dealt with in detail in chapter 45. All use a variant of the U. S. 1906 Model ammunition. These are based on a cartridge developed by the United States in 1906 after experimenting with the German 1905 pointed "Spitzer" bullet. Springfields are often described as "caliber .30-06," indicating the Model 1903 rifle chambered and adapted for the 1906 cartridge. The sights of the original 1903 were also changed and the cleaning rod bayonet was eliminated.

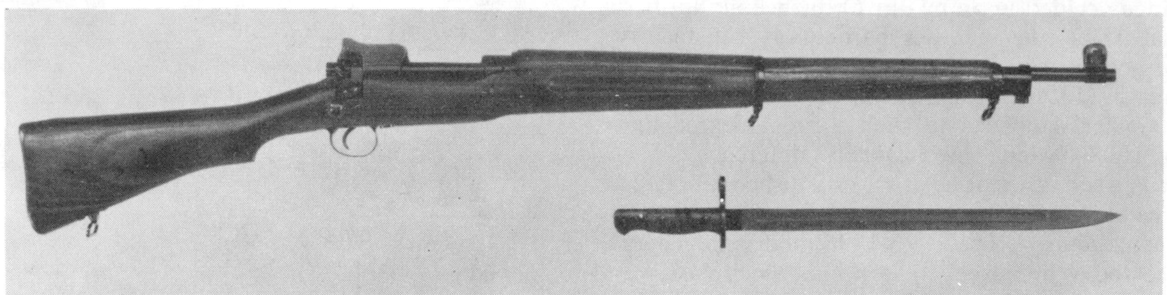

U. S. Model 1917 (Enfield) Rifle.

The "Enfield"

The "U. S. Model 1917" rifle was an emergency design only. Yet in two wars it served its purposes well. It was a modification of a British design and was first produced in 1917. The name "Enfield" is popularly applied to it from the British arsenal where it was developed.

The outbreak of World War I found the British experimenting with a new Mauser-pattern .276 rifle originally intended to replace the "Lee-Enfield" designs. British manufacturing facilities were not capable of handling additional production, so U. S. arms makers were asked to manufacture the new design, but chambered and altered for the British standard .303 cartridge to conform to regular issue.

When the U. S. entered the war in 1917, there was a shortage of Springfields. Since both Winchester and Remington were tooled by then for the British Pattern '14 (Enfield), the United States Ordnance Department had those companies undertake alterations of the design to handle the standard U. S. rifle cartridge.

This rifle has been issued to allies throughout the world. It is commonly referred to as the "American Enfield" to distinguish it from the earlier version chambered for the British cartridge. It, too, is discussed in chapter 17 in detail. While heavy and rather clumsy, it is one of the strongest military rifles ever built. It bears the mark of the manufacturer also, which may be Winchester, Remington or Eddystone; and these markings at times cause confusion to foreign writers.

With this short summary of American bolt action development, we now revert to an earlier day for the American story of repeating and magazine rifle development.

While the terms are very often used interchangeably, the word "repeater" in general use ordinarily indicates a tube-cartridge reservoir; while the term "magazine" ordinarily indicates a military type arm with cartridges held in a box below the bolt.

The Spencer—The World's First Successful Repeater

The Spencer (1860) was the first successful repeater. Of course, its development was made possible only by the introduction of the metallic cartridge case. It had a spring-fed magazine tube in the buttstock. Firing was by an external hammer. Operation was by triggerguard lever. A semi-circular breechblock operated by the lever had both a falling (unlocking) motion and a rotating (feeding) motion.

As an item of genuine Amercian history as well as firearms history, the Spencer story deserves to be told.

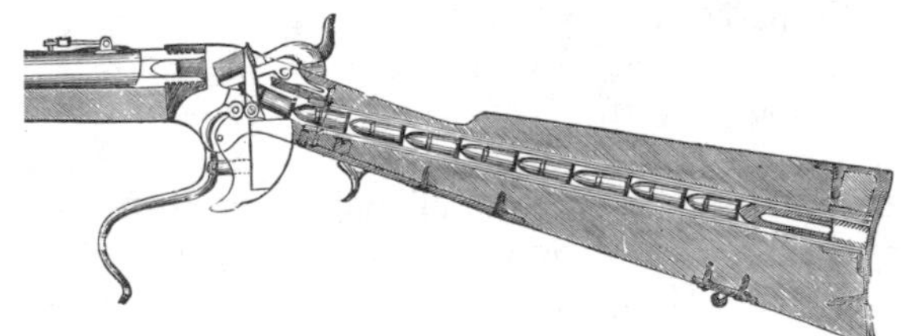

Spencer Civil War Carbine Magazine and Feeding Mechanism.

The story, part of another little known saga of American arms inventors, begins on a day early in the Civil War when a youth of 20, harried and self-conscious, haunted the corridors of the bustling War Department in Washington. He had run the customary gantlet of military red tape even to gain entrance to the sacred confines. To the busy Ordnance officers he was just another "young man with a gun": just another crazy inventor come to take up their valuable time with senseless talk of a revolutionary weapon. Every armory and every capable manufacturer in the North was turning all his efforts to producing more of those fine muzzle loading percussion rifles. Yet here was an adolescent talking gibberish about not only a metallic cartridge breechloader, but actually one which would fire repeatedly after being loaded with several cartridges! How could the war ever be won with all these interruptions of precious routine?

Dispirited, discouraged, ready to quit, Spencer complained bitterly to the one man he found who would listen to him: a humble doorkeeper at the War Department Building, not an arms "expert." Just a simple man who sensed in the manner of the boy something the experts had not taken time to observe. That plain American doorman examined the weapon the boy carried. He watched the dummy cartridges inserted in the tube in the hollow butt, watched the lever of the crude model thrown down to feed a cartridge into the chamber, studied the action as young Spencer brought the lever back to seat the cartridge and seal the breech. Another forward movement of the triggerguard lever and the dummy cartridge in the chamber was ejected and a second one fed; a closing movement of the lever and the breech was sealed again! Unbelievingly the humble man watched the stream of dummies ejected as Christopher Spencer worked the lever. Here was a development which might actually make killing so fast and terrifying that it might shorten the fratricidal war!

"You come back here after I am through for the day and I will take you to a man who will examine your gun." Those were the words the doorman spoke as Christopher M. Spencer recalled them in a later day. Heartened but doubting, the youngster left, alternating between hope and fear as the day dragged on.

Later that day the two made their way to the great White Mansion next door to the grim War Department Building. The man was confident that the great humble personage in the White House would have the time no Army man could spare; the boy was tense and unbelieving at the prospect of seeing the Commander-in-Chief himself.

Why President Lincoln had such confidence in the simple door tender we do not know. That he did is evi-

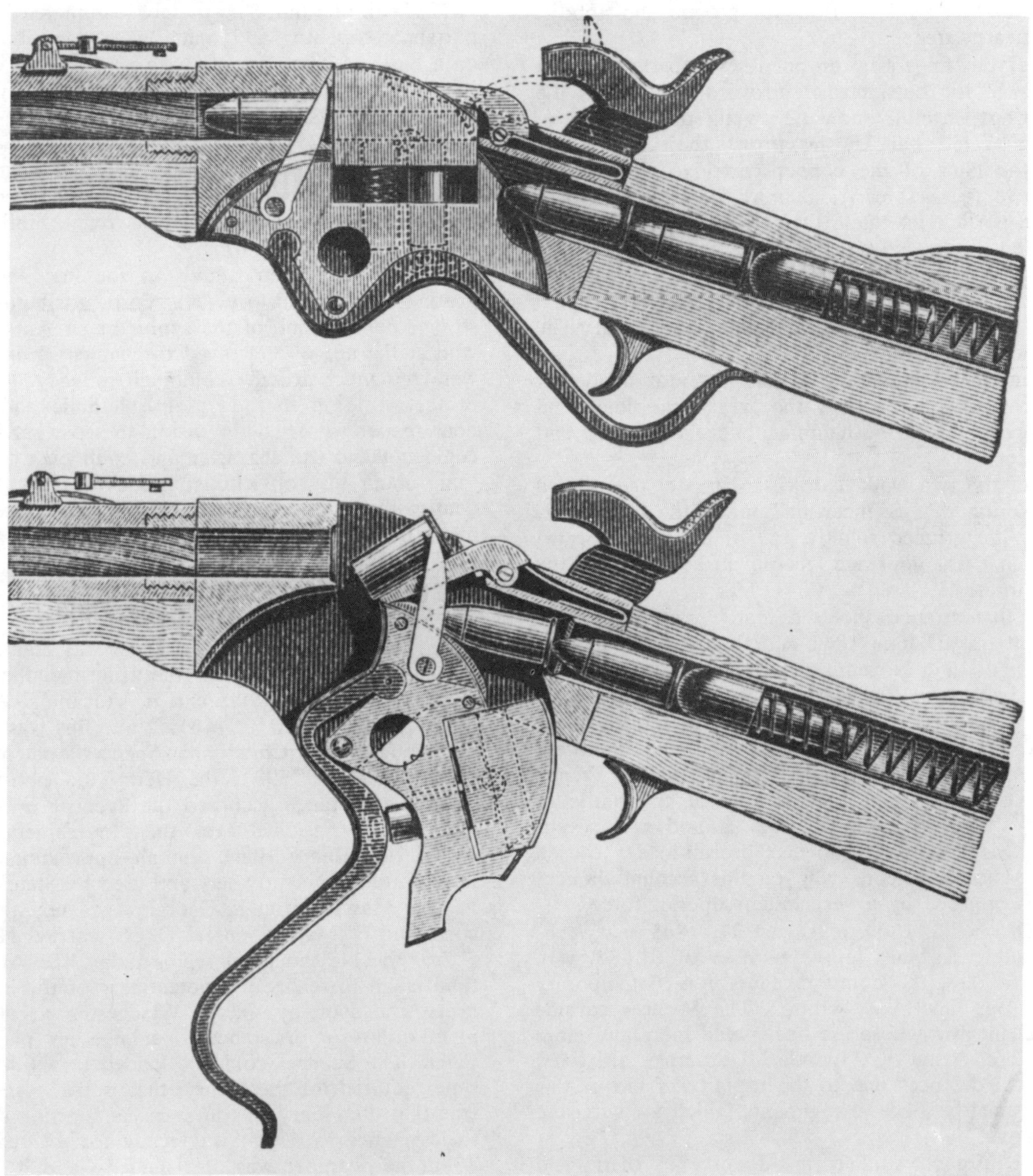

Famous American Spencer carbine action. Upper: Rifle ready to fire. Lower: Rifle ejecting empty case. The post-War II rifle developed by Birmingham Small Arms Company of Birmingham, England, uses, under the name of Ralock, a modification of the loading system here shown.

denced by his actions, for he saw them both in his chambers. His plaid shawl about his shoulders, Abe Lincoln sat gaunt and drawn, attentively watching and listening as the boy demonstrated the action with dummy cartridges. Slowly he rose. "It works all right," are those words Spencer recalled the President saying, "but the proof lies in the shooting. Let's go out and shoot it."

As they walked down the grounds of the White House, Lincoln absently noted that the pocket of his coat was torn. "This is a nice dress for the Chief Magistrate to appear in public," he said, as he asked for a pin. While the tall gray man pinned his torn pocket, young Spencer picked a weathered shingle from the ground and stood it against a nearby tree.

With nervous fingers he dropped seven cartridges into the hollow in the butt, pushed forward and locked the feeder spring. Carefully now he swung the carbine towards the target. Quickly he thrust the lever down, catching the glint of the copper cartridge case as the spring drove the first cartridge into the chamber when the breech-pin left its catch. Quickly he pulled the lever back, seeing the breech-pin thrust the cartridge home as it was rocked forward behind the head of the case. He thumb-cocked the bulky side-hammer expertly, aimed fleetingly, fired. Again he fired. Again, and again. The gun functioned perfectly!

The weapon reloaded, the boyish inventor handed it to President Lincoln. Gravely the great man aimed and fired; levered, cocked the hammer, and again aimed and fired. Again.

Together the two walked down to inspect the riddled shingle. Noting that Spencer had made the better pattern, Old Abe grinned slightly and in his solemn drawl said, "When I was your age I could do better." And the testing continued.

Out of that strange shooting match came the Navy Department test of June 1861 and the War Department tests of August and November that same year. The first delivery of the new Spencer .52 caliber repeaters was made on December 31, 1862. By June of the following year 7500 had been delivered. Many of these rifles were issued to the Michigan Cavalry Brigade, and a French Observer, Col. LeCompte, wrote that at the Battle of Gettysburg "The Michigan Brigade, armed with seven-shooter magazine guns, the Spencer breech-loader, caused a great loss to the enemy, who on this account thought themselves opposed by a very much superior force."

From October 3, 1863 to August 31, 1865 new Spencer .52 caliber carbines to the number of 61,685 were delivered. Of these the Comte de Paris in a contemporary history of our Civil War wrote: "The Spencer carbine is an excellent arm whose use has spread more and more in the Federal Army . . . Wonderful examples are given of individual defences due to the rapidity of fire of this arm. Many of the Federal regiments which used it were most effective."

Had the French studied the reports of their field observers on the use of the Spencer, the story of the Franco-Prussian War of 1870 might have had a different ending. Instead the overly conservative French entered that War with the hopeless paper-cartridge needle gun, the Chassepot, while reports on the marvelous new Spencer repeater mouldered in their files.

During the Civil War, the North spent nearly $3,-000,000 for Spencers—the arms could not be manufactured rapidly enough even to approximate the demand. The armory in the Chickering piano factory at Tremont and Camden Streets in Boston closed its doors in the Fall of 1869. The War ended, its financial backers saw no further market for their arms; and that more far-seeing Yankee, Oliver Winchester, promptly bought up surplus Spencer stocks at auction and sold them from 1869 to 1872. With one move he thereby eliminated his only important competitor and managed a good business deal on a basis of hard Yankee cash.

It was only after the Winchester 1866 raised havoc at Plevna in 1877 that Europe awoke to the value of the repeater. By that time the Spencer Repeating-Rifle Company was a part of history. It will remain a part of an important history as long as free men believe in individual initiative, and as long as free Americans maintain an interest in firearms.

The Spencer, then, stands as the first successful repeating arm in history, a record attributable to the strange combination of the genius of an American youth who at the age of 19 solved mechanical problems which were too much for the combined military design brains of the world in that day; of a humble and intelligent door tender who had the vision to see what the experts could not and the character and confidence to do something about his convictions; and of a truly great President without whose active support this new invention might have been hopelessly sidetracked in the vast wastes of departmental red tape.

The Henry Repeating Rifle

As we have seen, B. Tyler Henry was granted a patent for a lever-action repeating rifle using metallic cartridges, a direct evolution of the earlier Volcanic Rifle, on October 16, 1860 (No. 30446). While this was only a few months later than Christopher Spencer's patent of March 6, 1860 (No. 27393), the Henry did not receive the prompt acceptance accorded the Spencer in actual service. During the Civil War the Government purchased only 1731 Henry rifles, though approximately 10,000 more were bought privately and used by State Regiments. In the March through Georgia two regiments of the command of Major General Dodge carried Henrys.

Inexplicable though it seems today, the Army at that time failed to realize the potentiality of this weapon; for every endeavor by Oliver Winchester to get Government orders or assistance to enlarge his plant facilities failed. The Spencer could be loaded in a fraction of the time required for the Henry, that is true. And it is also true that the Henry was primarily a sporting rifle. Nevertheless, once loaded it was ready for 12 rapid shots—13 if the chamber was also loaded—and it could spew bullets at the rate of some 25 per minute, factors which should have impressed muzzle loader enthusiasts, but didn't.

The Henry magazine was below the barrel. To load, the magazine spring was first drawn up into the muzzle end of the tube. This muzzle section could then be pivoted to permit cartridges to be inserted head-first down the tube. The muzzle section was then pivoted back in place, thus allowing the compressed spring to force the cartridges back toward the breech.

The breechblock was toggle-locked. Pulling the trigger-guard lever down first disjointed the toggle to unlock it. From then on the toggle drew the breechblock back in a straight line. The rear of the breechblock rode down and thus cocked the hammer. A carrier block containing the first cartridge from the magazine tube now came in line with the breechblock. Drawing the lever back drove the cartridge into the chamber, dropped the block to receive the next cartridge, and on final movement straightened out the joint in the toggle to lock the breech firmly. The trigger was now in position to actuate the sear and thereby allow the hammer to fall on the firing pin.

A few Henrys were made in caliber .44-25-216 (meaning .44 caliber with 25 grains of black powder and a 216-grain bullet). They were stamped "Henry's Patent Oct. 16, 1860. Manufact'd by the New Haven Arms Company, New Haven, Conn." These rifles used .44 rim fire cartridges in which the bullet caliber was .44. The barrel however was bored .42 and rifled with six .005 inch deep grooves with a "gain twist" rifling.

In 1860 the Henry Repeating Rifle and Carbine Model 1860 was introduced. This had the "King improvement" —the spring loaded gate in the breech wall which allowed cartridges to be inserted from the breech end with ease.

The manufacturers, The New Haven Arms Company, dissolved in 1866.

Winchester Lever Action Military Rifles
The 1866 Model

The Winchester Repeating Arms Company was formed in 1866 at New Haven, Conn. It was merely a reorganization of the New Haven Arms Company. Its early records and catalogs show the Henry Rifle with the King loading gate being listed as the Winchester Model 1866. One Winchester catalog states, "The latest improvements consist in an entire change in the magazine and arrangement for filling it." Actually as hair-splitting collectors will point out, it was a very minor modification of the last Henry.

This 1866 Winchester is still another American invention which helped to revolutionize warfare in its day, yet has been passed by with rather scant attention in this country. Not normally rated a military arm, the lever action Winchester 1866 was responsible for two great Turkish victories over the Russians at Plevna. That story, seldom told and little known, deserves a place in this historical outline.

Plevna—The Last Days of the Single Shot Military Rifle

Little known today, and even less remembered, the 30th of July, 1877, cast shadows which even now are there for anyone with eyes to see. The great Russian army massed before the Turkish defenses of Plevna on the morning of that day stood in their might prepared to sacrifice themselves to the full, determined to storm the trenches ahead of them regardless of cost. They would not be halted; their front ranks would inevitably fall before the defense of the courageous Turks. They were prepared for that. So thought General Krudener and his Staff as they studied the quiet fields ahead on that eventful morning. In their trenches the Turks, barely half as numerous as the Russians, waited grimly, almost eagerly, for the beginning of the assault.

The Russian Guards soberly checked their Berdan rifles, their bottle-necked .42 caliber cartridges. Other units swung up the side locking blocks of their .63 caliber Krnka breechloaders, confident that the alteration of the Bohemian Sylvester Krnka had provided them with the speed of loading necessary to match the American Peabody-Martini rifles in the trenches ahead of them.

Bugles sounded. Officers shouted. The men roared. In massed formations the long lines advanced stolidly, inexorably. The solid lines marched on until, suddenly, a cloud of smoke rose from the black powder rifles in those trenches far ahead. Strangely and with terrifying accuracy a plunging hail of lead ripped into those massed Russian ranks before the reports of the rifles reached them. The Russian Staff stared aghast through their glasses as ranks thinned out before they were able to fire a shot. They claimed later that the slaughter began at a distance of two kilometers, some 2200 yards! Other observers on the Russian side claimed even more fantastic killing ranges for the Peabody-Martinis in the hands of the Turks—as much as 3000 yards! Perhaps the observers were too excited to measure correctly. Perhaps they were seeking to alibi their terrible mistake in ordering massed men to certain death. The true answer we can never know. But we do know that the American rifles had shown deadly efficiency at 700 yards; and it is possible that massed plunging fire at 1000 yards may have decimated the advancing Russians. Riflemen of today armed with Springfields or Garands could not hit consistently at the ranges claimed in 1877 for those old Peabody-Martinis. Of one thing, however, we are sure. At a range considered far beyond that of a rifle of those days, the Peabody-Martini began chopping down the numerical superiority on which the Russian Staff had counted for victory.

With the stoic calm of the true Slav, the Russian advance continued to ranges of 500 yards, 400, 300—200. In the Turkish trenches there was a momentary hush, a pause. The Turks laid down their single shot Peabody-Martinis. And the Russians charged madly ahead.

Russian Intelligence had duly reported the delivery of 30,000 Winchester repeaters to the Turkish cavalry. Those were Tyler Henry's lever action tube loaders with the new King patent side loading gate added, the first arm to bear the name "Winchester." The caliber was .44 Rim Fire Turkish. True, the arm had shown its merit in wild far away America; but what use would it be in real military combat on European fields? Little if any, they surmised.

Russian Intelligence had not learned that the cavalry had been disbanded and that their Winchesters had been issued to the defenders in the trenches. They had not known the intensive drill the defenders had been given in using the arms. They could not conceive what was about to happen . . . And so the charge went on.

At 100 yards the storm broke. All down the line a hail of rapid fire lead burst loose from the muzzles of 30,000 Winchesters. "Each Turk," wrote General Todleben, the new Russian commander, to General Brialmont in a letter dated January 18, 1878, "carried 100 cartridges, and had a box containing 500 placed beside him. A few expert marksmen were employed to pick off the officers . . . the Turks did not even attempt to sight, but, hidden behind the trenches, loaded and fired as rapidly as they could . . . The most heroic endeavors of our troops were without effect, and divisions of over 10,000 men were reduced to an effective of between 4,000 and 5,000." But the Russians were stubborn. Instead they repeated the attack on Plevna with the same tactics—and the same results—on September 11, 1877! In all they lost 30,000 men in the useless assaults!

Those Winchesters broke the back of the Russian attacks in their closing phases, after the long range Peabody-Martinis had whittled the advancing ranks down with harrowing fire. The "quick loaders" fastened to the sides of the Berdans and the Krnkas to hold cartridges ready for insertion in the breech were no possible answer to the true repeating arm.

A hush settled over the chancelleries of Europe that summer of 1877. Every European nation now set itself to re-arm with repeaters as rapidly as possible. The Turks turned first to Winchester for another 140,000 repeaters, then to Germany for a long succession of advanced Mauser designs.

In this day of the nuclear bomb it is difficult to conceive the way the success of the Winchester then altered the economic planning and the military thinking of the Globe. The hush that began over the Field of Plevna and spread throughout Europe was more than just another episode in the duel between Turks and Russians. It was a hush that presaged a development of arms and a course of diplomacy leading inevitably to the years of strain that lay ahead.

Truly, the day of the single shot military rifle was over.

Winchester Model 1895—Russian

One other Winchester Lever Action has played a part in military usage—the Model 1895 Box Magazine. This rifle was designed for Winchester by the late great inventor John M. Browning, about whom we must have more to say when we deal with pistols and machine guns.

The Model 1895 differs radically from the other lever actions which Browning designed for Winchester and whose uses have been sporting. It differs primarily by having a built-in box magazine in the receiver directly below the line of the breechblock. The magazine was designed to hold military cartridges in single line one atop the other, the column being forced up by a spring actuated follower as in regular military bolt action feeding.

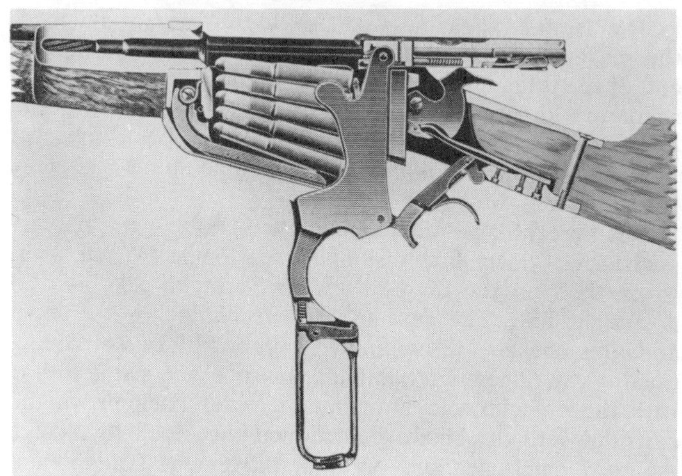

Action of the Winchester Model 1895 box magazine rifle ready for closing bolt stroke by operating the lever.
This is the same as the Russian version except for caliber and lack of clip slot loading element.

The positioning of the magazine required the locking bolt (which secures the breechblock to the receiver when firing) to be placed to the rear of the receiver. Working out a forward locking bolt to be lever actuated would have interfered with the simplicity and weight required. The action proved entirely strong enough for the normal military cartridges then in use (quite as does the British Lee-Enfield type with its rear-placed lugs).

During World War I, however, Russian purchasing commissions came to the United States to place orders for the manufacture of bolt-action rifles of their own pattern. One of these groups was impressed with the performance of the Model 1895 Winchester and a Russian Government order was placed for them. These rifles were chambered for the standard Russian rifle cartridge. A special alteration was made to allow these rifles to be loaded rapidly by inserting a standard Russian army cartridge clip in feed guides, then pressing the column of cartridges down into the magazine with a single thrust. This of course was merely an adaptation of the Mauser system of clip loading; but it is the only instance of its use in a lever action arm.

These Russian 1895's were used in both wars. Captured German intelligence bulletins reported them as in use on all fronts to some degree; probably indicating pressing shortages of small arms at the time of their use, of course.

Other American Lever Actions

At one time or another all United States sporting rifles have turned up in guerrilla use, of course, somewhere on the world's frontiers. The Winchester '73, '86 and '94 have all been encountered at some time or other in the course of troubles in South America, Asia, Africa and the Balkans. So have the old Burgess, the Colt Lightnings, the Marlins, Ballards, Savages and even the Adirondacks and the Kennedys.

Of all these, however, only the Savage 1899 has an action strong enough for military cartridge use as we know it today; and it was the only one to receive any serious official attention. It was tested, but not adopted, by our Navy in its early development form in the year 1895.

The Savage 1899

This American magazine lever rifle merits some attention because of its magazine system and its breechlock. The magazine is a revolving box type housed below the bolt. The cartridges are separated at all times so there is no danger of deformation of the cartridges or similar troubles. The magazine is a modification of the Spitalsky pattern which was perfected by Mannlicher and Schoenauer in Austria.

The breechlocking system is operated by lever, but can easily be altered to make a semi-automatic on the gas-actuation principle. As the lever is drawn down and ahead, it first lowers the strong steel breechblock out of locking mortises in the receiver walls. Once clear of its locking seat, the breechblock is then drawn to the rear by continuing lever action to extract and eject. Rearward movement of the triggerguard lever chambers a cartridge from the turning "spool" magazine; and then elevates the breechblock into locked position.

Experiments by Winchester and others on breech locks of this pattern have established that they are capable of sustained automatic use even with .50 caliber MG cartridges.

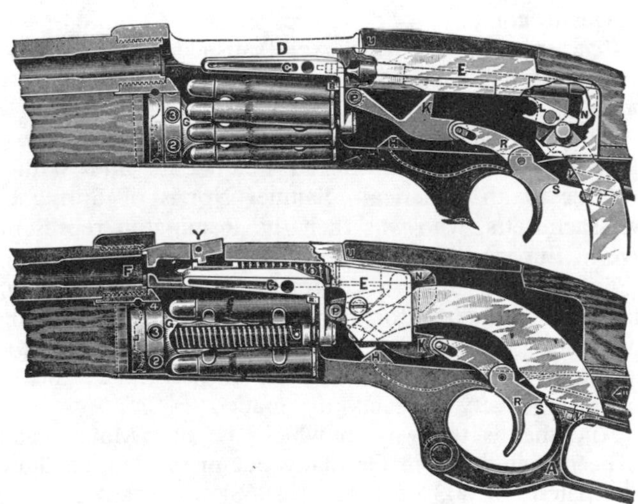

Savage 1899 Model Action.

Note on American Lever Action Repeaters

The foregoing outline merely touches upon the successful systems or those which played an important historical role.

The author's files alone list several hundred attempts by inventors at designing lever action repeaters for military use. It would be impossible to give space even to listing these abortive designs—though it is entirely possible that some of them may in time reappear. Inventors are forever turning up old and often discarded principles as something quite new!

The "Ball" for instance was patented in 1863 and 1002 were used by the Northern forces during the Civil War. This arm had a below-barrel magazine tube and was loaded through the receiver. Its feeding, locking, and ejecting systems however were mechanical freaks, and the design failed.

One of the weirdest of all was the Evans Rim Fire .44. It was patented in 1868 and was made to some extent by the Evans Repeating Rifle Co. at Mechanics Falls, Maine until 1880. This weird design had a buttstock magazine not unlike von Mannlicher's first design. The tube formed the small of the stock and extended through the buttstock to the butt plate. A four-fluted cylinder within this tube revolved one-quarter turn with each movement of the breechblock, the action being caused by a pawl. The magazine was loaded through the butt plate by dropping in a cartridge, then operating the lever. The magazine held from 26 to 34 cartridges. Loading was slow and had to be carefully done. A jam just about ruined the arm. No magazine spring was needed. These and similar oddities, however, had no part in the true evolution of the lever action system; they were and are collectors curios only.

The Evans in its day was the object of study by some Russian designers. And, of course, the Archimedian screw feature eliminating the need for springs might some day lend itself to a buttstock magazine to hold a year's supply of .22's say!

In any event, having covered in historical outline these lever developments, we must now turn to mention of the bolt action development in Europe.

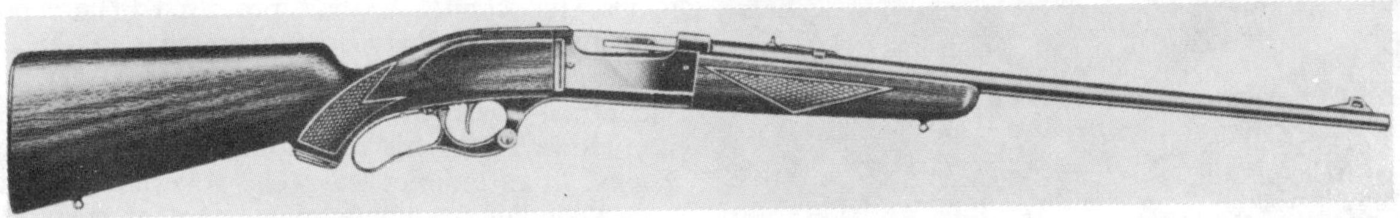
Savage Model 1899 Repeating Rifle.

Chapter 6. The Military Bolt Action in Europe

The Early Mausers

THE first successful metallic cartridge bolt action rifle was designed by Peter Paul Mauser of Oberndorf, Germany. One of his brothers, Wilhelm, was associated with him at the time in a business capacity. The mechanical brain, however, was that of Peter Paul, the youngest in a gunsmith's family of thirteen children.

Young Mauser graduated from elementary school in 1852, at the age of 14. He went to work as an apprentice in the Government Firearms Factory in Oberndorf. He was trained by his father and by four older brothers who also worked in the same factory. In 1859 he was drafted for military service. He was, of course, an expert on rifles. Military organizations being about the same then as now, it is perhaps not too surprising to find that he was assigned to the artillery.

During his military service he gave considerable attention to the Dreyse Needle Gun (Zündnadelgewehr) which was then the pride of his army. Naturally, he also spent some thought on the subject of artillery.

Upon completion of his term of active service, he returned to Oberndorf where he soon developed a model of a breechloading cannon. He had neither the financial, military nor social station to command any attention in the artillery field, as he soon discovered. Thereupon he turned to active work on the idea of a bolt action rifle. By 1865 he had worked out an action based on use of a metallic cartridge. An older brother, Franz, had emigrated to America and worked for Remington. Peter Paul had several sources of information on metallic cartridge developments aside from this one, however.

Peter Paul Mauser, the great German arms inventor and manufacturer, 1838-1914.

The unsuccessful attempts at bolt actions pointed the way for his invention, as step by step he overcame each drawback. First was his system of automatic cam cocking, whereby the firing pin was withdrawn at the opening movement of the bolt; this did away with the danger of firing accidentally as the bolt was closed, and also made way for easy extraction and fast operation of the weapon. Next was an effective breech seal and an ultra-strong lock which paved the way for the powerful military cartridges to come.

The Prussian authorities were satisfied with the Dreyse, so they rejected the new Mauser. Austria was interested, but had just been committed to the Wänzl design.

However, the Austrian ambassador was so impressed personally that he introduced Peter Paul and Wilhelm Mauser to an American, Samuel Norris of Springfield, Massachusetts, who was then the Remington representative in Europe.

Norris gave them a contract under which he would finance manufacture for them in Belgium, which was then as now a great small arms manufacturing center. Norris agreed to take out patents in the United States and was to pay a royalty on each rifle made.

And that is the way in which the first Mauser came to be patented not in Germany but in the United States! The patent, 78603 of June 2, 1868, was granted for the "Norris-Mauser" in the names of Norris and the two Mauser brothers.

When the news broke, Remington quite naturally went after their Mr. Norris. Norris found himself unable to raise the capital he had promised. Thereupon he tried to interest the Prussian Government in the arm, hoping to raise money on a government contract. The Mauser contract was breached when he did not succeed.

However, Norris had done the Mausers quite a lot of good in an indirect way. The government called Wilhelm to Spandau for conferences. Out of these developed a contract which resulted in the first successful military bolt action—the Infanteriegewehr M. 71.

Mauser's first rifle was truly basic. In later years it has

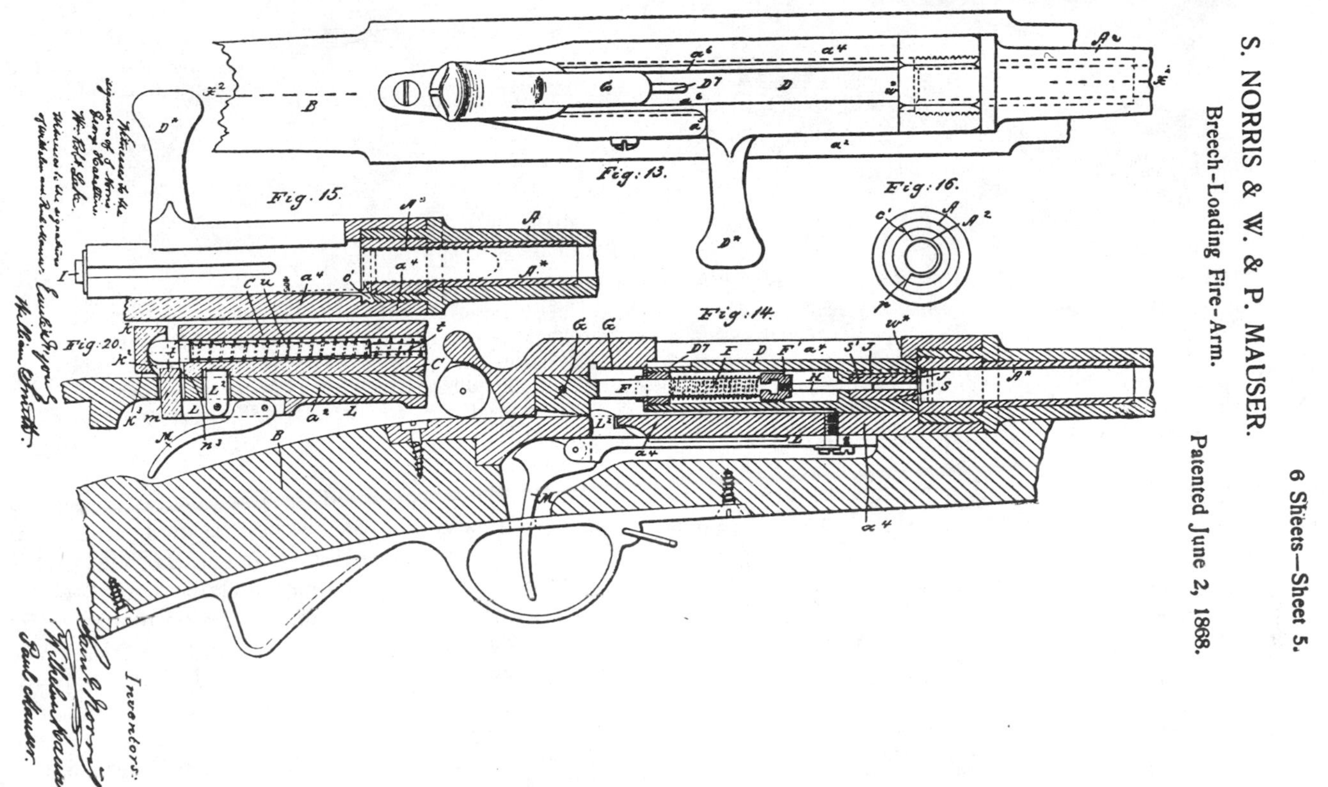

One of the six sheets of patent papers signed by Norris and the Mauser Brothers, now in the United States Patent Office. This was the first Mauser patent ever filed anywhere.

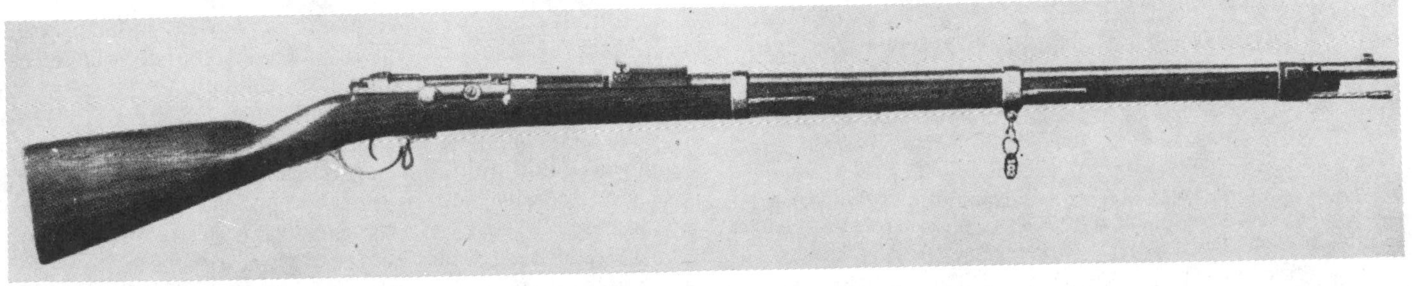

Model 71 German Infantry Rifle.

Right side view with action closed showing original Mauser single shot metallic cartridge rifle adopted by the German Army in 1871 and actually introduced into service in the following year. This model used the removable bolt head and split bridge receiver later used on turn-bolt Mannlicher rifles. The German Gew. 1888 bolt and receiver were evolved from the M. 71, not from Mannlicher designs. Model 71 rifles, both original and converted types, were used in the Balkans even in World War II.

been modified and improved. But it is safe to say that, except for the post-World War II improvement by Remington of the fully enclosed bolt head, no change of any importance has been possible except those made by Mauser himself. His personal mechanical efforts produced automatic cam cocking, the principle of bolt head design, elastic extractor, primary extraction, ejector, manual safety, and later improvements in the locking lug system.

The success of the Mauser was immediate. Initial production was at Spandau in 1872 where the Prussian government made them and paid Mauser a royalty. The Mausers raised enough money to set up a plant, but their work was given a serious set-back when the factory they opened in 1873 burned down a few weeks after the official opening. Württemberg gave the Mausers a contract of 100,000 rifles and sold them the government factory at Oberndorf. From there on development was rapid. By 1878 Peter Paul was intensively experimenting with repeating systems, having been influenced by the Turkish use of Winchester repeaters against the Russians at Plevna which we have already discussed.

He developed a wide series of magazine systems adaptable to his M. 1871. Since all military eyes were still on the Plevna battles, it is perhaps not surprising that his first production repeater was a below-barrel tube system along the lines of the Winchester 1866. Thus in 1880 we find him adding a tube magazine to the 1871—even though in the following year Serbia was still single-shot conscious to the extent of buying 100,000 Mausers of the type. These rifles were still encountered in the Balkans in World War II.

It was 1884 before the Prussian High Command ac-

Model 89 Belgian Infantry Rifle. Right Side View With Action Closed.
This is the standard rifle officially adopted by Belgium after experimenting with the Mauser Model 88 trial rifle. Note that in this weapon a barrel jacket is employed which covers the barrel almost to the muzzle. It was designed to protect the hands of the user from heat during firing and to protect the rather thin barrel from injury in field service. The magazine is considerably modified from the earlier design, and is adapted to rimless cartridges. Fabrique Nationale in Belgium made this model in quantity. Photograph from original Mauser design records.

cepted the Mauser tube repeater in caliber 11mm for general issue under the designation M. 71/84.

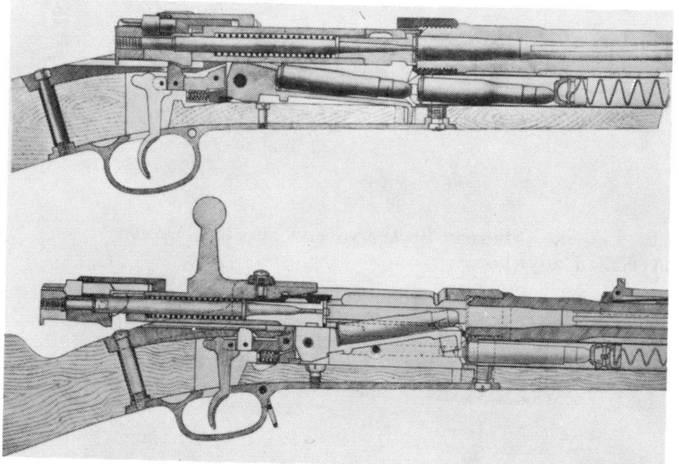

Drawing of the first Mauser Repeating Rifle. The Infanteriegewehr M. 71/84. Note that this is a below-barrel tube loader.

The German M. 1888 was *not* a Mauser development, but was the outgrowth of studies by an Army commission. The bolt was modified from the early Mauser, and the magazine system was taken from the Austrian Mannlicher.

The first truly modern Mauser came, of course, after the development of smokeless powder and the small bore caliber. This was the Belgian Model of 1889, using the strip-in clip system. This was followed in 1890 by a modified version for Turkey; others for Argentina, Bolivia, Colombia and Ecuador in 1891; by the Spanish model of 1893 which first successfully incorporated the staggered box magazine as used in our M. 1903; and by succeeding modifications culminating in the German Model 1898. (Note: Since all these systems are dealt with in chapter 26, there is no need for further examination of them here.)

Other Early European Bolt Actions

Having considered Mauser and his developments—some of them out of time context for purposes of continuity—we now turn to the story of bolt and repeater development in Europe generally.

While Mauser invented the first successful military bolt action, his was not of course the first attempt in the field. The Swiss were actually first in the field to combine the turn bolt and the copper metallic cartridge.

Swiss ordnance men, and more particularly Frederic Vetterli, had studied closely the first American Volcanic and its successful metallic cartridge counterpart, the Henry repeater, as well as the Spencer. They had watched, too, the growing might and arrogance of the Prussian Junkers. They saw Schleswig-Holstein overrun with the aid of the terrible new Dreyse Needle Gun, Austria fall before it, and France brace itself for the coming attack which was to be the disaster of 1870-71.

Grimly the Swiss set about to devise an arm which in case of dire peril might outshoot the dread German weapon. At this late date it is difficult to visualize the terror spread by the Dreyse, the first widely used European breechloader. But long before any major European power could think in terms of metallic cartridges, the Swiss actually had a repeater on the drawing boards, although by that time repeaters were an old story to the American sportsman. As their whole psychology revolved around defense of their precious homeland, the rifle-minded Swiss approached the design of their rifle from a far different viewpoint than either the Americans or the other Europeans. The American rifle being primarily a hunting or mounted-use arm, our inventors turned in the direction of the lever action repeater. The typical European military mind outside of Germany thought in terms of better needle guns, or of conversions which would salvage the tremendous stocks of muzzle loaders. German military thought itself was so oversold by the success of the Dreyse that Mauser had considerable trouble selling his first rifles! Characteristically, however, once the Prussians were sold, they went all out for further development. They stayed ahead of the rest of the world in military development right up to the day we introduced the Garand.

However, a few Swiss and Austrian designers saw the military value of the bolt repeater very early in the game. Since the vertical magazine system of Lee and Mauser and Mannlicher had not yet appeared, and since the successful American systems were tube repeaters, it is understandable that early European magazine design centered around tubes. Basically what the Swiss did was

Swiss Vetterli.

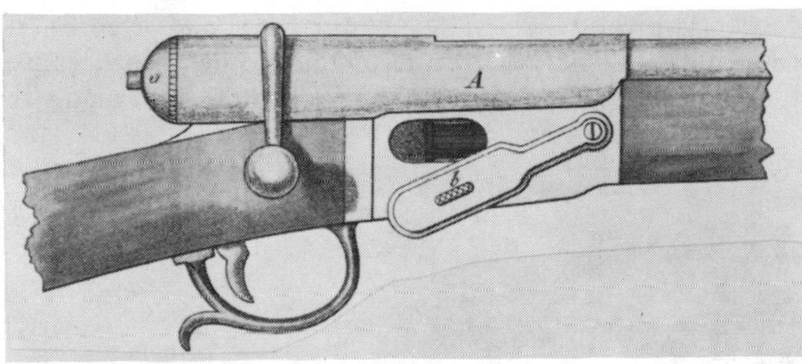

Vetterli Loading Gate, modified from American King type.

adapt the Henry-Winchester to their needs. They produced an improved Rim Fire .41 cartridge with copper case. They altered the King loading gate and the Henry cartridge carrier and applied them to turn-bolt actions which could be better handled prone than could the lever action.

The Federal Assembly of the Swiss Confederation meeting in solemn sessions in July and December 1866 officially approved the adoption of the repeating principle. Production of the Vetterli started in 1867, but it took two years to iron out manufacture. In 1871 and 1878 new models were produced at Waffenfabrik Bern. The rifle was used officially until 1889. As issued it had a 12-shot magazine. The caliber was 10.4mm. With 313-grain lead bullet, the rifle achieved a muzzle velocity of 1338 feet per second. Maximum range was given at about 3000 meters.

The next development of interest in Switzerland was in 1883, when Major Rubin designed a straight-pull bolt system. A special revolving cam turned the locking lugs out of receiver engagement and then brought the bolt back in a straight line to eject when the operating handle was pulled to the rear. Lugs for locking were at the rear of the bolt. A special detachable vertical box magazine was provided. The design was improved through the years as the model 1911 and model 1931. Caliber is special 7.5mm Swiss. The Swiss straight-pull has never been imitated elsewhere. It is today in course of being replaced by an assault rifle. (*Note:* Current designs are discussed in chapter 41.)

When the Swiss discarded these old Vetterlis they were sold to Bannerman in New York. He in turn sold them by mail throughout the United States. It is an eloquent testimony to the workmanship and materials of the Swiss that the Vetterli was still used in America to such an extent that cartridges were made for them in this country until just before World War II.

Austrian Früwirth 1869

Ferdinand Früwirth's bolt action tube repeater was in general use even before the Vetterli, though the design actually came later than the Swiss. Adopted as the official Austro-Hungarian rifle for Gendarmerie in 1869, it was generally issued in 1870. Its use was not extended to the military because when it was presented the Austrians had already been committed to manufacture the single shot Werndl block action.

The caliber was 11mm. The bolt handle turned down very close to the stock. A cocking piece at the rear of the bolt resembled a hammer.

Other Early Official Bolt Actions

When Germany (Prussia) officially adopted the Mauser in 1871, all other European nations frantically stepped up rifle manufacture. Beaumont, a Dutch engineer, produced a weird single shot bolt rifle using a center fire 11mm cartridge. Coil springs were not in too good repute at the time due to tempering troubles. The Beaumont had a freak V-spring in the bolt handle which powered the striker. Holland adopted the design.

Italy adopted the Swiss Vetterli in single shot pattern in 1871. The caliber of 10.4mm was kept, but the cartridge itself was a center fire type. The rifle was made under Swiss license in Italian arsenals.

In 1871 Russia and Bulgaria adopted the Russian bolt pattern known as the Berdan II already mentioned. Caliber was .42, muzzle velocity about 1440 feet per second. To compensate for slow fire, the Krnka and other "quick loaders" were developed. These devices were designed to be attached to the side of the rifle. The theory was that as the soldier ejected the empty case he could readily pull a loaded cartridge out of the loader and feed it into the rifle. This "poor man's repeater" was a failure, of course.

France recovered enough from the beating she had taken in 1870 so that by 1873 Chassepots were being altered to handle 11mm metallic cartridges. In 1874 the Gras conversion was adopted officially, work being done at Chatellerault and St. Etienne.

It is a commentary on French military thinking that although their ordnance groups had already done much experimentation with Winchester, Spencer and other repeaters, they still followed German thinking on design and caliber. The French Navy in particular at this period did exhaustive and intelligent testing of repeater designs; but all that came of them were reports. The new cartridge ballistically was almost a duplicate of the German. Among the rifles tested by the French Navy was a very unusual design—a falling block action with tube magazine. Firing was by a hammer. The design was not too practical, but in it may be found elements of later automatic design by the Norwegians who developed it. This arm was known as the Krag-Petersson.

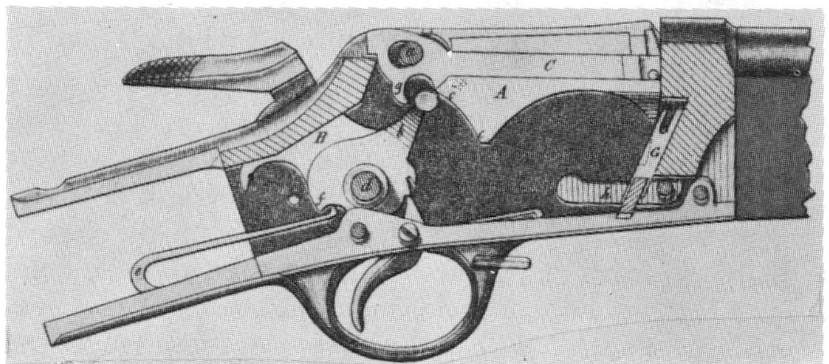

Sectional view of Krag-Petersson. Its locking and feeding features influenced later Danish designs.

The French tested and adopted to a limited degree a Gras system in 1874. In 1878 they first adopted on limited scale a repeater, the 11mm bolt action Kropatschek. It was issued to French Marines. The design was later improved in Vienna, by Gasser. No real use was made of the alteration, however.

In 1883 Russian designers at Tula Arsenal experimented with the impractical American Evans repeater already touched upon, but wisely stopped in the experimental stages. It was not until the smokeless powder era (actually in 1891) that the Russians finally adopted a magazine rifle. This was the Mosin Nagant, a turn bolt action which has never been adapted to any other designs. (Note: This and its variations are described in chapter 43.)

The year 1879 marked a great step forward in military rifle design. J. P. Lee introduced his vertical box magazine, which immediately became the subject of further experimentation; and which may have played a part in helping Mauser and Mannlicher to perfect their own designs in this line. Also in this year the first practical "spool" or revolving box magazine was introduced at Steyr Armory in Austria by Spitalsky. This was perfected later by Schoenauer and utilized by von Mannlicher.

Serbia in 1881 adopted a single shot known as the Mauser-Milovanovitch. They could have had a repeater at the time, but national pride dictated otherwise because of single shot modifications Milovanovitch had made in

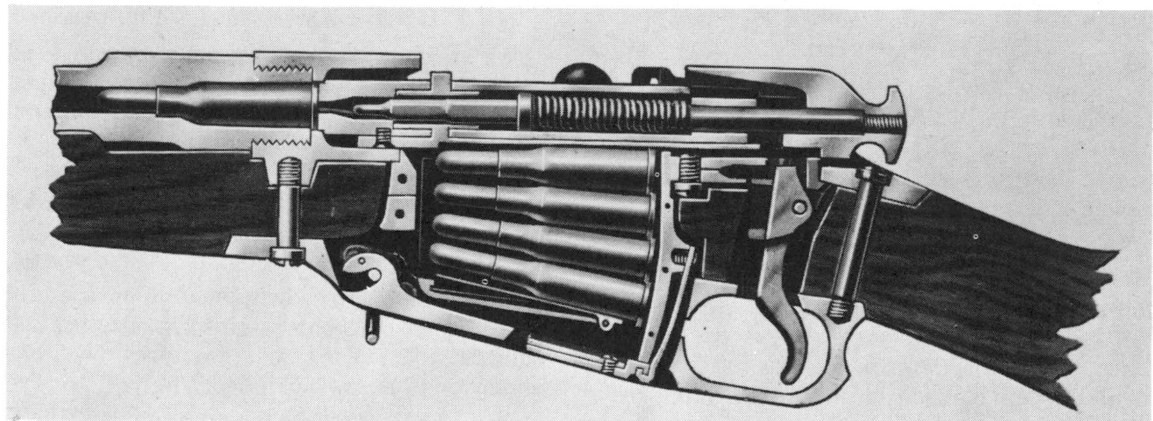

Sectionalized Russian Nagant Rifle. With very minor alterations this was the primary Russian military rifle of World War II. Also it was the basic rifle supplied to Chinese Communist forces in Korea.

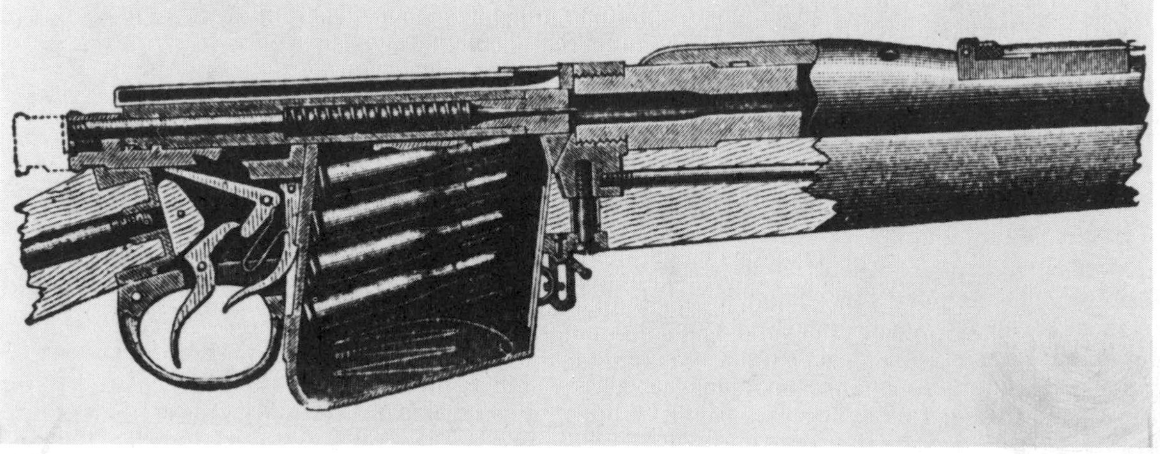

Sectionalized view of Lee-Speed magazine rifle.

the Mauser action which could not readily be applied to a repeater.

In 1885 Portugal adopted a single shot with a Martini dropping block action, the Guedes-Castro. Here was another instance where national pride in design overrode common sense in procurement. Even in 1904 when Portugal adopted a German-made Mauser she still had to clutter it up with "improvements" under the designation of "Mauser-Vergueiro." It and the current Mauser (98 pattern) are described in chapter 37, hence do not merit further attention here.

The Austrian Schulhof rifle was offered for use in 1882. This was a bolt action with thumb trigger and a most involved stock magazine of very large capacity. The side of the stock had a hinged plate which was lifted to expose several compartments for loading. A combination of gravity and travelling rail operated by the bolt controlled the feed. Later Schulhofs used spool magazines of a more practical nature, but the designs were just too complicated to compete with the Mausers, Mannlichers and Lees then available.

The Early Austrian Mannlichers

Von Mannlicher was one of the great firearms designers of all history. He was at all times in his thinking far ahead of the ammunition and metallurgy developments of his period. His automatic development work will be touched upon later. We can be concerned here only with his successful bolt action. All the important successful patterns are described in detail in chapter 15; but his-

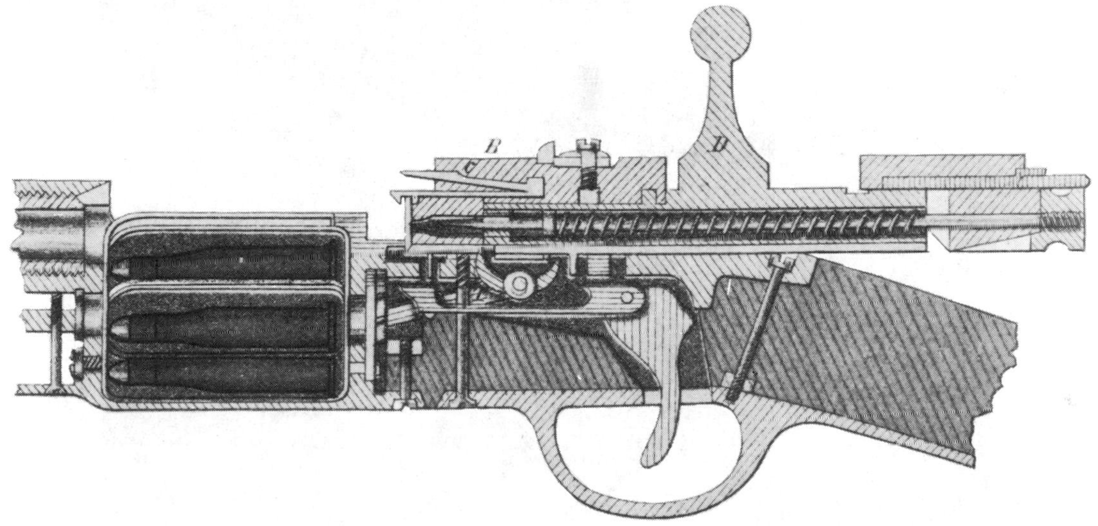

Spitalsky revolving box magazine perfected later by von Mannlicher.

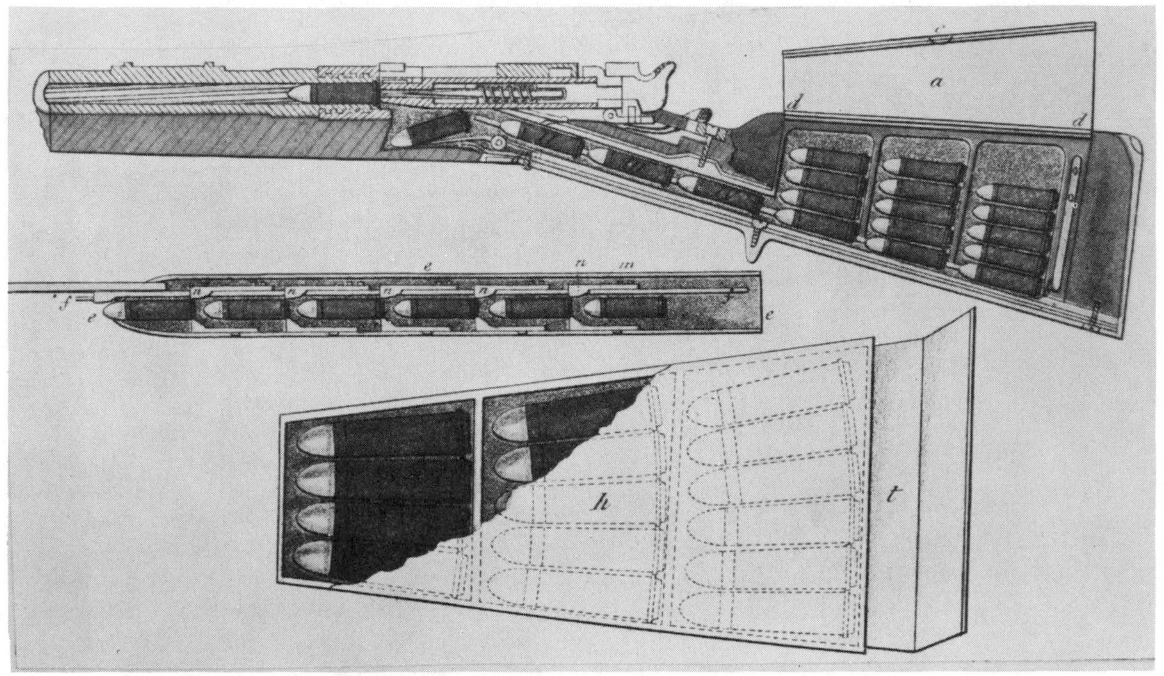

Austrian Schulhof, showing details of magazine system and cartridge transport.

torically some others require mention at this point in our historical outline. He actually produced over 150 designs. Had the Austrian Government backed up von Mannlicher financially as the Germans did Mauser, the arms history of the world would have been far different.

Note that the dates are those of the actual introduction of the items mentioned, not the times of design, for he was usually ahead of other designers.

In 1880 he produced a turn bolt action with 3- and 4-tube magazines in the buttstock. These worked automatically on bolt operation, and allowed 15 to 20 large cartridges to be carried within the rifle. These were chambered for the Austrian M. 77 cartridge.

In the following year a new design of turn bolt was offered. It also featured a slant steel box magazine from below. The magazine was detachable.

In 1882 he introduced a simplified turn bolt action with magazine tube below the barrel; and another one with box magazine positioned on the right top side of the receiver as in European machine rifle systems such as the Bren today.

Two years later came a very unusual item—a straight

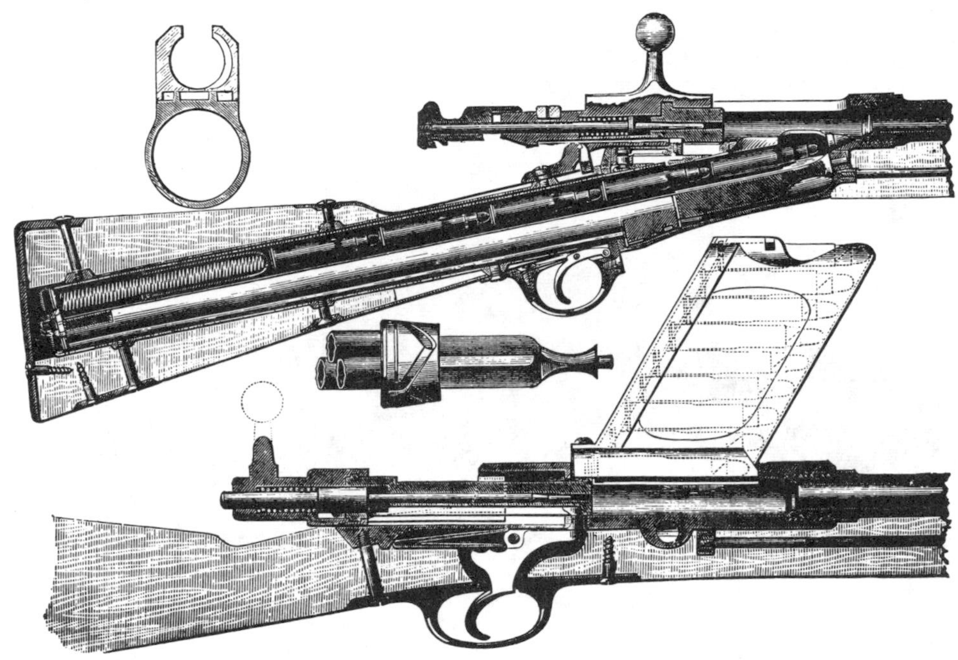

Early Mannlicher repeaters with tube and top box feeds sectionalized to show operation. Details of action and loading systems.

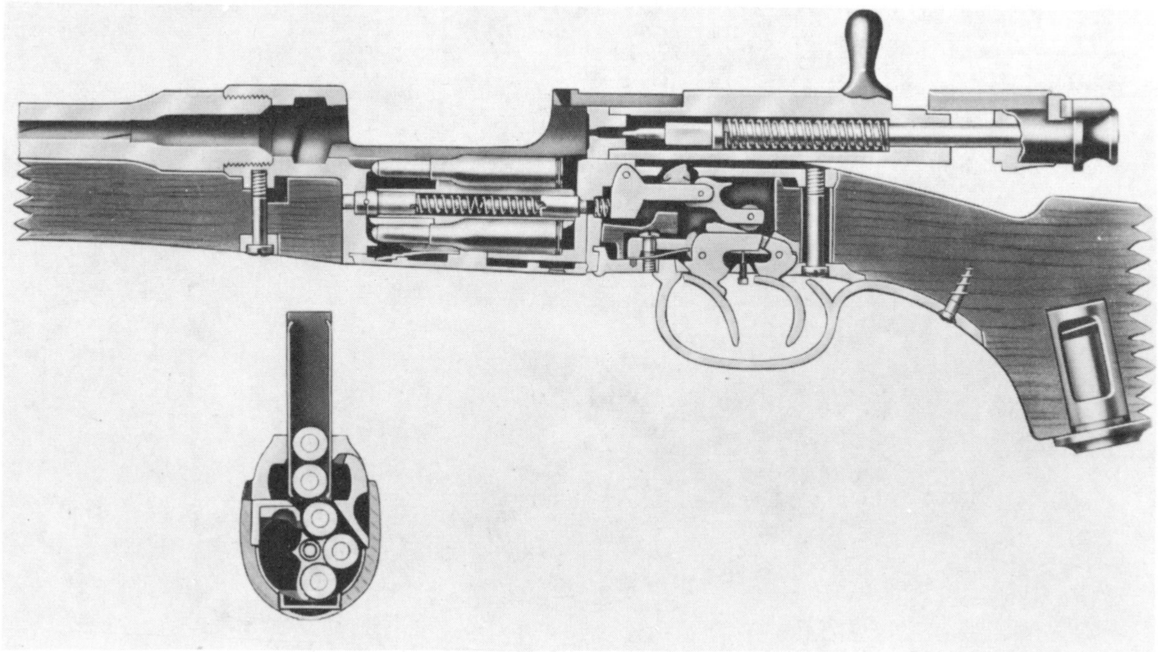

The Mannlicher-Schoenauer Rifle with turn bolt and spool magazine. Details of action and loading systems.

pull with revolving lugs positioned to the rear of the receiver well, and with a left-side box magazine. This was the forerunner of the famous 1895 breechlock.

In 1885 he introduced his straight pull, hinged wedge lock pattern. Here for the first time appeared the "Mannlicher" clip system in which the cartridges are loaded in a special clip which is loaded into the magazine complete. When the last shot has been fired, the clip is dropped out the bottom of the rifle. Our Garand clip is a modification of this 1885 Mannlicher pattern.

His 1886 model was adopted by Austria—a straight pull, wedge locked breech system. It used the perfected form of his new clip for loading.

The next year he brought out his first models with revolving box magazines. These used still another design of turn-bolt action. And in 1887 came the first "Mannlicher-Schoenauer" with turn bolt lock, special spool magazine for single shot or clip loading, and with cartridge release for rapid emptying of magazine.

German Model 1888 rifle system. The packet loading system was von Mannlicher's development. A variation of it is used in our M1 (Garand) rifle today.

The 1888 models included a new Austrian service rifle in 8mm caliber, straight pull with wedge lock; and the new German 7.9mm rimless cartridge rifle known as the Model 1888 already referred to. Here only the magazine and furniture were Mannlicher design (the breechblock having been modified from a Mauser by the German Commission); but the initial production of the arm itself was done at Steyr under von Mannlicher.

1890 saw the introduction of an official Austrian carbine with straight pull action and forward lug locking. In rapid succession then came developments and modifications in conjunction with other countries—Italy, France, Roumania, Switzerland, Greece, and Holland.

The most widely known of all von Mannlichers' military arms was the famous straight pull action of 1895.

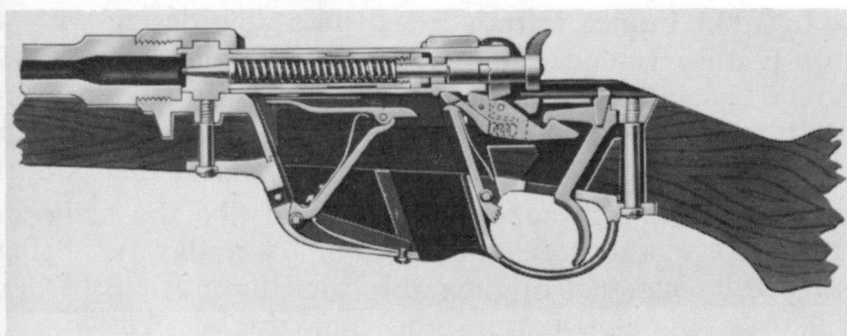

Sectional view of the straight pull Austrian Model 1895 rifle designed by von Mannlicher. Variants of this locking system appear today in many successful machine weapons.

With this brief summary, then, we must pass on to other early European bolt developments.

French 1886 Lebel

In the year 1886 France produced one of the best known rifles ever turned out for military use, one which is of prime historic importance as it was the first bolt rifle to handle the new smokeless powder. French chemists more than made up for the lack of ability in their arms designers. The new smokeless powder allowed the design of the first successful small bore (8mm) cartridge for military use. This compelled a revolution in military arms design.

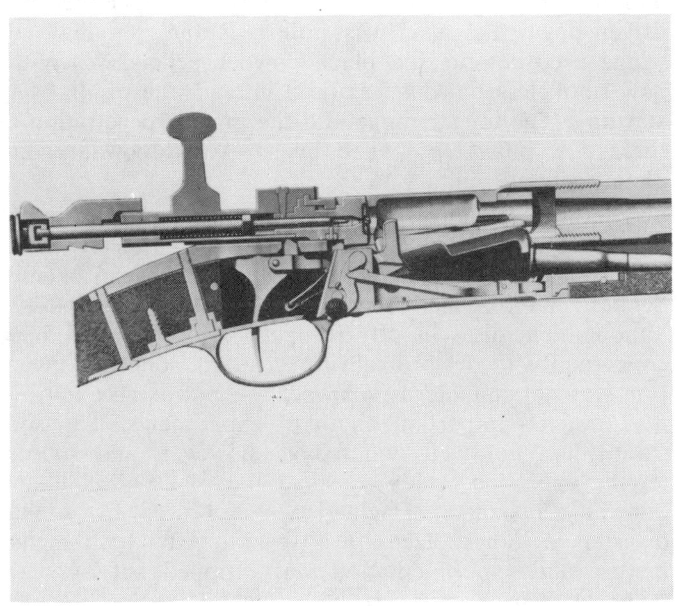

Section of French 1886 (Lebel). Tube repeating rifle showing operating system.

We must digress here for some historical notes on smokeless powder.

Smokeless Powder

The first successful smokeless powder for rifles was that developed by M. Vieille in 1884 for the French Government. His successful experiments followed the trails originally blazed by earlier French chemists, notably Pelouze and Braconnet in 1832.

The earliest researches into the problem of a smokeless propellant would seem to have stemmed from the military demand for a powder which would overcome the twin battle dangers of black powder. Riflemen opening fire in the early days at once disclosed their position to the enemy, a serious matter indeed in the day of slow reloading. In volley fire—more than ever with the introduction of the successful repeating and magazine arms—the clouds of powder smoke actually hindered vision of the firers to a dangerous degree.

Ironically enough, when Vieille perfected smokeless powder it developed that the comparative freedom from smoke was but one of the values of the new propellant! The new powders possessed a chemical and a ballistic stability far exceeding those of the best black powders. The ballistic efficiency, weight for weight, was far greater, thus permitting higher velocities without excessive pressures. As a result of the increased velocity, smaller, longer and lighter weight projectiles were necessary. The greater accuracy given by increased sectional densities of the longer bullets also changed tactics. Since the common lead bullet could not take the quick twist, jackets were introduced. A jacketed bullet was designed by a Swiss, Major Bode, in 1875. The improved copper-jacketed lead core bullet, introduced by Major Rubin, Director of the Government Laboratory in Thun, Switzerland in 1881, proved strong enough to stand the friction and torsion effects when a small bore long bullet was driven down the rapid twist rifling. Rubin's original cartridge used compressed black powder pellets. When the new smokeless powder was used instead, the results were startling. The longer range and the greater penetration of these new bullets propelled by smokeless powder completely altered military tactics.

The "invention" of smokeless powder was more in the nature of an evolution, actually. Its first reasonably effectual appearance was in 1846, when the German chemist Schönbein introduced his "cotton powder" (guncotton), although chemists in all European countries had been concerned with the problem for years. Schönbein's invention was not suitable as a propellant, but as an explosive it started an important chain of experiments. The substance was not well understood, however, and soon a terrific explosion which wrecked the plant of Hall and Son at Faversham, England was followed by similar disasters in other places. For several years both manufacture and experimentation was dropped out of sheer fear except in Austria.

General von Lenk of the Austrian Artillery persisted in experiments with guncotton which, while unsuccessful, were of value in pointing the way for British chemists to do further experimentation. As a propellant it still proved useless, however.

Dr. Hartig was able to control the combustion rate to some extent, and in 1867 the German Captain Schultz invented the smokeless powder which in improved form was used in shotguns as "Schultz Powder." It was not successful in rifle use, however. "Collodin," Frederick Volkmann's smokeless patented in 1871 was the first real approach to a successful smokeless powder for rifles. The next step was the entirely controlled powder of Vielle in 1884, which was originally a mixture of nitro-cellulose and picric acid. The picric acid was later dispensed with, the new powder being a mixture of nitro-cellulose, ether, and alcohol. In 1847, the Italian chemist Sobrero working at Turin first produced nitro-glycerine, out of which came Alfred Nobel's "dynamite" four years later. This development was not a propellant, but led the way for the mixture which Nobel patented as "Ballistite" which was a propellant. Out of Nobel's work the British Explosives Committee headed by Sir Frederick Abel developed a propulsive powder of good ballistic efficiency and excellent stability; this mixture of nitro-glycerine and guncotton gelatinized by a solvent, and to which mineral jelly was added as a stabilizer and fouling preventive, was named "Cordite" because of the cord-like shape it takes when manufactured. In modified form it is still used in Great Britain.

These, then, were the basic propulsive powders with which the modern small bore, high velocity rifles were first used. The further evolution is part of the story of Ballistics.

Added European Military Bolt Actions

France adopted in 1890 and in 1892 versions of the Berthier carbine, an individual turn-bolt breechlocking system with an adaptation of the Mannlicher clip-loading magazine system. Modifications were made from 1907 to 1916, barrel lengths varying and magazine capacities being either 3- or 5-shot. These arms, together with the Model 1886, all used the rimmed 8mm cartridge and were actually the basic rifles of the French forces during both World Wars!

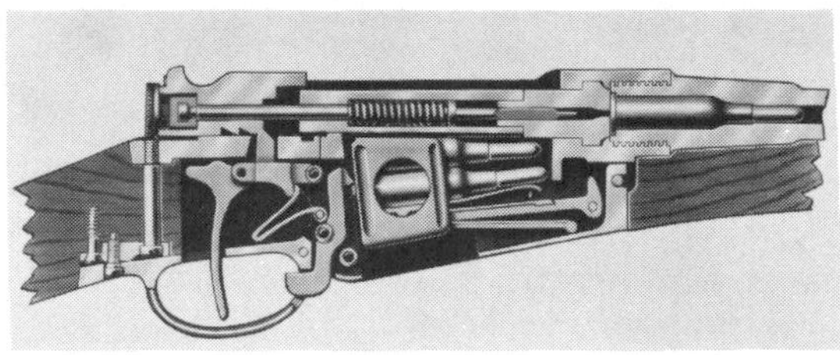

Section of representative French Berthier system carbine using Mannlicher type loading system.

French 1936 Rifle, top action view.

In 1932 France introduced a quite new design with a turn-bolt breechlock, and a modified Mauser staggered box magazine. An improved model was introduced in 1936, caliber 7.5mm rimless. (These are described in chapter 24, hence we shall pass over them at this point.)

Norway and Sweden both adopted the Jarmann in 1887, still another example of military authorities being swayed by national origin rather than by efficiency. This rifle was a below-barrel tube magazine design with a turnbolt lock. Caliber was 10.5mm. Basically it was merely the Jarmann single shot of 8 years earlier with a tube and lifter mechanism added. Norway, in 1894

Norwegian Krag-Jorgensen, Caliber 6.5mm.

Representative Italian Carcano pattern rifle.

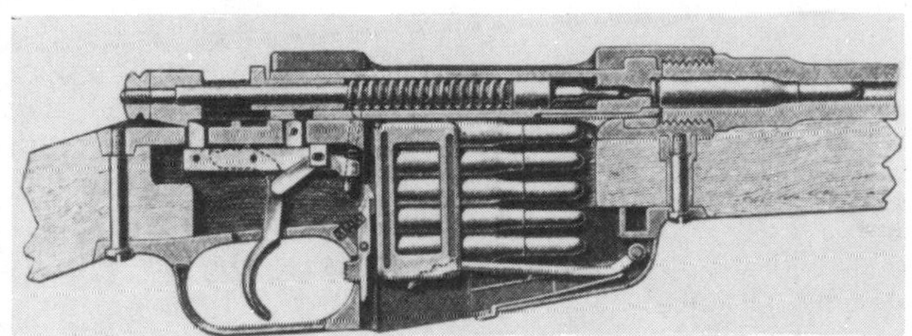

Representative Italian Carcano pattern rifle section.

adopted a version of the Krag-Jorgensen. Sweden in 1894 adopted the Mauser Carbine and in 1896 adopted the Mauser rifle.

Italy adopted the Vetterli in 1871 as a breechlock system. However, they altered it to utilize a vertical fixed box magazine in 1887. This magazine system used a special coil follower spring. This magazine is a variant of the Lee. Its inventor's name was incorporated with that of Vetterli, and the rifle was popularly known as the Vetterli-Vitali. The cartridge caliber of 10.4mm was retained, but the cartridge itself was center fire. Magazine cutoff and manual safety were provided.

The Italians adopted the Carcano in 1891. This was a modified arm incorporating elements of the Mauser breechlock with the Mannlicher clip magazine. As the M. 38 in 1938 it was modified to handle a new 7.35mm cartridge instead of the old 6.5mm.

Holland in 1888 adapted the Vitali pattern magazine to their old Beaumonts, the resulting hodge-podge being characterized as the M. 71/88. In 1895 Holland adopted a Mannlicher turn bolt design (not the Austrian service straight pull) which was made under contract in Austria and Holland. The magazine system is the familiar Mannlicher clip type. The bolt, however, has forward lugs as in the Mauser system, but has a detachable bolt head in distinction to the Mauser which features the much safer and stronger solid head. The caliber is 6.5mm Dutch.

A closing word must be said for an Asiatic country which had produced military arms in the period before World War II—Japan. The first Japanese service rifle was the turn-bolt Murata of 11mm caliber. In 1887 this design was modified from a single shot to a tube repeater and at the same time chambered for a new rimmed 8mm cartridge which was the cartridge of their China campaign in 1894. In 1897 a new rifle of Mauser pattern was de-

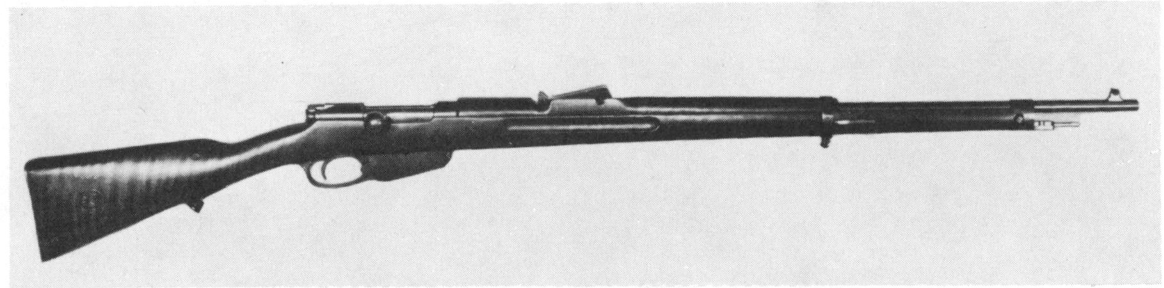

Netherlands (Dutch) Mannlicher turnbolt rifle.

signed by one Col. Arisaka. It was the Japanese rifle in the war with Russia, and was subject to criticism as it could be incorrectly assembled so as to be dangerous when fired. In 1905 this 6.5mm caliber rifle was again redesigned. It is one of the strongest rifle actions in existence. It was the basic Japanese rifle in World War II. An altered version in 1939 increased the caliber to 7.7mm.

Great Britain and Bolt Actions

The Lee-Metford already mentioned was adopted in 1888. The barrel had Metford rifling. The magazine was a Lee pattern holding 8 rimmed .303 caliber cartridges. It was listed in British practice as the Mark I. This was followed in 1892 by the Mark II, with double column 10-shot magazine and simplified bolt. In 1892 the Mark I was altered and was listed as Mark I*. The Mark II* of 1895 was the same as the Mark II except for a safety catch at the rear of the bolt.

The first of the long line of British Lee-Enfields—the real work horses of the British in both World Wars—was introduced in 1895. It was identical with the Lee-Metford Mark II* except that the rifling was the new Enfield pattern and the sights were changed. The L. E. Mark I*, just to confuse the soldier, was the Mark I without cleaning rod!

The succeeding Lee-Enfields and other British service designs will be found in detail in chapter 20. However, mention should be made of one colonial arm, the Canadian Ross. This was adopted in 1905 in caliber .303 to at least make a common ammunition supply with the Mother Country. It was an unusual straight pull arm with many of the strength features of the Mauser design. Bolt lugs were revolved by cam action on straight pull and thrust to unlock and lock the lugs into receiver seats directly behind the cartridge head. It was modified in 1910. Short trench usage in World War I established that the principle was not adequate for war use where regular attention cannot always be given to cleaning, and the rifle was replaced by the British Short Magazine Lee-Enfield.

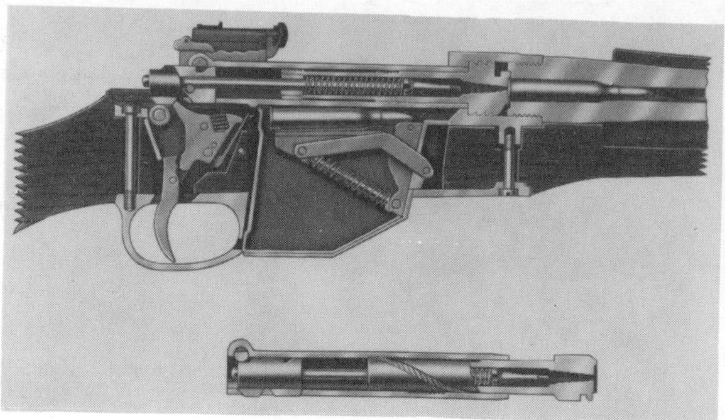

Representative Canadian Ross straight pull rifle and bolt in section to show operation.

* * * * *

The preceding is but a very brief outline of the development of the bolt action. Today all countries which can afford to do so are arming or preparing to arm with automatic or semi-automatic rifles. The history of the bolt action in the future, therefore, will be a history of sporting use in general. Its day as a military arm is waning, although doubtless there will be bolt actions used somewhere in the world a hundred years from now!

Chapter 7. Semi-Automatic Rifle Development and Carbines

A SEMI-AUTOMATIC rifle (often popularly but erroneously called an "automatic" rifle) is actually a self-loading arm. In appearance, general design, and weight, it approximates the standard manually-operated type of rifle. Its magazine system in military usage is commonly only a variation of the box magazine found in manually-operated rifles. In commercial arms it may be box or tube magazine fed, however.

It must be hand loaded for the first shot. For succeeding shots, however, only an individual pull on the trigger is required. A very small part of the energy developed as the cartridge is fired is made to unlock the rifle, extract and eject the empty case, cock the firing mechanism, chamber a cartridge, and close and lock the breech.

Successful military systems have narrowed down the types of operation. Gas through a barrel hole is by far the most efficient.

The gas cylinder may be below the barrel as in the case of our own Garand or may be on top of the barrel as in the case of the Russian rifles. In any event, a small hole is commonly drilled in the barrel. As the bullet passes over it, gas under pressure is passed through the hole into the cylinder where it drives the operating piston. The piston is connected or in contact with the bolt or other breech-locking mechanism. The rearward thrust of the piston does all the work normally done manually in getting ready for the second shot. In some designs, no piston is used; the gas itself goes through a tube and acts directly against a bolt carrier. A disconnector mechanism is incorporated in this design so that the trigger must be deliberately released after each shot before it can be pulled again for the succeeding shot. This is necessary to prevent the gun from mounting out of control in full automatic fire. When, as in some instances, 20-shot detachable box magazines are supplied with such an arm, a trained man can fire as many as 60 aimed shots a minute.

The only reasonably successful recoil-operated semi-automatic rifle thus far to appear commercially was the Johnson. It is no longer made. It utilized the recoil to drive the locked barrel and bolt assembly back a short distance, the barrel then being halted as the breech-locking mechanism was turned out of engagement. The

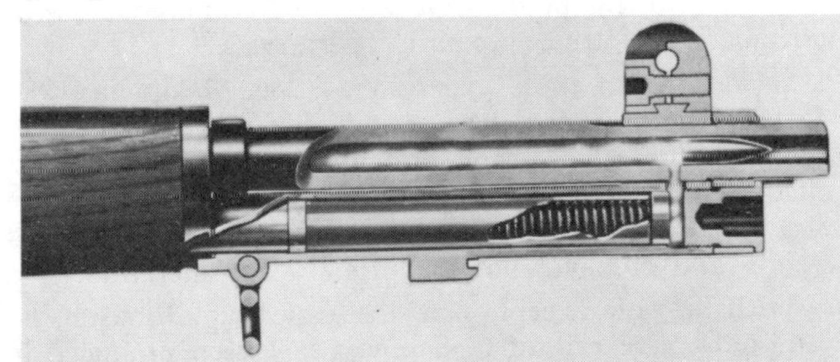

Garand Gas System. Gas passes through port in barrel after bullet passes over it. Expanding gas acts against piston and springs to operate weapon. Variants of this system represent the most successful form of actuation in light weight military rifle caliber arms.

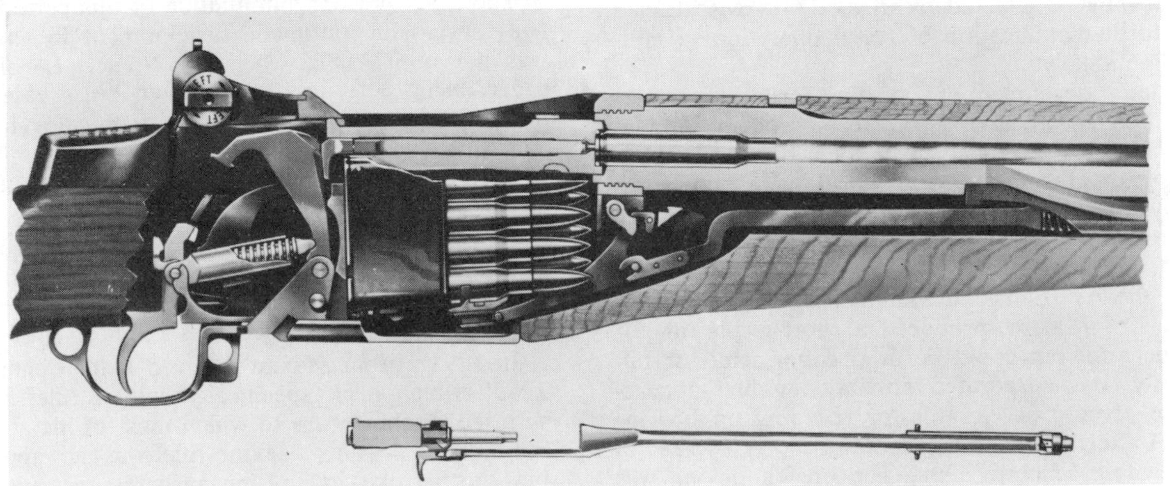

The U. S. M1 (Garand) in section. The trigger action requires release of finger pressure after firing each shot.

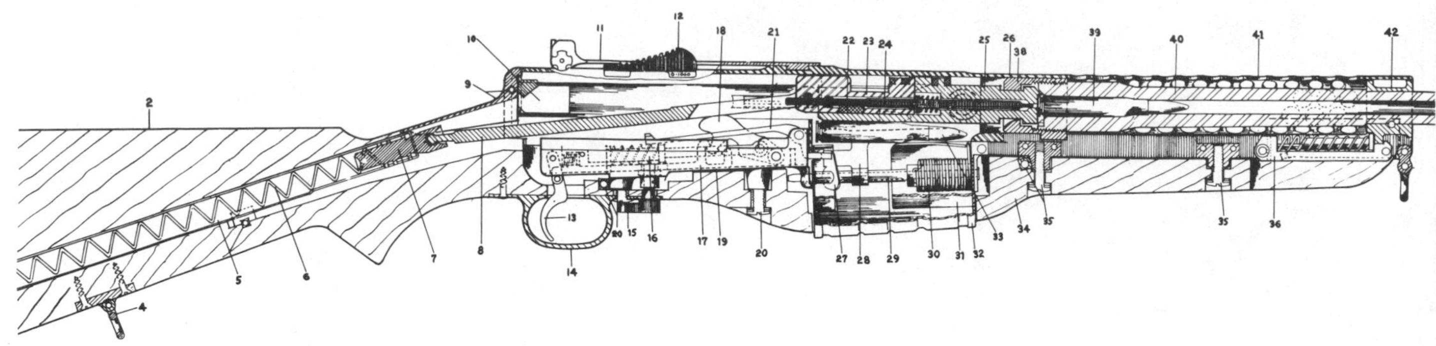

Johnson Semi-Automatic Rifle. Sectional view showing parts and operating system.

recoiling parts then cocked the gun and compressed springs so that on the return stroke the mechanism would chamber a cartridge, drive the barrel to forward position, and lock the breech ready for the next shot.

The American, Hiram Maxim, in his scientific experiments in 1881 and 1883 actually produced the first practical method of semi-automatic operation in a rifle.

While one of those early experiments was merely occupied with converting Winchester lever action repeating arms by linking up levers and springs with the recoil, these experiments pointed the way for Maxim's successful introduction of true automatic operation.

It was out of these experiments that Maxim in 1884 developed his original basic patent for locked breech recoil operation. This recoil principle has proven the most efficient one for machine gun use where high rate of fire and continuous volume is essential and where factors of weight and bulk are not the primary consideration.

With the sole exception of the American, Johnson, no semi-automatic rifle of high power has been produced in any quantity using recoil locked-breech operation. The Browning long-recoil hunting rifles all use medium-power cartridges. Because the desirable weight of the military rifle is preferably well under 10 pounds, and because military rifles require a minimum of exposed operating parts which may be affected by dirt or otherwise fouled in action, further application of recoil operation to military rifles is unlikely.

Maxim later developed one of the earliest gas-operated rifle designs which, like his recoil system, formed the basis for scores of related inventions. In the years between, designers throughout the world were widely influenced by all his automatic developments and he may be credited indirectly for scores of imitation designs at this period.

In 1885 the Austrian, von Mannlicher, following close on the heels of Maxim, produced a short-recoil rifle. It was a crude arm, but could be fired either semi- or full automatically. It incorporated possibly the first appearance of the pivoted accelerator for speeding up breechblock travel after the unlocking motion, the system found in the Browning Machine Gun. The breech-locking was effected by the camming up and down of a locking block from the floor of the receiver into the lower side of the breechblock. Cocking was on rearward motion by a lever which entered the breechblock and engaged a notch in the striker. The recoil spring was mounted in the receiver behind the breechblock. All these details are strikingly similar to those in the modern Browning Machine Gun. Since Browning did much of his design work in Belgium and von Mannlicher's efforts were well known and carefully followed there, it seems quite likely that the genesis of many of the Browning principles actually came directly or indirectly from a study of this earliest of the von Mannlicher automatic weapons.

Of the scores of developments in this field in the next few years, however, none was successful and few were worthy of even passing attention. The Schlund & Arthur British patent of 1885 deals with a long-recoil method of functioning, a form which has proved practical only in connection with shotgun and sporting rifle production. Most developments at this period were efforts to apply the automatic-loading principle to the military arms of the time. In England, for example, Needham & Paulson produced automatic unloading and cocking of the British Martini-Henry. Since this is a lever-action single-shot rifle, one which would be most difficult to operate from a magazine, the value of their efforts may be readily assessed.

The black powder ammunition of this period precluded truly successful automatic development in any event. It was not until 1886, when the French Lebel rifle cartridge, using a rimless solid drawn brass case, a cupro-nickel jacketed bullet, and a load of smokeless powder was introduced, that the semi-automatic rifle became really a practical design for experimentation.

Successful military weapon functioning requires that while the high point of pressure must pass quickly after firing, residual pressure in the barrel must still be sufficient to operate the action. Black powder pressure dissipates too rapidly to meet this requirement.

In 1891 Hiram Maxim received British patent number 22859 which dealt specifically with a rifle, rather than with the machine guns to which most of his attention had been directed. This Maxim rifle was an application of the short-stroke gas piston principle of operation. By bleeding off gas through a port quite close to the chamber, Maxim utilized the expanding gas to operate a piston for functioning the British Martini-Henry. Since his attention was basically given to his now successful machine gun, Maxim did not follow through on this gas rifle development, which, had it been applied to a magazine arm, might have been of tremendous importance.

In 1891 von Mannlicher in Austria introduced two rifles which were modified versions of his 1885 design. These rifles had very many of the most modern design characteristics, including a standard Mannlicher box magazine system which was clip-loaded through the top of the open action, a hold-open device to keep the breech open when the last shot was fired, and a standard pattern cocking handle on the right side of the weapon. Lack of military interest in Austria prevented general manufacture of either rifle. The inventor was ahead of his time.

John M. Browning's initial attempt at automatic rifle development followed pretty much along the line of Hiram Maxim except that he utilized gas instead of recoil to function a lever-action rifle. Variations of this muzzle cap design, which does not require drilling the barrel, have been tried at various times since Browning's original experiment, but the mechanical complications of the system offset its advantages.

Browning's next model, as discussed in chapter 9, used gas taken off through a hole in the barrel to operate an under-barrel piston. This design is actually a true forerunner of the modern military semi-automatic rifle, though its piston operation differs.

Browning utilized this gas principle for the production of the Colt Machine Gun and at the time did nothing about it in connection with rifle development.

Von Mannlicher in 1893 again gave evidence of his protean design ability by introducing two new semi-automatic rifles. One of these was an adaptation of his turn-bolt magazine rifle to semi-automatic action by adjusting the pitch of the normal locking lugs and their chamber seats. Actually the principle he utilized here was on the hestitation system, later found in the Villar Perosa and similar machine weapons. The opening action began immediately on the discharge of the cartridge, but the turning motion of the lugs in their helical grooves slowed the opening appreciably. However, even with the cartridges of the pressures of those days, breech opening was much too rapid for good operation.

The second rifle was an adaptation of the same lug principles to his straight-pull rifle. Again, the breech was hesitation operated and not fully locked against the discharge. These von Mannlicher designs were actually the forerunner of the much discussed Blish principle used in the first American Thompson submachine guns at a much later date. They directly influenced the later machine gun developments of the Austrian, Andrea Schwarzlose, also. By properly adjusting the angles of the receiver cuts, von Mannlicher sought to produce a condition where at the moment of firing the lugs would jam in their seats, serving as an actual full lock. As the pressure fell rapidly, and the residual gas continued its thrust against the inside of the case head, he sought to produce a condition where the friction would lessen gradually, and the action would open without too much violence. While devices of this sort do serve to slow down the action somewhat, the function is still frequently too violent for application to the standard patterns of military rifle cartridges.

In the following year von Mannlicher came forward with two new designs, this time solid breech actions with barrels blowing forward. The breech of the action being solid, as the weapon fired the movable barrel was thrust ahead in its guides and turned. Note that these arms were not true locked-breech weapons in the common sense of the term. The blow forward systems slowed recoil, absorbed a great deal of energy as the heavy barrel went forward and was literally pulled off the fired case to allow ejection. The later Schwarzlose automatic pistols utilized a variation of part of this principle. The Schwarzlose barrel, however, did not turn.

Also in 1894, the English Griffiths & Woodgate short-recoil rifle was introduced. This arm showed many promising possibilities, but lack of interest by the military halted further expensive development on it.

In the following year von Mannlicher introduced a gas-operated rifle with a true locked breech. This was a piston-operated rifle with a below-barrel gas cylinder. The bolt was cammed to the left on a hinge to open the breech by operation of the connected gas piston. A standard Mannlicher clip was used. This rifle utilized in elementary form many of the best operating principles found in our modern Garand military rifle.

While Mauser had done considerable experimental work since the introduction by Maxim of the short-recoil principle, it was not until 1898 that his first production rifle of semi-automatic operation was generally exhibited. This was a short-recoil operation using the standard Mauser box magazine. The arm is of interest basically because the locking principle of the breech was a development of the early Swedish Friberg principles.

The year 1900 saw the introduction of still another von Mannlicher rifle. For the first time he utilized a revolving box magazine, loaded, however, from a strip-in clip. This was a locked-breech arm operated by gas taken off close to the breech and utilizing a short-stroke piston. A cylindrical bolt was actuated by a stud on the

Gas Operated Danish Bang rifle (circa 1927).

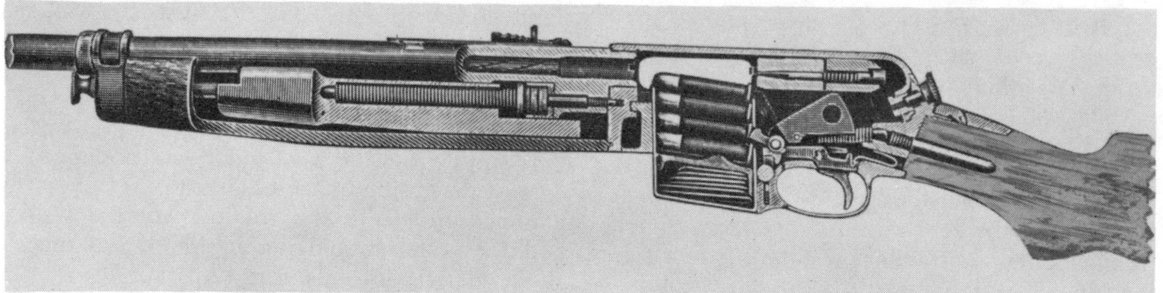

Winchester Semi-auto Blowback, Cal. .401 designed by T. C. Johnson, Action open.

operating rod, rather a forerunner of the later Lewis machine gun principle.

The Italians also had done considerable experimental work on semi-automatic weapons during the years after Maxim's initial work, but it was not until 1900 that a really worthwhile design was produced by them. Major Cei-Rigotti used a gas cylinder, with port in the barrel, and a tappet system for operating the bolt. This system was used in World War II by the Russians and the Germans in their successful semi-automatic rifles and is present today in the F.N. light auto rifle currently being used by many NATO nations.

Unlike the later adaptations of the tappet principle, however, this early Italian rifle hooked the system up to a rotating bolt with dual locking lugs at the forward end as in conventional practice. This rifle utilized the hold-open principle when the last shot was fired. Its box magazine was loaded from strip-in clips. Special magazines were provided holding as many as 50 cartridges. In one test in 1900, 300 rounds were fired in a model equipped with a full automatic switch. The 300 were actually fired in about one minute! The barrel heated so badly that it could not be used further.

This same year, 1902, saw the introduction of still another German Mauser recoil rifle for military cartridges. This however, was a long-recoil weapon which was on the principle later adapted by Browning to the Remington & FN commercial autoloading rifles. In some respects this early Mauser followed the Roth Austrian design of 1899, but the locking mechanism was quite distinctive. Mauser sought to make a practical military arm by using a box magazine, a cylindrical bolt securely locked to the barrel receiver by two locking lugs, and utilizing a striker firing design. The only truly successful application of this long-recoil principle to rifles is that of John Browning in the commercial medium-power rifles already mentioned; as a military design it has been a failure.

Mauser also introduced in 1902 still another semi-automatic military rifle operated by gas trapped at the muzzle in a blast cone. The gas was backed up to operate a rod on the piston principle to function the action for unlocking. (In World War II the Mauser factory introduced the experimental G 41(M) utilizing a slight variation of this gas principle. The design was not successful. The tappet system developed at the Walther plant along the old Cei-Rigotti line was a very efficient low-cost arm late in World War II.)

In 1903 a series of self-loading rifles were developed at Winchester by Thomas C. Johnson, one of the best of the commercial designers. These were elementary blowback arms of quite ingenious design but have no true military application, though in larger calibers they have been extensively used for police work and some gendarmerie operations.

Kjellman's development of the earlier Friberg principle was used in a rifle in 1904 in Sweden, in caliber 6.5mm Mauser. The operation principle was short recoil, the truly interesting feature being the locking mechanism which we have already mentioned.

Major Nambu of the Japanese Artillery also exhibited a semi-automatic rifle in 1904 which proved unsuccessful. However, Nambu turned his ideas to the development of machine guns along the same general lines. Actually these were variations of the French Hotchkiss machine gun principle. The only reasonably successful Japanese self-loading rifle was a World War II imitation of our Garand with modifications.

The Browning-designed Remington rifle introduced in 1906 was a long-recoil sporting rifle of medium caliber, employing the turning bolt principle and long-recoil action already mentioned as having been earlier conceived by Mauser. It had no military significance to warrant attention, though it has been used extensively for special police work.

In 1911 the Danish Bang Rifle was tested by the United States Ordnance Department and showed considerable promise. This operated on the principle of the cone about the muzzle trapping the gas and pulling the cone ahead to draw forward an attached operating rod which functioned the action. This, of course, was a variation of the original rifle experiments of both Maxim and Browning. (An improved form of the design was again offered in 1920 as modified by U. S. Captain James Hatcher. However, high production costs were envisioned and the design was passed over.)

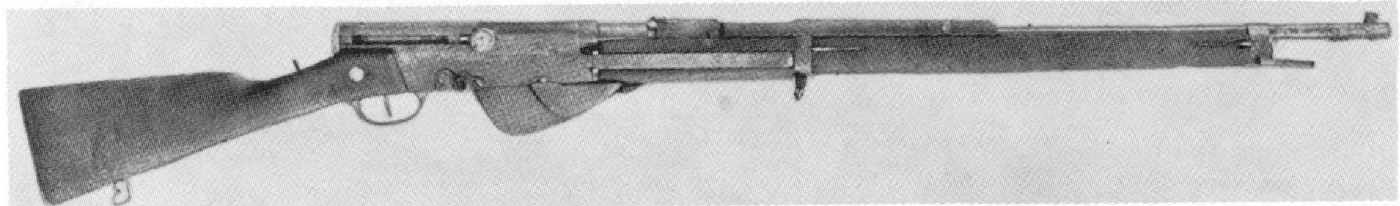

Representative French semi-automatic rifle made at St. Etienne. Model 1917.

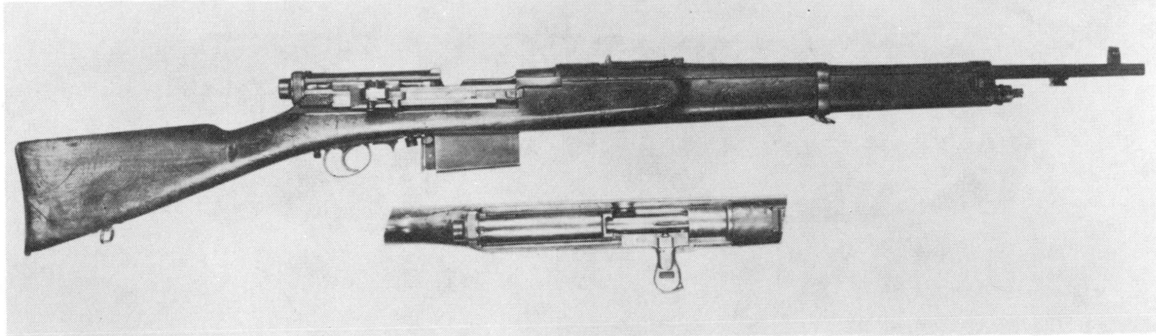

Mondragon Rifle. Side and top views. Made in Switzerland. Invented by Mexican General Mondragon. Used early in 1914 by German observers in airplanes before machine guns were mounted.

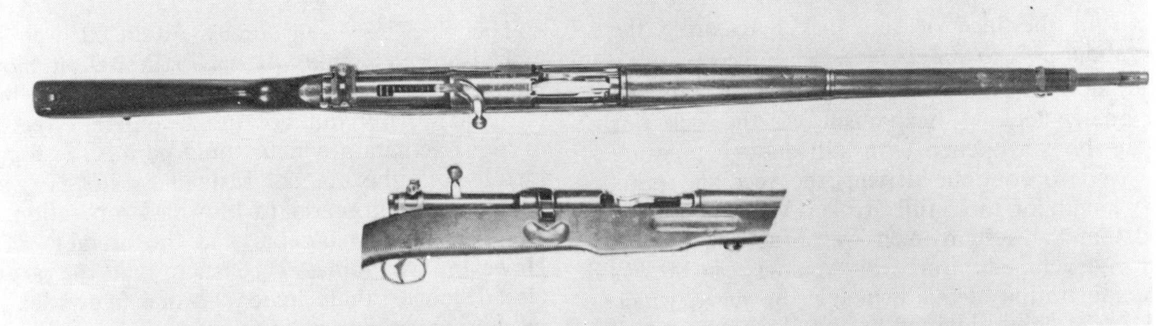

Thompson Semi-Automatic Rifle, Caliber .30. Top view closed. Insert shows breech open.

In 1911 the French began their experiments with the Fusil B and Fusil C, out of which came the later St. Etienne rifles. These designs, named after the arsenal of manufacture, were used to some extent by the French in 1917 and 1918 and were gas-operated, rotating-bolt rifles with box magazines. The operating rods were exposed on the right side of the forearm in these rifles, a condition which led to considerable field trouble. However, they represented the first actual use of semi-automatic rifles in general combat, though Mondragons and others had been earlier tried by the Germans for special duty use.

Passing mention must be made of this Mexican Mondragon. Invented by a Mexican Army Officer, the rifle was produced in small quantity in Switzerland. In several instances early in World War I, observers in planes were armed with these rifles. The Mondragon had a box magazine, a gas port about three-quarters the distance to the muzzle, and used a 10-shot box magazine. As in the case of all Swiss manufactured arms, the workmanship was excellent. The Mondragon was in production at the beginning of the war in limited degree, and actually saw battle service earlier than did the French, but the French rifles mentioned were the first ones to receive actual tactical battle tests.

Besides the Bang rifle already mentioned, as altered by Colonel James L. Hatcher, 1920 saw several other semi-automatic designs tested by the United States Ordnance Department. The Thompson rifle using a variation of the Blish hesitation principle did not prove satisfactory because of oiling requirements and because of jams and feeding trouble due to too rapid opening of the action. John C. Garand offered his semi-automatic rifle with primer-actuated mechanism at these trials.

In the Roth primer system, the primer was blown back in its seat against the head of the heavy striker. The striker, forced back inside the breechblock which housed it, was utilized to cam back locks to unlock the bolt from the receiver. The design was quite simple but the required special ammunition was not practical.

John Garand realized the impossibility of using other than standard cartridges. He therefore designed a primer-operated semi-automatic rifle action which would utilize a regular service rifle cartridge.

His firing striker had a cup-shaped face which would fit over the primer in the center of the cartridge case. When the rifle fired, the pressure of the gas inside the cartridge case as the powder was ignited, together with the pressure of the exploding primer itself, forced the primer back out of the case far enough into the cup

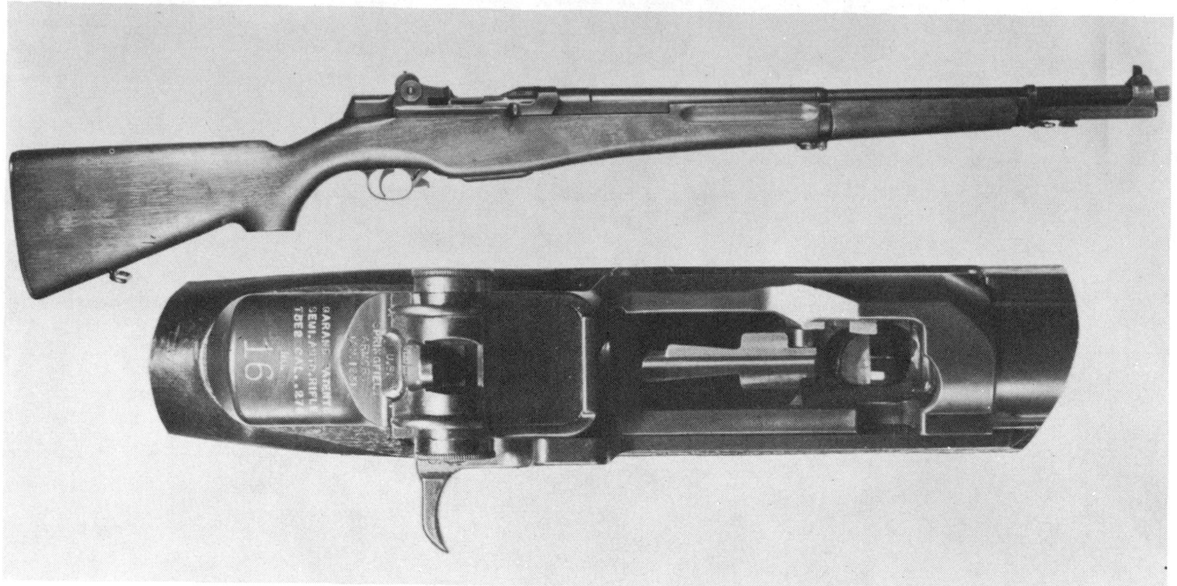

Early Garand for the .276 (7mm) Pedersen cartridge. Gas actuated.

shaped indent in the face of the striker to drive the striker back about .02 to .03 inches.

This small motion under high pressure was sufficient to open the breech locking mechanism. As the lock was withdrawn, the breech opened with still enough pressure left in the barrel to continue driving the recoiling parts back for the length of their full stroke. While Garand's tests showed that the system itself was practical, the individual rifles developed structural weaknesses. It was an earlier demonstration of this principle, however, which resulted in Garand being retained by the Government and given employment at the Springfield Armory to continue development of automatic arms. He, of course, is the inventor of our famous M1 service rifle, which is gas-operated.

Future development will unquestionably take into consideration this primer actuation principle of Garand's. It has a tremendous number of advantages over other systems. Unlike the short-recoil operation, for example, it does not require a recoiling barrel with all the necessary complications brought about by utilization of floating parts. With reference to the gas-operated system it offers simplification of manufacture, fewer parts and substantially longer operating life without attention. Naturally it has disadvantages, too, but those may be overcome.

The design points out one way to arms simplification, very few of which are possible so long as our current system of ammunition is utilized.

In 1923 another American, J. D. Pedersen, also was hired to do design work at Springfield. He was given unusual latitude, being permitted to develop a cartridge as well as a rifle. This is not standard procedure, rifles normally being designed around a specified cartridge. It is also not very practical, in view of the enormous investment every government has in equipment to produce the cartridges in general usage.

The rifle Pedersen finally produced was not a true locked-breech system. It was a hesitation blowback, actually. It utilized a toggle principle somewhat like the old Maxim, but did not utilize either a recoiling barrel or a gas actuation which would permit the toggle to completely lock the breech. Instead the toggle was designed to permit, as in standard blowback operation, immediate recoil of the moving parts at the moment of discharge. However, the joints were such that the arm was held closed longer than under normal blowback procedure, permitting an approximation of a locked-breech action by delaying the opening sufficiently to prevent burst case heads in most instances. The leverage was brilliantly worked out. As in all such systems, however, ruptured cases were encountered when the cartridges were not lubricated. Pedersen therefore developed a dry wax process for the cartridges to prevent such occurrences. This was impractical from a military standpoint and the design with its new .276 cartridge was not adopted. The military was sufficiently interested in the new cartridge, however, that it was approved by the Army as one to be eventually developed into our semi-automatic rifle cartridge, though time has proven this decision wrong also.

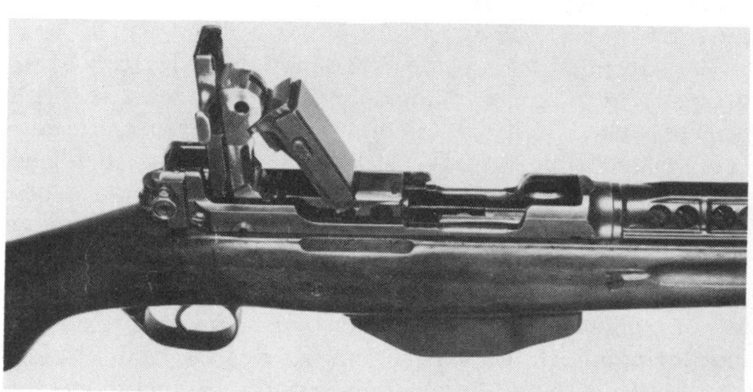

The Pedersen .276 open to show toggle system. This is a brilliantly conceived hesitation-lock system.

All arms entered in our official 1929 tests were in this caliber with the sole exception of the Garand which used our standard .30.

Fortunately, however, in 1932 a decision was made to retain the original .30-06 cartridge. In view of later developments, including the necessity for utilizing our huge capacity for manufacturing cartridges of this caliber and design, it is most fortunate that the change as indicated by the tentative acceptance of the Pedersen cartridge was not accomplished.

Pedersen had much to do with developing a magnificent line of firearms for Remington. These were commercial rifles and shotguns and a pistol, however. One item for which he is noted is the rather fantastic Pedersen Device which was one of the great United States "secrets" of World War I. In order to keep from the enemy any knowledge of this weapon, it was listed officially as "Automatic pistol, caliber .30, Model 1918."

This device was a self-contained unit which could be placed in the receiver of a Springfield bolt-action rifle when the regulation bolt had been removed. It was locked in place by modifying the cutoff mechanism of the regular rifle to serve as a lock. Its barrel was the exact length, size, and shape of the regular rifle cartridge case, in effect being merely a chamber at its forward end. When the device was installed, a short pistol type .30 caliber cartridge would chamber properly in it. A 40-round double line box magazine was provided which projected at a 45-degree angle to the barrel, the ejection port being cut in the rifle receiver to line up with the ejection port in the Pedersen Device. In practice a trained operator could remove the bolt from his Springfield and install the Pedersen Device in about 15 seconds. In actual field work it did not work that way. There is a considerable difference between what a trained operator will do and what an average infantryman under fire will do, as the course of all history including our own Civil War has shown. The idea was to provide these devices and ammunition to infantrymen going into battle. They were to use the regular ammunition and rifle for long range work, but at close-up work were to install the device and thereby become automatic riflemen for in-fighting.

The device was made a "top secret" item; 65,000 were actually made, and Springfield rifles altered as required to handle them. All but a few were destroyed after the war. It was intended as one answer to the development of the submachine gun by the Germans in World War I. Like most makeshifts, it was good in theory but not in practice. The few devices which escaped destruction are collector's items today. The cartridges too were "top secret," though they were little more than modified .32 auto pistol cartridges.

After 1929 tests at the Aberdeen Proving Ground ruled out other experimental rifles introduced, the Garand was adopted. General Douglas MacArthur was then Chief of Staff and fortunately he disapproved of the .276 caliber. As a result our Garand was developed for the standard .30-06 cartridge. In 1936 it was officially adopted.

Julian S. Hatcher's *Book of the Garand* deals thoroughly with the various experimental designs which were rejected in favor of the Garand, and the interested reader is referred to it.

In 1936 the first working models of our Johnson semi-automatic military rifle were introduced by their inventor, Melvin M. Johnson. Twenty-three models of this short-recoil arm were made before production was started.

The Johnson was the first truly successful application of the short-recoil principle to a rifle. In 1940 it was put into competition with the gas-operated Garand. By this time over 50,000 Garands were actually in use, and the field testing and manufacturing modifications which had been made had eliminated most of the difficulties from the design. Johnson's almost untried rifle was pitted against this thoroughly tested and modified design in competition. It is not surprising, therefore, that the Johnson came off second best in the tests. The Garand was put into production at Springfield and a contract for manufacture was also placed with Winchester. During the course of World War II the Garand performed beautifully and fully warranted the hopes which had been placed in it, except for the inevitable complaints about its weight.

The Johnson Machine Gun saw some service in the war but like the military shoulder rifle of the same caliber and same general design, it did not stand up too well in service, principally because it had not had the years of evolutionary development behind it that the other weapons had.

In 1940 a new gas-operated rifle was offered to the United States Marine Corps for tests by Winchester. This arm operated on a short-stroke piston of the type later utilized in the U. S. Carbine M1 (an arm which also was designed by Winchester). In this system gas is taken off near the breech and drives the piston back about .01 inches, the drive being passed on to the operating slide which in turn moves back to function the breech mechanism like the Garand method.

The breechblock mechanism itself in this first Winchester rifle design resembled that of the old Savage Model 99. It was a block lifted at the rear in mortises to lock position. When in position it was held up by a wide steel surface behind the action opening giving tremendous strength; the block was first lowered and then carried back after being so unlocked to function the mechanism. It required fluted chambers to ease extraction, a factor which also was found in Russian rifle design because of difficulty with extracting unlubricated cases where adequate primary extraction is not provided. This was the one real objection to the lock.

In 1916 the Russians began development of their semi-automatic rifle. One of their first products was the rifle developed by Simonov. It was issued in 1936. The arm in general is a semi-automatic military rifle though some designs have been encountered with full automatic features. It is a gas-operated arm of considerable effectiveness. The original wedge breechblock was very complicated. The design received a tryout by the Russians

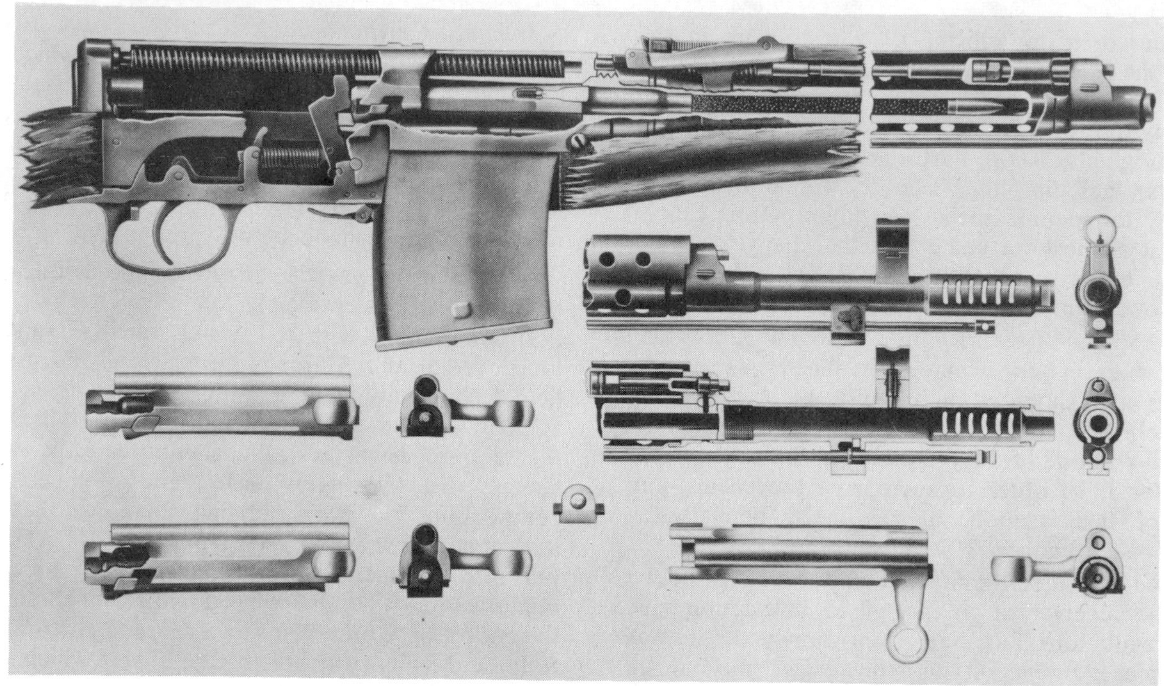

The Russian Tokarev Semi-Auto Rifle. Phantom view showing action locked at instant of firing. Details show the muzzle brake, gas operation and bolt locking systems.

during the Spanish Civil War when they provided a quantity to the so-called Loyalists so battle efficiency could be observed.

In 1938, therefore, they introduced their new design, the first of a line of Tokarevs. A modification was made in 1940 and additional changes have since been made, none of them drastic however.

The Russian designs are all rather crude in appearance but all are extremely simple both from an operational and a manufacturing standpoint. They represent a tremendous advance in automatic rifle design from the standpoint of simplicity of manufacture.

The only foreign design of any note before 1936 was in Czechoslovakia. Here the Holek Rifle was under development, which was known as the ZB 29, a tilting breechblock design on the gas piston system. These rifles were magnificently manufactured but had so much detailed hand work in them that general production was never attained.

They were used, however, to some limited extent in Ethiopia. Most specimens seen come from the Middle East. This design, by the way, was one of those entered in the tests we conducted in 1929; it was passed over for the Garand.

During 1941 the Germans, brought to a realization of the desirability of a semi-automatic rifle by use of the Russian arms against them in the Eastern theater of war, produced their muzzle-trap gas-operated rifles. These arms were in many respects similar to earlier Mauser experimental designs. Various types were issued, the 41M by Mauser and the 41W by Walther.

By 1943 Germany realized the necessity for an arm which could be manufactured at very low cost and under conditions utilizing high-speed production equipment. In a very short period they produced the crude appearing but highly efficient Gewehr 43. The designation K43 was later applied to a slightly modified form. The locking system was basically that of the early Mauser, which in its turn was an adaptation of the early Friberg.

Toward the end of the war Germany frantically pro-

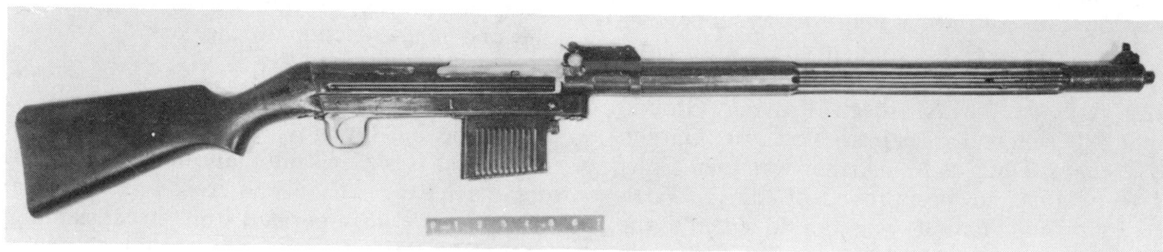

An early German Walther experimental gas-operated design.

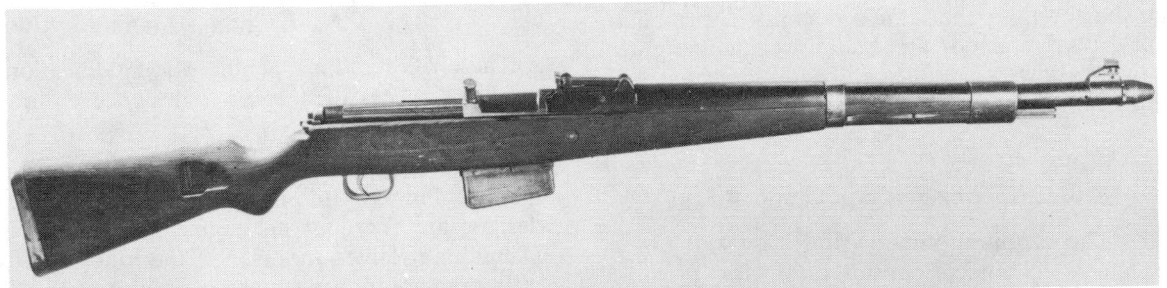

German 41 W. Designed by Walther. Gas operated. Muzzle cap design.

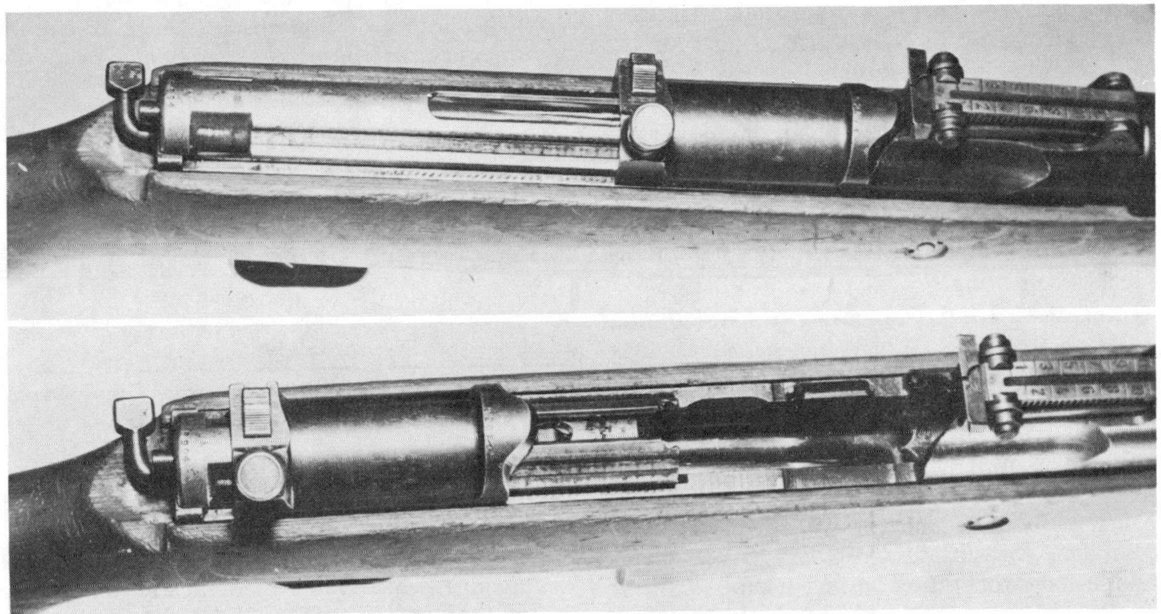

German Gewehr 41W. Breech closed and open.

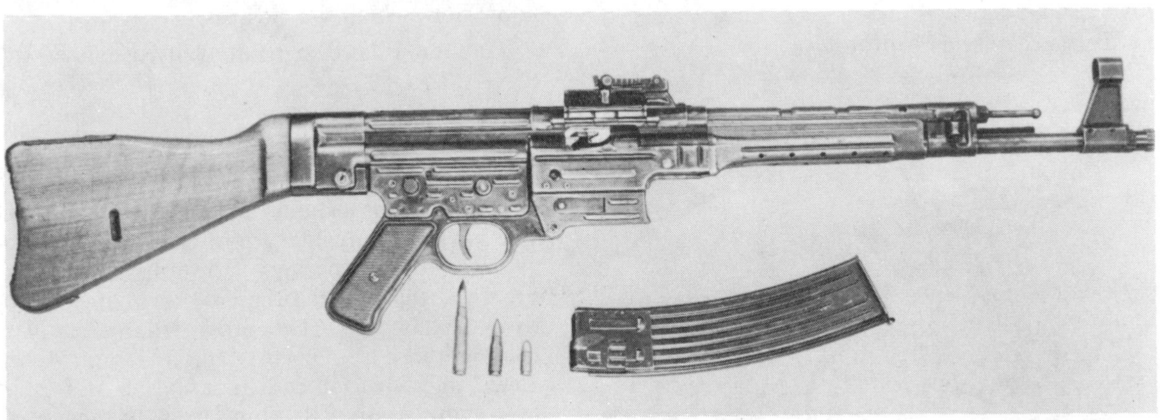

German M P 44. This arm was the first approach to the modern all-purpose military rifle. For comparison cartridges shown are the standard German 7.92mm, the short form 7.92mm for the M P 44 and the 9mm Parabellum used in pistols and submachine guns.

duced a number of potentially fine semi-automatic and full automatic arms capable of tremendous future development. Noteworthy among these is the Fallschirmjaeger Gewehr which will be covered in chapter 26.

Perhaps the outstanding German design was the MP 44. This is a locked-breech arm operated by gas. It uses a new short cartridge form intended to offset and go far beyond our own carbine experimentation. The magazine capacity is 30 cartridges. The arm is gas operated by piston having, of course, a locked breech. It is actually a machine or automatic carbine for special purpose use.

The Germans showed far more intelligence and imagination in developing a cartridge for this weapon than we did in our adoption of one for our own carbine. Their cartridge was merely a shortened version of their 7.92mm standard rifle cartridge. The case was bottlenecked but shorter than the standard case. The regular pointed bullet was retained, the bullet weight being reduced somewhat, however. Ballistically the cartridge was a tremendous improvement over the one that we developed.

United States Experimental Automatic Rifles

Two American semi-automatic rifles as well as a Belgian design were under consideration for possible adoption by the United States and troops of the NATO Nations.

The first was the T-44. This is a gas-operated rifle and basically the locking action of this arm is that of the regular M1 Garand rifle in all essentials. The weapon went through five modifications and the T44E4 has been adopted as the M14; it is covered in detail in chapter 45.

The second experimental rifle was the T47. This design utilizes a form of the common Browning automatic rifle lock, the principle of a section of the breechblock being hinged up into a locking recess in the top of the receiver to lock when firing.

When the rifle is fired the operating rod forces the hammer block to the rear. When the hammer block begins its movement it draws down the locking bolt linked to it out of a recess quite as in the manner of the BAR. The block continues backward and downwards opening the slide on top of the action. With the slide open, the empty case gripped in its face by the extractor is struck against the ejector and thrown out of the rifle. As the slide moves forward to close the action, under action of the tensioned operating spring, a new cartridge which has been fed up by the spring in the magazine is stripped out of the magazine and fed into the chamber for firing.

The T47 was made only as a prototype.

The F.N. Belgian Automatic Rifles

These rifles and a machine rifle modification are among the finest pieces of automatic design ever introduced.

Full advantage has been taken of the knowledge of the most modern manufacturing and firearms development techniques in producing these rifles. Basically the designs are those of an engineer at the F.N. Plant, M. Dieudonne Saive. In essence the rifle is a combination of a number of previously tried and tested factors. The locking system was patented by Monsieur Saive without knowledge of prior development. However, as a study of the history of firearms in this book will show, all the principles therein were experimented with to one degree or another in the past.

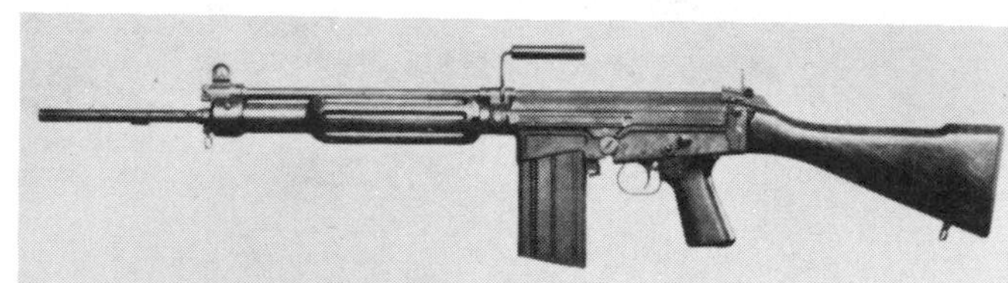

F. N. Belgian Automatic Rifle, Cal. 7.62mm NATO

This arm was originally chambered for the German 7.92mm short cartridge. Models have been made and tested, however, for the United States caliber .30 T-65 cartridge, which while theoretically not as efficient as the 7mm, has the saving grace of utilizing huge quantities of equipment and a tremendous background of ballistical know-how which we possess.

The new F.N. designs are fully discussed in chapter 16.

CARBINES

One of the classic Wallhausen military drawings dated 1616. It shows a carabineer firing a wheel-lock carbine—and is so described. The weapon is a short form for use from horseback.

A wheel-lock pistol carried in its holster slung across the "pistallo" or pommel of the saddle is also a historic item, as it is an early piece of evidence indicating that the term "pistol" quite probably derives from the position in which mounted soldiers first carried it.

A carbine is usually defined as a short rifle, generally one having a barrel length of less than 22 inches.

Like most of the very old terms used in the history of firearms, the actual origin of the name cannot be positively established. The most reliable early records, including those in Gays' Memoires pour l'Artillerie published in 1548, indicate that the short form of shoulder fired gun acquired its name from the fact that it was extensively used in Spain by cavalry groups then called "Carabins."

While some researchers indicate that the name originated from the fact that short shoulder arms were early used by Calabrian troops, and still others trace its derivation to its alleged use for repelling boarders on small ships called Carabs, the best documentation seems to support the theory of the Spanish cavalry origin.

In passing it might be mentioned that still another somewhat fanciful explanation for the derivation of the name carbine is that it stems from the Arabic "Karab," meaning a weapon.

Representative U. S. M1 Carbine. Unlike earlier U. S. carbines, this arm does not use the same cartridge as the M1 Rifle, nor does it employ any parts from the rifle.

Earlier U. S. carbines all used the standard rifle cartridge and most of the same parts, being modified only by shortening and decreasing the weight.

In military usage in the past for the most part, the carbine has been merely a form of the standard rifle. It features the same lock work but has a shorter barrel and modifications of the stock and forestock as required to lessen the weight. In general, in early times carbines were basically cavalry arms carried in a boot on the saddle.

Exceptions generally were in Italy and Spain where short lightweight rifled shoulder arms, using normally the 9mm Parabellum in Italy or in Spain the 9mm Bayard or Parabellum cartridge, have been designated as carbines. These have appeared in turnbolt full auto and semi-automatic weapons. However, such arms have invariably been intended for basic police work and for border patrol service, not for military usage as such.

In any event, even in sporting arms both here and abroad the term carbine has been used to designate a rifled arm similar to its rifle parent, except that it is

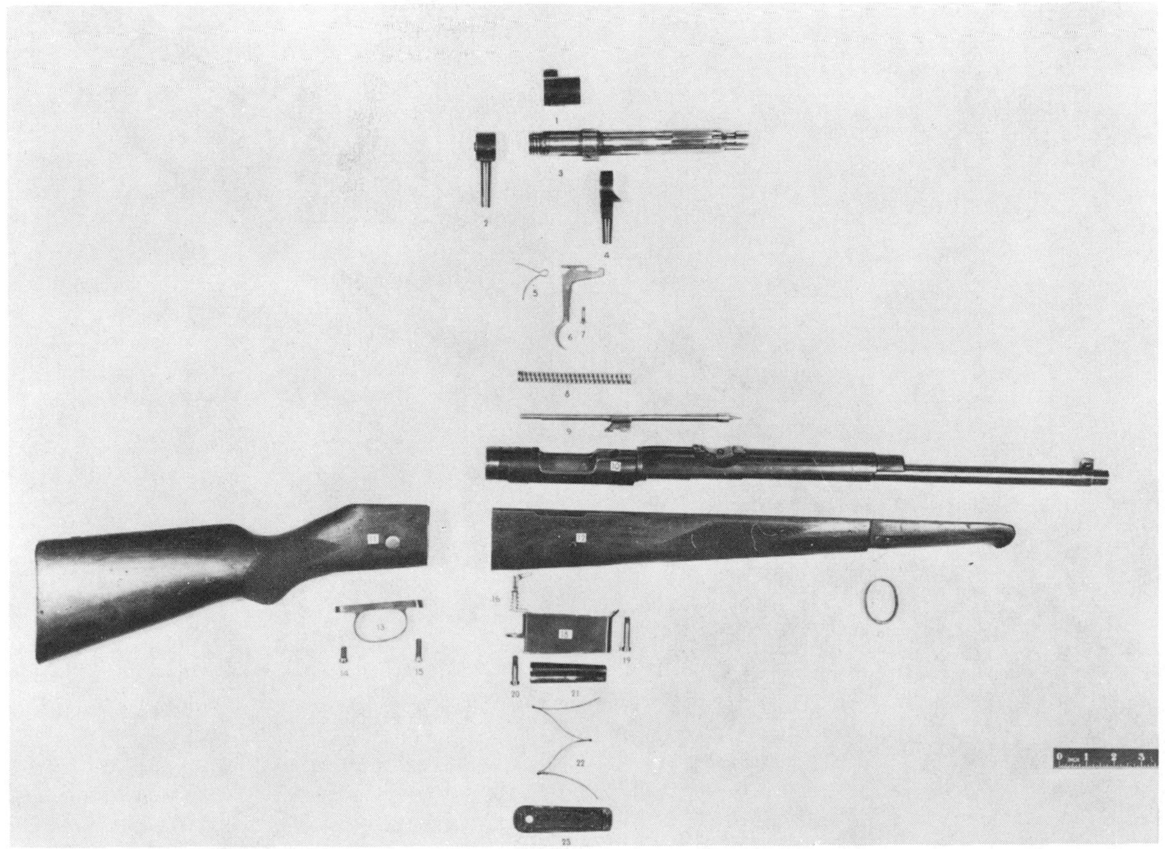

The Mexican Mendoza 7mm semi-auto carbine. Uses the official Mexican rifle cartridge. Gas operated. Field stripped to show simplicity of the design.

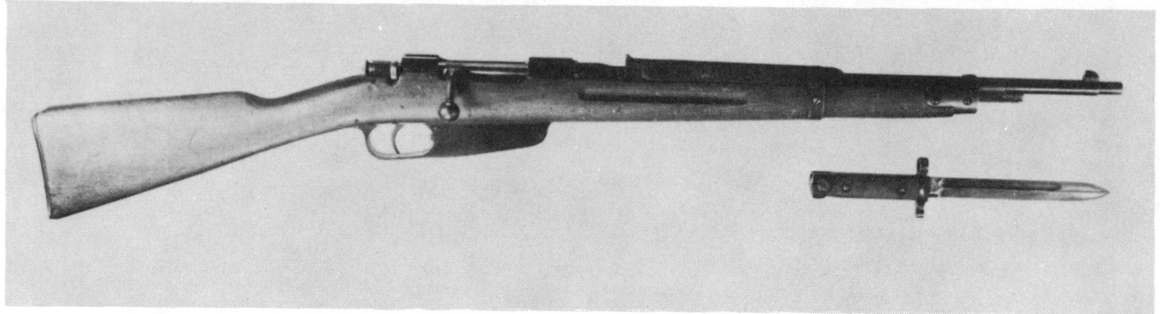

Italian Carcano M 38 Carbine. This is a true military carbine in the classical sense. It was made in two calibers—6.5mm and 7.35mm, both of which were official rifle calibers in World War II.

This carbine has a 21-inch barrel and is 40 inches overall.

Its counterpart in the rifle utilizes the same cartridge and the same receiver and operating parts and averages about 10 inches greater length of barrel and overall measurement.

shorter and lighter by reason of lesser barrel length and modified stocks, et cetera.

The United States Carbine M1 is the first arm in general military use to deviate from this definition, being a light and short rifled weapon—but one which uses a cartridge of its own and has no parts interchangeable with the Garand rifle.

In 1940 the Ordnance Department provided a set of specifications and called for designs to meet them. These were to be semi-automatic (and later also full automatic) carbines. In this instance an entirely new military cartridge was developed for the short lightweight weapon whose weight was specified originally at 5.5 pounds. Curiously the cartridge developed was almost identical with the original commercial .32 Winchester auto loading cartridge of 1905 except the bullet was shorter and lighter.

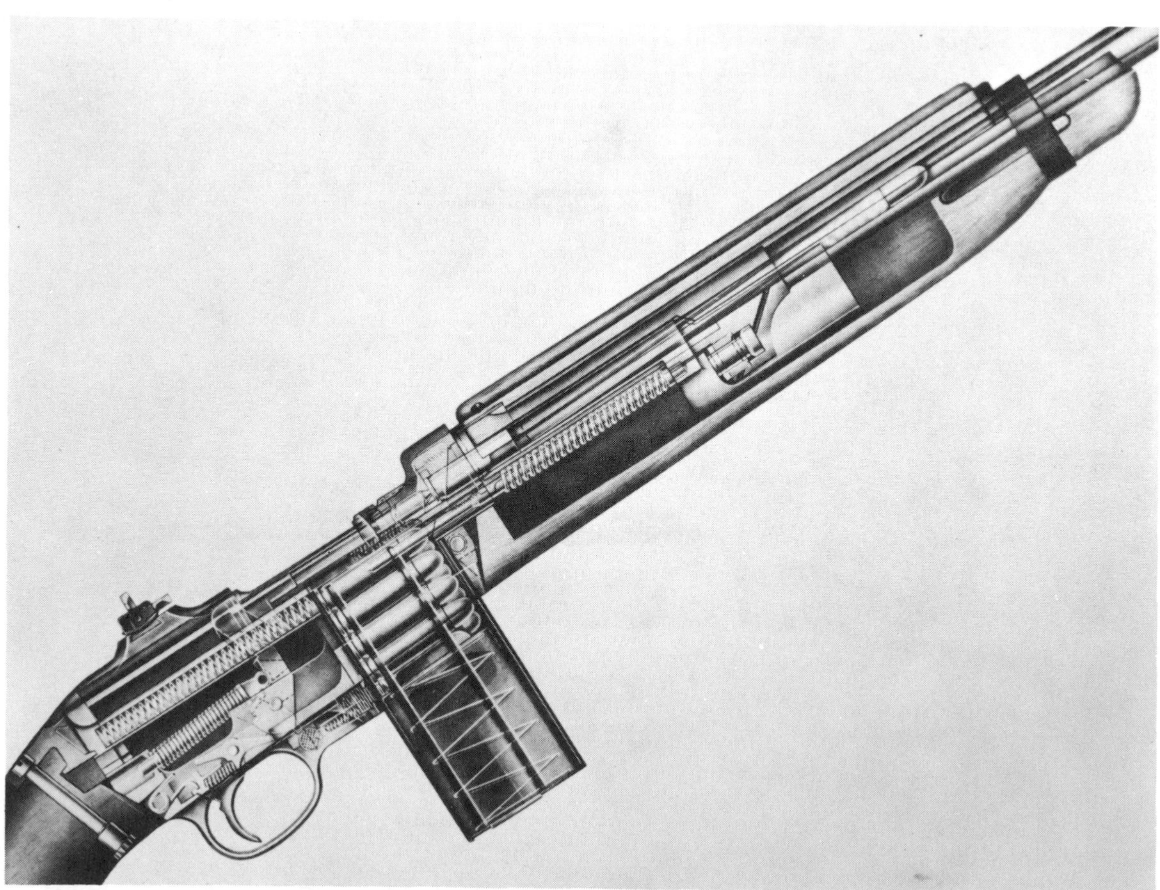

U. S. Carbine M1. A phantom drawing to show mechanism at instant of firing. Parts are not interchangeable with the Garand. Systems are related but not identical. Cartridges are of same nominal caliber but are entirely different in shape, size, and ballistics.

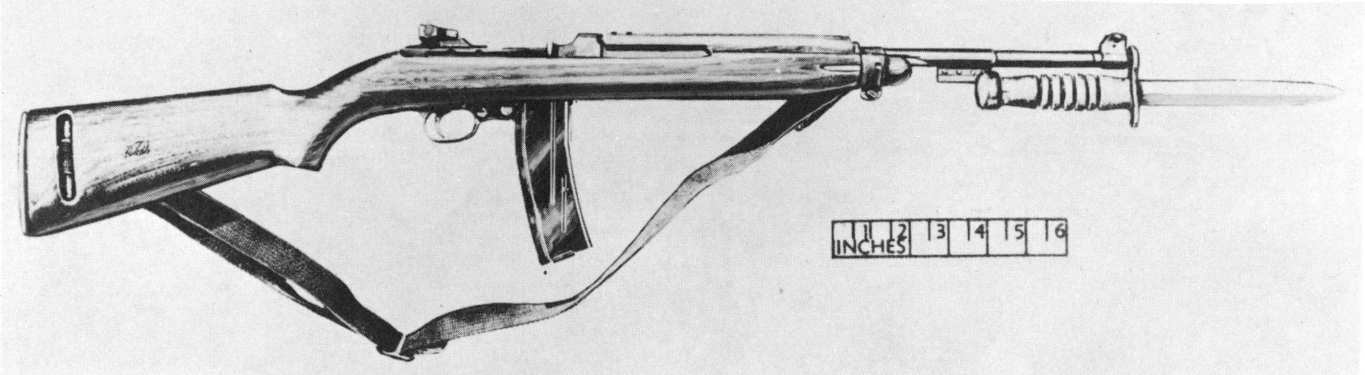

U. S. Carbine Caliber .30 M2. This is a modification of the semi-automatic carbine M1.

Guns made by Auto Ordnance, Harrington and Richardson, Hyde, Savage, Springfield Armory, Winchester, and Woodhull were submitted. The locked-breech Winchester with its short stroke action was selected, partly because of its highly efficient lock action which resembled the Garand quite closely. The gas operating system, however, was the type used in the Winchester 1940 rifle.

When adopted, this carbine was catalogued as the U. S. Carbine, Caliber 30 M1. It has since gone through numerous modifications, including paratroop models and full automatic designs, most of which will be found in chapter 45.

The U. S. Carbine, caliber .30 M1 is not to be confused with the U.S. Rifle .30 M1, the cartridge being shorter, lighter and very, very much less powerful. It is a special purpose arm not to be confused with rifle requirements.

The U. S. Carbine Caliber .30 M1 and its modifications represent one approach to the subject of increasing the efficiency of the very light weight, readily portable automatic weapon. German specialists investigated this subject thoroughly in 1933 and 1934, pointing out at that time the two ways of accomplishing it: either by enlarging the type of pistol ammunition in use or by decreasing the size of the standard rifle type ammunition as used in the light machine gun.

In its inception the U. S. carbine was intended to produce a compromise weapon having the general characteristics of a group of arms. Many hopefully expected it to actually replace the pistol, the submachine gun, and even perhaps the rifle. No truly serious military students ever had any illusions on this possibility however. Least of all the Germans.

The German design followed the second line of taking advantage of their vast technical knowledge and manufacturing experience and resources for producing the rifle cartridge, but shortening the case to produce an entirely new ammunition style which yet was related to

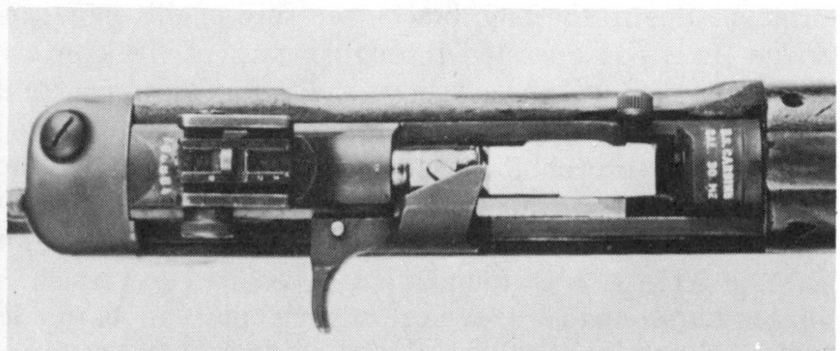

The M2 is a special purpose weapon. Shown without magazine. The full auto switch is seen at the receiver above the stock. Externally it resembles the carbine M1. This specimen has the folding M1A1 type stock.

Top view showing Selector (switch). Breech open.

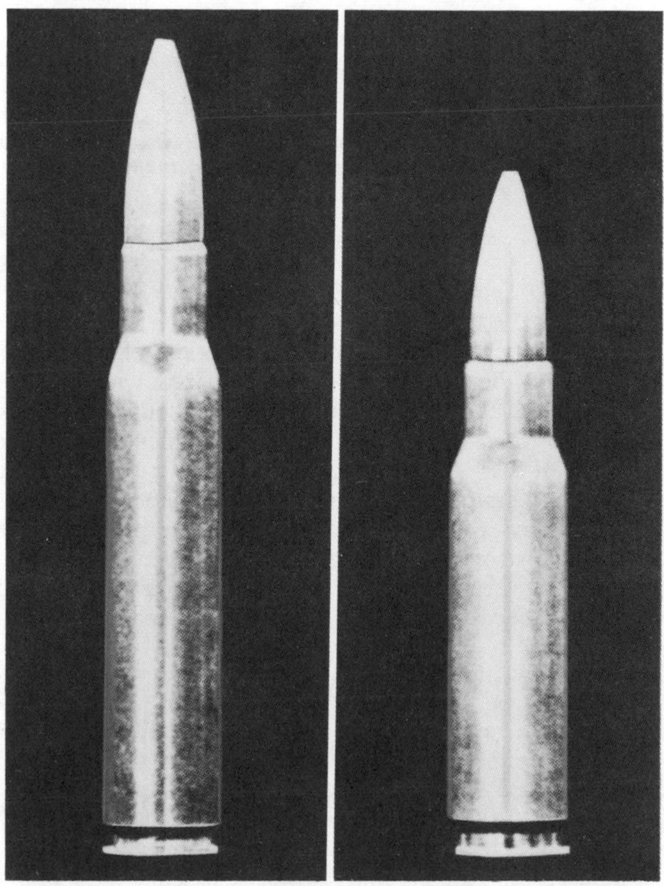

Comparison photos of standard U. S. Rifle Cartridge M2 and the 7.62mm NATO Cartridge. It is used in new auto rifles and other machine arms here and in NATO nations.

Upper: The German M P 44 semi- and full automatic rifle which introduced the brilliantly conceived short form 7.92 cartridge which was the forerunner of current automatic trends and design. Its actuation is by gas. Its low cost, high speed production design points the way to modern military small arms design.

Lower: 7.92mm MKb 42 (H), the predecessor of the MP44.

their rifle ammunition. Such ammunition of course has the relative disadvantage when compared with our carbine cartridge of having much greater bulk, which requires a larger magazine to carry the same number of rounds. It has on the other hand the tremendous advantage of simplifying ammunition production and also, in these days of advancements in powder production, of being able to utilize new powders in its short case which will give a very close approximation of the standard rifle cartridge because less case space is needed for the burning.

Since any mechanical or technical matter must always necessarily be a matter of compromise, this German compromise was unquestionably the better of the two. In evidence of this fact, one may point to the United States T65E3 (7.62mm NATO) cartridge case developed from our .30-06 on the same principle as the German MP 44 cartridge. This most nearly approximates the truly desirable all-purpose cartridge, since it is capable of utilization in rifles, carbines, light and heavy machine guns, and even as the Germans used it in a form of what might be called the assault rifle with locked breech.

On the other hand, the Germans first introduced it as the MP-43. However, in 1944 in recognition of the fact that it was an entirely new arm and not to be confused with the machine pistol design, it was renamed the StG 44 assault rifle. This arm utilizing the new German bottlenecked cartridge was not operated on the blowback principle due to the high breech pressure of this new cartridge. It is gas operated through means of the conventional barrel port, placed above the barrel, however, and the standard type of cylinder containing a reciprocating piston. The breechblock locking mechanism is of the tipping pattern operated by the piston extension in relatively conventional manner. As in the case of our own carbine M1, it was found also necessary to furnish a longer barrel than the typical submachine gun barrel in order to obtain good velocity. The butt stock as originally issued was a crude wooden affair but in development can be altered to provide a folding metal type for paratroop work. Remarkable factors are low cost production, rapid manufacture, and great inherent strength built into this gun through the most advanced use of steel pressings, as developed by the Germans in the manufacture of their machine pistols and light machine guns. These too are subject to considerable refinement, but do point the way to later design.

Experience and observation of this pattern has convinced the Germans that in any new armament in which they have a design hand, the MP 44 will be the basis for the new design. Since in production these can be manufactured at a fraction of the cost and with a fraction of the equipment necessary to produce the more formal types such as those manufactured in the United States, this design is deserving of considerable attention.

The German Volksturm Gewehr

This arm too is discussed and pictured in chapter 26. Developed in the closing days of World War II, it was issued in small numbers in 1945 and was intended for

Volksturm Gewehr.

Crude but efficient. This arm is covered in detail in chapter 26. It introduced a new form of gas controlled hesitation lock.

last stand defense of the homeland. By the time of its introduction, however, the will to fight had been broken.

This very crude weapon utilized the MP 44 cartridge with its exceptional ballistics. While the recoiling elements weigh about three times more than those of the breechblock assembly in the typical submachine gun, the design is such that the overall weight of the arm is still only about 9½ pounds. The breech locking depends on inertia of the moving assembly to halt too rapid breech action in opening, but is aided by expanding gas being bled off through gas ports into the gas cylinder in such a manner as to exert a forward thrust as the bullet passes the gas ports. While the design itself was elementary in its original appearance, it is capable of considerable development in this field.

.30 M1 Carbine Cartridge Note

This cartridge was developed in 1940 by the Winchester Repeating Arms Company at New Haven at the direct request of United States Ordnance Department. The Company was furnished with specifications calling for a compact, rimless cased cartridge with a bullet of 110 grains, developing a velocity in the neighborhood of 1800 feet per second from an 18-inch barrel.

The cartridge as originally produced by Winchester had an overall length of 1.67 inches with a case length of 1.29 inches. Originally head stamped .30SL by Winchester the cartridge later became our .30 Carbine M1.

It is a most unusual coincidence that the cartridge developed was actually one very close to the .32 Winchester Self Loading Rifle cartridge developed by that company for use in its model 1905 Self Loading rifle. This is a short, semi-rimmed cartridge case with straight side wall. The slightly altered version was issued to several developers to use in producing carbines for Government tests. Entered in the tests were two versions of carbines developed by John Garand. Among others Winchester had developed a 7½-pound carbine or experimental rifle for this cartridge. It proved so successful that Winchester undertook the development of a 5-pound carbine to handle the newly accepted cartridge.

They developed the first handmade sample carbine in the record breaking time of 14 days. The initial tests brought out several bugs as was inevitable in such a rush model. By working round the clock for 34 days, the Winchester organization rushed through the model which became the U. S. Carbine Caliber .30 M1.

Samples of this new Winchester were tested on September 15, 1941 against improved models from Springfield, and by Hyde and Reising, as well as a gas-operated rifle by R. J. Turner. The outstanding superiority of the Winchester design was clearly demonstrated.

Nomenclature

Great Britain has recently changed their terminology to designate as "submachine guns" in accordance with United States practice, all the various weapons heretofore listed by them as "machine carbines."

For all practical purposes, the term "carbine" will normally indicate, either in military or sporting usage, a rifled shoulder weapon with all the basic characteristics of the rifle version, except that the barrel will be shorter and the stocks and sights altered accordingly to reduce weight and make for a more compact weapon.

The tremendous number of "U. S. Carbines M1" and modifications now in use throughout the world will undoubtedly require the continuation of this designation, although the weapon itself actually falls into a new arms classification.

Chapter 8. Development of Automatic Principles in Firearms

AUTOMATIC FIREARMS are those in which forces of the discharge are utilized to reload, recock and fire successive shots until the trigger is released, or until the ammunition supply is exhausted.

Semi-automatic arms are those in which the forces of the discharge are similarly used to reload and recock, but in which a deliberate release and pull of the trigger are required to fire the second and successive shots.

The discharge forces utilized may be merely those of the recoil occasioned by the discharge as in the case of the common so-called automatic pistol. Strictly speaking, of course, these arms are semi-automatic. It is necessary to deliberately release the trigger, and pull individually for each successive shot. If this were not done, the discharges would be so rapid and the recoil so great because of the light weight of the weapon that the arm would mount out of control. Recoil actuated arms may be blowback (unlocked), hesitation (retarded opening) or positively locked designs.

A second principle of such operation is utilization of the gases either as they expand at the muzzle or as they are tapped off through a port in the barrel itself to operate an unlocking and reloading and firing mechanism. Such actions are locked-breech designs on all but freaks.

Still another type is that in which there is a combination of the uses of the recoil forces as such and gas either taken off at the muzzle or tapped off through a barrel port. These are locked-breech designs.

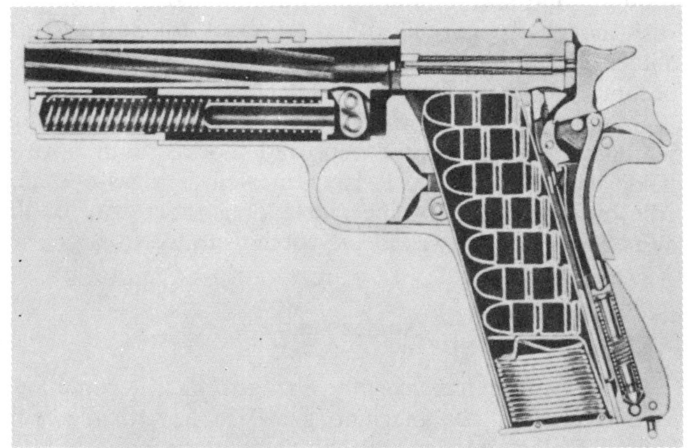

U. S. Government Model 1911A1 pistol. A representative "Semi-Automatic" weapon. Sectionalized. Chamber empty. Top barrel ribs locked into slide.

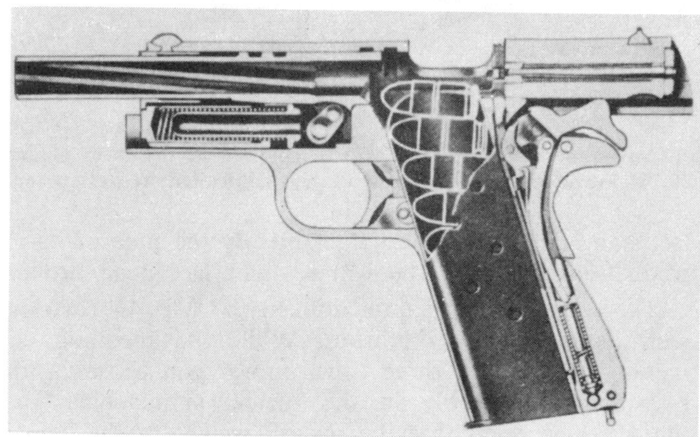

Representative locked breech type. U. S. Government 1911A1 pistol. Sectionalized, breech open. Barrel down on link out of slide engagement. Short recoil operation.

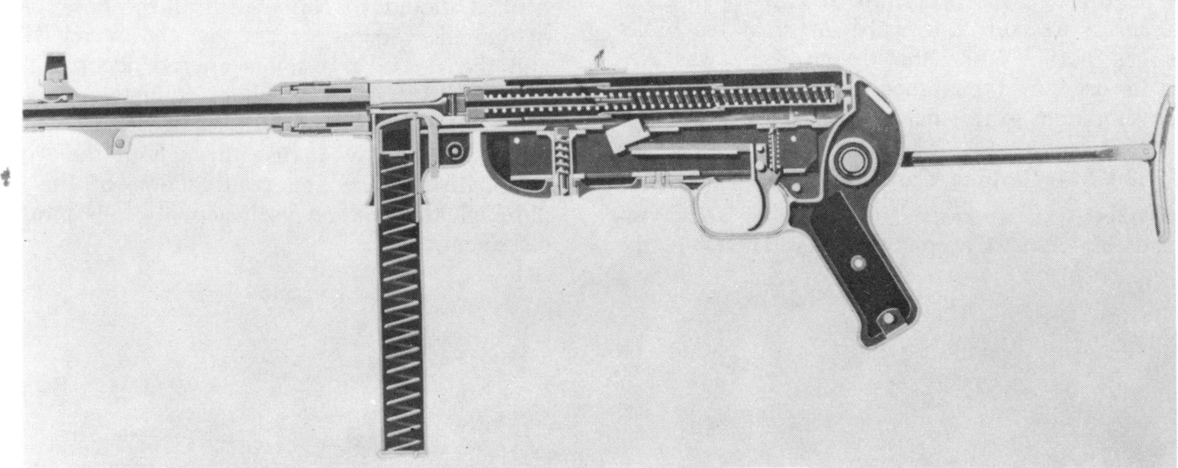

German M.P. 40. A representative true "Automatic" weapon. Sectionalized. Shown empty.

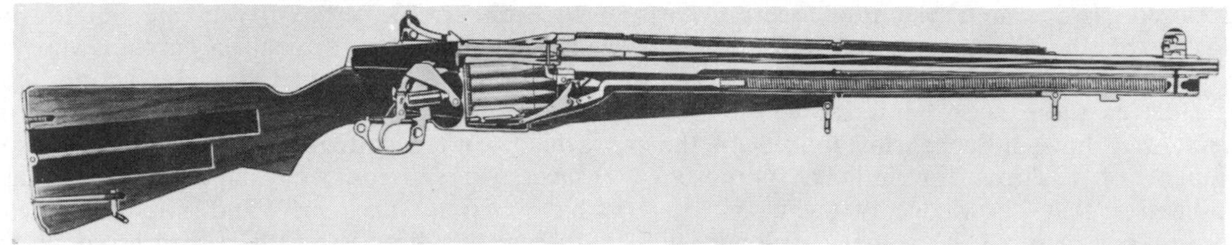

U. S. M1 (Garand) rifle. Gas taken off through barrel port near muzzle operates the mechanism as bullet passes over gas port. Sectionalized. Ready to fire. A representative gas port and piston operated arm.

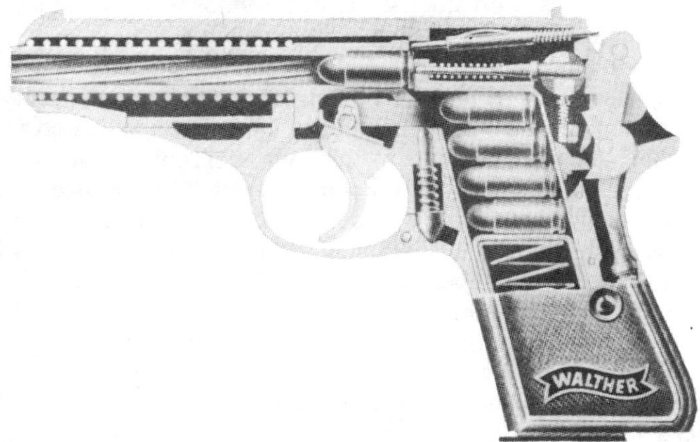

Representative blowback type. The German Walther PP pistol.

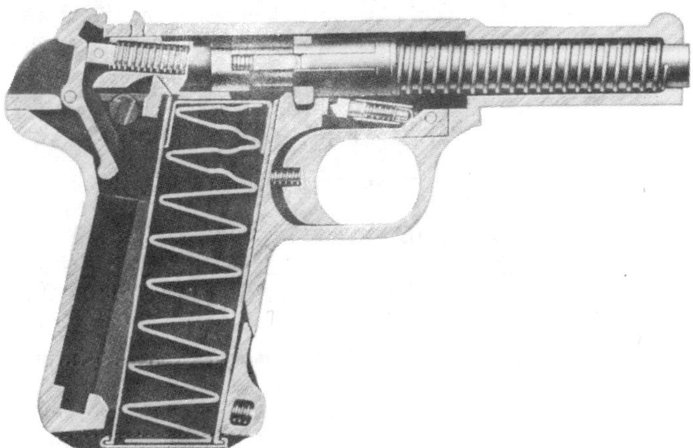

Representative Hesitation Lock. The American Savage Pistol.

History

Automatic firearms became a possibility only with the introduction of the successful metallic cartridge.

There is nothing new, however, about the knowledge of the principle itself as such. There is, for example, one very noted contemporary record shown in Birch's History of the Royal Society published in England. The records of the Royal Society for March 2, 1663 quote Sir Robert Moray, F.R.S. as telling that body "there had come to Prince Rupert a rare mechanician who pretended to make a pistol shooting as fast as could be presented and yet could be stopped at pleasure; and wherein the motion of the fire and bullet within was made to charge the piece with powder and bullet, to prime it and bend the cock."

On the basis of this and similar fragmentary records, the British "Text Book of Small Arms 1929 Edition" considers the automatic principle as having been an English invention.

In view of the fact that the records of the Royal Society show no further mention of the arm, such a claim is obviously rather farfetched.

Among other fragmentary records of the day one might quote that unearthed by the Abbe J. Rouquette, found in the archives of the Province of Languedoc, France. A document there states that on the 21st of August, 1688, one Abraham Soyer was arrested. When arraigned before the Inspector of the Mission of the Cevennes, a pistol was found in his luggage. He stated he was taking the weapon to St. Etienne, which was an arsenal and arms development center at that time in France even as it is today. The description given indicates that the weapon was a breech loading item using a crude cartridge which was loaded through the butt end of the stock quite in the manner of the common automatic pistol in use today! However, we find no further mention in French records of such a device until some 200 years later.

Still another mention which might possibly be descriptive of an automatic weapon is that found in the Pepys Diary for the 4th of March, 1664. Herein is mentioned a "new fashion gun brought by Lord Peterborough this morning, to shoot off often, one after another, without trouble or danger." Here again a search of the records of the period in which this was written does not disclose any further mention of such an arm.

One could quote equally vague and yet tantalizing reports from the Belgian, German, and Italian records of the early seventeenth century. In fact some of an even older date might be quoted. However, in no case are any of them sufficiently explicit to indicate that the arms actually were presented, but merely ideas about them were discussed.

For all practical purposes, therefore, we must face the fact that self-loading and -cocking mechanisms as such were not capable of practical development until the perfected metallic cartridge of the twentieth century came into being.

In the United States patent records for the year 1863 we find patent number 2998 to one Regulus Pilon, which describes a system for recocking the hammer of a weapon by utilizing the barrel recoil. We find similarly in our records for the year 1866, patent number 1810 to W.

Curtis for a proposed gas-operated system of firearms. An unsuccessful gas pistol, the Clair, appeared in France in 1863.

While items such as these are of interest to the true historical student, they have little bearing indeed on the actual development of firearms for military purposes. There is no indication that knowledge of such past developments were of any avail to the actual developers of our modern automatic weapons.

For purposes of simplification in the discussion of the history of the evolution and development of automatic arms, we will discuss the various weapons classifications individually, introducing overlapping developments in the fields of other types only when to do so may clarify the general discussion of the moment. That history really begins with the inventions of our own Hiram S. Maxim.

THE STORY OF HIRAM MAXIM

Hiram Stevens Maxim was born February 5, 1840 at Sangersville, Maine, the youngest of a family of seven children. He is the unquestioned father of automatic firearms as we know them today. He was one of the great geniuses in mechanics of all times. A short account of his astonishing life has a place here in these pages.

At the age of six Maxim was enrolled in the local school at Sangersville. His unusual mechanical abilities were discernible very early in life. At the age of twelve he encountered a former sea captain who taught him to read latitude and longitude. Having no money to purchase a chronometer, with his own hands he built one which worked perfectly. As in the case of so many other successful self-educated men, a few books seemed to have had a very early and important development in shaping his life. His father, impressed with the interest young Maxim showed in the subject of astronomy, purchased for him a book on the subject which he studied avidly. Another of the formative books to which he was subjected was Comstock's Natural Philosophy, together with of course the inevitable and invaluable family Bible. The Maxim family was of French Huguenot descent They had been driven out of France to England, and long after emigrated to Plymouth County, Massachusetts. Maxim himself tells us in his autobiography that the family emigrated "so they could worship God according to the dictates of their own conscience, and prevent others from doing the same." His wry sense of humor also was early developed! These characteristics stayed with him through his long and profitable span of life.

Hiram Stevens Maxim, 1840-1915. The father of the successful automatic system in firearms.

Maxim was apprenticed to a carriage maker at the age of fourteen. He was already noted for having built a boat and for being a natural mechanic. Working days of sixteen hours were quite common at that period, and from this very difficult early apprenticeship Maxim also developed many of the traits which stood him in such good stead later on.

This apprenticeship paid four dollars per month, not necessarily in cash. Maxim next turned his hand to manufacturing rakes for a few months. He returned to school and supplemented his income by selling the skins of animals he and his brother trapped. Hunting and trapping gave him a familiarity with arms and their mechanical principles as well as a rugged, healthy physique.

As an outgrowth of his apprenticeship, however, Maxim was able to get employment in the Flint Carriage Shop at Abbot Lower Village. This was a noted plant in its day, as it used machinery operated by water power. During this period young Maxim developed an ability at drawing. He spent considerable time designing parts and sketching various items he thought might improve the carriage business.

He spent four years at the Flint establishment. He left there while still a minor to operate a grist mill at Abbot, Maine. All grist mills, of course, were mice-infested and Maxim was compelled to turn his attention to the problems involved thereby. Legend has it that one must merely develop a better mouse trap and the world will beat its way to one's door. Unfortunately the maxim did not work very well for young Hiram Maxim.

He actually did invent a better mouse trap, one operating through the use of coil springs, on a rather clocklike design. As the trap was tripped on catching one mouse, it would automatically reset itself for another. He tells us that his first experiment with it caught five mice in the first night. Nobody seemed to be unduly interested in his better mouse trap, however.

Maxim, as so often happened during his life, was

ahead of his time even on mouse traps; years later this type of mouse trap was produced by dozens of small manufacturing plants for whom it earned large sums of money. Maxim, of course, never benefited.

The grist mill was successful but unfortunately payment was normally made in grain, not cash. When he couldn't buy clothes with grain, Maxim unloaded himself of the business and moved to Dexter, Maine. There he obtained employment as a woodturner, an occupation in which he was engaged when the Civil War broke out. He joined a local home guard company but soon tired of "playing soldier" as he called it. Shortly thereafter Maxim decided the war could not last very long, and that for him to enlist would be merely to leave himself open to having to hunt another job upon his discharge.

On the advice of a friend whose judgment he valued, Maxim left Maine and moved to Huntingdon, Canada. In later life this move was often brought up in the course of arguments he had with various business competitors. Many took occasion to point it out and to sneer that he had left the United States to dodge the draft. In all due justice to Maxim there is nothing in the record to indicate that he was so motivated. In fact two of his brothers did serve, and it was Lincoln's policy not to take more than two from any one family.

In Canada he worked at dozens of varying occupations ranging from painting signs to bartending and decorating sewing machines.

A rather strange incident resulted in his return to the United States. During the course of doing painting work, he was engaged to produce a new type of blackboard for a school house at St. Jean Chrisostome. He developed a paint which permitted the chalk to work well on a plain plaster wall, thereby saving the school hundreds of dollars.

He asked the huge price of six dollars for payment. The school board refused on the ground that although they were saving considerable money, Maxim himself had only used 40 or 50 cents worth of material!

From this experience he developed such a strain of bitterness against Canadians that he moved back to his old home in Maine. At this period he encountered still another book which had a great influence on his mental development. This was Ure's dictionary of Art, Mines and Manufactures. He tells us that he spent an entire winter reading and digesting this work, and that it marked a major step in his educational development. He recounts that the village girls teased and ridiculed him for spending time with a dictionary rather than with them. Curiously, he developed almost an antipathy for women as a result of this hazing, although a few years later he moved to Boston where he was married after an engagement of only a few months.

After traveling rather extensively through the West and South, working at one thing and another, he returned to Fitchburg, Massachusetts where he went to work for an uncle, Levi Stevens. Here he learned a great deal about casting methods and engineering generally. During this time his uncle had contracted to manufacture a number of automatic illuminating gas machines for the Drake Company of Boston. These were extremely important items in that day. Maxim made a study of the machines and was responsible for many improvements in them. As a result of this work the uncle determined to undertake the production of an improved version of the Drake machine. While it was in the course of preparation for manufacture, young Maxim developed an even better type! As a result the uncle took personal umbrage at his nephew and discharged him, apparently on the theory that Hiram should have had his second thoughts first.

Maxim went to Boston where he entered the employ of Oliver P. Drake whose basic business was instrument manufacture. He worked for him through the period of the closing days of the Civil War.

The Drake automatic illuminating gas machine on which he worked led directly to a number of other inventions of considerable importance in their day.

One outgrowth of the contacts made in the course of this work was the development by Maxim of the first successful automatic fire extinguishing system of which we have any knowledge. In response to a request from one of their Boston customers, Maxim developed an automatic sprinkler alarm which would shower water down on an area where the fire was burning and also sound an alarm in the fire house giving the exact location of the fire position.

The installation worked perfectly, but in spite of it Maxim was unable to interest other building owners in using it.

He did take out patents on the system. It is one of ironies of his business life that only after the patent had expired was the principle fully seized upon. Today practically all such sprinkler systems are based on the principles so early evolved by young Hiram Maxim.

His experience with trying to market the fire extinguisher system and the cost of patents led him directly to an attempt to sell his patentable ideas to other concerns rather than to invest in them himself.

At this point we see that he learned greatly from his sour business experiences. He proceeded to associate himself with Mr. A. T. Stewart, then one of the wealthiest men in the country. Together they formed the Maxim Gas Machine Company at 264 Broadway, New York City. From Stewart he received contracts to provide lighting systems for Stewart's mills and a hotel in New York City. By this association he was able to eliminate the problems of selling his ideas or his products. He proved the American truism that there is no substitute for capital.

About this time, however, electric lamps were becoming widely known and Maxim saw that the use of the illuminating gas system was on the wane. He turned therefore directly to the production of electric bulbs using carbon filaments. As a matter of record, the first electric lights to be used in New York City were those installed by Maxim's Company for the Equitable Insurance Company at 120 Broadway, the building wonder of its day.

As a result of this installation people from all parts of the country flooded into New York to see the new marvel. Out of this interest Maxim developed a rather amusing sideline which still produced money. Only direct current was used at the time. As people stood around watching the lighting equipment many had their watches magnetized and stopped. Maxim produced a machine to de-magnetize watches and charged one dollar for the service! The business came to take a great deal of his time. He patented the machine he had developed and then offered it to watchmakers and jewelers. Until the introduction of the alternating current, these de-magnetizers were still big money makers for many jewelers.

His next venture was with the United States Electric Lighting Company where he received the then very large salary of $5,000.00 a year. He gave himself the title of Engineer, one to which he was very well entitled though no school had granted it to him and he had no formal education to warrant such usage.

He was sent to Europe on a trip to attend an exhibition dealing with the electrical industry then being held at Paris. This was in August, 1881.

When he returned home the electrical items on which he reported created such a stir that he was assigned the task of preparing literature and explanations covering all electrical appliances and data of which he had any knowledge. He searched both the French and the Belgian patent files thoroughly in preparation of this manuscript. The resulting data was of tremendous value to the United States Electric Lighting Company in later years when it was utilized to defend against law suits for infringement.

His next trip was to London where he went to reorganize the British subsidiary called the Maxim-Weston Company. While he and other American inventors were primarily interested in electricity, Maxim found that Europe was interested basically in arms. As a friend of his, also an electrical engineer, said according to Maxim "Hang your chemistry and electricity. If you want to make a pile of money, invent something that will enable these Europeans to cut each others throats with greater facility."

After a visit to Vienna where he again saw the European interest being exhibited in rapid fire weapons, he turned his attention to the development of a new device in this field.

He tells us himself that his original idea for recoil operation of a weapon came as a result of some target shooting he did with an old Springfield .45-70 rifle years before.

The recoil of this monster left his shoulder black and blue and the thought came to him "Cannot this great force, at present merely an inconvenience, be harnessed to a useful purpose?"

Characteristically he filed the thought away. Characteristically, too, in due course he made use of it.

His examination of the European attempts at machine arms, all of which were operating on mechanical principles, convinced him that a single barreled arm, recoil operated, would be the answer to military requirements.

Maxim drew heavily on the toggle lock of the Henry-Winchester rifle and on the general design of the American Gardner mechanically operated machine gun for his automatic design. But the basic principle of recoil operation was his. So was the basic principle of gas operation, often erroneously credited to John M. Browning. Browning was the first to use the gas principle successfully, however. Maxim concentrated on the successful recoil operation.

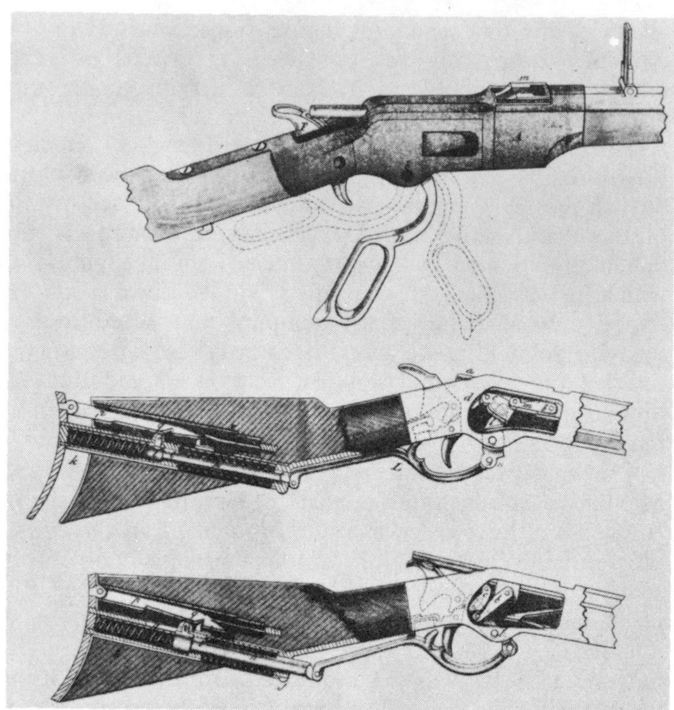

Gun as modified by Maxim to produce semi-automatic action. This design was produced in prototype but was not put into general manufacture. This weapon was not produced in quantity.

He turned his attention to the matter of making a standard lever action Winchester 1866 rifle operate through use of recoil. He attached a movable butt plate with a spring support on the stock of his Winchester. He arranged a series of jointed levers connecting it with the lever triggerguard.

The recoil driving the piece back and compressing the spring between the weapon itself and the butt plate operated the levers to open the triggerguard lever. This action of course ejected the empty case and cocked the rifle. The reaction of the now compressed spring under the butt plate at the end of the recoil action forced the arm ahead, and working through the compound levers closed the action on the chambered cartridge ready for the next trigger pull.

This was the first truly successful automatic functioning of any firearm of which we have evidence.

This epochal development occurred in 1883. It achieved tremendous attention throughout Europe. It was applied to many Turkish Winchester .44's, specimens of which are occasionally encountered in arms collections abroad.

In 1884 Maxim was granted his first basic patent. This covered a recoil operated lock breech system and was applied to machine guns. From it was evolved many of the important items which followed.

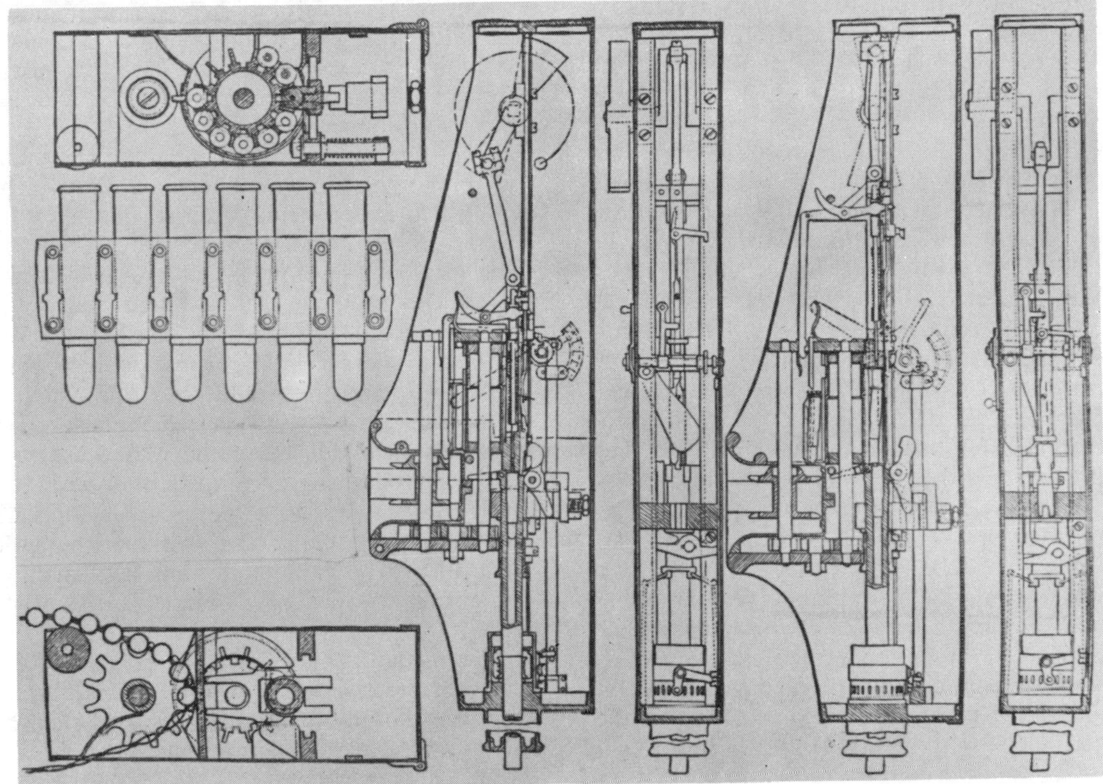

Drawings from Scientific American Magazine in 1884. The Maxim Gun basic mechanism has changed very little through the years.

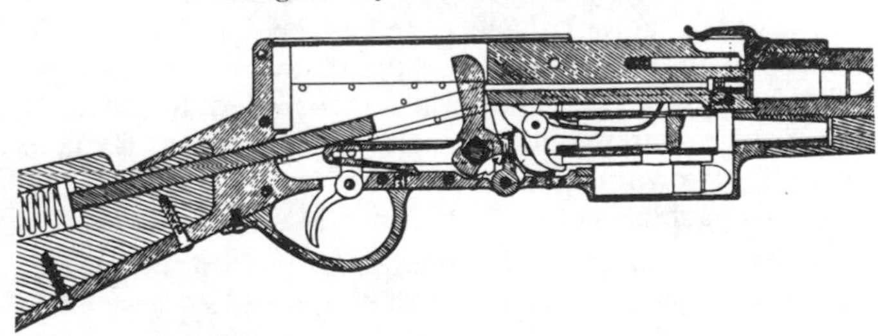

Early automatic rifle developed by Maxim. This weapon was not produced in quantity.

One of his early developments is a fully automatic rifle loaded from a revolving magazine based on the Roper system which was then being tried in repeating shotguns in the United States. A study of the drawings of this arm are of interest. They show positioning of the recoil spring in the butt of the rifle, much as in the common practice in some of the world's finest lightweight automatic and semi-automatic arms—rifles, shotguns, and machine weapons.

While Maxim invented several automatic rifles and automatic pistols in the course of his career, none of these was ever manufactured commercially. His entire successful developmental progress centered around the machine gun. It is to that field we must turn for most of our essential observations on his firearms developments, though his principles were exploited by others in lesser arms.

Maxim began experimental development of a machine gun at a small plant at 57 Hatton Gardens, London. Among the equipment he used was a new Browne and Sharpe milling machine recently imported from America, an item which itself had been developed primarily in relation to gun manufacture. He proceeded to develop all the tools for building the necessary parts, all the holding fixtures, jigs and gauges. The one thing he would not undertake to produce personally was the barrel; barrels were purchased.

The ability, genius, and hard work poured in by Maxim at this point is difficult to imagine. If one remembers that he had no guideposts, since he was operating in an entirely new field, one gathers some little insight into the tremendous problems he faced and overcame despite warnings from "experts" that he could not possibly succeed. He operated in the face of such criticism and foreboding at all times during his life, constantly upsetting the experts in the field.

When his first experimental model was ready for testing, he used a .45 caliber British Gatling gun barrel. Placing six cartridges in the feedway, he discharged them all in about half a second.

From this he knew that his principle was sound and he proceeded to develop working drawings and to lay out methods for actual manufacture of both models and production arms.

While his experiments were made with an orthodox vertical feed, he soon realized that continuous fire with formal systems of this sort would not be practical in automatic arms. Thereupon he developed the cartridge belt feed which was the deciding factor in long firing records with machine arms.

Maxim by this period was well aware of the danger

of demonstrating an arm before it was fully tested. He produced several handmade weapons before he released any press notices. Many of these were passed over with amusement by the British press which was generally skeptical of the statements that a single barrelled arm could possibly load and fire itself by recoil energy at a rate of six hundred rounds a minute as Maxim claimed.

However, his Royal Highness the Duke of Cambridge visited the shop to see a demonstration. He was very much impressed. As a result of this visit, important people in London generally traveled to Hatton Gardens to see demonstrations of this amazing new arm. Fashion followed the leader then as now.

On the advice of Lieutenant General Sir Andrew Clarke, Inspector General of Fortifications, Maxim proceeded to develop a system of parts so designed that they could be withdrawn from the mechanism without the use of tools. As a result he developed components which permitted change in case of breakage of practically any part in six seconds.

So sound was the original design that very little has been done to alter any basic features of the Maxim since the day of its introduction! Its modern version known as the Vickers differs very little except in styling and weight reduction and in the fact that the locking action of the toggle is inverted.

The principle of short-recoil operation itself is very simple. The bolt is locked to the barrel at the instant of firing. They recoil together customarily for a distance of about three-quarters of an inch. At this point the barrel travel is halted. The action is unlocked through movement of the toggle and the lock mechanism continues to the rear to extract, operate the feed mechanism, and compress the recoil spring for returning the action to battery and for firing the next round. The "toggle" system is like the human knee operation.

Maxim utilized a canvas belt based on that used by sportsmen to carry 333 cartridges. This belt was seven yards long. It had a clip device on the end to attach another loaded belt to give continuous sustained fire. Maxim's feed mechanism pulled the belt through the action automatically.

This first model was also equipped with an external rate control and firing arrangement which was later discontinued.

We must remember that Maxim was pioneering at this point, both in design and usage. The military itself had no conception of what could be done or even what was wanted in the field. Therefore, he had to develop the arm for use under practically any type of conceivable military situation. An indicator on the quadrant scale on the side of the gun gave the position for the selector at which the gun would fire at the rate of one round per minute. Moving the selector to the rear increased the rearward travel until a rate of six hundred rounds per minute could be achieved.

It was possible to fire in single shots or in bursts of ten, twenty, or one hundred per minute. The selector could also be set to maintain continuous fire at fast or slow speeds.

One of Maxim's ideas here was that should the gunner be killed, the gun would continue to function if so set until the cartridge belt had been exhausted. In actual practice this has never proven to be a desirable feature, so it is no longer encountered.

The rate of fire regulator was a simple hydraulic oil buffer system, modifications of which have been applied to many recoil systems since then.

Maxim also experimented with a drum type of magazine. It soon developed that the belt feed was far superior. He even adapted the belt feed to an automatic rifle intended to be fired from the shoulder, a device which did not prove practical because of belt-snarling.

At this period he produced a rifle which was intended to operate on a principle which has never been fully exploited, nor fully explored. The case was corrugated to permit of a slight elongation of it at the instant of firing. Such a system of course would permit the operation of an automatic arm without the utilization of a gas port or trap and without any movement of the barrel, yet permit the use of a simple lock and powerful cartridges.

The metallurgical knowledge of his day did not permit this system to operate properly. It is entirely possible, however, that in our present advanced stage of technology the principle might again be investigated for certain types of automatic weapons.

In the period from 1883 to 1885 Maxim filed patent specifications on just about every conceivable system under which automatic fire might be produced. The results of his tests were followed avidly in Europe. Mauser, Mannlicher, and others proceeded to intensify their own research into the field. And some years later John M. Browning developed the first successful gas-operated machine gun on an earlier Maxim principle.

To Maxim must be credited not only the short recoil system found in so many of the world's finest automatic arms today, but also such developments as adjustable head space (which controls safe operation of the arm); the accelerator (to transfer energy from the halted barrel during recoil to the bolt assembly); T-slot extractor, such as we find in all our Browning machine guns; and the special ejector system. Most guns throughout development all over the world have utilized one or more of these principles. None have particularly been improved since Maxim introduced them.

The first Maxim was designed for a black powder cartridge of its day. In later years it has been built to handle practically every type and caliber of rifle cartridge made in the world as well as a great many types of artillery ammunition. The basic mechanism has remained unchanged through the years. Only cooling systems, methods of mounting, weight, and fire control systems have been altered as required by different cartridges, different usages intended, and improved metals.

The British Government gave Maxim his first order for machine guns in 1887. The order was for three guns for test, and though they passed all tests provided by the Government, the Maxim was not officially adopted.

In the same year 1887 the inventor made a trip to

Switzerland where he entered his gun in competition with the Gatling, the Nordenfelt, and the Gardner, all being mechanically operated as true "machine guns."

Maxim's production guns were made by Albert Vickers, a steel manufacturer at Crayford, Kent. This relation between Maxim and Vickers continued to their mutual benefit and eventually evolved into the present "Vicker's gun" after the Maxim patents expired.

All Europe by then was awake to the desirability of a machine arm. Tests were conducted at Spezzia in Italy in competition against the Nordenfelt and also in Austria.

Archduke William, Field Marshal of the Austrian Army, was tremendously impressed with the demonstration. During the test British-made cartridges were used, of course. The Austrian officers desired to have a model tested with their own cartridge. In spite of the importance attached to the tests, Maxim still was unable to get a release from the Austrian government to carry a single Austrian service cartridge out of the country. The cartridge was classified as a top military secret by the Austrian brass of that day. In case this seems ridiculous we must point out that the same nonsensical military thinking continues to occur, particularly in our own country. Maxim made a mechanical drawing and took a sample of the brass which went into a case with him to England. The Birmingham Small Arms Company there produced cartridges for the arm. Not being conversant with the Austrian system of cartridge manufacture, they furnished ammunition with considerably less power than the Austrian.

In July 1888 the Austrian Commission conducted experiments with Maxim's guns in Austrian caliber and gave a very favorable report on them. Despite this, however, only a small number were purchased. The Austrians proceeded later to develop the Schwarzlose, an arm far inferior to the Maxim, which we shall discuss later.

Shortly afterwards Maxim tests were made in Germany. The Kaiser visited Spandau Arsenal where tests were conducted in his presence. The arm proved itself a terrific improvement over the Gatling which was operated by four men. The Kaiser was very much impressed by the one- or two-man Maxim operation. He specified that this be the gun that Germany adopt. It remained the basic machine arm of the German forces until the end of War I, and saw much use even in War II.

Later in 1887, Maxim took his guns to St. Petersburg for tests. The Russian military mentality was not as progressive as it is today. They absolutely refused to believe that the gun could operate at the rate of 600 rounds per minute, as Maxim had stated. Apparently the idea of automatic operation was completely unknown to them and they were completely unable to visualize it! Until the gun began firing they insisted that the handle could not be cranked back more than 200 times a minute, believing it had to be worked by hand. When the belt was placed in the gun and the entire belt load of 333 shots fired by recoil forces without stopping, the Russian staff for the first time realized the meaning of a true automatic weapon.

Despite the enthusiasm with which the military now accepted his product, the secret police proceeded to give Maxim a lot of trouble. He was summoned to Police Headquarters and called upon to give a dossier on himself. Talking with an English speaking official, he was very much disturbed to find that their principal interest seemed to be in his religion! He was advised that he could not remain in Russia unless he had a religion. Maxim said he had none. The official advised that Protestant would be the correct denomination. Whereupon Maxim tells us he said "Then put me down as a Protestant. I protest against this whole thing."

Note on Smokeless Powder

When Vieille developed smokeless powder in France in 1885 he accelerated the development of the automatic machine gun tremendously.

Up to that time Maxim, of course, had been compelled to use black powder ammunition in his gun. With black powder practically all the forces of the explosion are produced at the instant of ignition. Pressure drops very rapidly following its peak.

On the other hand, with smokeless powder ignition rapidly reaches its peak but there is a continuing expansion of gas in the bore following the achievement of maximum pressure. This is called "residual pressure." It continues to exert some rearward force for an instant after the bullet has left the barrel. By taking advantage of this continuing thrust after the pressure has dropped to safe limits, it is possible to fire submachine guns and low-power arms with unlocked breech safely; and also to use relatively light-weight locking mechanisms for the more powerful locked-breech machine guns.

This development had, then, a tremendous influence on the rapid development of machine weapons in other countries.

Early Rise of the Machine Guns

Maxim guns were first issued to the British forces in the year 1891. They very rapidly displaced the Gatling guns which had been used up to that time. The Maxim received its first actual battle trial in the hands of troops forming the armed police of the Rhodesian Charter Company in the Matabele wars of 1893-4. A group of fifty infantrymen armed with just four properly-emplaced Maxim guns faced a charge of five thousand of the savage Matabele Zulus. In less than ninety minutes the Rhodesians induced masses of over five thousand spear-armed natives to charge several times. In the course of the various charges, the Maxim gun fire was held until the tribesmen were close in. Over three thousand dead were piled up in front of the British fortifications by these four guns. The next effective use of the Maxim came soon thereafter in yet another British outpost, the Northwest frontier of Afghanistan. In the Chitral campaign there in 1895 the Maxims again stopped fanatical tribesmen attempting to rush the guns. When the British infantry finally charged the positions occupied by the natives they found nobody alive to oppose them.

These were considered police campaigns, however, not

Early Maxim. Marked on receiver is "Maxim Nordenfelt Maxim's Patent 1893. Guns and Ammunition Company, Ltd." Gun at West Point. Mount is for display only. This is typical of the early Maxim gun, which mechanically is relatively unchanged.

truly military. It was in the Sudan that real military effectiveness was first realized, and it was there that foreign military attaches, including the Germans, had their first opportunity to watch the results possible with this new type of arm.

The most effective use was made at Omdurman. This is the campaign in which the then Leftenant Winston Churchill figured in one of the last cavalry charges in British history. At that time, incidentally, Churchill carried one of the new German Mauser automatic pistols, the first time this weapon saw service. British casualties in this battle amounted to less than two percent of the relatively small forces involved. On the other hand over twenty thousand of the ferocious Dervishes were wiped out. Over three-quarters of those slain were officially credited to the machine gunners.

The gunners as yet were not familiar enough with the handling of the weapons to avoid considerable feeding trouble, a fact which makes even more remarkable the terrible effectiveness they showed. The heavy-wheeled mount used with the gun was unsuitable for such campaigns. It became the practice with the British to leave the mount to attract enemy attention and carry the gun to an emplacement. Up to this time, military men generally assumed that the gun could be used only for covering fire in an attack or as a defensive weapon protecting fortifications. It was some time later that the effectiveness of the machine gun as an attack weapon was forced on the attention of the military experts of the world.

In the Boer War the Maxim gun was first used on land by white men against other white men armed with the same terrible weapons. In this instance the Boers were also armed with the new Maxim 37mm "pom-pom."

A special gun was developed by Maxim at the request of the British for a gun to be used against light naval craft.

The British government did not promptly purchase the gun. Instead it was manufactured in England for sale to France. African natives in discussing the arm gave the sounds equivalent to "pom-pom" in attempting to tell what it sounded like. This name stuck to the gun through its continuing use.

The Boers made astonishing use of this new weapon. Since it used smokeless powder, they could use individual shots fired at British artillery positions to get the range without worrying the artillerymen particularly or disclosing position. Once they had the range zeroed in properly, the Boers would then cut loose an entire belt of 37mm cartridges into the area. This tactic was used time after time and was terribly efficient in destroying British artillery groups. The rate of fire of the pom-pom was about three hundred rounds per minute, although the belts normally held only twenty-five rounds because of the large size of the cartridges.

Unlike the British who had been responsible for its development, the French recognized the efficiency of this new Maxim gun and placed orders with the Maxim firm for them, primarily for use with the French navy and for resale.

It was during the Russo-Japanese war of 1904-5, however, that the automatic machine gun really came into its own. For the first time large numbers were used by each side under military conditions. They were grouped in batteries of from six to eight pieces in most engagements. Russia used the Maxim with a high-wheeled carriage for a mount. These proved to be unwieldy in action. They also exposed the gun crews to sharpshooter fire. Therefore the Russians substituted low mounts instead. These proved extremely efficient. They were equipped with shields, incidentally.

The Japanese were armed with a gas-operated gun, the French-made Hotchkiss with which we shall deal later. In the battles between the Russian and Japanese forces, the recoil-operated Maxim proved much the more efficient. German observers of this campaign noted the fact and the German army went into very serious examination and production of the Maxim gun. This was their really terrible infantry weapon at the opening of World War I.

The Japanese in a report after the war stated that at the battle of Hei-Kou-Tai cartridges jammed in the Hotchkisses once in about three hundred rounds as an average. This was considered quite dangerous. However, except for refining the gun the Japanese did relatively little about the design until well toward the end of World War II. The Hotchkiss guns used by them are covered in detail in chapter 32.

Maxim on wheel mount. With very slight modifications this pattern was used by the Russians in both world wars. Also by the Chinese Communists in the Korean War.

It is of historical interest that even the Russian Maxim guns in their newly adopted 7.62mm caliber were made by Vickers Sons & Maxim. The usage initially made in this caliber was at the Yalu River which has become known to every American as a result of our recent Korean troubles. It was here that the desirability of a low mount and a shield to protect the gunners was established by the Russians.

While the British army introduced the Maxim gun in 1891, it is noteworthy that no attention was given to the design in the United States. This was largely due to the fact that oceans at that time constituted a natural barrier and our military saw no need for rapid firing guns of the type. The Germans did not adopt the Maxim, even though they had been very much impressed with its early tests, until 1899. However, from that point on they worked intensively on it as already noted. The Maxim gun designated by them as Model 08 was actually produced at the German government armory at Spandau. This name is often given as generic for machine guns both of this type and others in some quarters in Europe today.

The Spandau was equipped with a very heavy sled mount. The mount was later altered and a lighter one produced at the Erfurt Arsenal. The caliber was the standard German 7.92mm Mauser. The German gun used a belt feed of 250-cartridge capacity.

Maxim demonstrating the light weight of his L. M. G. and Mount. This was one of his favorite photographs.

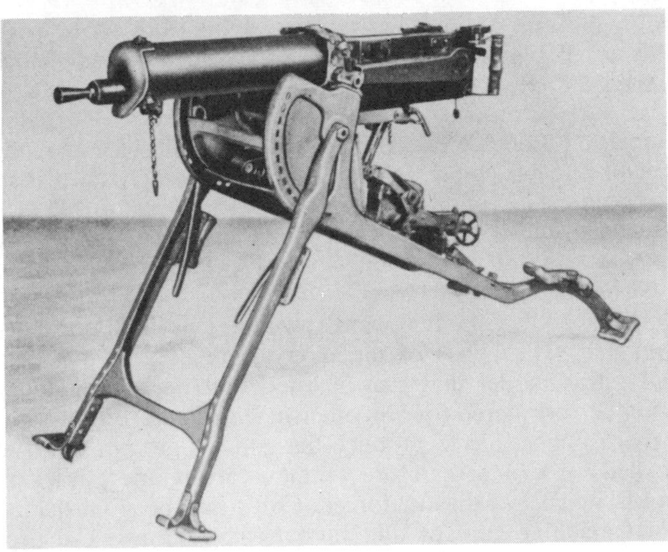

Spandau with folding sled mount. This was a prime German weapon in World War I and saw service in World War II also.

Russia continued, on the other hand, to purchase its guns from Vickers & Maxim. However, it adopted the Russian Sokolov mount. This mount uses two small wheels for field transport and can be equipped with a heavy steel shield to protect the operator. The gun is chambered for the standard Russian 7.62mm rifle cartridge.

When the young Turks deposed Abdul Hamid in 1908, Turkey was so severely disrupted that Bulgaria was able to declare its independence. Other provinces were seized by Austria. A Balkan League was soon formed consisting of Greece, Roumania, Bulgaria, and Serbia. This group in its war against Turkey in 1912 seized all the European Turkish possessions except the city of Constantinople. The basic machine arm used by all these groups was the Maxim. Some even used the pom-pom. The machine guns made in the varying calibers of the different countries involved were in use during World Wars I and II.

American forces during the Philippine insurrection seized some Maxim machine guns in the official British .303 caliber. These had been manufactured as early as 1895. Despite this we as a nation did nothing at that time to purchase any automatic machine guns.

The first official trial given to the Maxim in the United States was in 1888. None were bought. Our Navy did purchase a quantity of Colt 6mm guns which were used in the Spanish-American war.

Due in part to public apathy and Congressional lethargy, our military did little about machine arms until World War I was looming and we found ourselves hopelessly outdistanced by all other major nations.

In 1903 tests were made with the Vickers, the modified Maxim, so named after the Maxim patents ran out and some few changes had been made. The guns were then being built at Hartford by the Colt's Company. These guns were practically identical as to operating mechanism with the one Maxim had shown at the 1888 trials when he used black powder cartridges. The United States Army adopted the model as manufactured by Colt's to use our standard caliber .30 cartridges. It was designated the 1904 model Vickers. In 1916, as a result of tests made against seven competing machine guns, the Army Board recommended purchase of 4600 Vickers guns, M1915. At the time we did not have one machine gun in the country which was actually of a type we would care to use on the European front.

Meanwhile the famous Browning gun had been developed. The heads of the Army were now so impresed with this model that they insisted that no official adoption be considered for any other machine gun. But in 1917 it was impossible to produce the gun for prompt use. We called on Colt's therefore to manufacture more Vickers with which to arm our forces. Colt's had been producing that machine gun for the Russians in 7.62mm. The necessary retooling to produce it for the United States caliber .30 cartridge hindered production and it was July, 1917, before initial deliveries were made. Altogether during the period from then to September 12, 1918, 12,125 of these guns were made. Over 7,000 American Vickers were shipped overseas.

There is a lesson here which we as a nation might learn if we would. It is shown by the figures of World War I, when the Germans at the outbreak of the war had 12,500 of the Spandau-made Maxims ready to throw into service. Remember that we did not have a single acceptable machine gun ready for active military field use then. And at the end of the War we still had very few of our own at the front.

The Germans proceeded after War I to lay the groundwork for replacing the Maxim with another recoil-operated system which would be far simpler and far cheaper to make with the improved technical and manufacturing knowledge and developments. As a result, when War II started the Germans were again equipped with the finest and most advanced type of machine arms, while we in the United States were still armed with the Browning types which we had developed in World War I. Fortunately, experimental shakedowns had made the Browning a fine field weapon by that time, though not as advanced as some others.

So much for the Maxim story here. We may now turn to a consideration of the developments which led to the automatic guns.

Chapter 9. The Evolution of the Machine Gun Principle

THE idea of using rapid fire, volley fire, and concentrated fire, particularly for defensive purposes in military practice, is almost as old as the history of gunpowder itself. Of course it was not until the development of the metallic cartridge that even the manually-operated machine type of arm was feasible, much less the fully automatic type with which we are basically concerned today.

In passing, however, some historical mention might be made of the early items such as the "Orgue" or Organ gun and the Ribauld which appeared as early as the Fourteenth Century.

In general they were a series of barrels or arms positioned together in a frame or on a wheeled carriage. These were intended to be moved in for a direct attack or to be

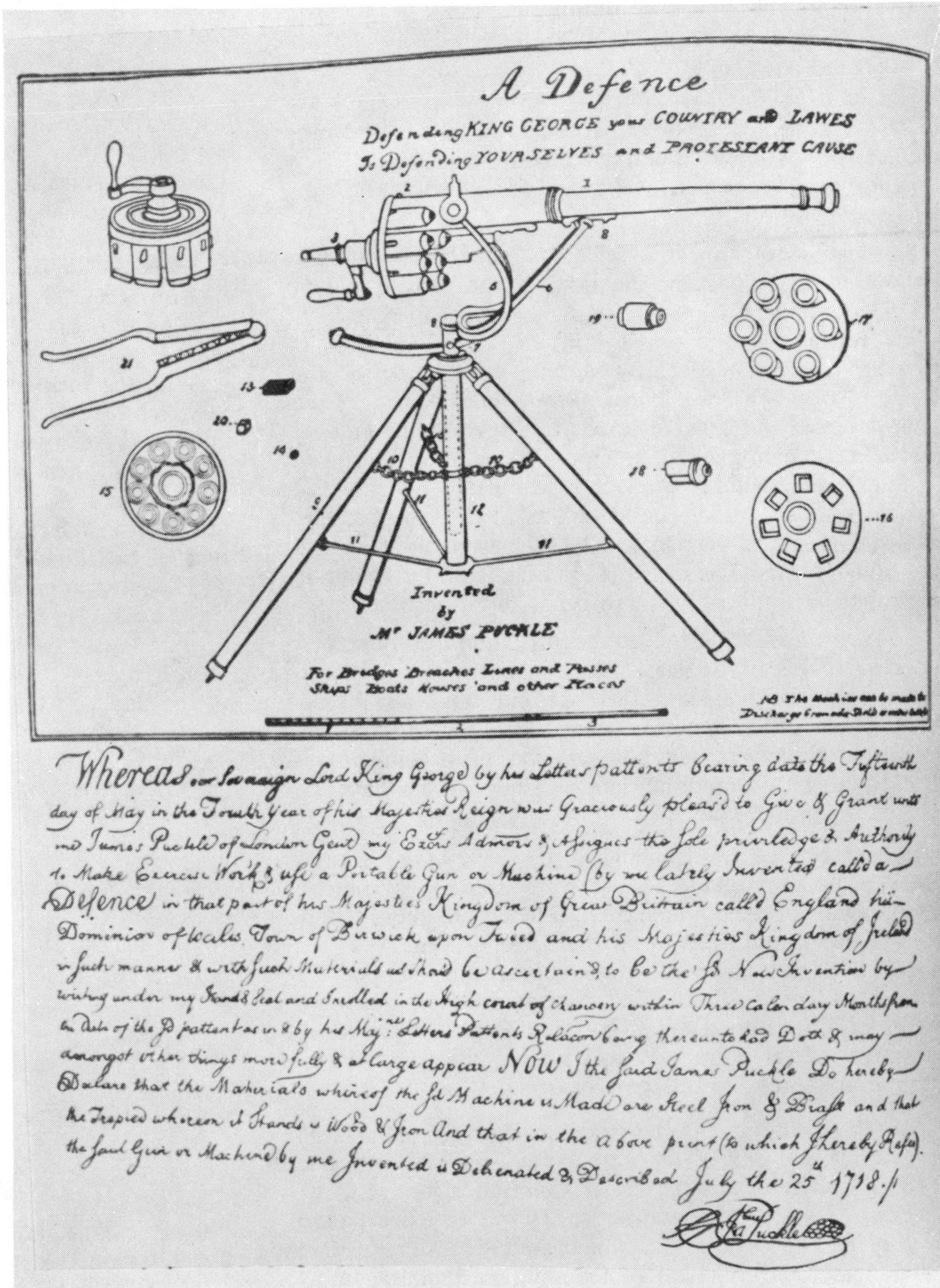

Whereas our Soveraign Lord King George by his Letters pattents bearing date the Fifteenth day of May in the Fourth Year of his Majesties Reign was Graciously pleas'd to Give & Grant unto me James Puckle of London Gent my Exors Admors & Assignes the sole priviledge & Authority to Make Exercise Work & use a Portable Gun or Machine (by me lately Invented) call'd a Defence in that part of his Majesties Kingdom of Great Britain call'd England his Dominion of Wales Town of Berwick upon Tweed and his Majesties Kingdom of Ireland in such manner & with such Materials as should be ascertain'd to be the sd New Invention by writing under my Hand & Seal and Inrolled in the High Court of Chancery within Three Calendar Months from the date of the sd pattent as in & by his Majties Letters Pattents Relation being thereunto had Doth & may amongst other things more fully & at large appear NOW I the said James Puckle Do hereby Declare that the Materials whereof the sd Machine is Made are Steel Iron & Brass and that the Tripod whereon it Stands is Wood & Iron And that in the above print (to which I hereby Refer) the said Gun or Machine by me Invented is Delineated & Described July the 25th 1718./

Jas Puckle

The famous Puckle Design. So far as records show, it was never made in England.

A version of this gun was actually built in Russia about 1850.

placed in front of artillery gunners as a protection against cavalry charges. The Army of Burgundy as early as 1411 listed two thousand special carts having a number of barrels attached thereto for field use.

At the battle of Ravenna, Pedro Navarro, in command of the Spanish forces, positioned thirty of these carts, each mounted with a large number of arquebuses, in front of his infantry to protect them from the charge of the mounted French armored forces. They were most successful.

Leonardo Da Vinci in his life span developed a large number of volley type guns. Some of these fired in banks straight ahead, while others would fire fan-shaped volleys.

Da Vinci apparently even had provided some sort of rudimentary cartridge for loading this device. It is interesting to note that even during the period of our own Civil War very extensive use was made of this system of firing.

For that matter, as late as World Wars I and II, instances were known of arms being set to be fired mechanically in volleys, much on the order of these early Organ guns. Of course, most usage of this sort was from defensive positions.

No history of machine weapons could be complete without at least passing mention of the British patent No. 418 issued on May 15, 1718, to James Puckle. This called for a revolver type of firearm on a mount. Its drawings are very specific. Nothing ever came of the weapon so far as we know. Many claims have been made for it as the progenitor of arms such as the Gatling gun. The revolving block intended to be used as shown by Puckle could hold seven or nine bullets. He specified that they should shoot round bullets in ordinary warfare against Christians; but square bullets when used against the infidel Turks! His drawing even showed his intention to provide cylinders for these types of projectiles.

Toward the close of the last century, qualified observers reported scores of Russian museum pieces at St. Petersburg, Tula Arsenal, and the Kremlin built on Argne, Puckle, and other systems. Many were for cap-and-ball operation. None were actually very old, most being copies of early items from other lands. Thus far we have no verified records of actual use of these types.

In both France and England in the Eighteenth Century, volley arms were made. These were a group of barrels having one common touch-hole. They were mounted in a single stock and fired by a single flint. As many as ten barrels appeared in these arms, which were intended for defense of fortifications. The famous London gunsmith Nock, who developed the Knox Form which is found on the barrel of the former British service rifle, was one of the manufacturers of this type of arm.

Scores of attempts were made to develop multi-firing weapons in the day of the percussion cap. The only one of these worthy of any particular attention is that of C. C. Barnes of Lowell, Massachusetts. He was issued a patent on July 8, 1856 for a gun which suffered from the fact that it was too far ahead of the military thinking of its day and too far ahead of cartridge technology.

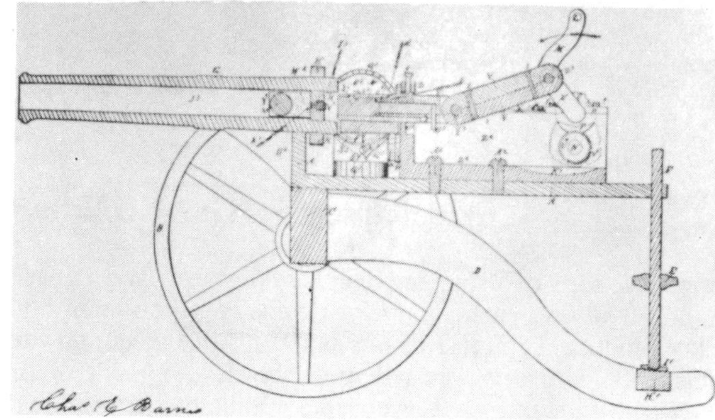

Barnes Gun 1856. From United States' Patent Office drawing. This gun suffered from being designed too early. It was not produced commercially.

This was a crank-operated gun using a special linen cartridge. Of course, the percussion cap had to be fitted separately over the firing nipple. This, however, was done mechanically after the weapon was locked.

The breech lock itself was a toggle joint arrangement. This, too, was in line with the final successful development in its field.

However, the metallic cartridge was on the verge of coming into its own about this time, and nothing much was done about the Barnes gun.

With the introduction of the paper or linen cartridges, in which the powder for propelling and the ball itself were combined so they could be readily loaded down the muzzle end of a chamber, as was done with the original Colt percussion revolvers, several inventors turned their attention to developing machine arms to handle this new type of cartridge.

The most original one was that of Ezra Ripley of Troy, New York. He developed a gun idea in which a series of barrels were grouped about a common axis. A special breech block, made somewhat like a revolver cylinder of the day was loaded with paper cartridges. Of course, percussion caps were then placed over the nipples at the

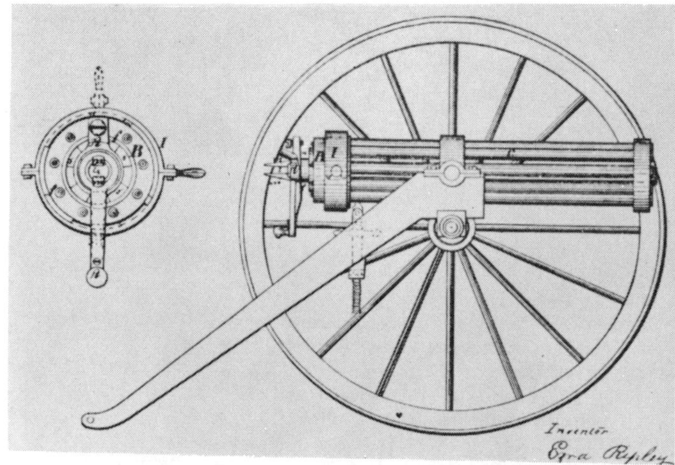

Ripley Machine Gun. From drawings in the United States' Patent Office. This gun was designed in percussion days. The development of the metallic cartridge halted its production.

rear of each chamber, as in common revolver practice in that day. This cylinder was then placed over the breech end of the weapon, the holes lining up with the breech ends of the individual barrels. The breech was then locked into place. An operating crank was provided. When turned it fired each chamber in succession as rapidly as the action permitted. By having on hand a number of these cylinders already loaded, the Ripley might have been capable of use as an early form of the later successful Gatling gun. However, again because of rapid cartridge development, nothing came of this idea. It is of historical interest only, although it does have a bearing on the development of the later multi-barrel machine type arms.

The Billinghurst Requa Battery

During our Civil War, volley guns were used to a considerable extent. One of the best known of these came to be called "the Covered Bridge Gun." The name stemmed from the fact that most of the bridges in those days were covered or enclosed. Roof and sides were provided to protect the floor of the bridge and the supports from weather conditions. Because of this type of construction, the bridges could be easily protected by use of a volley type gun. The best known of these probably is the Requa Battery. This was a .58 caliber gun manufactured by Billinghurst at Rochester.

Billinghurst Requa battery gun. This is the original working model which stood in the window of the Billinghurst shop in Rochester, New York. It demonstrates clearly the system of operation. This gun was percussion fired.

Billinghurst Requa volley gun. The name stems from the fact that it fired all barrels as a single volley.

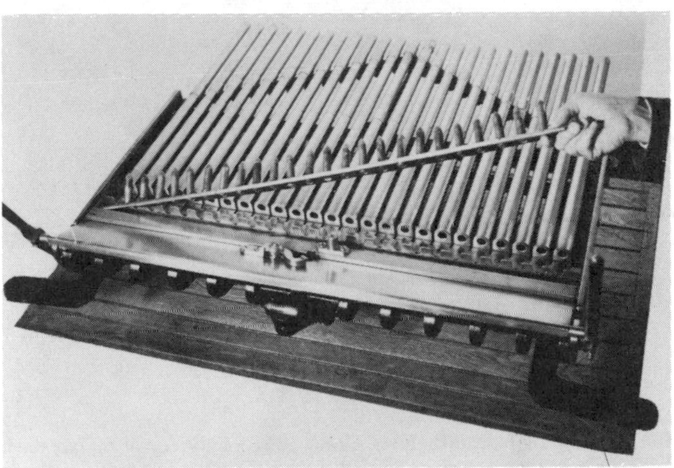

The breech mechanism is shown loaded ready to be inserted. The mount is a display mount used only at West Point. The gun has 25 barrels of .52 caliber. It is loaded with individual steel cartridges.

Twenty-five barrels were mounted flat side by side on a light platform. A sliding breech mechanism was loaded with individual steel chambers. The powder and ball were inserted exactly in the manner used in early days of the flint lock as shown in some of the exhibition pieces still to be found in the Tower of London.

The ignition system was interesting. When the breech was locked into place by its lever the openings or touch holes of the various cartridge chambers were exposed. A train of powder passed the hole in each of these chambers. A single ignition percussion cap ignited this train firing the twenty-five barrels. Only one hammer was used. It was cocked by hand and, when released by pulling an artillery type lanyard, fired all 25 barrels.

This, of course, was a very crude arm. Nevertheless, its barrels could be adjusted to height and width to cover the entrance to a bridge. A three-man crew normally operated the gun. Firing could be done at the rate of seven volleys a minute. The effective range was well over one thousand yards.

The gun's use was confined largely to bridges and fortifications where it could be enclosed, since any dampness which reached the powder train would prevent the firing of the arm. A confederate specimen of this type of gun was used at Charleston, South Carolina. It was of large caliber and weighed some 1300 pounds.

Still another type of our Civil War period is the Ager Coffee Mill gun. Its name derives from the fact that it resembles a coffee grinding machine of that day. It, too, was a hand-cranked machine of .58 caliber. Unlike the Requa it only had one barrel. Cartridges of steel were loaded and fed into the hopper. Operation of the crank pushed the cartridge forward and held it in alignment as the wedge-lock was cammed forward. The barrel was stationary. A detailed report was made on this gun by Major Fosbery of the British Army, quite a noted

Ager Coffee Mill Machine Gun, 1862. Caliber .58. This uses a short muzzle loading chamber or charger capped with a percussion nipple. The loaded chambers were fed into a hopper at the top. As the crank was turned they were fed to firing position, after which the empty charger was ejected to be recovered and reloaded. Barrel, bullet, and charger into which the bullet and powder were loaded are seen below the gun. The mount and shield are those on a specimen at West Point. In use, the gun was normally mounted on a wheeled carriage.

authority of the day and one who had been employed by the government in India to report on machine arms for adoption by the Indian Army.

While tests indicated that the Ager was a serviceable and potentially terrible weapon, the military authorities of the day refused to definitely commit themselves on recommending it. The matter of purchase was even carried to President Lincoln, who in turn refused to authorize purchase unless the military would specifically request it, since he did not pretend to be an authority in this field. The war passed without any action being taken.

The Williams Machine Gun

The first use made of the machine gun in actual battle of which we have any positive knowledge was that of the Confederate States of America during the Civil War. This gun was invented by Captain Williams of the Confederate Army who was from Covington, Kentucky. He developed a very unusual arm in the form of a one-pounder gun having a 1.57-inch bore. It was mounted on a howitzer type limber to be drawn by a horse between shafts. The Confederate Bureau of Ordnance adopted the gun at the outbreak of the Civil War. It was considered a very serious secret weapon at the time.

This gun was operated by turning a crank. It had a single barrel. The crank pulled back and pushed forward the breech block. Self-consuming paper cartridges were dropped into the piece by assistants as the operator turned the crank. This gun could be fired at the rate of about 65 shots a minute. A battery of them proved particularly

Confederate Williams Rapid Fire One Pounder. Probably the first machine gun actually ever to see battle service. Several were used by the famous Pickett's Brigade.

William's Civil War Confederate Rapid Fire Gun. Gun open ready to load.

efficient in battle use on May 3, 1862, at Seven Pines, Virginia. Several of the guns under the control of Captain Williams himself were used by Pickett's Brigade. These arms received considerable use throughout the period of the Civil War.

Vandenberg Volley Gun

This weird item is a massive instrument which was based on the earlier Belgian Montigny Mitrailleuse. The Vandenberg had from 85 to 450 individual barrels! A special breech held cartridges in individual drilled chambers. This could be inserted and screwed into the rear of the barrel arrangement so that the cartridges came in a direct line with the individual barrels. A center charge was ignited by a percussion cap and the entire volley was

Vandenberg Volley Gun. 85 barrels. Caliber .50. Made by Robinson & Cutton of London, England. The breech is being opened to load.

The Vandenberg Volley Gun. Rear view showing mechanism ready for loading.

simultaneously fired. The resulting recoil of course was terrific. The accuracy of the gun was surprisingly good. One British test with a 191-barrel type showed that ninety percent of the volley hit a six foot square at one hundred yards. Its weight, of course, limited its value in land warfare. It was used to some extent experimentally by the British, who intended it for naval use.

Confederate revolving cannon also used in the Civil War. These arms were remarkable developments in the percussion period.

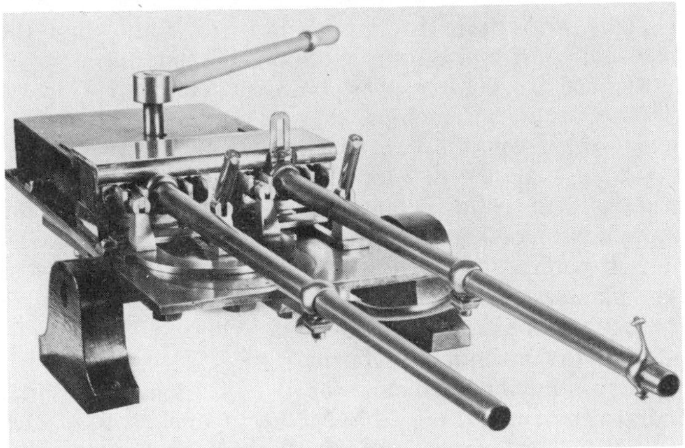

Claxton invention commonly called after its British makers, the Guthrie & Lee Machine Gun. Caliber .69.

It has two barrels. Behind these barrels is a breechblock containing four removable cartridge chambers. There are also four loading troughs with loading pistons. They are located near the rear ends of the barrels on each side. The gun is operated by a long arm which is moved back and forth for a limited travel. This is a percussion fired gun.

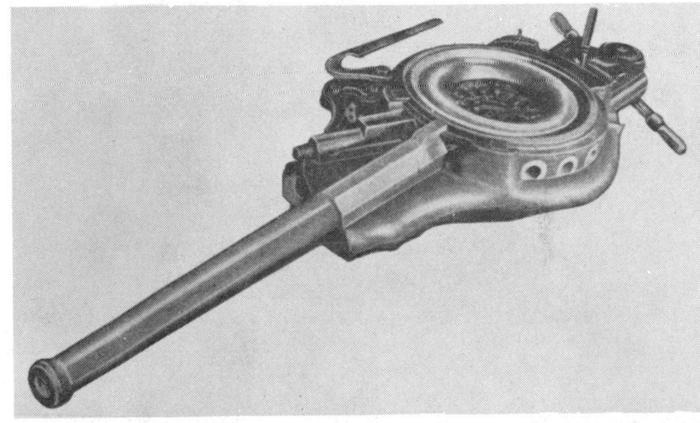

Confederate Gorgas Gun on a variation of the Cochran principle.

Throughout the Civil War the Confederate States showed far more initiative and imagination in design than did the North. There were many other very unusual developments, several of which are to be seen at the United States Military Academy at West Point today. Notable among the types developed was one not unlike that of a common revolver.

We must now move on to one of the great advances in this field, the American-invented Gatling guns.

THE GATLING GUN

The Gatling goes down in history as the first successful mechanical machine gun. It is to be differentiated from the later Maxim which was automatically operated by recoil of the individual cartridges as they were fired.

The Gatling falls into that classification of machine arms where operation by manual effort, usually by hand crank or lever, causes the gun to fire repeatedly, doing all the functions of loading, cocking, firing, extracting, ejecting and reloading. (Note: Later day Gatlings have been motor driven.)

These arms were so important in their day that the historian must make some mention of their inventor.

Richard J. Gatling was born in Hertford County, North Carolina, September 12, 1818. His most notable achievement was the gun which came to bear his name.

Gatling's father developed several machines in connection with cotton planting. His son assisted in the manufacture of some of these mechanical aids, and by himself patented a machine for planting rice. He adapted this planter to handling other grains and he traveled through various cities in Indiana, Ohio, and Missouri offering the invention to farms.

After studying medicine for two years at La Porte, Indiana, he entered the Ohio Medical College where after a year he was given a degree. So far as is known he never practiced medicine. However, he always used the title and throughout his life was known as Dr. Gatling.

Gatling and one of his guns with modified Accles feed. Dr. Gatling in his time thought his weapon was so deadly that the terror it induced would prevent wars.

At that time smallpox periodically swept the country. Legend has it that Gatling studied medicine merely to be able to protect his own family in case of illness. There is no documentation for this interesting story however.

His real vocation was mechanics and invention. In 1851 he developed the idea for a gun which he patented in 1862. He designed it to defend covered bridges and general installations. He seems to have studied both the Ager and the Ripley guns which we have already mentioned. His early model, which was a far cry from the later successful gun, was actually a combination of the fundamental system of the Ager coupled with an improvement of the multi-barrel system of the Ripley.

His early gun used paper cartridges and also could be adapted to handle steel chambers as in other models which we have discussed. The model, while good for its type, obviously could not be too efficient with the type of ammunition available. With the advent of the metallic cartridge he was able to build a practical model of a new revolving barrel design.

After receiving some assurances that his arm would receive military attention if it could pass tests, he raised enough capital to start manufacture of six guns. Before the work was completed, however, the factory was destroyed by fire. The blueprints, all his data, and all the work were destroyed. After a period of reorganization, he raised enough capital to again attempt gun manufacture, this time at Cincinnati, Ohio. He produced twelve new guns. Gatling then hit on the idea of using new copper case cartridges instead of the steel cylinders or paper cartridges he had been using. He utilized the new metallic cartridges of rim fire pattern. Numerous mechanical changes were required in connection with the new ignition system, and this gun really should be listed as number two in his design series.

However, these early Gatlings operated on a principle analagous to the common revolver. There was a gap between the chambers holding the cartridges and the barrels themselves. Gas leakage, of course, was considerable because of the impossibility of keeping a tight joint.

These initial models had six barrels grouped around a central axis. The caliber was .58 rim fire.

Gatling was not a believer in nonsensical secrecy. Realizing that the success of his gun would hinge on general knowledge of its operation and how it could be made, he invited attention by publishing illustrated accounts giving full details of his design. European nations immediately fastened on the subject, but he received practically no support in this country.

In his attempt to have the arm considered by the Chief of Ordnance in Washington, he was refused. Even in Civil War days we had our cloak-and-dagger mentalities. One reason later given for the refusal of the Ordnance Department to even test the Gatling was that confidential reports had been submitted indicating that Dr. Gatling was actually in sympathy with the South; and it was feared that he might have an ulterior motive in presenting the gun which might in some mysterious way be injurious to the Union!

There is little doubt that Gatling's sympathies were with the Confederacy. But official blindness in confusing his politics with his invention cost the Union a heavy toll.

However, the gun was brought to the attention of General Benjamin F. Butler, later to become infamous in Confederate history for his treatment of the women of New Orleans. General Butler was nevertheless one of the most remarkable people of his period. A self-made man, who during his lifetime amassed a huge fortune for

Gatling Machine Gun, Caliber .58. One of the earliest models of the Gatling gun. Made in rifle caliber of the period. The feed is missing.

those days, he later became Governor of Massachusetts. Butler early developed an antipathy to professional militarists as an outgrowth of his inability, in spite of marked superior mental capacity, to get admitted to West Point. He made his way up the military ladder by sheer force of ability and drive.

Butler saw at once the terrific potential of the Gatling. He ordered twelve purchased at a price of $12,000 for the guns on carriages, together with twelve thousand rounds of ammunition. General Butler personally directed the use of these guns during the siege of Petersburg, Virginia, with telling effect. Official policy nevertheless was able to block further purchases.

In 1863 Gatling offered the guns to the French Royal Artillery. The offer was given considerable attention by French personnel but nothing was done about it. In 1870, seven years later, we find the French obsessed with the idea of a "secret weapon" based on the notoriously ineffective Montigny volley type gun. The Gatling might have altered French history.

Gatling in 1865 entered into a contract with the Cooper Firearms Manufacturing Company of Frankford, Pennsylvania, to produce improved models of his Gatling gun. This new model did away with the separate chamber system and incorporated the chambers in the barrel breeches themselves.

This new model introduced a modified bolt and a cam arrangement for performing the functions of loading, firing, extracting, and ejecting. This basic gun is representative of all the successful Gatlings which followed it. While a loader places cartridges in the feed, the operator aims the gun and by turning a side crank fires it. A series of beveled gears turns the main shaft. The barrels, carrier, and cylinder all turn with it. Cartridges drop into the grooves of the carrier from the feed as the barrels are rotated by this action. The bolt, engaging in cam surfaces, is moved forward to push the round into the chamber. A cocking lug on the striker compresses the spring. When released at its high point, the striker is driven forward by the spring to hit the primer and discharge the cartridge.

The bolt starts to the rear as the rotation is continued. The extractor hooks free the empty case and draws it to a point where the face of it hits the ejector. The empty case is thus thrown out of the gun through an opening in the housing.

Each barrel is fired as it reaches the lower right hand position. The cycle of operation of each bolt and its barrel assembly is completed with one revolution, and fire continues as long as the crank is operated.

After a successful Army test in 1864, Gatling was granted a patent on his changes in May of 1865. Tests were run on a new design of one-inch caliber which had been recommended by the Chief of Ordnance. These were made at Frankford Arsenal at Philadelphia. All were highly successful.

In 1867 Gatling contracted with Colt's at Hartford to build 100 guns. These were delivered and all proved eminently satisfactory. The Colt's Company continued manufacture of the Gatling through the life of the gun's existence. The next development was the introduction of a new .50 caliber center fire cartridge to replace the old .58 rim fire. This too was developed into an eminently successful gun. We adopted this 1865 model.

Shortly afterwards Gatling licensed Paget & Company at Vienna and W. G. Armstrong Company in England to manufacture the design. Both produced ten-barreled types to handle the cartridges used by the various governments for which they manufactured them. In addition, some one-inch models were produced with both 6- and 10-barrel types, the latter being of course extremely heavy and intended basically for fortification work. One celebrated test of the efficiency of the Gatling was that conducted at Carlsbad, in 1869. One hundred crack infantry troops with the Dreyse Needle Gun, men who had been trained for volley fire, were pitted against the Gatling gun

The range was 800 meters. The one hundred riflemen and the one Gatling of rifle caliber were to fire the same number of bullets. The soldiers succeeded in making 27% of their bullets hit the target, while the Gatling scored 88% hits. Strangely, this devastating demonstration of the Gatling potential still was not enough to awaken the Prussians in that day to the fact that their Needle gun was already obsolete.

We have already noted the Battle of Plevna in 1877, where American arms in the form of long range rifles and rapid firing Winchester 1866 rifles broke the back of the Russian assault on the Turkish position. Curiously enough, the Russians during that battle were equipped with some Gatling machine guns which they used, however, only for night firing and for use on bridge and approach covers. They had at hand the means to equalize the tremendous advantage the Turks had over them in the way of rapid repeating arms, but failed to recognize the potential of the Gatlings in their possession. The Turks, too, had a few Gatlings, and they made better use of theirs, though they still did not understand all the implications of their use.

The British purchased Gatling guns but insisted that they handle the already outmoded British Boxer cartridge. This, of course, was not suited for machine gun use and the gun therefore was not too efficient. Usage was generally confined to the Navy.

The British used Gatling guns in the Zulu War of 1879. Their firepower proved of tremendous value in stopping charges of hordes of savages, but their liability to jam with the Boxer ammunition then used offset much of their value.

The gun was later improved by the addition of the Accles feed, a drum-type gravity feed much more positive than the vertical type which had been used theretofore. The guns finally adopted by Russia were purchased from Colt's in Hartford. The head of the Russian Commission in 1871 was a General Gorloff. He had the guns chambered for the Russian infantry rifle cartridge, four hundred being made and delivered. He insisted that each one have his name stamped in Russian.

Colt-made Gatling with Accles drum feed.

Colt Gatling with feed removed to show direction of cartridge insertion. Gun is at West Point.

Quite as today, it was just a question of time before the Russians forgot all about the inventor of the gun. The Gatling was later made in Russia's own arsenals. However, it bore there the name "Gorloff." In the Russo-Turkish War, the identical guns, except in different calibers of course, were used to some extent by both forces, as we have noted. The only difference was that the Turks used them under the American name of Gatling, the Russians called them (and still call them) Gorloff's.

From then on until the adoption of the Maxim, the British, too, used increasingly large numbers of Gatlings, even manufacturing them themselves under license.

One ironic note in American history is always brought to mind by any historical discussion of Gatling. This is the famous Custer Massacre. In 1876, when Custer's command was wiped out at the Little Big Horn, his headquarters actually had in its possession four Gatling guns with a rate of fire of approximately 1,000 rounds per minute! These were the perfected types chambered for the .45-70 center fire rifle cartridge, the cartridge with which Custer's troops were equipped. When Custer was surrounded by the Indians, his troops were armed with the single shot cam-locked Springfields (which were still in use, for that matter, at the time of the Spanish-American War). A few Indians had the terrific advantage of firepower from Henry and Winchester rifles which they had bought from traders. Custer had, in the availability of these Gatlings, the solution to any such Indian tactics as those which resulted in the annihilation of his command. No use, unfortunately, was made of the Gatlings and another epic of history goes written on the wrong side of the ledger.

At the time of the Spanish-American War in 1898, Captain John H. Parker, recognizing the value of the Gatling, requested permission to organize a Gatling battery. His immediate superiors refused to permit it. He went directly, however, to his Commanding Officer and received permission to get both the equipment and the necessary skilled men to operate the guns. Parker made most effective use of these during the campaign in Cuba. He took up where General Benjamin Butler had been compelled to stop thirty-six years before at Petersburg, Virginia. To "Gatling" Parker goes much of the credit for developing the ideas which first led to our machine gun tactics.

As the years went on, Gatling worked constantly to improve his device. The introduction of the automatic Maxim, of course, doomed the mechanical principle on which the Gatling operated. However, Gatling was not to be dissuaded. He developed a strip-type feed and an electric motor built into the rear of the gun casing. The motor could be detached and the gun fired by a hand crank if electricity was not available. This and other attempts at power driving the gun gave a tremendous rate of fire, as much as 3,000 rounds per minute. A final development incorporated some actual gas operation. However, although his guns were chambered for the .30-40 Krag and even the .30-06 Springfield cartridge, they were never adopted by the U. S. armed forces.

As a closing note it might be mentioned that in the past few years special applications have again occurred where the mechanical operation of the Gatling system has received attention. In present arms, particularly in the aircraft gun field, it is of military value, being used in the current U. S. 20mm M61 aircraft cannon.

THE MONTIGNY MITRAILLEUSE

In this period when American inventors were introducing the wide range of new rapid fire mechanisms we have mentioned—and hundreds for which we have no space here—European developers generally were blinded to anything but alterations of then-outmoded systems. The one most concentrated on by military and independent designers alike was the "Mitrailleuse."

The name literally means "grapeshooter," the implication being that the system was intended to hurl the equivalent of grapeshot but under directional control. It was just another version of a volley gun.

While the design originated with Belgian Army Captain Fafschamps in 1851, it was actually produced by a brilliant engineer of the day named J. Montigny, also a Belgian.

In 1867 Napoleon III was so impressed with versions of Montigny's Mitrailleuse that he placed it in secret manufacture at the French Arsenal at Meudon. And thus began another chapter in the long history of military misadventure based on undue secrecy. The Montigny in its day duplicated all the nonsense of the Maginot Line of a later day. And with the same result.

The French press of the period really had a field day. The new "secret" weapon had such dread possibilities that none save the initiate might even receive a hint of its nature. Its transport was guarded, its presence covered at all times. The precautions taken in transporting our first atom bomb were amateurish alongside the measures taken by the French to hide the nature and identity of their secret weapon of 1870. All this, remember, in connection with a design familiar to every military observer in Europe for a period of well over a decade! And all this, too, in face of the fact that our own Dr. Gatling had shown his metallic cartridge machine gun at the Paris World's Fair in 1867; that the French had actually taken this gun to Versailles for firing tests; and that the Gatling had proven itself, though it must be admitted that the French Chassepot cartridge was so inferior that it probably couldn't have been adapted to the Gatling.

When the Prussians launched their attack in 1870, the Mitrailleuse was the laughing stock of most military men in Europe outside of France. The French populace, frightened by the stories of the Prussian Needle Rifle, were lulled into a false sense of security by mysteries which were mysteries only to them.

When the test came the French authorities paid dearly for hoodwinking the people. The first use of the "new" arm was only a skirmish, but the press was fed stories which made it appear that the war had already been won by their secret weapon. Actually the Germans were fully aware of what the gun could and couldn't do, and they merely deployed their infantry so the Mitrailleuse would waste ammunition.

While the French papers continued to report after each engagement that the new weapon had mowed down the enemy in fantastic numbers, the German artillery actually was disposing of them every time they made an appearance. Had the French followed up the occasional successes they had when the guns were employed as infantry support, they might have given a far better account of themselves. Instead, they were considered and used by the French as artillery arms. Before the war ended, some Gatlings as well as other American machine arms reached France, but the secrecy surrounding the Mitrailleuse had blinded the French to the proper usage of such arms, and they played a very small part except for fortified defense use.

And what were these "secret" arms? The Montigny is typical. It consists of 37 separate rifled barrels positioned inside an iron jacket. There is a loading plate provided with holes to receive cartridges to match up with the barrel positions. The plate when loaded is dropped into grooves in the breechblock. A hand crank is turned to drive the breechblock forward against the barrels, the plate providing the firing chambers. The firing mechanism is cocked by the closing of the breechblock, and the cartridge necks are forced into the barrel mouths. The gunner now releases the loading and locking crank and gives his attention to the right hand crank which does the firing. As he turns the firing crank the 37 barrels are fired in succession, the speed depending upon his rate of turning. When the plate is empty it is withdrawn and replaced with a new loaded one.

This secret wonder mounted on an artillery-type carriage weighed with its limber well over two tons. It was a worthy forerunner of the Maginot Line guns which pointed only in one direction, and the other items of French military blindness which originated from confusing secrecy with security. And its results were much the same for the French nation.

THE FRENCH HOTCHKISS CRANK OPERATED MACHINE GUN

The original Hotchkiss machine gun, with which we will deal in passing, is the hand-operated machine type based somewhat on the Gatling. At a later point in this work we shall consider the gas-operated automatic arms made by the Hotchkiss organization. These and modifications were in use in France and in Japan through both World Wars. All gas-operated Hotchkiss patterns were developed after the death of the man whose name they bear.

Benjamin Berkley Hotchkiss was an American. He was born in Watertown, Connecticut, in 1826. He achieved his early knowledge of firearms while working at the Colt's Patent Firearms Company at Hartford. Many of the early improvements in the Colt revolver were accredited to Hotchkiss.

Like practically all great American arms inventors, he received little cooperation from the United States Government, but much attention from foreigners. In 1856 he sold a rifled field piece to the Mexican government. Our Government did later adopt a percussion fuze which he developed for projectiles. While he did much small arms designing off and on throughout his life, it is in the field of light artillery that he is perhaps best known. Only his repeating rifle received any appreciable attention in his own country.

Hotchkiss Revolving Cannon. Caliber 1.5 inch. Developed in 1881. 5 barrels. The gun shown was made outside Paris. It is numbered 596. A shell is shown being loaded into the gun.

Hotchkiss was in charge of the City Arsenal at New York during the draft riots of 1863. He was given this appointment, of course, because of his knowledge of arms.

He went to France in 1867. His improved metallic cartridge case, which had received little attention here, was seized upon by the French to replace the combustible paper types used in the Chassepot rifle. However, the military failed to rush production until too late for use in their dire need in 1870.

Hotchkiss organized a manufacturing company in France in 1875 at St. Denis, and proceeded to produce his new machine gun there.

This Hotchkiss had five rifled barrels of compressed steel. These are mounted parallel to each other about a central axis. They are held between two metal discs, and they rest in the frame which carries the trunnions. Turning a hand crank at the right side gives the necessary rotation for loading, firing, and extracting. While the gun externally resembles the Gatling in many ways, its design is completely original.

Hotchkiss began manufacture of a 37mm gun for both land and naval purposes. By 1884 the business had developed to such a large extent that additional works for production were necessary. Manufacture was begun by Armstrong in England.

The French plant sold over 10,000 cannon and 4,000,000 rounds of ammunition to the French Navy. During the period of its general use it was at one time or another employed by all the major nations in connection with naval operation. Details of its use will be found in the literature of Austria, Denmark, England, Germany, Holland, Italy, Russia, Turkey, and the United States.

Hotchkiss died in 1885, recognized and honored as one of the great inventors of his time. He did a great deal to push forward the development of repeating mechanical mechanisms. What is perhaps more important is that he trained the men under him to continue the operation of the plant after his demise. As a result, the name of Hotchkiss continues even to this day in connection with the gas-operated arms developed by his highly trained staff after his death.

It is France's misfortune that in recent times the effort, energy, and intelligence of the once-great Hotchkiss group has been allowed to diminish. Its history is considerable.

OTHER AMERICAN MECHANICALLY OPERATED MACHINE GUNS

Among the machine arms to appear in this general period must be mentioned the American Gardner. It had a certain degree of acceptance in Great Britain, though in spite of very successful tests in the United States we did nothing with it.

William Gardner was a Captain in the Northern army during the Civil War. He designed and built his original gun in 1874. He was unable to finance it. He turned manufacture over to Pratt & Whitney at Hartford, Connecticut on royalty. Francis Pratt had been a master mechanic at the Colt's plant in Hartford and knew not only design but also production techniques. Within a year he actually was producing the gun in the Pratt & Whitney factory for military sale.

This organization was the parent firm of the great Pratt & Whitney group which today is so noted for its aviation engine developments in the United States.

The Gardner gun was composed of two barrels placed parallel to each other, about an inch-and-a-quarter apart. They were housed in a single casing. Loading, firing, and ejection were all handled by turning a crank as in the Gatling system. In all crank-operated arms accuracy is not too good, partly because of torsion produced as the crank is turned. Yet the system was an efficient one in its era.

The Gardner was purchased in some quantity by the Royal Navy to supplement its Gatling guns. It was simpler, cheaper, and easier to transport. Some were used by British Navy land groups in the Sudan and

American Gardner Machine Gun, Model 1879, Caliber .45.

Upper Nile campaigns in 1884 and 1885. Later attempts were made to convert the system to a belt feed operation using smokeless powder cartridges, the modification being popularly known as the Robertson, after the British modifier. However, the approach of the recoil automatic

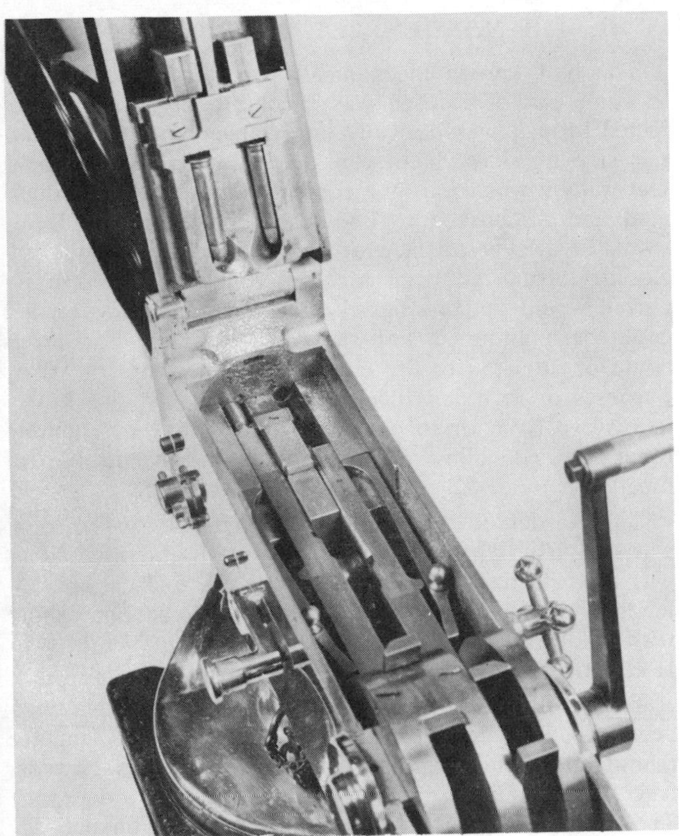

Gardner American Machine Gun, Model 1879. Showing method of feed, breech open. Barrels are hinged open. This system had several meritorious features.

operation of Maxim doomed all such hand-operated attempts at machine arms.

Another gun externally resembling the Gatling, but otherwise quite different, was the Lowell, manufactured at the city of that name in Massachusetts. It was designed by De Witt C. Farrington in 1875.

Lowell Machine Gun from a contemporary drawing. Barrels are hinged open. It was used to some extent and for developmental purposes by the Russian Navy.

Our Navy gave some attention to this unusual gun. The Russian Navy also purchased twenty of them. As an interesting aside, it must be noted that the State of California purchased three for protective use in its prisons. The city of Cincinnati, which had a very forward-looking police organization in those days, also purchased one for possible riot use. However, nothing of any true importance came from the development because its mechanical system had already been superseded by more developed design. In recent years the Italian designer Alfredo Scotti utilized a variety of the Lowell's 3-barrel system in a gas-operated machine gun. (The principle is that of having three barrels so mounted that as one overheats the next can be brought immediately into position to sustain fire.)

The Wilder gun developed in 1876 at Hillsborough, New Hampshire, by Elihu Wilder was another instance of a gun coming too late to be of practical value. Wilder arranged his barrels in a half-circle instead of in the full circle of the Gatling type. This permitted use of a smaller number of locks and smaller parts, making for a far more reliable weapon. However, the inventor turned his attention to adapting the system to a 37mm gun which,

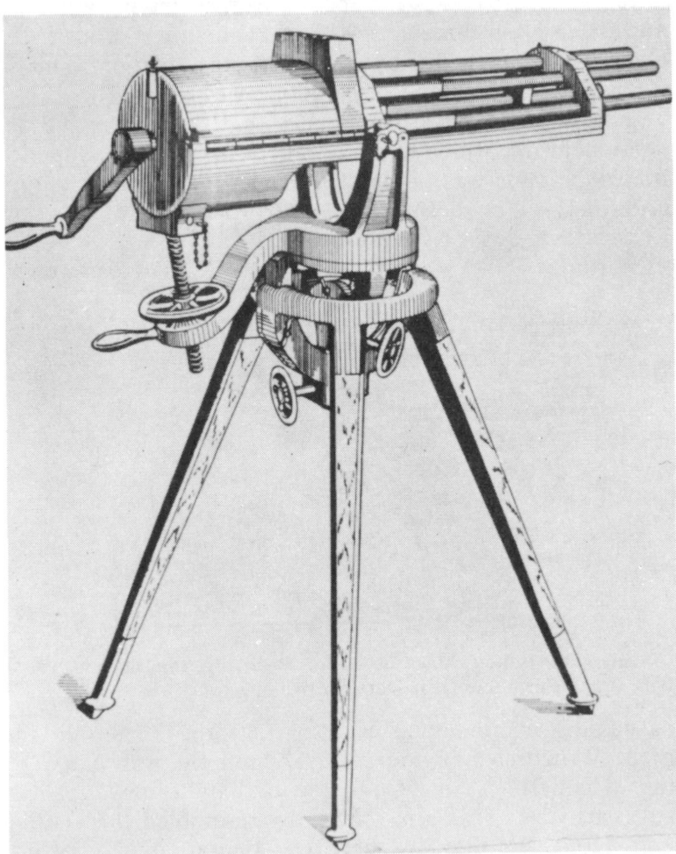

American Wilder Machine Gun. From contemporary drawing.

had it been produced, might have been a tremendous competitor for the Hotchkiss. Wilder died before completing this model and the Wilder gun never was put into production.

Some passing mention must be made of the "McLean Peace Makers." These were a highly publicized group of promised weapons offered by a Scotch gentleman who was quite a medicine man in his day. None were ever made. Barnum probably took lessons from McLean.

McLean made a fortune in the patent medicine game. And then he met one Myron Coloney of New Haven, Connecticut, a gentleman who considered himself an inventing genius. In fact he admitted it! These two men proceeded to issue extravagant pamphlets (and to offer stock for sale in ventures) describing an amazing range of alleged gun developments, none of which were ever actually developed, but all of which laid the groundwork for our modern Buck Rogers.

In a 200-page brochure these gentlemen offered such little items as a 48-shot repeating pistol—a 128-shot self-loading rifle—machine guns capable of firing 2,000 shots a minute and sweeping an area of 6 miles—and a host of other fantastic items rivalling our H-bombs.

Amazingly enough, out of this tremendous hodgepodge of impossible promises, McLean actually presented some drawings which did have an effect on the development of firearms, though he personally did nothing in this connection! One of his illustrations shows a cannon with a tubular feed. To produce the proper type of operation, the artist showed the cartridges having no rims and having an indentation (or cannelure) around the heads of the cartridge cases to permit extraction! This in a day when the rimmed case alone was known!

This depiction of a true rimless cartridge case, the development of which did so much to produce superior machine arms, was a direct influence on actual weapons and ammunition designers in the production of the rimless cartridge case as we use it today.

Fortune Bailey's machine gun of 1874 is worthy of passing comment, as it is part of the history of the great Winchester organization. A sample was made by the Winchester Arms Company to handle a .32 caliber rifle cartridge. This arm externally resembled the Gatling gun. However, it was a belt feed operation of very unusual design. The amazing feature in the belt feeding was that the rounds were never removed from the belt as it passed through a conveyor and was fed through the gun for firing. Again, although this arm had a number of features which would have made it an extremely important weapon some thirty years earlier, it too was doomed by the recoil operation which at that time was getting worldwide attention.

American Bailey Machine Gun. Probably the first to use a belt feed. From contemporary drawing.

THE NORDENFELT MACHINE GUN

The best known mechanically operated machine arm to come out of Europe was the Nordenfelt. In its perfected form it was basically an arrangement of four barrels side by side which were fed by individual hoppers. Generally it was fixed on a conical mounting. It was operated and discharged by movement backwards and forwards of a lever at the rear end. The arm was fully enclosed. It suffered from the fact that any stoppage incurred would put one barrel out of action. However, fire could be maintained with the remaining barrels. Barrels could be adjusted to fire either simultaneously for volley purposes or in quick succession. They could also be set to diverge from or to converge upon a line of sight, in other words to allow a dispersion or a concentration of fire.

The Nordenfelt is of interest in that one version of it was the first lightweight machine arm to be used. This was a single barreled British version in rifle caliber, intended basically for use by the Navy to be put ashore with landing parties much in the line of our World War II commando tactics.

The actual inventor of this system was a Swedish engineer named Heldge Palmcrantz. He was unable to finance manufacture and therefore interested a fellow Swede, who was then in the banking business in London, one Thorsten Nordenfelt. This man agreed to finance the gun provided it carried his name.

The Nordenfelts were manufactured in varying calibers and styles with numerous barrel systems. The light versions used a lever toggle locking system which Palmcrantz had developed, but the heavier guns for shells were fitted with dropping block mechanisms. The Nordenfelt saw relatively limited service, since its day was numbered by superior designs.

Note

As will be seen from this outline, most of the truly efficient developments in the mechanically-operated machine gun were of American origin. However, it is also noteworthy that without exception all designers and inventors had to turn to Europe for financial support. They were indeed prophets without honor in their own country.

All these figures, together with still later developers such as Borchardt and Browning, were compelled to go to European plants where they were able to utilize their inventive genius. In general, many of these inventors took with them skilled mechanics from the United States. They and their knowledge of productive methods, as well as of American-made equipment, did much to develop armaments abroad at a time when we ourselves paid no attention to such development.

Definitions

The general term "machine guns" is loosely applied to a wide variety of automatic arms. In the interest of clarity, the general characteristics of the various classes must be understood.

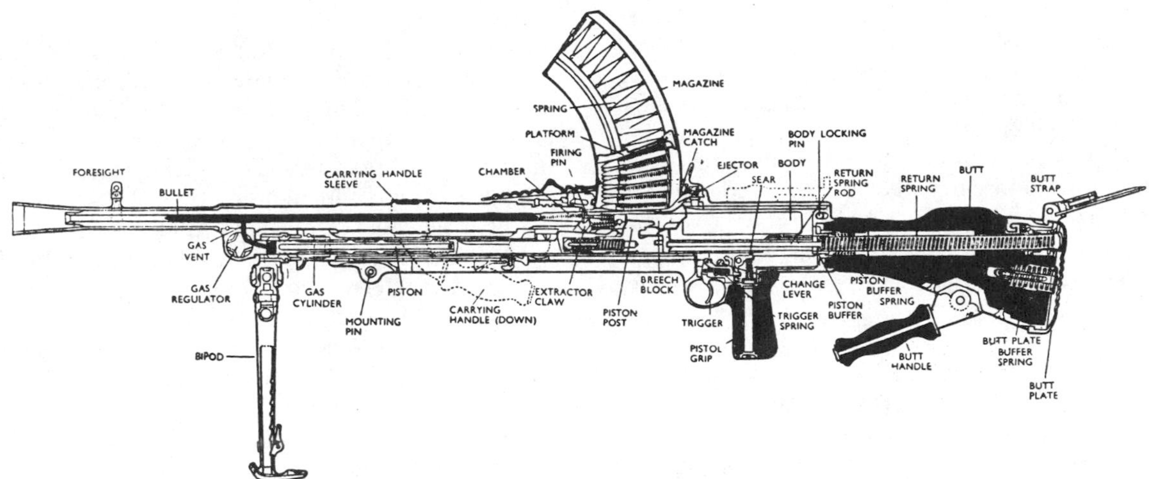

Sectionalized view of British Bren Gun. This gun evolved from the Czech ZB.

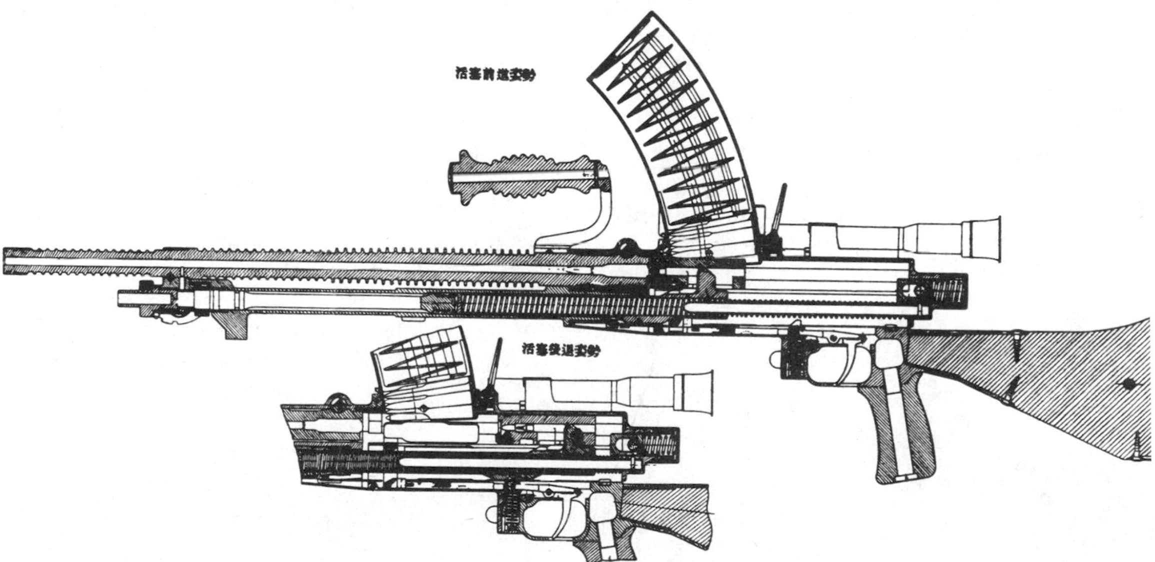

Sectionalized drawing of representative World War II Japanese light machine gun fed from top mounted box.

Light Machine Gun. This term customarily designates a weapon which can be fired full automatically and which may or may not be furnished with a device to permit semi-automatic or single shot fire. The light machine gun normally fires the same cartridge as the military shoulder rifle of the using nation, whether bolt action or semi-automatic. The normal weight of this weapon is from 15 to 30 pounds. It is customarily fitted with a butt-stock like a standard rifle and is intended normally to be fired from shoulder support while in prone position. The front end is commonly supported when firing by a mount, usually a folding two-legged steel design. Like everything in firearms there are exceptions—the Germans in World War II adapted their LMG's to special quadruple mounts, etc. as shown in chapter 26.

The light machine gun is capable of use by a single man under emergency conditions. Normally, however, it is operated by at least a two-man crew, the gunner and an ammunition carrier who feeds the weapon. Furthermore, it must be recognized that this form of weapon uses ammunition at such a high rate under combat conditions that it really requires additional support in the form of reserve ammunition carriers or providers.

The feeding system may be any of the types found in

A representative Light Machine Gun. The Russian Degtyarev in field action. Note drum shape magazine.

other machine guns, though the most common types utilize detachable steel box magazines. Drum feeds are common in some European designs, notably German and Russian, but the belt feed is uncommon, normally being encountered only in designs where quick barrel change is a part of the design of the arm. This is because of the rapid overheating under continuous fire from a belt feed with its great ammunition carrying capacity in comparison to the box magazine patterns.

Operation may be either gas or recoil, and in some occasional experimental designs may even be blowback.

Machine Rifle. This term is often used to designate a light machine gun. It is all a matter of national terminology. In the United States the common form is the "Browning Automatic Rifle" or BAR. The designation automatic comes from the fact that the arm can fire in full automatic operation by merely holding back the trigger with the selector in the proper position. The characteristics under this name are the same as those given under the designation Light Machine Gun. At times the name is also applied to the post-War II forms of shoulder rifles having full-auto switches—the true "automatic rifles."

In general, the designation "automatic rifle" or "machine rifle" in the past was commonly employed with arms such as the Browning Automatic Rifle or its European equivalents. Today it is not generally used.

Weapons classed as machine rifles and light machine guns have the advantage of very high mobility. This together with their ease of handling by one man in an emergency make them the perfect weapon for frontline operations. Since the weight and bulk are low, these guns must be fired in bursts, and are not suitable for sustained firing except where extra barrels are readily available for interchange. Regardless of the firing rate, it is actually not practical to fire much more than 100 per minute from the light machine gun except in case of direst emergency.

Medium Machine Gun. The "medium machine gun" (commonly referred to merely as "machine gun") uses the same rifle cartridge as the light machine gun.

The medium machine gun of modern design weighs between 25 and about 60 pounds. While it has a firing rate of 500 rounds per minute or more, in actual usage it normally will deliver a maximum of about 250 rounds per minute from belt feed. Clip or drum feeds holding fewer cartridges provide substantially lower fire volumes.

Even when several interchangeable barrels are available, a gas-operated medium machine gun is seldom capable of sustained fire of more than 6,000 rounds per hour actually delivered. The water-cooled varieties on the other hand have been known to fire up to 15,000 rounds per hour, because of their more efficient but far bulkier and heavier cooling systems.

The medium machine gun is normally mounted on a folding portable tripod. This arm also, of course, requires a gun crew to sustain it, or even to put it into action, since the minimum handling crew must be one man for the tripod, one the gun, and at least one for ammunition. Once the gun is fixed, of course, it can in emergency be operated by the firer alone.

American Johnson Machine Rifle of World War II.
This too is a representative Machine Rifle. It is short-recoil operated. It feeds from a box magazine inserted in the left side of receiver.
The gun was designed and manufactured by Capt. Melvin M. Johnson, U. S. M. C. R.

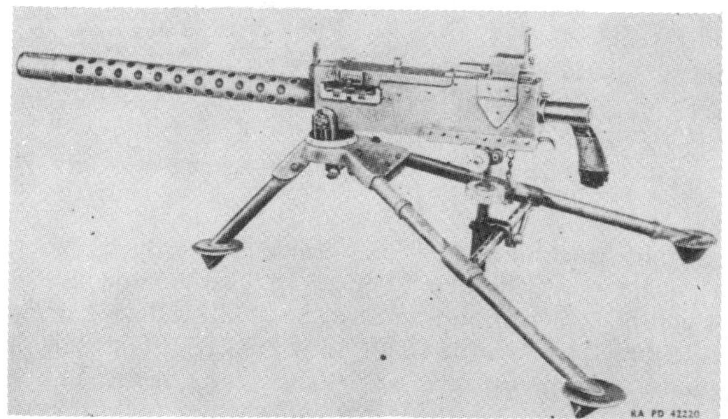

Browning Machine Gun Cal. .30. A typical medium machine gun using the standard rifle cartridge.

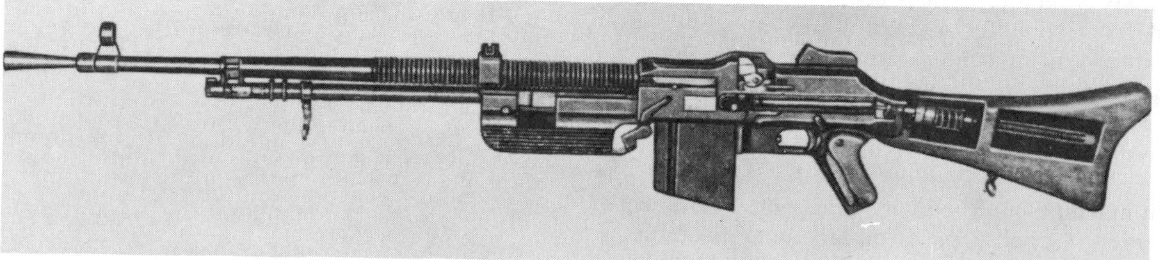

Polish Browning Machine Rifle cutaway. This gun is based on the Browning as made in Belgium. It differs in some design features from our BAR.

Because of its weight, cooling system, and stable mounting, the medium machine gun can be used effectively at ranges three to four times greater than is possible with the light machine gun.

All the operating systems used in the light machine gun are also applicable to the medium machine gun.

General Purpose Machine Gun. Sometimes called a *dual purpose* machine gun. These are weapons which are intended to be used on bipods as light machine guns and on tripods as medium (heavy rifle caliber) machine guns. They are normally belt fed, but frequently use small ammunition boxes attached to the gun when used in the light machine gun role. The U. S. M60, the French M52, the F. N. type M.A.G., and the German MG 42 fall in this category.

Heavy Machine Gun. In general the characteristics are those of the light machine gun except that the weight of all components is greatly increased, as is their size also. The term heavy machine gun is correctly applied today only to cartridges .50 caliber and larger. In general, these arms are merely scaled up models of the equivalent medium machine gun pattern, as in the case of our .50 caliber Browning. Such guns today play a considerable part in various forms of motorized equipment carrying machine guns and are used to some extent for low anti-aircraft fire, often in multiples. Since the cartridges they use are too powerful for normal use in standard rifle pattern weapons, and since their mechanical and design characteristics are but minor modifications of the medium machine guns, no further coverage of them is required here.

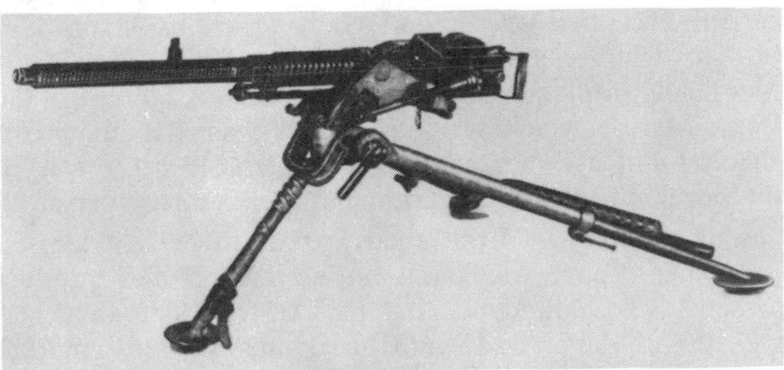

French Hotchkiss Cal. 13.2mm Heavy Machine Gun.

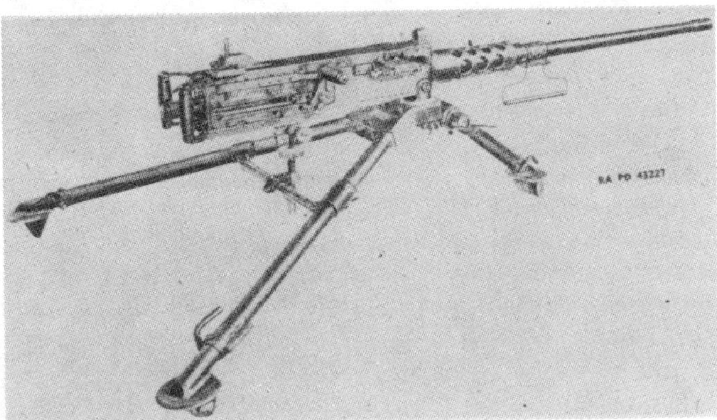

U. S. Browning Machine Gun Cal. .50. A typical heavy machine gun using the heavy .50 caliber cartridge which is too powerful for standard rifle use.

THE EVOLUTION OF THE AUTOMATIC MACHINE GUN

As we have seen, our own Hiram S. Maxim was the real father of automatic arms operation. He not only developed to the full the principle of recoil operation for automatic weapons systems but also did tremendous experimental work in the field of gas actuation, some of his systems being utilized by others.

We have space here only for passing mention of the various great foreign inventors and the arms for which they were particularly noted. All such arms as are in general use today, which means all those which were truly successful, will be found completely detailed in Part II. We shall content ourselves here with historical background on these developments as they emerged.

The Skoda Gun

Skoda at this writing is the world famous Czech center of development for all types of arms, both light and heavy, now unfortunately in Communist hands. Actually Skoda is a tremendous group of what we would call job shops, not fully integrated factories along the general American plan. As a metals center it also has no superior.

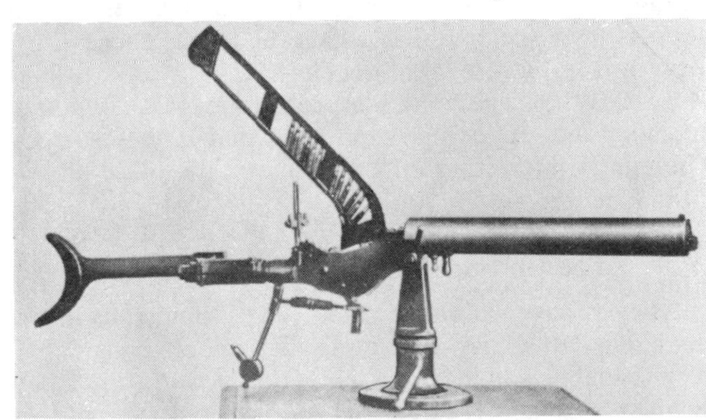

Upper, the Skoda of 1893.
Lower, the Skoda of 1909 with shield.

Soon after Maxim's gun appeared, an automatic machine gun was introduced by the Grand Duke Karl Salvator in conjunction with Colonel Von Dormus of the Austrian Army. The gun was patented in 1888. Manufacture began at a plant for arms manufacture, built in 1859 by the Count of Waldstein, which was acquired by Monsieur de Skoda in 1869. The works were at Pilsen, then in Austria-Hungary. This soon became one of the great armament plants of the world.

This first Skoda gun was a delayed blowback. It operated on the principle of being locked only by spring pressure and by the weights of the moving elements, though a retarding mechanism was provided which still further, through spring pressure and friction, slowed down the rapidity of opening so that the barrel pressure would be safe by the time the action had opened enough to permit extraction. This system has the advantage of simplified design and manufacture, but is not adaptable to truly high power ammunition.

It was officially adopted in Austria in 1893. In general it was intended for naval and fortification protection. It saw some service in the hands of an Austro-Hungarian detachment in defense of their legation at Pekin in 1900 at the time of the Boxer Rebellion.

This Skoda gun was completely redesigned and issued as the Austrian Model 1909, at which time the original hopper feed mechanism, which had not been satisfactory, was replaced with a belt feed.

In tests the original Skoda proved incapable of standing up alongside the competition to which it was subjected. The gun is interesting only because of the place and conditions of its production.

The Hotchkiss Automatic Machine Guns

As we have already noted, the American inventor Benjamin Hotchkiss died in 1885, but left behind him a very capable engineering and production organization devoted to the development and manufacture of arms.

To this organization in 1893 went Austrian Army Captain, Baron Adolf von Odkolek with a new type of gas-operated machine gun which he had developed at Vienna.

The Hotchkiss Company by that time had expanded into a dual organization, though both were under French control. The original organization was changed after the death of Hotchkiss and in 1887 it became officially the Société Anonyme des Anciens Establissements, Hotchkiss et Cié. Its offices were in Paris, but manufacture continued at St. Denis. The English branch set up originally in 1884 with Armstrong at Elswick now became the Hotchkiss Ordnance Company Ltd. with offices in London.

Laurence V. Benét, an American who had been associated for years with Hotchkiss, was placed in charge of promotion and engineering—a rather unusual dual position. The fact that Benét's father was General S. V. Benét, then Chief of Ordnance in the United States, just might have had something to do with the appointment and the jobs. In any event it was he who arranged originally for his son to enter the Hotchkiss employ.

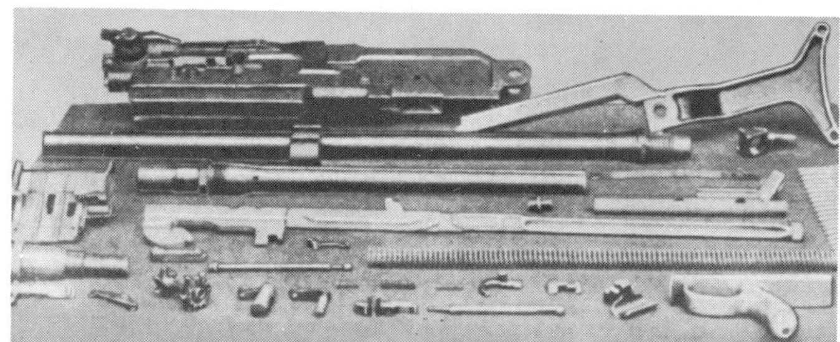

Upper: Laurence Benet, assistant to Hotchkiss, testing the original Hotchkiss.
Lower: The first Hotchkiss field stripped to show simple parts.

Mr. Benét had the faculty so important for the successful executive—he knew how to pick assistants and how to delegate authority to them. One such was Henri Mercié, a brilliant and tireless worker. Aside from the Benét-Mercié Machine Gun which was not to prove successful, these men played a very considerable role in the development and advancement of automatic arms.

Von Odkolek had the good fortune to present himself just when Benét was badly in need of a new product to sell his stockholders. And the Austrian definitely had something. Maxim had ruined the Hotchkiss world market with his superior automatic designs and he had the patents on recoil operation so sewed up that Hotchkiss couldn't find a way to compete. Von Odkolek provided the way. While his gun itself was not very good, being basically an early inventor's model, he had a new application of gas-powered operation. This was the now familiar gas piston housed in a cylinder below the barrel.

The Hotchkiss people drove a pretty hard bargain, refusing a royalty deal and paying instead a flat sum for outright purchase. The inventor in later years tried in many ways to get around his own patent, but he had done too good a job in the first place; and the Hotchkiss group through the years controlled the world market until the patents expired.

Benét and his associates re-worked von Odkolek's system until in 1895 they came up with the first version of the successful gas-piston-operated automatic arm. The gun was chambered for the 8mm Lebel cartridge and through the intervening years nothing basic has been done which could really improve it. The 1914 gun as detailed in chapter 24 is typical of all the variations, being itself a slight variation of the 1897 model.

The gun is locked-breech, clip-fed, gas-piston operated and air-cooled. Gas is taken off to operate the piston through a port drilled in the barrel, the gas being exhausted as the piston passes back over an exhaust port.

The United States Navy was furnished a model for testing in 1896, the tests being unsuccessful because of lack of proper metal usage and tempering of parts. An American, Edward Parkhurst of Hartford, Conn., was engaged upon recommendation by our Navy to make design changes and manufacturing suggestions; and as a result of his work the 1897 Hotchkiss modification was produced.

Benét retained his American citizenship, leaving France to serve as an ensign during the Spanish-American War, but returning to Hotchkiss after his discharge.

While the French adopted the Hotchkiss gun in 1897 and placed a limited number in African desert service, it was not until the 1900 version with improved steel cooling fins was introduced that the gun really received serious military attention. We made exhaustive tests at Springfield under which the gun stood up well, but in which the feed superiority of both the Maxim and Colt-Browning belt systems was established. The Japanese early purchased large quantities of Hotchkisses. In the Russo-Japanese War of 1904-5, the machine gun as such really came into its own when these Hotchkisses were pitted against the Russian Maxims in numbers. The German observers advised immediate concentration on machine guns as a result of their observations, and their government acted.

The Hotchkiss influence spread to other guns—or more correctly to modifications of the Hotchkiss, for that is all that they are. We must now mention the more celebrated of these, since much confusion exists on the subject.

The French Puteaux Machine Gun

This gun takes its name from the fact that it was first produced at the French National Arsenal at Puteaux in 1905.

It is actually only a minor modification of the 1900 Hotchkiss, the various "features" developed by the French army designers being useless gingerbread for the most part. They built in, for instance, a firing regulator permitting firing cycle changes of from 8 to 650 per minute. This of course was merely a variation—and not a good one—of the regulator Hiram Maxim placed on his very first gun; and which he very soon discarded. Brass circular fins covered the barrel from breech to muzzle, and in desert campaigns these heated up faster than the standard pattern did. As a result of its desert failure, the Puteaux was withdrawn from field service and issued for use in fortifications. It is often referred to as the "Fortifications Model," though it was never actually intended as such, but just happened to end up there because in field use it was just too undependable for issue.

The French St. Etienne Machine Gun

This gun represents yet another unsuccessful attempt to improve the basic Hotchkiss. It takes its name from the fact that it was designed by officers and made at the French Arsenal at St. Etienne. .

Just about the most stupid thing any design group can do is to make a change just for the sake of change—or for private empire building. The St. Etienne gun is a fine example of this technique.

The gun merely reverses the successful gas piston system of operation. The gas is utilized to drive the piston forward to unlock the bolt—instead of to the rear. This requires a gear rack and spring-loaded rod hooked up to the piston. The gear rack in turn is engaged with a spur gear which in turn is secured to an operating lever. This lever in forward position engages a cam slot in the bolt to lock it when firing.

As the gun fires, tapped-off gas blows the piston forward. This compresses the spring attached and also forces the spur gear to rotate. The operating lever turns with the gear through a half turn, thereby withdrawing the bolt and halting it in rear horizontal position. The operating spring now reacts to drive the piston to the rear. This in turn brings the bolt back to firing position. The operating spring under the barrel is behind the piston and must be exposed at all times as otherwise heat would destroy its temper in very short order.

In War I complaints by soldiers resulted in its replacement in the field by the Hotchkiss. Its heavy cast brass receiver immediately identifies it.

The French Benét-Mercié Machine Rifle

About 1908 the Hotchkiss Company introduced a completely new design. It was the combined work of Benét and Mercié.

Their idea for a light-weight machine weapon was very good and most sound. Some of their design changes were excellent, too, resulting in a reduction of the number of parts to about 25. In Europe where it was adopted by the French in caliber 8mm Lebel in the year 1910 it was widely known as the "Hotchkiss Portative." The American terminology for the model we adopted in 1909 in our caliber .30-06 was "Benét-Mercié Machine Rifle" —from the inventors' names and the fact that it was light and had a shoulder stock.

It varied in two design ways from the Hotchkiss—both bad: In method of breech locking and in feeding the clips upside down. Cartridges were on the lower side of the clip during feeding. The locking was by a cylindrical fermature nut. A lug on the nut engaged the gas piston and locked the breechblock when firing. During operation the nut also did the unlocking after gas pressure had dropped.

The barrel in the gun could shift forward if a lock nut on the action worked loose; but the big troublemaker was the feed system. To fire the gun the feed clip had to be inserted upside down, and very carefully, in the right side of the receiver. The cocking handle, was then pulled back to draw the operating units to the

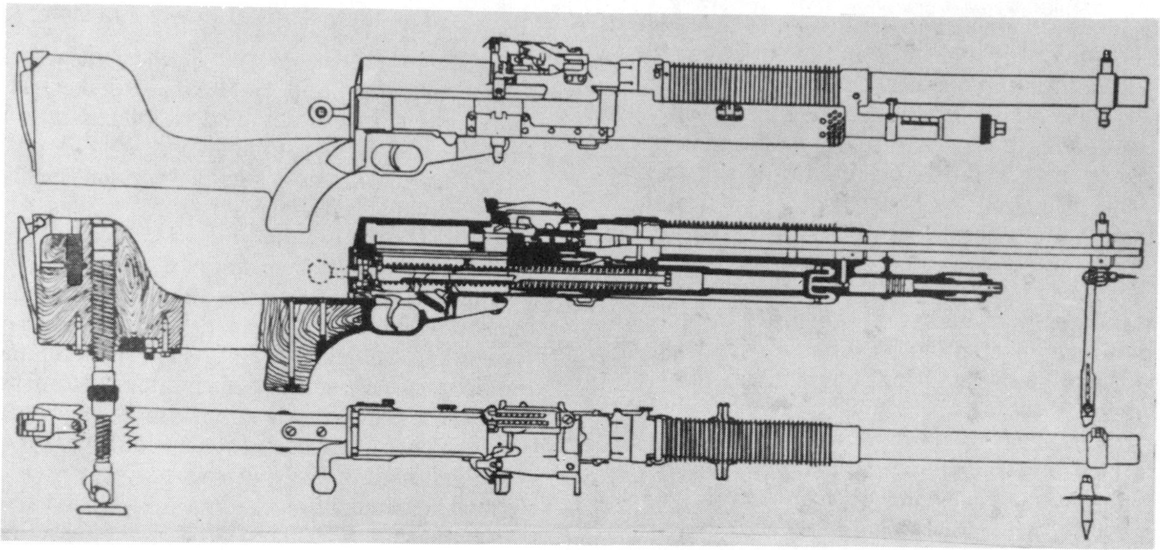

Sections of the Benet-Mercie 1909, modified from the original Hotchkiss.

rear. The handle was then pushed forward as far as it would go, at which point it could be lined up with the letter "A" for full auto fire, or with the letter "R" for single shot or repetitive fire by turning it to the right.

This was our official machine arm until 1916. Fortunately we didn't send any overseas, keeping them at home for training purposes where they were at least heavy enough for the purpose, something that couldn't be said for the broomstick guns with which so many War II soldiers were trained.

In all fairness, the author must point out, however, that we purchased only 29 of these guns from Hotchkiss. Over the years Colts and Springfield Armory made only 670 more. In the face of the small orders, it is obvious that we could not hope to get either manufacturing or operational "bugs" out of any design. These facts must be considered in appraising our failure to improve the Benét-Mercié.

When Pancho Villa raided Columbus, New Mexico, in 1916 the town was "defended" with Benét-Mercié Machine Rifles. According to newspaper stories and some military historians, not one of them fired a shot. The gun squads had a perfectly good alibi—Villa attacked at night, and the feeding of their guns was so delicate and ticklish that they just couldn't get the guns started. So goes the story.

American newspapers lampooned the Benét-Mercié mercilessly, even to the point of suggesting that the rules of war be changed to prevent night fighting so we could use our machine arms. They thus became famous as the "daylight guns."

The Mexican guerrillas had some Colt-Brownings, as well as some early Hotchkiss guns they had captured from their own armed forces. These all worked very well when we managed to capture and test them.

What actually is the truth? Quite different. The raid was completely unexpected—but then so was Pearl Harbor. One of the most reliable and unbiased arms experts of all time is Major General Julian S. Hatcher, U.S.A., Rtd. Throughout his long years of service and experience his reports have always been noteworthy for accuracy and detail. In the Saturday Evening Post magazine issue of November 10, 1917 will be found an article by him dealing with these stories. His investigations showed that after the shock of surprise, the crews actually got their four Benét-Merciés into action and fired 20,000 rounds, despite some jams. Fire was often withheld because of darkness and lack of targets; but the guns did contribute positively to the defense of the town. The journalistic outbursts should have been leveled at those responsible for permitting a surprise attack—just as they should have at Pearl Harbor and Hickam Field.

The French Hotchkiss Model 1914

Although the Germans made no secret of their stock of Maxim guns, the approach of war in 1914 found the French desperately short of machine weapons. In

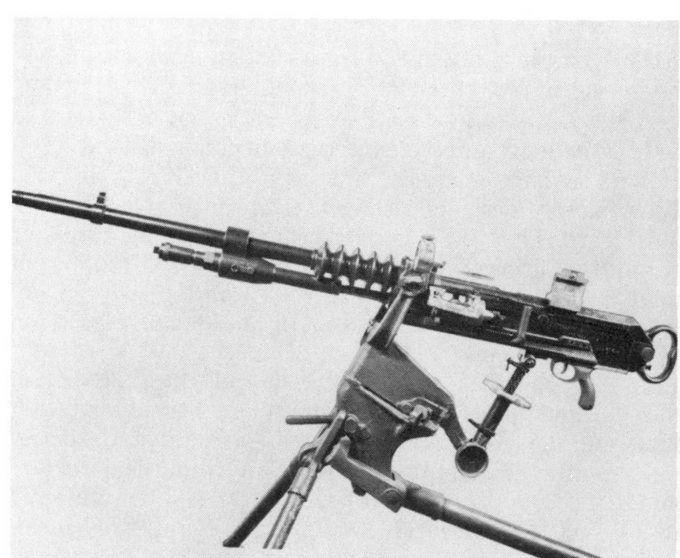

The French 1914 Model Hotchkiss, caliber 8mm French. A famous gun in World War I. Still used by the French for special duty. This is a West Point specimen.

their need the French called upon the Hotchkiss organization to produce in quantity, the Arsenal production and manufacturing methods being entirely inadequate. Hotchkiss performed miracles of production for that day. By 1916 they were really pouring guns out, and the quality and reliability astonished all observers—a real tribute to the design and the manufacturers. By 1917 the French troops were demanding Hotchkisses to replace the St. Etienne and other hybrids; and on July 15, 1918, it was the Hotchkisses which Gouraud's Fourth Army used to break up the all-out German attack which really folded up German offensive ability in War I. More than fifty percent of the attack force was left on the field dead or wounded.

American forces in France were armed with these 1914 Hotchkiss guns using the French 8mm cartridges in the opening stages of the war.

The French Hotchkiss Balloon Gun

This gun, a typical Hotchkiss beefed up to handle an 11mm (.472) caliber cartridge was introduced late in the war by Hotchkiss. It was originally intended as a long-range machine gun for use against artillery crews at ranges too great for standard rifle caliber guns to reach.

Its surprise use, however, came with the widespread introduction by the Germans of observation balloons for artillery spotting. These new Hotchkisses with their large size bullets were able to carry a heavy enough incendiary charge into the hydrogen-filled bags of the balloons to raise havoc. Firing at a rate of 400 to 500 per minute, they used not only conventional 20-shot clips but also a special metal belt holding 250 rounds.

While still in the prototype stage this gun was observed by our Colonel John Parker, who recognized in it features we could use in developing a heavy caliber arm of the type. He arranged for samples to be sent here from France, and while the gun was not adopted because ballistically its ammunition did not meet our requirements, it really pointed the way for the eventual development of our famous .50 caliber cartridge and gun.

The famous World War I Hotchkiss Balloon Gun. Ready to fire.

The French Nordenfelt Machine Gun

In 1897 there appeared in France a gun which is of some historical interest, the Nordenfelt.

Like his previous gun designs, this automatic arm produced by Swedish Thorsten Nordenfelt was not invented by him. Where previously he had been a banker in England, at this period he lived in France.

He bought the new gun patents outright from Swedish Captain Bergman and proceeded to build a model of the new automatic arm, hoping thus to re-enter the arms field from which he had been retired when automatic systems outmoded his hand-operated arms.

This machine gun was a belt-fed, water-cooled heavy type. The feed was unusual, and the belt was a metallic link type almost identical with our best present day variety. The gun was a locked-breech, recoil-operated type. One unusual feature was that it could be set for either automatic or hand operation. Nordenfelt believed this feature very important, as he was convinced that automatic operation just wasn't here to stay!

The gun might well have been successful but for the fact that its owner just didn't believe in the principle even though he owned the gun. It was never produced in quantity.

The American De Knight Machine Gun

This gun was produced only in prototype. It is of interest basically because it represents another abortive attempt by Pratt & Whitney to enter the machine gun field —their first having been with the early mechanical Gardner, as we have noted.

The gun was invented by Victor De Knight of Washington, D. C. in 1898. It was a tripod-mounted gun for the .30-40 Krag service cartridge. Water cooled, it looked like a conventional recoil operated arm externally, but actually was a rather complicated gas-operated weapon. A pivoting block lock was used, actuated by a gas piston. Feed was by belt.

When we saw war coming in 1916, the De Knight gun was brought out of moth balls and subjected to test for possible adoption. It failed rather miserably. The

De Knight machine gun made by Pratt & Whitney.

original gun was made by Pratt & Whitney under arrangement with De Knight. It is doubtful, however, that it ever had a chance because of its involved design.

The Danish Madsen Machine Guns

The machine guns marketed as the Madsens have been chambered for every conceivable military cartridge and been used in every corner of the world at one time or another since their introduction in 1902. Their widespread use stems from a variety of causes and reasons. First, the gun is a good design and is always at least reasonably well made. Its cost has always been relatively low. Also, it has had an aggressive worldwide sales group behind it. But perhaps most important of all, Madsen has stayed in the business of making machine guns and in emergencies all military groups have been able to turn to Madsen—not for what they wanted necessarily but for what Madsen had to offer in the line.

In the 1880's, a light machine gun was constructed by Mr. W. O. H. Madsen, who was then a captain of the artillery and later major general and minister of war, in cooperation with Mr. Rasmussen, technical foreman at the Arsenal. In Denmark, this weapon was called a recoil rifle, whereas in the rest of the world it became known by the name of the Madsen Machine Gun.

Both Captain Madsen and Mr. Rasmussen were employed by the Technical Services of the Danish Army, and therefore the utilization of the invention in Denmark was reserved to the Danish Defense Authorities.

In order to utilize the invention abroad, in which the constructors had great confidence, a syndicate was founded in 1896 by the name of "Dansk Rekyl-Riffel Syndikat" for utilization of the invention in all countries outside of Denmark.

In 1900, the syndicate was changed to a joint stock company which kept the same name.

In 1936, the name of the company was changed to "Dansk Industri Syndikat, Campagnie Madsen, A/S."

From a very modest start the production increased gradually as the weapon was improved. However, it was not until the end of World War I and the years thereafter that the boom occurred, especially after the factory was modernized. Thereby the quality of the weapon was improved and the capacity for competition greatly increased.

In spite of all improvements and modifications, the weapon, which in the production of the factory was called "The Standard Machine Gun," still operates on the recoil principle.

However, there is never any question about the Madsen to one who knows the elements of its design. It is the only "non-ramming" action used in machine guns. While all other patterns utilize the breechblock or its equivalent to drive or ram the cartridge out of the feed into the chamber, the Madsen system does not.

The breechblock is a variety of the original American Peabody and the Martini lock. The breechblock is pivoted at one end. On the opening action stroke it is swung up to expose the head of the cartridge case in the chamber for extraction and ejection. On its next action the block is dropped below the barrel line to permit a fresh cartridge to be chambered. The final motion brings the oscillating breechblock back up again into position to

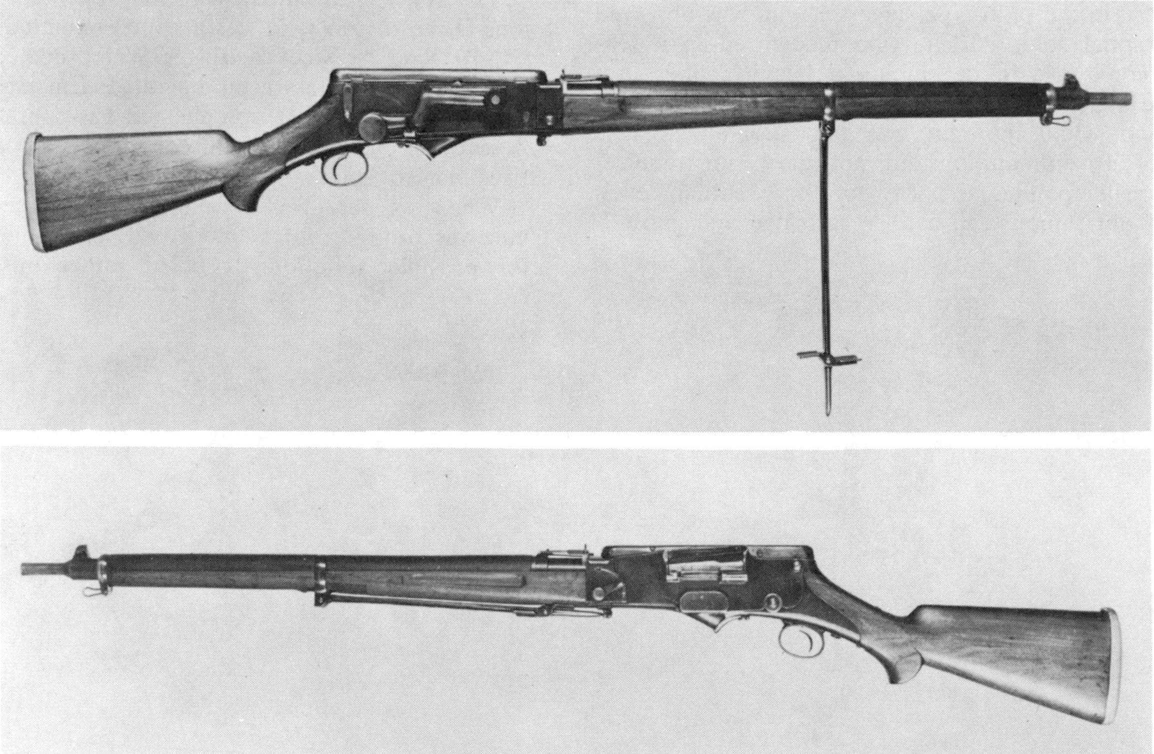

Model 1896 Danish Semi-Auto Rifle made by Madsen. This rifle did not receive the attention given to the full automatic machine gun version. It is relatively unknown.

support the chambered cartridge as it is fired. A simple circular stud on the barrel extension operates in corresponding grooves in a switch plate secured to the receiver, to function feed and lock; all actions take place as the barrel extension recoils when the gun fires. The original feed was a top-mounted clip magazine; but improved belt feeds are also used on later models.

Experts for years have "proven" time and again that the Madsen is not a "sound" machine gun principle. Each round as it is rapidly chambered is somewhat distorted into an arc. Their theory can be proven by high speed photography. However, the gun works in spite of it; and in usage in every clime through the years it has built up a remarkable reputation for reliability. it is more fully covered in chapter 21.

The German Bergmann Machine Gun

While the Bergmann never achieved in Germany the success of the Maxim, it still was a machine gun to reckon with. In view of its many fine points, plus the fact that it was designed by a German, the noted inventor Theodor Bergmann of Gaggenau, it is noteworthy that the German Army passed over it as a first line gun and adopted instead the foreign Maxim. The German policy has always been to try and create the best, but not to hesitate to put their own aside when a better product appeared. Most other nations could learn something militarily from this attitude.

Bergmann is noted for his production of automatic pistols, and also for the fact that he developed the first truly successful submachine gun as we shall see later.

M. G. Model 1910. Inventor Theodor Bergmann demonstrating his first type machine gun.

Bergmann water-cooled machine gun Model 1910.

His first machine gun was patented in 1900 and initial production at the Bergmann works in Suhl appeared two years later as the M. 1902. Modifications in 1903 related only to mounting and feed details, and indeed others in 1910 were again little beyond mount modifications. As in the Maxim and the Hotchkiss, the design itself was so simple and correct that later mechanical improvements could only be minor ones. This is the true measure of any design genius.

The Bergmann utilized an exceptionally fine feed, the belt being a non-disintegrating type made of aluminum links in a day when only the canvas belt was in general usage. The feed extractor claw would engage, withdraw, and position cartridges inserted under conditions which would jam any other feed mechanism.

This simple gun was a water-cooled, short recoil-operated, belt-fed weapon with a quick-change barrel system unique in water-jacket types. Many of its general design features appeared in later machine guns, including our own Brownings. The back plate carried the grips and trigger mechanism and could be easily removed. The cover plate enclosed the feed system and was locked to the receiver, and when the cover was lifted the gunner had access to all the lockwork. The barrel could be removed without loss of water from the jacket by turning the muzzle down, pressing the bayonet-lock release catch on the receiver, and then pulling the barrel and its connected extension out the rear of the receiver. An assistant shoved a stopper in the barrel opening in the jacket as the barrel was withdrawn. The stopper was pushed out by the new barrel as it was inserted.

The parts recoiled locked for approximately one-half inch, after which the barrel and extension travel was halted, and the rising block lock was cammed down out of engagement with the breechlock, thus allowing that member to continue rearward travel to produce the action for extraction, ejection, feeding, and reloading.

The gun was very compact and had a straightline action of a very desirable type. Probably the long successful record of the Maxim dwarfed the Bergmann. Whatever the reason, though it saw battle service to some extent in both World Wars, it never achieved large scale production.

The German Dreyse Machine Gun

The Dreyse is still another of the endless line of arms which have created confusion in military circles because of its name, much as in the case of the Madsen we have discussed.

In the first place, Johann Nikolaus Dreyse had been dead many years before the machine gun named in his honor was patented by Louis Schmeisser of Erfurt. That was in 1907. And it was five years later before the first model appeared. The gun was named in honor of the inventor of the needle gun by the heads of the factory where it was made—the factory originally founded by Dreyse, incidentally—the plant known as the Rheinische Metallwaren und Maschinenfabrik A.G. at Düsseldorf.

German Dreyse Machine Gun. The gun was named in honor of the inventor of the needle gun who was dead many years before it was designed.

This organization, as we shall see later, was the primary concern in setting up the small arms might of Hitler through its machinations with the Swiss Solothurn and other foreign arms makers.

The Dreyse 1912 and its 1918 modification rather resemble the Bergmann at first glance, and are often confused with that earlier gun. Actually they have little in common except appearance and the fact that both are recoil operated, water cooled, and belt fed.

Like the Bergmann, the Dreyse gave great consideration to feeding—one of the basic weaknesses in belt-fed guns. Its feed featured a three-clawed cartridge withdrawal unit, one of which was bound to pick up the cartridge regardless of how poorly it was positioned in the belt.

The 1918 Model replaced the tripod mount for most purposes with a bipod which allowed close-to-ground firing positions for the gunner. The receiver was equipped for telescopic sight. Unlike the Bergmann, the Dreyse incorporated an accelerator and buffer, giving a firing rate of about 600 per minute as against the other's 450.

The breechlock was a pivoting design pinned at its lower end to the barrel extension. During recoil its rear section rode up a ramp in the receiver, thus lowering the locking section out of engagement. Firing was by an internal hammer through a firing pin, the hammer utilizing the hammer-hook safety principle not unlike that on our modern Garand rifle.

At the close of War I the victors sought to prevent fast German rearmament by prohibiting the manufacture of water-cooled machine guns—on the theory that only relatively heavy guns of that type constituted a real military threat.

The developers of arms such as the Dreyse found little difficulty in designing better and simpler light arms which could do just about everything that the heavy water-cooled types could—plus. And the makers of the Dreyse were also the manufacturers who arranged for parts manufacture outside Germany in preparation for the day of resurgence. Those who studied the Dreyse and its construction often foretold what its makers were capable of doing; but in a world of politics their warnings went unheeded until World War II broke and it was too late to take preventive action.

The Italian Perino Machine Gun

The Perino is little more than a historical name in the field of automatic weapons. But for the stupid secrecy with which the Italian military surrounded the gun, Giuseppi Perino's 1901 invention might today be one of the world's outstanding arms developments.

In their determination to keep the gun a secret, the Italian army went to the fantastic extreme of buying Maxims to equip its forces as a "cover-up" for developing the new Perino. Machiavelli in his wildest dreams never conceived the hare-brained ideas his descendants hit upon in their attempt to be devious.

While Italian designers have always been noted for unusual—and generally impractical—feed systems, Perino actually produced something new in feeds which still has an undeveloped potential. His gun was compact, had an unusual recoil operating system with a rather long stroke which was used to mechanical advantage, featured both air-cooled and water-cooled systems well ahead of the time, and had a host of other features which placed it, if perfected, actually ahead of the fabled Maxim.

In its early form the Perino feed was by metal trays of 25 cartridges fed through the gun from left to right. Trays could be started only when the bolt was forward, the mechanism locked—a safety feature in itself. Pulling back the cocking handle opened the action and cocked the mechanism, meanwhile indexing a cartridge in line with the chamber.

On forward motion of the firing mechanism when the trigger is pulled to release it, the bolt pushes the cartridge out of the tray into the chamber, actually passing over the tray itself. Five 25-shot trays were placed in the ammunition feed box, and, as the gun fired, the trays fed from the bottom layer, thus allowing the loader to replace loaded trays in the top of the box for continuous fire.

A most unusual arrangement withdraws each fired case from the grip of the extractor as it emerges from the

Italian Perino machine gun. Never produced in quantity, yet one of the outstanding designs in its field.

chamber on recoil and snaps it down into its place in the loading tray under the bolt. This, of course, does away with the need for an ejection chute and for much of the involvement of belt feeds. As the 25-shot tray receives its 25th empty case, the next loaded tray follows it into the gun, the empty one being expelled to the right.

The breechlock is actuated by lugs thereon which engage receiver cams during the movements of the barrel, barrel extension, and bolt. The lock is a pivoted type. A unique linkage provides simple acceleration not only of the bolt in its rearward movement to the buffer, but also in its forward movement to chamber and lock. Part of this linkage is a forked lever which does away with the need for a separate driving spring behind the bolt, and also positions the bolt to compel breechlocking before the gun can fire.

A later feed was almost equally unique, consisting of a flexible strip of brass holding the cartridges coiled in an ammunition drum. The strips could be separated at 2-foot intervals.

In case of feed trouble with the Perino one had only to press a release button and take the ammunition box off to remove the troublesome round from the gun. In case of failure of any mechanical part, the right side of the gun could be hinged down instantaneously to expose the entire mechanism for attention. This could be done close to the ground, affording protection to the gunner while he made repairs without exposing himself.

In the watercooled model, the recoiling barrel functioned as a small reciprocating pump, giving constant water circulation so that the gun in tests would fire long after the regular Maxim pattern had boiled its water supply. A built-in muzzle booster utilized the gas trapped after the bullet left the barrel to give added rearward thrust, thus giving a high cyclic rate in a gun whose normal recoil length was much too great to allow it with the formal arrangement. This long recoil, incidentally, afforded slow extraction to prevent ripping off case heads.

By the time the aura of secrecy wore off this gun, the Italians were too embroiled in other matters to do anything with it. Had this gun been put into production in the day of its development, it would have affected all later machine gun design.

The Austrian Schwarzlose Machine Gun

This gun is remarkable for being the only machine gun on the retarded blowback system which met with any degree of success prior to 1950 and which was put into general military production.

It was invented by Andreas Wilhelm Schwarzlose of Charlottenberg, Germany in 1902 and was first produced by Steyr in Austria three years later. Schwarzlose is familiar to all students of the history of automatic arms as the developer of early pistol and rifle types. His production included an early short-recoil system and also several unusual "blow-forward" pistols, one of which was commercially manufactured and sold in the world market. These are touched upon in their proper place. At this point we are concerned with his successful ma-

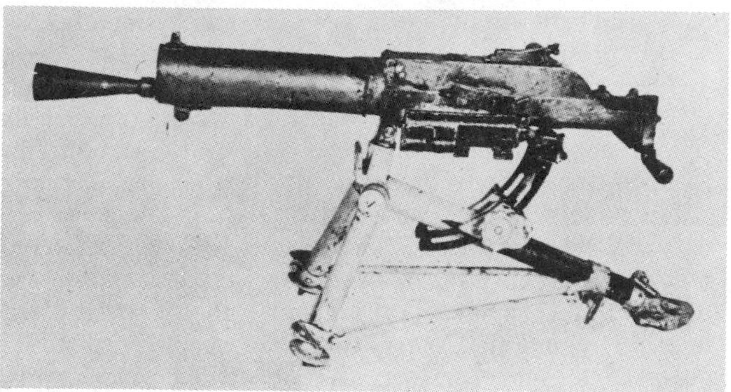

Representative Austrian Schwarzlose M. G. with cover open. This gun is discussed in detail in chapter 15.

chine gun primarily.

All gas- and recoil-operated machine weapons involved high-cost machining and fitting in the early days of development. As a matter of fact, it was not until the introduction of the Russian and German developments in World War II (notably the German MG 42) that locked-breech systems were developed which were capable of fast production at low cost; and their manufacture was a matter of improved metals and manufacturing equipment even more than design.

Schwarzlose, therefore, turned his attention to a weapon having a fixed barrel, few moving parts, and rugged construction. His development, like all such attempts, had many limitations. But it was successful within those limits. The gun saw service in both World Wars, and in several armies.

In this system the breech is at no time truly locked. When the gun fires, the rearward thrust of the exploding gases actually starts the action opening at the same instant it starts the bullet down the barrel. However, by using a very short barrel and a combination of very heavy recoil parts and springs, plus a system for developing a mechanical advantage in the mechanism, Schwarzlose produced a machine gun which permitted the use of military rifle cartridges without an impossibly heavy breech mechanism.

The gun was water cooled. Originally chambered for the 8mm Austrian military cartridge, it was modified at times for other calibers. The 1905 and its 1907 modification required lubrication of cartridge cases to prevent case ruptures caused by the action opening so fast that it drew the case back while the bore pressure was still too great, and the case was still sealed by expansion to the barrel chamber walls. The designer built an oil pump into the gun to overcome this difficulty. On each stroke oil was squirted into the firing chamber to lubricate the incoming cartridge case. In the later modification in 1912 the pump was eliminated by considerable re-design.

A study of the Schwarzlose and the illustrations in chapter 15 will give a clear understanding of its operation. In general it may be stated that the operation required the use of a short barrel to allow fast dissipation of the gas pressure, unusually heavy and sturdy recoil spring and bolt to furnish the initial inertia, and a system of jointed levers which placed the bolt at a mechanical disadvantage in its action of compressing the huge recoil spring.

The mechanical disadvantage is produced through an elbow joint attached to the bolt and having another arm pivot-pinned to the heavy receiver. As the action starts to open, the elbow must move through an arc. The angle between this linkage and the operating crank is slight when in closed position. This results in much of the primary thrust being taken up by the receiver rather than the breech elements. The ingenuity in the parts design is truly remarkable, even the huge recoil spring being designed to serve the several purposes of recoil spring, buffer spring, and firing pin spring at the instant each function is required. The cartridge feed is equally unusual, having only two working parts. One, a roller, is acted upon by the moving belt to pull the belt into the gun, the cartridges passing through a wheel-section of the roller and being cammed back slightly before complete withdrawal—a form of initial extraction of the loaded round to be fed which is far better than the abrupt jerking motion customarily encountered in belt feeds. The only other part is a detent slide of relatively simple design.

The 1912 Model introduced a still heavier bolt and spring, plus a more angled linkage. This design, which of course is a form of toggle action, permitted the placing of the operating crank well off center, the effect being to control the pressure and make the receiver absorb even more shock. The bolt movement was still further slowed, as the initial thrust must first raise the off-center crank out of line. This additional disadvantage was sufficient to permit the designer to discard the lubricating pump of his earlier models.

Even with the relatively low-powered military cartridges used in the gun, so much flash was encountered at the muzzle that a large cone-shaped hider was required over the muzzle for night firing. The construction requires such heavy and sturdy parts that it did not have very much effect on other design development in portable weapons, though some cannon utilize varieties of hesitation or retarded blowback operation.

With the recent developments in permanent magnets and special metals, and in ammunition advances, new possibilities suggest themselves in this design, and the future may see it receiving more attention than it has in the past for special duty use.

The French Chauchat Machine Gun

Like so many others we have considered, the Chauchat gun is known by the name of the man who pioneered it. Col. Chauchat was chairman of the French Commission which decided upon its adoption, and it was named in his honor. Many American soldiers swore by this gun, which was one of their arms in World War I. Many more swore at it as one of the clumsiest and balkiest pieces of equipment ever encountered, and they were by far the more numerous.

The gun is sometimes listed as the "C.S.R.G." This, too, is in the European tradition of "honoring" officials, for it represents the initials of the entire adopting Commission—Chauchat, Suterre, Ribeyrolle, and Gladiator! After World War I it was distributed to Belgium, Turkey, Rumania, and many other countries. In British circles the gun is often listed—incorrectly—as the "Chauchard."

It is ironic to recall that our own supply of automatic arms was almost nil when war broke out, and that we were forced first to equip our troops with this monstrosity in its 8mm French service caliber and to purchase some 37,000 of them from the French. Nine of our combat divisions were issued Chauchats in the United States before sailing, some in caliber 8mm, some altered for our .30-06 cartridge.

As a matter of record, it might be mentioned that the alterations were easily made, but they reduced the magazine capacity from 20 to 16 cartridges. As might have been expected when altering such poor equipment to handle far more powerful ammunition, the .30-06 models were even worse than the originals. Cases stuck in the barrel after even moderate fire, parts broke—particularly springs—and the gun jammed under almost all field conditions. Still, the B.A.R.'s were not in production and we were compelled to accept the philosophy of Chauchats being better than nothing at all. To make matters even worse, alterations and inspection were under French control, and little heed was paid to American suggestions and requests for improvements.

One French Chauchat training tactic was too much

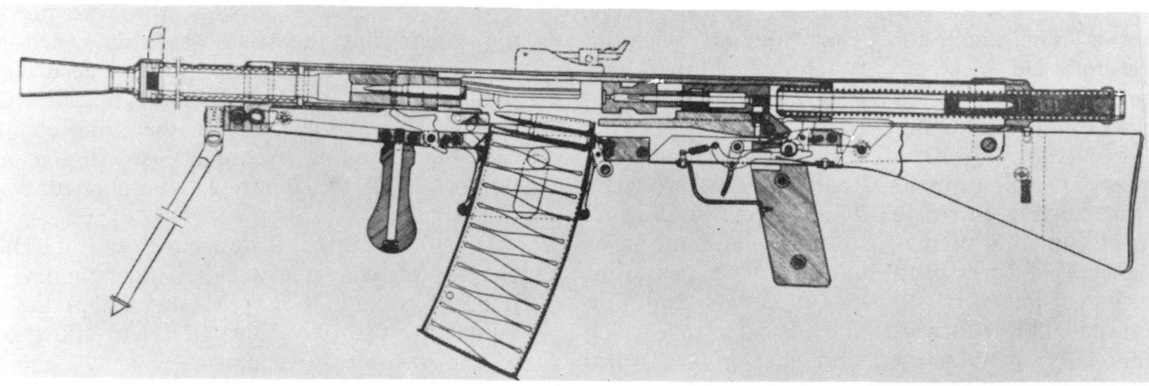

French Chauchat M. G. in section to show operation. See chapter 24 for photos and description.

even for their own long-suffering troops. This was the "brilliant" idea of rear echelon experts that the way to use the Chauchat was to advance in line, each soldier firing a burst from the hip as he planted his left foot! Fortunately for the French, not much use was made of this and similar instructions, since it was difficult to keep the gun firing for more than two very short automatic bursts even in spite of its leisurely rate of operation.

The gun was a pretty accurate copy of a turn-of-the-century rifle designed in Hungary by R. Frommer, the father of the long recoil system of operation which works well in automatic shotguns, fairly well in pistols, and not well at all in machine arms.

The basic feature of this system is that the recoiling members, including of course the barrel, travel back the entire length of the cartridge case, fully locked. Compressed springs then assert themselves. The barrel is pushed ahead. Through cams acting in a non-recoiling sleeve, its movement causes a turning movement of the bolt head to unlock—the bolt tail being suitably held back at this point. As ejection occurs and a new round comes up for feeding, the bolt is released to chamber the cartridge as its spring drives it home. Cams turn the bolt head to lock the action. This is the basic Frommer action.

The gun could be fired only when the action was fully locked—when it could be fired. The quality and construction of the gun was undoubtedly the crudest ever to appear in any military arm. Despite a complete lack of normal tolerances, the gun parts still were not interchangeable. The arm was unique in that it utilized stampings, tubing, and lathe-turned parts throughout. The principle of manufacture was most sound. The trouble was in the crudity and carelessness of manufacture. The principle used in building the Chauchat was utilized by both the Germans and the Russians during World War II and produced some superb weapons, some very cheap ones—but all reliable because of care in manufacturing plus improved manufacturing methods. Even our own M3 submachine gun is built on this manufacturing principle, as are many other of today's best foreign arms in that category. However, thus far only the Germans have been able to take full advantage of this form of design and manufacture in high-power designs, though the Belgians are successful in their new auto rifle built on this manufacturing idea.

The French Berthier Machine Gun

This gun is usually listed as French because its inventor was a French Army Officer, Lt. (later General) André Berthier. His first patent was in Belgium in 1905. This was for a straight pull rifle similar to the Mannlicher, but with an external gas cylinder housing a piston on the right side of the rifle where it could move the operating handle in straight line. Similar applications of this system were made at Steyr Armory before Berthier, yet he achieved considerable attention for the design.

In 1908 he introduced the first model of his machine

Model 1911 French invented Berthier M. G. was manufactured in Belgium.

gun, the arm being made at the plant of Anciens Establissements Pieper at Herstal, Belgium, an organization set up in competition to the F.N. plant by one of its original founders. This is of interest since at the time there was great rivalry between the two firms, and John M. Browning was then a member of the F.N. combine as his heirs are today. Browning's later famous B.A.R. has much in common with Berthier's first Belgian produced gun, particularly in the matter of its gas operation and its breech-lock system.

The gun was light, well-made, and streamlined. It was designed for both infantry and cavalry use. A unique water-cooling system used a very tight barrel jacket with two compartments, water being circulated through them from rubber water bags squeezed by an assistant during firing. This method did away with the bulky jacket design of standard guns of the type.

The cartridges were fed down through the top of the receiver from a spring-operated magazine which had a capacity of 30. Firing rate was about 450 per minute. The breechblock was the prop-up type which is locked as its rear end is raised into a locking seat in the top of the receiver, allowing the actuating gas piston to continue ahead and its firing device to discharge the round in the chamber.

General Berthier visited the United States in 1916 in an attempt to set his gun up for mass production. After tests in June 1917 orders were placed by our Army for 5000 and by the Navy for an additional 2000. The guns were to be made at Norwich, Conn. by the arms firm of Hopkins & Allen—a manufacturer no longer in existence. The firm had set up a special division (The United States Machine Gun Company) for manufacture. They had financial troubles and the gun was not put into production.

With the end of the war, all U. S. interest in such developments also ended. The Berthier went the way of many similar arms. Some of its principles found their way into successful designs—e.g., the Vickers Berthier Mark III.

The Swedish Kjellman Machine Gun

The important operating principles of this unusual design were patented in 1870 by Swedish Army Lt. D. H. Friberg. Peter Paul Mauser in Germany did some work along similar lines at about this time also.

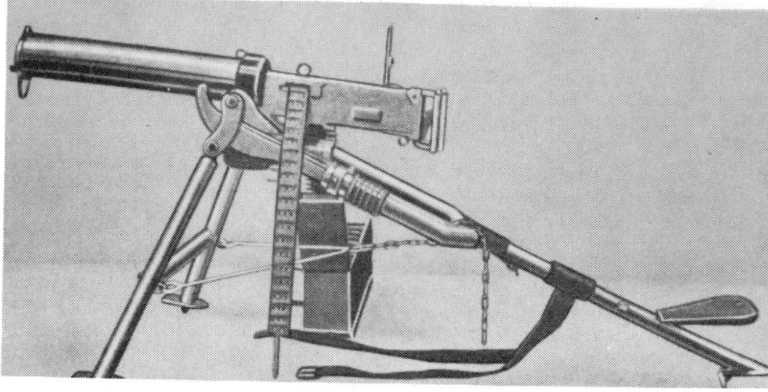

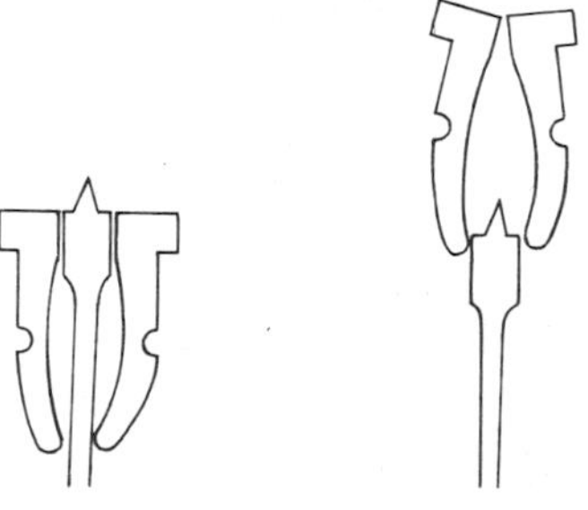

Swedish Kjellman Heavy M. G. locking system illustrated. Firing striker in movement cams lugs into and out of engagement in locking recesses. Modification of this system is used in Russian Deg. L. M. G.

However, the ammunition then available did not lend itself to successful automatic action, and at the time nothing came of Friberg's brain child. With the development of advanced ammunition at the close of the century, however, the Friberg principle again received attention. Its principles were seized upon in 1907 by Rudolf Henrik Kjellman of Stockholm, Sweden. Variations of this intriguing locking system were experimented with by Mauser who developed several rifles and experimental automatic pistols using variations of it. In World War II variations of the system appeared both in the gas-operated Russian light machine guns and in the famous German MG42 recoil-operated gun, which interestingly enough was developed at the Mauser factory.

The feeding systems in all these variations differed distinctly from those employed by Kjellman and Friberg. But the breechlocks have similarities.

The original gun was water cooled and furnished with a tripod mount. It was belt loaded from the right-hand side. A later model with a bipod mount and with an arc type magazine positioned on top of the receiver was also introduced. However, although Sweden conducted various experiments on it, it was never officially adopted.

Perhaps the outstanding characteristic of the arm is the fact that the extremely short recoil was so utilized that it made for a breech-locking mechanism more secure than most of the other systems of its time. Spark photography showed the bullets traveling some 98 feet out of the rifle before the actual unlocking of the breech commenced.

The Italian Revelli Machine Gun

In chapter 31 due attention is given to the Italian Model 1914 Revelli (or Fiat) machine gun in caliber 6.5mm.

The gun is mentioned here because of the unusual nature of this arm and of the background of its inventor.

It was developed in 1908 by Bethel Abiel Revelli of Rome, an officer in the Italian Army.

The design itself is a combination of short recoil and blowback. Locking by wedge is so slight that the gun is not a locked-breech weapon in the true sense of the word, but actually is a hesitation pattern blowback.

Models were manufactured at the Fiat Automobile Works at Turin, Italy and the name Fiat is often applied to the arm. It was tested both in the United States in 1911 and in Italy, of course. It utilized a 100-round magazine in the 1913 test.

One very unusual feature of the gun is the magazine system of so called "mousetrap" type. Theoretically it provides better flexibility than does the belt-fed mechanism. However, in actual practice as the mousetrap maga-

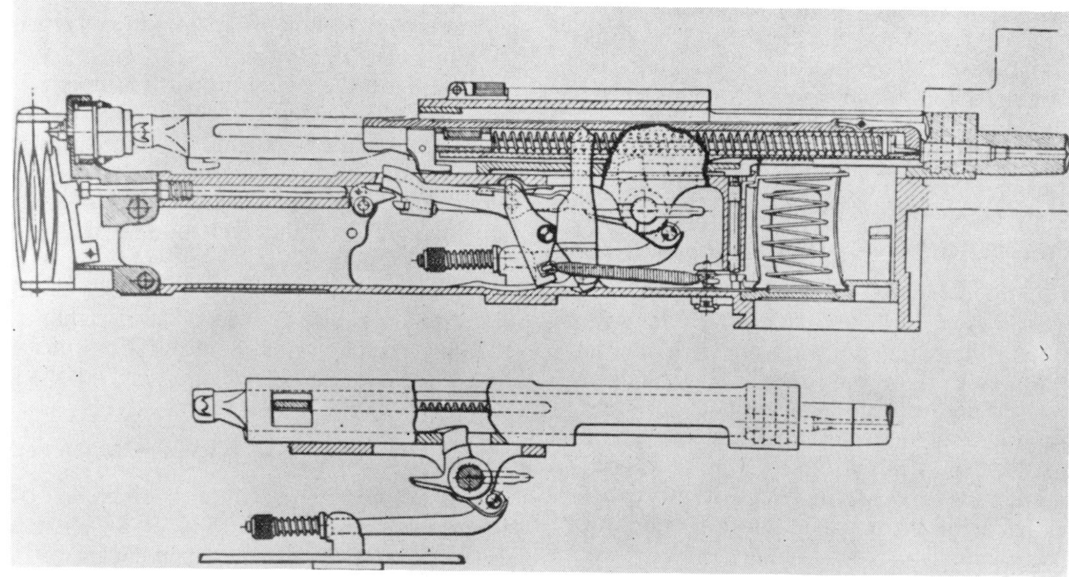

Italian Revelli M. G. This gun is pictured in chapter 31.

zines are ejected, they are easily dented and rendered unserviceable.

All of Revelli's experimental and developmental work was of considerable value both to Fiat and the Italian government.

Laird-Menteyne Machine Gun

One of the final tests of off-trail machine arms was that conducted at Springfield Armory in September of 1913 when a test was made of the so-called Laird-Menteyne Automatic Machine Gun.

The arm was produced at the Coventry Ordnance Works in England. A representative of the company, of course, was with the gun to assist in the test.

The design was invented by two French mechanical engineers, one of whom was Paul Menteyne. Development work and original patents seem to have been done in 1909 but it was several years before the Coventry organization undertook development of a sample model.

It was an air-cooled, recoil-operated machine rifle to use the standard service cartridge. The arm had several items considerably in advance of its day, particularly in the matter of safety features. However, it failed to pass the rigid test to which it was subjected and was not put into production.

The American Lewis Machine Guns

Since the various successful designs of the Lewis gun are discussed in detail in Part II, we have place here only for its influence on the history of automatic weapons development.

Colonel I. N. Lewis, U. S. A., the developer (not the inventor) of the famous gun which bears his name. The system was actually invented by Samuel McClean.

Most noteworthy perhaps is the fact that the Lewis constitutes the first aerial machine gun, having been tested in June, 1912.

The test was made when the gun was taken up in a Wright pusher-type plane equipped with a crossbar on which the pilot and observer rested their feet during flight. The gun muzzle was rested across this bar while Captain Chandler fired the gun at the target as they flew over it.

This first experimental firing of a new type of machine gun from an airplane stirred the interest of the newspapers and magazines to great heights. Hundreds of writers recognized the import of this new development and it was given tremendous publicity.

First aerial use of the machine gun. Infantry type Lewis tested from plane in 1912. From news photograph.

The promoter of this gun was Isaac Newton Lewis, born on October 12, 1858 at New Salem, Pennsylvania. He graduated from the United States Military Academy at the age of 21 and was assigned to the Coast Artillery.

In 1910 the Automatic Arms Company of Buffalo, New York approached Lewis with a business proposition. They offered him stock in the Company if he would produce a machine gun for them. They owned a number of patents which they offered as a starting point. He accepted and his first prototype weapon was ready in 1911. The machine gun was the now well-known air-cooled, gas-operated Lewis with magazine mounted on top of the gun.

Despite successful tests by the United States Ordnance Department, Lewis received no orders. Like so many technicians before him, he went to Europe with his guns in 1913. His first stop was at Liege in Belgium where he demonstrated the four guns he had manufactured for testing for the United States Army. Out of this grew several similar demonstrations for various foreign military groups. As a result a company was organized at Liege under the name of the Armes Automatiques Lewis. Manufacture was done at Liege in the opening stages. Later however the production was moved to the British Small Arms Company at Birmingham, England. The Lewis gun was revolutionary in its time. With either 47 or 96 cartridges depending on the height of the magazine pan, and not being burdened with belts or jutting clips, it was possible for one man to operate the weapon and move rapidly with an infantry organization while carrying it.

It must be noted that Lewis was not the inventor of the gun. Actually Samuel Neal McClean was its developer and he assigned all patent rights to his machine gun to the Automatic Arms Company before Lewis joined the firm in 1910. The original design is generally known as the McClean-Lissak rifle, an unsuccessful pattern never produced.

Lewis' contributions aside from acting as a salesman were still very considerable. It was he who introduced the draft cooling system which is characteristic of the common variety of Lewis gun. He also developed the rate of fire regulator, the clock-type mainspring, and several other modifications.

When World War I began, the Birmingham Small Arms Company turned over all production facilities to making Lewis guns, since six could be manufactured in the same time as one Vickers.

Even the combined efforts of the British and Belgian factories, organizations which work together today even as they did in early World War I days, could not produce the number of guns desired.

Contracts were let to the Savage Arms Corporation at Utica, New York to manufacture them in the United States. Within two years the Savage organization was turning out four hundred Lewis guns a week.

The Lewis gas-operating system was actually not original in any true sense; its principles had been known for years. But it was the first truly successful portable arm of its class. We find its prototype in early Mannlicher automatic and semi-automatic rifle design and in the principle of the Mannlicher straight-pull rifle. An interesting observation is that the Germans utilized this same principle in a weapon developed just prior to the closing of World War II, the F.G.42; this was a highly efficient model designed for paratroop use.

In August of 1914 two British airmen carried a Lewis gun aloft with them without authorization. At an altitude of 5000 feet they emptied a drum at a German plane. They missed. This represented the first active use of the machine gun in aerial warfare.

When the pilots reported their adventure, instructions were immediately issued that planes were not to be so equipped because of the danger of inciting retaliation on the part of the enemy. Nevertheless, force of circumstances soon compelled the issuance of Lewis guns for airplanes. By September of 1914 British aircraft armed with the Lewis gun were in active service.

A considerable controversy was stirred up in the United States in 1916 because of the Lewis gun. Colonel Lewis complained that our War Department was taking a negative attitude toward his gun. The Ordnance Department on the other hand claimed it was unable to get the Automatic Arms Company, manufacturers of the Lewis, to submit guns for testing. Regardless of the merits of the controversy, it is an established fact that some 40,000 Lewis guns had already been tested on the field of battle at a time when our Ordnance Department still could not make up its mind whether or not the gun should be adopted here.

It developed later that some unsatisfactory tests were the result of dimensional changes in the gun. These had been made without Lewis' knowledge because of the appalling blanket of secrecy which was then as now thrown over the most elementary developments in these fields. The United States Ordnance Department at one time contended that the gun could not satisfactorily handle the .30-06 United States Government cartridge because its velocity and chamber pressures were higher than those of the British .303 for which the Lewis was generally chambered. The Savage Arms Company then manufacturing the Lewis exploded this idea by building test guns chambered for our cartridge.

In very rigid U. S. tests the early Lewis guns did not stand up. This may have been due to faulty construction and manufacture or may have resulted from too rigid testing. Their battle service in British hands speaks for itself, though the .303 cartridge cannot compare with ours.

Astonishingly enough, although our combat Marine groups were equipped and trained with Lewis guns prior to landing in France during World War I, they were compelled to surrender them when embarking. They were not permitted to use the Lewis in service. Instead the fantastically inferior Chauchats were issued to them. This matter has never been satisfactorily explained. It indicates at once the confusion and the difficulties encountered by Colonel Lewis and by the Savage Arms Company in their dealings at the time.

Representative Lewis machine gun, infantry type. This gun is covered in detail in Part II of this book.

During World War I the Germans produced a terrifying psychological weapon in the famous Zeppelins.

They attempted raids on England, to counter which incendiary ammunition was developed at London by George Buckham. This was issued for tests with Lewis guns. Buckham's work was duly reported by agents to the German government, but fortunately somebody slipped up in evaluating the information they obtained. Twelve Zeppelins were destroyed in attacks over London, ten of them being officially shot down by Lewis guns firing the Buckham incendiary bullets. These bullets had flat nosed jackets of cupro-nickel. The nose of each bullet held a charge of yellow phosphorus. This charge of eight grains was retained by a serrated plug of lead which was backed up by a larger base plug. A hole through the jacket near the juncture of the two plugs was filled with an alloy which would fuse at low temperature. When the bullet passed down the barrel the alloy melted and permitted the phosphorus to ignite. The yellow phosphorus, when it passed through the bags of the Zeppelins contacted the highly inflammable hydrogen gas therein. This exploded the gas, completely wrecking the dirigibles.

The Lewis gun, therefore, must be given full credit for destroying the power of that early German terror weapon, the Zeppelin, over England in the first World War.

Lewis guns have been officially used by the United States, Belgium, Great Britain, Portugal, Holland, Honduras, Nicaragua, France, Russia, Italy, and Japan. During World War II they were used throughout the Balkans and even by Russian troops, as indicated by specimens captured and reported by the German Intelligence Organizations at that time.

During World War II, 80,000 Lewis guns were obtained by England from various friendly powers, including the United States. These were issued to the British Army after the defeat at Dunkirk where they lost so much of their equipment. And as more advanced arms later became available, these Lewis guns were issued to Home Guard units and to small ships in the fleet.

One closing note on Colonel Lewis is necessary. He sent checks for over $1,000,000 as donations to our Treasury Department. These represented his portion of royalties on Lewis guns which were purchased by the United States during and after World War I. He made a point of stating, "I will not accept one cent of royalty for a single Lewis gun purchased by the Government of my country."

An interesting sidelight, in view of the difficulties Lewis encountered in his earliest attempts to deal with the Ordnance Department, was that General Crozier, the Chief of Ordnance, even fought the acceptance of the first of these checks! Disparaging remarks were passed which embittered Lewis very much. Still, our Treasury kept Lewis' donations.

The German Maxim Model 08

These arms will be found generally discussed in chapter 26. As a historical note, however, it might be stated that the German Army had over 12,500 of them for immediate use at the outbreak of World War I and many more were in course of manufacture or on order. Only Germany was awake to the importance of the machine gun.

German Maxim light model 08/15. These guns appeared to some extent even in World War II.

These Maxims were also mounted as part of the equipment on Zeppelins to fight off attacks.

The German Parabellum Machine Gun

During World War I the Germans utilized the so-called Parabellum as their prime aircraft machine gun. Mention of it is made here only because a certain number of these guns equipped with special jackets and mounts were issued for infantry use or for use on mounts in Zeppelins. During War II the Parabellum again made its appearance to a certain extent. The gun is basically a highly refined version of the German Maxim. It was developed at the Deutsche Waffen Und Munitions Fabriken at Berlin. This was the plant which produced the world-famous pistol known to us as the Luger. (In Germany it is known in military circles as either the Pistole 08 or the Parabellum, the latter name being merely Latin "for war," indicating a military type arm.)

In 1911 Karl Heinemann was assigned at the D.W.M. plant to work over and lighten the Maxim gun to handle the standard Mauser rifle cartridge. He produced the Parabellum, a name which was the telegraph code address of D. W. M.

It varies in action from the Maxim in that the locking toggle moves up as in the Luger instead of down as in the original Maxim. By other refinements Heinemann managed to reduce the weight to 22 pounds with a firing rate of about 700 rounds per minute.

The Parabellum was utilized by the German aircraft designer Fokker. He developed from an earlier Swiss patent a device for permitting safe fixed firing from an airplane through the movement of the propellers. This enabled the pilot to fire effectively while in flight.

Fokker was born in Batavia, Java. As a designer he offered his services to Great Britain before World War I broke out. He received absolutely no attention then from either the French or the British in this connection. The Germans however utilized his services with tremendous success. The British Secret Service during the war offered Fokker sums up to 2,000,000 pounds to try and inveigle him away from Germany!

The American Marlin Machine Guns

At the outbreak of World War I the Marlin-Rockwell Corporation at New Haven, Connecticut, received a contract to produce Colt-Browning Model 1914 machine guns to be used by infantry for training.

In view of the need for aerial machine guns, Marlin-Rockwell undertook to alter this infantry design. The pendulum type of operating lever below the barrel of the gas-operated Colt-Browning gun was impractical, of course, for aircraft work.

The modification was actually worked out by A. W. Swebilius, a Swedish-born American who began work at the age of 16 with Marlin and developed into one of the finest firearms designers in the country. Swebilius later organized the High Standard Arms Co. whose pistols and shotguns have achieved considerable commercial success.

He substituted a reciprocating piston below the barrel for the pendulum lever of the original Colt. The gun was lightened throughout and other modifications were made as required, including a cocking mechanism consisting of a handle on the right side of the gun itself.

It is a great tribute to the skill of Swebilius that in the course of a few weeks time he completed a major transformation in the original gun. The Marlin was used throughout the war and for several years thereafter as the principal synchronized machine gun of the American Air Corps. It was also produced in a design for tank use and one was also designed for potential infantry service.

The Parabellum and the Vickers had been synchronized for aircraft work, a relatively simple matter since they were recoil operated. The Marlin was the first gas-operated weapon to be successfully synchronized.

As issued, the Marlin 1918 model was belt fed and gas operated. Cooling was by air. It weighed only 22½ pounds and had a fire rate of 630 per minute.

The tank version could be used with a tripod mount. A longitudinal-finned cooling jacket was placed about the barrel. The grip section was copied from the Colt Model 95.

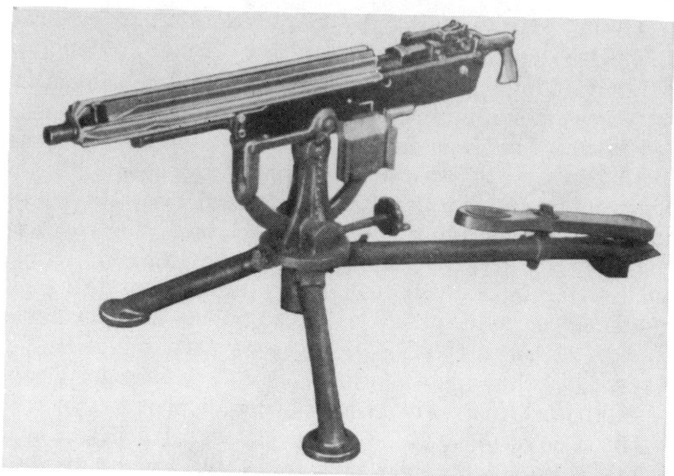

Marlin modification of the Colt-Browning machine gun for tank use. This gun was made primarily in aircraft types.

The Marlin ground gun patterned its barrel on the heavy design of the original Colt. The operating handle and the general design was that of the Swebilius modification.

The Japanese Nambu Machine Guns

In chapter 32 all the basic Japanese machine arms are treated in detail. We have room here only for a historical note concerning their inventor and their development.

The first Japanese machine gun known as the Nambu

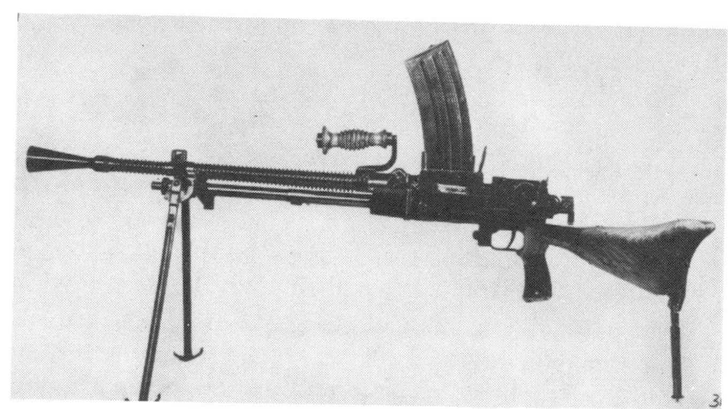

Typical Japanese light machine gun. Type 99.

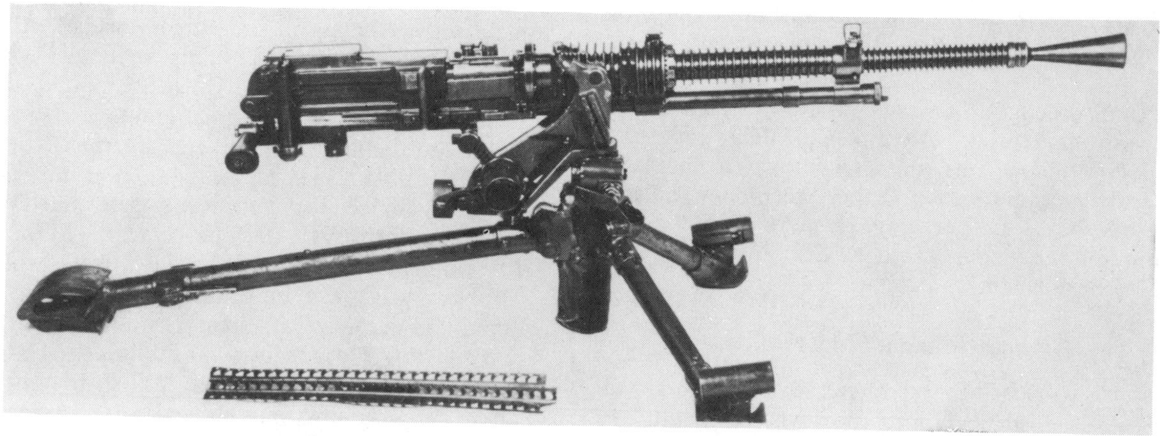

Typical Japanese Heavy Machine Gun. Note Hotchkiss-type lines and clip.

was developed by Lieutenant (later General) Kijiro Nambu. The design was based strictly on the old French Hotchkiss which had been in use by the Japanese since the days of the Russo-Japanese War.

His first gun was a heavy machine gun produced in 1914. In 1922 he developed the type 11. In 1927 the general founded a company for the manufacture of firearms at Tokyo. Here he developed the Type 92 machine gun. This led to the arm which appeared in use against our forces during World War II known as the Type or Model 96.

Nambu's organization merged with that of the Chuo Kogyo Kaisha Company at Tokyo in 1937. In 1939 they introduced the Type 99 light machine gun.

The Nambu operating system was strictly that of the Hotchkiss, but the ejection principle of pivoting the cartridge out over the bolt body was a steal from the Lewis system. All essential details of these types are discussed in chapter 32.

Italian Revelli (Safat) Machine Guns

The Fiat Company, the original producer of the Revelli gun, offered a light-weight machine gun in response to an Italian government request in 1926. In theory this was a new gun. In actual practice it turned out to be just another modification of the earlier Revelli.

The Italian government placed an order for 2,000. Fiat set up a new organization to handle this government contract under the name of Societe Anonina Fabrica Armi Torino (SAFAT). This organization actually manufactured the guns which were officially known as Fiat Model 1926. The nameplate however bore the initials of the technical manufacturer, "Safat."

Italian Revelli (Fiat) Machine Gun.

Very much confusion often develops in considering Italian arms because of methods such as these. The Italian system has been to contract for machine guns based on identical specifications with various companies. Tests are then run to see which company produces the best gun. Often guns which are practically identical will be produced bearing various names, usually those of the individual manufacturers.

The Model 1928 did away with the retarded blowback system of the Revelli. It introduced a positive locking system developed by one of the Safat engineers named Mascarucci. This gun with tripod or shoulder piece weighs about 21 pounds. It can be taken apart in a few seconds without the use of tools. Feeding is from a special metal loader.

At the moment of firing a latch locks the bolt, barrel extension, and barrel together. After a travel of about ½-inch the link begins to elevate the bolt latch slowly.

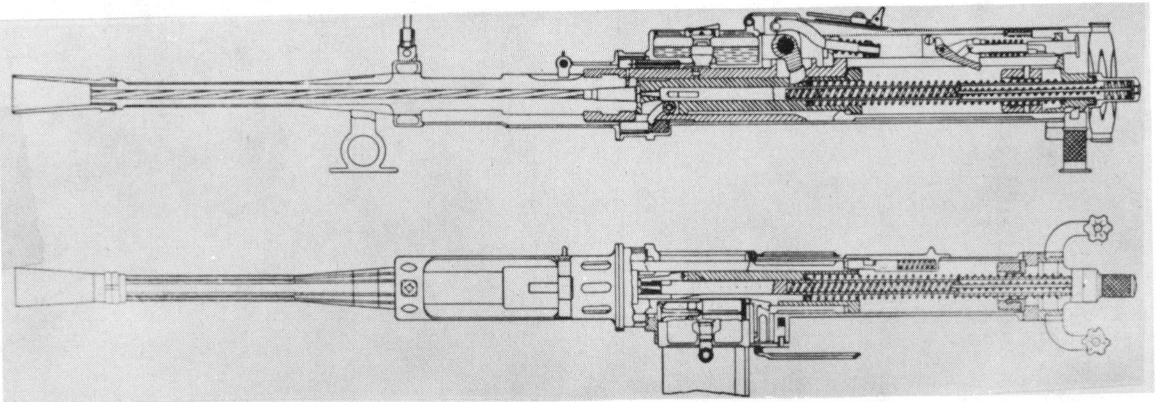

Section Drawing of Model Revelli 1926, a hesitation locked weapon.

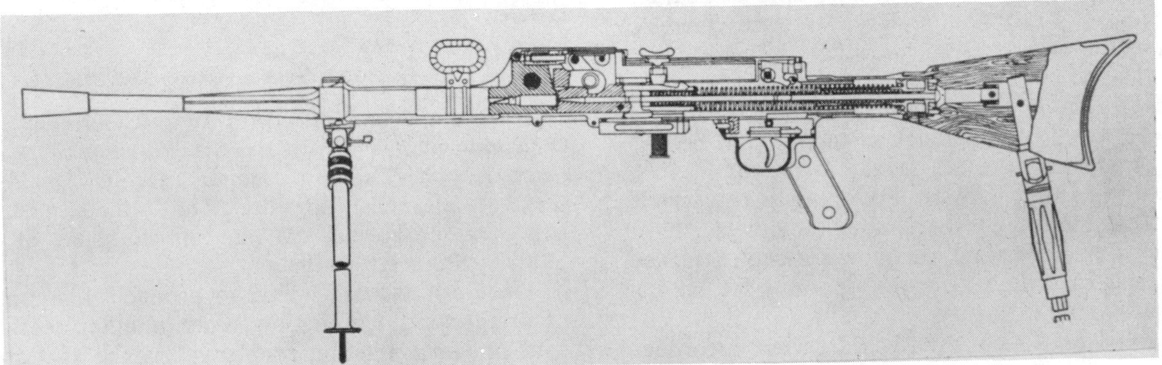

Italian Model 1928 with Mascarucci locked breech and quick change barrel. This arm influenced many current designs.

The recoiling parts then are suddenly released. This slow unlocking gives the effect of primary extraction, preventing ruptured cases. This original Fiat was chambered for the standard Italian 6.5mm rifle cartridge. A later model was designed for a 7.7mm cartridge. In 1935 Fiat produced a new model. This was merely a redesigned 1914 model Revelli. Strangely enough, they reverted to the retarded blowback system in preference to the locked bolt which had been successful.

The German Model MG 13

When Hitler achieved control of Germany, action was taken immediately to rework the thousands of Dreyse Model 1918 water-cooled machine guns on hand. They were converted to more efficient air-cooled types. This work was done by Simson & Company of Suhl. The resulting modifications altered the appearance of the gun very much indeed.

During this period automatic weapons were given an identification number. The designation MG 13 was assigned to this particular modification. Until 1935 it remained the principal machine gun of the German Army.

The improvements over the old Dreyse consisted of eliminating the water jacket and furnishing a ventilated air-cooled barrel. A light-weight shoulder stock and a pistol grip were provided for prone shooting. Instead of the belt, a spring-loaded curved 25-shot magazine was provided. This could be loaded directly from the standard 5-shot army rifle clips.

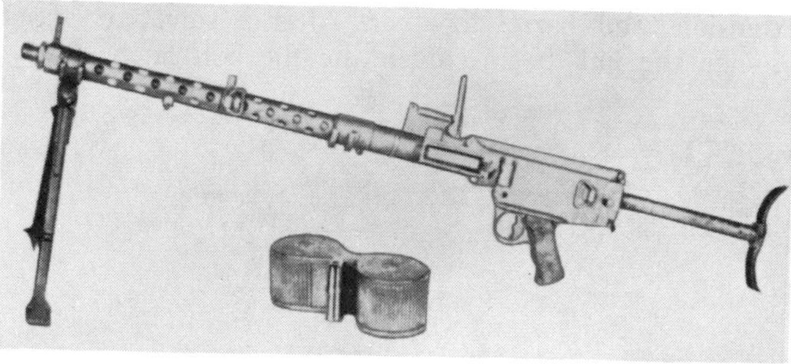

German MG 13.

The firing mechanism stayed open, held by a slide catch when the last shot had been fired. This, of course, notified the gunner and also permitted rapid reloading. A special system of cover operation was devised whereby the cover assembly was raised, allowing the back plate to be lowered. The two operations permitted immediate access for inspection of all operating parts.

The action also allowed a quick change of the heated barrel. This circumvented the League of Nations idea of preventing the Germans from developing arms which could have sustained fire, theretofore obtainable only by very heavy barrel versions or by water-cooled jacket patterns. A selector switch gave the operator his choice of single or automatic fire.

Later a muzzle booster and flash hider were incorporated in the design, as well as a saddle-type drum magazine to hold 75 cartridges.

When these guns were superseded by large quantities of the perfected MG 34, the Germans sold MG 13's to Spain and Portugal. Spain kept the designation MG 13. Portugal described them as "Dreyse M1938." Confusion sometimes results from this designation. The "1938" merely indicates the year in which these used guns were adopted by the Portuguese.

Italian S.I.A. Machine Guns

The S.I.A. guns were actually built first in Italy in caliber 6.5mm Italian service. They are described in general in chapter 31.

The name derives from the fact that the inventor, Giovanni Agnelli, transferred patent rights to the Societa Italiana Ansaldo at Turin. The designation S.I.A. comes from the initials of this organization. They were given a substantial order by the Italian government but their guns were not issued during World War I.

They were, however, introduced into service prior to the World War II period. These air-cooled guns are retarded blowback design and are provided with vertical feed top magazines. The heavy barrel and large aluminum fins extending to the flash hider at the muzzle give good cooling to the weapon.

The S.I.A. is of interest only historically today, far better designs being commonly available.

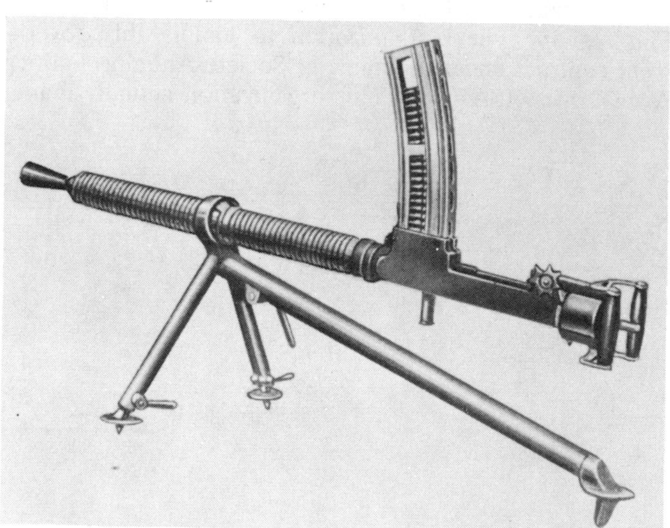

Italian S.I.A. used in both wars. Initials indicate the manufacturer.

The German Secret Gast Machine Gun

Toward the end of World War I Germany was concentrating intensively on the development of a top secret machine gun. This was named after its developer, Carl Gast of Barmen, Germany. The principle curiously is closely allied to one patented in England in the year 1886 by Bethel Burton.

The Germans had hoped to produce this gun, capable of firing some 1,600 rounds per minute, as the answer to their aerial fighting problems. At the end of the war our Ordnance organization located drawings and details of the weapon and requested delivery to Springfield Arm-

German Gast Machine Gun. A secret development in World War I.

ory of at least one gun with 4,000 rounds of test ammunition. When it finally did arrive, strangely enough it was unaccompanied by the drum magazines necessary to fire it. This again delayed testing at the Springfield Armory. It was not until 1923 that we were finally able to test this gun.

The Gast proved to be a dual-barreled affair with unusual drum magazines (spring fed) positioned on each side of the gun. The mechanism operated on the recoil locked-breech principle. These guns were provided with high-powered telescope sights for installation in aircraft. One of the most remarkable features of the design was the easy disassembly. Thumb pressure on the back plate latch permitted the gun to be field stripped within one minute.

Our tests (as usual) produced a report to the general effect that while the gun was mechanically good and operated reliably, it did not have sufficient advantage over the Browning gun to be of interest to us at the time.

The French Darne Machine Gun

The original Darne guns were the invention of Regis and Pierre Darne, who operated a factory near St. Etienne. During World War I they produced small quantities of Lewis guns. The French Government gave them an order for their new gun and some were delivered in 1917. At the close of the war they continued their experimentation on this arm and eventually produced types which were used basically for aircraft work by French units and by some of the countries in the Balkans.

The Darne is not, as had been suggested, just another type of Hotchkiss, though like that gun it is gas operated. Fundamentally however, it is quite a different arm. The feed system differs radically. Its unique design permits a very short bolt stroke. The functioning of the feed occurs during the course of the recoil. The Darne is capable of a very high rate of fire, as much as 1700 rounds a minute with the 7.5mm French rifle cartridge used in War II.

In view of the high quality and extremely high selling price of the famous Darne shotguns in commercial use, it is difficult to reconcile the poor quality and workmanship of its very cheap machine gun.

The quality of the arm seems to have been deliberately sacrificed on the theory that the life of an airplane was short anyway and it was not worth while spending a lot of money on guns for it!

Darne machine guns were furnished to the government of France in 1931 at a price of approximately $28.00 American. In the period from 1918 to 1931 11,000 went to Brazil, Italy, Serbia, and Spain as well as to France. The gun was also adopted by Lithuania after competitive tests in 1934, again on a price basis. In the following year a British commission visited the Darne plant. While the weapons passed French tests, they did not measure up to the British standards.

Darne produced a light and a heavy machine gun for infantry use as well as an antitank automatic gun of 11mm caliber at this time.

For all its terribly crude appearance, the Darne is potentially an efficient gun and probably the cheapest arm of its type ever produced anywhere. It is quite remarkable for not having one forged piece in its entire construction. It depends upon screw machine pieces and stampings for most of its parts. The action of course is gas operated. Primary extraction is provided and ejection is quite satisfactory. The bolt is quite heavy and is securely locked at the instant of firing by a shoulder on the gas piston which cams the rear of the bolt up into a locking recess in the receiver. This design, if better constructed, could easily be one of the finest weapons of its particular type. The answer to arms manufacture, for all practical purposes, should actually fall midway between the preposterously poor manufacturing methods, equipment, and materials of the Darne and that of the super finish and unnecessarily strong and costly designs with which we as a Nation are afflicted. There is considerable room for thought and action in this connection.

The English Beardmore-Farquhar Machine Guns

The Beardmore Farquhar was submitted for tests to the Royal Air Force in November, 1919. It also was

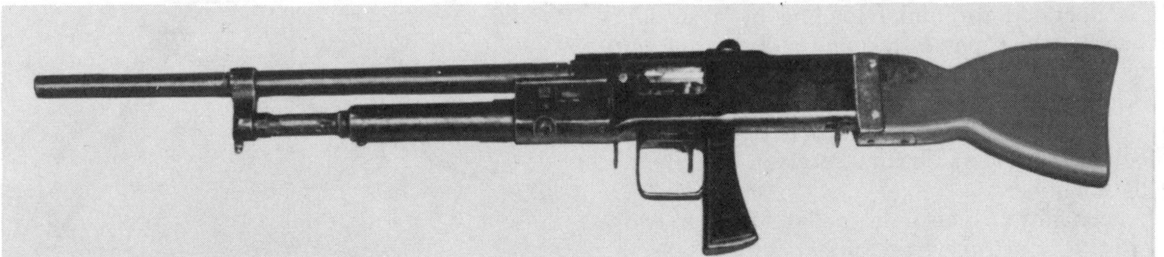

French Darne Light Machine Gun. Probably the cheapest machine gun ever built. Good design but very bad manufacture.

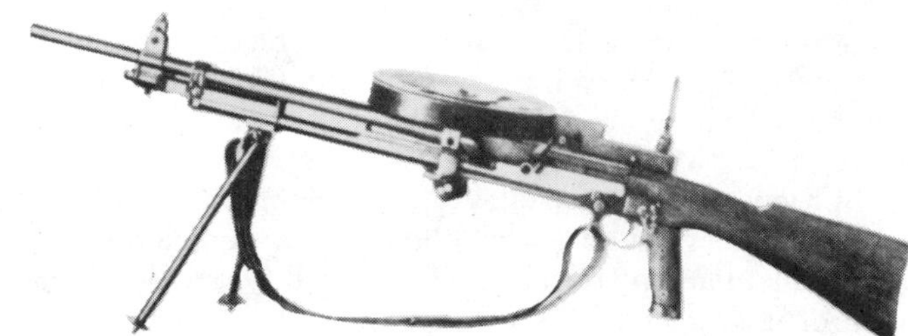

English Beardmore-Farquhar Machine Gun. Original in design but quite complicated.

intended for possible use as an infantry machine gun of the light pattern. Despite favorable tests it was not adopted. No further development has been done on the gun. However, because of its unusual nature, it requires some passing historical comment.

In general lines the gun resembled rather closely other patterns. Its outline for instance is not too dissimilar from that of the Russian Degtyarev now in use. The mechanism, however, is quite different.

This arm is a strange combination of gas and spring functioning.

The forces of the explosion do not act directly on the unlocking mechanism of the bolt. Instead they compress and store up spring energy until the pressure within the bore has dropped to safe operating limits. At that point the bolt is unlocked by a very smooth action of the spring. This furnishes positive unlocking and yet does not give the sudden jerking effect found where a standard piston mechanism is employed.

The piston itself is in a tube below the barrel and connected to the bore by a drilled hole as in standard practice. The main spring is in the front end of a special spring tube having a sear device within it. A special spring for closing the bolt is housed about a central rod at the rear of the spring tube below the barrel.

The bolt remains locked until such time as the force required to unlock it is lower than the strength of the compressed mainspring, thereby preventing varying gas expansion factors from having any effect whatever on the operation. In other words, regardless of the gas pressure of varying cartridges the operation of the functioning of the piece remains constant.

As the weapon is fired, the expanding gas in the cylinder forces the piston to the rear, thereby compressing the mainspring until it reaches a position where it is caught by its sear. This spring remains under compression until the resistance to turning the bolt head is so reduced that the strength of the spring overcomes it.

The bolt is operated for initial loading by a straight pull on the handle which passes through a slot in the left side of the gun. The bolt itself is composed of a non-rotating cocking piece and a head which rotates, the locking lugs being at the front of the bolt head and engaging in locking shoulders in the receiver directly to the rear of the chamber.

The feed mechanism is also distinctive. It is a two-layer rotary drum. Cartridges are under spring tension and are spring indexed and stopped as well. It is possible to unload the drum by pushing the two feed stops simultaneously, thereby releasing the full pressure of the springs to eject the cartridges.

The arm was so designed that the drum magazines which held 77 rounds could be replaced, if desired, with a 5-round magazine using infantry clips, thereby permitting it to be used as a shoulder type automatic rifle.

The gun was rated superior in many ways, especially in lighter recoil and less liability to jamming than the other guns then used. However, the design was not considered sufficiently advanced over the existing patterns to warrant the expenditure of producing it.

The Italian Brixia Machine Gun

The Brixia is an interesting Italian machine gun which was produced in 1920. Its manufacturers are producers of the unusual Brixia mortar.

It derives its name from the initials in Italian of its manufacturers, the Brescia Metallurgical Company. This organization had considerable experience in the manufacture of Fiat machine guns during World War I.

While the Brixia has never been produced in quantity, many of its design factors are such that it is deserving of some attention here for possible future design reference.

One of its unusual characteristics is a special rate-of-fire control system. The regulator is in the form of an eccentric bolt, whose cylindrical section is moved along an axial plane. The periphery of its other half has two grooves, placed at variable distances from the axis of rotation. Projections resting in the tops of the grooves act to either accelerate or slow down the recoil action. Pushing down the regulator button at the left of the gun, with the trigger depressed at different levels, controls the forward and rearward distance to which the bolt is permitted to travel. This regulates the speed of motion of the recoiling parts and hence the rate of fire.

The locking system is short recoil. The bolt, barrel, and bolt extension travel to the rear at the instant of explosion securely locked for a distance of some five millimeters. When the unlocking point is reached, the breechlock is flipped over backwards, thereby functioning as an accelerator.

The barrel extension being stopped by its buffer, the bolt which is now unlocked from the barrel, continues

Italian Brixia water-cooled machine gun. Very short recoil operated.

to the rear under the forces imparted to it. The empty case in the grip of the extractor in the bolt face strikes a projection on the receiver which forms the ejector. Ejection is to the upper left. The recoil of the parts is halted in standard fashion by a back plate buffer, at which time the recoil spring and buffer drive the operating parts forward for the next cycle. The bolt has a circular section. A rectangular projecting unit is attached to it. During the counter recoil movement, the projection is moved into a housing slot in the upper part of the receiver. Movable units in the upper section of the bolt projection act not only to unlock the bolt at the proper moment but are also the fire regulators already mentioned.

The gun was offered in both water-cooled and air-cooled models, the latter having an aircraft-type barrel with radiation flanges along its length. The feed is peculiar, consisting of rectangular boxes which are attached to the receiver. This is another instance of the involved mechanical feeding box to which Revelli originally gave so much attention.

One very unusual feature of the arm is the complete enclosure of all recoiling members. This not only prevents dust, sand, or other foreign matter from entering to interfere with the operation but also serves to protect the gunner in case of defective cartridge explosion.

The gun is mechanically designed to prevent firing until the breechlock is in closed position. This is accomplished by the mechanical positioning of the bolt in relation to the loading and the recoil mechanisms.

The Mexican Mendoza Light Machine Gun

The Mendoza is described generally in chapter 33 and calls for merely historical observation at this point.

It was developed by Señor Rafael Mendoza, then a foreman at the National Arms Factory at Mexico City. The design was started in 1920. The finished gun was not offered until 1932.

A very low number of parts (22), ease of barrel removal, and the relative simplicity of manufacturing requirements all rate the Mendoza as a very unusual light machine arm.

Some refinements and production changes were suggested by M. H. Thompson of New York City, a mechanical engineer with previous experience in production at the National Arms Factory.

The gun was adopted by the Mexican government in 1934 after the conclusion of successful tests.

It was issued to Mexican troops to replace the conglomeration of Colt, Hotchkiss, and Vickers guns with which they were then equipped. The standard Mexican 7mm rifle cartridges were used in the Mendoza.

While the gun itself utilizes principles already established by the Hotchkiss and Lewis guns, it possesses a number of unique developments of its own. The Lewis-type action is improved with the incorporation of a double cam slot, which helps to equalize the torque. Locking friction is materially reduced thereby.

While the gas cylinder is modeled somewhat after the Hotchkiss, the piston system of the Hotchkiss is not employed. The gas assembly is in the form of a cup shaped projection on the barrel. Within it is housed a short piston. The operating stroke is very short, and at its limit the gases are dissipated openly into the air, thereby reversing the operation of the typical gas mechanism of this sort. A firing switch on the left side of the receiver forward of the triggerguard may be set for full or semi-automatic fire in the standard manner.

The cocking handle projects from the left side and is placed well forward. The gun fires from an open bolt position. A special firing pin is provided which carries a firing tip at each end. In the event of firing pin breakage, it is necessary only to reverse the pin to continue firing.

The ejector is an integral part of the hold-back assembly. The quick-change barrel is not threaded. As a result no provision is made for head spacing.

When the gun is cocked, the barrel latch at the forward end of the receiver can be pressed in. A large lug, which is holding the barrel to the receiver, is thereby

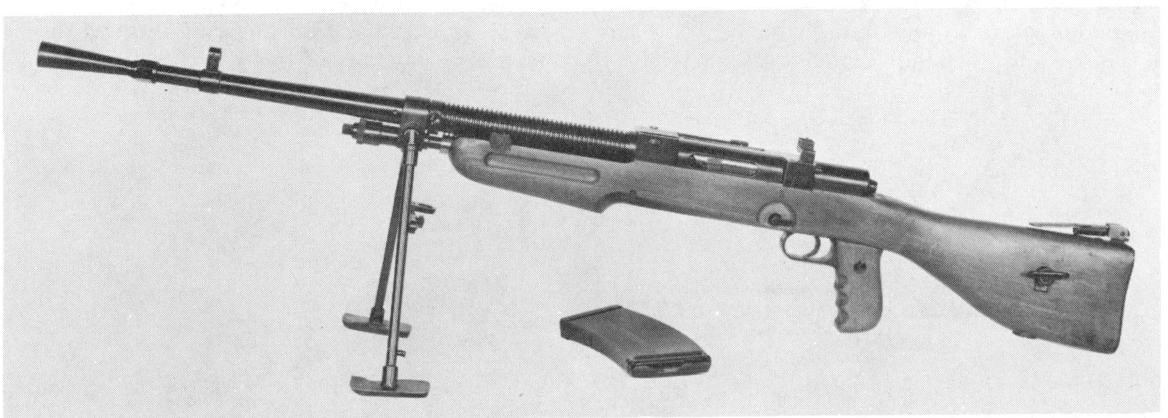

Mexican 7mm Model 1932 Mendoza Light Machine Gun.

freed. The barrel can then be pulled forward out of the receiver.

The rear of the barrel is slotted to permit the locking key to pass through. This key, of course, passes through corresponding receiver slots and is retained by the retaining pin.

A three-corner stop on the magazine follower rises above the lips of the magazine into the receiver as the magazine is emptied. This interferes with the movement of the hold-back pawl. Insertion of a loaded magazine releases the rear sear and allows the bolt to move forward enough to engage a notch in the actuator. Pulling the trigger releases the sear. The operating parts are driven ahead by the tension of the operating spring. The bolt face passes over the double column magazine and drives the first cartridge ahead. The extractor cams itself over the cannelure of the cartridge.

As the cylindrical bolt chambers the round and stops, the light locking lugs on the bolt are in line with the fixed lugs. The bolt extension is still three-fourths of an inch from firing and is continuing forward. It rotates the bolt, locking it firmly to the receiver.

The gas port is about 11 inches from the breech end of the barrel. When the bullet passes over it, gas is released into the piston area. The bolt extension starts rearward some three-fourths of an inch before its lug hits the cam in the bolt slot. The firing pin is started backward with the actuator. Continuing rearward movement unlocks the bolt and carries it to the rear.

Note on Mendoza

A new version of the Mendoza in caliber .30-06 is currently being produced in Mexico. This version is potentially one of the world's finest designs. The barrel is not quickly removable as in the 1932 type. However, provision is made for hinging down on the butt section for quick removal of all operating parts much in the manner incorporated in the Belgian F.N. Auto Rifle. See chapter 33 for more detailed description.

The French Chatellerault Machine Gun

The Chatellerault was introduced in prototype in 1921. Its first official adoption was in 1924 after modifications. Basically it is a combination of the American B.A.R. and the earlier Belgian Berthier. Its name derives from the point of manufacture, Manufacture d'Armes de Chatellerault. This is a French government arsenal.

After the introduction of this new gun, which was prepared in utmost secrecy in common with such matters, the French newspapers proceeded to give ecstatic reports about it. Among other things it was stated that the soldier could fire 30 shots at one burst from the shoulder and that eventually every French soldier would carry this new weapon.

The Chatellerault design required the introduction of a new cartridge instead of the old rim case 8mm cartridge. The 7.5mm rimless now in use in the French service was developed to permit this gun to operate.

Before the gun was even in production the French government offered it to Yugoslavia in 1925 at a very low price of 2,000 francs. A Yugoslav Military Commission went to France to check on the Chatellerault gun. The price by that time had risen since the French found it could not be produced within the original offering figure; but it was still far below that of other machine arms. The Yugoslav army needed machine arms badly and asked for demonstrations and competitive tests. Tests were so poor that Yugoslavia turned to Germany and Czechoslovakia instead of to France for its equipment.

Similar conditions arose when the gun was offered to Romania. During the Romanian tests at least one gun operator was seriously injured by an explosion in the receiver of one of the guns. The French immediately claimed sabotage. Tests were made to produce the same type of premature explosion in the Hotchkiss, which resulted in merely a swollen barrel. There was no such explosion as occurred in the then inferior and lighter Chatellerault.

For several years the French troops themselves were much afraid of the design after the early stories they had heard about it. They continued to demand the heavy Hotchkiss. Eventually, however, the manufacturing bugs, particularly those in relation to poor heat treatment and metals, were overcome.

Special models were made between 1934 and 1939 to adapt the 7.5mm arm to use as a fixed aircraft gun. Another design was intended for use as a tank, armored car, and fortress model. The so-called "fortress model" could be furnished with a drum-type magazine on either right or left side, ejection being through the bottom of the gun. The capacity of this weird magazine was 150 rounds.

Chatellerault as modified. Used in Indo-China.

This "fortress model" Chatellerault was another one of the great "secret weapons" of the French which tied in with their Maginot Line psychology. It was actually fitted with a device operated from the recoil and the counter recoiling motion of the bolt to inject water into the chamber end of the barrel for cooling. This action took place as the case was extracted and before the new round was chambered. This represented a tremendous military secret to the French. The theory was that in the Maginot Line the attack would be made directly from the front and any gun which could maintain long bursts of fire would unquestionably annihilate the Germans coming forward in mass formation! Like the forward-facing artillery of the Maginot Line, the guns did not get an opportunity to demonstrate themselves.

Chatellerault also furnished an aircraft version allegedly capable of firing 1600 rounds per minute. On actual tests it proved to be much nearer 1300. The magazine was a monstrosity intended to hold 500 cartridges. The big "secret" in the design was allegedly a new type of spring having at least double the life of the customary type—according to the production men at the Chatellerault Arsenal.

Actually the spring had already been used by the Russians. Aircraft machine guns on planes sent to Spain by Russia during the Civil War in 1937 utilized this type of spring. It consisted in coiling several smaller diameter springs of piano wire together to replace the single thicker coil. There is no question about the efficiency of the spring. The only question is about the secrecy with which its alleged development was surrounded.

The Danish Madsen

In 1923 the Madsen syndicate altered its production considerably to bring it more into line with requirements of the time.

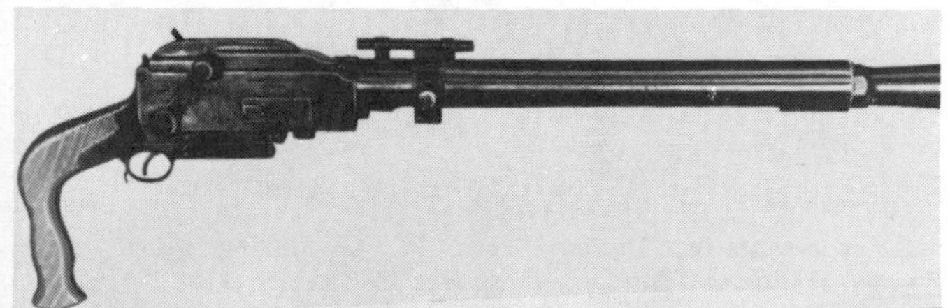

Representative Danish Madsen, tank pattern. The Madsens are dealt with at length in chapter 21.

An aircraft type and tank version of the machine gun were produced. Weapons were made in a wide variety for almost any type or caliber. The general mechanism was not altered to any significant degree. The guns were made more streamlined in appearance and some were fitted with muzzle boosters to speed up the rate of fire.

The arms are discussed in detail in chapter 21. Because of the tremendous spread of the Madsen arms throughout the world, these weapons may be said to be of more than passing interest.

The English B. S. A. Machine Gun

The B. S. A. is of interest only as a historical item today.

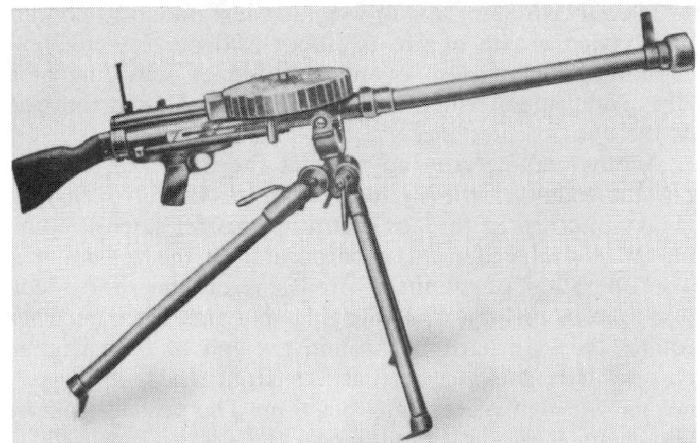

English Birmingham Small Arms Machine Gun.

It was developed in 1924 by the Birmingham Small Arms Company with the intention of making it a .50 caliber gun, basically for use by airplane observers.

Externally it resembles the familiar Lewis gun. Its system is radically different in every respect, however. The ammunition was the same as that used in the .50 caliber Vickers aircraft gun. Besides the aircraft version, another water-cooled gun was provided for naval use.

The drum feed resembles the Lewis only externally. It carries 37 rounds of ammunition. This is much too small for practical use with the bursts involved.

Unlike the Lewis, which it resembles so closely in external line, this gun is technically a short-recoil action. However, it is a freak in its category. Instead of the normal travel to the rear of the barrel, bolt, and extension mechanism, this weird mechanism traversed a distance of 2⅞ inches fully locked before the unlocking operation commenced. No explanation was given for this unnecessarily long stroke. It must be remembered that it has all the characteristics otherwise of a short-recoil action.

Because of the long locking stroke the rate of fire was very low, about 400 rounds per minute. This is much too low for aircraft purposes, but is ideal for a land gun.

Nothing was done with general manufacture of this gun in light of the advances and tactical developments after its introduction. It was not produced in quantity.

The Italian Breda Machine Guns

While the Breda guns are covered in chapter 31, the background of their development is sufficient to merit historical mention at this point.

Societa Italiana Ernesto Breda at Brescia was originally a locomotive manufacturing plant. During World War I it produced the Model 1914 Revelli gun which we have already discussed, operating on sub-contract from the Fiat Company which held the Revelli patents.

Breda constructed a separate plant near the locomotive works to produce arms. Considerably enlarged, this works today is producing some of the world's finest automatic shotguns, which are commonly exported to the United States.

At the close of World War I Breda undertook development work on machine guns which resulted in the Model

1924 caliber 6.5mm, a gun weighing just under 20 pounds and having a rate of fire of about 500 per minute.

Its magazine system is entirely unique, consisting of a clip arrangement which can be pivoted out from the side of the gun for loading.

Another noteworthy advance at the time and still important today is the system of quick barrel exchange. Heavy interrupted threads secure the barrel extension and barrel. A flash hider was incorporated in the gun muzzle. The operation of all these Bredas is on the short-recoil principle. A locking ring engaging six cams in the receiver rotates the lock partially around the end of the barrel in closing. The locking lugs at the front end of the bolt engage the two pieces into position. The recoil stroke is about three-eighths of an inch.

Cartridges are loaded from a cardboard container directly into the magazine, which has been hinged out from the side of the receiver for loading. In closing the action, the last cartridge to be inserted in the magazine is picked up by the bolt.

The normal extraction on this arm is extremely violent. An oil apparatus is provided, which is operated by the recoil and counter recoil of the mechanism to squirt oil into the chamber between shots. This lubrication of the ammunition is necessary to prevent the violent breech opening from tearing the heads off cartridge cases while being extracted.

When finally issued, the first Breda was listed as a Model 1926. Much confusion at times is encountered in Italian arms designation because the Fiat produced in their "Safat" plant another model which was also designated Model 1926.

After some minor changes, Breda issued a modified model in 1928, the modifications being relatively small. Late in 1930 Breda absorbed Fiat. It assumed control over all machinery, patents, and equipment for the production of machine arms and automatic rifles. A new plant called the Breda-Fiat was opened at Piacenza.

The first product of the new plant was the 1930 model Breda. This appeared in the standard Italian 6.5mm caliber and also in 7mm and 7.92mm calibers for export, the latter, of course, being the standard German cartridge which is in common use in countries where Mauser rifles have been sold.

The Italian Breda Model 1937 Machine Gun

This model was an outgrowth of experimental work done in 1931. It is a gas-operated arm entirely unlike any of the preceding Bredas.

It too was noteworthy for still another freak type of feeding system. The feed is by tray, the cartridges being inserted from chargers holding 20 rounds, each of which is housed in a separate compartment.

In operating this model which was made in an 8mm caliber, the gunner inserts a loaded 20-cartridge tray in the feed slot in the left side of the receiver. The cocking handle on the right side is pulled back to withdraw the gas piston and locking mechanism. This action also indexes the feed tray to bring a cartridge into feeding position.

There is no provision for single shot fire. Pushing the trigger off the safe position and forcing the trigger in releases the sear from the gas piston assembly. The assembly, driven forward by the compressed spring, chambers the cartridge in its path.

The bolt stops directly behind the head of the cartridge case but the piston continues its forward movement, camming the breechlock up into recesses in the top of the receiver. As the movement continues a projection on the gas piston strikes the firing pin to discharge the cartridge in the chamber.

The gas port on the underside of the barrel is some two-thirds of the distance down from the breech end. The barrel weighs close to 10 pounds, being unusually heavy to permit firing large bursts.

As the gas passes through the orifice into the gas cylinder, pressure is exerted against the piston therein. The initial opening movement withdraws the firing pin and lowers the breechlock to free the bolt. Some initial extraction is provided. As the bolt is unlocked it first moves the cartridge case back sufficiently to loosen it from its chamber.

From this point on the action is distinctive. As the cartridge case is extracted and drawn back by the extractor in the face of the bolt, its motion is halted by a dog on the receiver. Simultaneously a cam thrusts the empty case up into the space it originally occupied in the feed tray.

When the 20 cartridges have been discharged, the

A representative Italian Breda M. G. during quick barrel change. Important Bredas are shown in chapter 31.

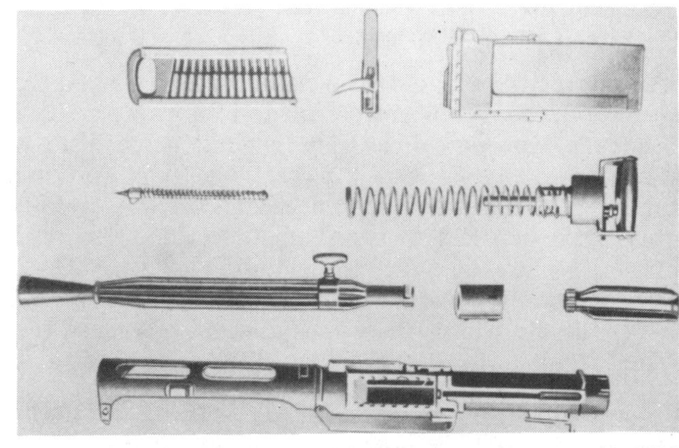

A representative Breda field stripped to demonstrate simplicity of design.

clip which contains all the empty cases is thrown out of the gun to the right.

The theory of this clip system is that it will make it easy to reclaim cartridge cases since they may be picked up in units of 20. In actual practice the clips are damaged so often that reuse of the clip or of the ammunition cases is seldom practical.

The Italian designers themselves came to this conclusion after exhaustive tests. As a result, in 1938 they issued a modified tank model which also saw considerable service during World War II. This design has an overhead clip-feed. Cartridge cases are ejected out the bottom of the receiver. The arm is furnished with a pistol-type grip. Beyond this, however, the mechanism and the principles are the same as with the 1937 model already described.

The Italian Breda-Safat Model 1935

These guns represent a combination of the old Mascarucci locking principle already discussed and design improvements developed by the engineers at the Breda Works.

Basically these were intended as aircraft machine guns. The lock was inverted to place it on the bottom. Muzzle boosters were furnished to increase the rapidity of action and hence rate of fire. Recoil-operated accelerators were also incorporated.

The guns were issued in 7.7mm caliber using the same cartridge as the British, the .303 rimmed. They were also made in 7.92mm German caliber and in 13.2mm for use against vehicles. These guns were designated Breda-Safat Model 1935.

A disintegrating metal link belt was provided for feed. It was so arranged that feeding on the aircraft model could be from either side. Ejection was through the bottom of the receiver. The chambers in the barrels of these guns were fluted. This was required to expedite extraction. The principle is that of allowing the gas expanding as the cartridge fires to "float" the empty case momentarily until pressure is lowered.

The Swiss Furrer Machine Gun

Swiss small arms in general have had very little direct influence on gun design, and even less throughout the world because they are normally very expensive to produce. The designs of Colonel Adolf Furrer are worthy of considerable attention both from a historical and design standpoint, nevertheless.

His prototype gun produced in 1925 was an 18-pound air-cooled ground machine gun with a shoulder stock. His principle of locking and operation has been applied to a wide variety of arms from rifles and machine arms through submachine guns and cannon. All have been mechanically successful. Few have seen any service outside of Switzerland.

The locking principle of the Furrer is the toggle joint system, basically as found in the Luger pistol design. As we have seen, this toggle action was developed long before Borchardt, the developer of the predecessor of the Luger, entered the field of firearms. It is also the basic locking principle of the various Maxim guns.

The Luger pattern of pistol was the official side arm of the Swiss army from early in the 20th Century until 1948. It is most likely that Colonel Furrer, who was Director of the Swiss Government's Small Arms Plant at Berne for some time, got the idea for his mechanism from that pistol. However, he went beyond the customary pistol locking procedure and developed a number of refinements.

The first Furrer gun was the Model 1925. This was an air-cooled, 18-pound light machine gun with shoulder stock. It was fed from a 30-shot clip magazine using the standard 7.5mm Swiss rifle cartridge.

Barrels were made by Hammerli of Lenzburg, still one of the world's finest custom gun and barrel makers. They are producers of some of the finest precision pistols made and are today making auto target pistols based on the German Walther Olympia pattern.

Manufacture of the initial gun proceeded slowly while tests were made on its efficiency and also on methods of manufacture. In 1928 a sufficient number had been delivered to warrant full-scale adoption after it had survived all possible field and endurance tests. The Hammerli barrels, a feature of the weapon, are commonly considered to be accurate for at least 20,000 rounds.

Because of the light weight of the barrel and the relatively small surface allowed for heat radiation, the gun required cooling after about 400 shots had been fired from the full automatic position. Each gun carried a complement of 34 spare magazines. A flash hider, muzzle booster, and blast suppressor were incorporated in the gun construction. As customary in all Swiss firearms, the parts were magnificently machined but were so intricate that mass production was never possible.

A very unusual feature in the Furrer is the construction, which permits exceptional timing of the operations. The barrel and barrel extension are held in rear position after the unlocking stroke. The action, of course, is a typical short-recoil fully-locked system. Nevertheless, it incorporates an interesting operational feature not commonly found.

This feature is an arrangement whereby the gun is actually fired a small fraction of a second before the moving elements are stopped by the receiver. In this design, unlike the blowback, the barrel and bolt are securely locked, but firing actually occurs while the recoiling parts are moving forward under tension of the spring behind them. In effect this permits the gun to fire and start recoiling before the bolt metal strikes the receiver metal. This gives a buffing action which produces a very smooth firing cycle. It also cushions all the parts and adds greatly to their length of serviceable life.

The design was adapted for airplane use also. Guns of both flexible and fixed type were made. Belt feeds were arranged for these types, the belts normally being disintegrating. In these patterns longer barrels were employed on the aircraft guns than on the ground types.

The fire rate of the aircraft types was stepped up from the 450 per minute (normal for the infantry version) to about 1,200 rounds a minute through the use of a trap to utilize the expanding gases as the bullet leaves the bore. The backward thrust against the barrel muzzle accelerates the recoiling action. In addition, heavily spring-loaded buffers provide a faster return to step up firing rate.

The barrel and all the attached firing mechanism may be withdrawn from the rear of the receiver as an assembled unit. A new assembly can be inserted to continue operation during parts replacement in case any defects in operation are encountered. This is a rather farfetched provision which is not normally of value except possibly for fortification or defense work. It must be remembered that the energies of the Swiss have been concentrated for generations on just such employment, so the design makes sense in Switzerland, at least.

In operating the gun, a magazine is locked into position in the side of the receiver. The operating handle is pulled back to unlock and open the action. When the trigger is pressed, the sear is lowered allowing the compressed operating spring to thrust the firing mechanism forward.

When the bolt comes to the position of the feed a loaded round is driven forward from it into the firing chamber. On the last fraction of an inch of travel, the toggle locking joint is forced into line. As it locks, by cam action, it also cocks the piece. The sear holding the firing pin can rotate inside the frame of the bolt. It pivots and releases the firing pin which has its own spring. The pin is driven forward to fire.

As already noted, however, the action is still moving forward at the instant of firing, although all the elements of barrel, bolt, and barrel extension are rigidly locked at this point.

As the recoil starts, the barrel extension and bolt and barrel are still locked together during the first fraction of an inch of rearward travel. There are suitable guides for them, of course, in the receiver. The bolt is carried in a frame which is also traveling to the rear at this point. It connects by a link with the forward end of a pivoted member which is also a link. This rear link is mounted in the frame (so it can rotate on a pivot). The front end is attached to the barrel extension and the rear end connected by pivot pin to one of the support links.

As the unlocking point is reached, a stationary projection in the receiver breaks the joint of the toggle, allowing the bolt to open slowly to furnish primary extraction. As the unlocking motion is continued past the locked point, the further action draws the loosened cartridge case held by the extractor until the case hits the ejector in the receiver wall. The empty case is pivoted and ejected through the ejection port.

The barrel and barrel extension unlocked from the bolt remain in rear position. As the bolt completes its recoil stroke, stored-up operating spring energy drives it ahead to feed. The bolt compresses the firing pin spring to cock it only in the final act of locking the breech. This gun fires from a closed breech.

Detailed characteristics of weapon will be found in chapter 41.

The Czech ZB Machine Guns

Since these guns are dealt with in chapter 20, only historical references are required at this point. However, in view of the importance of the ZB Works, at this time when Czechoslovakia is under Communist domination, their designs cannot be too strongly emphasized.

A producing company set up at Brno (Brunn) was established in 1922. Today, of course, it is under Communist control. Little information about its operational heads is currently available, though the arms being manufactured there are well known because of worldwide distribution.

In addition, sporting rifles based on the Mauser pattern actions made at this plant were sold in the United States until quite recently. Sporting rifles using this action and automatic pistols of the pocket variety, which are used in police and military circles abroad, were also imported into the United States by both east and west coast importers in very large quantities.

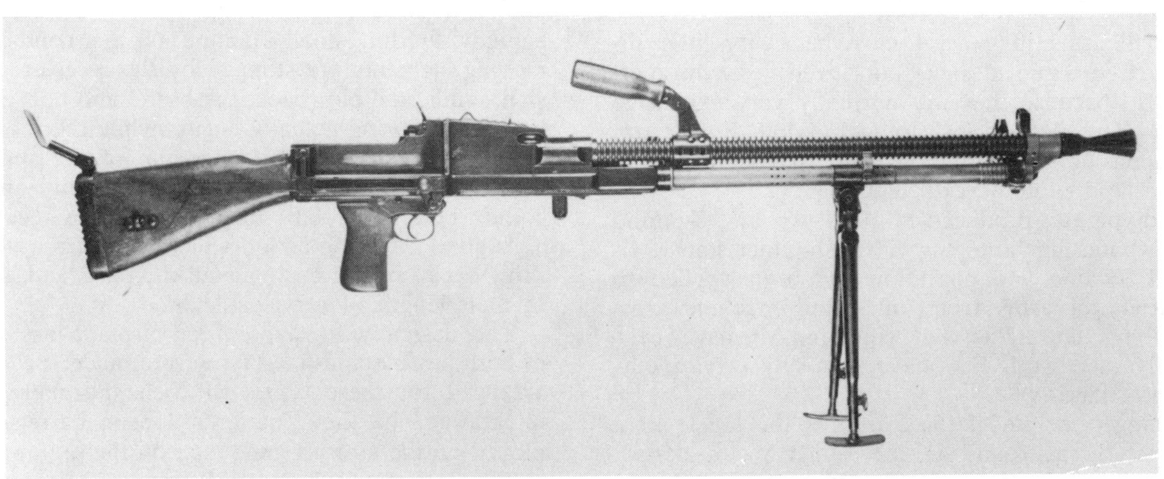

Representative Z. B. Machine Gun. Weapon captured by General George S. Patton in World War II. On the right side of receiver is marked Kulomet-26.

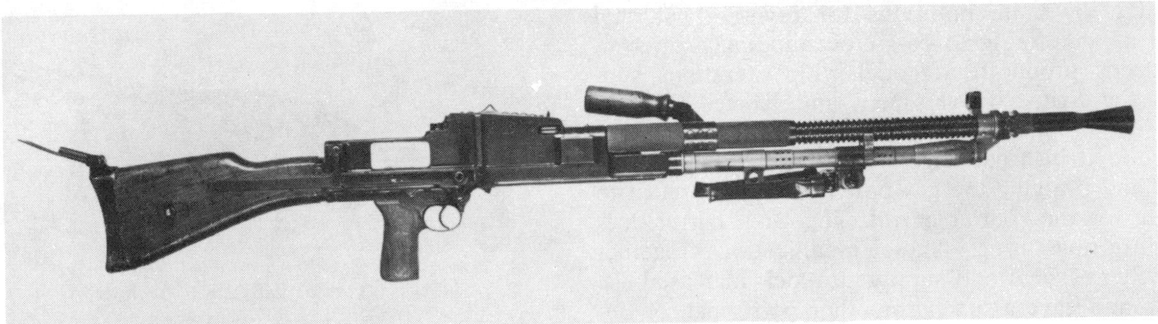

Representative Z.B. as made for Yugoslavia (ZB30J).

Representative Z. B. showing quick barrel change lever. Magazine mounts on top of gun.

The original company was named Ceskoslovenska Zbrojovka Akciova Spolecnost v Brno. Upon its formation in 1922, 75% of the stock was retained by the Czech government and 20% was held by the Skoda Works, the remaining 5% being distributed among employees.

At this time very close liaison was developed with the French authorities. French technicians were supplied to aid in the development of the plant. In short order, however, they became subsidiary to the Czechs both in importance and ability.

In 1922 the ZB Works produced their first light machine gun, a Hotchkiss model of French design. It was modified, of course, but was still the French pattern.

By 1924 they had developed a prototype light machine gun based on the principles of the commonly known Berthier, the Hotchkiss, and the American and Belgian Browning Automatic Rifles.

When this gun was put into production it was introduced as the Brno ZB Model 1926 and was offered for world sale under that designation. The name probably was determined upon because of the difficulty foreigners would have in otherwise identifying it or pronouncing it.

The principal designers were two Czechs, Vaclav and Emanuel Holek, brothers. An Austrian engineer, Marek, and the Polish engineer, Podradsky, were also influential in design.

Vaclav Holek is a designer of outstanding ability. He is responsible for the production of a very remarkable semi-automatic rifle which was intended largely for sporting use but was curtailed by the beginning of the war. This gun is a masterpiece of simplified operation on the gas principle and is designed for high-speed production. It uses a large number of easily manufactured parts, including stampings and screw machine parts, and leans heavily on the utilization of torsion springs of very simple design.

This Holek rifle was manufactured for a number of Mauser type cartridges, notably the 7.9mm German military cartridge. It fires from a closed breech, utilizes an internal hammer, has an extremely simple takedown system, and is clip fed with a detachable box magazine. The cocking is rather unusual, being done by a sling strap attached to a swivel at the forward end of a sliding element over the gas tube.

Vaclav Holek is credited with the principal features of the combination he made in the design of the ZB light machine guns. It is worth noting that his remarkable ability was recognized and that he became a very wealthy man as a result of the international sales of the products of his genius which were manufactured in the ZB Works.

The ZB is one of the finest light machine guns ever developed. Because of the exceptional quality of the steel provided by the Skoda plant, spare barrels could be easily interchanged after rapid fire. Even red hot barrels of this steel can be plunged into cold water without injuring them. A quick change barrel feature was an important element in the design, since the gun could stand only about three complete magazines in full automatic fire before requiring cooling. The Japanese Type 97 tank gun is a slightly modified ZB26.

The British Bren Gun

This gun, which is discussed in chapter 17, is of historical interest also, because of its evolution from the ZB arm, and because during the war many technicians from the Czech Works, who had contacted the British during the development of the Bren, left their native land and joined the military and engineering forces of Great Britain and the United States. When Great Britain instituted a series of tests for a new light machine gun in 1932, Madsen and the Vickers-Berthier were ranged alongside the ZB model for testing. The ZB out-performed competition to such an extent that even at the expense of losing face the British decided to go outside the confines of the Island to obtain their new design. This took a considerable amount of moral courage on the part of the British military authorities. Practically all countries including our own are notorious for favoring National designs even when foreign ones are outstandingly superior.

The Czechs produced a model with alterations submitted by the British Government and labeled the gun the ZBG. The modifications, aside from rechambering the barrel for the British cartridge, were basically shortening the barrel and bringing the gas port nearer the breech to compensate for the shorter barrel. The Bren barrel does not move during firing. These modifications together with a newly designed and supported stock increased the rate of fire and gave a much smoother performance. Because of the recoil mechanism redesigning, the stock on the Bren as it is now known cannot be hinged.

The British Government was licensed by ZB to manufacture. In January, 1935, drawings were received from the ZB firm. By September, 1937, the Enfield Government Arms Plant produced its first guns. They were called the Bren. The first two letters were taken from Brunn (Brno) in Czechoslovakia. The last two letters were from Enfield, the British Arsenal.

In January, 1938, 200 guns were assembled. By the middle of the same year production had been stepped up to about 300 a week. That rate of production continued until September, 1939, when it was increased to about 400 a week.

The guns themselves continued to be made at the Royal Small Arms factory, but the B. S. A. and the Austin organization received contracts to produce spare magazines. Considerable initial trouble was encountered until it was found that the drawings had provided for magazines to hold rimless cartridges while the British ammunition of course was rimmed. In spite of this it was found that the magazine could be loaded with 29 instead of the customary 30 cartridges and still work well.

Upon the outbreak of World War II the Bren gun was manufactured in very large quantities in England and also in Canada for British service use.

The Canadian manufacturing plant also furnished large quantities of the gun to China in caliber 7.92mm, most of the military rifle equipment there at that time being of German Mauser type using the German service cartridge.

The Czech ZB 50 Machine Gun

In 1932 the Czechs developed a new gun under the designation Model 50-1932. This gun is a short-recoil arm in caliber 7.92mm. This represents the first recoil-operated arm produced at ZB, although experimental work had preceded it.

The bolt assembly resembles that of the gas-operated models. However, the gas piston principle is eliminated. An accelerator transfers the energy at the time of recoil and at the instant of unlocking to transmit full force to the bolt, speeding it to the rear. This accelerator works very much like that of our own Browning machine gun.

Feed is by a non-disintegrating metal belt. The belt is expelled and the gun held open on the last shot. The design of the gun is largely credited to and patented by Anton Marek. A feature of his design is that only a loaded cartridge is needed to completely dismount the gun. The point of a bullet is used to depress a number of spring loaded detents, a system also utilized in many experimental designs by Holek.

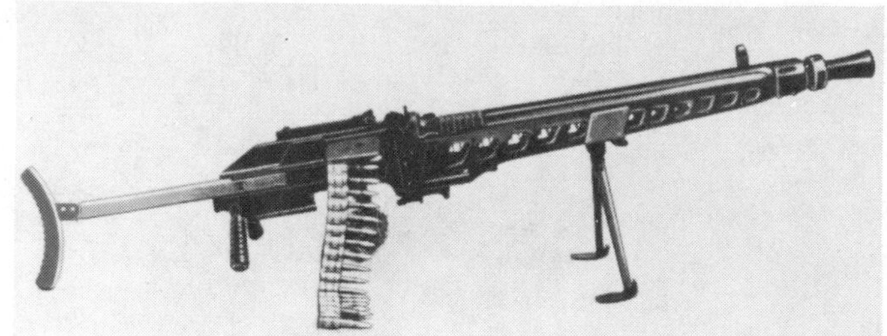

Czech Z.B. 50 Machine Gun.

A combination of a muzzle booster and the accelerator gave a firing rate of about 600 rounds per minute, the booster being also made to serve as a flash hider and forward barrel bearing. The influence of this design on later German developments can be seen.

A most unusual safety design is incorporated. It acts not only to lock the sear to prevent its release, but also lowers the bullet point of the cartridge in line with the bolt so that if by any breakage or freak action the sear might be slipped, the bolt going forward could not chamber the cartridge to fire it.

The British Besa Machine Gun

The ZB Plant was seized by the Germans early in World War II. It was operated under their control during the war as the Waffenwerke Brunn A. G.

The Germans maintained the working organization of ZB and used the arms produced there throughout the war. Currently the work is similarly progressing under Communist domination.

The British Besa machine guns of World War II are also of Czech design. They stem from the 1937 gun of Vaclav Holek. The plant designation was ZB 53 model 1937.

Officially this gun was known in Czech service as the Model 1937.

Its performance impressed the British to such an extent that again they secured licenses to manufacture this new product of the ZB Works.

The name Besa was applied to this gun. The B is for Brno. The E means Enfield. The SA are the initials of the Birmingham Small Arms Corporation which entered into the manufacture.

The introduction of this gun represented still another instance in British procedure in the line of accepting efficiency before national pride. Since the gun was chambered for the very efficient German 7.92mm rimless cartridge, the British continued use of this instead of their own .303, even in the face of possible ammunition complications. As a secondary advantage, however, it might be pointed out that captured German ammunition could be used in the gun.

This gun and modifications were known as Besa 7.92mm Mark I, II, III, and III*. Later a 15mm caliber was designed to utilize a high-velocity anti-tank cartridge.

The new weapon was listed as the Besa 15mm Mark I and is a copy of the ZB 60 (Czech 15mm M1938 machine gun).

Again we find that in the interests of engineering design and manufacturing economy, the basic operating parts of the gas models were kept. Alterations were made only as required for the new operation.

The cocking system of these guns is unique. The grip is pushed forward. A sear catches the extension of the gas piston. The grip and triggerguard are then pulled straight back, bringing all the operating parts to the rear and held by the sear. Grip is then returned to a normal position, care being taken to keep the finger away from the trigger during this motion as otherwise the gun will fire.

By the use of very heavy barrels, some flanged and others not, Holek succeeded in reducing the necessity for barrel cooling or replacement.

Because the shoulder stock of previous items in this field was removed (since the guns were basically intended for either tripod or tank mounting), the spring-loaded buffer system had to be housed within the receiver itself.

This buffer system permitted an increase or decrease of firing rate. By elevating the buffer system, the bolt was permitted a further rearward travel on its recoil stroke and the compressed operating spring alone served to return the parts to battery. This combination resulted in a slowing down of the action. The buffer of course functioned as an accelerator, though actually in effect it was not. Its function was to interfere with the length of the bolt stroke and by shortening it and compelling a faster recoil to move the gun back into battery at faster rate.

Thus it did not add energy to speed up the recoiling parts, but effected the same result by interfering with the length of travel and the rapidity of return.

Gas pressure could be increased if desired by turning a circular piece having two holes of different size. By rotating this member between the port in the barrel and the gas piston cylinder, control was obtained.

After the grip has been pushed forward to catch the piston assembly, pulled back to cock it and compress the operating spring, and then returned to position, the arm is ready for firing. A selector switch on the side of the handle permits single shot or full automatic fire.

Pressing the trigger releases the sear. The firing mechanism moves forward impelled by the powerful operating spring. A projection at the forward top of the bolt passes through the center of a cartridge link, pushing the cartridge ahead of it directly into the chamber.

As the bolt reaches firing position, its rear end is directly under the locking recess in the bolt extension. An extension on the gas piston is held to the rear by a beveled locking lug. It continues forward as the lug cams the rear of the bolt up into the locking recess and out of the piston extension path. The final travel of the piston extension serves to free the barrel holding catch. The barrel, bolt, piston, and extension move forward to firing position. The locking lug on the piston extension strikes the firing pin and fires the weapon. As in similar designs, such as the Swiss Furrer already discussed, the recoil movement in this gas-operated arm starts slightly before the forward-moving parts contact the stationary receiver, thereby giving a cushioning effect and smoothing out the operation of the gun itself.

The gas port is about one-third of the way forward from the breech end. Gas striking the face of the piston drives it rearward in recoil. The back of the lug on the piston extension pulls the bolt down out of its locking recess.

The cartridge extractor is standard but the ejector is positioned in the belt guide. Ejection is through a slot in the piston extension and in the receiver.

A barrel recoil spring is mounted in the cover group to reduce the upward jump of the muzzle and increase accuracy.

The British Vickers-Berthier Machine Gun

The Vickers Company purchased the manufacturing rights to Berthier Machine Guns in 1925 and started limited production.

The light machine guns so produced were not particularly successful, although organizations such as the Latvian Army did adapt them for their rifle cartridge. Spain and South America bought limited quantities and the gun was also officially adopted by the Indian Army. It received relatively little service use during World War II.

This was a gas-piston-operated machine gun. It was modeled along lines somewhat like the Bren but was quite different in functioning. Its aircraft version appeared in 1928. It was outmoded because the turrets in the planes were fitted with belt-fed fixed-type weapons.

The bolt locking was by a tipping-up operation of the bolt itself. The magazine in the aircraft design resembled externally the Lewis but did not rotate. This gun has had no particular effect on armaments development, although at the time of its introduction it represented a step ahead in the small number of parts, the complete enclosure of those parts, and the ability to be dismounted and assembled without the use of tools.

The Finnish Lahti (Suomi) Machine Gun

These very interesting arms are dealt with in chapter 23. However, a note concerning them has a place here.

The designer was Aimo Johannes Lahti. Another of his noted products is the Lahti pistol. He served as Chief of Finland's Government Arsenal for a number of years. His inventions also cover rifles, submachine guns, and cannon. All of them were good; all of them were simple. His developments included both gas and short-recoil-operated arms.

The weapons themselves were first produced in 1926 at the Valtion Kivaaritehdas which, translated, is State Rifle Factory. This is at Jyaskyla, Finland. The Lahti machine gun was a primary arm of the Finns in the defense of their country against the Russian invasion. Originally designed in 1926, it was modified in 1932. It is recoil-operated, air-cooled, and can be fired both full automatic and single shot.

When the gun went into manufacture, the producers hoped to sell it to either the Germans or the British. As it happened it served a far better purpose in its part in defending Finland during the Russian attack.

The German Rheinmetall-Borsig Machine Gun

The noted German Solothurn Machine Guns were made by the Rheinmetall-Borsig A. G., one of the largest munitions industries in Germany in World War II.

The parent of this organization was the original Rheinische Metallwaren und Maschinenfabrik A. G. founded in May, 1889.

It was set up by the firm of Horder Bergwerk of Westfalen in that year to manufacture new jacketed bullets for the German Army. The plant was at Dusseldorf in one of its suburbs. The company prospered in the armaments field. When World War I began it was second only to Krupp in the production of munitions. Among its products were the German version of the Maxim gun, the Model 08.

The plant was dismantled by order of the victors under the Versailles Treaty after World War I. However, the Germans managed to get some 23,000 tons of tools, dies, patents, and drawings out of Germany and into Holland where they were stored in warehouses at Rotterdam and at Delfzyl.

The Inter-Allied Control Commission allowed Rheinmetall to build, for the reconstituted small German army and navy which was authorized, all guns below 17cm bore diameter.

In effect this ruling concentrated *all* army weapon developments in this company from 1925 to 1927. Special facilities were instituted for development work.

After unsatisfactory arrangements with Holland, the German company in 1929 obtained control of the Waffenfabrik Solothurn A. G. in Switzerland. This plant was originally a watch manufacturing concern. It was purchased by a Swiss who had previously worked for the Deutsche Waffen und Munitionsfabrik A. G. in Germany.

He set up to manufacture weapons but failed financially. The notorious Fritz Mandl of Hirtenberg, Austria then obtained control. Rheinmetall worked with Mandl in the development of the Solothurn Plant to bypass Allied restrictions on machine gun manufacture and development.

The German authorities had complete stock control of this works. Arrangements were made with armament works in Austria and in Hungary to produce component parts for automatic arms.

Within a few months of the time Rheinmetall took over the Solothurn firm, weapons began appearing with the new name. The plant, of course, was used merely as an assembly point.

The Germans utilized this plan to sell throughout the world outmoded equipment as they developed new and improved forms for their own use.

This was common knowledge in arms circles at the time and it is incredible that government agencies and intelligence organizations either had no knowledge of it or failed to properly evaluate the information received. This permitted Germany a tremendous edge in rearmament which actually hastened World War II.

The Solothurn Model 29

The Model 1929 gun was offered for sale to military groups throughout the world just two months after Rheinmetall purchased the stock control.

The actual development of the gun is credited to Louis Stange, a German designer who worked originally in the Bergmann factory at Suhl under Schmeisser, who was one of the great developers of automatic arms systems.

Schmeisser, whose pistols and submachine guns we shall touch upon later, was also affiliated with Rheinmetall. It was no secret at any time that many of his patents were assigned to this company.

The first Solothurn was short recoil operated. Cooling was by air. The gun weighed only 17 pounds when chambered for the German 7.92mm cartridge.

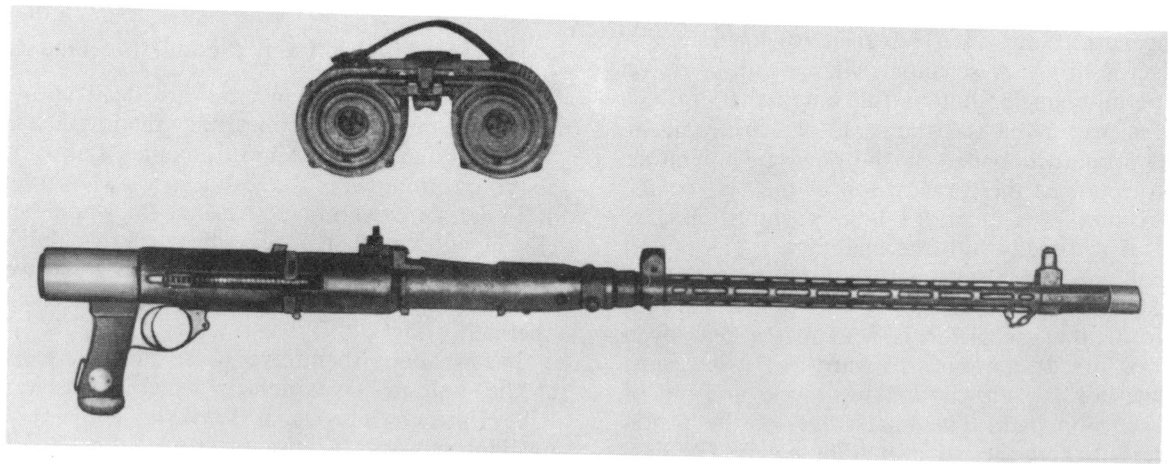

German R-B Machine Gun. Customarily an aircraft gun, this pattern was at times adapted for ground use. MG 15.

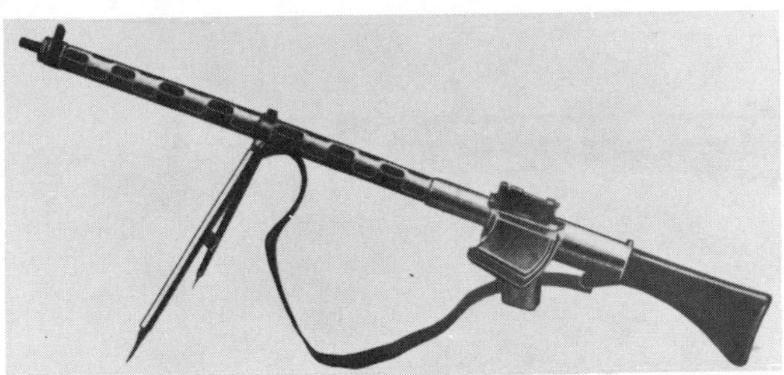

Model 29 Solothurn made in Switzerland.

This gun is extremely interesting in connection with current world design, as it pointed the way to the first really low-priced, high-production, dependable automatic weapons. A large number of the units were lathe turned or made by screw machines. Since this type of manufacture can be conducted by semi-skilled or at times even unskilled help, the guns had considerable acceptance in countries where mechanical skills are not highly developed. Replacement parts for the guns could be made in an emergency by almost any commercial metal turning shop.

Single shot or automatic fire is provided in the Solothurn.

The breech-locking action developed by Stange is most unusual. It is cylindrical in shape. A central locking ring rigidly holds the bolt and barrel together by six interrupted threads. Only in the fully-locked position is an obstruction removed from the path of firing pin. This prevents accidental discharge.

The magazine holds 25 cartridges. After the last shot is fired the bolt is held open.

A safety is provided to lock bolt and trigger together. This permits inserting a loaded magazine while the bolt is locked.

A refined version, the S-2-200 appeared in 1930. It was also called the MG30.

The Austrian Solothurn Model 30

The Solothurn was technically Swiss, but since Rheinmetall was the only outlet it obviously was German. Hence the gun is usually so recognized throughout the military world.

Austria purchased this same model, also designating it Model 30, in 8mm caliber. The Steyr Arms factory in Austria actually furnished most of the parts for the Solothurn, manufacturing them under the noses of control authorities and shipping them to Switzerland for assembly.

Hungary adopted this model as the Model 31 in the following year. As an index of the volume produced, it might be pointed out that from 1930 to 1935 Austria and Hungary alone purchased over 5,000 of these machine guns.

The trigger system of the earlier model was retained. Its face has two curved depressions, pressure on the top one giving single shot operation, and a pull on the lower one giving full automatic fire. This system allows the operator to fire single shot or full automatic without any movement of the hand except the index finger and without shifting aim from the target.

Although German army tests firing 100,000 rounds on this model produced very good results, other and more advanced designs were already on the way, and the Germans did not adopt it for general use although they did use many for drill.

The MG30 featured a special quick change barrel system. Pressing a locking piece allows the shoulder stock to be turned 60 degrees to the left and pulled to the rear. The operating spring and guide remain in the rear section. The barrel with the attached bolt and other assembly are then shaken out the rear of the receiver. By disconnecting the barrel from the rest of the assembly, a cool barrel can be inserted.

To fire, a magazine is inserted with the bolt either open or closed. Assuming it to be closed, the operating handle is then pulled to the rear. The mechanism is held to the rear by the sear ready for discharge. When the trigger is pulled the bolt moves forward under the drive of the compressed operating spring. It picks up a cartridge from the magazine and pushes it into the chamber. The bolt (carried in a special carrier) drives the carrier, the barrel, and the barrel locking ring ahead under its spring thrust. The locking ring is turned under the influence of its lugs engaging in spiral grooves and locks the assembly. The firing pin is released as the action.locks in its fully forward position.

As the arm fires and the mechanism recoils, when the unlocking position is reached the rollers on the locking ring engage the spiral grooves machined into the walls of the receiver.

The rearward movement turns the locking ring to free the bolt. The barrel, bolt extension, and locking ring are halted by a buffer and held in rearward position. The bolt and the mainspring guide continue rearward under the acceleration imparted by the spiral grooves. The extractor pulls back the empty case. As ejection takes place the continuing rearward action of the parts is finally halted. The firing pin spring is compressed as the bolt starts into counter recoil position. At the end of the stroke and if the automatic trigger is being held, the action continues until the magazine is emptied.

In 1932 Rheinmetall introduced the MG15, an aircraft-type gun for the German forces.

This gun was only a modification of the MG30, a muzzle booster allowing an increase in rate of fire to as much as 1,000 per minute. Special drum magazines of the saddle type holding 75 rounds each were furnished

Austrian Solothurn Model 30 made in Switzerland.

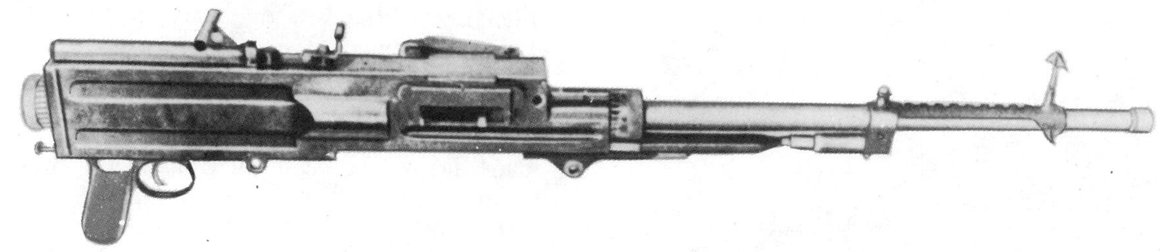

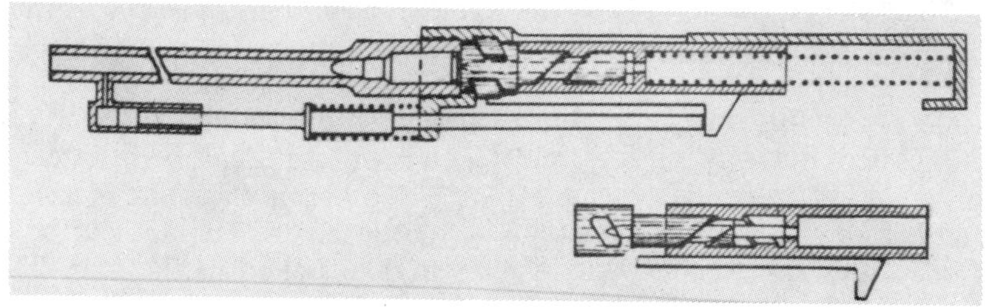

Italian Scotti Machine Gun and sectional drawings of mechanism.

for this gun. Each half of the drum is fired alternately, thus preventing the center of gravity from being affected as the firing continues.

Later aircraft models designated as the MG17 incorporated solenoids for electrical firing of the guns. A heavy model, known as the MG131 used a 13mm cartridge with a velocity of 2,560 feet per second. This design also used the locking ring principle of the Solothurn.

The Italian Scotti Machine Gun

Scotti, an Italian engineer in Brescia, Italy, introduced in 1928 the first of a long series of machine guns which he designed.

His production utilizes in all instances the delayed blowback system, with breech locking based on the earlier Mannlicher straight-line function of a turning bolt head.

While a very wide range of automatic and semi-automatic weapons including submachine guns and light machine guns appeared based on the Scotti patent, only his automatic cannon received any real attention.

His guns were manufactured largely by the Isotta-Fraschini Company, Italy's great automobile and aircraft engine plant. An organization he set up in Switzerland was eventually taken over by the great Swiss Oerlikon firm.

As we have indicated, his action was always based on the elementary principle of the gas port in the barrel tapping off gas to operate an under-barrel piston to unlock a rotating bolt which opens under residual gas pressure.

His use of feeding systems was considerably more varied, ranging all the way from the Perino system of metal clip loading, in which the empty case is reinserted automatically in the clip after being fired, to belt and drum feeds of all types.

The only really unusual gun produced under the Scotti patents was a machine gun utilizing three barrels. In operation (at least in theory) when one barrel was overheated the gunner operated a mechanism to rotate a new barrel into position, thus giving continuous fire. The device was never accepted as truly functional, however.

Danish Bang Machine Gun

The Danish Bang of 1929 was a machine gun in prototype. It was based on the operational principle of the forward moving muzzle cone as mentioned in chapter 7.

Italian Sistar Machine Gun

The Italian Sistar patented in December, 1932, also was produced only in prototypes in caliber 6.5mm and 7.92mm. The Sistar used one of the original swing-out magazine clips to permit rapid loading. Operation was short recoil on the rising or lifting block-locking principle.

The German MG 34

The MG 34 was developed at the Mauser Works in Oberndorf. We have dealt at some length with the Mauser organization in our section on rifles.

After World War I, when the equipment and plants of the Deutsche Waffen und Munitions-Fabriken (or D. W. M. as it is commonly known in America) were put out of operation by action of the Allies, the equipment, patents, and drawings covering the Luger "Pistole 08" were transferred to Mauser from D. W. M.

The work and models done by Heinemann in modifying the Maxim machine gun to the version we have discussed as the "Parabellum" were also transferred to Mauser.

No overt machine gun development was undertaken at the time, although considerable covert attention was given to the subject. It was not until 1934 when Hitler came into power and Germany began to rearm openly that active work was begun by Mauser on a new machine gun. The organization at that time was officially Mauser Werke, A. G.

A special all-purpose type machine gun to use the infantry ammunition was desired. It was specified that the new design must be adaptable to light and heavy machine gun use, as well as to tank and antiaircraft work. The general specifications to be met were provided by the German Military High Command. It was decided to begin

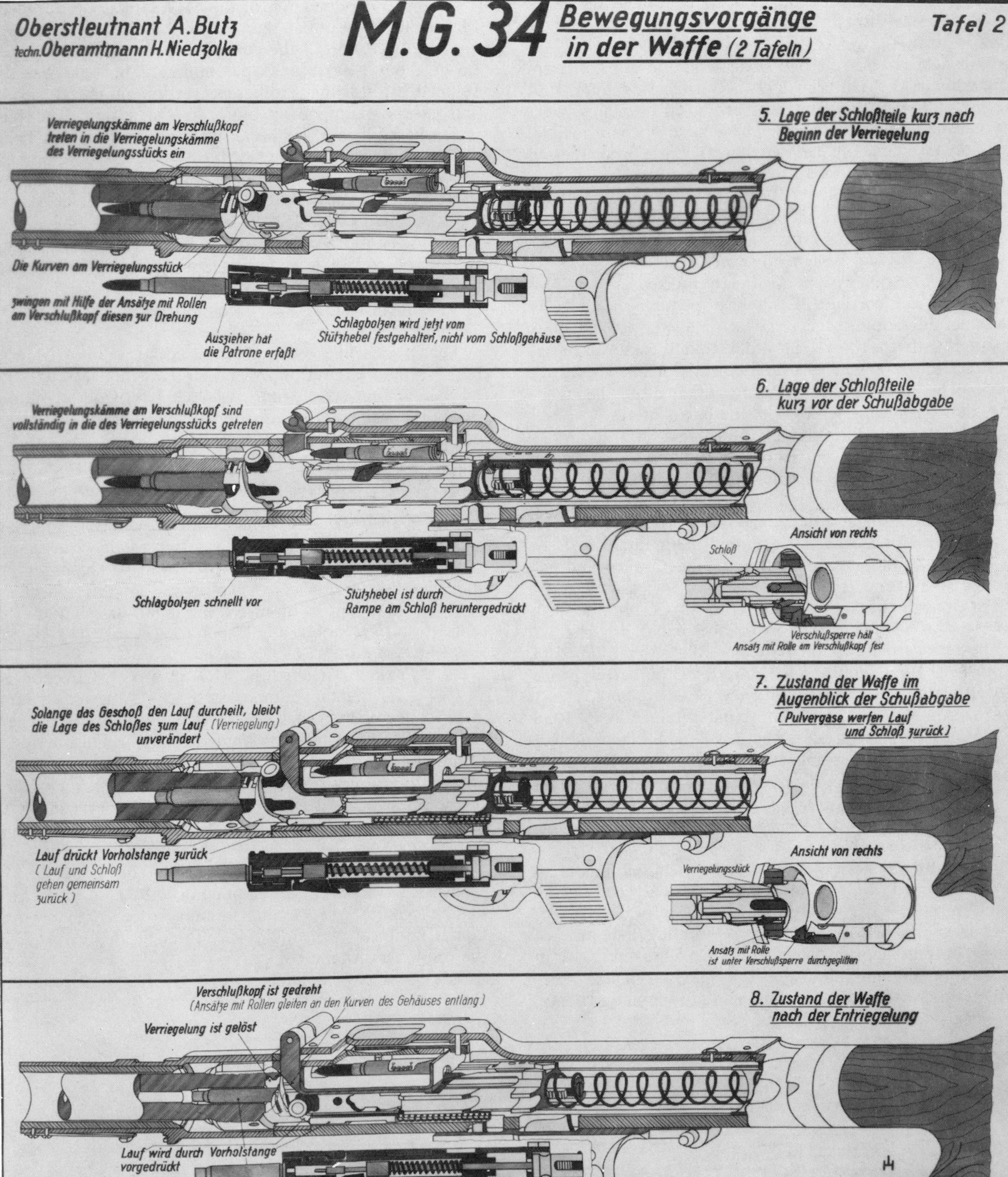

German Machine Gun 34. Sectional drawings showing operation as presented by German Ordnance.

work on the basic lock mechanism of Louis Stange of the Rheinmetall-Borsig Organization with which we have already dealt.

Paul Mauser himself had done work on a mechanism very similar to the breech lock now suggested for manufacture, although the version as produced by Stange went beyond the application Mauser had made of the principle. It might be stated in passing that all basic principles in this field were developed in the early periods by Maxim, Mauser, and Mannlicher. All designs since that time have been merely extensions of or improvements on the basic principles. Stange deserves considerable credit for furthering the original design however.

The locking ring system as already utilized on the Solothurn was not considered the best possible because its construction required the removal of all the locked units together with the barrel in order to effectuate a barrel change. It was sought to overcome this deficiency by replacing the locking ring with the rotating bolt head design, thus permitting removal of the barrel alone.

The Stange modification of the original Mauser rotating bolt head actuated by recoil utilized the energy of the barrel together with an accelerator to increase the travel of the bolt to the rear after unlocking. Most previous efforts utilized the residual chamber pressure to furnish this power. This modification among other things assisted greatly in developing reliability of functioning and increased rate of fire.

The muzzle brake was utilized also as both a flash hider and as a forward support for the recoiling barrel.

The rearward thrust of the expanding gases trapped in the brake, impinging upon the muzzle of the barrel, drove it back to operate the arm with increased force.

This gun was first put into actual production in 1936 in infantry form with shoulder stock and bipod mount. Elimination of the locking ring permitted a quick barrel removal system to be incorporated. This and all other general details of the gun are fully discussed in chapter 26.

The MG 34-S and MG 34-41 are the same as the earlier models except for the styles of the barrel jackets. All these modifications differ from the initial model in being equipped for full automatic fire only; in having larger muzzles to permit greater surface for the brake-checked gas to bear upon; a larger buffer; elimination of firing pin nut; shorter barrel and incidental changes in the feeding method; and single trigger of standard design instead of the pivoted swinging dual-operation trigger. This trigger immediately identifies the modifications.

A further modification of the MG 34 was produced by Mauser in 1939 under the designation MG 81. This was an aircraft version of the gun with the rate of fire stepped up to about 1200 rounds per minute. This rate was developed by utilizing a different version of muzzle brake and exceptionally heavy buffer return spring. The feed was generally from flexible disintegrating metal link belts.

It must be noted that the MG 34 after its development by Mauser was also produced by Maget at Berlin, by Steyr-Daimler-Puch A. G. at Vienna, by Gustloff at Suhl; and, after the German occupation, at Waffenwerke-Brunn A. G. in Czechoslovakia. The distribution of manufacture of course left these plants, some of which are today in Russian control, in full possession of equipment, methods, know-how, and even personnel utilized by the Germans.

The MG 81 likewise was produced not only by Mauser but also by a large group including Krieghoff at Suhl and by the Waffenwerke Brunn A. G. It is obvious therefore that the designs are common knowledge to all anti-democratic experts as well as to our own.

The German MG 42 Machine Gun

This gun is one of the most remarkable machine weapons ever produced anywhere by anyone. Its design has influenced production methods and will continue to influence machine arm production in the years ahead.

While the gun is discussed in detail in chapter 26, some historical notes are essential here because of the unusual background of the design.

As its name indicates, the MG 42 was first introduced in 1942. Its first appearance so far as American troops were concerned was at the terrible battle at Kasserine Pass, where its value was immediately recognized by all observers.

This gun is not an original invention. Rather it is one of the finest examples of what can be done by composite design and manufacture that the firearms industry has ever seen.

Without wasting unnecessary energy on trying to establish it as a purely developmental design of their own national genius, the German military proceeded to combine a group of elements of fine foreign guns to produce the result they wanted.

The quick barrel change system the Germans produced enabled maintenance of a terrific fire volume with a light machine arm.

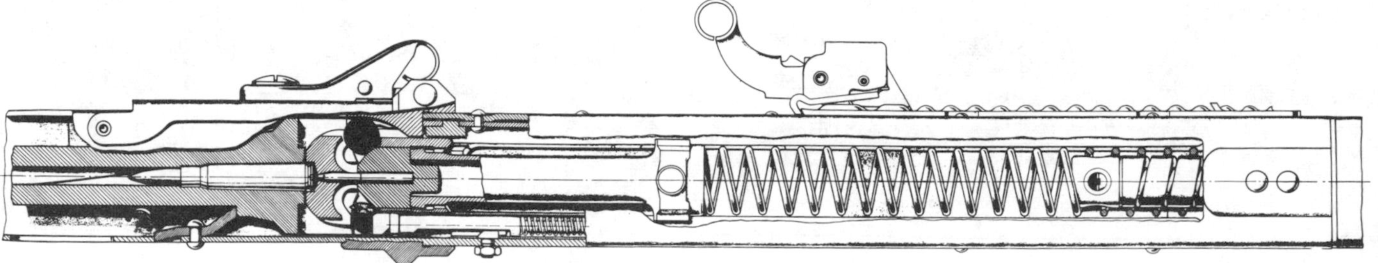

German MG 42. Top phantom view showing gun locked and about to fire.

By utilizing a dual feed pawl system wherein one round was positioned while the other one was being chambered, a feeding operation with metal belts was produced. This gave a smooth belt movement to prevent interference with the aim of the gunner by the customary violent jerking.

The muzzle device served to support the forward end of the barrel, to act as a booster by backing up expanding gases against the barrel muzzle to increase rearward motion during the recoiling action, to serve as a flash hider, and by slotting to serve as a muzzle brake to stabilize the arm when short bursts were fired at high rate.

The most remarkable aspect of the entire design of the MG 42, however, is its method of manufacture.

This is the utilization of the finest high speed techniques for mass producing metal stampings to form an arm which might be crude in appearance by gun standards, but which could be made at a fraction of the cost and in a fraction of the time required for an equivalent gun as produced by formal methods.

This part of the design was undertaken by a noted German industrialist, Doctor Grunow, a specialist in metal stamping work (or pressing, as it is commonly known abroad).

By working out a system of pressing, riveting, and spot welding, he was able to turn out the guns with heavy duty stamping equipment of the type normally utilized in automotive production.

A great deal of nonsense was poured out at the time by military intelligence circles and others attempting to prove that the Germans were in dire need of materials. Otherwise it was argued they would not produce so crude a gun. A considerable time passed before it was generally understood that the reason for the design was to produce the finest arms in the shortest time at the lowest cost; that this development stemmed from mechanical genius—not from shortages or desperation.

The gun was put into production in the plant where Doctor Grunow supervised the initial work, the Johannus Grossfuss Metall und Locierwarenfabrik at Dobeln in Saxony. Mauser Werke at Berlin also later manufactured it as did Maget at Berlin. The gun was also produced at the Steyr Works in Vienna and at the Gustloff Works at Suhl. These items are mentioned again to establish that since many of the areas involved are in Russian hands, the methods are as fully known to the Russians as to United States technicians. There is nothing secret about the production techniques.

In 1943 an attempt was made in the United States to produce prototypes of this gun, the work being delegated to the Saginaw Steering Gear Division of General Motors, at Saginaw, Michigan.

The guns as produced in 1944 simply wouldn't work. The arm was modified and was again subjected to tests and again found wanting. The American-made version was listed as the Machine Gun Caliber .30 T-24. The reason for the failure of these American-made versions of the MG 42 to operate was really very simple. The United States .30 caliber cartridge is, as almost all shooters are aware, merely a somewhat lengthened version of the German 7.92mm cartridge, the common Mauser cartridge from which ours was originally developed. In the course of attempting to manufacture a gun to handle United States ammunition, our design and engineering groups overlooked entirely the elementary matter of the difference in the length of the cartridge cases.

As a result, the bolt face could not recoil far enough behind the ejection slot in the receiver to permit ejection, the receiver yoke interfering with the cartridge guide plate by about a quarter of an inch! On such oversights as this often rests the matter of savings of countless millions of dollars.

The German FG 42 Machine Gun

This gun represents still another amazing German experiment in the field of machine arms improvisation.

It was designed and manufactured at the Krieghoff Works at Suhl. Krieghoff, before the war, had developed a gas-operated sporting rifle which would have been placed on the world market except for the war.

The FG 42 was also designed on the principle of utilizing stampings and machine screw parts to the full, with the intention of issuance for service as a light-weight

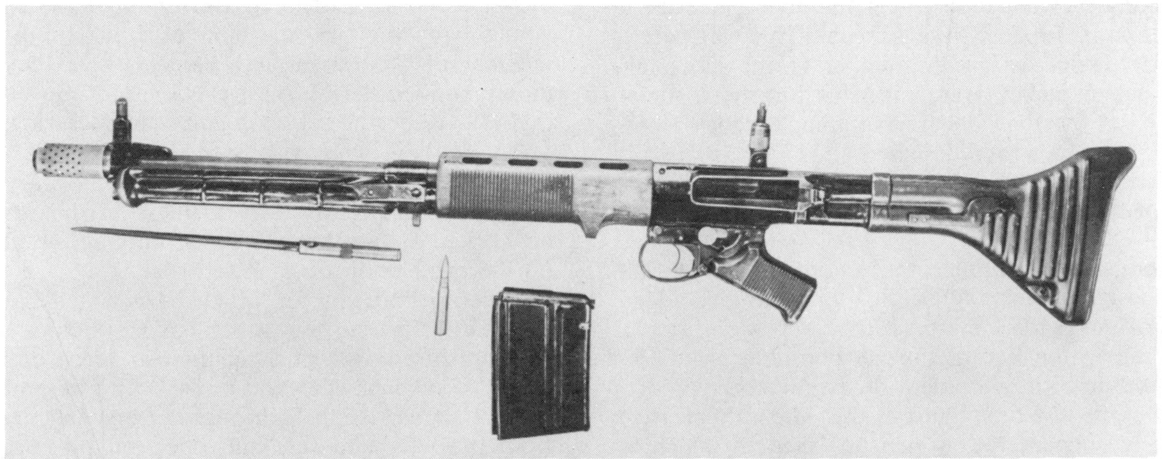

German FG 42. This is one of the most remarkable of all light automatic weapons. Shown with clip, cartridge, and detached bayonet.

machine weapon for airborne troops. It was so utilized in its first appearance at the raid on Crete. The designation FG 42 which sometimes leads to confusion with the entirely different MG 42 derives from the name "Fallschirm-Jaeger Gewehr," the paratroop machine rifle.

The operating system of the mechanism was not taken from the Krieghoff sporting modification, which is under-barrel operated. It was a utilization of a form of the Lewis gas system.

A description of the gun and its operation including the gas system is to be found in chapter 26.

The receiver is a stamping. The barrel is fixed, being permanently secured at front and rear end by swaging and by having the added security of locking pins. The muzzle brake is particularly efficient, and also serves as a flash hider. The gas selector, by affording access to different size port holes, allows the gunner to increase or slow down the action.

The trigger mechanism is sheet metal, welded, as is the unit containing the sear, the firing change lever, and safety latch system. In common with some arms like the American Johnson, it permitted firing from either an open or closed bolt, thus giving the gunner the opportunity for keeping the action open for cooling in case of full automatic fire or giving him the desirable feature of a non-slamming breech operation for accurate single shot firing.

The locking action is the basic Lewis gun system in which, after the bolt has completed its travel and chambered a cartridge, the still moving piston hits a cam in the bolt body, turning and rotating the bolt and its head so the locking lugs engage in their recesses to lock the weapon securely and get the obstruction out of the path so the firing pin on the gas piston can strike the primer and fire the cartridge.

On rearward action the gas piston has a travel of approximately one inch. During this time, of course, the bullet is well clear of the barrel before the unlocking action starts, through the cam rotation of the bolt. In addition to the operating spring, a heavy buffer spring is provided as required by the light weight design.

Russian Firearm Developments

The first reported machine gun manufacture in Russia was undertaken in 1905 at Tula Arsenal. This was purely the standard Maxim design. A number of the parts, including the water jacket, were made of bronze, a metal easily worked at the time but having great weight.

The 1905 model was redesigned in 1910 as an all-steel model, reducing the weight notably. The Navy continued use of the earlier models because of anti-corrosion factors.

Later modifications altered the smooth water jacket to a ribbed design modeled after the Vickers to give added strength. Various other minor alterations were made, particularly along the line of muzzle boosters, again following in the line of development of the Vickers.

In recent usage in Korea, guns of this Maxim type have been regularly encountered as first-line medium machine gun equipment. They have only one notable new feature, in the form of a special large-size cap on the top of the water jacket which allows rapid filling when the water tends to boil off. Earlier patterns are slow to fill.

The best known of the modern Russian designers is Degtyarev, born in 1880. To him is credited the light machine gun which is described in chapter 43, one of the most notable manufacturing and efficiency developments in the field of small arms.

He was engaged in work of experimental nature at Tula with the designer, Federov, on developing special ideas for light machine guns as far back as 1908.

The Degtyarev was adopted over various Maxim modifications because of the ease of manufacture and the simplicity of general design.

In addition to the infantry version, there is a tank adaptation utilizing a larger capacity drum. A modified version, the DPM, was produced to house the driving springs in a tube at the rear of the receiver, as overheating of the barrel affected the springs when housed as in normal infantry gun fashion below the barrel. This overheating, of course, was aggravated by the sustained rate of fire utilized in the tank modification.

In 1938 Degtyarev introduced his 12.7mm caliber gun. This is merely an oversized version of the original infantry model, with modifications. The drum feed is replaced by a belt feed of rugged and simple character to increase the volume firing potential. A 1939 7.62mm version introduced to utilize 250-round belts was otherwise very much in the regular Degtyarev tradition, except that it had a heavily flanged barrel to furnish greater radiation surfaces for more adequate cooling.

A recent development in the field in Russia is the Goryunov 1943 model. This arm also utilizes the standard 7.62mm rimmed Russian rifle cartridge. This gun is a subject for consideration from a design standpoint by military authorities throughout the world today.

JOHN M. BROWNING AND HIS GUNS

The most famous of all American arms designers is the late John M. Browning. Born in Ogden, Utah in 1855, young Browning was the son of Jonathan Browning, a member of the Latter Day Saints, or as they are commonly known, the Mormons. His father moved to Ogden in 1852, where he set up a gun manufacturing shop.

The father, who was born in Tennessee, served an apprenticeship as a gunsmith and at the age of 21 was already operating his own business in that trade. While he worked at farming and blacksmithing, he also worked on the production of guns to order.

Among the items for which he is noted is an original repeating rifle of the so-called Harmonica type. The mechanism consists of a rectangular piece of iron chambered to take powder and balls, which resembles a harmonica. It was slipped through an opening in the breech from the left hand side and operated by finger pressure on a small lever on the side of the rifle. As the magazine was inserted and the lever pressed, the action was jacked

John Moses Browning 1855-1926.

Original photograph of the great American arms inventor taken at the F. N. Factory in Belgium in 1913. He is posed with his superb .22 autoloading rifle.

forward to form a tight seal between the individual chamber and the barrel. The arm, of course, was a cap and ball design since it was produced before the metallic cartridge era. It not only enabled a considerable number of shots to be fired rapidly from one loading, but furnished an opportunity to carry extra magazines fully loaded ready for sustained fire. In addition to this, Jonathan also produced a breech mechanism containing a six-chambered cylinder rather like that of the standard revolver of the time.

From all this it will be seen that young Browning had

GUNSMITHING.

THE subscriber is prepared to manufacture, to order, improved Fire-arms, viz: revolving rifles and pistols; also slide guns, from 5 to 25 shooters. All on an improved plan, and he thinks not equalled this far East. (Farther west they might be.) The emigrating and sporting community are invited to call and examine Browning's improved fire-arms before purchasing elsewhere. Shop eight miles south of Kanesville on Musquito Creek, half a mile south of TRADING POINT.

JONATHAN BROWNING.

Advertisement of September 19, 1849, which appeared in the "Frontier Guardian" in Kanesville, Iowa.

a family background to interest him in arms design. He went, however, far beyond the confines of the typical gunsmith. He became in his lifetime one of the most noted and legendary figures in the entire history of armaments.

Before he reached the age of 20 John Browning was actually building rifles himself, one of which he made for his brother Matthew. This was so good that even his father admitted it was the finest he had ever seen.

Jonathan had hauled a foot-operated lathe with him in his ox cart on his trip across the plains from Council Bluffs, Iowa. John served an apprenticeship of 10 years, his particular interest being in the operation of this lathe.

Young John's first design and patent was a single shot rifle of the dropping block type. Lowering the triggerguard dropped the block to open the breech, extracted and ejected the empty case, and cocked the hammer. When the triggerguard was returned to battery position the hammer was below the line of sight, an obvious but quite noteworthy improvement in general rifle design. It was this rifle which first attracted the attention of the Winchester Arms Company of Hartford, Connecticut.

Upon the death of Jonathan, John Moses and his brother, Matthew Sandefur Browning, took over the operation of the business, John devoted himself to production and Matthew, the better business man, turned his attention to handling the all-important matters of sales and money.

Matthew realized the pitfalls of building individual guns for individual cranks, a lesson which many fine gunsmiths find out the hard way even in this day and age. He interested his brother in the idea of producing a group of identical arms for sale. With this idea in mind, they actually built 600 of the drop block

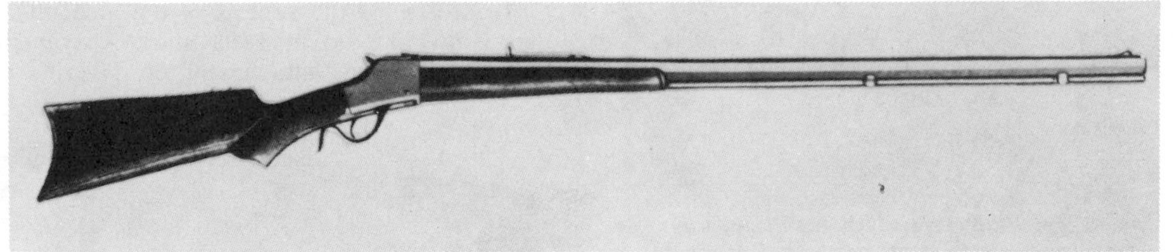

The world famous Winchester dropping block single shot rifle. This rifle was designed by John M. Browning.

action rifles which John had invented and patented before offering any on the market. This simple piece of strategy probably marked the difference between their doing business and not doing business with Winchester.

The quantity produced enabled them to set up an assembly line of sorts, and by duplication of parts with common machine set-ups, allowed them to produce a gun which could be sold at a price well below that of any comparable weapon produced by the large gun manufacturers.

As a result of this investment of theirs in 600 rifles, the Winchester representative was impressed not only with the arm itself but with the danger that the Browning brothers might become a definite competitor in the West.

Winchester not only purchased the rights to manufacture the gun but bought out the entire stock of 600 rifles. The brothers opened a sporting goods store on the lower floor of the building they occupied. They sold standard arms of other manufacture as well as their own. The upper floor was turned into a workshop and a pattern-making shop where John did much of his early experimental design and development work.

He was only 26 when he designed and patented in 1884 the rifle which Winchester marketed two years later as their famous Model 1886.

This lever action, tube magazine arm was originally produced in .45 caliber. It remains today one of the sturdiest of all the medium-power hunting rifle designs.

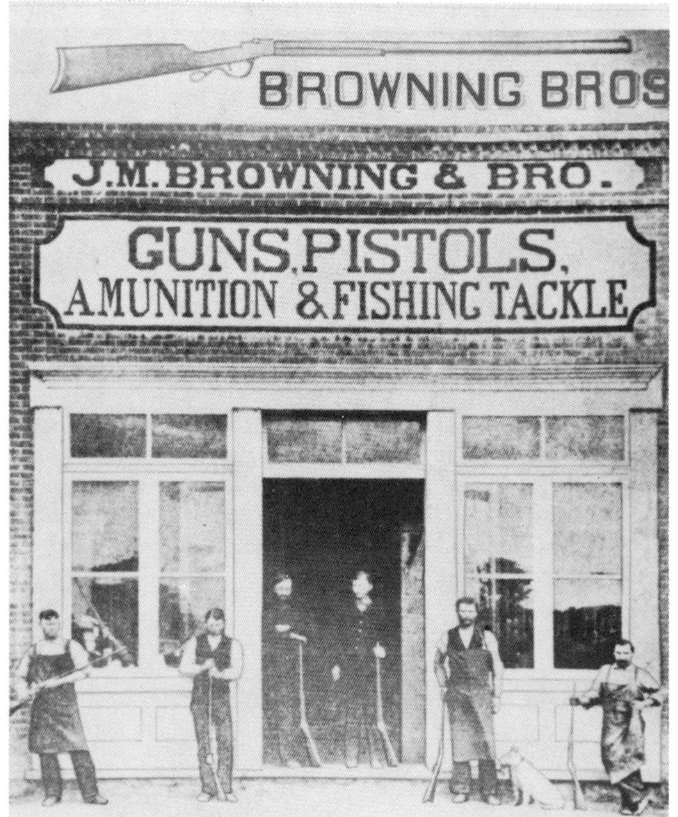

The first Browning gun shop, Ogden, Utah. The factory was on the second floor. From left to right are: Sam, George, John, Matt, and Ed Browning and a gunsmith whose name passed unknown.

Young Browning also designed the Winchester pump action rifle Model 90 in .22 caliber, the prototype of most of the familiar shooting gallery rifles. This was followed by the famous 92 and 94 Model Winchesters, the latter still among the most popular for deer hunting in the United States. After that came the pump shotgun, the Winchester Model 97, and the famous Model 95 box magazine rifle, specimens of which during World War I were purchased for use by Russia in their own 7.62mm caliber. The Model 1906 .22 Winchester repeater is also a Browning development.

The story of Browning's other Winchester developments and his problems with that company do not form a part of the historical section of this book, since we are concerned primarily with matters military. However, we must note that as the result of an argument between him and Winchester, growing out of difficulties over an automatic shotgun which he offered them for production, Browning discontinued his contacts with Winchester and did not again enter the plant until World War I when he returned there to do work on machine arms in the interests of the United States Government.

The years in between were spent largely at the F. N. Works in Belgium, where his first automatic pistol was manufactured, and where his first automatic shotgun, the most widely imitated arm of its type, was first produced.

Out of the early model automatic pistols, most of which he designed at F. N., came the long line of automatic pistols known to us as Colt's, including the .25, .32, .380, .38, and .45 Government models. All were designed by Browning and were manufactured under license in the United States by Colt's. Several of the models were also made in slightly varying forms at F. N. for world sale.

According to folklore, John Browning in 1889 hit upon the idea of the possibility of automatic operation by utilization of gas. While out hunting he fired while walking through some bulrushes and noticed that the blast disturbed the rushes for some distance from the muzzle. The story goes on that Browning's mechanical mind realized that this represented a power source which could be utilized.

Since the principle of gas operation had been very widely exploited in Europe well before this time, and since Browning was practical enough that he was thoroughly familiar with patent office procedure, it is much more likely that his original ideas were based on knowledge of some of the European experimentation. The Browning in the bulrushes yarn is unlikely, even though his middle name was Moses.

Regardless of the genesis of the idea, the fact remains that Browning did in 1889 start experimental work by utilizing a muzzle attachment on his rifle to determine

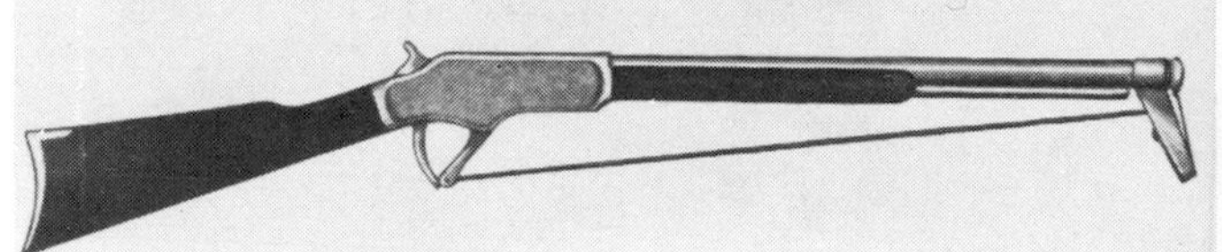

Browning's first experimental rifle, gas actuated by muzzle blast.

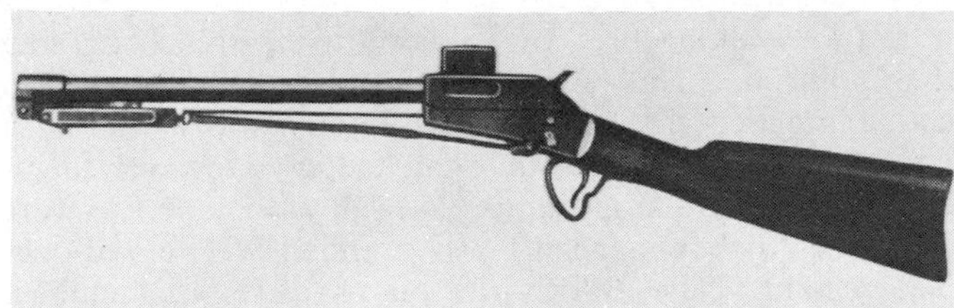

Brownings second experimental gas-operated rifle. Actuation here was by gas through a barrel port acting on a piston. This was one of the first approaches to the modern successful system found in nearly all light weight automatic and semi-automatic weapons of military rifle caliber.

the effect of the blast. He placed a 4-inch square chunk of iron weighing some five pounds at a distance one inch forward of the muzzle of the rifle. A hole was drilled in the center of the block and the rifle was alined with the hole. A lanyard attached to the trigger fired the piece. The bullet passed through the drilled hole and the blast of gas following the flight of the bullet blew the iron block across the room. Browning proceeded next to produce a concave steel cap with a hole in the center which he secured over the muzzle of his rifle. By connecting this with a hinged arrangement to a spring-loaded operating lever he secured a condition where the blast blew the cap down, thereby pulling the loading trigger-lever forward. A spring returned the lever to lock position, thus preparing the arm for firing again merely by pulling the trigger. The next progression was tapping gas off through a hole in the underside of a magazine rifle and allowing the gas to actuate a piston to operate the action for unlocking, extraction, and reloading. This action was made fully automatic.

Out of such elementary experimentation in a little shop in Ogden, Utah, Browning evolved the basic design for what was to become the famous first successful gas-operated machine gun.

The gun was offered for production to Colt's in a letter from Browning on November 22, 1890. Prototype manufacture was undertaken, since the original gun was actually in .44 Winchester caliber, hardly a military arm even in that day.

In 1893 the United States Navy undertook some tests on the new Colt's gun. The design still had bugs. In 1895 guns were developed to handle both the .30-40 Krag cartridge used by the Army and the 6mm Lee cartridge then used by our Navy.

This first Colt's 95 Model was nicknamed the "potato digger," a name it still carries in some of the far corners of the earth where models of this gun are still in use. The name derives from the fact that there is a very heavy operating lever below the barrel which swings in a half arc. If the tripod is mounted too low, or the earth happens to be soft at the point of mounting, the gun tripod burrows in and the operating lever will churn up the ground.

A United States Navy Board was so impressed with the gun that in January, 1896, it ordered 50 guns from Colt's. At that time Colt's was also manufacturing the gun in various other calibers for Austrian, Mexican, and even German ammunition. While the Navy was farseeing enough that in 1898 it ordered 150 more of these Colt guns, the Army still remained adamant on the matter of retaining the crank-operated Gatling.

These Colt "potato diggers" in the hands of United States Marines were the decisive element that saved the lives of the inhabitants of the Foreign Legations at Pekin in the Boxer uprising.

The Navy Colt guns, originally in 6mm Lee caliber, were rechambered for the .30-40 rim Krag cartridge when a decision was made to standardize all service ammunition. These were later modified further to let them handle the .30-06 cartridge when that cartridge was introduced for general service use.

So fixed was the American military mind on the matter of mechanical gun operation as opposed to automatic that, as late as June 14, 1895, an Ordnance Board at Springfield Armory turned in a detailed report of a highly negative order on automatics! To quote directly from the closing of their opinion, "The Board is of the opinion that in its present form as shown by the tests made, this arm is not suitable for ordinary service and has no place in the land armament." This is the same gun which turned up in use even in War II in many places.

When World War I began we still had practically no machine arms available. Although no public information was released, in April, 1917 we had on hand 670 Benet-Mercies, 282 Maxims, and 158 Model 95 Colt machine guns, a total of some 1,100 outmoded pieces to begin a war of the scale in which we embarked!

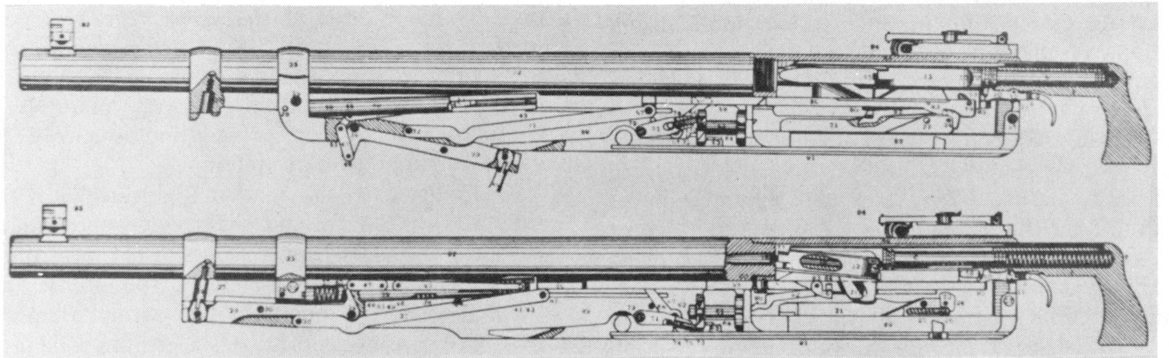

Sectionalized drawings of the famous 1895 Model Colt (Browning invented) gas-operated machine gun, popularly called "The Potato Digger."

For use as a training gun, Colt's was authorized to produce these "potato diggers" and several thousand were turned out by 1918. As we have already noted, the design was altered by the Marlin Rockwell Company to a piston operation rather than a lever type; and those constituted the important machine gun equipment of our planes during the war and for some time thereafter.

The Browning Recoil-Operated Guns

Browning's own experience with machine guns early convinced him that Maxim had been right on heavy arms for which the short-recoil principle was the ideal operating system. In 1900, therefore, he filed an application, which in 1901 was granted, covering a water-cooled short-recoil operated gun. The patent covers all the basic features of the present line of Browning Automatic Machine Guns which are the mainstay of our forces and those of our allies whom we are currently supplying with machine arms.

Because the government would not cooperate financially toward the design or production, Browning put the item aside and concentrated on the production of designs for pistols, shotguns, and hunting arms for which there was a wide commercial market. On these he built a very large personal and family fortune.

Since there is a tendency to believe that this recoil-operated gun, which is our standard today, was not developed until the period of World War I, it should be pointed out that Browning presented in 1900 a written description of the operation of the gun he had then designed. This is in all essential features the same as the later Brownings which will be found in our discussion of the Browning arms in chapter 45.

As we have seen, Germany started World War I with 12,500 improved Maxim guns on hand and many more under construction. Against this we had 1,100 obsolete guns. Browning and other inventors were called upon to submit gun designs after the declaration of war. Such was the state of our military preparedness at the time.

Some time earlier Browning had delivered to Washington a sample of his heavy water-cooled machine gun and also of the light gas-operated machine rifle which was later known as the Browning Automatic Rifle (or BAR).

The Browning automatic rifle is covered thoroughly in chapter 45 so only historical note may be made here. It was offered for tests and in due course public firing demonstrations of the light portable gun were made on February 27, 1917, outside the city limits of Washington, D. C. at Congress Heights.

Over three hundred people were invited to attend the Washington tests of the BAR. Included in the list were representatives of the armed services of Belgium, France, Great Britain, and Italy, and for a refreshing change representatives of the Press were also allowed to view the new secret weapon.

Even the breathless prose of those newspapermen hardly did justice to this new development of John Browning. At that time French military opinion was that a light automatic weapon was needed which could be used for "walking fire" by soldiers in the trench fighting then going on. This was a most impractical concept. In actual practice the arm proved tremendously useful in later days, but for quite different tactics. However, demonstrations of walking, semi-, and full automatic fire were given. A 20-shot magazine was emptied in two-and-one-half seconds. The BAR's 70 pieces were disassembled and assembled in 55 seconds—a marvelous record at that time.

While the design was excellent, the writers seemed to forget that we were already on the threshold of war and did not have the tools to permit it to be produced in volume. It was evident that numerous manufacturing facilities would be necessary to turn out the BAR as well as the heavy Browning in quantity, and arrangements were made for the Government to buy the rights to manufacture of these Brownings from the Colt's Patent Firearms Company of Hartford, Connecticut. Colt's held an exclusive contract with Browning for the production of these arms and his automatic pistols in the United States; and since they were the best qualified they provided the drawings and the all-important gauges to the other companies assigned to manufacture.

Most of the early development of the BAR was done by Browning at the Colt's plant. Browning had not entered the Winchester plant in years, as the result of the early disagreement with them over production of his automatic shotgun which drove him to Europe to seek a manufacturer. Now, however, in the face of war involving his country, Browning pocketed his resentment. The great Winchester organization turned its full facilities to preparing and correcting working drawings. Many of the important refinements of the gun were developed there. Work actually began on the BAR at Winchester in February, 1918. As an inevitable result of the working pressure, some manufacturing bugs developed which resulted in parts not being completely interchangeable. After some delay in production, the necessary corrections were made and when the war ended Winchester was turning out these very difficult to manufacture weapons at the rate of 300 a day. This was a most remarkable performance which reflected great credit on the Winchester engineering and production groups.

In June, 1918, additional BAR production was commenced by the Marlin-Rockwell Corporation in a plant especially acquired for the purpose. When the war ended on November 11th of the same year, this producer was turning out 200 guns a day, also a remarkable achievement. Before the war ended some 52,000 BARS were delivered, only about 9,000 being made by the Colt's Company since they were simultaneously heavily engaged in other war production.

Our 79th Division landed in France in 1918, in July, armed with BARs, and their guns were put into action on the 13th of September. Historical note must be taken of the fact that Val Browning, son of the inventor and then a First Lieutenant in our Army, demonstrated the use of the arm against the Germans. Today he is the active head of the Browning family organization which still manufactures pistols and shotguns developed by his

World War I photo of then Lt. Val Browning demonstrating his father's great BAR somewhere in France.

Val Browning today is one of the active heads of the unique Browning family arms sales organization.

father at the F. N. Plant in Belgium and sells them under the Browning Bros. name in the United States.

The French in particular were very enthusiastic about our new weapon, experience with their own Chauchat and other inferior French machine rifles having been very disillusioning. It is interesting to note that Browning's water-cooled machine gun did not receive nearly the enthusiastic reception accorded the BAR. There were many who felt that in spite of its fine features, it still was not superior to the Vicker's and other guns of the time. As a matter of fact, the smooth feeding from the improved Browning belt and feed system was in itself so great an advance that only the prejudiced could have bypassed its superiority. About the BAR there could be no question, since there was no true competition.

The Browning Machine Gun Model 1917

While our government seized upon the BAR for immediate adoption after its initial demonstration, and history since then has proven the judgment sound, action on the water-cooled Browning machine gun was not handled so expeditiously.

Under tests at Springfield Armory in May, 1917, the gun fired 20,000 rounds at a cyclic rate of 600 a minute without malfunction or breakage. This in itself was a truly remarkable performance. Browning personally ran another 20,000 cartridges through without failure of any of the component parts. A second gun was introduced to demonstrate that it was the design rather than the individual gun which was responsible for this sterling performance; and by securing together long belts loaded with ammunition, Browning succeeded in operating the gun for 48 minutes and 12 seconds continuously.

Here, too, for the first time demonstrations were made of dismounting and reassembling the gun blindfolded. This demonstration started the era of training which sought to enable gunners to become so proficient in handling their weapons that they could function almost subconsciously. Familiarity with the weapon is even more important than actually being able to make repairs.

Entirely aside from the reliability the Browning showed, the adoption was fully warranted by the fact that the design was suitable for high-speed production methods of that era. Colt's (who originally controlled the patents), Remington Arms-Union Metallic Cartridge Company, and New England Westinghouse were given contracts to produce this gun, which at the time was known as a "heavy" machine gun though today its classification is that of a "medium."

The performance of Westinghouse in this production was a tremendous tribute to the gun design and also to the flexibility and intelligence of the American industrial system. While in theory the gun companies with their knowledge of firearms should have had a manufacturing edge, the Westinghouse group produced a handmade pilot model in 29 days from the time of the con-

John M. Browning and his famous Model 1917 Machine Gun. It is in use throughout the world.

tract! A mere 34 days later they brought the first production gun off the assembly line. By the end of the war, Westinghouse was turning out 500 Browning Machine Guns a day.

Remington produced 12,000 during the war as compared with Westinghouse's production of 30,150. The Colt's organization turned out only 600, though this figure is not truly representative of their capabilities since their facilities were largely engaged in preparing various gauges, tools, and mechanical drawings for other plants, as well as turning out British Vickers' guns.

As it happened, the Brownings reached Europe entirely too late to be given any extensive battle practice. Again Lieutenant Val Browning served as instructor to introduce this new machine gun of his father's design to our troops, but European observers were unable to evaluate the design because of its very limited war use. In very minor combat use in September by our 79th Division, which had a small detachment armed with them, four Brownings stood up very well indeed.

In a way, it was fortunate indeed that the Brownings did not get into extensive use in World War I, since some relatively minor weaknesses which did appear (and were not the result of the design necessarily) would have given the gun a bad name from which probably it would never have recovered.

One such weakness which may be cited is the bottom plate in the receiver. The original metal used for this part did not stand up under continuous fire. In view of the rapidity with which the gun had to be put into production, this metallurgical slip-up is understandable. When this inadequacy was recognized, however, immediate steps were taken to correct it by introducing a reinforcing "stirrup" to fit over the weak area on the outside of the receiver.

Over 25,000 original Brownings required this particular modification. Later production was altered, of course, to make this modification unnecessary.

During the period between World Wars I and II, manufacture and development of the Browning machine gun went ahead both in the United States Ordnance Department and at the F. N. Plant in Belgium. The guns made abroad were sold commercially throughout the world.

The Browning since 1918 has seen service everywhere in the world under all types of weather and battle conditions. The modifications made in it, while all relatively minor, have evolved a design which for the purposes intended is probably the equivalent of any produced since Browning developed it. No higher tribute can be paid Browning than recognition of that fact.

The Browning .50 Caliber Machine Gun

Colonel John Parker, in charge of the United States Army Machine Gun School at Gonducourt in France, was very much impressed with a new 11mm machine gun and cartridge the French introduced for particular use against observation balloons. He secured samples for shipment to the United States.

Colt's was given the task of altering eight Brownings to handle this new 11mm French cartridge. Aside from

The inventor posed firing an early model of his basic .50 caliber gun at the Colt's plant at Hartford, Conn.

its use as a balloon gun with an incendiary bullet, the round was also used with armor piercing bullets against armored vehicles and defensive shields which were then appearing in use by the enemy.

The ammunition as designed by the French did not meet military needs as General Pershing saw them. He insisted that the bullet weight and muzzle velocity both be substantially greater. Pershing's attention to this seemingly minor matter proved to be of great importance.

The Winchester Repeating Arms Company at New Haven were by this time working with Browning on the development of a larger caliber machine gun cartridge than the standard rifle .30-06. They merely scaled up the standard .30-06 rifle cartridge to try and make it usable in both the heavy machine gun and this antitank gun, and in the course of doing so added a rim to the cartridge case.

Fortunately Pershing, who was following ammunition development very carefully, saw the new specifications and insisted that the case be redesigned to be rimless. His instructions were followed and a dummy cartridge of this pattern was sent to Browning at the Colt's Plant. Browning, meanwhile, had scaled up his .30 caliber machine gun, keeping all the mechanical features but adding weight, size, and strength to handle the larger cartridges with their increased pressures. A test gun was ready.

Browning moved the model from Colt's to Winchester, since the latter was making and developing ammunition as well as arms. The work developed so well that he stayed on at the Winchester Plant. Since Colt's had no ammunition manufacturing facilities, this move greatly accelerated the eventual development of the .50 caliber machine gun.

The first of the new .50 calibers was actually assembled on September 12, 1918, and Winchester proceeded to produce six duplicate handmade testing models. Although the new bullet developed was heavier than the minimum demand of General Pershing, the velocity was still low by several hundred feet per second.

During infantry tests it was found that even with the gun and tripod weighing 160 pounds, the increased energy engendered during firing the heavy rounds made it almost impossible to hold the gun on the target during full automatic fire. Other tests indicated that its rate of fire (then 500 per minute) was not great enough for antipersonnel use from tanks, and that the bullet lacked sufficient penetration against improved enemy armor.

While the Browning design was still under way, our troops captured some German antitank rifles with a new variety of 13mm ammunition which fired an 800-grain bullet at a muzzle velocity well over 2,700 feet per second. This bullet was able to penetrate an inch of armor at 250 yards range. This was a fantastic performance at the time. Under normal conditions, allied military policy is to keep such developments top secret since any admission of enemy superiority is decried. The more practical German approach has been to seize immediately upon an advance regardless of its origin.

Fortunately, the normal system of nonsensical military secrecy we throw up about such matters did not prevent some rounds reaching Winchester. The engineers there began immediate work on bringing their .50 caliber cartridge into the ballistic range of the German. After Win-

The outstanding productions of Browning's inventive genius.

chester had worked out all the technical aspects of the new ammunition, development was transferred to the Government Arsenal at Frankford, Pennsylvania. The transfer was not effected until 1918. Much of the credit for our .50 caliber development belongs to Winchester and to their energy in taking advantage of the new German development so rapidly.

The new .50 caliber cartridge required, in addition to the scaling up of the .30 caliber parts, various other alterations. An oil buffer was added with the dual purpose of helping to absorb energy and providing a fire rate regulator. The pistol grip of the .30 caliber had to be replaced with a double spade grip as encountered generally in Maxim design, since the gun really needs both hands to be controlled. The gun is covered in detail in chapter 45.

Note on Browning

The range of the development genius of John M. Browning is breath-taking. Unlike Maxim and Mannlicher, Browning did not develop any principles. He did adapt known principles to a vast range of firearms developments from the early Winchester single-shot .22 rifle through the entire field of medium- and high-powered rifles (bolt actions excepted), shotguns, automatic pistols, and machine weapons, even to 37mm automatic cannon. From the standpoint of commercial success, no other designer even approaches him.

His commercial specialties were lever-action rifles such as the Winchester Model 94, .22 semi-automatic rifles such as the Remington Model 24, high-powered semi-automatic rifles such as the F. N. and the Remington Model 8, .22 pump rifles like the Model 06 Winchester Hammer Model, and the hammerless F. N. .22 caliber Trombone. His shotgun developments ranged from the early 97 Winchester Pump Gun with its exposed hammer, a shotgun used for military service in both wars in guard capacity, through the hammerless Stevens Model 520 pump gun to the world-famous Browning Automatic shotgun with its long recoil action, the most imitated automatic shotgun ever produced.

The Browning over-under (or superposed) shotgun is without peer in its field, one of the finest combinations of American genius and Belgian craftsmanship that the gun industry has produced. His range of automatic pistols starts with the Colt's, such as the .22 Woodsman, the .38 Pocket and Militaries, the .25, .32 and .380 Hammerless Pocket Models, and, of course, our own official .45 Automatic. His modification of our military pistol, the 9mm Belgian 1935 High Power, has influenced automatic pistol design all over the world. In no instance has any of his commercial designs ever been a failure.

A character portrait study of John Moses Browning, the most successful arms inventor in history.

Few men in history have done more for the development of defensive weapons for their governments than John M. Browning. His patriotism may be summed up in the fact that he discussed payment with the War Department, through his representatives, only after his guns had been officially adopted by our government and their production had reached their greatest heights. His instructions to his fiscal agents then were to accept any price the government cared to set without hesitation or bargaining. He actually accepted royalties at a rate about one-tenth of that normally allowed.

In his development of military, sporting, and commercial arms, Browning achieved the heights of quality and reliability. The standards he set have been maintained to this very day. The Fabrique Nationale d' Armes de Guerre plant at Herstal, Liege, Belgium, is also the seat of the Royal Belgian Arms Factory and the Belgian Government Proof House. These establishments are without doubt among the top design and producing groups in small arms today; and it may safely be said that most of their stature can be attributed to the influence of John M. Browning and his long years of association with them.

Chapter 10. Submachine Guns—Historical Development

A SUBMACHINE gun is a light-weight weapon designed to use pistol ammunition and to be fired with two hands. It differs from the standard type of semi-automatic pistol (from which it was originally evolved) by the fact that it can fire cartridges full automatically so long as the trigger is held back. It may or may not, according to its design, incorporate a switch to permit the typical semi-automatic pistol type of action where an individual pull and release of the trigger is required for each shot fired. In general practice it fires from open bolt position.

The submachine gun as we know it was called in Great Britain the "machine carbine" until recently—now they conform to our terminology. It is known generally throughout Europe under various terms which translate "machine pistol." In most cases it is a very simple weapon operating without a breech-locking device of any formal kind, since the low-powered pistol cartridges do not require such locking mechanisms. More attention will be given to the technical phases of the submachine gun at a later point, but at the moment we are concerned basically with the history of its origin and its development, about which there has been a great deal of confusion.

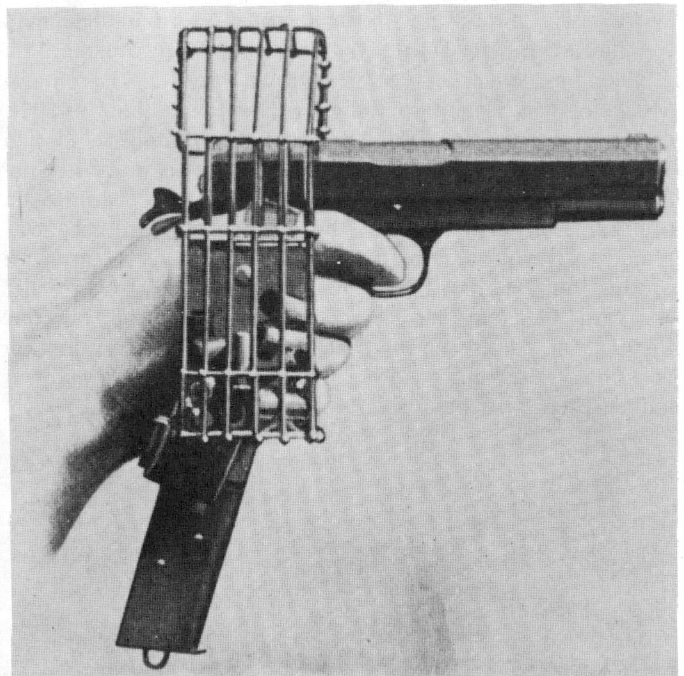

World War I Cartridge Cage designed for use by airmen in combat before the appearance of machine guns.
The cage prevented ejected cases from possibly injuring any delicate plane mechanism in that day. Oversize magazine was also provided.

Curiously enough, the submachine gun which has come to be a prime infantry arm, and also an invaluable adjunct to tank and transport groups, began as an aircraft weapon!

Early in 1914, before any general recognition had been made of the desirability of equipping aircraft with protective weapons, British and German observers in airplanes engaged in duels with pistols, rifles, and even shotguns. There is one recorded instance of a German plane being downed by shotgun fire from a British observer!

About this time, and before the first Lewis gun was mounted in an airplane, there appeared a number of weird devices to attach to automatic pistols. The most common form used was that of a wire cage attached to the right side of a .45 automatic pistol. Used in conjunction with an over-sized magazine, it enabled the aviator to fire 20 rounds in standard pistol fashion, each ejected cartridge case being caught by the wire cage. This precaution was necessary to prevent the ejected cartridge case from striking the pilot or any sensitive part of the plane.

The credit for designing the first full automatic arm to fire pistol type cartridges goes, however, to Bethel Abiel Revelli, about whom we have considerable to say in the discussion of machine gun design. This Italian was the inventor of the fully automatic arm which is commonly known as the Villar Perosa. The name derives from the company to which he originally assigned the patents he took out on April 8, 1914. This was the Villar Perosa Company of Pinerola, Italy. At a somewhat later

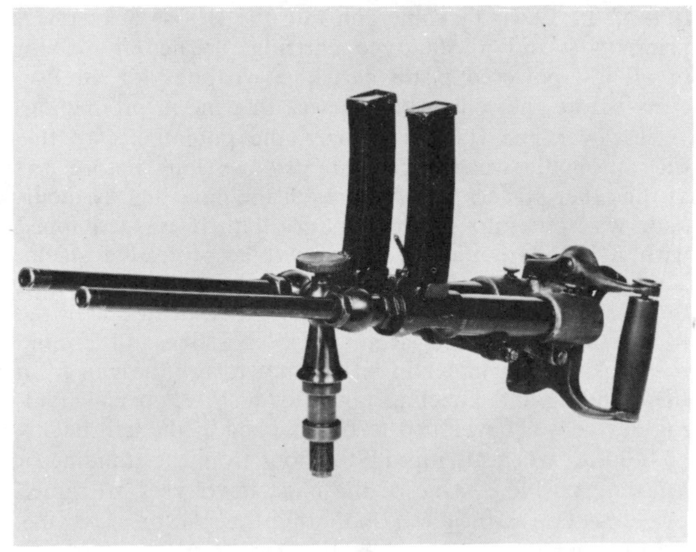

Italian 9mm Villar Perosa Submachine Gun of 1915.

date the weapon was put into production at the great Italian Fiat Factory, principally for intended infantry use. From this fact the gun is often designated as the "Fiat Model 15."

Revelli originally designed the arm, however, for aircraft use. It was substantially the same weapon as the later infantry version discussed in chapter 31. It was extremely light, weighing only 14 pounds 4 ounces with dual loaded magazines in place, the magazines normally carrying 25 rounds each, although special ones for 50 were available. The cartridges were stacked in double rows. The gun actually consisted of two barrels each complete with a firing mechanism held rigidly together by a crossbar at the front end with a handle at the rear. The barrels were stationary. The action was retarded blowback or hesitation, each bolt being so designed that it was compelled to turn slightly to the left when recoiling and slightly to the right during its forward motion of chambering and firing.

At the instant of firing a camming action took place which delayed the bolt opening, adding greatly to the inertia required at the instant of the explosion to open the action. Each mechanism was provided with an individual trigger in the handle and each one could be fired individually by the thumb of one hand. Alternatively both could be fired simultaneously by jamming both triggers with the thumbs of both hands. Since the bolts and strikers weighed only about 10 ounces each and had a travel of less than 1¾ inches, the rate of fire of the weapon using the standard 9mm Parabellum pistol cartridge was extremely high. With the standard Italian service cartridge used at that time in the Glisenti pistol, neither the velocity nor the striking energy were comparable to the German 9mm pistol cartridge which, except for charge and bullet weight, was the same as the Italian. With the Italian service cartridge, each barrel of the Villar Perosa would fire at a rate of about 1500 rounds per minute.

The weapon soon proved unsuitable for aircraft use due to the under-powered cartridge it fired. The institution of the Lewis machine gun into the British air service, firing as it did a rifle type cartridge, sealed the doom of all low-powered pistol cartridge weapons for air use, even before the Villar Perosa was in general production.

However, the Italians realized the potentiality of this full automatic weapon for infantry use long before any of the other powers did. As a result the gun, slightly modified, was put into production at Fiat. It was equipped with a bipod mount and also with a protective shield. This made it difficult to handle the arm except when in the prone position, but the Italians experimented with the use of straps secured around the crossbar and around the neck of the gunner in an attempt to fire the gun from the standing and kneeling positions also. A special holding device was developed to be attached to the belt buckle of the firer when attempting to shoot from the standing or kneeling positions. One of the most novel uses attempted in connection with it was mounting the gun on a bicycle. The rate of fire was so high, the dispersion so great, and servicing of the weapon so difficult that the gun was quickly outmoded for practical service use. Nevertheless, this model was the first actual use of a submachine gun in military service.

Early German Developments

Early in 1917 the German Army realized the necessity for a rapid firing lightweight arm for close-quarters use. They tested automatic pistols, both Mauser and Luger types with lengthened barrels, shoulder stocks, and in some cases special magazines.

The principal German weapon of this sort was the Pistole 08, or Luger as we know it, of 1917. It was equipped with a special 7.87-inch barrel. A special snail-type magazine to hold 32 cartridges was a feature of this new weapon. Although this model required an individual pull for each shot, the fact that it was supported by two hands greatly increased the number of aimed shots which could be fired per minute. All 32 shots in the snail could be aim-fired in about 45 seconds. Basically the arms were issued to noncommissioned officers, primarily those attached to machine gun units. They were also utilized for defense work at close range.

In October 1917, the Germans and Austrians folded up the Italians in the terrific disaster of the battle of Caporetto. Very large numbers of the Villar Perosas were captured there. German intelligence recognized the possibilities in these arms, and samples were sent to the major arms development centers in Germany.

As a result of intensive studies, particularly at the Bergmann Plant, a rather clumsy but extremely efficient weapon was designed there by Hugo Schmeisser at the Suhl Plant of Bergmann. Schmeisser even before World War I was one of the primary German designers of small arms. His World War II designs are outstanding.

The first weapon, often known as the Bergmann Muskete, was issued to the German forces late in 1918 under a designation MP-18, meaning Machinen Pistole 1918. While the Germans recognized that a more powerful cartridge than the standard pistol type would be preferable in such an arm, the ammunition industry was already overburdened in attempting to keep up with production. Hence the arm was designed to fire the standard German service pistol cartridge, the familiar Pistole 08. This 9mm cartridge used in conjunction with heavy recoiling parts obviated the necessity for a locked-breech mechanism.

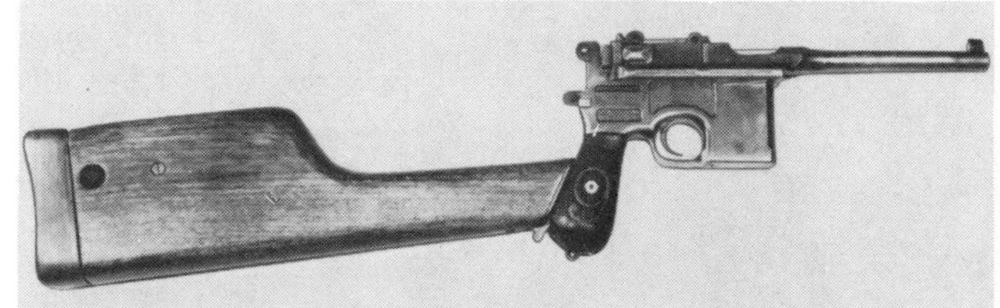

World War I Mauser Pistol converted to caliber 9mm Parabellum and fitted with detachable shoulder stock and holster. Experimental models were full auto.

After the war the design was also issued commercially with a full auto switch. This design is too light for practical true submachine gun use.

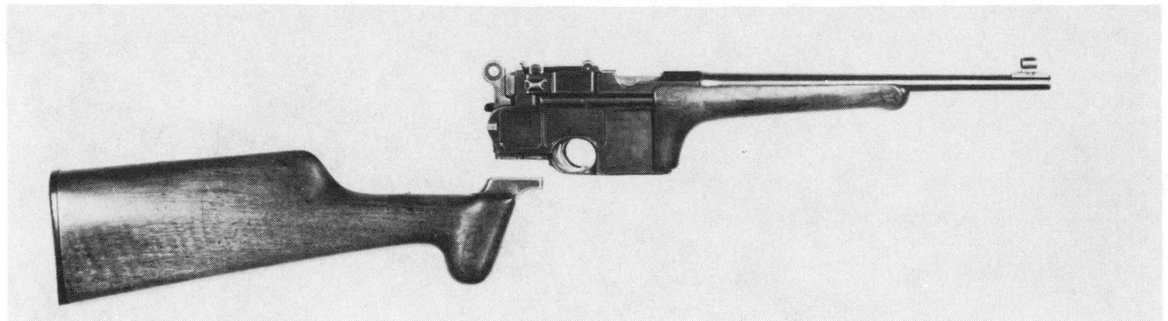

Early Mauser Pistol-Carbine, stock detached. Magazine built in. While this model was not originally intended to fire full auto, some were altered to allow selective fire. Like the Thompson this pre-War I Mauser was manufactured to use pistol cartridges. This weapon fires from a fully locked breech. Whether full or only semi-auto, this arm is legally classed as a machine weapon in the U. S.

Entirely aside from the ammunition factor, manufacturing facilities were available for producing the extra length barrels more suitable to this design and also the snail type magazines already used in the Luger or Pistole 08. For simplicity of action this initial design has never been surpassed. It fires only full automatic, but because of the weight of the recoiling parts, the cyclic rate is good for the purposes intended.

Since this weapon is treated extensively in chapter 26, only general details are necessary at this point. It utilized a rifle type stock, fed from the side with a snail magazine, was fitted with a perforated jacket for cooling the barrel, and consisted only of the stationary barrel, the moving bolt driven forward by the recoil spring, and the simple trigger, sear, extractor and ejecting mechanism.

The design was so extremely simple that it was possible to issue the guns without any special training. As a matter of routine, all officers and noncommissioned officers and 10 percent of all the men of the infantry companies were given instruction in its use. The original idea was to furnish a squad armed with six of the MP-18's to each company. Gunner and ammunition carrier were also to be armed with a standard rifle. A hand-drawn cartridge transport cart was assigned to a company.

Probably because of the terrific pressure the Germans were under in the summer and autumn of 1918 while events were turning steadily against them, very few official records were kept of the actual value of this new gun in service. However, the allies placed tremendous importance on its use. That is, all except the British. As a result, under the treaty of Versailles the 100,000-man army which was permitted Germany was denied the right to use these machine pistols or submachine guns. Some small use was authorized for police details. The manufacture of such weapons was ordered completely discontinued. The order was not particularly effective because German design went ahead on an underground basis and in other countries.

Early U. S. Developments

Early in 1918 appeared the only American World War I attempt at even an approximation of such an arm. This was the device which was listed as a top military secret and classed as the automatic pistol, Caliber .30 Model 18. This of course was the now familiar Pedersen conversion which we have discussed under rifles, a unit intended to replace the conventional turn bolt in an altered Springfield and allow the insertion of a special magazine to hold a small .30 caliber pistol type cartridge. In theory the Springfield rifle could thus be converted to a semi-automatic arm for close-up use. Since the user would have to carry two types of ammunition, two bolts, and a special magazine, and there was constant danger of

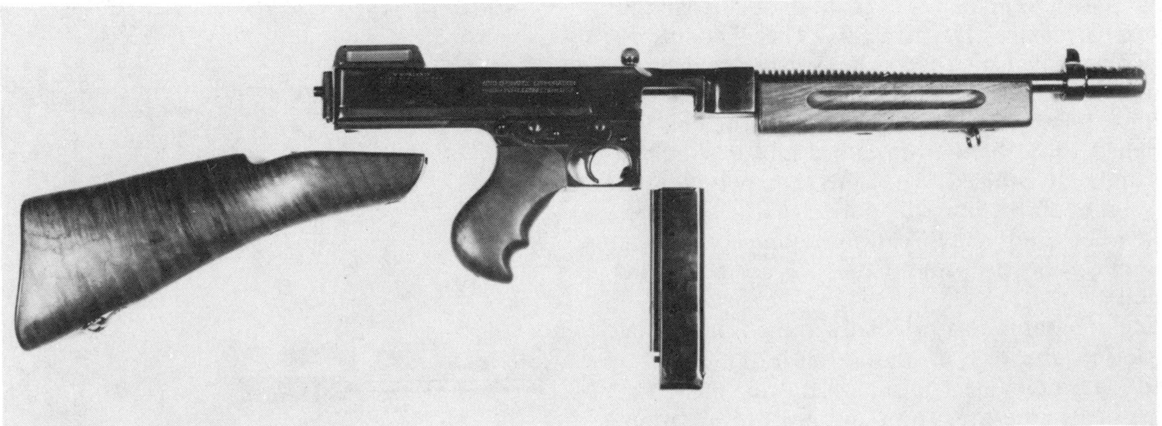

The famous Thompson Submachine Gun showing stock and magazine detached. Blowback with inertia lock. (Current models are blowback only.)

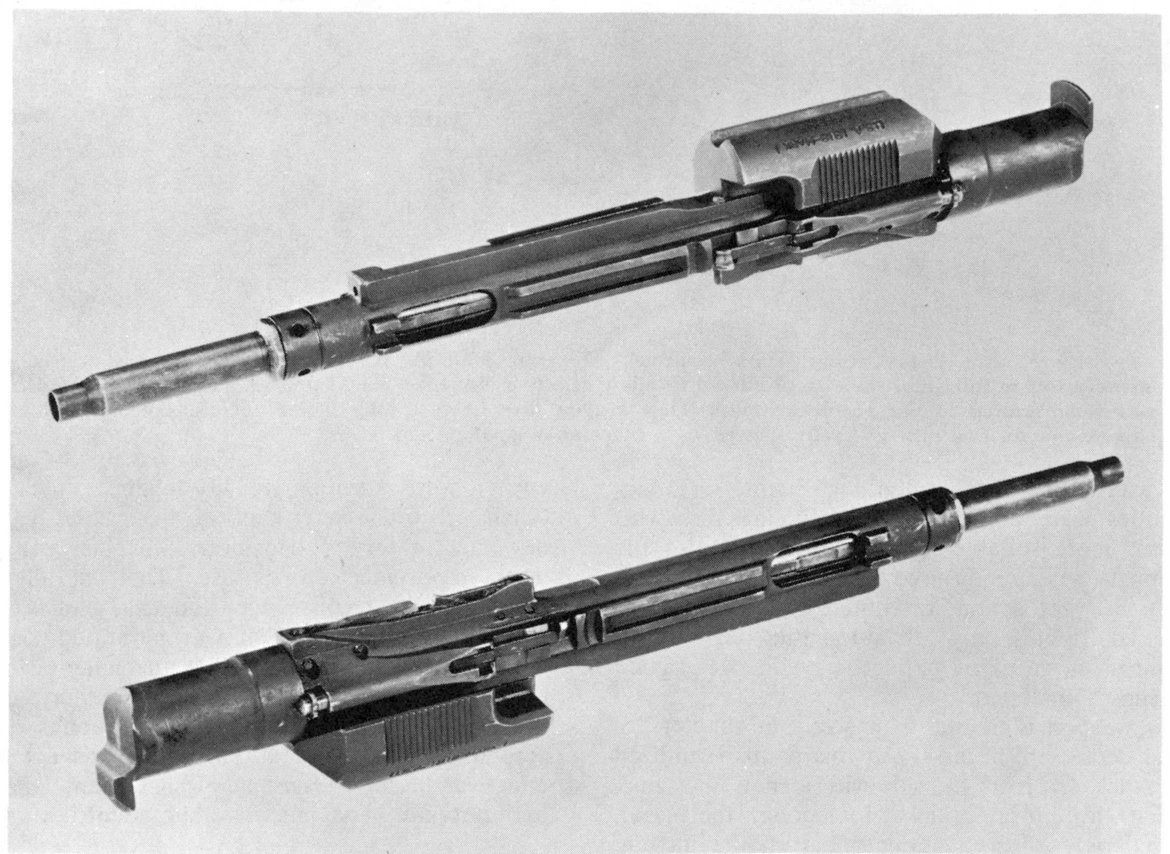

Pedersen Device, Caliber .30.

losing equipment which had to be changed in the course of the heat of battle, the Pedersen was doomed to failure from the start.

The first American submachine gun was the now world-known Thompson. Designed by General John T. Thompson, and first placed on the market in 1921, it is ironic that the weapon was immediately seized upon not as a law enforcement gun but by the bootleggers in Chicago. The reputation it made there at that time was grim indeed. Police and prison units now saw the necessity for an arm of this type to counter the number which had found their way into lawless hands.

At this point the weapon received attention from the United States Ordnance Department. The Thompson, as originally made by Colt, had a removable buttstock. It was fitted with two pistol grips, one below the barrel for left hand hold and the other conventionally behind the trigger. Designed to be fired from either hip or shoulder with both hands, it utilized the Cutts compensator to control the climb of the muzzle during automatic fire. Unlike the earlier Bergmann, it was equipped with a switch to permit either full automatic fire or to require a pull for each shot.

The cocking apparatus was originally a knob projecting through a slot in the top of the receiver. Drawing it back cocked the bolt mechanism ready to fire. The arm like most of its type fires from an open bolt position. The cartridge originally used was the .45 Colt auto pistol cartridge, but the weapon was furnished in other calibers including 9mm Luger and .38 Colt automatic; 50-shot and 100-shot circular drums were provided, but in actual practice the 100-shot drum because of its weight and feeding factors was not found too practical; 20- and 30-shot detachable clips were also issued. The original cyclic rate was of the order of 600 to 800 shots per minute. The original Thompson was equipped with the involved Thompson idea of a hesitation locking principle under which the factor of adhesion was utilized, in theory at least. In actual practice the gun would fire as well with-

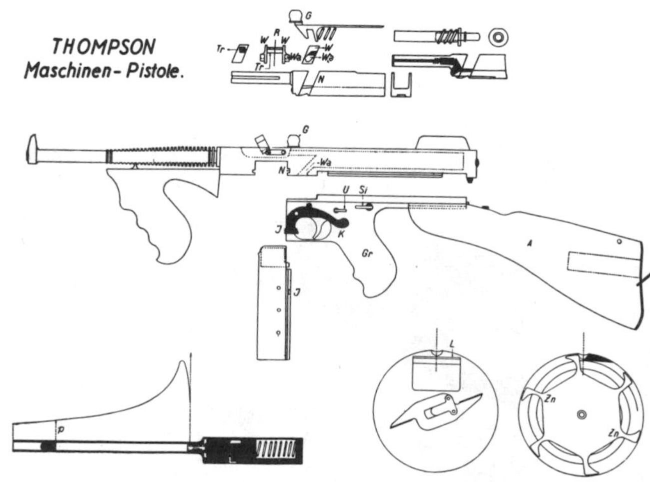

A German detail drawing showing locking details of the Thompson. This gun received considerable attention from German military officials.

out the inertia wedge block as with it, though perhaps at a somewhat faster rate.

In later models of the arm as redesigned for the United States services the hesitation system was dispensed with entirely. The last of this famous arm is a straight blowback operation, the cocking handle now being placed on the right side of the arm in standard practice. It is far simpler and quite as efficient.

It might be noted in passing that the so-called "Blish principle" on which the original Thompson was intended to operate is very much like that which Revelli developed for the original Villar Perosa. These submachine guns, of course, are operated on the elementary blowblack principle. The theory of this method of retarding the breech opening is that the design is such that the rapidity of opening is controlled. In theory, because of the rapidity with which the barrel pressure reaches its maximum, the bolt is firmly locked by the adhesion of the inclined surfaces provided until the pressure has dropped to a safe value. Any successful application of such a principle depends very largely on the constant and equal lubrication of the surfaces of the sliding elements. The Thompson originally provided lubrication by an oil pad.

In theory at least, because of the very high friction resistance with normal gas pressure even when the lock is oiled, it is impossible for the bolt to slide freely in the receiver. As the projectile leaves the barrel, the gas pressure drops. The decrease of the friction resistance occasioned by the high pressure is immediately encountered. The lock is thereby freed. The residual gas pressure in the barrel pushes the bolt mechanism back to extract, eject, and cock the firing mechanism ready for the next shot. The breech oiler automatically keeps the bolt lubricated so long as it is not subjected to dust or dirt. As we have stated, in actual practice these systems operate as well without the frictional device installed as with it.

As originally listed in early catalogues by the Auto Ordnance Corporation, the Thompson sold for $200. While the price was high, the amount of machining and fitting involved entailed a great deal more work than in the later forms of the same gun. Since no other submachine gun was available in the world market until 1928, it achieved worldwide attention in all theaters where police troubles or minor military troubles were developing.

Later World Developments

Meanwhile, although manufacture of submachine guns was prohibited in Germany by treaty, the development work was not interfered with. Hugo Schmeisser, then working with the Haenel firm in Suhl, acquired manufacturing rights for the MP-18 I which he had developed. Under his guidance the arm was modernized and prepared again under the name of the MP Schmeisser 28-2. The design perfected, the Germans very easily sidestepped the Peace Treaty by transferring the manufacturing rights in name to the Pieper Firm at Herstal in Belgium. It was manufactured there for world distribution.

This new MP Schmeisser 28-2 was offered for the standard German 9mm Parabellum cartridge. (The word Parabellum from the Latin "for war" is the commercial designation for the pistol ammunition known in Germany as the Pistole 08.) The design was also made for the 7.63mm and the 9mm Mauser pistol ammunition which had been manufactured in Europe for years and which had received worldwide distribution through the Mauser firm. Thus the elements of the pre-war Mauser organization were able to offer a submachine gun to their former customers in calibers they desired.

The snail drum of the early design of Schmeisser was replaced with a box magazine carrying the ammunition in staggered column as in the familiar military rifle. Moreover, it was equipped with a switch to permit single or continuous fire. The switch was in a form of a button in the shaft above the trigger. Where the recoil spring of the first model had been provided with a guide, this was eliminated in the new model and instead the spring diameter was increased to utilize the interior dimension of the receiver tube.

Ironically, the fullest acceptance of this weapon in military circles as an official weapon was by the Belgian army in 1934. They listed it as the Mitraillette Model 34. (Mitraillette was a designation used in Belgium and in France for the submachine gun, indicating a small caliber full automatic arm.)

While the United States was adopting the Thompson for special duty purpose, and England and France ignored the new weapon, the Russians proceeded in 1934 to develop a submachine gun. Operating on the theory that pistols were no longer adequate defense arms for the protection of heavy weapons by their crews, nor for the leaders of infantry units, Russian concentration on submachine gun development, while it came slowly, did eventually develop on a very wide scale.

The Tikkakoski factory in Finland began production of a machine pistol or submachine gun under the designation of Suomi. It was promptly adopted by the Army of Finland and some were brought by the Swedish, Swiss, and Danish armies. It is a well made elementary blowback design. The recoil spring is positioned directly behind the bolt, the point of the firing pin protruding constantly. The arm fires as the bolt is still moving forward, providing an additional inertia factor to slow down the rapidity of opening. The operating handle is stationary during the firing period, an advantage in itself. The Suomi was fitted with a barrel which could be speedily changed without the use of tools. This too marked a step forward in design. Both box and drum magazines were provided.

This Suomi was developed by the Finnish designer Lahti. When the Russian attack opened on Finland in November of 1939, one of the weapons with which the Finns defended themselves was this submachine gun. Its deadliness and particularly its adaptability impressed the Russians tremendously.

In passing it may be noted that Lahti had produced his submachine gun in 9mm caliber. This, of course, represented German influence at the time, as well as the fact that Finland and Sweden also used the 9mm Parabellum cartridge.

At the close of World War I the Russians' sidearm equipment had been a hodepodge of revolvers, mostly in 7.62mm Russian caliber with an intermingling of German Mauser pistols. The revolvers of course had rimmed cartridges which will not function effectively through box magazines of the type used in submachine guns. The Russian designers, therefore, turned their thoughts to a new automatic pistol cartridge. Since Mauser military model automatic pistols have been used extensively in Russia since early in the century, the 7.63mm bottlenecked high-speed cartridge used by this weapon had been given considerable attention by the Russian development groups.

The Russian designer Tokarev, using the Browning-Colt system as a model, worked out a very unusual development in low-cost production of that pattern and introduced in 1930 a new service Russian automatic pistol designated as caliber 7.62mm. This actually used the slightly underpowered 7.63mm Mauser ammunition. Up to this point American experience had leaned toward the large caliber in submachine guns, as witness the fact that our pistols and the Thompson both use the .45 automatic pistol cartridge. The Germans and their supporters leaned toward the 9mm. The Russians felt that the 7.63mm caliber with its bottlenecked case, higher velocity, and greater range was more in line with their requirements. (Also, the same barrel-making equipment used for making their service 7.62mm rifles could be adapted to this pistol and submachine gun caliber.)

It will be noted that, in later modifications of this first Russian submachine gun and in most later types they have adopted, the Russians have adhered religiously to the principles set forth early by Hugo Schmeisser. They have sought to produce a weapon at an extremely low price, using the common machinery available in their country, utilizing to the full the application of stampings and metal turnings which are the simplest form of manufacture. While the resultant arms have all been crude in appearance, they have been very effective. Their low cost and rapid production possibilities have enabled the Russians to follow through on the original German idea of issuing them to all noncommissioned officers and to all special groups. In addition, also in line with the original theory, the guns have been kept so simple that the most ignorant and illiterate soldier can be taught to use them without extensive training.

In 1934 there also appeared the first of the Swiss-made Solothurn submachine guns (or machine pistols as they are called in Europe). As we have discussed in some length in our section on machine guns, the Solothurn Works was controlled by the great German Rheinmetall firm which had been authorized to produce rifles for the 100,000-man German army authorized by the Peace Treaty. Design work had continued, even though they were denied the right to manufacture machine pistols. Parts were manufactured in Denmark and also at the Steyr Plant in Austria and shipped to Switzerland to the Solothurn Works for assembly under German control.

The first issuance of the MP Solothurn 34 was in caliber 9mm Mauser. This is not to be confused with the 9mm Luger, the so-called Parabellum or official German Pistole 08 cartridge. It is a longer and much more powerful cartridge which was manufactured originally for the Mauser 9mm export model pistols, most of which were sold in South America. The original Solothurn idea was that this overpowered 9mm cartridge would be a step in the right direction in connection with future machine pistol development. They recognized the importance of a more powerful load for the submachine gun which, being heavier and intended to be used with two hands, was much more stable than the pistol.

The 9mm Solothurns were delivered to the Austrian Army where they were adopted as the MP-34. Since the Austrian police were basically equipped with still another type of 9mm automatic pistol, their Model 1912 or Steyr, a quantity of the guns were chambered for this cartridge for police use. Later, during the Spanish Civil War, considerable quantities of these weapons were sold by Solothurn to the Spanish Franco groups. In fact, it was the testing done in this Civil War with this caliber which led German observers to the firm conclusion that for machine pistols the 9mm Parabellum, whatever the theoretical considerations, in actual practice was as desirable as the 9mm Mauser patterns.

In the Solothurn the recoil spring is positioned in the

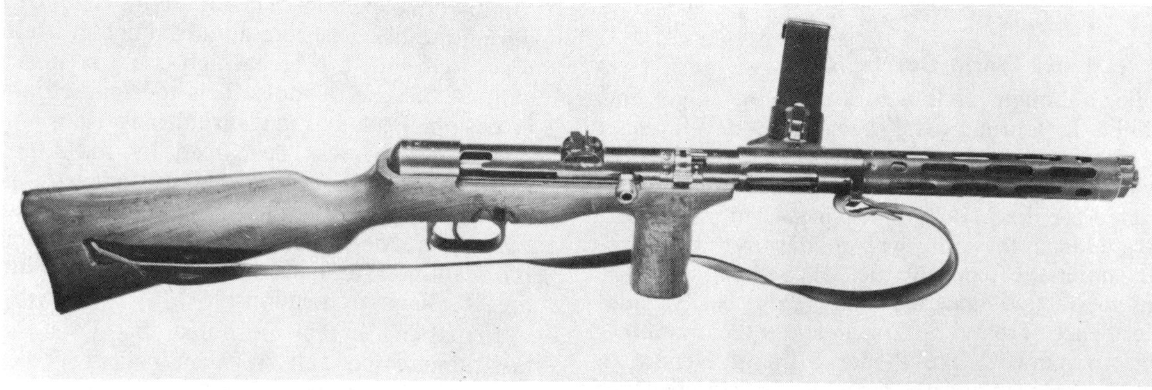

Erma Machine Pistol. Designed by Vollmer, this gun was made in both Germany and Spain. Its name derives from the manufacturer, Erfurter Maschinenfabrik.

rifle-like butt stock, being compressed by a rod hinged to the bolt. A change lever on the left side of the receiver permits single or automatic fire. The magazine is a double line box. A special loading attachment is provided. Since the arm was primarily designed for close quarters work, it was equipped to be fitted with a bayonet. Still another accessory tested in the Spanish Civil War was a container to be mounted over the ejection port. This was for tank and vehicle work where flying empty cartridge cases might be undesirable.

By 1932 the Bergmann Company then at Berlin had produced a very unusual modification and improvement of their original MP-18I. This weapon (Model 34) had been turned over to the Schultz & Larsen Manufacturing firm at Otterup in Sweden. This arm, slightly modified, was adopted by the Swedish army as its Model 39.

While this 34 Model is blowback as in the case of the original Bergmann, it varies in many mechanical respects. The receiver is completely enclosed. The operating handle does not move during firing. The bolt may be withdrawn and dismounted without tools. A special firing pin device was incorporated, the firing pin protruding from the bolt to fire just before the end of the closing bolt stroke. The trigger system is a variation of one utilized in various Solothurn arms. The trigger is pivoted at its center, and a pull at the upper section fires a single shot, the breech staying open until the trigger is released and then pulled again, while the pull on the lower half gives continuous fire until the trigger is released. The barrel has a cooling jacket and is fitted with a compensator to counteract the muzzle climb and also a device to reduce recoil.

Originally issued as the MP Bergmann Model 34, the

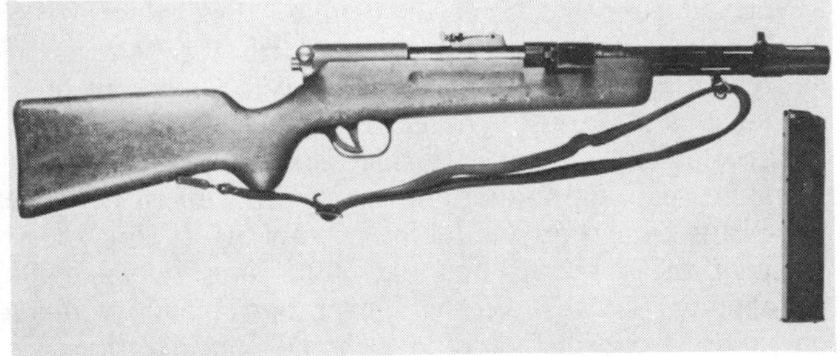

German Bergmann 9mm 1934 machine pistol or submachine gun. This and the other German designs are covered in chapter 26.

gun had obvious advantages over its earlier model. However, so much simplification was lost that the cost, naturally, increased considerably.

Also in 1935 the Spanish Echeverria firm at Eibar introduced a machine pistol. (Star is the trade name of this firm which manufactures pistols, submachine guns, and shotguns.) This initial Spanish machine pistol, like so many of the Spanish developments, was a modification of an American arm. An attempt was made to utilize the bolt system of the American Thompson. The gun was offered in various calibers including the standard 7.63mm and 9mm Parabellum and others.

It might be noted in passing that the various arms factories in Spain have for years issued copies and modifications of Mauser military pistols and of Colt automatic pistols. Star currently produces a pistol externally and in locking arrangement very much like the .45 Colt automatic. It can be fitted with an extension magazine. It also can accommodate a detachable buttstock. A firing switch permits the use of single shot or full automatic fire. Even when used with a stock, however, this design is too light for practical machine pistol usage. Star also makes a German pattern submachine gun (Model Z-45).

The Russian MP-34 and its modification the Model 34/38 as well as their Model 40, which are very much of a pattern, were not originally Russian in development. Their designs were evolved directly from the MP Schmeisser 28-2.

Still another German submachine gun (or machine pistol) developed during this period was the Vollmer. Manufactured at the Erfurter Maschinenfabrik (The Erfurt Machine Works), it is also a blowblack weapon. Its recoil spring is positioned directly behind the bolt, enclosed in a telescoping tube to protect it from dirt, a system which was utilized during the World War II by the Germans in their superb submachine guns MP-38 and MP-40.

This arm was equipped with a right thumb switch to permit single or continuous fire and had a forward pistol grip to steady the arm as in the case of the early Thompsons. It was manufactured not only for the standard 7.63mm Mauser cartridge and the 9mm Parabellum, but also for the Luger 7.65mm cartridge and for the 9mm Bergmann, this last being a cartridge seldom seen except in Spain and in some areas in Scandinavia. It too was one of the submachine guns sent to Spain to the Franco forces during the Civil War there.

Hungarian Submachine Gun

In 1939 the Hungarian Army adopted officially their M-1939 machine carbine in caliber 9mm Mauser. While it was never produced in quantity, it is an interesting example of the better type of retarded blowback or hesitation system.

In general lines it resembles a short rifle and is furnished with a box magazine which can be folded up below the barrel when not in use but can be swung into position quickly in case of necessity.

The breechblock has two connected parts, a pivoted lever being positioned in the front one. The upper end of this lever bears constantly against the rear section of the breechblock which is thrust forward by the recoil spring. The lower end of the lever rests in a slot in the lower section of the receiver.

As the cartridge is fired and the breechblock starts back, since the lower leg of the lever is positioned in the receiver, the bolt thrust against the upper half compels the lever to rotate. Consequently, the upper end of the lever thrusts the rear half of the brechblock backward. This causes the front section to be forced forward by reaction through the lever axis. By thus utilizing the opposing reaction which, of course, is equal to every action, the forward section of the block which supports the recoiling cartridge case is slowed down after the initial thrust, but when the rear section of the connected breechblock reaches its limit of rearward travel its transferred kinetic energy pulls the forward section back to completely open the breech.

This delaying system permits the use of a very much lighter breechblock than does the standard blowback arm using the same 9mm cartridge. On the other hand, of course, this system has several offsetting disadvantages. It is a much more complex design requiring more parts and more machining and fitting. However, this is one of the best of the delay systems and does offer experimenters a principle worthy of more intense study than it has received for application to other types of arms.

Italian

A form of machine carbine, based originally on the Villar Perosa principle of the lightweight turning bolt to retard the blowback, is common in Italy. The magazine is the typical box magazine fed in through the top of the rifle. Ejection is through the bottom. This arm, while normally encountered as a single shot or semi-automatic design, was also made to some extent as a full automatic. It uses the standard 9mm Italian service pistol cartridge and is commonly known as the Beretta Moschetto, after the factory manufacturer.

Italian Beretta

In 1938, however, the Beretta factory produced a true submachine gun of the very highest order. Heavily built and of rifle type (it weighed 10.3 pounds with a loaded 40-round magazine) it was equipped with barrel jacket for cooling, compensator, bayonet mount, dual triggers for single or full automatic fire, and was intended to be used with a heavily loaded 9mm cartridge popularly known as the M38. This gun was put into service in Africa. It was also issued to police in areas where smuggling was rampant. Because of the heavy weight of its recoiling parts, and the fine quality of the materials and the machining, this is one of the most efficient arms of its sort ever designed, although its weight and bulk are considered by many to take it out of the standard classification of the common machine pistol.

In 1942 technicians in the Italian factory proceeded to modify the Beretta. The new version was listed as the MP-38/42. The barrel was shortened and its forward end cut to furnish a built-in compensator. The cooling jacket was dispensed with in the interests of lessening weight.

German

In 1938 the Germans introduced their MP-38. This was a standard simple blowback gun in 9mm caliber. It was a magnificent example of the utilization of the latest design and in the use of elementary turned parts. The operating spring, housed in telescopic tubes somewhat like the earlier Vollmer, prevented kinking of springs and gave complete protection from dirt or dust. Since this gun is covered in detail in chapter 25, only passing reference is needed here. It introduced the idea of the folding butt stock which could be folded so as not to interfere with hip firing. In 1940 a modification of this arm was

German Schmeisser 41 modification. From the West Point Collection. This pattern was not common.

introduced. The cyclic rate of fire of about 450 to 540 per minute is nearly ideal for submachine gun operation according to European theory, although American theory favors an even lower rate. In any event, a trained gunner can tap off single shots with this arm. In view of this, the Germans dispensed with the idea of a special single shot trigger, thereby still further simplifying manufacture and reducing costs.

General

It is a matter of German record that when the German Armies entered Poland, Norway, and the Balkans they encountered very few submachine guns, most of those they did meet being early Bergmanns or American Thompsons.

Despite the fact that both Germany and Russia were testing several types of submachine guns of their manufacture or control in Spain during the Spanish Civil War, the British army failed to recognize the importance of this type of arm. Both the Germans and the Russians learned during the Spanish conflict the value of the machine pistol as a close combat arm for both attack and defense, with particular reference to its use in house to house and forest fighting. Its light weight and easy transportability gave it a terrific edge over even machine rifles in such close-quarters work. Its superiority over the pistol from the standpoint of rapidity of fire, possibility of firing bursts, and the extra range which could be obtained because of the longer barrel and two-hand operation, were all factors given great consideration.

The British Army was not then equipped with submachine guns. The immediate use in quantity of this design by the Germans compelled them to turn to America as a source of supply at the outbreak of war. Large quantities of Thompsons were purchased. These were both the 1928 commercial patterns with two hand grips and the military patterns with one grip and forestock. In the African campaigns trouble was shortly encountered with the involved locking mechanism on the Thompson. The locks were commonly removed. Large quantity orders were placed with Savage in the United States for manufacture of Thompsons. Over 1,000,000 were made.

Meanwhile the British, examining samples of the German MP-38, set out to design a low-cost submachine gun. The standard British side arm at that period was a .38 caliber revolver which, of course, used rimmed cartridges which would not feed properly through an automatic pistol magazine. This fact led the British developers to produce their submachine gun to handle the standard 9mm German pattern cartridge. This enabled them to utilize stocks of captured ammunition. Their own and United States ammunition factories had a table of experience on manufacture of the 9mm Parabellum cartridge, a fact which eliminated design and development work on a new type of cartridge.

British Sten

While they were greatly influenced by the German idea of utilization of stampings and machine turnings, the British did not have either the German machine equipment nor the manufacturing know-how to produce arms of a like quality. They developed, therefore, an ultra-cheap type of arm which could be manufactured in the most elementary machine shops. This weapon was really a masterpiece of design from the standpoint of low cost and rapid production. This is the famous Sten gun. The name derives apparently from the initials of the designers and the point of manufacture, Enfield Armory. Both the bolt system and the feed mechanism are a direct imitation of the Schmeisser MP-28.2 However, the firing pin is stationary in the bolt. The gun was designed to be easily dismounted and carried hidden by paratroopers and guerrillas. The arm originally met with considerable derision by German technicians, but its actual battle use very shortly established it as an arm capable of doing anything that the most expensive types of submachine guns could hope to do. The cost was brought down as low as the fantastic figure of $9.00 per gun during the height of the war and under intense manufacture in Canada!

This gun led the way to later manufacture in Australia of the quite unusual Austen or Australian Sten gun, which together with the Australian Owen, is completely described in chapter 17.

French Development

Like the British, the French paid little attention to submachine gun design in the period between World Wars I and II. The outbreak of war found them using a certain number of Thompsons in .45 caliber which had been purchased from the United States, and also a version of the Vollmer Erma produced in Germany and originally sold to the Communist groups in Spain. The French Army itself produced only the MAS 38 (the name comes from the point of design and manufacture, Manufacture d' Armes, St. Etienne). This gun too will be found completely described in chapter 24. An elementary blowback, it utilized a 7.65mm long pistol cartridge. Since the French were armed with a wide variety of revolvers and automatic pistols in varying calibers, they designed a special cartridge for this submachine gun. The cartridge is little more effective than the common American .32 automatic pistol cartridge. The cartridge is actually so close to the U. S. .30 Pederson device cartridge of War I that it would seem that French designers merely "borrowed" the caliber.

This submachine gun was issued in considerable quantities to French Colonial troops in the recent Indo-China campaign. When the Germans stormed over France, they permitted the French police to use these weapons.

U. S. M3

During the War the United States Ordnance Department developed its own stamped type of submachine gun based on the British Sten gun and the German Schmeisser. This gun is fully described in chapter 45. The United States design, which was promptly dubbed the "grease gun" by our troops because of its crude appearance, is actually one of the most efficient submachine guns in the world today. It went through several modifications before finally getting all the bugs out, but the design was such as to lend itself to a maximum of high-speed production with stampings and screw machine equipment commonly available on a large scale in the United States. Neither as crude as the Sten nor as well-made and finished as the German, it still has all the elements of simplicity and ruggedness needed in this type of arm.

U. S. submachine gun. Cal. .45 Serial #5. Experimental model of M3 submachine gun. From the West Point Collection. The production models are covered in chapter 45.

Other U. S. Designs

Another elementary blowback was made at Philadelphia by Sedgley, though this too was an expensive type of arm and with the coming of the M3 was completely outmoded. Our Ordnance M2 was also by-passed in test stages for the superior M3.

The U. D. developed at High Standard Arms for the Dutch in limited quantities was but an elementary blowback also.

The very unusual delayed blowback Reising gun which we also cover in chapter 45 did not stand up too well in use by United States Marines. This gun too was outmoded on a basis of cost, simplicity, and reliability by the M3. It is rather extensively used by law enforcement groups who purchased Reisings while the Thompson patterns were available only for military use.

Russian

As we have seen, the early Russian submachine guns were basically little more than modifications of the German Schmeisser MP-28-2. These included the Model 1940 machine pistol equipped with a 71-round drum. This modification was ascribed to the Russian inventor V. Degtyarev. The usual designation is Model 1940: PPD.

In 1941 the Russians introduced a new one, the Model

1941: PPSH, the name stemming from the name of the designer Shpagin. This design differed radically from the earlier ones and is of true Russian origin. For the most part it is a series of simple stampings. The receiver cover and the barrel jacket are a one-piece design. An extension of the barrel cover over the muzzle acts as a muzzle brake. The front end is designed to counteract muzzle climb. A switch provides for single and full automatic fire. The safety is a sliding design copied from that of the Model 34/38, and the drum magazine is similar except for the type of lip required.

In 1942 and again in 1943 new Soviet submachine guns appeared. The clumsy wooden one-piece butt stock was replaced with a folding steel stock modified along the lines of the German MP-38. These arms were designed for box type magazines only, the normal magazine capacity being 35 rounds.

The Role of the Submachine Gun

The history of the submachine gun is small in relation to other arms types, as we have seen. It really began in 1915 in Italy with the Villar Perosa.

However, due to the intense development and the widespread usage both during World War II and in the various so-called police campaigns throughout the world since then, it is technically very far developed. Relatively few changes of any importance can be expected in this type of arm unless and until more powerful types of ammunition are available or adaptable.

While technical details of the various arms differ, of course, all use ammunition which was originally designed for one hand firing in pistols where effective ranges are necessarily short.

None handle ammunition which warrants usage against human targets at ranges of much more than 200 yards. While many are equipped with sights graduated up to 1,000 meters or more, such sights are useless except for possible, plunging fire. Submachine guns have proven to be very essential arms equipment for both the Army and for certain types of police work, all, however, at close range.

For all practical purposes probably the 9mm Parabellum cartridge is the most suitable for this type of arm. In connection with standardization of equipment, it is quite likely that the .45 automatic cartridge in due course will give way to this smaller caliber. The advantage of greater bullet weight is more than offset by the greater weight of the ammunition and of the weapon itself.

Magazines for normal tactical purposes require a capacity of 25 to 30 rounds. Except for the possible development of the staggered 4-column box issued in Sweden and Finland, there is no practical way of increasing the magazine capacity much beyond this point without incurring disadvantages which will nullify the increased magazine capacity. The 70- to 100-round drum magazines proved unsatisfactory in the field wherever used and by whomever used. They are much more given to jams than are the simple straight line box types of magazine.

In practically all instances, firing from the open breech is and will continue to be the ideal method of operation of the submachine gun. Because of the heat generated in automatic fire the chamber must be left empty, as otherwise cartridges would "cook off" in a closed breech. There is little to be gained by increasing the barrel length, since the distance between sights is not particularly important in view of the relative inaccuracy of this type of arm and cartridge at distances over 200 yards. The short bullet travel permits simple design and construction of a blowback action, whereas the longer barrel would have the effect of increasing velocity somewhat but would introduce serious design factors with relation to the operation of the breech mechanism.

Cooling systems are unnecessary not only because of the relatively low power of the cartridges used and the relatively heavy weight of the barrels involved, but also because the amount of fire which can be put through a gun at any one time would hardly ever warrant the weight and complication of a cooling agent or section.

As we have mentioned, the Hungarian Model 1939 is an instance of a delaying device or hesitation device which might be the subject of some investigation, though its complicating factors with use of pistol ammunition more than offset the value of the lower weight breechblock which it permits. Madsen, as we have seen, tried to utilize a lighter breechblock by compelling it to carry with it the receiver cover, but here again the complication offsets the value of the weight saved, which in no case is likely to be more than six ounces. If more weight than that is saved, the cyclic rate of fire will be too high for proper submachine gun use.

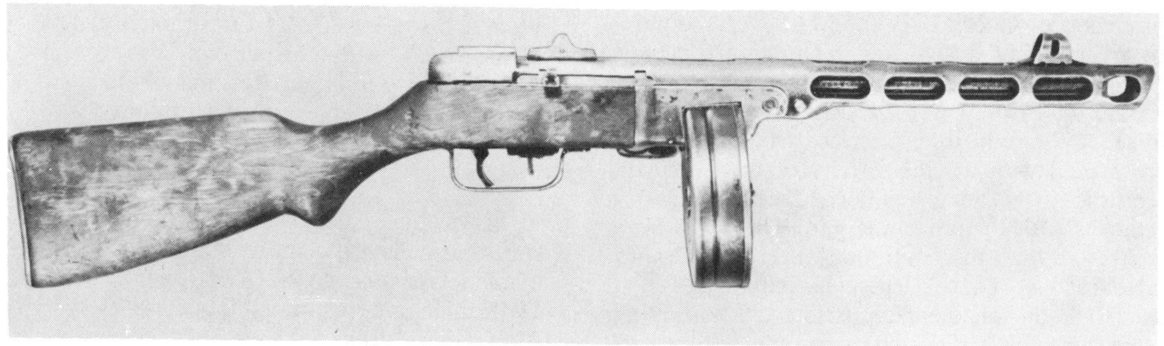

Russian Model PPSH 41, One of the cheapest yet most efficient submachine guns ever built, despite its crudity. The large capacity drum magazine is being replaced in Russian service by the box type.

Probably the one truly valuable field feature to be introduced in any new gun is that in the Swiss pattern in which the magazine may be swung from horizontal to vertical position. In all other types of submachine guns, either the magazine protrudes so far below the receiver that the gun cannot be fired from the prone position without exposing the shooter, or in side feeding it is clumsy and awkward in anything but prone shooting.

Much attention has been given in some quarters to the idea of using precision castings to simulate machined parts with an ease of manufacture which is expected to be comparable to that of stampings. In actual practice this just does not work. There is no process of manufacture which begins to approach stampings or pressings for low-cost production. On the other hand the design of an arm to utilize such procedures and to hold them to the tolerances found in the M3 submachine gun and in the German MP-40 is beyond the technical skill of any but the world's finest arms factories and metal working factories. As to precision castings, it is impossible in quantity at low cost to hold these to the types of tolerances which are commonly required in the firearms manufacturing business. They are excellent for developmental and prototype arms, but in production even the most formal methods of forging and machining permit a faster and far cheaper rate of manufacture.

Developments such as the so-called German MP-44 and the U. S. carbine M1 series constitute locked breech weapons utilizing cartridges of far higher power than can be handled in standard submachine guns. Such arms form an entirely new classification of weapons. Although they are often loosely placed in the category of submachine guns, and varieties of them may be used in full automatic fire, they actually constitute a new field weapon whose uses are being explored.

A study of the submachine guns in Part II covers pictorially every design which has been produced in any quantity.

Note on Design

It is generally agreed that the most efficient cyclic rate for a submachine gun is of the order of 450 rounds per minute. This is extremely difficult to achieve, particularly with a relatively light weight breechblock. Most designs have far higher rates which result in ammunition wastage through uncontrollable fire. While the heavy breechblock will reduce the rate materially, the weight of the moving block itself is such a sizable part of the entire weight of the arm that its movement creates vibration to a degree that interferes with accuracy. The M3 submachine gun minimizes this through use of a relatively heavy breechblock but by providing it with balanced recoil spring and by keeping the bolt completely guided on metal guides at all times during its forward and rearward travel.

Compensators are definitely valuable, particularly on the lighter variety of arms, because by deflecting some of the muzzle blast (upwards as a rule) they oppose the tendency of the barrel to climb during full automatic fire. The Beretta system of cutting slots in the upper section of the muzzle forward of the front sight is relatively effective, as the escaping gas produces a reaction equal to its own momentum.

The Russians and their allies generally have come to utilize the submachine gun almost to the complete displacement of the pistol for offensive purposes. For standard military purposes there can be no question that the submachine gun as formerly produced by Russia costs even less than a pistol to manufacture, and, by producing a tremendous volume of fire which is usable and directable at greater ranges than normal pistol shooting, has made the pistol obsolete as a practical offensive weapon.

Chapter 11. The Revolver—Historical Outline

THE revolver is an arm intended to be fired with one hand ordinarily. It consists of a single fixed barrel positioned in a frame, and a revolving cylinder which contains several chambers for cartridges, one chamber being lined up and locked in line with the barrel at the moment of firing.

While the terms "revolver and pistol" are customarily used interchangeably in common lay practice, no firearm is actually a revolver except as described above.

From the earliest times attempts have been made to produce revolvers, however crude.

The first actually successful revolver was, of course, that of our own Samuel Colt. However, it must be noted that his original patent was granted in England in 1835 and he did not seek out United States patents until later, the first being granted on February 25, 1836.

Samuel Colt. From a painting made at the height of his success.

Romantic legend has it that Samuel Colt conceived the idea of his revolving system while traveling on a schooner as a cabin boy and studying the operation of the spoked steering wheel. It is not strange that a person with the fantastic background and personality of Samuel Colt should be the subject of legends, though this one is considerably farfetched.

There is in the Royal United Service Museum in Whitehall, England, a Snaphaunce revolver of the days of Charles the First of England. Its date of manufacture is before 1650. This is a brass-barreled giant of .500 caliber which weighs about 6¼ pounds. In every essential of cylinder operation it is so similar to Colt's original firearm that the researcher looking at it cannot help but wonder if Sam, one of the great opportunists of all times, did not see this model on one of his early trips to England. A ratchet is cut into the head of the cylinder and is set with six teeth. When the hammer is cocked, a metal hand attached to it pushes up against the ratchet to line a chamber up with the barrel. The familiar spring catch locks in a positioned notch in the cylinder to lock the action at this point.

Whatever the origin of his design, whether individually conceived or subconsciously borrowed, Samuel Colt is unquestionably the father of the successful revolver.

His original British patent covers the revolving of the cylinder by a hand attached to the hammer as the hammer is brought to full cock. It also specifies in great detail center fire ignition produced by percussion caps firing through horizontal nipples separated by partitions to prevent accidental firing of adjoining chambers. It also deals in detail with the lockwork.

Colt's first model was made by an East Hartford gun-

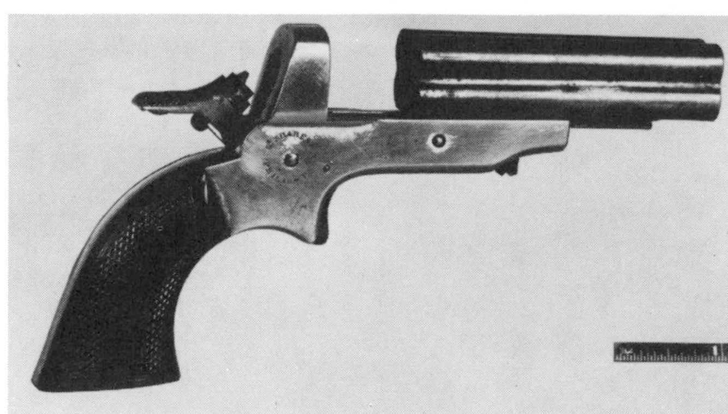

Early American Sharps 4-barreled pistol for metallic cartridges. Note that this and variant types which do not have revolving cylinders are not technically revolvers.

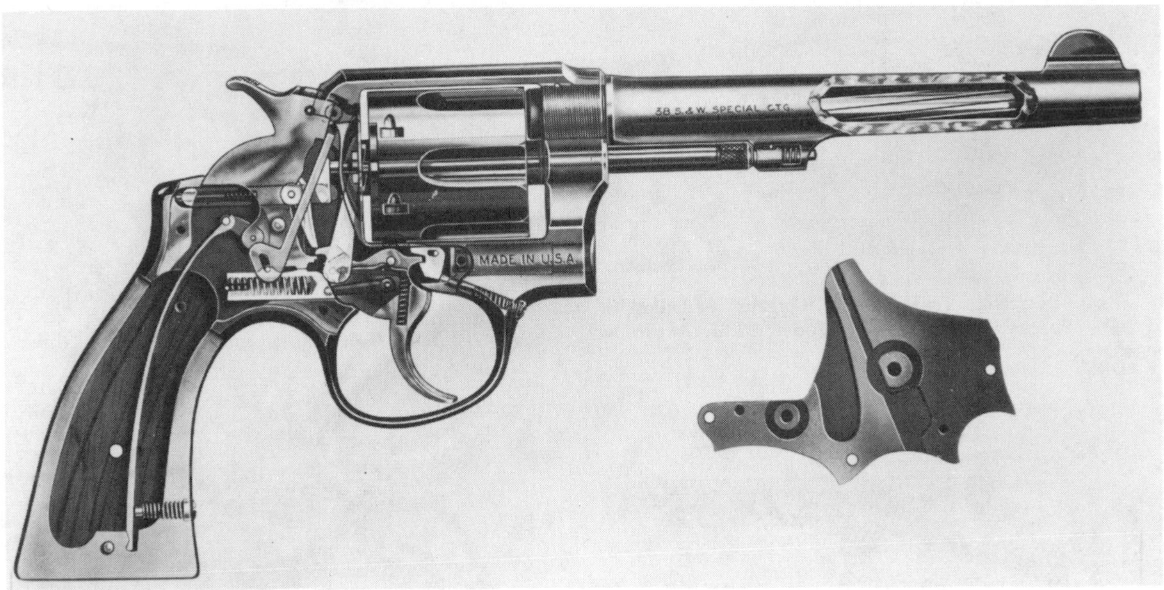

A revolver. The cartridges are loaded into individual chambers in a revolving cylinder.

Sectionalized view of the current Smith & Wesson modern revolver; 95% of American police units use this type of side arm. Working mechanism is exposed by removing the side plate shown below.

smith named Anson Chase. Sam lost the hard-earned dollars paid to Chase when the model blew up as fire flashed from one chamber to another. The failure was due to lack of the protective partitions between the chambers which he later specified in his patent. The famous "Anson Chase Model," Colt's number 2 design, is still to be seen at the Colt's Museum at Hartford. In weight, measurements, and general appearance it is a close relative of the Single Action Army Model of 1873 which was in manufacture until recent years, the famed "Peacemaker" of Wild West fame.

Colt's original weapons, of course, were developed in the percussion era. All the chambers were loaded with powder and ball (or with combustible cartridges which contained the powder and the ball) from the front end. Percussion caps were then positioned over the nipples on each of the chambers. These nipples had holes drilled in them to permit flash of the percussion fire into the powder charge inside the individual chambers. Partitions between the nipples confined the percussion flash and prevented accidental firing of adjoining chambers.

Colt's original patents were so well drawn that they prevented the actual manufacture here and abroad of any but freak revolvers until 1850. He promptly squelched with law suits anyone attempting to infringe upon his idea.

Colt's first revolvers were manufactured at Paterson, New Jersey. Today these are among the world's prime gun collection pieces. Very few are in existence. That original manufacturing company went bankrupt, but six years later Colt was back in production at Whitneyville, Connecticut. With the cooperation of one of the great assembly line production geniuses of all time, Eli Whitney, Colt proceeded to act upon suggestions from Captain Walker of the Texas Rangers to produce the heavy revolvers used at the outbreak of the Mexican War. From this business Colt managed to raise enough money to open his own factory at Hartford, still the best known revolver manufacturing plant in the world.

By 1850 Colt was exporting revolvers to England and elsewhere in Europe. In 1853 he opened a plant at London, using men he had brought from the United States as foremen to train the manufacturing groups there.

The English Deane-Adams revolver, patented in 1851, was the only arm which at that time offered any serious competition to Colt. This English revolver was the first true solid frame design. Since the barrel and frame were a single forging, this arm was a much stronger design than the Colt of the same period. Also, the English revolver was a double-action type in which a pull on the trigger turned the cylinder and cocked and dropped the hammer, a design favored by the British even in recent years. However, neither this nor other British revolvers such as the Lang & Witton and the Daw were able to compete commercially with the mass production Colt had initiated. His system of manufacture played quite as large a role in the introduction of his revolver as did the design itself.

The English Beaumont of 1855 furnished a true advance in lock work, permitting the revolver to be thumb-cocked and fired by trigger pressure as in the Colt, or fired by direct double-action pull on the trigger as in the case of the Deane-Adams. The Beaumont action, in fact, was soon incorporated into the Adams revolver, the weapon then being officially adopted by the British as their service revolver.

The Colt cocking system was excellent for accuracy since it allowed a relatively light pull on the trigger to drop the hammer for firing without affecting the line of sight. However, it was relatively slow in operation in the hands of the average shooter. The Deane-Adams, on the

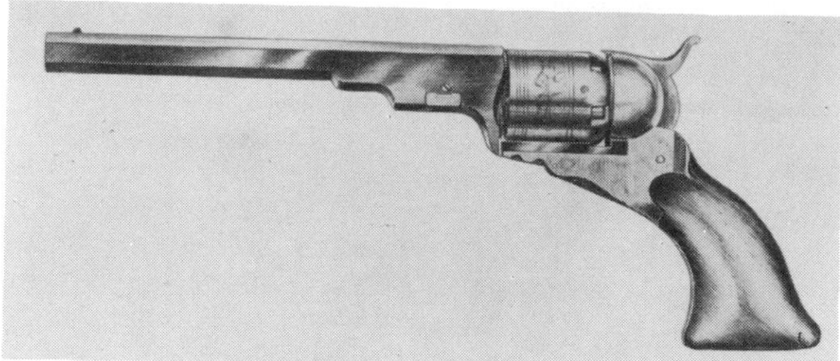

The Colt Texas Paterson. Caliber .40. Muzzle loaded with powder and ball. Percussion cap fired. Model 1836. Made at Paterson, New Jersey.

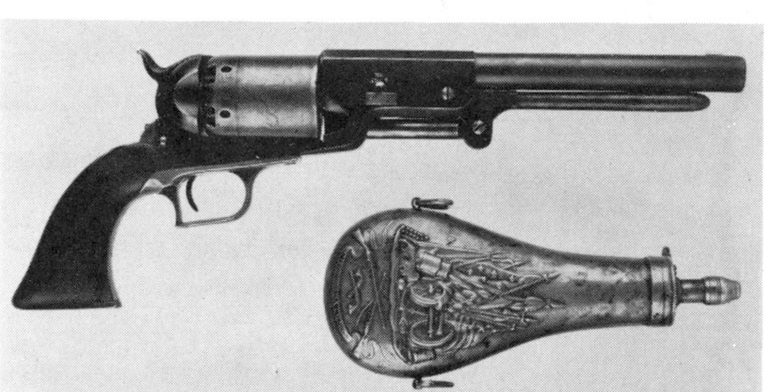

U. S. Percussion Revolver. Whitneyville-Walker Colt. Model of 1847. "C" Company No. 154. Caliber .44, six shot, single action.

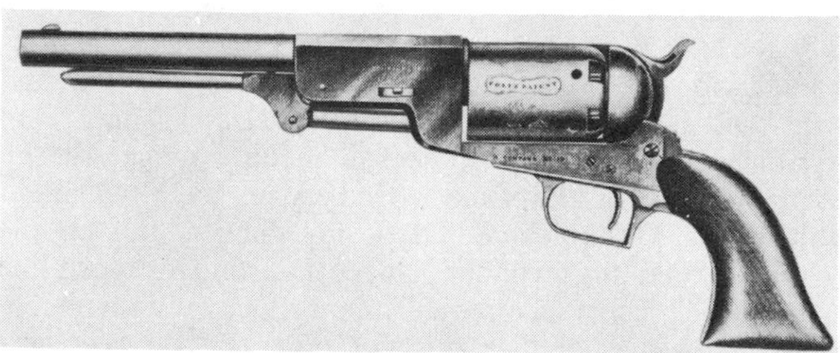

The Colt Walker model 1847. Caliber .44.

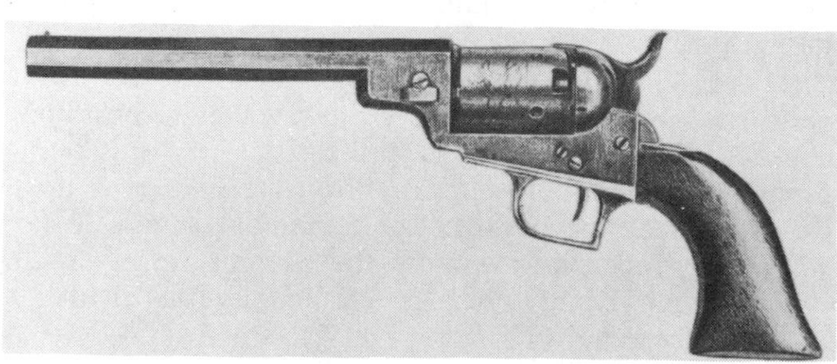

The Colt Wells Fargo model 1848. Caliber .31.

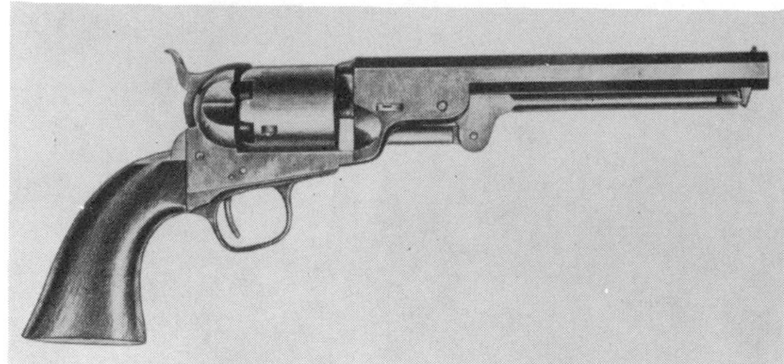

The Colt Navy model 1851. Caliber .36.

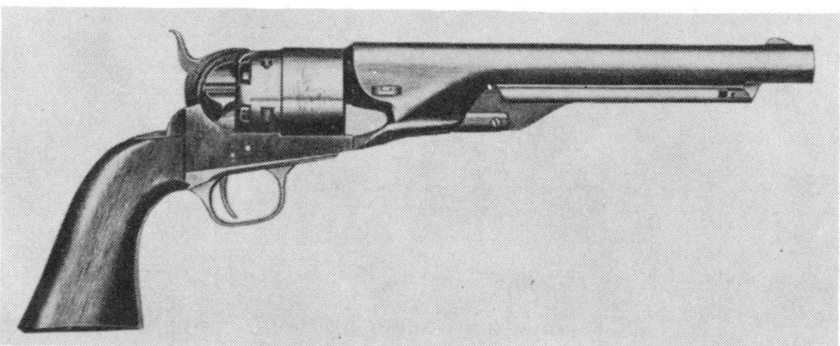

The Colt Army model of 1860. Caliber .44. Still muzzle loaded and cap fired, this was nevertheless the major revolver in our Civil War.

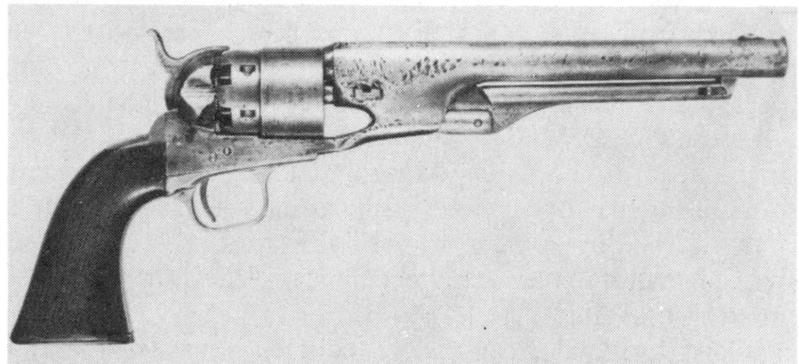

Colt Army 1860. Caliber .44 six shot, single action. The principal revolver of the Civil War. The first of the "Streamlined" model Colt revolvers, 107,156 were furnished to the War Department between Jan. 4, 1861 and Nov. 10, 1863. Was known as "New Model Army Revolver" at time of issue.

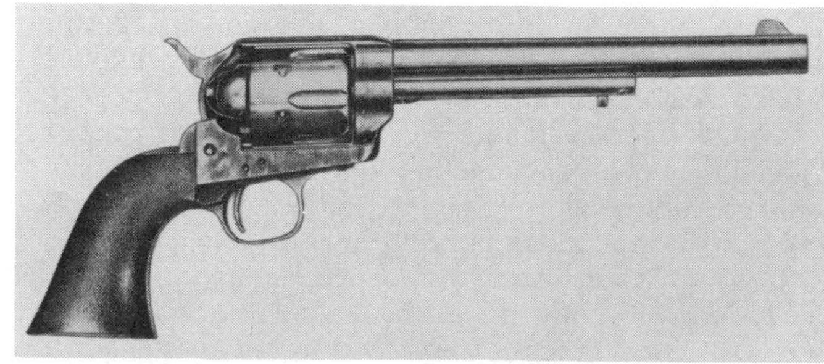

The Colt Peacemaker model of 1873. Caliber .45. The most famous revolver in history and legend, this is the revolver that "made all men equal" in the pioneer days of the West. Metallic cartridge pattern.

Evolution of the Colt revolver from muzzle loader to metallic cartridge single action.

other hand, with its double-action system allowed far greater rapidity of fire than the Colt, but gave relatively poor accuracy because of the long pull on the trigger and the additional force necessary to compress the mainspring and revolve the cylinder.

The value of the Beaumont double-action system becomes immediately apparent when we see that it lends itself either to thumb cocking for accurate shooting when time permits, or for straight pull through on the trigger when several shots must be fired in rapid succession or at close quarters.

None of the later percussion weapons, whether the Tranter, Webley, Kerr, Westley-Richards and similar English designs, or the Belgian Comblain or Amangeot, were of sufficient merit to affect Colt's markets.

When the Colt's patents expired, however, the United

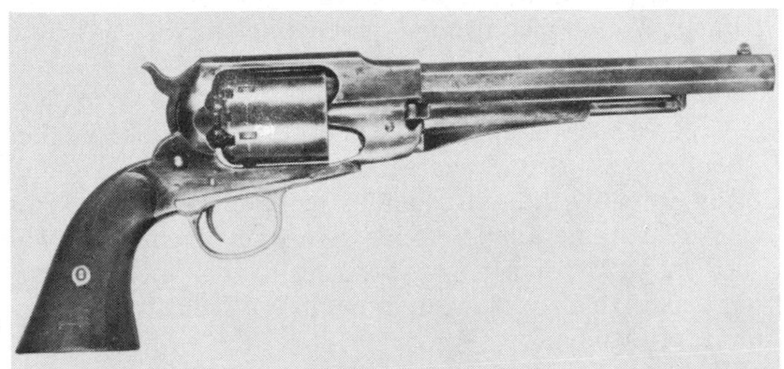

Remington Army, new model (Civil War). Percussion revolver, caliber .44, six shot, single action. 125, 314 Remington revolvers were purchased by the U. S. Government during the Civil War. The most advanced design at the time, with the top strap, Second only to Colt in number and popularity during the Civil War. The most accurate of the cap and ball revolvers.

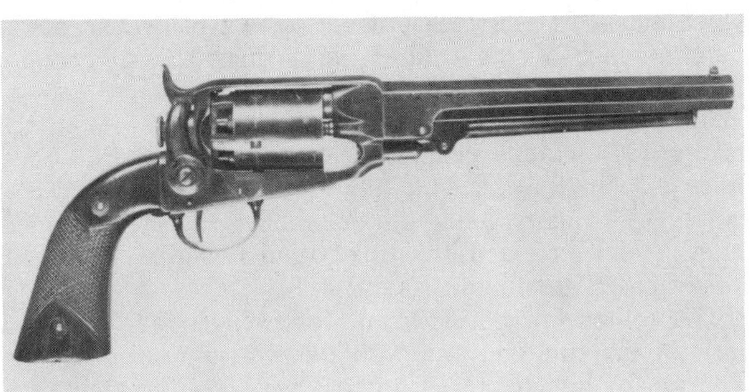

Joslyn Army percussion revolver (Civil War). Caliber .44, five shot, single action. A total of 1,100 Joslyn revolvers were purchased by the government during the Civil War for Army and Navy. Of these 875 were purchased in 1862.

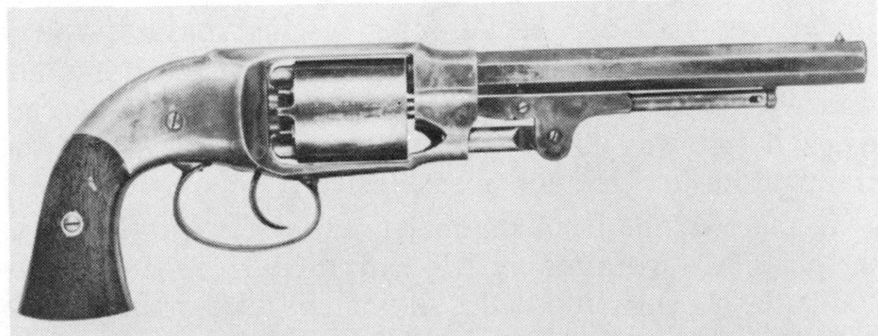

Pettingill Army percussion revolver (Civil War). The first and only hammerless U. S. martial revolver. Caliber .44, six shot, double action. 2,001 were delivered to the government on contract during the Civil War. It did not prove serviceable, since the mechanism was complicated and delicate, and could not stand rough usage under field conditions.

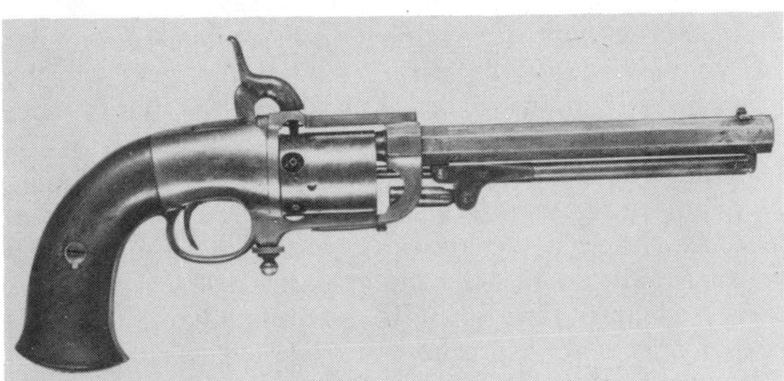

Butterfield Army percussion revolver. Caliber .44 five shot, single action. There is no record of government purchase during Civil War. This weapon used a mechanical feed for a disc primer fed from a magazine.

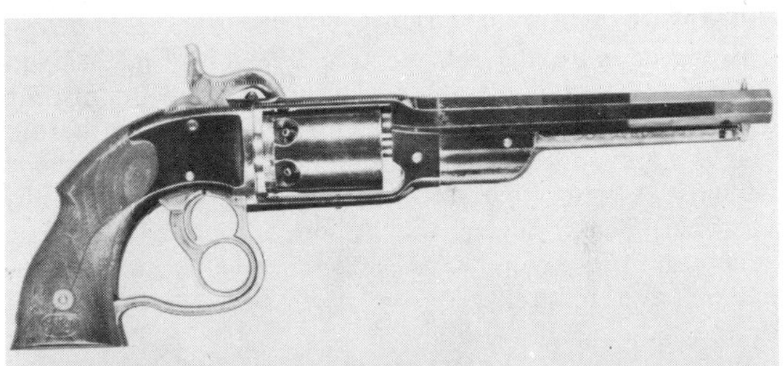

Savage Navy percussion revolver. Caliber .36, single action. 11,284 Savage Navy revolvers were purchased by the government during the Civil War. This is a transition from the single action to the double action revolver. The only U. S. revolver with the mouth of the chamber covering the breech of the barrel at the time of firing, giving a nearly gas tight seal. This system of gas sealing is used in Russian revolvers today. It is not efficient. Any American Colt or Smith & Wesson revolver gives better sealing because of close tolerance manufacture.

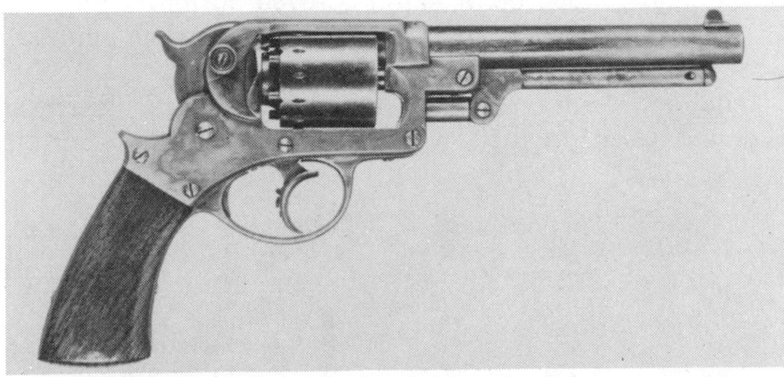

Starr Army double action. Civil War. Caliber .44, six shot, double action. 47,952 Starr revolvers were purchased by the government during the Civil War.

Representative samples of a few of the Colt imitators of Civil War days after Colt's patents expired. All are percussion fired. Smith & Wesson was the only firm at that time manufacturing their newly developed metallic cartridge revolver.

States was flooded with a tremendous variety of domestic percussion pattern revolvers, most of which were merely variations of the Colt. These included the Remington, which was a relatively standard design single action percussion cap revolver. In the double-trigger Savage, the first trigger cocked the hammer and revolved the cylinder and the second trigger tripped the hammer to fire. The Pettingill had an enclosed hammer (so-called "hammerless") and quick removable cylinder design. The Savage double action with a ring trigger and chamfered cylinder was reminiscent of the earlier Collier flintlock and the present day Russian Nagant gas seal revolver, the cylinder being moved forward as the weapon was cocked so that the individual chamber was actually thrust forward over the mouth of the breech of the barrel in an attempt to prevent gas escape at the juncture. (Many of these revolvers were later altered to fire metallic cartridges.)

All of these early patterns were familiar Civil War weapons, as were also a host of lesser types.

We tend to think of the military revolver as being a large caliber weapon, which in normal American usage it is. Even the early day Colts were of the .36 or .44 caliber pattern when used for regular issue Navy or Army service in the United States, though in Europe the caliber was often considerably smaller.

However, with the introduction by Smith and Wesson of their .22 metallic cartridge in 1859, their astonishing little 7-shot .22 caliber revolver with its hinged-up barrel, removable cylinder, and single action firing lock became the most sought after sidearm of both Union and Confederate officers during the American Civil War. The combination of compactness, light weight, rapidity of loading, and reliability of the new cartridges accounted for the demand.

With the coming of the Lefaucheux pin fire system of cartridges, revolvers to handle such ammunition were extensively made in Europe, although the design never was produced in the United States except experimentally. This design, of course, requires that each chamber be so notched that the cartridge dropped into the chamber will have a resting place for its projecting pin in the cylinder face, where the hammer can strike it a downward blow. Although such designs were widely used in Europe until recent years, many being captured even during World War II, pin fires never actually constituted serious military weapons.

The first Smith & Wesson rim fire .22 revolver was actually based on the design of Rollin White of Lowell, Massachusetts. His patent of April 3, 1855 for a cylinder bored through to permit the insertion of cartridges from the breech end was purchased by Smith and Wesson who applied it to their new .22 caliber metallic cartridge. Smith & Wesson exercised a monopoly on the system, which permitted insertion of cartridges from the rear of the cylinder, until patents expired in 1869. During this time, Colt attempted various hybrid systems including the Thuer alteration in an endeavor to get around the Smith & Wesson controlled patents. None of these expedients worked out.

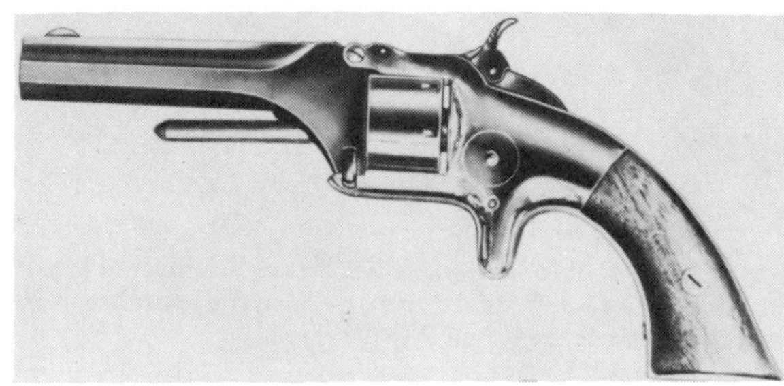

One of the first Smith & Wesson cartridge revolvers. Caliber .22 rim fire. A favorite officer's model in the Civil War.

The most important revolver of our Civil War was the Colt 1860 Model. Over 200,000 of these .44 caliber 6-shooter percussion revolvers were made. Yet another Colt is probably the most famous revolver in history. This is the solid frame Single Action Army revolver which was issued in 1873 for a new .45 Army caliber metallic cartridge, and which was a direct evolution from the percussion 1860 Model.

When the Smith & Wesson patents expired, inventors and manufacturers throughout the world proceeded to turn out a tremendous assortment of breech loading revolvers in calibers from .22 to .50. Many of the revolver developments which today are considered quite modern first appeared at this time. These include features such as the recessed-head cylinder and counterbored chambers which allow the entire case heads to rest below the outer circumference of the cylinder to protect the shooter in case a weak cartridge head ruptures. The early Italian Glisenti revolvers, several Austrian patterns, and in America the Colt House pistol and the Remington Elliot all utilized such devices. The rim fire was made in a wide variety of calibers, only the .22, .30, .32, .38 and .41 really achieving extensive distribution however. All used copper cases in standard practice.

The center fire development followed so hard on the heels of the rim fire, and with their brass cases were so superior for higher powered cartridges, that the major revolver manufacturers promptly concentrated on weapons to fire them. Only the .22, which is difficult to prime centrally because of its small case head diameter, has survived.

Colt was able to take immediate advantage of the center fire cartridge because his original basic revolver design had been developed with an idea of mass production. With relatively few alterations the new metallic cartridge design was quickly put into major production, while competitors had to tool up extensively.

In place of the front rammer used to seat the bullets in the chambers from the muzzle end, the altered Colt heavy frame design introduced the sliding rod ejector below the barrel. A hinged loading gate was provided on the right side of the revolver which when swung open gave access to individual chambers. Bringing the hammer to half cock freed the cylinder from its lock and permitted it to be turned by hand to bring each individual chamber in line with the loading gate for successive loading with center fire cartridges. For ejecting, with the gate opened, pressure on the ejector rod rammed the rod up in the chamber in line with the loading gate to push out the empty case. Releasing the rod permitted its spring to return into place, whereupon the cylinder could be turned to line up the next chamber for unloading. Slight variations of this ejecting system were immediately applied to revolver designs throughout Europe. However, this efficient but slow method posed an immediate military problem.

The next advance was that produced by a W. C. Dodge, an American. He projected the idea of a hinged frame revolver in which the act of bending the barrel down after releasing the locking catch would allow the extractor to be automatically raised out of the center of the cylinder in the barrel assembly to extract and eject all empty cartridge cases simultaneously. At the end of the stroke, an escapement permitted the extractor spring to return the extractor to its seat in the head of the cylinder. The arm was now ready for rapid reloading. This is the fastest revolver loading system ever devised, but hinging the frame results in structural weakness, unless construction is very heavy.

The European Galand, in which the barrel and cylinder were slid forward while the empty cases were retained by an extractor until clear of the chambers, is often cited in European records as the first instance of automatic extraction. Dodge effectively repudiated this claim in his day. The awkward Galand system has not survived the test of time, incidentally.

Dodge had applied for British, French, and Belgian patents. The boat on which his check was carried in the mails covering his patent fee for the British patent arrived a few days late. On this technicality his British patent was voided. Similar action was taken shortly thereafter in France and Belgium. Dodge always insisted, and the weight of the evidence bears him out, that agents of the British patent office released information on his application before the patent was granted. In substantiation of his claim, it is possible to point out that a very large

A Belgian-made hinged frame revolver, now obsolete.

number of Birmingham manufacturers released revolvers utilizing the Dodge patent within six weeks of the time the British patent was invalidated. The Liege Small Arms Company also produced a revolver utilizing the Dodge principle in a matter of weeks after the invalidation of the Belgian patent. Some revolvers, apparently manufactured by the English firm of Webley although they did not carry a manufacturer's name, were released at this time; these were an exact copy of an original Smith & Wesson .22 which incorporated the Dodge principle, S&W having purchased the Dodge extracting patent.

English revolvers made by Adams and Tranter as well as by Webley were customarily solid frame types provided with hand-operated ejectors for removing cartridge cases individually along the general system of the single action Colt. Developments on the Continent at this period were also confined to the solid frame construction whether the design was Belgian, German, Austrian, or Italian; only the freak Galand system was different. The Pryse English patent of 1876 covering a revolver of the general Smith & Wesson design was the next true advance. It utilized the now common cam-functioned ejector. Its breech-locking system was operated by dual spring catches, one on either side of the standing breech. Truly monstrous revolvers in this general design were manufactured by Webley in England in calibers as high as .476, while the Belgian manufacturers produced arms of the type of the Montenegrin .45. Occasional freaks were made in calibers approaching .600!

These were the first European arms to incorporate the principle of the rebounding hammer. This is the safety system by which spring tension, applied through various systems direct and indirect, automatically withdraws the hammer from possible contact with the cartridge case as the trigger is released. In some of these systems the hammer rebounds automatically before release of the trigger pressure by transferrence of mainspring thrust from a firing to a withdrawing position on the hammer.

This Pryse system also incorporated the safety device (even then familiar in Europe though not in the U. S.) of a metal block or bar rising automatically between hammer and frame to prevent the hammer from striking the cartridge or firing pin at any time except when a deliberate pull on the trigger caused the hammer action.

The most famous publicized example of this safety wedge system is that in our own current so-called "Colt Positive Lock." Varieties of this principle actually appeared in Austria and in Italy as early as 1871. Because of inadequate firearms research by patent attorneys, the Colt's Company in the United States was able to exercise an American monopoly on this system of safety during the life of a group of patents.

Early in the twentieth century American firms such as Hopkins and Allen produced safety revolvers in which the hammer operated on an eccentric. In this system, the hammer could strike the firing pin only when the pull on the trigger dropped the hammer and during the course of the period in which the trigger was held back. Release of the trigger automatically worked the hammer on its eccentric to bring it to a position where it could not accidently hit the firing pin.

The famous Iver Johnson American system of so-called "hammer-the-hammer safety" was another expedient to get around this Colt positive lock system. In the Iver Johnson system, cocking the hammer raises an independent steel bar between the hammer and the firing pin face. If the trigger is deliberately pulled, the hammer blow can be transmitted through this bar to the firing pin. At all other times the hammer is resting on the face of the standing breech above the line of the firing pin and no external violence to the head of the hammer can be transmitted to the firing pin.

Smith & Wesson achieved the same general idea through use of a recoil block, a spring-actuated wedge system. In recent years, however, all Smith & Wesson revolvers have utilized a form of the locking principle found in the Colt Positive Lock. While the operation is somewhat different, the effect is the same. A steel bar is mechanically interposed between hammer and cartridge access at all times except when the trigger is deliberately pulled.

In an endeavor to evade the Dodge patents, numerous manufacturers such as Thomas in England, Galand in both Belgium and France, and Merwin and Hulbert in the United States all developed freak systems in which the barrel assembly could be unlocked and swung away from the standing breech for cartridge case removal and reloading. These were all too complicated to stand in the face of the superior, simple hinged-frame system of Dodge and the later swing-out cylinder systems.

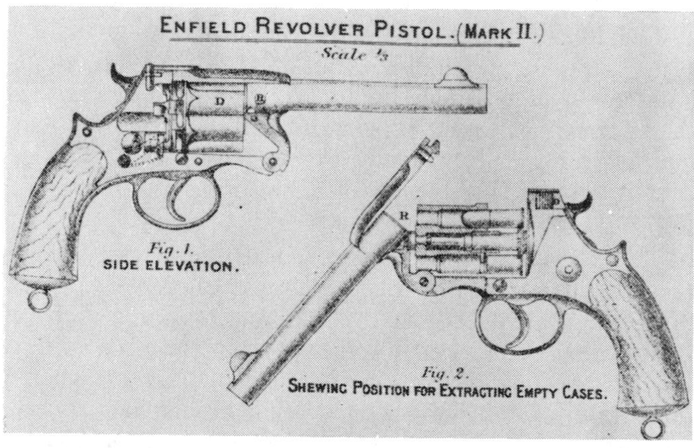

This Enfield saw some service in the early days of the Royal Canadian Northwest Mounted Police. It was replaced by Colts. Today the organization has become the Royal Canadian Mounted Police armed with Smith & Wesson revolvers.

Passing mention must be made of the fantastic method in which the Government Enfield Small Arms Factory in England attempted to develop a unique service revolver which would bypass any of the patents then existing. This was the 1882 model Enfield in caliber .476. Releasing the lock on the standing breech first permitted the barrel to be tipped down and then the cylinder to slide straight ahead to eject! This impractical design illustrates again the futility of permitting nationalistic pride to determine firearms design for government use. It was rapidly supplanted by the hinged frame Webley of 1882.

In 1887 the British government adopted as the Mark I Webley, a slightly modified version of the original Webley hinged frame. Unlike the American systems in which the breech lock is fastened to the extension of the barrel, Webley introduced the stirrup lock which is pivoted on the standing breech and which locks over the barrel extension. This is the strongest hinged frame system ever devised. Through the years it has remained the official British service pattern whether used in the original .455 caliber or in the World War II .38 caliber. It has, of course, been supplemented in times of emergency by Colt and Smith & Wesson revolvers purchased in America. It will be replaced in British official service by the Belgian Browning-type 9mm automatic pistol in due course, partly because of ammunition standardization since this automatic pistol cartridge is the one used in the official British submachine guns such as the Sten.

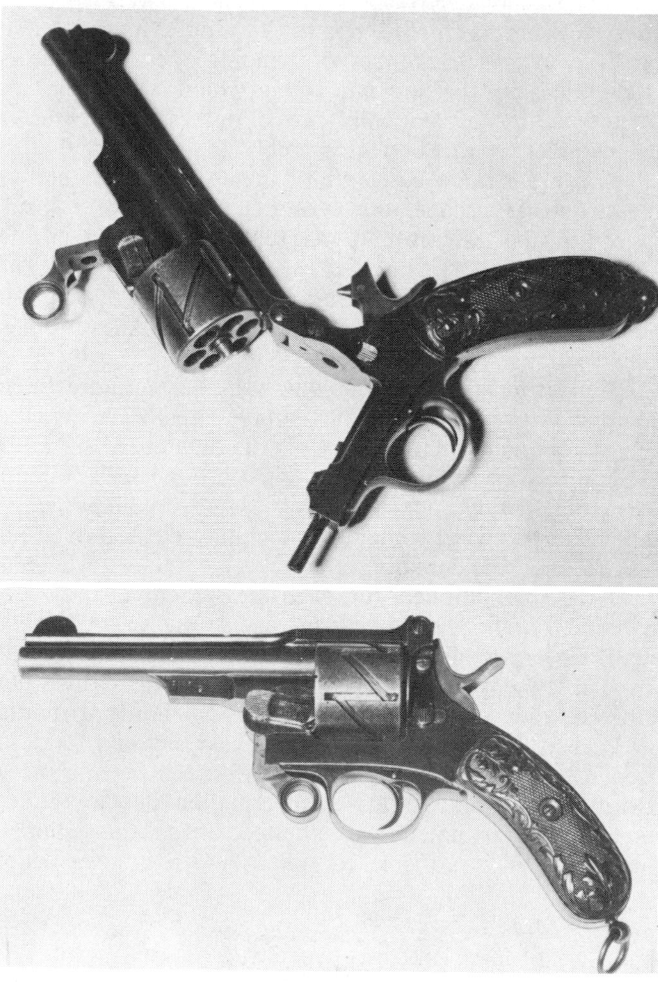

Early Mauser Revolver open (above) and closed (below). The cylinder turning mechanism appeared later on the Webley-Fosbery Automatic Revolver series.

The revolvers of the 1871-1880 period in France, Italy, and the Balkans are still in use in many instances. Such revolvers will be found fully covered in Part II. Mauser designed several solid frame and hinge-up pattern revolvers in Germany in 1878 and 1879. They were noteworthy only for their novel system of cylinder rotation through zig-zag cylinder slot operation. German interest in repeating and auto pistol design nullified most German attempts at revolver design.

Passing notice must be made, however, of one development of the period about 1885. This was a solid frame revolver of the Nagant pattern originally manufactured in Belgium by Pieper.

This development was a cylinder design which, as the arm was cocked, not only permitted turning the cylinder to line up a chamber with the barrel for firing, but which also thrust the cylinder forward so that the chamber to be fired was slid forward slightly over the mouth of the breech of the barrel. As in the old flintlock Collier and even earlier arms, the idea here, of course, was to attempt to minimize the escape of gas at the juncture of the chamber and the barrel. In actual practice no such system works effectively. However, Pieper incorporated this device into solid frame rod ejecting revolvers in both single action and double action designs which were adopted by the Russians as standard equipment in 1895. Revolvers of this type using the 7.62mm Russian cartridge were widely reported by the Germans as used in World War II.

In this same general period, many other solid frame revolvers appeared both here and abroad using various forms of the double action firing systems. This elementary solid frame pattern continues in manufacture commercially. Its use is confined almost entirely to low priced protective and plinking arms. It was never utilized in the United States as a military weapon. On the other hand, weapons of this elementary sort were encountered even during World War II in use by many of the European powers, notably France and Italy.

The Swing Out Cylinder System

The next system appeared as early as 1892 in France and the United States. This utilizes a solid frame into which the barrel is screwed. The frame is machined to receive a crane mechanism which carries the cylinder. Releasing a catch, usually on the standing breech (though some European variants have the release at the forward end of the extractor rod) permits the cylinder and crane to be swung out to the side for loading. Pressure on the extractor rod which passes through the center of the cylinder actuates the star-shaped extractor head to withdraw all cases or cartridges from the cylinder simultaneously. The extractor spring returns the extractor to its rest position when rod pressure is released.

This form has a far greater strength than the hinged frame system as a general rule. As a result, for large caliber use it has completely replaced the hinge frame in the United States. While the normal system of swing-out cylinder operation is for the crane to operate from the left side, many European versions such as the French swing out to the right.

In all production forms, this revolver incorporates a double action firing system, single action systems of this type being always inventor or freak models. Colt and S&W make only solid frame revolvers of this type. Hi-Standard is currently preparing to manufacture one.

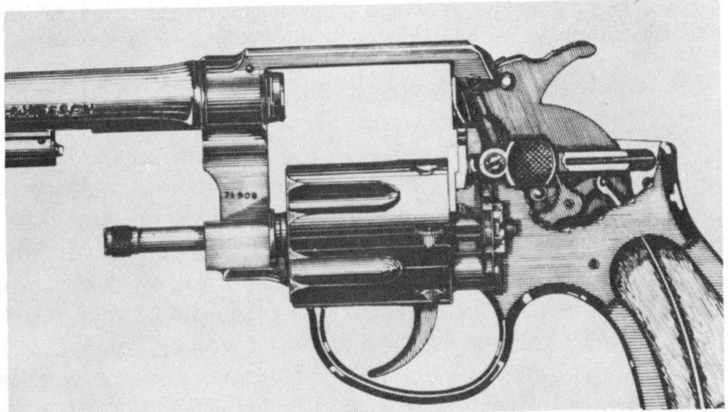

Typical swing-out cylinder revolver with mechanism sectionalized.

The Revolver in Military Service

As we have seen, the revolver received its first great impetus as a military weapon during the American Civil War, though attention had been focussed on its possibilities in the earlier Mexican-Texas encounters. While basically this War was fought with muzzle-loading cap-fired revolvers, the earliest Smith & Wesson .22 and .32 caliber rim fire cartridge revolvers were also used, particularly by officers who were fortunate enough to be able to purchase them. They were in extremely short supply at that time.

The S&W .44 American was actually the first breech loading revolver officially adopted for U. S. Army service. Its service was short and limited. This was a single action hinged frame design.

Colt's first successful breech loading revolver was issued after the expiration of the Smith and Wesson patent coverage. This Single Action Army .45, popularly known as the Colt "Peacemaker," was adopted for Army use in 1873.

First Cartridge Colt Revolver, Model 1872. Note that it does not yet have a solid frame with top strap over cylinder.

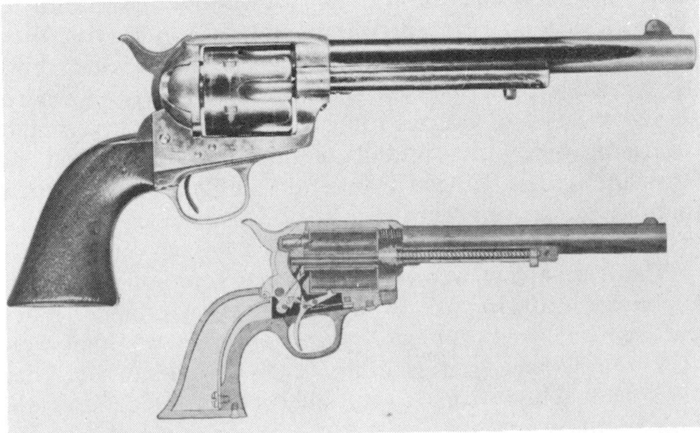

Colt Army Revolver, model of 1873. Caliber .45, six shot, single action. Manufactured for nearly 70 years with little change. The first solid frame U. S. military Cartridge Revolver. Note top strap.
Insert shows the 1873 sectionalized.

Smith & Wesson Schofield, model 1875, Army caliber .45, six shot, single action. Insert shows sectionalized view with action open. This is one of the strongest hinged frame models ever built.

Coincident with the adoption of the solid frame Colt .45, a new model Smith & Wesson .45 Schofield was also introduced in 1873. A special barrel catch was furnished on this revolver. Military theory at the time required this on the grounds that the more common latch form permitted an opponent in hand-to-hand fighting to free the formal type of catch and permit him to open the weapon, thereby rendering the revolver useless. While in theory such things can happen, in actual practice such a contingency is almost unthinkable. While wasting time on this sort of technicality, ordnance authorities overlooked the matter of cartridge standardization. The .45 ammunition used in the Colt and the S&W were not interchangeable.

The double action system was not favored at the time on the grounds that the basic use would be by the cavalry, and that a mounted man during the course of firing might discharge a double action weapon accidentally if his horse bucked or shied unexpectedly.

The Russian Grand Duke Alexis came to the United States at this time intending to purchase Colt revolvers. After a demonstration of the hinged frame Smith & Wesson system, he went on a hunting trip to the West with Buffalo Bill Cody, during the course of which both used the Smith & Wesson revolver extensively. As a result of the Grand Duke's report, the Russian Government placed an order for 150,000 of the Smith & Wesson .44 Russian Models, hinged frame and single action. Even in this day, no more accurate heavy revolver or cartridge has yet been designed!

These revolvers were so sturdy that some of them were encountered during World War II by the Germans. When our own troops occupied Japan, quantities of them were also found there, representing revolvers which the Japanese had taken from captured Russian officers at the turn of the century.

Ironically enough, this tremendous order (for those days) occupied the S&W plant to such an extent for export work that Colt was left master of the field of domestic supply of revolvers for the development of our

Smith & Wesson Army six shot, single action, center fire revolver. Model 1869. Caliber .44 Center-Fire. The first breech loading revolver adopted by the U. S.

own West. The name and fame of the Colt spread largely because of this monopoly.

When Colt's applied the double action cocking system to the revolver they called the Double Action Army Model, a small quantity was purchased for Army experimental use. It was never, however, officially adopted. This pattern is often known as the "Bird's Head Model," the shape of the grip when turned upside down having some resemblance to a bird's head. Varieties of this model with large triggerguards (so a gloved finger could be inserted) were used in the early days of the Klondike, and are popularly known as "Alaskan Models."

The next official United States Army adoption was the 1892 version of the Colt with swing-out cylinder in .38 caliber double action. This used the new .38 Long

Colt Army Revolver, model of 1892, six shot, double action. The first solid frame, swing-out cylinder, .38 caliber U. S. service revolver. The modified 1894 version was used in the Spanish-American War, and later in the Philippine Insurrection.

Colt cartridge, a load not so powerful and far less accurate than the later .38 special.

This .38 Colt saw service in the Philippines campaign. Field tests indicated it did not have sufficient man-stopping power for use against savage groups. On the other hand, the .45 single action proved an effective man stopper. The British in their African and Indian campaigns had already established this principle to their satisfaction and were using a .455 caliber revolver, the Webley.

In 1909 our Army officially adopted a heavier version of the swing-out cylinder Colt, the New Service .45 caliber. This revolver was also made commercially and for export in various heavy calibers. It was used in both Canada and Great Britain in caliber .455.

Smith & Wesson introduced their version of the swing-out cylinder revolver to compete with Colt's. Both types have seen War service since the time of their adoption in wars throughout the world.

Revolvers in World War I

While the .45 Colt Automatic Pistol was the primary sidearm of United States Forces during this War, the shortage of such weapons compelled the adoption of swing-out cylinder double action designs of both Smith & Wesson and Colt manufacture. These were substitute standard weapons. Under the designation of Model 1917, both patterns were chambered to take the standard .45 automatic pistol cartridge to minimize ammunition supply problems.

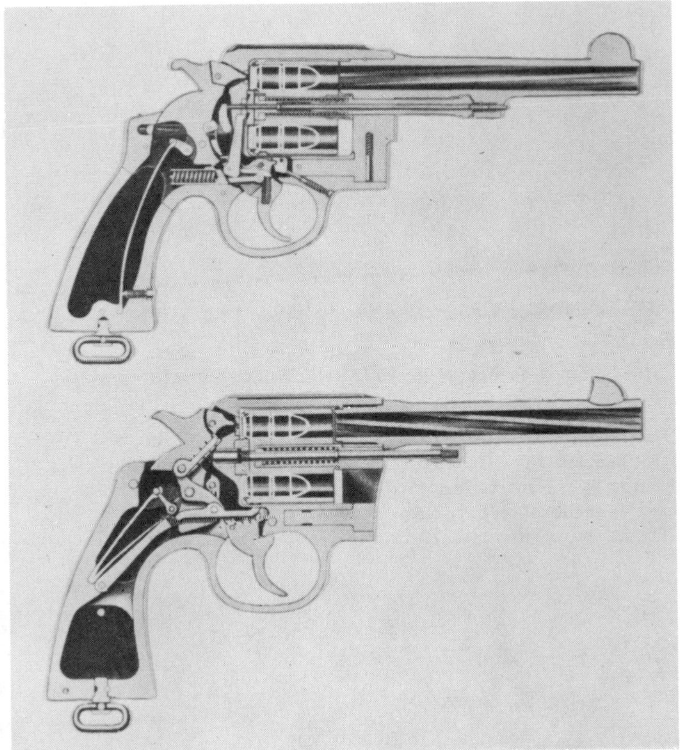

Sectionalized views of World War I U. S. revolvers. Lower: Colt. Upper: Smith & Wesson. Both are shown loaded with hammers down. Caliber .45 U. S. government.

Smith & Wesson developed a special half-moon type clip which would hold three of these rimless cartridges. Using these clips the revolvers could be loaded and unloaded very rapidly. The Smith & Wesson chambers permitted firing the cartridges in an emergency without the use of the clip. This was possible because the .45 ACP cartridge is designed to seat in the chamber on the mouth of the case. In such an instance the standard rim-type revolver extractor could not operate. As these cartridges have no rims, it was necessary to punch or pry the empty cases out of the chambers. The Colt, on the other hand, was so chambered that normally the cartridges passed too far into their chambers to be fired at all unless their heads were supported by the half-moon clips.

Colt's and S&W revolvers were also manufactured for use by Canadian and British forces in caliber .455 Eley, the official rimmed cartridge of the British Government during World War I. These required no modification except caliber.

Because of the tremendous number of these .45 A.C.P. caliber revolvers available after the War, the Peters Cartridge Company (now a division of the Remington organization) produced the .45 automatic cartridge with a special rim under the designation of .45 Auto-Rim. This cartridge of course does not require the use of the half-moon extracting device. Some World War II use was made of this revolver and cartridge combination.

The official revolver of the British forces during World War I, though supplemented by Colts and Smith & Wessons as required, was the Webley hinged-frame in caliber .455.

The other revolvers then in European use were those of France, Italy, Russia, and to a limited extent Austria. All these are covered in detail in Part II.

Military Revolvers in World War II

At the outbreak of World War II, Great Britain again found herself very low on sidearms. While the .455 Webley was still in general use, the official revolver was now a weapon of the same general design made at Enfield in the new .38 British caliber.

This .38, the equivalent of the low-powered American .38 Smith & Wesson cartridge, is not to be confused with the ultra-powerful .38 Smith & Wesson Special types of cartridges used in general by American police.

The original .38 Smith & Wesson cartridge is practically identical with the .38 British service cartridge. The cases are shorter than the American .38 special, while their case diameter is greater than the .38 special. This stems from the fact that when the .38 special powerful cartridge was designed for swing-out cylinder revolvers, it was necessary to develop a form which could not be inserted in the weaker hinged frame .38 models. As a result, the .38 Smith & Wesson cartridge and the British service .38 cartridge are too large in diameter to be inserted in the American .38 special type of revolver. Conversely, the .38 American Special cartridge is too long to permit it to be inserted in the cylinder of the .38 British type of revolver or of S&W or Colt's revolvers chambered for British use during World War II.

Tests led the British to the belief that for close-quarters work the .38 was even more efficient in the hands of the average military user than was the larger caliber. The lower recoil, the lighter weight of the weapon, and lighter weight of ammunition were all contributing factors to the adoption of this lesser caliber.

Great Britain turned to Smith & Wesson of Springfield, Massachusetts at the outbreak of the War to manufacture large quantities of revolvers for the British .38 caliber cartridge, since Smith & Wesson in their Military and Police Model had a revolver easily adaptable to the British cartridge. Large numbers of the equivalent Colt's model were also adapted to the British cartridge and sent to England during this period.

General Patton's Famous Revolvers.

General George S. Patton Jr.'s Colt Single Action Army Revolver, Caliber .45 (No. 332088; ivory grips, silver plated, barrel 4¾" long).

One of the most popular revolvers ever produced. Its production was begun in 1873 and continued without interruption until 1941. A total of 357,859 were sold.

The de luxe model was purchased by the then Lt. Patton in 1916 and was carried by him until his death in 1945. He wore it during the Punitive Expedition to Mexico in 1916-1917; in World War I (where he saw action as commander of the Tank Corps); at his landings in North Africa, Sicily and Normandy. Many legends surround General Patton's famous revolvers. Contrary to general belief, they are not matching. They are not pearl-handled and were rarely worn as a pair. Actually he wore them so that his troops could easily identify him in the field.

General George S. Patton Jr.'s Smith & Wesson .357 Magnum. It was purchased by Colonel Patton in Hawaii in 1935 and is one of the first of this model to be sold. This revolver shows signs of much service.

As a result, the British service during World War II used a wide variety of revolvers. The primary ones were their Enfield, not only in the standard double action hinged frame, but also in a special close-quarters model with a special hammer which allowed only double action firing, plus the Smith & Wesson and Colt's revolvers chambered for their cartridges as indicated above. In addition, of course, considerable stocks of the earlier .455 calibers were pressed into service during this emergency.

During this same period the United States again issued some 1917 Model Smith & Wesson and Colt's .45 caliber ACP revolvers for service, but did not manufacture additional ones. However, both Smith & Wesson and Colt's produced very large quantities of .38 caliber revolvers using the .38 Smith & Wesson special cartridge for special purpose work in our Navy, Marine Corps, Aviation and various guard services.

Russia at this time used some revolvers chambered generally for their 7.62mm cartridge. In general, however, it may be stated that the Russians early came to the conclusion that the submachine gun could be made cheaper and faster than the revolver, and throughout the course of World War II they concentrated on furnishing the former weapons. Revolvers saw minimal service.

French and Italian services at the beginning of the war also used earlier revolvers of solid frame and swing-out cylinder construction as substitute standard arms. These were generally not important, but all are considered in Part II.

Except in the United States, experience with revolvers during the course of World War II convinced military thinkers that this arm should be replaced by automatic pistols utilizing the same caliber ammunition as the submachine gun. This will unquestionably be the foreign military trend of the future.

During World War II the Japanese troops used revolvers only to a very limited extent. Most of these were very crude Japanese-manufactured forms of the early Smith & Wesson hinged frame type chambered for a freak Japanese rimmed cartridge of approximately 9mm caliber. They fired double action only. Such other revolvers as were used were generally of American manufacture.

Postwar Developments in Revolvers

In general it may be stated that for all practical military purposes, the revolver design has reached the zenith of its perfection. The preferred form is the solid frame swing-out cylinder revolver manufactured by Colt's and Smith & Wesson. Mechanically, these revolvers cannot be substantially improved. Changes since the end of the war are basically those which stemmed directly from ammunition improvements and from metallurgical advances; design changes as such are relatively inconsequential.

To be of military value revolvers must be relatively light in weight and compact in size, and must be effective within the limitations of their sighting equipment. For all practical purposes, a revolver cylinder cannot be made large enough to take more than six cartridges of relatively large caliber. This is an elementary matter of dimension. In this respect, of course, the revolver must always be inferior to the automatic pistol where the cartridges are in a magazine one on top of the other without the necessary metal separation of the revolver chambers. As to weight, research by the aviation industry on aluminum developments has produced qualities of aluminum forgings which are entirely suitable for all practical revolver frame purposes, though in field use it has been determined that high tensile steels are still necessary for ultra-powerful cartridges insofar as cylinder and barrel construction are concerned.

Since the bullet must jump a gap between the chamber and the barrel, there must always be a substantial loss of gas at the juncture. Colt and Smith & Wesson both hold tolerances at this point to an absolute minimum, but any device to give a better seal must inevitably require mechanical complications which would offset its value.

As metallurgical knowledge advances, titanium will unquestionably influence revolver design from the standpoint of producing a lighter weapon with the approximate strength of the standard steel patterns, though such use will probably be confined to cylinder and barrel production as the lighter aluminum has proven itself sturdy enough for the frame sections. In all practical use, if the cylinder holds during the course of firing, the frame is not subject to any great pressures. Because of this factor, both Smith & Wesson and Colt's, after extensive development of the .38 special revolver using aluminum cylinders, found it advisable to return to the use of high tensile steel in their smaller models. While the forged aluminum cylinders as produced by these firms are adequate for factory loaded ammunition, they will not necessarily hold up under the terrific hand loads introduced by experimenters. In the interests of safety, therefore, the steel cylinders are still recommended.

For practical military use, the power of cartridges also cannot be substantially increased without unreasonably increasing the weight of the revolver. Otherwise the shock to the firer frightens the amateur and interferes with both accuracy and rapidity of operation by the expert. Any major increase in revolver power must depend basically upon ammunition advances, not on any possible improved revolver design.

As to increased accuracy, we have already pointed out that the original .44 Smith & Wesson Russian revolver cartridge of 1873 cannot be substantially improved upon today from the viewpoint of accuracy. For all practical purposes, almost any modern revolver will shoot far more accurately than any human being can hold.

As a military arm the revolver is normally intended for use at ranges under 10 yards. An expert can use it effectively at 50 yards. It seldom has any true value at longer ranges, though of course exceptions do occur.

As to mechanical perfection, the utilization of coil springs and of parts held to absolute minimum tolerances, as now evidenced in the Smith & Wesson and Colt's manufacture, has resulted in the simplest form of mecha-

Smith & Wesson Centennial Model Hammerless (enclosed hammer) with grip safety. For the very powerful .38 Smith & Wesson special cartridges. A special close quarters arm.

nism capable of reliable functioning.

Only one slight form of improved revolver for special duty purposes might have military application as distinct from those commonly available, and it is merely a new application of an old principle. This is the form represented by the Smith & Wesson "Centennial Model" revolver. This is their standard solid frame swing-out cylinder revolver for the .38 special cartridge, but the frame is designed to completely enclose the hammer. Colt has produced a "hammer shroud" to enclose the external

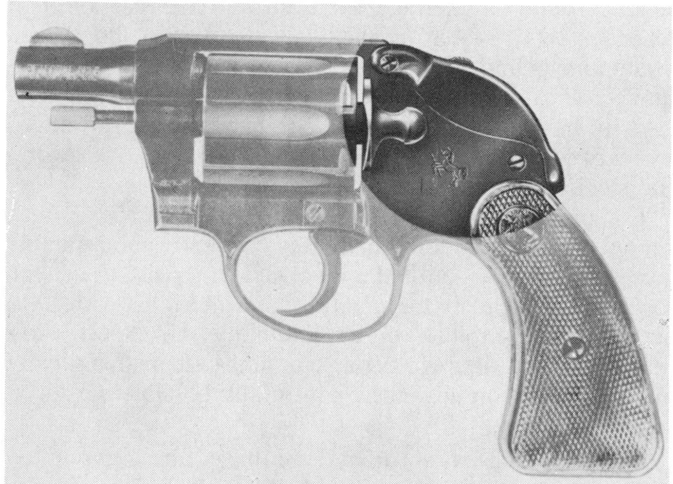

Colt "Hammer Shroud" to cover hammer and permit quick draw or firing through pocket.

hammers of some of their small frame revolvers. The intent here is the same as in the Smith & Wesson design, which is basically to furnish an arm which can be fired only double action for close-quarters work. The advantage of this system over the typical exposed hammer revolver might lie in an enlarged triggerguard; troops could carry it in the side pockets of reefers or overcoats in extremely cold climates. Such an arm provides a very efficient close-quarters defense weapon. In case of emergency it can be fired through the pocket of the coat until the cylinder is emptied without any danger of mechanical interference with its operation. The standard type of service revolver given the same usage will normally foul because the exposed hammer will snag in the coat lining. An automatic pistol under similar conditions will not function after the first shot because the reciprocating slide and ejected case will inevitably jam the action.

The original Smith & Wesson intent in introducing this model (which is equipped with a grip safety to prevent firing except when the weapon is held firmly in the hand, was in the interests of a safe weapon for home use. The general intent was to provide an arm which, because it required a relatively large hand to hold it and simultaneously operate both the safety lever in the back of the frame and the trigger, would preclude children accidentally firing the arm.

Its use for special service purposes in cold areas has not yet been explored. It is worthy of military attention, however.

Smith & Wesson Combat Masterpiece. A favorite U. S. Marine revolver in Korea. Caliber .38 Special.

Based on experience, the United States Navy, Air Force, and to some extent the Marines and Army have found that under some circumstances a revolver utilizing the .38 special cartridge is a more practical close quarters defense weapon than the bulky .45 automatic pistol. As a result, very large quantities of S. & W. short-barreled light-weight revolvers of this pattern utilizing aluminum frames and cylinders with steel barrels have been

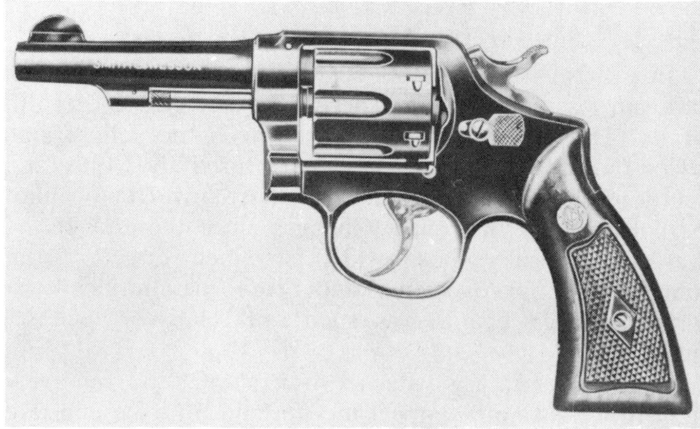

Smith & Wesson Military and Police Model. Caliber .38 Special. Used by most U. S. Police Departments and by the Royal Canadian Mounted Police.

furnished to the Government services for special use. Colt's also has developed equivalent arms to handle the .38 special cartridge for similar service use.

In passing it must be noted that since the close of World War II there has been a tremendous resurgence of interest in the use of the revolver as a sidearm in South America and Asia. This is generally in accordance with American police tradition. In Japan, for example, the police and quasi-military bodies are being generally equipped with the short Smith & Wesson .38 caliber special revolver known as the Chief's Special, the name deriving from the interest it excited as an undercover weapon among police chiefs in the United States. Huge quantities of this and other models in both steel and aluminum patterns, and in calibers as small as .32, have been sold to police and military organizations in South and Central America and in some areas in Asia. Calibers above .38 are normally not well received in such areas, due to their excessive recoil and weight. In general, of course, revolvers in use by the military are actually used for police purposes.

The only other areas in which revolver manufacture is proceeding at a rate worthy of attention are Spain and Italy and to a minor degree in Belgium. All these areas are currently manufacturing basic imitations of Smith & Wesson and Colt swing-out cylinder type re-

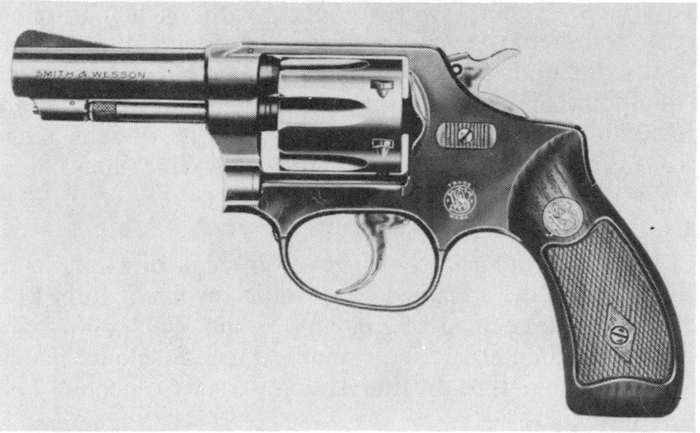

Smith & Wesson .32 Hand Ejector. Used by police and military in many South American nations.

Smith & Wesson Chief's Special (steel or airweight). Used in steel by Japanese police units. An airweight (aluminum frame) model is used by various U. S. government services. Handles the powerful .38 Special cartridges.

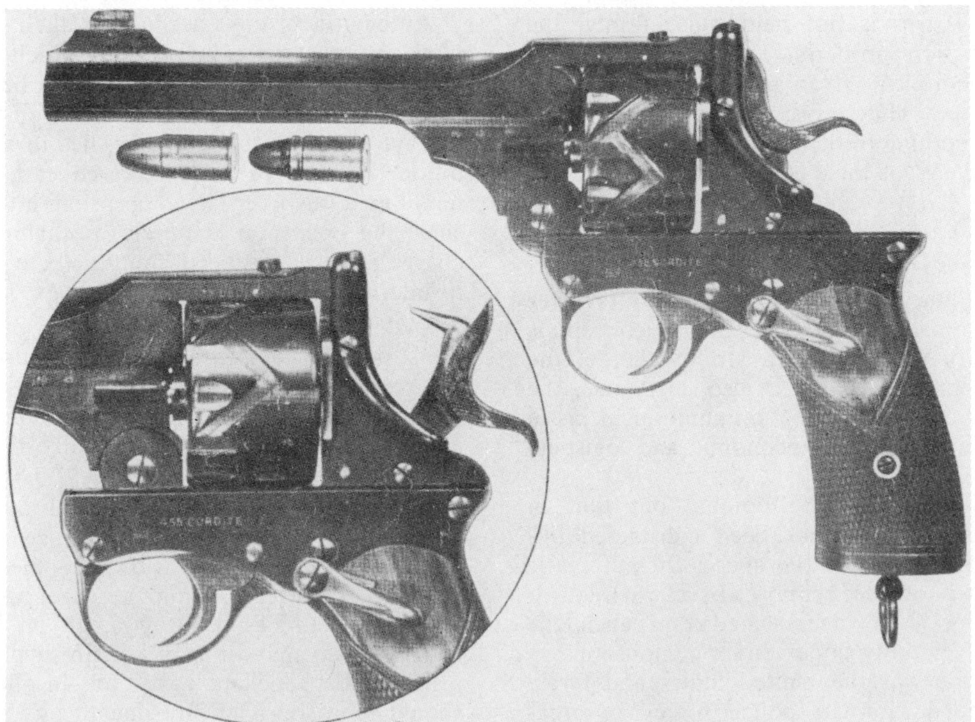

Webley-Fosbery Automatic Revolver. Insert shows barrel and cylinder assembly in full recoil. Cylinder has been revolved halfway to next chamber and hammer cocked. Recoil spring will thrust assembly home and revolve cylinder ready for next shot. Model shown is the .455. This revolver was also made in Cal. .38.

volvers for general world export, with particular reference to South American export in competition to the Colt and Smith & Wesson patterns. Such arms from the standpoint of material, manufacture, and tolerances are invariably inferior to their prototypes; the designs range from direct copies to manufacturing modifications.

Automatic Revolvers

The only other type of revolver requiring any consideration is the so-called "automatic revolver" form produced for some time in England as the Webley-Fosbery. It had its counterpart in a small American model manufactured for a time by the Union Arms Company. This was unsuccessful.

This pattern of revolver is basically the Webley hinged frame type, so designed that the barrel and cylinder assembly can recoil within the grip-frame. The revolver must be hand cocked for the first shot. It is hinged open for loading and extraction as in the standard hinged framed Webley revolver.

As the Webley-Fosbery fires, the barrel and cylinder assembly recoil in the frame. This causes a stud to act through a zig-zag series of cuts in the cylinder to perform the action of turning the cylinder the distance of the next chamber, and to lock the chamber in line with the barrel upon completion of the return action. The return of the assemblies is brought about by a recoil spring mounted in the grip which stores energy during the recoiling operation. The recoil also causes a barrel extension to cock the hammer ready for the next shot. This design was made in England in .38 and in .455 calibers. It was made in the United States in .32 and .38 calibers. While the design is ingenious, it suffers from complication. If the grip is not held quite firmly, the action will not function properly. Designs of this sort have at best only theoretical advantages over the standard double action system. They must be considered as a passing phase, with nothing to recommend them for future experimentation because of their complexity and inherent unreliability.

The Revolver vs. the Automatic Pistol

In England the military trend is away from the revolver and toward the automatic pistol. The British concept is becoming like that of the Continent, strictly that of the practical military approach. There is also, of course, the fact that the utilization of the same ammunition in pistol and submachine gun is a distinct economic and logistical factor.

In this connection it must be pointed out that in Europe generally the revolver has been considered obsolete since the introduction of the successful automatic pistol about the turn of the century. In Germany, for instance, this feeling is so deep-seated that even the police will use revolvers only under direct compulsion.

At the close of the war the United States and Great Britain both equipped German police forces in areas under their control with quantities of Smith & Wesson revolvers. As rapidly as possible, these police organizations found ways to trade these excellent revolvers as part payment on decidedly inferior automatic pistols manufactured in Spain and France! Many of these revolvers were then sold in the world market, some going to the Israel police organizations. Others went to South America. In short, the German military psychology is such that the police felt better with an inferior automatic pistol than they did with a superior revolver.

In the United States, on the other hand, and in areas which have benefited from or been influenced by American police psychology, the revolver is an important defensive arm. In the United States, for example, some 99% of all police organizations are equipped with revolvers to the exclusion of automatic pistols.

In closing, some mention must be made of the superiorities for which the revolver is noted, as well as its inferiorities with reference to automatic pistols. The mechanism is much simpler than that of the automatic pistol. It is easier to train the police officer or soldier in its use. It is inherently safer because when loaded the rims of the cartridges can be clearly seen at all times. If the cylinder is swung out on its crane, a glance will tell if the cartridges are loaded or fired. Firing in single action fashion from a cocked hammer, the revolver gives a far better pull than can be incorporated in a typical automatic pistol. This, of course, is a great assist to accuracy as it simplifies holding the sights in line during the instant of firing. None of its springs are compressed except when the arm is in the course of being fired or is fully cocked. As a result there is no spring fatigue; this can develop in automatic pistols. No hand-actuated safeties are required, although some are found on occasional European freak designs. As a result, there is nothing to remember or forget when bringing the revolver into action.

Automatic pistols, because of their nature, require in most instances external safeties which must be mechanically thrown off before the arm can be discharged.

Perhaps the most valuable asset of the revolver over the automatic pistol, however, lies in the field of ammunition. If weak or underpowered cartridges are encountered in a revolver, they occasion little or no difficulty since the operation is purely mechanical. If the powder charge is weak or the priming defective, there is nothing to interfere with the firing of the next shot.

With the automatic pistol, on the other hand, when a weak powder load will open the action only part way, the resulting jam can cause a serious tieup. Automatic pistols require a certain minimum amount of blowback action for functioning. And finally there is the matter of the misfire.

A misfire in an automatic pistol is an extremely serious thing in combat. In truly modern arms where the automatic pistol is equipped with a double-action mechanism as in the revolver, pulling the trigger a second time will allow the hammer to drop again on the defective cartridge, which may or may not fire it depending upon the primer and propellant condition. In all automatic pistols, should there be a misfire due to any one of the several failures which may cause it, the slide or bolt mechanism must be withdrawn by hand to eject the empty cartridge case from the chamber and to permit the feeding of the next live round for firing. With the revolver, of course, in case of a misfire, another pull of the trigger finger will move the dead cartridge out of line and bring the next one into line for firing. For defensive purposes this is the most serious consideration of all.

European (more specifically German) military psychology accepts the personal danger in the course of operation of an automatic pistol because of defective ammunition and the like. It operates on a basis of the average, not of the individual.

American psychology is more aligned to individual and police thinking that the possible advantage of greater magazine capacity or higher rate of fire is more than offset by the dependability factor. In passing it must be noted that ammunition manufacturing variables, as well as age and storage conditions involved, contribute far more to stoppages and malfunctions in firearms than do the mechanical designs or effectiveness of the weapons themselves.

Chapter 12. Military Pistols—Historical Outline

A PISTOL is defined as a short firearm intended to be held normally with one hand. Its chamber is generally formed by reaming and enlarging the breech end of the barrel so it will receive the cartridge case.

The term "pistol" unless otherwise qualified means a single shot weapon. It is often popularly—but incorrectly—applied to mean a revolver or an autoloading pistol.

During World War II the United States actually issued a considerable quantity of single shot pistols for military use, although for all practical purposes the single shot has been outmoded since 1872. The pistol in question was a single shot arm very cheaply made from stampings, tubing, and screw machine parts. It fired our standard .45 caliber service auto pistol cartridge. The arm had a trap in the butt where a few extra cartridges could be carried. With each weapon went cartridges, a short stick to be used in pushing the empty case out after firing (no extractor was provided), and a simple set of line illustrations showing without words how to load, fire, and empty the weapon. The single shot was distributed to guerrilla forces in several theaters of war. It was reported as being used very effectively against the Japanese in particular. The barrel was not rifled. As a close-quarters weapon it was extremely deadly, not only because of the heavy slug it threw, but also because the user knew that he had only one chance. He stopped his enemy the first time or he was in trouble. There is reason to believe, on the basis of data furnished by intelligence groups, that more killings were actually done with this simple, crude pistol than with all the service .45 automatics issued! In general these pistols were issued to natives by the O.S.S. (The Office of Strategic Services, headed by General "Wild Bill" Donovan. This organization was a highly specialized military intelligence organization.)

American made single shot pistol, caliber .45 automatic. Made for our Office of Strategic Services and distributed by them to the various underground movements during World War II. The lock lifts up as in the early German Theiss rifle.

In the Balkan areas some use was made of the huge "Bavarian Lightning" single shot produced at Nuremberg in 1867; but these were merely arms which had been in family or police possession since time of manufacture, not current war period production as was our own pistol mentioned above.

Passing mention might also be made of two "secret" weapons which were dreamed up during War II, but which were completely impractical. One was a small tube-and-pocket-clip affair resembling a fountain pen. It was to be carried attached to coat or shirt by the clip. When ready for use, the clip was pulled all the way back and let slip. It was under spring pressure, and releasing it fired a .22 short cartridge housed within the barrel section. Cloak-and-dagger operators who carried such items explained that they were to be used as suicide arms in case of capture. Others were supposed to use them in fights for very close-up use, particularly shooting at the exposed area of the medulla oblongata. The only actual use authoritatively reported was when someone carrying such a device shot himself accidentally but not fatally!

Yet another freak was developed in Naval Intelligence circles. This beauty was a flat steel plate device holding one husky .38 S&W special cartridge. It was attached to a heavy leather glove with rivets. A firing release protruded from the front. The idea here was that the wearer of the glove could crack a skull with a blow; and in case

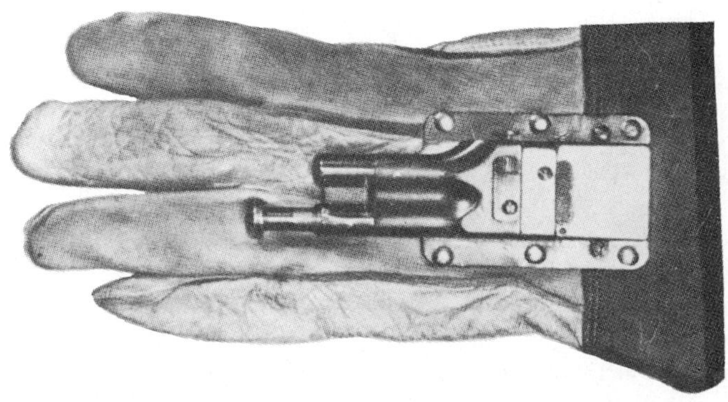

Glove pistol of World War II. When fist is closed the projecting striker will fire the pistol when struck against the opponent's body. Made in caliber .38 S&W and also in caliber .38 S&W Special.

of emergency could jam the striker release against the face of an opponent, discharging the .38 into said opponent. Such inane devices crop up in every war period.

At the other extreme were single shot pistols used by all services, but most highly developed by the British Intelligence, for close quarters use with silencers. Some were useful on Commando raids. Others were frankly weapons for military or political assassination. Revolvers are not efficient with silencers because gas—and hence noise—escapes at the jointure of barrel and cylinder. Auto pistols are not too effective because of noise as the breech opens and gas is blasted out, and because of the mechanical clatter as the slide slams home. The single shot was used because it made a truly silent arm when properly constructed. Arms such as these are intended only for specialist use, hence will not be dealt with in this volume.

Of course, there have been multi-barrel pistols, revolving pistols, magazine pistols, and a host of other freaks and legitimate variations in the course of the evolution of the pistol. We can touch here only on those which have had some relation to military usage, or which have some special historical value.

Derivation of the Name

There are almost as many explanations of the source of the name "pistol" as there are types of pistols. Reference works generally state the name came from the fact that the weapon was "invented" in 1540 at Pistoia, Italy by a gunmaker named Vettelli. This is quite unlikely. In fact the weight of evidence is against it.

Short firearms of the "pistol" type existed a good 200 years before 1540. The Chronicles of Modena, Italy, for the year 1364 A.D., just to cite an Italian instance, list "four little scioppi for the hand" as part of the town's inventory. "Scioppi" evolved from the Latin "sclopetum" which is the authorized Latin word for pistol. Perugia's historical records of about the same period list "500 portable bombards a span's length." The Roman "span" in use at that period was about 7½ inches. Hundreds of similar records in various European centers show that the one-hand small firearm was in use long before Pistoia ever heard of it.

Still another explanation is that the name derived from the fact that the caliber was originally the diameter of a common coin, the "pistole." Historical records and such early samples as are known do not bear this theory out. There was a tremendous divergence in calibers in the early days, and standardization was unknown.

Researchers who combine a knowledge of languages with etymology and also with knowledge of firearms (and these are few indeed) lean to the explanation that the name derived from the fact that the early pistols were used by cavalry; and that "pistol" evolved from the fact that the arms were commonly carried in holsters positioned on the "pistallo" or pommel of the saddle. Henry II of France named such troops "pistoleers."

Whatever the derivation of the name, there is no question that the history of the pistol parallels that of the longer firearms—and may even have preceded them.

Contemporary illustration showing use of the Petronel. From Lat. Mss. 7239 in the Bibliotheque Richelieu.

Early Pistols

In the early period of the Cannon Lock, the German Black Knights terrified the French forces when they introduced the "secret weapon" of that day, the "petronel." This was a one-hand gun commonly hung around the neck on a lanyard. When firing the butt end was rested against the chest (poitrine) for support. A lighted match was applied by the other hand to the touch-hole to fire the piece.

The German Ritters about 1520 employed wheel-lock one-hand guns. At the battle of Renty (1544) they used them with terrifying effect against the French. This was the first use of the dread "caracole" where a line of horsemen galloped in close to the massed French soldiers, fired their pistols at point-blank range, then wheeled to the rear to reload while a second line of Ritters galloped in to repeat the performance. These Ritters were mostly paid mercenaries, and Henry II finally hired them himself and named them "pistoleers."

A novel called "Jewel House" published in England

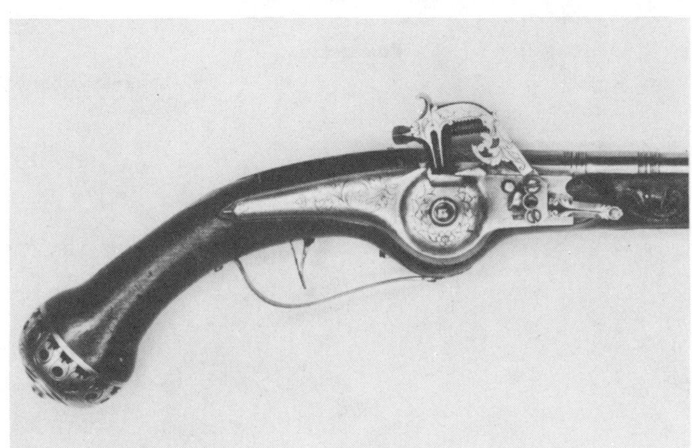

Early German wheel-lock pistol. There were thousands of varieties of this type.

Pair of George Washington's flintlock pistols made in England, now at West Point. Note engraving details.

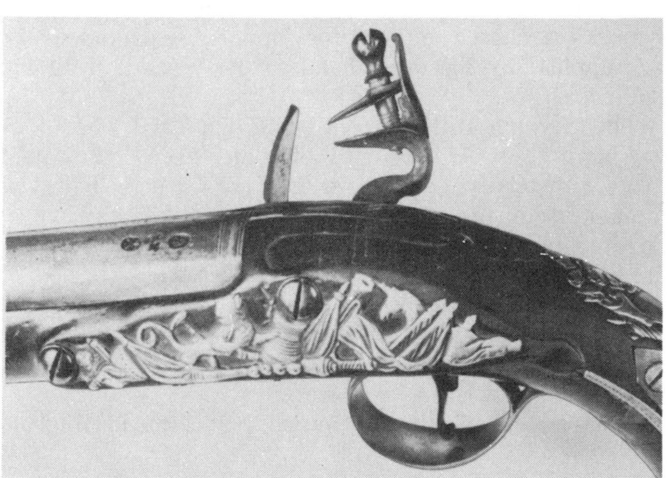

Side detail.

Butt detail.

North & Cheney flintlock pistol model 1799.

French 1777 pattern flintlock pistol made in Connecticut by North & Cheney for American forces.

in 1594 carries an account of a rifled pistol, an interesting item in view of the fact that English patent records disclose no records of rifling before 1635. This is another instance of the difficulty of being definite about dates and names in the history of firearms.

In the days of the Snaphaunce and the true Flintlock, the pistol was known in all these early forms. We have place here only for passing mention, since books could be written on each type. We can no more than note the existence of hinged frame and other patterns of breechloaders, 3- and 4-barreled pistols, magazine pistols of the "Cookson" type already mentioned, over-unders and every other design which had appeared earlier—and was to be repeated later as ignition systems advanced.

The early pistols used in our own country were largely for defense, of course, and authentic records disclose very little about them. Hubbard's "History of The Pequot Indian Wars" (published in 1677), for instance, tells of the use of "pieces laden with ten or twelve pistol bullets," but says nothing of the arms themselves except that they were used against the savage Pequots. Another early history, Bodge's "Soldiers in King Phillip's War," tells of an attack in which Captain John Gallup was "armed with two guns and two pistols and with buckshot for bullets." Beyond the fact that pistols were used, the historian tells us nothing about them.

John Kim, a gunsmith, advertised in The Boston News Letter, in the year 1720, that he manufactured pistols to individual order. These, of course, were flintlocks. During the early days of our Revolution when General Gage, British Commander at Boston, called on citizens to surrender their arms, we learn from Frothingham's "Siege of Boston" that 634 pistols were turned in. This is an index of the use of pistols; yet it is strange how little is authentically known of what they were or who made them. The famous "Pitcairn Highlanders" carried by the British commander at the Battle of Lexington are still to be seen in the little museum in Lexington. One of these captured pistols probably fired "the shot heard round the world" which set off the shooting on Lexington Common. These are flintlocks made in Scotland. They were carried, of course, in holsters across the saddle pommel, which accounts for their capture. Pitcairn's horse was shot and the major was thrown. Minute Men took the pistols from the stricken animal's back.

The earliest official American military pistol of which we have record as having been made in America is the "Rappahannock Forge" Flintlock. The locks were imported, but the rest of the pistol was made and the assembly was done in Virginia, where the Legislature set up a forge. It was destroyed early in the Revolution, and the pistols are rare. North & Cheney in 1799 produced flintlock pistols patterned after the French army pistol of the day, the caliber being .69. Deringer's Flintlock made in Philadelphia is representative of the general patterns used by our forces in the early days through the War of 1812.

The first U. S. Government-made flintlock pistol is the Harper's Ferry 1806. This .54 caliber pistol had a rifled barrel and its general design conformed to that of the rifles produced at Harper's Ferry Armory. Among the best known of these early American pistols for military use are the various models made by Simeon North at Berlin, Connecticut. The 1819 model featured a safety catch behind the hammer. Springfield Armory produced pistols in 1818, but the locks were imported from England. The final official U. S. flintlock pistol was the Model 1836, developed at Springfield, but made by private contractors also until about 1844.

It is a strange fact that despite very large scale early pistol manufacture in America, there is little to indicate that any particular attention was given to multi-barrel or freak types. Manufacture and design in this period held very closely to single shot design; while during the same

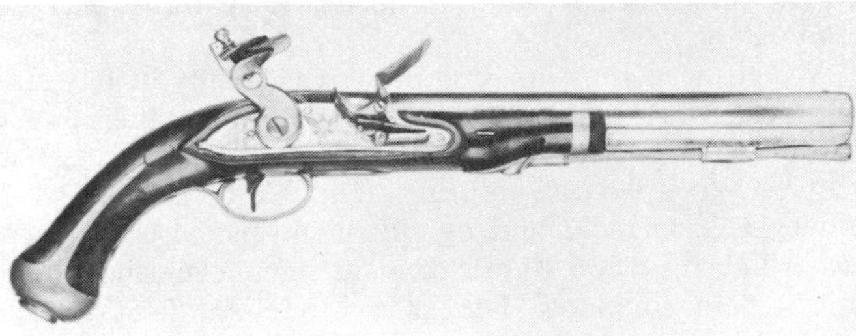

Harper's Ferry. Army and Navy Model 1806 flintlock pistol.

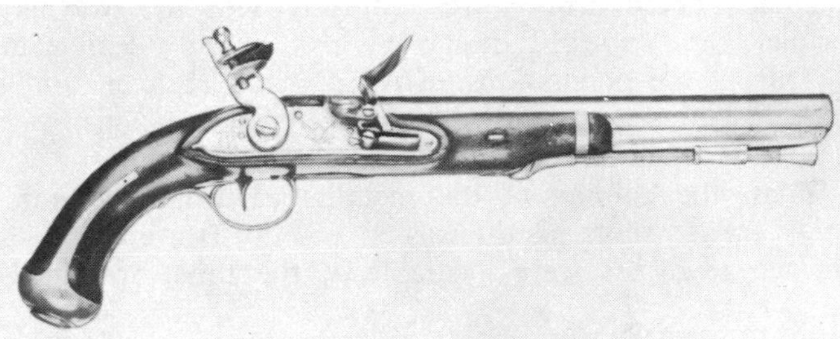

Harper's Ferry. Army and Navy Model 1807 flintlock pistol.

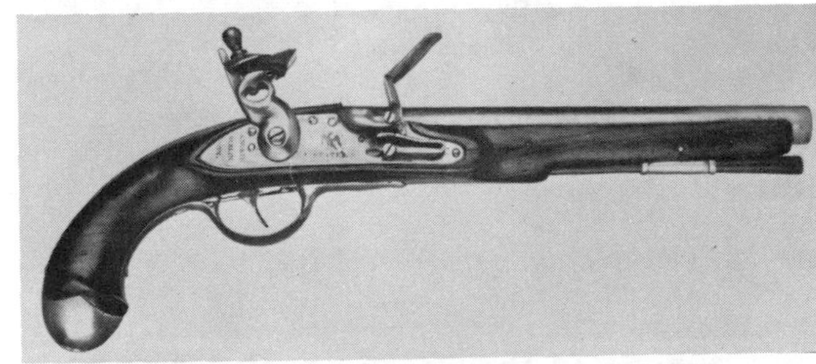

U. S. Pistol Model 1808 by S. North, Navy caliber .69.

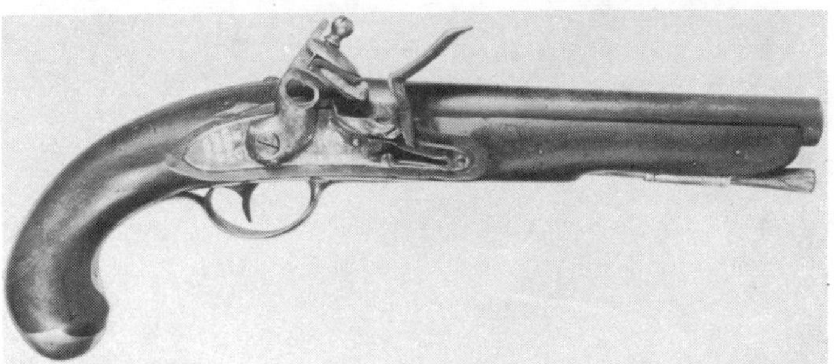

United States' Flintlock Pistol Model of 1810.

period in Europe every conceivable pattern was attempted.

When the percussion system arrived, many of the early flintlocks were altered to the new ignition pattern. New manufacture varied very little in overall design except as required for percussion firing. The U. S. Model 1842, made at Springfield and by private firms, also was very much like the 1836 Flintlock in its lines, even the caliber of .54 being retained. The 1855 Model U. S. Springfield was issued as a pistol-carbine. It had a pistol form, but was fitted with a detachable shoulder stock for use as a carbine. These arms were equipped with the Maynard primer, the "cap-roll" design we have already dealt with.

During the percussion era there was a rash of double barrel, pepperbox, and similar designs, but none were officially accepted for military use.

With the coming of the metallic cartridge, the military single shot pistol was doomed. However, even though revolvers were available at the time, Springfield

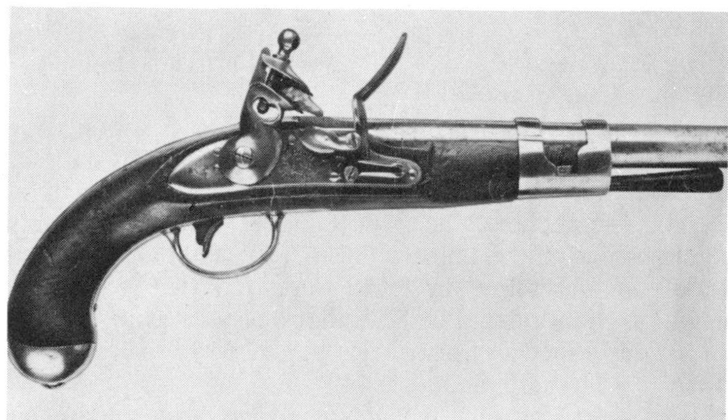

U. S. flintlock pistol Model 1813 by Simeon North. Used by Army and Navy.

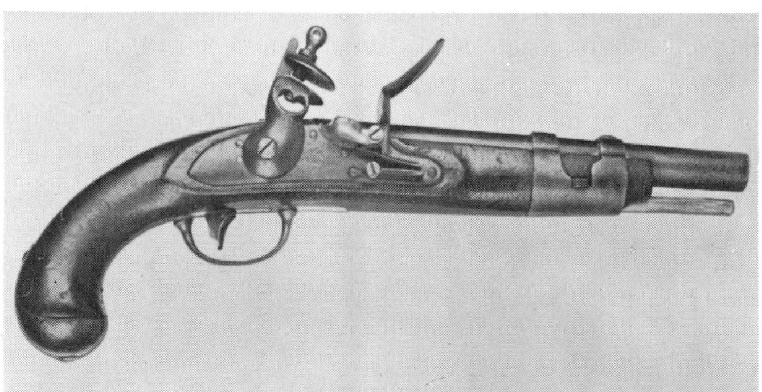

U. S. flintlock pistol, Model of 1816 by S. North. Caliber .54.

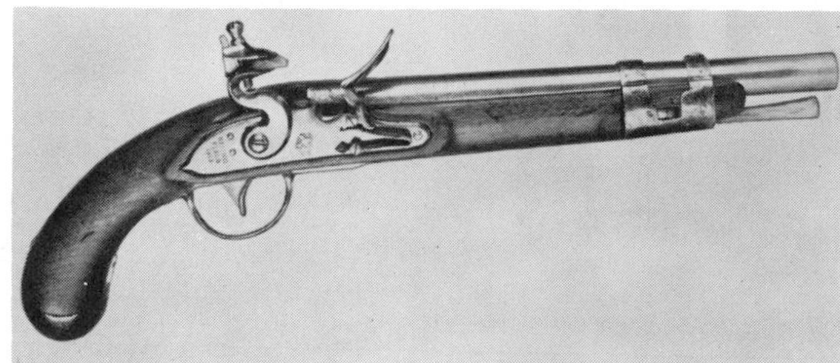

U. S. flintlock pistol. Model of 1818, U. S. Army. Made at Springfield Armory.

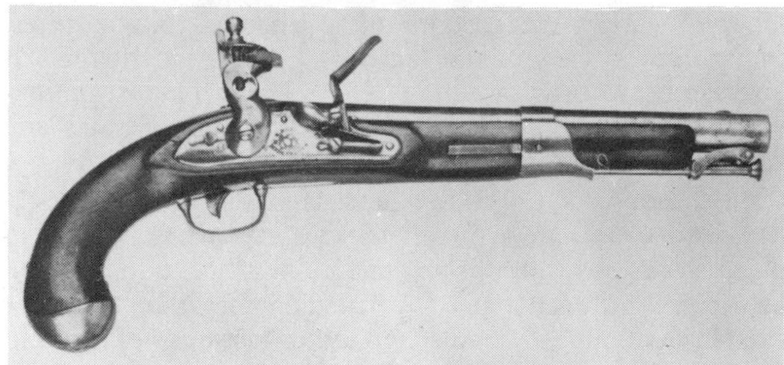

U. S. flintlock pistol, Model 1819 by S. North.

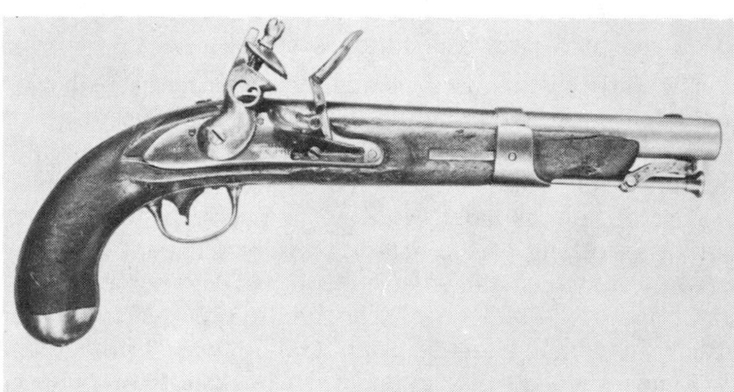

Simeon North Army and Navy flintlock pistol Model of 1826. Caliber .54. The last of the Simeon North contract U. S. Martial pistols. Three thousand of these pistols were contracted for.

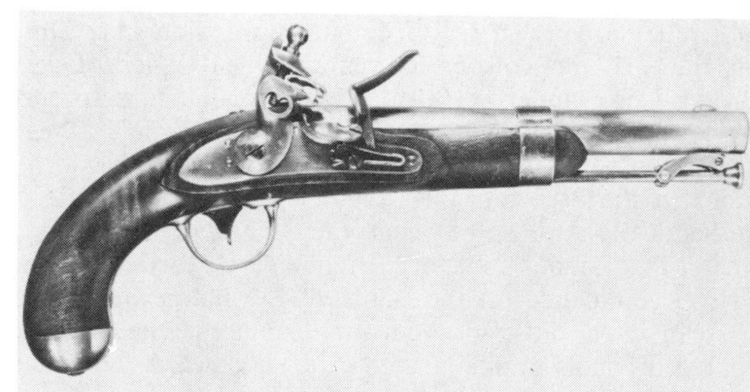

U. S. flintlock pistol, Model 1836 by R. Johnson. Caliber .54 taking a one-half ounce spherical ball and a charge of 50 grains of black rifle powder. In 1848 the flintlock arms in government armories were inspected and the serviceable weapons were ordered to be altered to the percussion system.

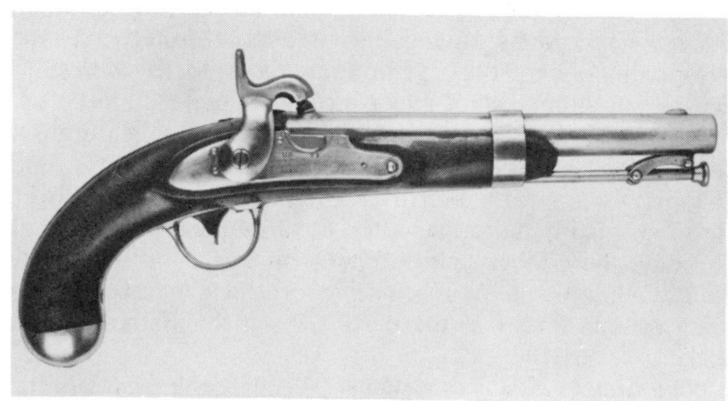

R. Johnson Army Model, Caliber .54. Model of 1836 converted to the percussion system.

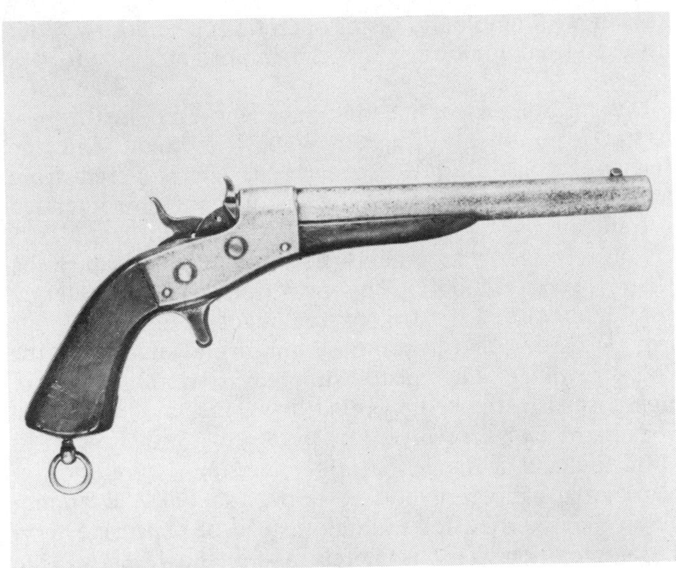

U. S. single shot Navy pistol. Early Model of 1866 by Remington. Caliber .50 rim fire. This was the first metallic cartridge pistol issued to the U. S. services. Later model Remingtons employ the more secure rolling block lock and the formal trigger and triggerguard.

Armory actually designed a .50 caliber pistol with the cam-lock system used in the rifle of the day! This 5-pound wonder was never issued, but models were made. Our Navy did purchase a quantity of Remington Rolling Block pistols Model 1867 to handle a .50 caliber cartridge. This was followed by the Army purchase of the improved Remington Model 1871 in .50 caliber. This pistol is still sought by gun enthusiasts for conversion to handle modern cartridges because of its strong lock and its fine balance.

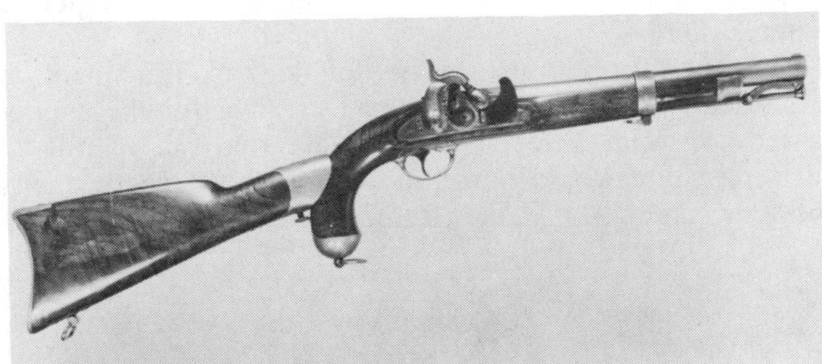

U. S. Percussion Pistol with detachable carbine stock. Although such stocks are of little practical value, recurrent use is made of the principle. Spanish machine pistols currently made employ it.

The "pepper-box" design came into its own for a period in percussion days. It is a question just who first introduced it here at this time. Ethan Allen patented his in 1845, and it was a favorite weapon of those who went to California in the gold rush days of 1849. At about the same time, the system was widely manufactured in England and on the Continent.

This design had little military significance. It is interesting, however, as an early form of the "double action" lock mechanism where a pull on the trigger operates both the hammer and the feed mechanism as in the

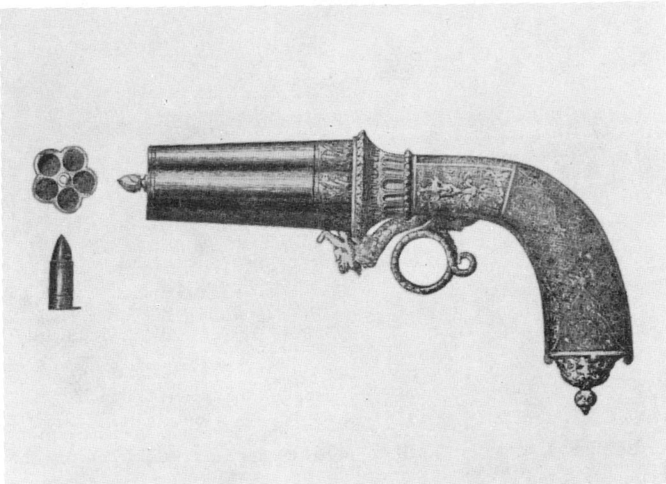

Original Lefaucheux Pepperbox pin fire shown at London 1851 exhibition. The pepperbox is usually percussion fired and there are thousands of variations.

case of modern revolvers. Pepper-box patterns were used in Matchlock days, but the 19th century use of the system is the first known where operation of the mechanism was mechanical by springs and finger pressure. All previous patterns required manual turning of the barrels.

The pepper-box design consists of a series of barrels around a central axis, or alternatively a series of barrels all drilled out of one solid piece of metal much like an elongated revolver cylinder. Usually there were six barrels —sometimes more, sometimes less. Each one was loaded from the muzzle end. Caps were then placed over nipples on a band at the breech. Pulling the trigger raised the hammer, turned a barrel into firing line, and dropped the hammer on the cap to fire the barrel. They were heavy and not very accurate; at best they constituted a transitional design.

Among the earliest developers of small percussion pistols was Deringer in Philadelphia. One of his pistols, as every arms enthusiast knows, was used to assassinate President Lincoln. While soldiers often carried such arms for defensive purposes, they were never official issue.

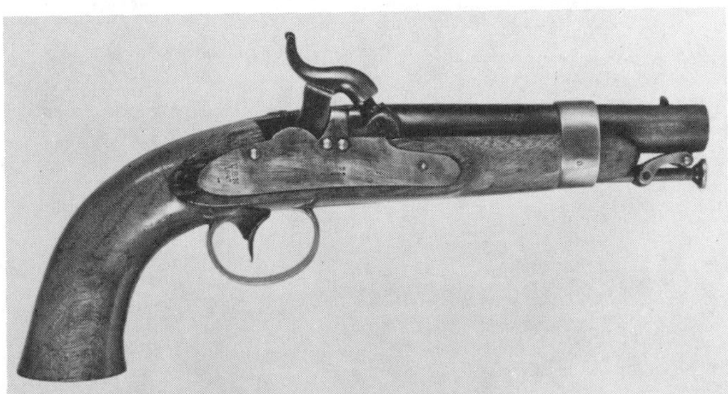

U. S. Percussion Pistol, Model of 1843 by Deringer. Navy Model, Caliber .54. The first U. S. Martial percussion box lock pistols actually issued to the service. Although a Model 1843, these pistols were made and issued before the Model 1842. This was a matter of manufacturing production.

English Lancaster Caliber .476 center fire, 4-barrel pistol.

England produced one fantastic multi-barrel type before accepting the revolver design. This was the Lancaster, a 4-barreled pistol to take .476 caliber cartridges. The design was a strong hinge frame breechloader. Barrels were stationary. Pulling the trigger actuated an internal striker mechanism which acted through individual firing pins to discharge each barrel in succession by double action as the trigger was pulled. This monstrosity saw some little private use by the British in Africa and Asia, but was not officially adopted.

Today some single shot pistols are again being introduced for training purposes. One such is the S-M Pistol being sold by Sydney Manson of Alexandria, Va. This arm is made in .22 caliber and is intended for training in the handling of automatic pistols. It resembles an automatic pistol in general outline and balance. The bolt is drawn back manually to load the chamber. A release catch is pressed to close the breech as in regular service auto pistol use. When the trigger is pressed the arm fires. The action opens automatically and ejects the empty case. The action stays open ready for reloading. This system simulates quite well the action of a service pistol and affords training of value. At the same time its single shot feature precludes any danger from accidental firing of successive rounds as happens at times with novices unfamiliar with automatic pistol operation. The cost of both pistol and ammunition is low, an important element in a trainer.

Designs somewhat like this have appeared in the past in the form of the English Webley & Scott and the Belgian Pieper. Both these early designs suffered from being more expensive than the pistol they were intended to train for.

Colt's formerly manufactured a single shot called the "Camp Perry Model." This was intended as a target pistol and also as a trainer for revolver use, since its grip, lockwork and loading system were similar to the Colt's revolver. This pistol suffered from the factor of high cost also, the selling price being higher than that of a standard Colt's revolver.

In England a single barrel conversion is sold to replace large caliber revolver cylinders so that .22 ammunition may be used for training instead of expensive service ammunition. This is merely a unit, however, not an actual pistol. In the United States special barrel and slide devices have been produced to allow use of the service .45 auto as a single shot .22 trainer. Here again they have not been accepted because of the high cost of such conversion units. Colt's, Springfield Armory, and Sedgley Arms Corp. all introduced such units without success.

Double Barrel Pistols

All through the course of firearms history double barrel pistols have been known. The common military forms in early ignition periods were side-by-side barrels as in the modern shotgun construction. None are of value to this outline.

In the early percussion era, as we have seen, much attention was given to small designs, a few of which were used as auxiliary side arms. Again none are of particular interest here.

The one truly outstanding double barreled pistol in America was the old Remington Derringer for the copper cased .41 Rim Fire cartridge. Note that such arms in varying calibers and barrel systems were made by many other makers. Only the Remington warrants attention

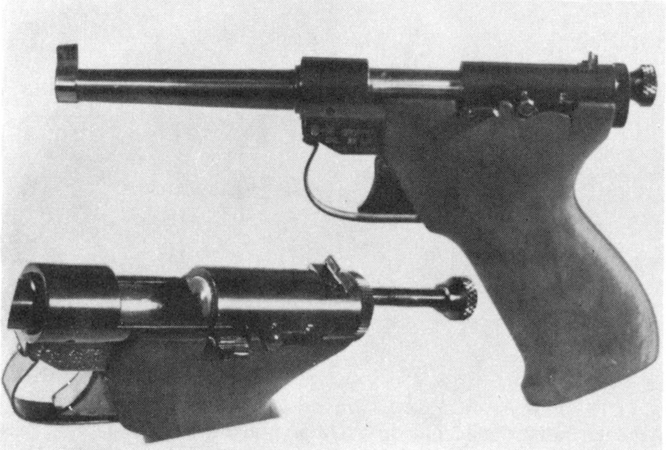

American S-M single shot pistol closed. Insert shows action open after firing.

American Derringer by Remington. Caliber .41 rim fire. Still highly regarded as a defense weapon by police in some areas, though both gun and cartridge are long obsolete.

here. It is still a weapon carried by many police officers in the West and Southwest as an auxiliary "hideaway" weapon. The two barrels are placed one above the other. They are hinged at the top of the breech. Turning the release catch allows them to be swung up for loading. A manually operated extractor is provided on most of these. The pistol must be thumb-cocked to fire each barrel in succession. The heavy, slow-travelling slug is deadly at close range.

During both World Wars many U. S. officers carried these deadly old Remingtons as hidden arms, much as the German officers tended to carry small and rather ineffective .25 auto pistols concealed for emergency use. Note that such arms are called "Derringers," with two r's. This spelling stems from the fact that the original inventor of the early "Deringer" refused to allow competitors in the short pistol field to capitalize upon his name; so they evaded by doubling the "r."

Multi-Barreled Pistols

The only military use of pistols with several barrels in recent times was the appearance of freaks such as the early 4- and 6-barreled designs made late in the 19th Century by Braendlin Armory in England and the Lancaster already mentioned. These were hinged frame types fired by a double action pull. They could be used with modern .455 British service ammunition, and after Dunkirk even relics such as these appeared, so desperate were the British for arms.

In general, designs of this type have been made with all the barrels drilled in a single steel block; but a few freaks have consisted of several barrels brazed together. They have no historical importance here except as indicated.

Other weird forms such as the European "Regnum" and "Reform" pistols were occasionally found on prisoners during World War II, but did not constitute military issue as such. The former has four barrels drilled one above the other in a solid block. The caliber is usually 6.35mm (.25). Each barrel is fired in succession as the trigger is pulled. This pistol hinges open to load. The "Reform" has a somewhat similar barrel structure. The action is different, however. The first pull fires the top barrel. Each succeeding pull moves the barrel block up and gas from the exploding cartridge ejects the empty case from the barrel above it! The sole value of such pistols is their flat shape allowing easy concealment as an auxiliary arm.

Captured German belt buckle pistol World War II. Property of the Honorable Gordon Persons, former Governor of Alabama. A very rare specimen.

The Germans during War II made a unique belt-buckle pistol. The only samples the author has ever seen were hand-made models. However, Governor Gordon Persons of Alabama, an ardent collector of unusual arms, possesses a sample which seems to be a production item. Production was probably halted by events of the war. The pistol is a great rarity, a collector's prize of the first order. Pressing a catch on the buckle allows the face of the buckle to spring away and the barrels to emerge and fire—a dangerous close quarters gadget to be used upon the unsuspecting.

Magazine Pistols

None of these are worthy of more than passing notice, since none were ever practical military arms. They have appeared all through firearms history in one form or another, however.

In metallic cartridge days, the early Austrian Schwarzlose magazine pistols were experimented with by the Austro-Hungarian Army but were not adopted. (These are not to be confused with later Schwarzlose auto pistols.)

These freak arms differ in operation from the so-called "automatic" pistol where the forces of the explosion function the action. "Magazine pistols"—the Schwarzlose, Bittner, Fiala, and others—looked like auto pistols of their day. However, after firing each shot, the action had to be opened by hand to eject the empty and feed in the next cartridge in the magazine. Such transition arms and freaks have a single barrel and chamber, but carry a reserve supply of cartridges in the butt to be fed in as the action is manually functioned.

Repeating Pistols

These too are freaks, having a single barrel and chamber and a reserve stock of cartridges usually in the handle section. The actions are mechanically or spring-operated as the trigger is pulled. They are more advanced than the "magazine" types mentioned above in that a pull on the trigger feeds and ejects without use of the other hand. They are inferior to the automatic type in that the ejection and feeding is mechanical rather than by utilizing the explosive forces, hence they are slower and more clumsy. The French and Belgian plants which made these types were never successful in selling them for military use, though again some were taken from prisoners during World War II—"hideaway" arms they had personally bought.

The Single Shot Auto Ejector

The final form of true pistol is that in which the cartridge is manually inserted, but in which the forces of the explosion are utilized as in the automatic pistol to open the action ready for reloading.

We have already mentioned this pattern as having some value as military trainers when, as in the case of the current American S-M .22 pistol, they sell at low price. As they appeared in the discontinued Belgian Pieper and the British Webley & Scott, their training value was offset by their cost.

Chapter 13. The Military Automatic Pistol—Historical Outline

THE principle of the so-called automatic pistol design was familiar almost from the inception of gunpowder. We find written references to arms utilizing the principle as far back as Sir Robert Moray's report to the Royal Society in 1664. However, the practical application of the principle was never truly possible until after the development of the successful metallic pistol cartridge and smokeless powder.

As we have seen, American patent office records as early as 1863 showed attempts to develop gas-operated arms. Historically, however, the first successful automatic pistol was that marketed in Austria by the inventor Schönberger.

Section view of the original Borchardt. From a contemporary drawing.

The successful automatic pistol was also dependent to a large degree upon the development of the rimless and semi-rimmed case. These were at once strong enough to stand the violent jerk of immediate automatic extraction, utilized a metal jacketed bullet which could be securely seated in the case and would feed easily, and permitted cartridges to be placed one on top of the other in the familiar box magazine design.

The 1893 barrel-recoil-operated pistol of Andrea Schwarzlose of Austria was never put into production, but it paved the way for his later designs.

The first automatic pistol which was truly successful commercially was of German manufacture but of American design, the 7.63mm Borchardt. Hugo Borchardt of Connecticut early in life worked at the Winchester Repeating Arms Company in Hartford. He developed a very clumsy but nevertheless thoroughly efficient automatic pistol with a toggle-locked breech and detachable box magazine in the stock. For it he developed a special cartridge of bottleneck design with a jacketed bullet. With very little modification, this cartridge is the familiar 7.63mm Mauser cartridge today. An even smaller modification makes it also the Russian 7.62mm automatic pistol and submachine gun cartridge.

Borchardt was unable to interest American manufac-

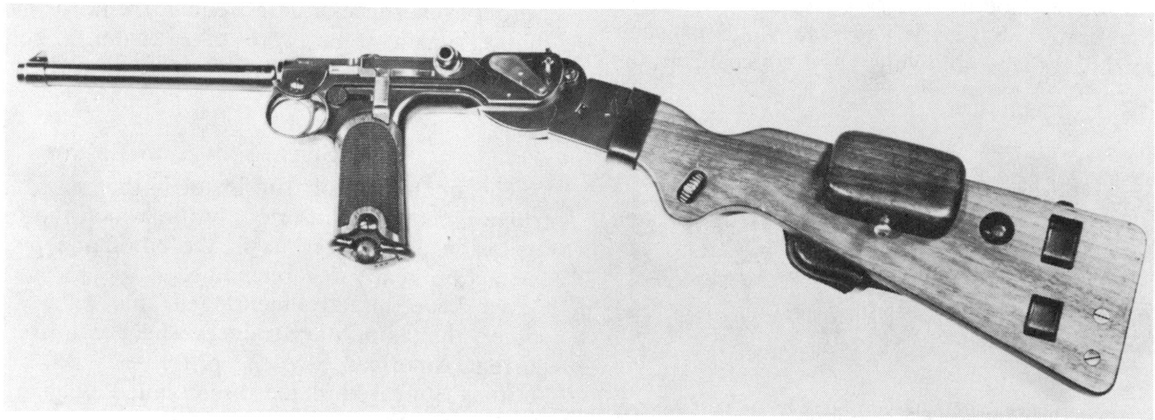

The American designed Borchardt with shoulder stock attached. The weapon was manufactured in Germany. The Luger evolved from it.

turers in producing the design. He went to Germany with it. The Berlin firm of Ludwig Loëwe and Company at that time was engaged in production of Mauser rifles. They employed Borchardt as an engineer and put his pistol into production. It was marketed in 1893. As originally issued it was accompanied by a detachable rifle stock, the idea being to make it either a one- or a two-hand weapon for short or long range firing. In practice, shoulder use of pistols is not desirable.

One of Borchardt's assistants at the Loëwe plant was George Luger. He redesigned the mechanism to produce the first model of the world-famous Luger pistol, an arm which from 1908 until 1938 was the official side-arm of the Germany military forces.

The long line of German Bergmann pistols began in 1894. These models included locked and unlocked breech types, exposed and internal hammers, in-built and detachable magazines, and many calibers and styles. One of these Bergmann's was manufactured in Belgium under the name "Simplex." It utilized an 8mm cartridge developed specially for it. This cartridge was modified by John Browning and the F. N. Works in Belgium and is familiar throughout the world today as the .32 Colt Automatic Pistol cartridge or the 7.65mm Browning Automatic Pistol cartridge. No other pocket pistol cartridge in history achieved the success this one did.

In England in 1896 the American, Hiram Maxim, patented a blowback automatic pistol and made samples in various calibers. These were never put into production, however. The design was noteworthy in that it was one of the first to successfully use the rimmed .455 British service cartridge. An American design, the Reifgraber, later duplicated this feat by using the .32 S & W rimmed cartridge.

However, until the development of the special magazines used by the .22 Colt Woodsman, automatic pistols generally would not operate satisfactorily with rimmed ammunition. Much work is being done today in sporting and quasi-military circles on the development of automatic pistols to shoot the super-accurate .38 Smith & Wesson Special rimmed cartridge.

The automatic pistol as a truly military arm began its history in 1896, when Mauser introduced his 7.63mm Military Model, a pistol still in wide general use throughout the world. Hugo Borchardt was officially credited by German ammunition manufacturers, who first produced this cartridge, with not only the cartridge design but also with having done much of the experimental engineering work on the Mauser pistol itself, although the basic design was that of Mauser.

Winston Churchill as a Leftenant in the British Lancers used a Mauser automatic pistol in the cavalry charge at Omdurmann. He recommended the pistol highly, stating that because of its efficiency and magazine capacity he was able to shoot his way out of a native trap, killing several of the fuzzy-wuzzy warriors in the course of saving his own life. However, it was many years before

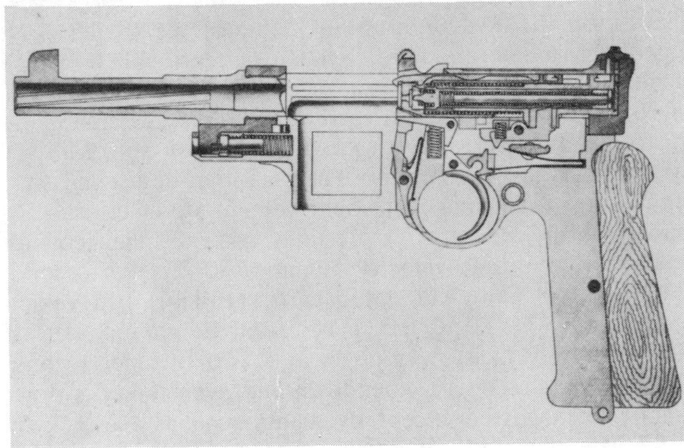

Sectionalized drawing of another of Mauser's semi-automatic pistols. This was not produced commercially. A variant of its locking mechanism is used in some automatic arms today.

the British service gave particular attention to the general adoption of automatic pistols for military service.

The first automatic arm to provide a device to hold the action open when the magazine is empty was that used in 1898, again by Andrea Schwarzlose of Austria. The short-recoil locking principle found in this pistol is basically that of the German machine gun of 1934 and the American Johnson light machine rifle. The pistol used 7.63mm Mauser cartridges, but was never generally used for military service.

By far the most successful of all automatic pistol designers, of course, was our own John M. Browning. As in the case of so many other inventors, he had to go to Europe to have his original design manufactured. His first pistol was introduced there in 1899. It had been patented in the previous year. This arm was manufactured by the F. N. (Fabrique Nationale D'Armes de Guerre, Europe's largest arms manufacturer today, is at Herstal, Belgium.)

Browning's first pistol made in the so-called 7.65mm or .32 automatic caliber has been used as a side arm in practically all military groups in the world at one time or another. It has in all instances, however, been a substitute standard weapon or one purchased by officers personally.

In 1900, Colt introduced a new model Browning automatic pistol to handle a newly-developed cartridge, the .38 Colt automatic. The first model of this arm made by Browning was actually a full automatic enclosed hammer model, a single pull on the trigger emptying the magazine.

The arm fired so rapidly and uncontrollably that it was almost impossible to hit anything with it, the rapid successions of recoil throwing the muzzle up so fast that anyone nearby was in danger.

In June, 1900, Browning wrote to the editor of American sporting magazine that he had experimented with various types of safeties, both grip type and thumb actuated. He also explained his reasons for designing the

.38 automatic with a rotating hammer, his earlier F.N. pistol having been fired by a conventional rifle-type striker.

From this design he evolved the Colt .38 automatic pistol in Pocket Model with short barrel and Military Model with six-inch barrel. The cartridge developed was, and still is, a remarkable achievement. Our official .38 caliber Army Revolver at the time, using a black powder load, had a muzzle velocity of only 750 feet per second. The new .38 Colt Automatic cartridge developed velocities as high as 1,350 feet per second in unofficial tests! The official velocity was given at 1,260 feet per second. The penetration was tremendous, and even today is practically unsurpassed except by giants such as the S & W .357 Magnum and some special freak loads. The initial penetration was given as 11 inches in pine. The penetration of this pistol resulted in its use throughout the world by big game hunters who carried it as an extra weapon for close quarters use in case of emergency. The pistol itself introduced Browning's first recoil-operated, locked-breech mechanism, varieties of which are today in use in all the locked-breech Colt and Browning pattern pistols as well as in those of many imitators ranging from Poland and Spain to Russia.

The angle of the grip and the size and balance of the arm were all poor. Moreover, the slide was secured to the receiver by a cross wedge, the receiver being so machined as to permit the slide to travel in it. When, as occasionally happened, the wedge crystallized and gave way, the slide could be blown off the back of the pistol.

Browning's next military design in .45 caliber was quite similar to the .38 and was equally a failure.

However, his later .45, as developed for our government tests, was in all except minor details the same superb arm it remains today. This locked-breech short-recoil-operated weapon was so constructed that the slide could be removed only from the forward end of the receiver. The pitch of the grip was improved, as was the balance and weight distribution.

Mannlicher introduced an automatic pistol in 1901. This was not particularly successful, although it is still occasionally encountered. One of its defects was that it used a special cartridge obtainable only from Austria.

In 1900 the great Deutsche Waffen and Munitions-Fabriken, world renowned before World War I as "DWM," produced the pistol popularly known after its designer as the Luger, which was a refinement of the American Borchardt. This was originally introduced with still another bottlenecked cartridge of considerable velocity and power, the 7.65mm.

In 1908 the German government adopted the Luger as its official service pistol but the caliber was increased to 9mm. However, the 9mm cartridge itself is similar to the earlier one in body diameter. The 9mm case was developed directly from the 7.65mm so that interchangeability of the two cartridges is very simply effected merely by replacement of barrels. Only the chambers and the bores differ. These pistols have never been manufactured commercially in any other calibers than 7.65mm and in 9mm. Early in the century a quantity were hand-manufactured in caliber .45 for United States government tests. These are collector's arms, and although they were advertised commercially they were never manufactured in commercial quantities.

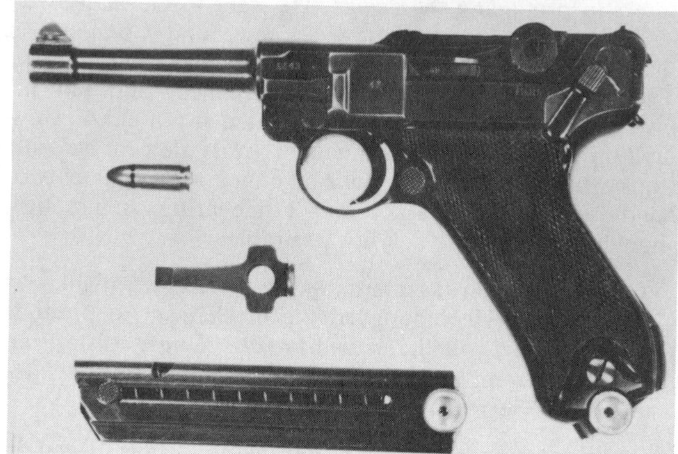

A representative Luger. The "08" stamp indicates German Pistol Model 1908, caliber 9mm.

World War I Luger with 32-shot snail magazine. This was a forerunner of the submachine gun.

The F.N. Model of 1903 developed by Browning appeared as the Colt Hammerless .32 Automatic Pistol. The design was blowback, the hammer was enclosed, and a grip safety provided. From this development came a modification in 1910 from the F.N. factory. Hundreds of variants of this pistol have been manufactured in Belgium, Italy, France, Germany, Spain, and Czechoslovakia since the introduction of the arm itself.

The German designer Bergmann negotiated manufacture of a locked-breech powerful design with an external hammer and a magazine forward of the trigger-guard which first appeared in Belgium under the name of Bergmann Bayard, and later simply as the Bayard. These were issued in 1908 and 1910 and are still encountered in Scandinavia and in Spain where they were official military arms for a time.

The 1904 Webley automatic pistol manufactured in England was produced in .455 caliber and was not a successful design. In 1913 a new and highly improved Webley locked-breech design in .455 caliber was adopted under the designation Mark I by the Royal Navy. It saw some limited use in both World Wars. In general the arm is too heavy and clumsy to be compared with the Colt pattern of automatic pistols. The Webley pocket type automatic pistol, an elementary blowback form of 1906, was used for some time in British police circles and constituted a defense issuance arm to some extent during the war periods.

American Savage .45 automatic. A collector's item.

In the United States the Savage Arms Company in 1906 produced in limited quantity a .45 caliber automatic pistol of interesting design with a hesitation locked breech in which the barrel rotates slightly to unlock. The angle of rotation is only five degrees, which actually furnishes a delaying or hesitation action rather than a true locked-breech pattern. This pistol was submitted for United States Government tests, but did not stand up in the face of the opposition from the .45 Colt pistol developed by Browning. It is encountered as a collector's item only. It was followed, however, in 1908 by the first of a series of very fine pocket automatic pistols by Savage utilizing the same general principle. Some models of this design are in official military use in caliber .32 in Portugal. They have had little military usage, however, except of course as emergency arms.

The Italian official Glisenti pistol was introduced in 1906, but was not adopted by the Italian Army until 1910. This interesting but weak design is discussed in detail in chapter 31.

Austro-Hungary in 1907 adopted for cavalry use a freak 8mm pistol by Roth-Steyr. This had been patented several years earlier. It was never a successful design although it saw military usage in both World Wars. This arm used a firing system which was spring operated, though ejecting and loading were produced by recoil forces.

In 1908, Browning's small pocket pistols of the so-called vest pocket type (which have seen extensive military use by staff officers in various European armies through both wars) were introduced in the United States as the .25 Colt Vest Pocket Automatic model and in Belgium as the F.N. Baby Browning. This too represents a type which has been tremendously imitated and copied throughout the world. Items resembling it very closely may be encountered with literally hundreds of varying trade names, representing pistols manufactured in Spain, Italy, and Belgium for the most part.

In 1913 Webley introduced an elementary blowback which they called a "9mm high velocity" but which in effect was an unlocked breech arm for the inferior 9mm Browning long cartridge, a cartridge seldom encountered.

The year 1910 saw the introduction in England of a locked-breech Webley following closely the design of their .455 Mark I Navy pistol but in caliber. 38 automatic. This did not meet with general success and was abandoned.

The United States .45 Colt Government Model Automatic Pistol designed by John M. Browning was introduced in 1911. With very few modifications, this is still the official pistol of the United States forces. Post-War II commercial models have been altered to utilize aluminum frames and a modified hammer.

Also in 1911, Austria introduced its 9mm Steyr-Hahn, a form converted later in World War II to the German service caliber of 9mm Parabellum or cartridge pistol 08. This interesting rotating barrel design loads with a strip-in clip instead of a detachable box magazine.

Hungary introduced the long-recoil pistol made by Frommer in 1912. This is a very unusual form of locked-breech action entirely unnecessary for the type of cartridge for which it was designed, the .32 automatic. This arm saw considerable use in the Balkans as a military arm despite its ineffective cartridge.

In 1915, Italy introduced the Beretta, another elementary blowback pistol which in modified form has since

A representative Italian Beretta pistol stripped to show simple design. The quick removable barrel is a feature of this type.

received tremendous manufacturing attention, both as a military arm and for export.

After World War I, Remington produced a .380 automatic pistol with a hesitation-locked breech of very unusual meritorious design. However, the American field for pocket automatic pistols at that time did not warrant production continuing and the pistol was discontinued. The locking mechanism in this pistol, functioning on the two-part breechblock hesitation mechanism, is susceptible of considerable development for possible application to other automatic arms.

During the succeeding years, very extensive manufacture of automatic pistol design was carried on in Spain for export use. In general these were modifications or direct copies of known locked-breech types. Copies and modifications were made of the Colt system also for .38 caliber, 9mm, and .45 automatic calibers. All were inferior in workmanship and materials, though in recent years they have been much inmproved.

In 1922 C.Z. in Czechoslovakia introduced the Nickl pattern of locked-breech pistol in .380 caliber, some parts of the mechanism other than the lock closely resembling that of the German pocket Mauser. This weapon was officially adopted by the Czech Army. Some later patterns involved one of the early forms of double action trigger mechanism commonly found in revolver construction. Next came a standard 7.65mm or .32 automatic of the blowback pattern marketed in 1927, which also saw use in the Czech military services.

In 1928 a Military Model of the Le Francais blowback pistol was introduced in France. An elementary blowback, the pistol had some unusual design features. Its firing mechanism is not cocked by the opening of the slide as in most pistols of the design. While the slide functions in normal fashion to permit extraction, ejection, and reloading, the firing mechanism is not cocked thereby. A long pull on the trigger is necessary to cock and slip the firing striker for each shot.

Only minor modifications of design were undertaken in the United States during this period. Great Britain paid no attention whatever to such production. In 1935 the F.N. plant in Belgium introduced its 1935 Browning High Power, a modification of the familiar Browning pistol with several interesting items added. In the original Browning locked-breech design as it appears in the .45 Colt automatic pistol, the movement of the barrel traveling in a vertical plane is utilized to lock the breech. The rear end of the barrel is secured to the receiver by a link, locking ribs on the top of the barrel engaging in mating cuts in the underside of the slide. The front section of the barrel serves as a pivot. The 1935 model, while essentially the same, replaces the swinging link with a solid nose section cam which is shaped to ride up and down in the receiver during the locking and unlocking motions. In the 1935 pattern the barrel is supported by a lug at its lower section which is an integral part of the barrel forging itself. Through a cut in this lug passes a transverse bar in the receiver. As the barrel and slide recoil, a cam-face on the lugs strikes the bar forcing the barrel down to disengage the locking lugs on the barrel from their seats in the slide. At this point, the barrel motion being halted, the slide can recoil the remaining distance to extract and eject.

Poland shortly thereafter introduced the Radom pistol which is a relatively minor modification of the Belgian Browning High Power.

In 1925 Japan introduced the Nambu. This locked-breech design is fully described in chapter 32. Originally introduced in 8mm service caliber, small production was later instituted on a 7mm caliber of reduced size. This is a short-recoil-operated arm with a hinged locking block cammed up from below the receiver to lock the breechblock well to the rear of the firing chamber. It is striker fired. While the design is interesting, it is doubtful that it will ever again be considered as an important design factor in military arms. The cartridge itself is ineffective by modern military standards. The experience of the Japanese military and police groups with small arms of American manufacture since the close of the war will undoubtedly influence Japanese design in the future. We have supplied both .45 and also latest model .38 S&W and Colt's revolvers to Japan recently. The latter take the .38 Smith & Wesson special revolver cartridge, a cartridge so much more powerful and efficient than the original Japanese 8mm that its superior characteristics cannot be ignored.

Spain during this period added to its line of imitations of Colt automatic pistols and Mauser automatic pistols by offering items such as the Star, Astra, and Azul pistols. Except that some of these are fitted with full automatic switches to permit continuous fire on one pull of the trigger (a totally useless device on a small arm), their production was purely that of uninspired patterns. In Argentina pistols such as the Criolla appeared; they were merely imitations of the Spanish Star.

The French modification of the Browning pistol locking system, the MAS pistol made at St. Etienne in 1935, is again merely a minor Browning variant utilizing the

Spanish Star. General design and appearance are Colt-Browning.

The design is often fitted with full-auto switch on right side of frame.

Latest models have improved takedown system. Calibers from 9mm luger to .45 A. C. P.

Argentine Semi-Auto Cal. .45 A. C. P. Made by HAFDASA. This is a slightly modified version of the Colt M1911.

common principles of the short recoil action. The cartridge, based on the "mysterious" American Pedersen device cartridge of World War I, is little more efficient than the .32 Colt automatic pistol cartridge, which may make it a desirable light weight arm for staff officers but labels it impractical for basic military usage.

In 1923 and later in 1934, several modifications were made in Italy of the basic Beretta pistol, all of which are covered in chapter 31. None are important particularly from a military standpoint because of the relatively ineffective cartridges of .32 and .380 caliber which they used. The same applies to a considerable degree to Austrian types and other development during this period; except that they produced some forms of the double action automatic system, whereby a pull on the trigger will fire the first shot mechanically without the hammer being cocked. These, however, were all small pocket arms for commercial use. The 1937 Hungarian modification of the Browning system, too, is merely of passing interest.

The Lahti is a short-recoil locked-breech pistol of 9mm caliber originating in Finland. It was later made in Sweden. Externally resembling the familiar Luger, but involving its own locking system, it is a relatively heavy and clumsy arm of its type by today's standards. It is no longer in general production.

Czechoslovakia improved its Strakonice double action automatic pistols, introducing a .380 model with a barrel hinged at the muzzle end for ease of cleaning. The design generally, however, was heavy and clumsy for the cartridge used.

French 1935 Pistol and section view showing mechanism.

Germany, during the period before World War II, saw the introduction of a wide range of advanced pistols basically of pocket type, but most were later pressed into military service. Perhaps the best known of these were the Walther PP and PPK automatics, the designations indicating Polezei Pistole and Polezei Pistol Kriminal or plainclothes model—from the fact that the latter had a shorter barrel and was intended to be concealed, while the police model was intended basically for holster use on the belt.

Representative Walther pattern PPK Model, engraved.

The basic function of the double action as provided by Walther was to allow carrying the pistol with complete safety with a cartridge in the chamber yet ready for instant action. While the thumb safety was provided, it was not necessary to apply it as the arm could only be fired by direct pull on the trigger. Carried in this manner, a long pull on the trigger would fire the first shot, the hammer being cocked by the mechanism for succeeding shots in standard automatic pistol fashion. The varieties of these designs will be found covered fully in chapter 26. It may be stated, however, that the Walther designs were a radical improvement over any of their predecessors. Mauser later introduced its HSC and Sauer and Sohn also introduced double action enclosed hammer models with some interesting features in an endeavor to compete with Walther.

None of these initial pistols were in other than the pocket calibers adaptable for blowback action. Walther next turned their design ability to producing the Walther-Heeres Pistole (Army Pistol) in caliber 9mm Luger or PP 08 to use the German military terminology. A slightly modified form of this double action locked-breech pistol was officially adopted in 1938, the German Government intending to use it to replace the celebrated Luger. As the P-38 it was the basic German sidearm of World War II although it was supplemented, of course, by Lugers, Mausers, and in the final stages by all types of available small arms.

Norway introduced in 1914 a .45 caliber automatic pistol which was merely a minor variation of the familiar Colt and Browning system. The arm was not produced in quantity and has nothing original about it worthy of notice here.

World War I type 9mm blowback.

Hammerless version of the P-38. Very few made. Locked breech.

Remarkable late World War II stamped pistol intended for ultra-low-cost production. Production did not get under way before war ended.

Unusual Walther Pistols.

Russian Tokarev Pistol, caliber 7.62mm, Russian. Will handle the Mauser 7.63mm cartridges if made to European specifications.

World War II Colt Government Model 1911A1, steel.

In 1930 the Russians introduced their Tokarev automatic pistol. This pistol is credited to their designer Tokarev. It resembles quite closely in most external lines except hammer the familiar Colt .32 automatic pistol. However, it is unlike it in that it is a fully locked-breech pistol. The locking system is patterned after that of our .45 Automatic Pistol, also a Browning development, of course. Tokarev's contribution to the Browning design was basically a highly simplified form of manufacture and a compact firing mechanism. While the arm itself is crude in appearance and does not have the balance nor the pointing qualities of the American product, it is cheap to manufacture and completely reliable as a military design. It is chambered for the 7.62mm Russian cartridge which is a bottlenecked rimless cartridge practically identical with the 7.63mm Mauser cartridge. One interesting note on this caliber is that the cartridges as made in Europe for the 7.63mm Mauser may be efficiently used in this pistol, as may those of American manufacture where the cartridge specifications were obtained from European sources. Some varieties of American ammunition, where the specifications were taken from cartridges themselves rather than obtained directly from European manufacturers, will not chamber efficiently in this design. This, of course, is due to minor differences in tolerance only. The cartridge is the one used also in the Russian submachine gun.

Military Use of Pistols During World War II

Statistics compiled by American military authorities during the course of the war indicate that the actual casualties inflicted upon enemies with the automatic pistol were so few as to render the combat value of the arm questionable. This is, and will continue to be, a subject for military discussion for years to come. The psychological value of the pistol to many military personnel is unquestionable, though its efficiency or its usage in general combat would hardly seem to warrant the expenditure of great sums of money in attempting to further develop the arm.

The standard sidearm of the American Forces using a pistol during World War II was, of course, the familiar .45 Colt Government Model. (Officially this is the United States Government Model 1911 or M1911A1, these arms having been made in various plants besides Colt's on government contract. Ithaca, Remington Rand, and Union Switch & Signal all did some production.)

The British used substantial quantities of 9mm Browning High Power auto pistols, most of which were manufactured in Canada by the firm of John Ingles. These pistols proved of considerable value in Commando tactics since they had a large magazine capacity (13 shots as against 7 in the Colt .45) and since they used the same ammunition as the Sten and other submachine guns which were the basic weapons of the British specialists. Since these pistols were used by the highly trained troops of an "elite guard" nature, their efficiency and effectiveness, which was considerable, is no gauge of the value of the arm for general troop use.

The German forces at the outset of the war leaned heavily on automatic pistol distribution to officers and noncoms. As war progressed, with particular reference to the campaigns against the Russians, the German military thinking tended to follow that of the Russian, i.e., to issue submachine guns (Machinen Pistoles) to special service troops and to noncoms in place of pistols.

The Russians early came to the conclusion that in the hands of their troops offensive arms of the nature of submachine guns were cheaper to make and far more deadly than the familiar pistol. They, therefore, tended to minimize the issuance of the one-hand gun in any form.

Japanese use of the pistol was confined largely to officers. Their Nambus with their relatively inefficient cartridges were not in very wide usage at any time. The widespread issuance of American revolvers to Japanese quasi-military forces may later affect their thinking with reference to pistol issuance for military purposes. Their past experience has tended to minimize both revolver and pistol usage, however.

The Italians issued very large quantities of varying forms of Beretta and lesser known automatic pistols, mostly in .32 and .38 caliber, with of course available supplies of the earlier 9mm calibers such as the Glisenti. The fighting record of the Italian forces, of course, gives no index to the actual value of the pistol as a modern weapon of war any more than does the experience of the French forces. Certainly a study of casualty statistics of forces opposed to these units would not indicate that in their hands the automatic pistol was a particularly efficient arm. Its most noted use occurred during the Italian attack on Ethiopia when official films showed Italian officers using pistols to execute natives, the natives being held by Italian troops while the pistols were presented against their heads for firing. This hardly constitutes combat use.

All later reports from the Korean and Indo-China theaters of activity indicated a concentration by Communist-controlled Chinese and Vietnam troops on submachine guns, usually of Russian pattern. Pistols as

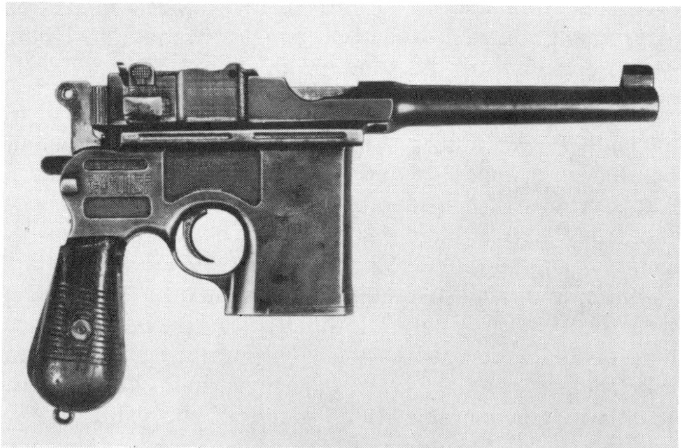

Chinese made Mauser Military Pattern, Cal. .45 A. C. P. Except for caliber (the Germans made these in production only in calibers 7.63mm and 9mm Mauser and in 9mm Luger) the Chinese version follows the German design very closely.

This is the only commercially successful semi-auto pistol to use any magazine style except the butt type. Here the magazine is positioned forward of the trigger.

a class have been relegated to use by officers and were not normally encountered when engaging regular troops. Guerrilla use, of course, inevitably produces large quantities of pistols because of the possibility of secreting them on the person. On the other hand, among our own troops on Asiatic duty, there has been a persistent demand particularly for revolvers, but the influencing factors appear to be psychological rather than directly military.

Post-War Developments in Automatic Pistols

In the United States since the close of the war, Colt has produced a variation of the familiar government Model 1911 .45 caliber pistol using aluminum slide and receiver to reduce weight. The hammer form has been changed to conform with that of the typical H.P. Browning pattern. Other changes have been inconsequential. The basic design has not been altered or appreciably improved.

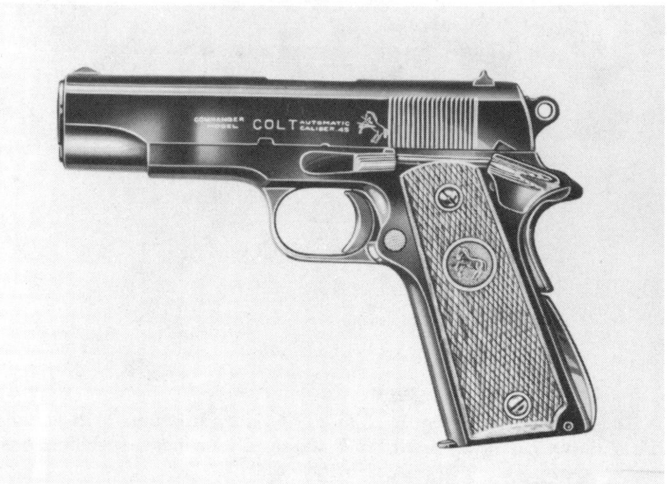

Post-World War II "Commander" Model, Colt .45, aluminum frame. Weight reduced to 26.5 ounces. Barrel shortened one inch. Hammer modified.

Smith & Wesson are in small scale production at this time of an automatic pistol currently designed to handle the 9mm Luger pattern cartridges. This pistol is basically only a modification of the familiar Browning 9mm High Power, whose locking system it utilizes. The locking lug with cam nose on the barrel affords, at least theoretically, better barrel stability when firing than does the familiar link type found in the Colt pattern, but technical matters such as these are of interest only to the ultra precision shooters.

Smith & Wesson has adopted and adapted several of the Browning modifications as found in the Belgian and also in the Polish variant of the 9mm Browning High Power, specifically such items as a magazine disconnector which prevents the firing of a round in the chamber if the magazine is withdrawn. Many accidents occur during the course of cleaning automatic pistols when the soldier withdraws the magazine and fails to recall that

Smith and Wesson 9mm auto pistol. This is the new military model with new double action trigger. Barrel 4 1/8 inches. Over all 7¼ inches. Weight with light alloy frame 28 oz.

The new Smith and Wesson 9mm auto pistol. Military model with standard single action trigger. Specimen shown is a factory hand engraved model from initial production. Pistol will be produced in steel frame and also light alloy frame.

there may be a cartridge in the firing chamber. Another adaptation is that of a slide safety device which permits dropping the hammer on a bar which is automatically interposed between the hammer and the firing pin for purposes of safety. Another common source of accidents in military usage of automatic pistols is that encountered when the inexperienced man attempts to lower the hammer while there is a cartridge in the firing chamber and a slipping of the hammer may fire the pistol accidentally.

Smith & Wesson have also made arrangements to produce their new military type pistol with a double action trigger, under which, as in the case of the earlier Walthers and others, a cartridge may safely be carried in the firing chamber without a manual safety being applied and without any springs being compressed. In a critical moment, it is only necessary to pull the trigger without having to cock the hammer (a very clumsy operation with the typical automatic pistol). The pull on the trigger mechanically actuates the hammer to fire the first shot, the slide automatically cocking the hammer for the next shot.

Other developments in automatic pistols in the United States have been confined, as far as production is concerned, to .22 caliber varieties. The Hi-Standard Company at New Haven, Connecticut has introduced a very fine line of improved versions of its earlier .22 target and plinking pistols, though none are of military design. During the war this firm produced a quantity of .380 caliber blowback automatic pistols which were not suitable for military purposes, being much too heavy for the cartridge they employ. They also did experimental production of both blowback and locked-breech pistols for our Navy to use the standard .38 S & W revolver cartridge. These were discontinued when no order materialized. These designs may, however, be introduced at a later date because of the interest among target shooters; though it must again be noted that, because of the variety of loads required by the target shooter plus the fact that the automatic pistol will operate satisfactorily only on a relatively stable type of loading, the development may not be practical commercially. Certainly it will not be militarily.

The postwar Sturm-Ruger organization developed and produced in considerable quantity a very popular, low-priced automatic pistol in .22 caliber, the external lines resembling very closely those of the familiar Luger. This, however, is a straight blowback weapon intended for plinking and in some models for target use. The design is ingenious, the low price being made possible by the utilization of stampings, screw machine parts, and furnace brazing techniques. Except as a military trainer, of course, this type of weapon is not of military application, though Ruger's manufacturing methods could be applied to low-cost military designs without loss of reliability.

Several small independent organizations are currently engaged in the development of automatic pistols in the United States. Almost without exception these are of the blowback type intended for small caliber target or low-powered pocket pistol cartridges, the relatively large imports of arms of this sort from abroad having demonstrated the continuing market for them in the United States. These again are of only correlative military interest, being arms which would be usable only in an emergency. They require no particular attention here.

Postwar Automatic Pistol Developments Abroad

In Switzerland, the Societe Industrielle Suiesse Neuhausen introduced in 1944 their new model pistol based on the Colt-Browning design in accordance with the Charles Petter patent modifications. The French model 1935A automatic pistol which we have mentioned was the first pistol designed by this inventor. The Swiss firm introduced their pistol to handle the familiar 9mm Parabellum (Luger) cartridge. The barrel locking system while still on the familiar Browning pattern utilizes a modified version of the Browning high power 1935 lock. This pistol and its modifications will be found described in chapter 41. The pistol was introduced in two modifications, the SP44/8 and the SP44/16. They differ only insofar as grip and stock modifications required in relation to magazine capacity, the 8 being a straight-line single column magazine holding 8 cartridges, the other being a double line staggered box holding 16 cartridges. Very few of the Model SP44/16 were made. An interesting feature of the Petter design is a hammer assembly which is a modification of the Russian Tokarev incorporating hammer, mainspring, sear, and disconnector assembly in a single unit easily removed from the frame or receiver. Switzerland adopted the 8-round version.

Since the barrel is a floating unit easily removed from the slide and receiver assemblies without tools, as in the case of the Colt .45 and the High Power Browning designs, the Swiss have taken advantage of this feature to furnish the pistol in calibers 7.65mm and 9mm Parabellum. Only a different barrel and recoil spring are needed with the basic mechanism to change the caliber from 9mm to 7.65mm.

This changeover is possible because of the original cartridge design developed by George Luger in Germany at the turn of the century. His original cartridge was a bottleneck 7.65mm which as we have pointed out in discussing German production was later altered when the German high command demanded a pistol of large caliber. Removing the bottleneck in the case and providing a bullet of 9mm caliber to replace the 7.65mm effected the change. Thus, the only difference in the two barrels is in the forward end of the chamber and in the barrel bore and rifling. In the Luger design the barrel is screwed into the barrel extension and requires tools for removal. It is, therefore, basically a gunsmith's job to change one caliber to another, although only barrel removal and possible recoil spring adjustment is needed to accomplish this since all other parts including the magazines are interchangeable.

In this new Swiss pistol, however, any amateur can take the pistol apart and replace the 9mm barrel and recoil spring with a 7.65mm barrel and recoil spring to convert the arm. The Swiss Army prior to the official adoption of this pistol was equipped with the 7.65mm Luger pistol in the 06-29 variations, which are minor modifications of Luger's original design. The new Swiss Service pistol, by featuring interchangeable barrels and calibers, permits use of ammunition stocks on hand while awaiting complete changeover to the 9mm caliber.

As an added, but not particularly practical group of accessories, this Swiss pistol can also be furnished with special recoil spring, barrel, magazine, and slide to convert the frame to a .22 caliber pistol for practice work. Theoretically, this is an excellent arrangement. In actual practice, the cost and the difficulty, slight though it is, of the interchange have never permitted this type of element to achieve financial success in the United States.

As evidencing the liaison between Switzerland and Denmark, it is interesting to note that the SP47/8 has been adopted as the official Danish service pistol, also in 9mm caliber.

The Czech national arms factory in 1946 produced under the designation CZ a modification of their wartime pistol. It is a double action operated weapon in which the hammer is cocked and dropped by mechanical pull through on the trigger, the slide serving only to eject the empty and reload from the magazine. Unlike the Walther type of double action, it must be kept in mind that this Czech design is mechanically actuated at all times, which means that the trigger pull is uniformly bad. The Czech military consider pistols basically defensive weapons only for the closest use and the safety factor inherent in a weapon where the springs are compressed only during the firing cycle, and where a long heavy pull is needed to fire the chamber cartridge, is actually considered an asset. The caliber has been increased to 9mm Parabellum from the previous less powerful .380 cartridge. Where the previous form except for experimental models was blowback operated, the CZ47 is short recoil, still another variation of the familiar Colt-Browning lock, though again the actuation is caused by a barrel lug rather than a swinging link. This weapon is not in common use in Czechoslovakia.

The German Walther PP and PPK designs are being manufactured in small quantity under license by a Turkish factory for government use. These same designs, also from the blueprints and working drawings of the Walther organization, are being used in the manufacture of .22, .32, and .380 caliber pistols identical with the Walther PP and PPK models. These were manufactured in France under Walther license and are now being manufactured in West Germany.

In Spain, Astra pocket pistols are being produced in calibers .22, .25, .380, and 9mm. These are all blowback weapons of elementary design but excellent manufacture. The Model 600 using the powerful 9mm Luger cartridge is equipped with special recoil springs to stand the shock of this very heavy load which in other pistols of lesser weight utilizes locked-breech designs. These designs are refinements only of earlier blowbacks, however.

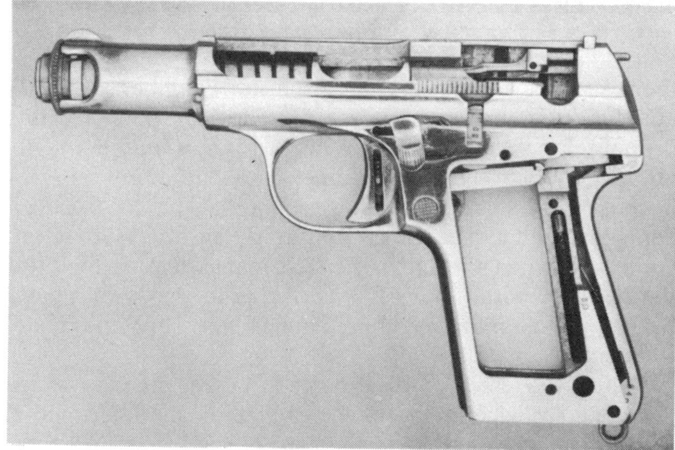

Representative post-war Spanish Astra pistol cutaway to show mechanism closed, hammer down.

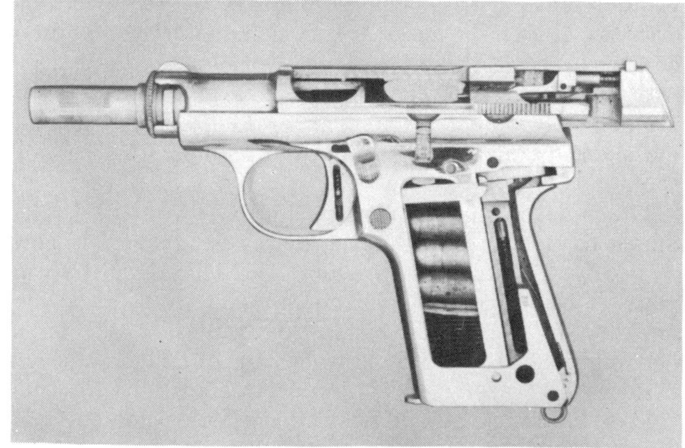

Astra cutaway open. Magazine partly loaded to show feed system.

Also from Spain are coming considerable quantities of elementary blowback pistols in calibers .22, .25, .32, and .380, under the Llama trademark. These for the most part are minor modifications of the Colt-Browning systems.

Echeverria of Eibar in Spain is marketing under their trade name (Star) a wide variety of pistols which are basically modifications of the Colt pattern. These include blowback arms in the .25, .32, and .380 caliber classifications in pocket types, plinking, and target pistols, which are basically the same design but with elongated barrels and locked-breech modifications of the Colt-Browning system in calibers 9mm, .38 Colt Automatic, and .45 Automatic.

Czechoslovakia is exporting elementary blowback pistols in .25 caliber in small vest pocket designs, as well as double action models in .32 caliber, all being blowback design, of course.

A wide range of pocket pistols in calibers .25, .22, and .380 are also being produced and exported from Italy. These include the Bernadelli, the Galesi, and a wide line of Berettas. None of these are in any true sense military pattern arms. None have any essential improvements likely to influence design in any particular way; and currently, at least, none are in competition in the United States because these calibers are not as yet being manufactured here in automatic pistols.

Post-war Italian Bernadelli .25 (6.35mm) auto. Arms such as these are used at times by European staff officers.

Post-war Italian Bernadelli .32 (7.65mm). A representative modern blowback auto. Derived generally from an earlier German Walther pattern, the mechanism has been modified in the U. S. A. for production of a low-priced .22 pistol.

In France the Manufacture d' Armes Bayonne is producing a formal pattern blowback automatic in calibers .22, .32, and .380 principally for export.

Also in France the Manufacture d' Armes Hendaye are producing good blowback pistols in calibers .22, .32, and similar pocket designs. These pistols, as well as some of the Spanish Astra and Star patterns, have been sold to German police agencies. None of them, however, including this French line which is trademarked Unique, have any military features or design features of any importance from an American developmental standpoint. They are elementary patterns of blowback weapons.

Special Features of the Automatic Pistol

As we have previously mentioned, the automatic pistol is actually misnamed. It is truly an automatic loading pistol. Since a truly automatic weapon requires a minimum weight of about 8 pounds to permit holding it down during full automatic fire, and since a pistol for personal use cannot be permitted to go much beyond 40 ounces in weight and should preferably be very considerably below that, it is obvious that pistol design must incorporate a device which will allow only one shot to be fired for each individual pull of the trigger.

However, the name "automatic pistol" has come to be generic. In discussing it herein, therefore, we have adhered to that terminology.

The automatic pistol has several advantages over the revolver from a military standpoint, though for sheer dependability and for close quarters defense for all but truly military use, the revolver is unquestionably superior.

The design of the typical automatic pistol in which the magazine is housed in the grip permits a very much larger ammunition supply to be carried in the weapon than does any revolver. The standard number is 7 or 8, but staggered box designs such as the Browning High Power hold 13 cartridges and the Swiss SP44/16 held 16 cartridges. For military pattern cartridges of 9mm or larger, the single line box with 8 cartridges is accepted as the optimum, however. Because a supply of loaded magazines can be carried, the arm can be reloaded so much more rapidly than a revolver that it can pour out a tremendously higher volume of fire than the revolver after the first loading has been exhausted.

It is a much more compact sidearm, caliber for caliber, than the comparable revolver. Since the arm in most designs is cocked by action of the slide during recoil, it can place a larger number of aimed shots in a given period than can the comparable revolver.

It is true that a revolver expert may occasionally fire six shots as fast as from an automatic. But because of the revolver disadvantage of long trigger pull to achieve this rapidity of fire, accuracy suffers correspondingly except at close quarters. Since the cartridge chamber is part of the barrel itself in an automatic pistol, this type of arm is not subject to bullet shaving and gas wastage as occurs in the revolver where the bullet must jump the gap from the chamber in the cylinder to the barrel. In addition, a properly designed automatic pistol is far simpler for the amateur to dismount, maintain, and assemble than any comparable revolver.

For military purposes, even at close quarters where a sustained volume of rapid fire is desirable, the superiority of the automatic pistol cannot be questioned. For all other practical military and police use, however, the additional reliability of the revolver seems more desirable. The automatic pistol when loaded and carried for service use has many springs constantly under compression, the magazine spring at all times, and the hammer and main springs when the arm is carried cocked. The susceptibility to mechanical failure is therefore necessarily higher in the automatic pistol than in the revolver.

However, in all arms as in all things mechanical, there is no all-purpose item. The needs and requirements of the individual services under individual conditions must inevitably lead to compromise. This factor explains and justifies U.S. purchases of light-weight revolvers, for example.

Possible Future Advances in Military Automatic Pistol Design

Like the revolver, the automatic pistol would appear to have approached the zenith of its design. Further important developments must depend entirely upon advances in ammunition or metallurgical technology.

In face of the world efforts toward standardization of armaments in non-Communist countries, and in the face of the ballistic background of the 9mm Luger cartridge both for the pistol and submachine gun use, there is great likelihood that this cartridge in the future will be the basis for most military design.

On the other hand, the tremendous United States investment in both weapons themselves and manufacturing tools for both .45 caliber automatic pistols and ammunition, has limited the rapid changeover.

Even before the war, Walther experimented extensively with aluminum frames for their PP and PPK designs in automatic pistols. Sauer did likewise. One of the postwar developments now underway with Smith & Wesson at Springfield is the production of their new 9mm automatic pistols in both single and double action, made with aluminum frames as alternates for the steel construction. Further advances may be expected in relation to the materials used in automatic pistols with a view to reducing weight or increasing tensile strengths. However, the requirements in the way of weight because of inertia factors, which are a necessary part of any automatic pistol design, must obviously control the minimum weights of the arms with relation to the power of the ammunition used. For all practical purposes blowback pistols must continue to be confined to cartridges with relatively little power. All conceivable forms of springs to compensate for lack of the necessary weight factor in moving breechblocks have been experimented with from the earliest days of the development of this type of weapon.

The long recoil system for pistols has been invalidated by experience. It is and must continue to be unnecessarily complicated for use in a weapon intended to be fired from one hand. Gas operation in all its forms can be truly successful only with weapons involving considerable weight, hence it is ruled out. The types of mechanisms required for its proper functioning are not applicable to lightweight compact pistol design.

Hesitation, or delaying the blowback, involves the utilization of mechanical factors calling for considerably more cost, skill, and technical engineering than is advisable in a pocket or one-hand type arm.

The short-recoil system, therefore, is likely to remain the most practical for relatively high-power automatic cartridge pistols.

Potentialities do exist in connection with the principle of primer projection for unlocking, and for utilization of some of the fields of applied inertia through utilization of permanent magnets. However, for all practical purposes, no major developments are to be expected in the field of automatic pistol mechanisms unless and until a new form of ignition is evolved.

Automatic pistols are normally arms to be used within a distance of 30 feet. In the hands of the target shooter and the expert, given optimum conditions, the pistol is an extremely dangerous weapon at 50 to 75 yards. There are very occasional shooters who can use this one-hand weapon effectively at ranges of 100 yards and even more. But for all practical purposes, the limitations set up by the requirements for light weight and compact form, taken together with the inability of the average shooter to effectively handle an arm with too heavy recoil, plus the sighting deficiencies inherent in a short arm with a minimum distance between sights, all conspire to hold practical pistol development within its present confines.

Of the practical limitations involved in one-hand gun design, it might be pointed out that during World War II the firm of Smith & Wesson conceived the idea of producing a revolver which would use the half-moon clip design they originally developed during World War I for the .45 automatic pistol cartridge, but which would actually chamber the .30 M1 Carbine cartridge. The general theory was that such a revolver issued to paratroopers armed with carbines would give them an additional close-quarters weapon with all the value of interchangeability of ammunition.

When these .30 M1 revolvers were tested by average personnel, it very soon developed that the shock of firing the arm more than offset any possible logistical gain in ammunition supply. Although the carbine cartridge was designed to have its best results by having the powder burned in an 18-inch barrel, the resulting ballistics were generally inferior to those of standard hand gun cartridges.

It is quite possible with improved metals to produce a Smith & Wesson revolver of relatively light weight to take even their ultra powerful .357 magnum cartridge. However, the shock of successive firing of this cartridge in a lightweight weapon not only destroys accuracy but actually hampers the use of the revolver by all but the most expert shooters.

There will, of course, continue to be modifications in practically all the accepted designs, but the basic physical facts involved in automatic pistol design preclude the possibility of any startling mechanical developments in weapons of this type.

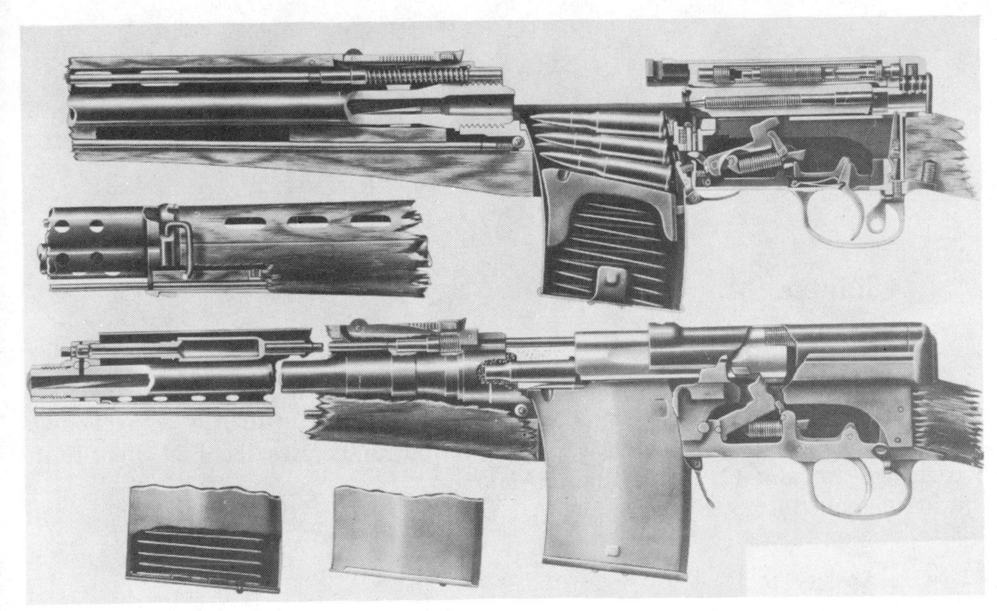

PART II

CURRENT WEAPONS

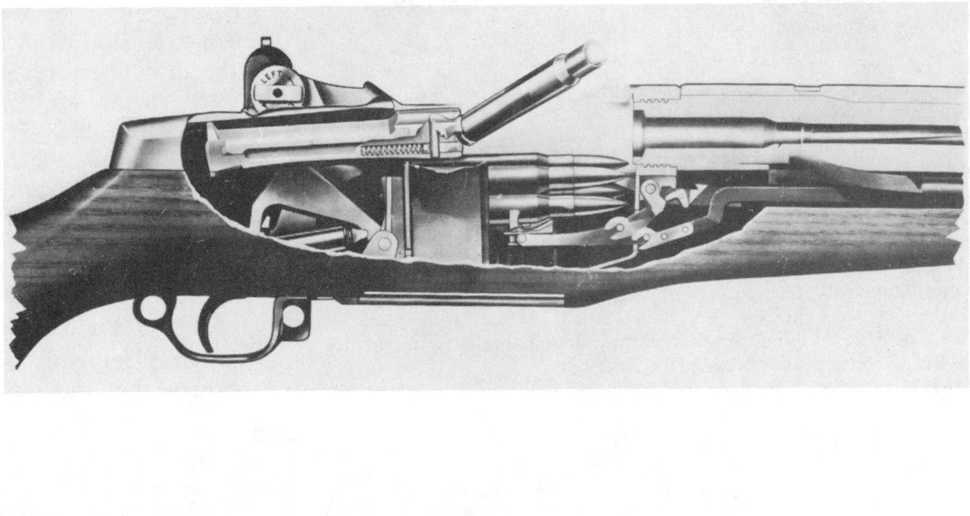

Chapter 14. Argentina

THE principal military rifle of Argentina was the 7.65mm Mauser. The original rifle is the Argentine Model of 1891. Later Mauser rifles of both Belgian and German manufacture for the 7.92mm cartridge are also encountered, however, while some Argentine manufacture is also in use.

Arms plants are in production on a wide variety of arms in Argentina today. F.N. rifles, submachine guns of blow-back design and automatic pistols of the Colt system are produced.

With the assistance of German technicians who emigrated from Europe after World War II, enough pilot production has been developed, not only in relation to small arms but also to elements such as 81mm trench mortars and even 37mm antiaircraft guns, that there is little question but that the coming years will find the development of quite efficient arms factories in Argentina.

Pig iron is being produced by an Argentine plant at Zapala near the Andes while steel is being produced at a new plant at Balentine Alsina.

The Argentine Army uses some United States types of weapons; it also uses many weapons of European origin and some weapons of native design and manufacture. Some of these weapons have appeared on the shelves of American gun dealers recently; therefore, they are being given more coverage in this edition than was given them previously. Argentina currently uses the F.N. light automatic rifle (FAL).

Caliber .45 Ballester Molina Pistol.

Caliber: .45 M1911 automatic pistol cartridge.
System of operation: Recoil, semi-automatic fire only.
Weight, empty: 2.25 lb.
Length, overall: 8.5 in.
Barrel length: 5 in.
Feed device: 7-round, single-column, detachable box magazine.
Sights: Front, Blade; Rear, Notched bar.
Muzzle velocity: 830 f.p.s.

ARGENTINE PISTOLS

Argentina manufactures several pistol types. The cal. .45 Ballester Molina and the Ballester Rigaud are manufactured by HAFDASA of Buenos Aires. A cal. .22 pistol similar to the Colt "Ace" has also been manufactured by this firm, as well as several submachine guns. The Argentine government arsenal has also manufactured the Ballester Molina pistol.

The Ballester Molina is basically a slightly modified Colt cal. .45 M1911A1 pistol. Its loading, firing, and functioning are the same as those of the United States pistol.

Major Differences Between the Ballester Molina and the Colt M1911A1

Hammer strut: The hammer strut is much smaller than that of the U. S. M1911A1. It is 0.75 inches in length and 0.158 inches in diameter.

Firing pin stop: The firing pin stop is not recessed on the sides, as it is on the U. S. models.

Safety lock: The safety lock is redesigned and the pin is larger in diameter than the safety lock pin on the U. S. model.

Mainspring housing: The mainspring housing, although arched as in the U. S. Model M1911A1, is an integral part of the receiver.

Trigger: The Argentine pistol has a pivoting trigger. An extension from the trigger, along the right side, cams the disconnector and engages the sear.

Magazine and magazine catch: The magazines are interchangeable. The magazine catch is located in the same place as the catch on the U. S. M1911A1. The assembly of the catch is somewhat different, but it operates in the same manner as the U. S. model.

Slide: There is no slide stop disassembly notch as on the U. S. models.

Field Stripping the Ballester Molina

Disassembly is the same as for the U. S. M1911A1, except that the pin for the hammer and the sear must be driven out. The trigger is held by a trigger pin. Upon removing the trigger and the trigger extension, the disconnector can be removed downward. After the sear has been removed, the main spring can be removed.

ARGENTINE RIFLES

The Argentine government has been selling some of its older Mauser rifles lately, and quantities of these weapons have come to the United States. The two weapons on sale in the United States at present are the 7.65mm M1891 and the 7.65mm M1909 Mauser rifles. Both of these weapons were manufactured in quantity in Germany for Argentina.

The M1891 Argentine Mauser is quite similar to the 7.65mm M1890 Turkish Mauser. The M1909 Mauser is a slight modification of the German Gewehr 98 (rifle 98).

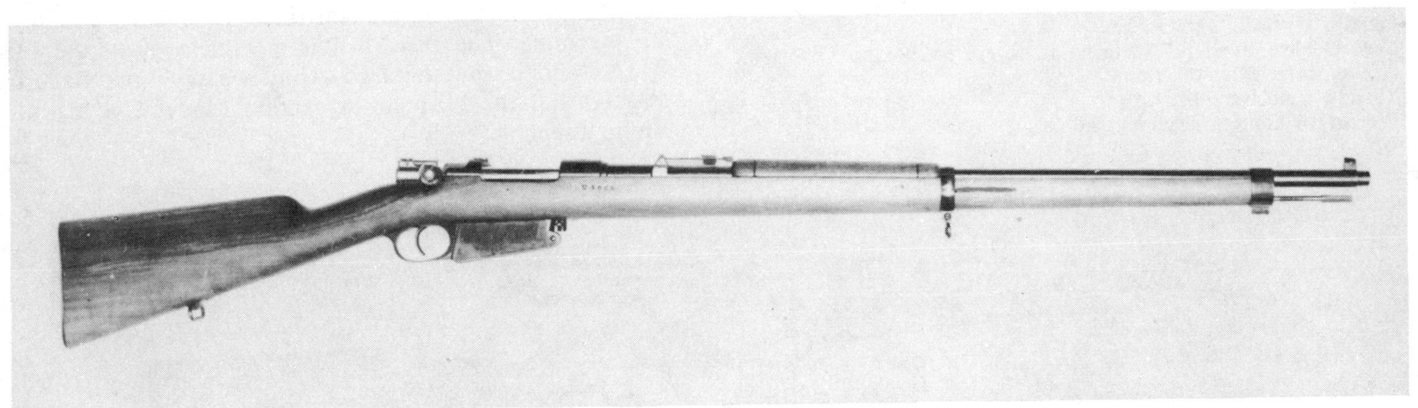

7.65mm Model 1891 Argentine Mauser.

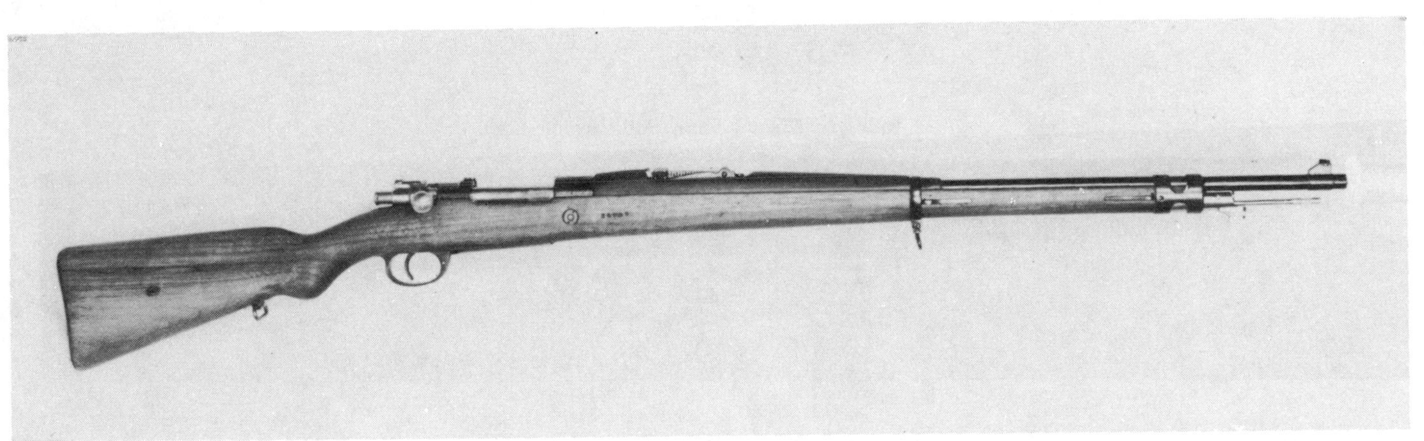

7.65mm Model 1909 Argentine Mauser.

	M1891	M1909
Caliber:	7.65mm rimless	7.65mm rimless
System of operation:	Manually operated bolt action	Manually operated bolt action
Length, overall:	48.6 in.	49 in.
Barrel length:	29.1 in.	29.1 in.
Feed device:	5-round, single column box magazine	5-round, staggered-row box magazine
Sights: Front	Barleycorn	Barleycorn
Rear	Leaf	Tangent leaf
Muzzle velocity: (w/spitzer-pointed ball)	2755 f.p.s.	2755 f.p.s.
Weight (empty):	8.58 lb.	9.2 lb.

ARGENTINE SUBMACHINE GUNS

Several submachine guns have been designed and produced in Argentina. Among these are the Ballester Molina caliber .45 Type C3 and the Halcon caliber .45 M1946. Both are blowback operated, selective fire type weapons. Major characteristics are as follows:

Ballestar Molina Type C3

Caliber: .45.
Length, Overall: 33.2 inches.
Feed Device: 40 round—detachable, staggered, box type magazine.
Cyclic Rate: 500-600 r.p.m.
Muzzle Velocity: 900 f.p.s.
Weight (without magazine): 8.6 lb.

Halcon M1946

Caliber: .45.
Length, Overall: Stock folded—24.4 inches. Stock extended—31.1 inches.
Feed Device: 17 round and 30 round.
Cyclic Rate: 700 r.p.m.
Muzzle Velocity: 900 f.p.s.
Weight (without magazine): 8.9 lb.

The Halcon comes in a fixed wooden stock version called M1943 as well as a folding metal stock version. In addition, a number of submachine guns chambered for the 9mm Parabellum cartridge have been produced in Argentina. The P.A.M. 1 is a 9mm copy of the U.S. M3A1 and is the standard Army weapon; the Ballester Rigaud and the Hispano Argentina Model C-4 are also 9mm weapons.

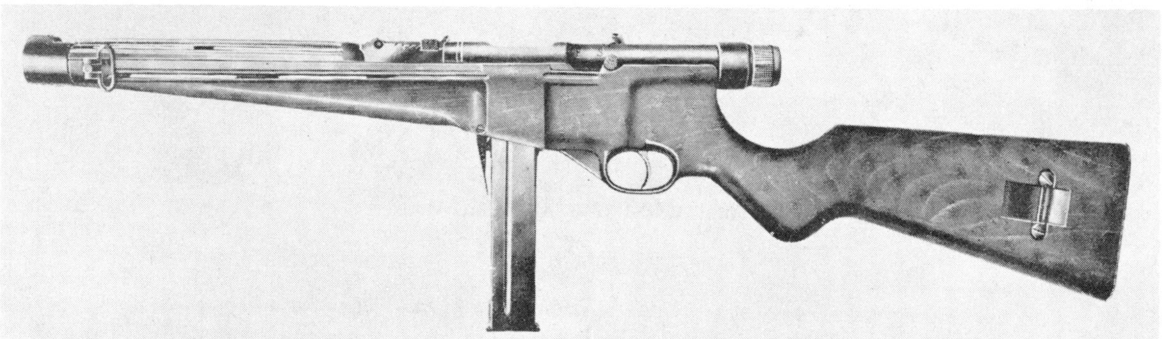

Ballester Rigaud 9mm Submachine Gun.

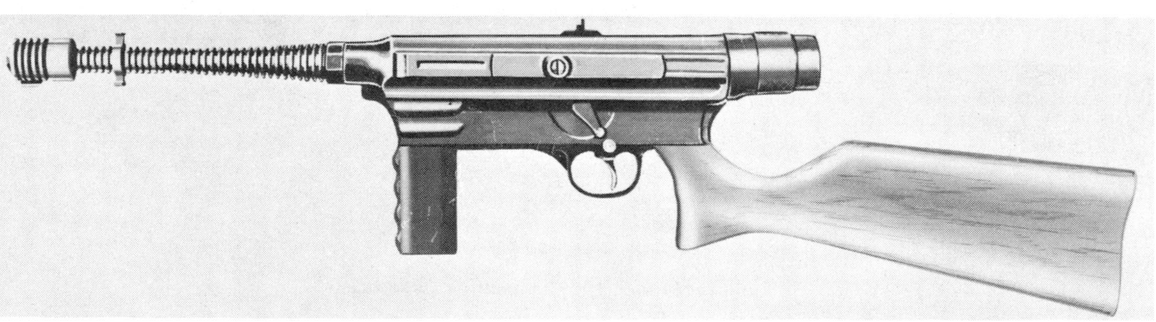

Halcon .45 Submachine Gun M1943 with wooden stock.

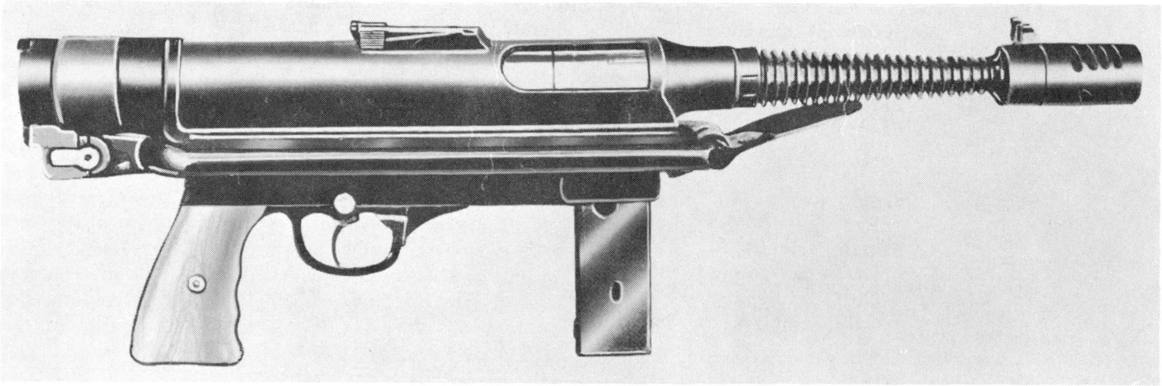

Halcon .45 Submachine Gun M1946 with folding stock.

Chapter 15. Austria

AS a neutral state in the Cold War, Austria has picked a middle ground in the matter of small arms for her small army. The Austrians were given some United States weapons, some Soviet weapons, and some British weapons. They have also ordered some FN NATO light rifles. Although commercial rifles are now being produced in Austria again, at Ferlach and Steyr, no native military small arms designs of post-World War II origin have appeared. Austria is now using the 7.62mm MG42 (MG 42/59) machine gun.

AUSTRIAN PISTOLS

These are elementary blowback pistols. Recoil spring is housed in special bore above barrel. Pushing down a lever on left side of receiver tips barrel muzzle down, disconnecting it from breechblock. Chamber may be loaded directly. Breechblock may be drawn back without effort, since it does not have to draw recoil spring with it. Snapping barrel back into place and inserting a loaded magazine in the handle leaves the pistol ready for use. Magazine is standard detachable box.

Identification. Tip down barrel. Breechblock mounted in receiver. Thumb safety to rear of left stock.

Ammunition. These and all other standard late model Austrian pocket pistols are customarily caliber 6.35mm or 7.65mm Browning. The 6.35mm will use the U. S. .25 Colt Auto cartridge. The 7.65mm will use the U. S. .32 Colt Auto cartridge.

Evaluation. Good materials and workmanship. Unusual loading feature permits ease of chamber loading along lines advocated by Smith & Wesson in their original auto pistols based on Pieper's patents.

From the American viewpoint the good features are outweighed by the lack of an automatic grip safety and by complex machining.

Typical 6.35mm Steyr Auto Pistol. Length 4.5". Barrel 2". Weight 15.5 ounces. Magazine capacity 6.

Typical 7.65mm Steyr Auto Pistol. Length 6.5". Barrel 3.5". Weight 23 ounces. Magazine capacity 8.

Steyr Pieper Pistols.

Austrian Roth-Steyr 8mm Pistol M1907.

Caliber: 8mm, special metal jacketed bullet.
Magazine: In handle of pistol. Cartridges stripped in from top.
Capacity: 10 cartridges.
Muzzle Velocity: About 1090 feet per. second.
Weight of Bullet: 116 grain.
Barrel Length: 5⅛ inches.
Overall Length: 9⅛ inches.
Weight: About 34 ounces.
Sights: Fixed.
Accurate Range: 50 yards.
Maximum Range: About 1500 yards.
Pistol Operated by: Recoil.
Locked: By recoiling, revolving barrel.
Magazine Loading Arrangement: Clip guide on top of slide. Special loading clip is inserted in the guides.
Position of Slide When Last Shot is Fired: Open.
Slide Release: On left hand side plate above grip.
Note: The striker on this pistol is cocked and tripped by pulling the trigger.

Instructions for Loading and Firing

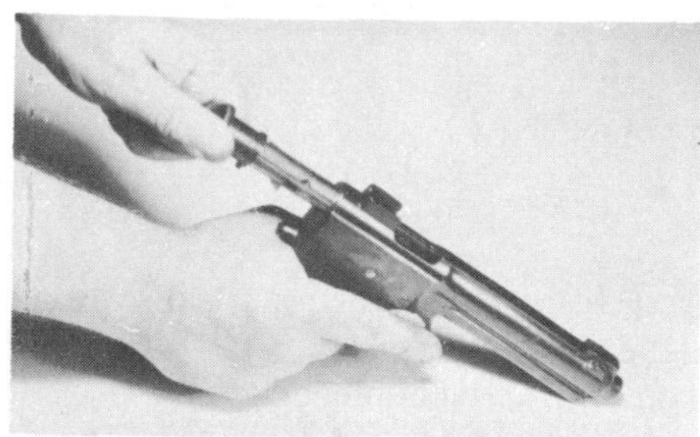

Draw back bolt as far as it will go. Magazine follower will hold it open.

Insert special clip in the clip guides. Press down on feeding slide which will force the cartridges into the magazine.

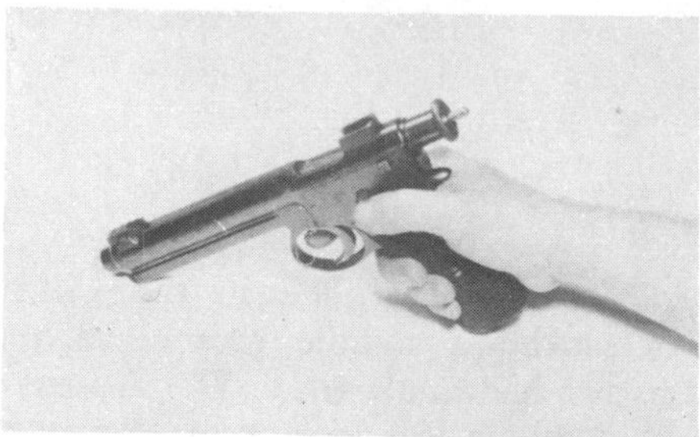

Withdraw clip and let bolt go forward.

Special Feature

This weapon was originally designed for use by cavalry. The recoil of the weapon ejects the empty case and strips a new cartridge into the firing chamber as in other automatic pistols. However, it does not cock in the regular fashion. The striker is drawn back and released to fire the cartridge by pulling the trigger, exactly as in hammerless revolvers. This makes the weapon safe to handle but difficult to shoot accurately.

Both pistol and cartridge are generally considered obsolete.

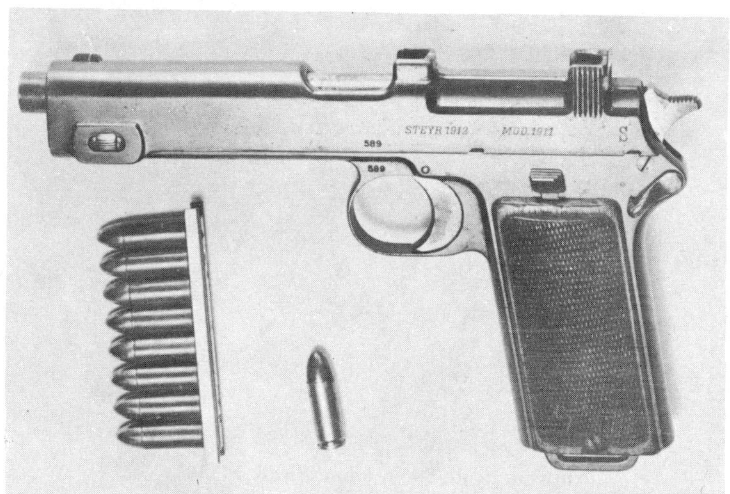

Austrian Steyr 9mm Pistol M12.

This pistol was widely used in Balkans and Austria.

Caliber: 9mm Steyr. Note: This is a **special** 9mm cartridge.
Magazine: Is **not** removable. Located in handle, but cartridges must be stripped into it from the top of the pistol.
Capacity: 8 cartridges.
Muzzle Velocity: 1200 feet per second.
Weight of Bullet: 116 grains.
Muzzle Striking Energy: 370 foot pounds.
Barrel Length: 5".
Overall Length of Pistol: 8½".
Weight of Pistol: 34 ozs.
Sights: Fixed.
Accurate Range: 75 yards.
Maximum Range: About 1800 yards.
Pistol Operated By: Recoil.
Locked: By cam ribs on barrel which lock in cam slots on inside of top of slide. As bullet passes down barrel, barrel tends to twist to the right. As barrel and slide move to the rear under recoil, cam rib twists barrel to the left and opens lock permitting slide to continue backward and function the action.
Type of Fire: Single shot only.
Magazine Loading Arrangement: Clip guide on top of slide permits insertion of loaded clip when action is opened, and slide is locked back with safety.

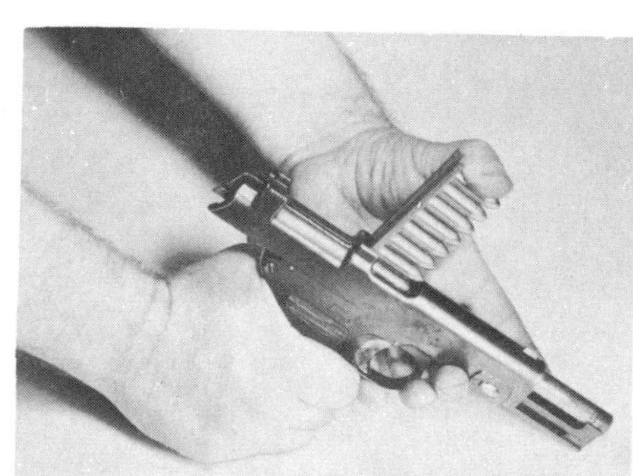

Position of Slide When Last Shot is Fired: Open.
Safeties: (a) A thumb safety somewhat like that on the Colt .45 Automatic will be found on the left side of the pistol just below the hammer. Turning this up into its notch in the slide makes the pistol safe. (b) An automatic disconnector on the right side of the pistol under the slide prevents this pistol from being fired until the action is wholly closed. Note: This pistol resembles the Colt .38 Automatic, and to some extent, the Colt .45 Automatic in **exterior** appearance. However, its locking and loading arrangements are entirely unique.

Note on Ammunition

This cartridge has an overall length of 1.37 inches. Parabellum (or Luger) 9mm type cartridges have an overall length of 1.14 to 1.16 inches. Thus the 9mm Steyr cartridge will not function in weapons designed to handle the Luger type cartridge. The Steyr bullet is lead with an actual steel jacket (not alloy cased), and although this jacket is plated over, these cartridges rust very readily. The range and penetration is exceptionally great. It was very widely used in Austria and in the Balkans. During World War II, it was used to a limited extent and some of these weapons were rebarreled for the 9mm Parabellum cartridge. These are marked 08 on the slide.

Instructions for Loading and Firing

To prepare to load: Grip the milled surfaces at the rear of the slide and pull the slide sharply back to the rear. The magazine follower will keep it open. Pull it still farther back and push the thumb safety up into the locking notch. This is necessary to permit clip loading.

To load magazine: Place a clip of cartridges (they come 8 to a clip) in the clip guides. Press firmly downward on the cartridges and strip them into the magazine.

Pull out the empty clip. A lip on the magazine will retain the cartridges in place.

Press down the thumb safety and the slide will go forward to load the firing chamber. When last shot is fired the magazine follower will act on the magazine lip to hold the slipe open.

Note: This weapon has a unique unloading system. If the slide is held back by the safety catch, pushing down on the release on the left side of the receiver above the stock will permit the magazine spring to force all the cartridges up out of the handle without any manipulation of the slide as in the typical automatic pistol.

Field Stripping

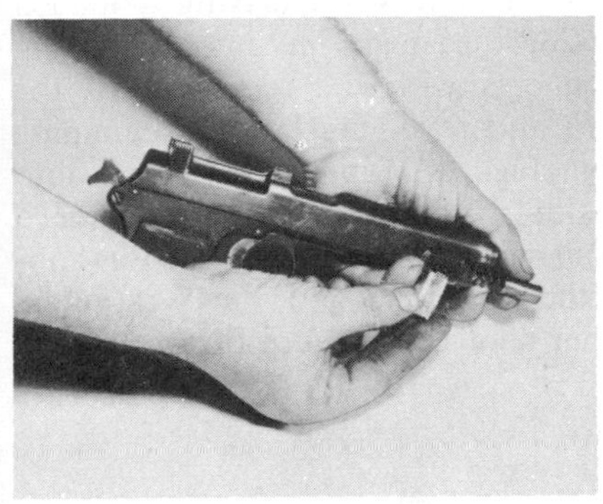

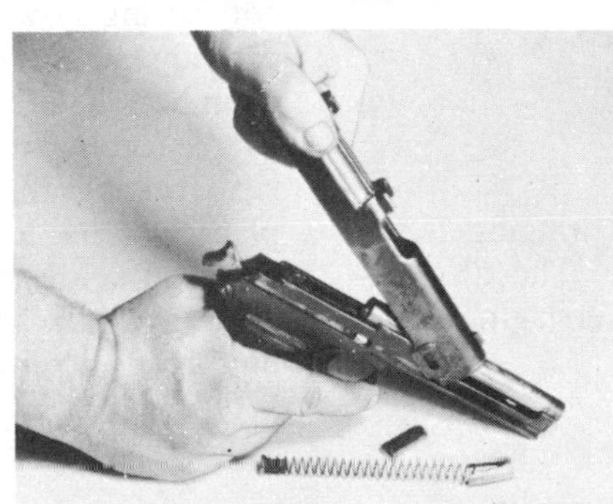

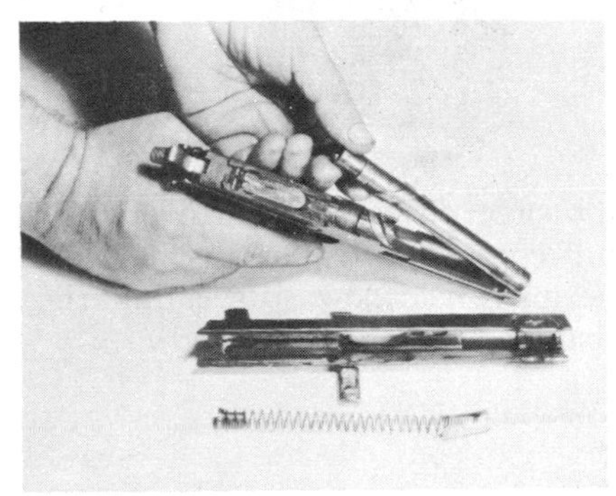

At lower front of slide is a spring locking block. Press together its spring points which protrude on the left side of the pistol, and push through and extract from the right side. Be careful that recoil spring and its housing do not slide from pistol. Ease them out.

Now pull slide back about 2" then raise and draw back and up. It can thus be lifted clear of the receiver. Barrel can now be lifted out.

How the Steyr Automatic Pistol Works

Starting with the pistol loaded and cocked, the action is as follows: The trigger being pressed, the hammer strikes the firing pin, driving it forward to explode the cartridge. The bullet following the rifling down the barrel tends to turn the barrel to the right, locking it securely to the locking slot in the slide. Under the rearward action of the recoil, barrel and slide recoil together a short distance when the barrel is stopped against the barrel stop. The cam surface on the barrel, riding on the cam rib in the receiver, twists the barrel to unlock it from the slide. The slide goes on back carrying the empty cartridge case gripped by the extractor; the empty cartridge case strikes against the ejector and is hurled up and out of the pistol. The magazine spring forces the next cartridge up in line with the bolt. The rear of

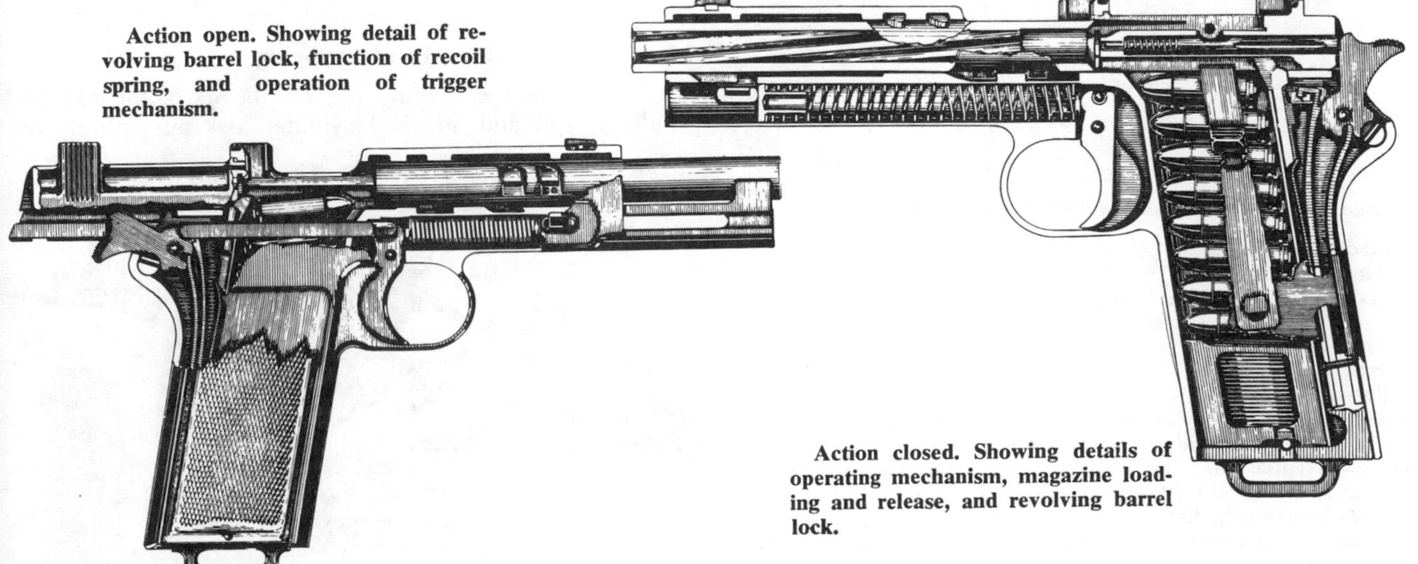

Action open. Showing detail of revolving barrel lock, function of recoil spring, and operation of trigger mechanism.

Action closed. Showing details of operating mechanism, magazine loading and release, and revolving barrel lock.

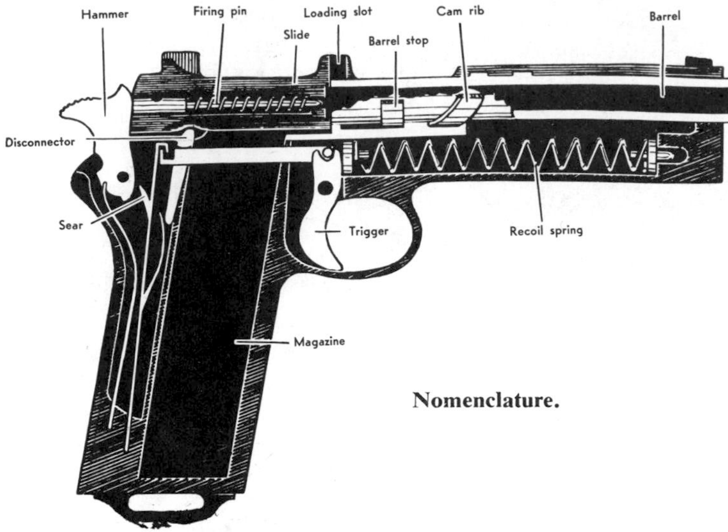

Nomenclature.

the slide pushes up and over the hammer bringing it to full cock. The hammer is held by the sear. The disconnector is held down preventing trigger from engaging with sear and hammer.

During all this action, the recoil spring has been compressed; this compression being brought about by the combination locking piece and recoil spring compressor riding back in a slot under the slide and pressing against the recoil spring housing. The rearward motion is now completed.

Return Movement of the Action: The compressed recoil spring now pulls the slide forward driving a loaded cartridge from the top of the magazine into the firing chamber. The slide connects with the rear face of the barrel forcing it forward and revolving it in its camming rib, twisting the locking lugs on top of the barrel into place in the locking slot in the slide. As the breech closes, the disconnector moves up into its groove connecting the sear and the hammer, and the weapon is now ready to fire another shot by pressure of the trigger.

AUSTRIAN REVOLVERS

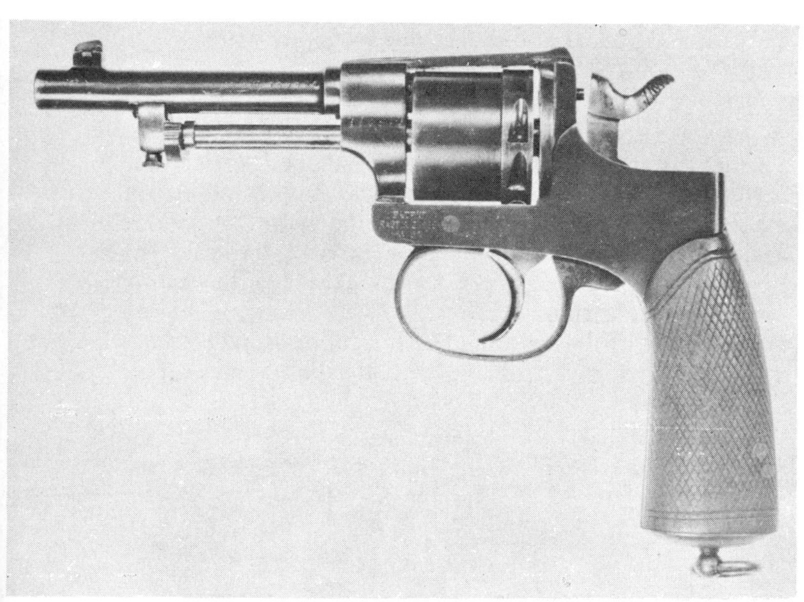

Austrian Rast-Gasser Revolver Cal. 8mm, Model 1898.

Caliber: 8mm.
Cylinder: 8 chambers.
Muzzle Velocity: About 750 feet per second.
Overall Length: 9¼ inches.
Weight: 33 ounces.
Barrel: 4½ inches.
Sights: Fixed.
Accurate Range: 50 yards.
Type of Action: Solid frame; rod ejector.
Double Action: May be fired by thumb cocking and pulling trigger, or by straight pull through on the trigger.
Safety: Rebounding hammer which strikes the firing pin, which is set in the frame, only when the trigger is pulled through its entire length.

Loading and Firing

The loading gate on the right side behind the cylinder is opened and the trigger pulled. The cylinder is then turned to bring a chamber in line with the open gate and a cartridge inserted. This is continued until the cylinder is completely loaded. The gate is then snapped back into place.

Ejecting. The locking lug at the front end of the extractor rod is turned to permit the rod to be drawn backward. The loading gate is then opened and the trigger pulled to turn the cylinder. The rod then pushes up into the chamber to eject the empty cartridge case.

Field Stripping

First open the locking lug on the extractor rod and pull the rod and attached cylinder axis pin entirely out

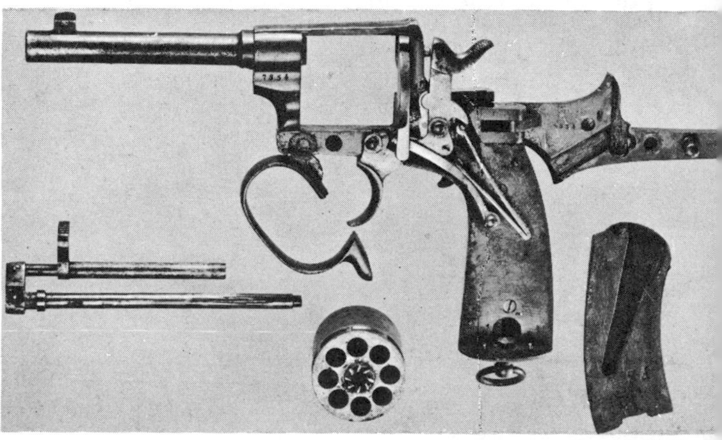

of the frame. The cylinder may now be removed from the frame. The triggerguard is hinged to the frame at its front end. Pull down the triggerguard behind the trigger. Remove the left hand stock. The left hand side plate may now be swung back on its hinge exposing all working parts of the revolver.

Special Note: Other models of this revolver will be encountered with 4½-inch barrel but with a shorter frame, giving an overall length of only 8½ inches. This weapon is obsolete.

AUSTRIAN RIFLES

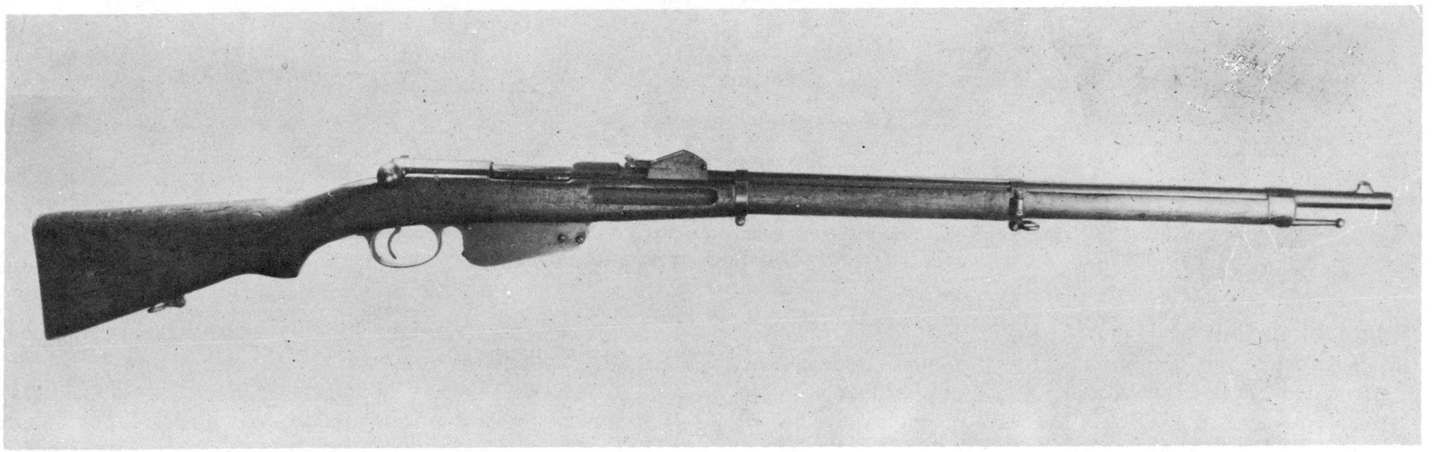

Austrian Model 1888/90 Straight Pull Rifle, Caliber 8mm Austrian Service.

Caliber: 8mm Austrian.
Barrel Length: 30.1".
Overall Length: 50.4".
Weight: About 9 lbs. 11 oz.
Sights: Barleycorn front and quadrant rear.
Operation: Straight pull on bolt handle unlocks and opens action for loading with clip. Straight push loads chamber and locks breech.
Magazine: Mannlicher vertical box, clip loaded. Clip can be inserted only one end up.
Breech Lock: Hinged wedge on underside of bolt forced down into receiver cut when handle is pushed forward.
Bolt Removal: Pull bolt handle back. While pushing trigger forward, draw bolt assembly out of receiver.

AUSTRIAN MODELS 1886, 1888, 1888-90 RIFLES

Mechanically and in overall design these rifles are practically identical. They differ in caliber as described below. These are straight pull actions, but have very little in common with the later M. 95 series except the system of loading and firing.

These types may be immediately identified by pulling back and examining the bolt. THERE ARE NO LOCKING LUGS ON THE FRONT FACE OF THE BOLT. The action is locked by a hinged block which swings down from the underside of the bolt body and is wedged into a recess in the receiver to the rear of the magazine. No part of the bolts in these rifles has any turning motion.

Identification of 1886, 1888, and 1888/90 Series. Straight pull bolt with original locking wedge on underside. Wedge locks into receiver above trigger. Mannlicher clip magazine.

Evaluation: Model 1886. This was the first Mannlicher officially adopted by Austria. It is 11mm (.433) Austrian caliber for black powder ammunition. The M. 1886 was in manufacture less than two years. Large numbers were used in World War II in Austria and the Balkans, but all specimens are about 50 years old. These rifles should be classed as collection pieces. They are not worth the cost of converting. The caliber automatically identifies this rifle.

Model 1888. Same as the 1886 except for caliber. This model introduced the first of the series of 8mm Austrian Service cartridges. The original 1888 cartridge used a charge of 62 grains of black powder with a steel jacketed bullet.

The date and the sights identify this model.

Model 1888-90. This model is mechanically the same as the earlier ones. However, it was designed for the then new smokeless powder, and is a much stronger action because it employed better steels in manufacture. The cartridge is the same as for earlier and later models in exterior dimensions.

The date and the sights identify this model. Rear sight is customarily graduated 600-3000 paces (1 Austrian pace equals 29.53").

Good Features. Simple straight pull action. Rifle cannot be fired until action is closed and locked.

Poor Features. No primary extraction. In all models extraction is difficult except when perfect ammunition is combined with a very good rifle.

Bolt lock is not suited to modern ammunition. The extreme distance between the face of the bolt and the point of locking (to the rear of the magazine well) causes bolt set-back with resultant extreme head space. As the bolt is locked only at one point, undue strains are also induced.

These models use the early Mannlicher loading clip. Unlike later patterns, these early clips can be inserted only one end up. Some M1888/90 rifles have been converted to use 7.92mm rimless ammunition.

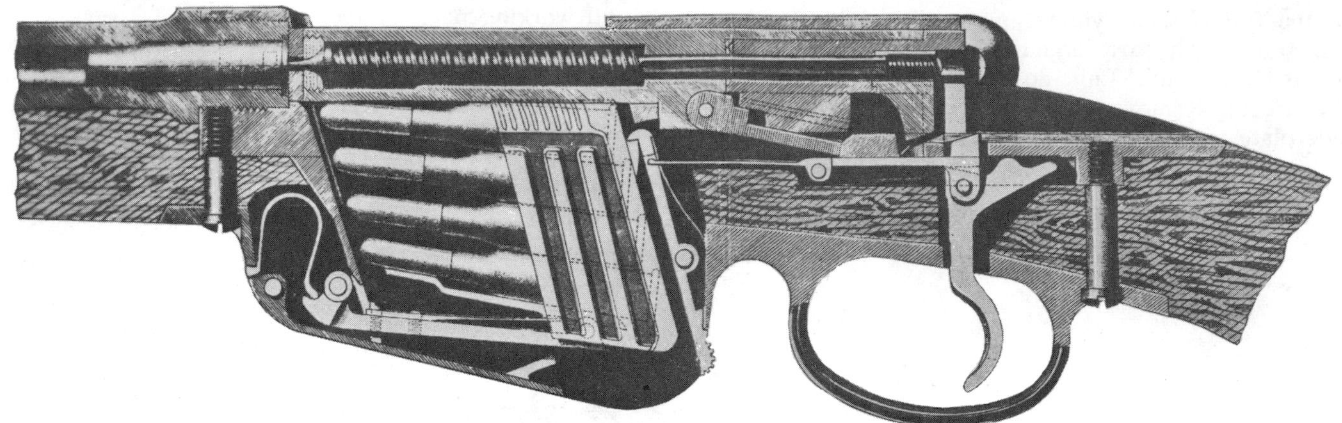

Austrian M. 1888 and 1888-90. Note Engagement of Clip Catch above Clip Projection. Locking Block is Wedged Down into Locking Position in Receiver.

Ammunition. Caliber 11mm Austrian. Not made in U. S.
Caliber 8mm Austrian. The standard ammunition mentioned under the Model 1895 will chamber in both the 1888 and the 88/90. Its use is not advisable in the 1888, and should be used in the 88/90 only when headspace and receiver locking seats have been adequately checked.

Conversion of any of these models to U. S. calibers is too costly and unsatisfactory to warrant recommendation.

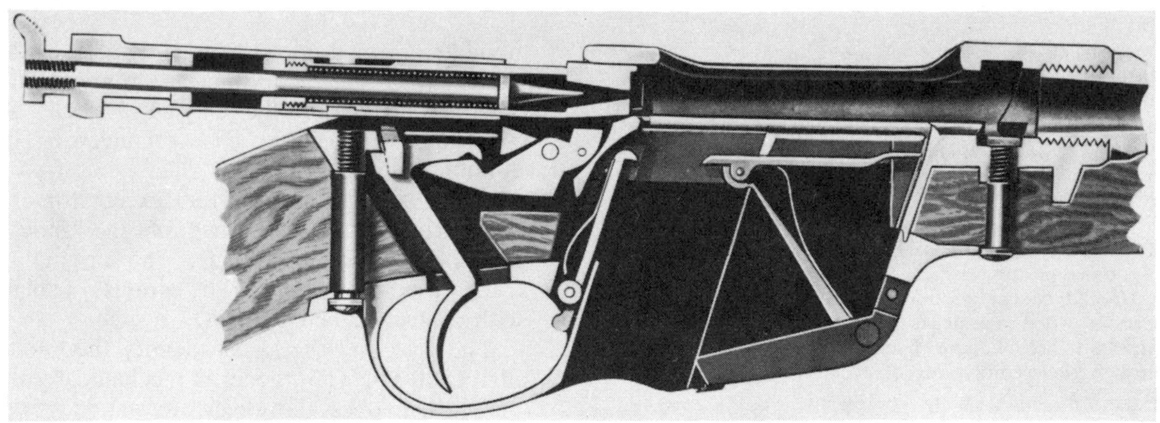

Austrian Model 95 Mannlicher straight pull section and mechanism.

MODEL 1895 AUSTRIAN SERVICE RIFLES

These arms have been successfully converted to handle the German 7.9mm rimless cartridge in Austria, Hungary, and Yugoslavia. The conversions are loaded with strip-in clips, the magazine being altered and having a bottom plate.

A Stutzen (short rifle) was also made with a 19″ barrel. This type differs from the carbine in that its sling swivels are positioned under the butt and forestock and it is equipped for bayonet and stacking as is the standard rifle. The Stutzen was primarily an artilleryman's. rifle.

The first of this series was actually the carbine issued in 1890. It differs from the later model in having a circular cocking piece.

Conversions. While these arms are commonly encountered in caliber 8mm rimmed, they may be found converted to take the 7.9mm German Service cartridge.

Identification of 1895 Series. Straight pull bolt with revolving bolt head. Two opposed lugs at front of bolt head. Mannlicher clip type magazine. Thumb grip at end of cocking piece.

Identification of 1890 Carbine. Same as M. 1895 except that cocking piece head is circular.

Evaluation. All arms in this series were well made of the best materials. When in good working order and condition they are very good lightweight rifles. However, they were designed to be very lightweight military arms. If converted to other calibers, care should be exercised to use cartridges within the pressure limits of the original M. 95 Austrian cartridge. The receivers are made of special steels permitting the use of a small mass of metal for the cartridge used; any extensive receiver alterations are not advisable.

Good Features. Straight pull action permits rapid operation.

Rotating bolt head with dual front lugs assures maximum breech seal.

Cam faces on bolt lug and receiver give some primary extraction.

Bolt design prevents firing until action is fully locked; and prevents firing pin or gas from blowing back into firer's face in event of a blown primer or cartridge case.

Poor Features. Weak primary extraction. Straight pull actions lose the advantages of great leverage found in turn bolt types, resulting in extraction troubles.

The magazine system employed requires that the clip be inserted with the cartridges, making it impractical to recharge magazine except when empty.

Ammunition. 8 x 50mm. Not manufactured in the U. S. When available will probably be imported from England.

English makers class the cartridge as: 8mm (.315) Mannlicher (Austrian, Bulgarian, and Greek). Powder charge 41 grs. N.C. Bullet weight 244 grs. Several bullet types made for hunting. Commercial pressure: 31,500 foot pounds.

These cartridges are not interchangeable with the 8mm Mannlicher Schoenauer or with any of the common German 8mm types.

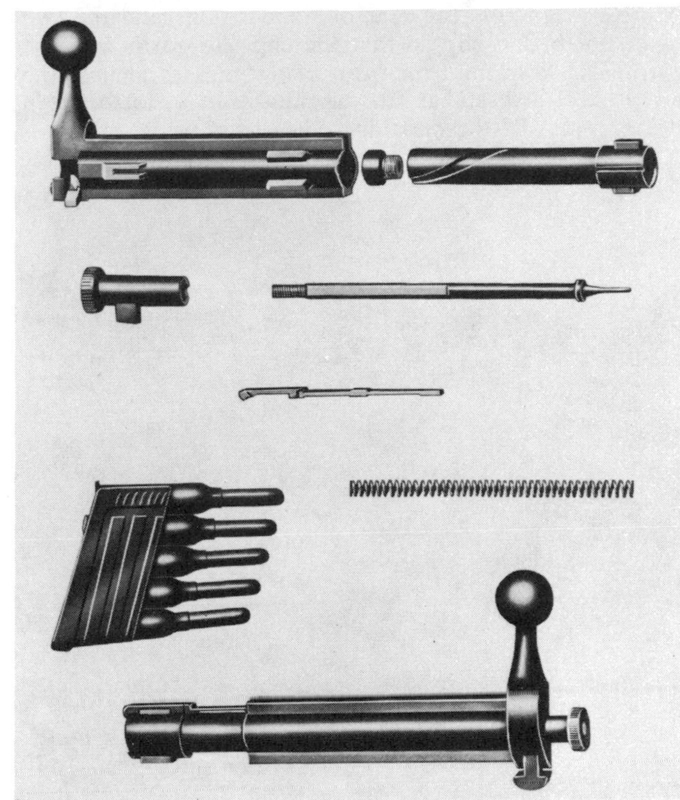

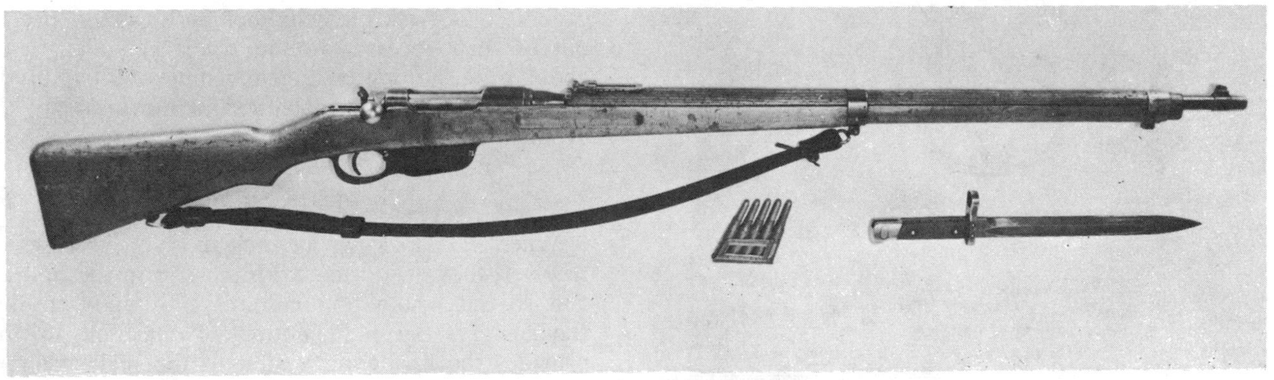

Austrian Steyr-Mannlicher 8mm Rifle Model 95.

Model 95 weapons marked with an *S* on the barrel ahead of the receiver have been converted to use the 8mm M30 cartridge (8x56mm); they can not be used with the 8x50mm cartridge. Rifles and carbines marked M95M are chambered for the 7.92mm Mauser rimless; they were used by Jugoslavia after World War I. Rifles marked M95/24 are also chambered for the 7.92mm cartridge and were used by Greece.

This weapon was in very wide use in eastern Europe. It was the official rifle of Austria and Bulgaria, and was much used also by the Italians. It is a straight-pull rifle having very little in common with other types. Its effective operation requires special knowledge.

Caliber: 8mm Austrian Service cartridge.
Barrel Length: About 30 inches.
Overall Length: 4′ 2″; with bayonet 9½″ longer.
Weight: About 8 lbs. 6 oz.
Sights: Barleycorn front and V-notch open rear adjustable from 300 to 2600 meters. No wind gauge provided.
Operation: The bolt on this rifle is drawn **straight back** to the rear to unload and thrust **straight forward** to load. Note that this bolt handle **does not turn.**
Rate of Fire: Because of the straight-pull action, the rate of fire of 35 unaimed shots per minute is possible with this weapon.

Magazine: Mannlicher type. This clip and five cartridges are inserted from the top. When the last cartridge has been chambered, the empty clip falls out the bottom of the rifle.
Note on Carbine: Carbine is identical with rifle except for length and weight.
Safety: Thumb safety at rear of weapon.
Cutoff: None possible with Mannlicher magazine system.
Magazine Follower: Together with its spring may be hinged forward from bottom of rifle to permit cleaning.

Loading and Firing

Pull bolt handle straight back to the rear as far as it will go. Insert Mannlicher-type clip loaded with five cartridges in top of receiver. Press down into rifle exerting the pressure across the rear of the cartridge and the two upper lips of the clip so that the clip will go in with the cartridges. A spring arm from below presses against the bottom cartridge and is free to ride up in a slot between the two sides of the cartridge clip.

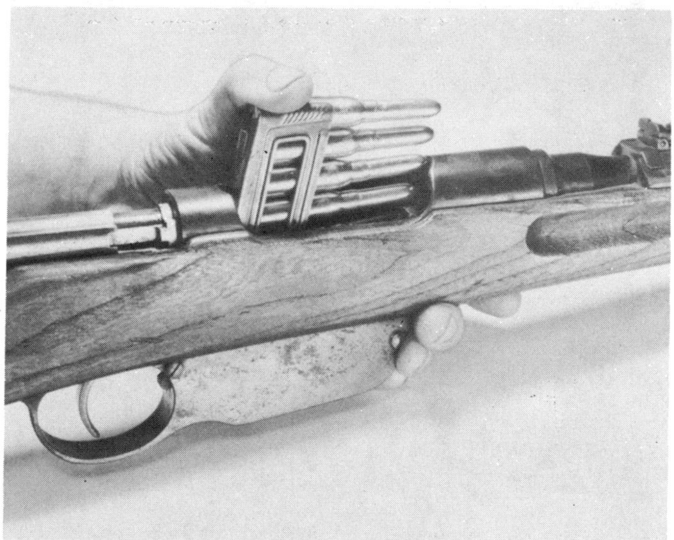

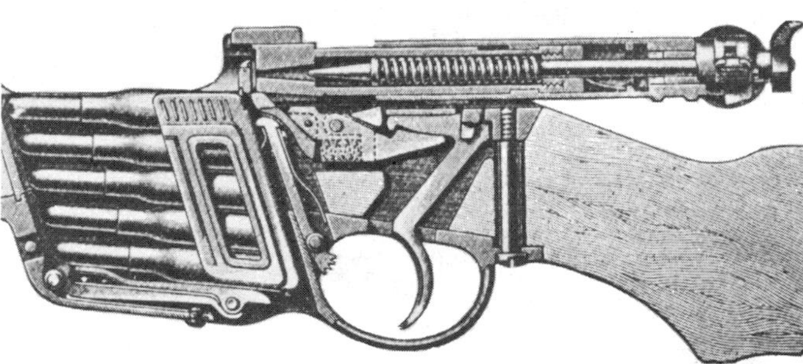

Bolt rear. Magazine loaded.

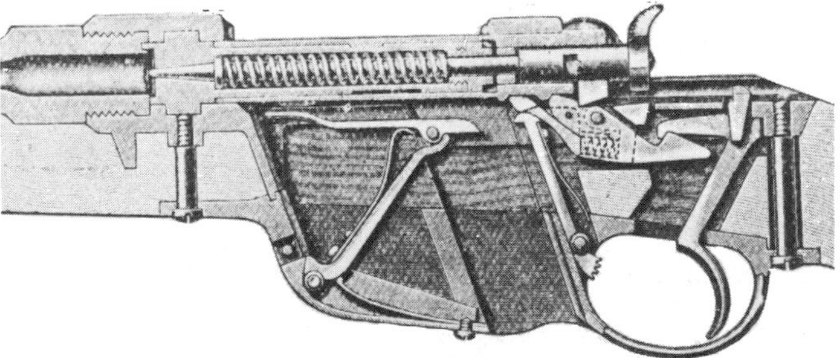

Bolt forward. Magazine empty.

Push bolt handle straight home as far as it will go. Weapon is now ready to fire.

Press the spring retaining catch on the bottom of the magazine just ahead of the opening through which the empty clip drops. This will permit you to hinge forward and downward the magazine bottom together with the follower and the supporting arm and spring.

Pull the bolt handle straight back as far as it will go.

Push trigger forward, and while holding it, pull straight back on the cockingpiece which will permit the removal of the bolt from the rifle.

Note on the Steyr Straight Pull Action. The bolt in this type of action is complicated by comparison with the turning-bolt type. This type of bolt action has never achieved wide popularity. While in theory it is very much faster to operate than a turning bolt, in actual practice the British-type rifle can be operated as fast or perhaps even faster. This is due to the fact that in the turning bolt the primary extraction of the fired cartridge case, which fits very tightly in the chamber, is achieved by the direct leverage of the bolt handle in its upward movement. In a straight-pull type, this leverage is not present.

As the bolt handle is pulled straight to the rear the full cylinder is prevented from revolving by its ribs which ride in the grooves of the receiver; and by centers engaging in the undercut groove in the tang. The bolt head cannot come back until the locking lugs have been turned out of their recesses in the receiver, which is brought about by a turning motion given to the tail of the bolt head by the feathers machined in the inside of the bolt cylinder working in the bolt head tail.

Field Stripping

When the locking lugs clear their recesses in the receiver, they are in line with the ribs in the bolt cylinder and so the whole bolt can travel directly to the rear. Incidentally, the first motion of the bolt to the rear provides the first compression to the mainspring.

A Canadian rifle, the Ross, using the straight-pull principle, was employed for a time in the Canadian Army during the first World War. It was not a satisfactory weapon. Switzerland uses a straight pull rifle known as the Schmidt-Rubin, which is an excellent weapon in every way.

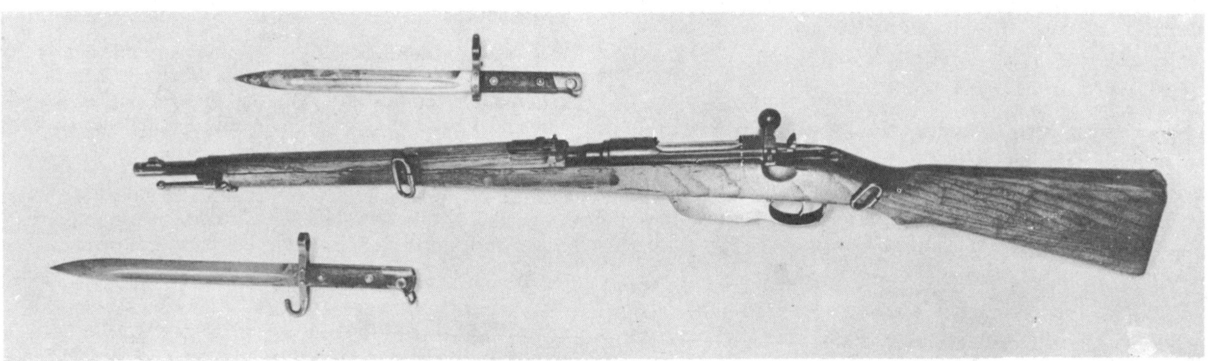

Austrian Steyr-Mannlicher M95 short rifle.

OTHER AUSTRIAN-MADE RIFLES

Model 1914. This is a Mauser rifle made at Steyr Armory. Before World War I Austria was manufacturing these rifles in 7mm caliber for Mexico. Adoption of the rifle for the Austro-Hungarian services was prevented by the coming of World War I.

Evaluation. When in good condition, these Steyr-made Mausers have no superiors. They combine all the good Mauser mechanical features with the finest Austrian steels and workmanship.

Ammunition. This ammunition is manufactured for sporting use by U. S. and British manufacturers under the designation 7mm Mauser.

Pressures. From 37,000 to 42,000 foot pounds, varying with type of loading.

Identification. Standard Mauser except for STEYR stamp, Cal. 7mm, and slightly different handguard.

Mannlicher-Schoenauer (Greek Service 1903/14). See chapter 27. Except for stocks, sights, and caliber, these are the same as the M S sporters.

Hungarian Mannlicher. See chapter 28.

Romanian and Dutch Mannlichers. See chapters 38 and 34.

Sporting Model Mannlicher-Schoenauers. These rifles were widely sold in the U. S. by American gun houses before the war. Actions are Mannlicher turn bolt. Magazines are rotary box types. The name Steyr-Werke A.G. customarily appears on the left side of the receiver.

These arms were made as both carbines and rifles, both full stocked and half stocked. They were made in standard and magnum (large size) receivers in a wide range of American and foreign calibers. M-S rifles are among the finest ever manufactured anywhere from the standpoint of design, materials and workmanship.

Ammunition. Before the war U. S. manufacturers made 6.5mm M-S and 8mm M-S cartridges. Other European calibers were normally imported.

Late M-S rifles listed in Austria as 6.7mm and 8.2mm will handle respectively the cartridges made here under the designations 6.5mm M-S and 8mm M-S.

Note: Mannlicher-Schoenauer actions are suitable for conversion to any American calibers within the power and style ranges of the original European calibers.

AUSTRIAN MACHINE GUNS

Austrian Schwarzlose 8mm Machine Gun M 07/12.

While this gun was originally of Austrian manufacture its use has been very widespread. Together with other types it was used during World War II by the Dutch, and specimens captured by the Japanese were probably used by them. It was widely used in Czechoslovakia, converted to take the 7.92mm ammunition of German type. It was also an official weapon in caliber 6.5mm in Sweden. There were large numbers of these guns in Italy; the Italian Army made extensive use of them from stock taken from Austria during World War I.

Caliber: 8mm (.315 inch), also in other calibers as noted.
Feed: Fabric belt, feeding from right to left.
Muzzle Velocity of Cartridge: About 2030 feet per second.
Weight of Bullet: 244 grains.
Barrel Length: 20¾".
Length Overall: About 42".
Weight of Gun: 44 lbs.
Mounting: A tripod is provided with this weapon, weighing about 44 lbs.
Sights: Barleycorn front. Rear V. Elevation provided up to 2400 meters.
Accurate Range: About 500 yards.
Gun Operated By: Delayed blowback principle. Backward thrust of gases in firing chamber presses head of cartridge against face of the bolt.
Locked: This is strictly an unlocked weapon. Instead of a fixed positive locking system, the action is kept closed by the inertia of a very heavy breech block supplemented by powerful springs and mechanical leverage.
Cooled: Water. Water jacket surrounds barrel. Hose leading from water jacket to tank and pump gives forced circulation.
Cyclic Rate of Fire: About 400 rounds a minute.
Type of Fire: Full automatic only. If single shot fire desired for any reason, it is accomplished by removing alternate cartridges from loops in belt. It is necessary to throw the rocker arm for each shot.

Loading and Firing

See that the feed box is properly positioned on the right side directly below the feed opening. Then insert the tag end of the belt into the guide on the lower right side of the feed. Pull the belt tag up and over the toothed wheel and pull it through as far as possible to the left. Pull the crank handle (or rocker arm) back as far as it will go and let it fly forward. The crank handle in this gun must be pulled back and allowed to go forward three times before the firing chamber is loaded.

Firing: This weapon is provided with traversing handles which may be set either horizontally or vertically. It also has a dual thumb trigger. To fire this weapon, it is necessary with the thumb of one hand to push an automatic safety catch (positioned between the dual thumb pieces) over to the left before the thumb trigger will go inward to fire the weapon.

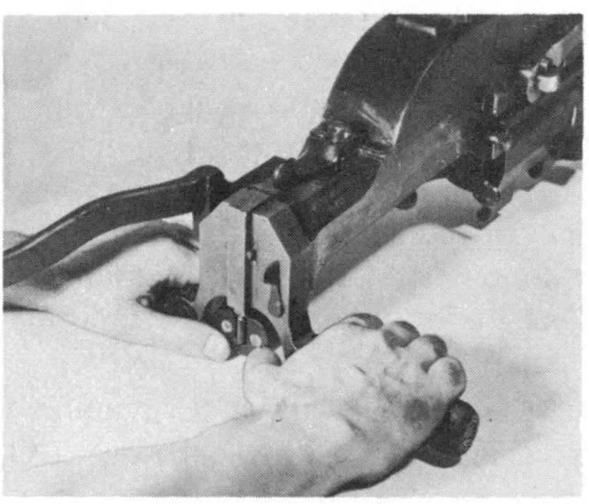

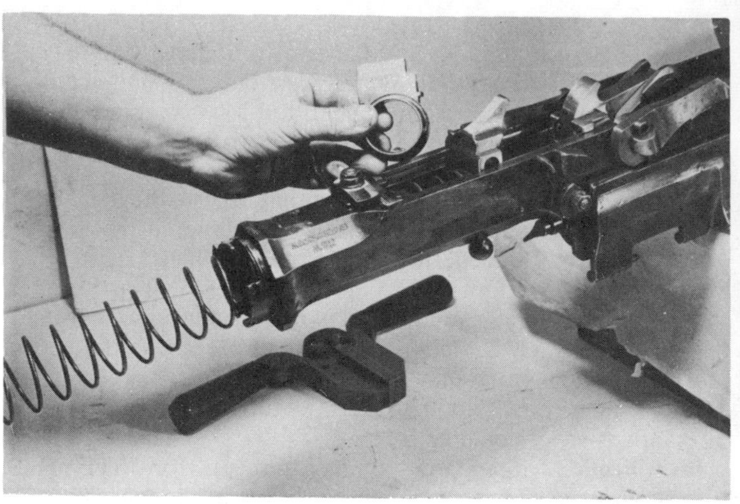

Field Stripping

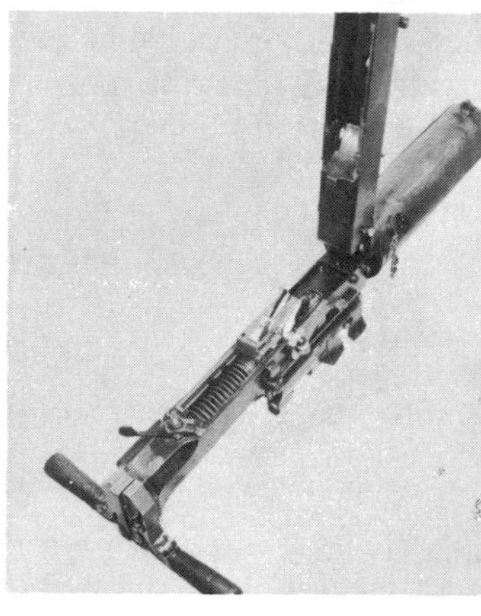

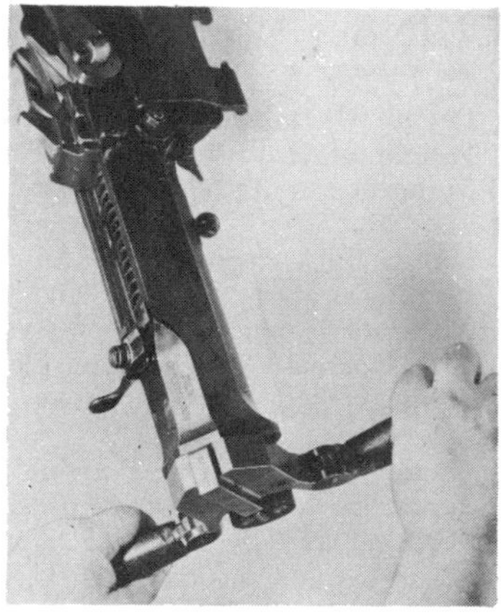

Turn the heavy lever at the rear of the top of the receiver to the left as far as it will go, then pushing the lock lug near the hinge of the receiver cover (directly above the feed opening), lift the cover up as far as it will go. This exposes the complete, massive mechanism.

Above the right hand part of the trigger is a rotating locking pin. Unscrew this and remove it. If the shoulder piece is attached, pull it out of its engagement.

Exerting forward pressure and with extreme care, turn the end cap and butt group to the right.

The unusually powerful recoil spring will force the butt group back once they are unlocked. Remember that this is not a normal recoil spring, but is one specially made to hold the action closed under terrific breech pressure. This spring may injure you if it gets away from you. Remove the recoil spring and the recoil spring guide plug from the gun.

The breechblock, firing pin, crank link and crank may now be lifted out of the gun. This completes field stripping of this weapon.

How the Gun Works

Starting with the gun loaded and cocked the action is as follows: Safety catch being pushed over to the left by the thumb, the thumb trigger is free to be pushed in. As soon as pressure is released on the thumb trigger, safety slips back into place automatically stopping the firing and locking the firing mechanism. When the trigger thumb piece is pressed in, the trigger bar is drawn down to the rear and the firing pin extension disengaged from a place in the breech block. A stud on the breech block link keeps the firing pin extension from slipping out of engagement with the bent until the breech block is almost entirely home.

A well in the top of the cover, directly ahead of the front sight is kept filled with oil; and a fine spray of

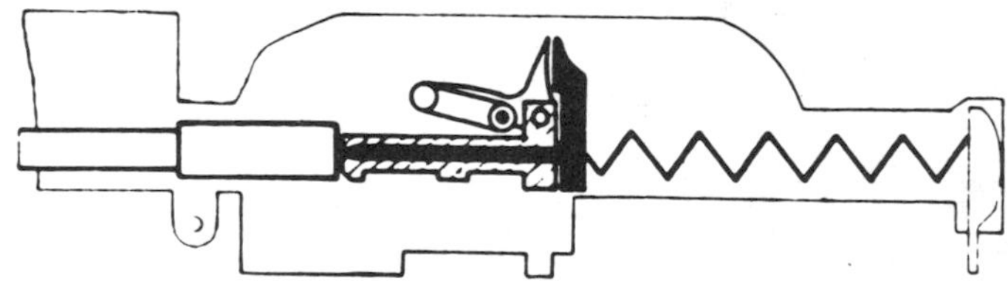

Position of Parts at Instant of Firing.

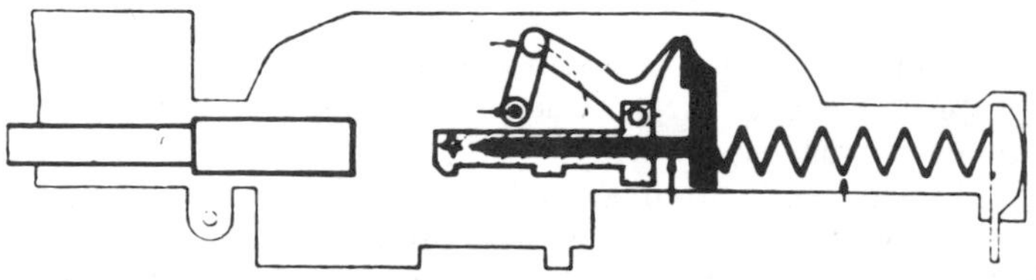

Hesitation Position of Parts.

lubricant is forced over each cartridge as it is driven into the firing chamber by the breech block. This lubrication is extremely important in guns such as this, and in the American Thompson submachine gun, since absolute uniformity of feeding is necessary when the gun is unlocked.

When the cartridge in the firing chamber is discharged, the bullet goes down the barrel. Note that the barrel in this gun is very short. This is a necessary factor in an inertia operated gun. If the barrel were very much longer, the action would open before the bullet had left the muzzle, and the results might be disastrous.

The moving parts in this weapon are extremely heavy, and the recoil spring which must be compressed is unusually powerful. Further resistance is offered to the opening of the breech by an elbow joint attached to the breech block which has another arm pivoted to a fixed axis in the receiver.

During the backward movement of the breech block, this elbow joint moves through an arch and since there is a very small angle between crank link and crank when the breech is closed, much of the force of the recoil is transmitted to the fixed axis of the crank and crank handle in the receiver. The striker is cocked during the backward action by a cammed toe on the crank link which acts against a corresponding toe on the striker. Note: Because of the nature of the recoil spring, assembling this gun is a two-man job at the least. While the assembly steps are comparatively simple, it is necessary for one man to guide the recoil spring while the other attaches the rotating butt cap.

Chapter 16. Belgium

THE F. N. PLANT

MILITARY small arms development in Belgium today is unqualifiedly superior to that of any nation in the world with the sole exception of the United States.

While the military small arms developments in Belgium are usually accredited to the Government, as a matter of fact the basic design, engineering, and production genius is that of the great commercial Fabrique Nationale d'Armes Guerre, S.A., of Herstal, Liege.

Military production is controlled in this plant by the Belgian Government. The basic businesses, however, are very closely intertwined in that both sporting and military weapons are produced under one roof with the same production and testing facilities and are exported throughout the world. Because of the tremendous world stature it has developed, and because of the remarkable small arms achievements of recent years there, this plant and its background require some passing comment.

The F. N. organization was originally founded in 1889 by a combination of a Lüttich Belgi syndicate together with L. Loewe and Company of Berlin to manufacture a new Mauser magazine rifle for the Belgian Government. The military division prospered from the start, and through the years has been a major military small arms purveyor throughout the world.

Early in the present century our own great John M. Browning offered his new automatic shotgun to the Winchester Repeating Arms Company. All his previously designed firearms had been turned over to Winchester under a contract which stipulated a nominal payment for each design. The financial returns to Browning hadn't been very satisfactory, to state it politely. Browning felt that this new long-recoil automatic shotgun was much too valuable a property to sell outright. When Winchester refused to operate on a royalty basis with him, and approaches to other American manufacturers were unproductive, Browning took his design to the F. N. plant in Belgium.

By that time F. N. had a worldwide sales organization, excellent plant facilities, and the finest technical skills. In addition, they had a highly enlightened management which recognized in John Browning a tremendous design and promotion potential. They saw immediately the world value of his new shotgun, too. Equitable arrangements were promptly made with him.

Browning stayed on at the F. N. plant and did much of his original early development on automatic and semiautomatic arms there. His first automatic pistol to be commercially established was the famous Browning 1900 in .32 caliber. In July, 1912, the factory held an official jubilee in celebration of the production of the one millionth model of this pattern!

The long series of successful Browning's sporting developments included the range of .25, .32, .380, .38, and .45 automatic pistols marketed in the United States under the Colt's name. The .25, .32, and .380 versions were also produced in Belgium under the F. N. Browning name for world distribution. Here also Browning developed .22 automatic rifles marketed in the United States under the Remington name and in Belgium under the F. N. name, medium-power trombone rifles, sporting pump shotguns, and the world-famous Browning over-under shotgun manufactured only at the F. N. plant.

From the earliest time of Browning's association with F. N., members of his family have worked in the F. N. plant as learners originally and as supervisors eventually. The Browning sons have carried on well at F. N. the traditions of their father.

After World War I, F. N. took over large-scale manufacture of Mauser rifles to supply the markets which had been serviced formerly by Germany. Most of the nations of South America and Asia have been armed at some time and to a very considerable extent with Mauser rifles produced at this plant. In general it must be recognized that all the F. N. rifle designs were basically the German Mauser, and that the later variations developed by the German manufacturers tended to appear almost simultaneously in the F. N. production.

Also on the military side, F. N. undertook the production of Browning's machine rifle and light and heavy machine guns for worldwide military sale after World War I. In 1935 they introduced Browning's last modification of his automatic system as found in our Government service automatic pistol, the modification known as the F. N. High Power in caliber 9mm Luger.

When the Germans overran Belgium in World War II, the key engineering and production personnel of the plant fled to England and Canada. The part they played in assisting production in both those countries cannot be overestimated. In Canada the 1935 High Power pistol, with slight modifications as required for production in Canada, was turned out in considerable quantity with the cooperation of these Belgian technicians. It will almost certainly be the Canadian and British pistol of the near future.

At close of World War II, when the factory was returned to its owners, it was found that while the Germans had done no damage to the plant, they had moved out tremendous quantities of the very fine equipment there. Much of this was rescued by United States Service teams and returned to the factory.

The management, which had returned from exile, recognized that the American factories were still helplessly overloaded with government production and saw that the worldwide sporting market for high-power rifles was an open field for any one prepared to produce for it. While design engineers turned their attention to improved prototypes for later production, the production facilities were immediately employed to turn out vast quantities of the arms which the production engineers knew how to turn out in volume and for which they were tooled. As a result, not only the famous Browning automatic shotguns but also huge quantities of the Mauser rifles adapted for sporting purposes, as well as actions on which foreign gunsmiths could build rifles for commercial sales, were exported.

In addition, of course, much work was received at the F. N. Plant in the nature of offshore contracts, since F. N. alone had the necessary space, facilities, and know-how for much of the work necessary to assist in rearming and equipping allied European groups.

The F. N. Plant is quite unlike similar American organizations. It is far more efficient than most. It is set up on a strictly production line basis analagous to that employed by the automobile manufacturers in the United States. The apprentice system of training, still in use in Belgium, develops a continuous source of highly trained personnel far greater than that available to most American producers. This item alone is extremely important in fine gun manufacture.

In addition, the engineering facilities of the plant have been made to embrace a very wide field of the arts allied to metallurgy. This development has kept them in constant contact with the British aviation interests, whose designs and production have consistently stayed several years ahead of that in any other nation in the world, despite their comparatively limited production facilities.

With this vast knowledge of military requirements throughout the world, its businesslike approach to the matters of production and costs (which no purely government body ever achieves), and with its magnificent engineering and design facilities, many instituted under the direction of John Browning, the F. N. organization proceeded to develop a series of automatic weapons eventually to be distributed on a world scale to replace the bolt action Mausers which are currently considered obsolete by many military powers.

Under the designation Type 30, the F. N. Plant modified the original Browning automatic rifle as produced in the United States to meet specialized requirements stipulated originally by the Belgian government. These incorporated a gas regulator and also a firing rate regulator.

BELGIAN PISTOLS

The Belgian Browning 9mm Hi-Power Model with Tangent Sight.

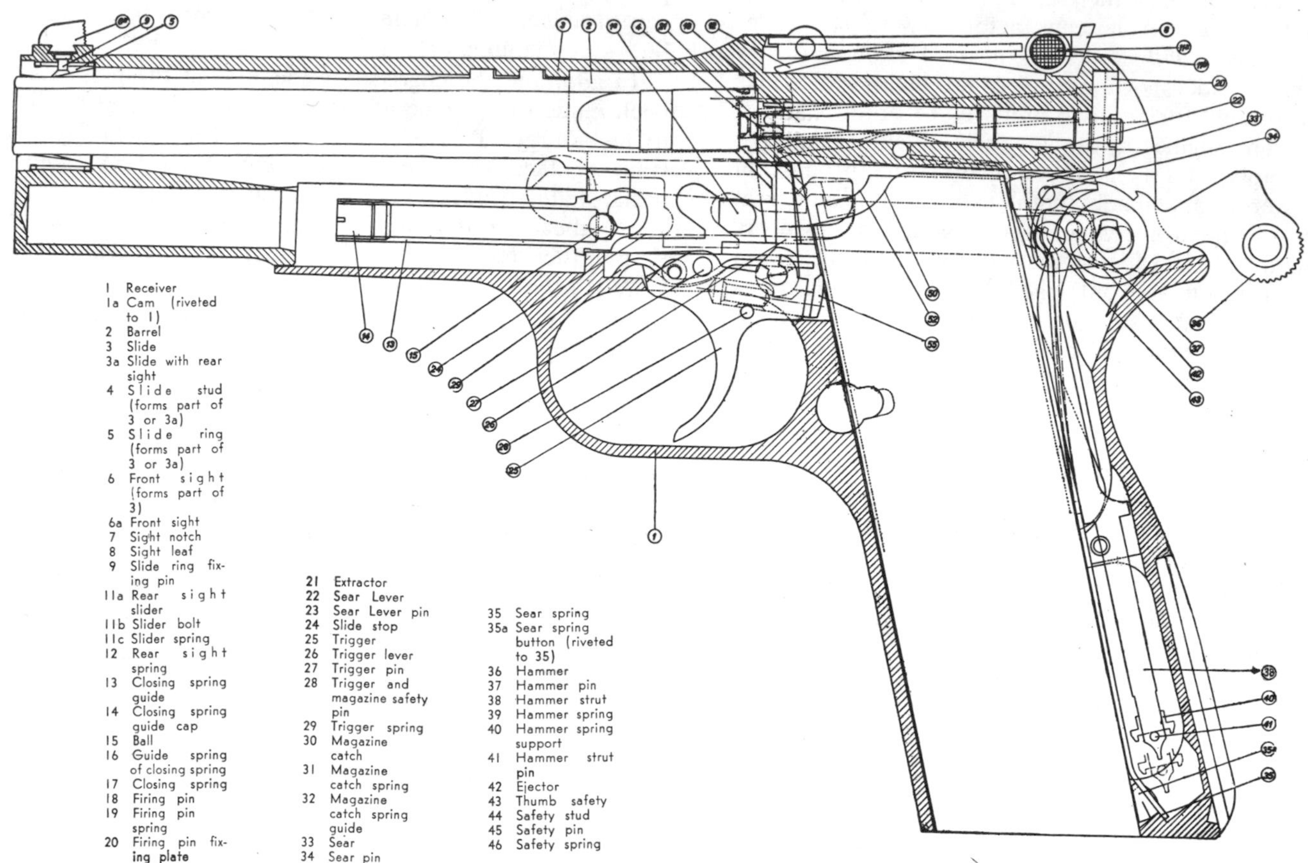

Caliber: 9mm Ball Ammunition, flat point or round point (Cal. .35). Luger type.
Magazine: Box type, double line staggered. Capacity 13 cartridges.
Muzzle Velocity: 1040 to 1500 feet per second depending on type and manufacture of ammunition.
Weight of Bullet: Variable.
Muzzle Striking Energy: 365 pounds average.
Barrel Length: 7.64 inches.
Overall Length: 7.34 inches.
Weight of Pistol: 2.06 pounds empty.
Accurate Range as a Pistol: About 50 yards.
Accurate Range with Shoulder Stock: About 200 yards.
Maximum Range: About 1200 yards.
Pistol Operated by: Recoil.
Locked: Parallel ruler system.
Type of Fire: Single shot only. Has positive disconnector.
Magazine Release Catch: Button on left side near trigger. Pressing it will eject magazine from handle.
Position of Slide When Last Shot is Fired: Open. Step on magazine follower forces slide stop up into locking notch in slide.
Safety: Thumb safety on left side of pistol.

Special Note: This pistol is issued in two types. (1) As a standard pistol with fixed sights, and a lanyard ring. (2) With a shoulder stock attachment similar to the Mauser Pistol. In this type the pistol is carried in a hollow inside the stock. Sights on this model are graduated to 500 meters.

Identification of 9mm Browning Hi-Power. Modified Colt-Browning lock using a barrel nose sliding on a ramp instead of the familiar Colt swinging link to raise and lower barrel for locking and unlocking. Double line staggered box magazine holding 13 cartridges.

As made in Belgium (the pistol was also made in Canada) it may have fixed or elevating rear sight; and may come with smooth grip or with grip machined to permit attaching pistol to a wooden shoulder stock which serves as a holster.

Evaluation. Pre-war models were good quality. This was John M. Browning's last design. F. N. manufactured Browning arms in Europe.

Many war-made pistols have been reported unsatisfactory due to sabotage during the German occupation. Germany manufactured 200,000 of these pistols after seizing the plant.

In the Browning design the slide is mounted from the front end to prevent its being blown off in case of serious accident. This fact and the mass of metal are reasonable assurance against serious trouble; but if these pistols bear German proof marks, they should be checked by a competent gunsmith. The barrel nose, its receiver seating, the barrel locking lugs, and the slide recesses should be examined.

When in good condition this pistol, like all Browning's late patents, is an arm of outstanding quality.

Ammunition. 9mm Luger ammunition is made in the U. S. This pistol functions best with late type round nose bullets, rather than with the old flat point Luger-type bullets.

Field Stripping

Pull slide back and push thumb safety up into the second notch.

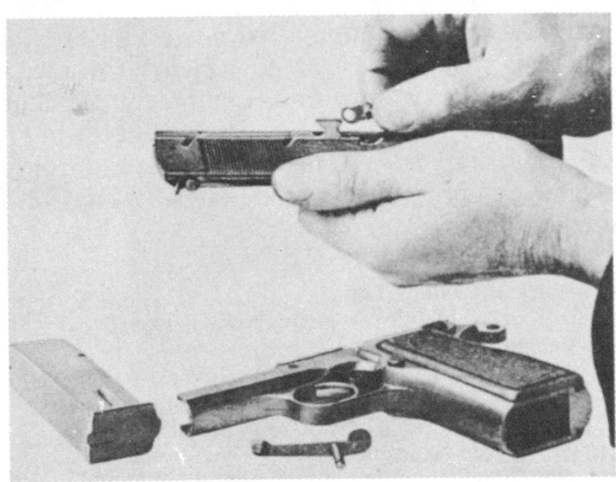

Press magazine catch and withdraw magazine.

Push pin from right side of receiver and lift out the pin and slide stop unit.

Holding firmly to the slide, depress the safety catch and permit the slide assembly to go forward and off the receiver runners.

Holding slide assembly upside down, pull recoil spring toward the muzzle and lift it out of engagement. Remove it and the spring.

Remove barrel from rear of slide.

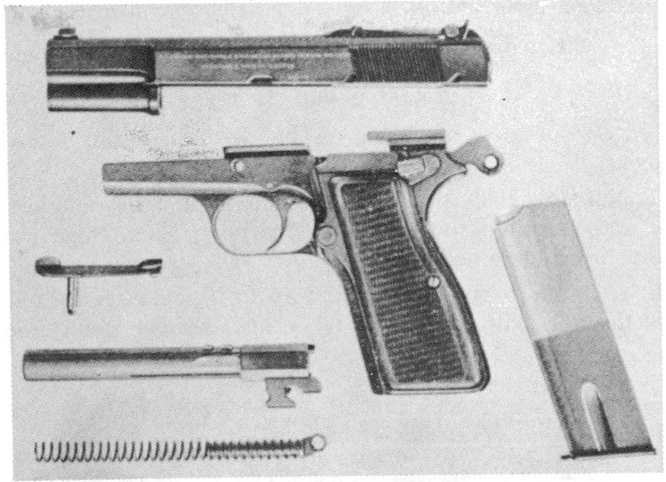

Description of the Mechanism

The use of a double row staggered magazine gives greater magazine capacity but at the same time necessarily increases the thickness of the grip. This additional width, together with an arched lower section of the handle section of the receiver, gives the pistol better than usual instinctive pointing qualities.

While in general the design follows that of the Colt .45 Automatic, in detail it is quite different. The positive hammer safety is positioned as in our service pistol. When it is forced up into its notch in the slide, a projection on its lower side fits at the rear of the sear to prevent the release of the hammer.

The slide stop, which is forced up by the magazine follower to hold the pistol open when the last shot has been fired, and the button magazine release both follow the standard Browning form. No grip safety is provided. This is held to be non-essential on a military pistol.

Other new features include a magazine safety. When the magazine is withdrawn the safety spring forces this safety out, swinging the trigger lever forward out of engagement with the sear. Inserting a magazine presses the safety against its spring tension and swings the trigger lever back and under the sear to permit finger pressure to be transmitted. The military value of this feature is questionable.

Caution. Many of these pistols made for the Germans in World War II had the magazine safety removed.

In place of the Colt stirrup-type trigger, this weapon is fitted with a comfortable trigger which when pressed forces a trigger lever upward. This rotates the sear lever which acts upon the sear arm, causing it in turn to swivel and release the hammer.

Unless the slide is fully forward and the barrel securely locked to it, this sear lever remains at the rear and the trigger lever cannot act upon it. This acts as a positive disconnector to prevent the weapon from being fired. Should the trigger be held back after a shot has been fired, the trigger lever is retained in raised position but is also forced forward by the sear lever on the forward motion of the slide. This prevents the trigger lever from acting upon either the sear or the sear lever, and so the hammer cannot fall until the trigger is permitted to move to its normal forward position. Thus only one shot is possible on each pull of the trigger.

The slide in particular is an improvement over the original Browning design. Its forward end has only one opening, that for the barrel. The front of the slide below the muzzle opening is solid, doing away with the weak barrel bushing of previous models. The recoil spring and its guide seat in the hollow below the barrel, and the head of the guide sets into the barrel nose (or lock) where it is securely retained by the transverse slide stop pin.

The barrel lock is also improved. While it retains the basic Browning locking idea (that of ribs on top of the barrel fitting into corresponding grooves inside the slide at the moment of firing) this new Browning does away with the swinging link and pin used in our service pistol. It provides instead a "barrel nose" which is part of the barrel forging itself. This barrel nose is placed directly below the heavily reinforced chamber section, and has a guiding slot which is controlled by a cam machined into the receiver. This arrangement gives a much more rigid barrel support and permits simplification of the recoil spring system.

How the Pistol Works

At the moment of discharge the barrel is locked securely to the slide as the top locking ribs engage in the locking slots in the slide. As the slide starts back in recoil carrying the barrel with it, and the bullet leaves the barrel, the sear lever is disconnected from the trigger lever.

As the barrel pressure drops to safe limits, the lower section of the notch of the barrel nose contacts the cam in the receiver, and the rear end of the barrel is thus drawn down until its ribs are free from the locking slots. At this point the rearward barrel movement is stopped as the barrel nose brings up sharply against its receiver stop.

The slide continues on backwards, riding over the hammer to cock it. The extractor claw carries the empty cartridge case back until it strikes the ejector and is tossed out of the pistol. Meanwhile the recoil spring is compressed around its guide. Rearward motion of the slide stops when its lower part strikes against the forward end of the receiver.

For the return motion, the recoil spring pushes the slide forward to strip the top cartridge from the magazine into the chamber. The breech end of the slide strikes the barrel; under the action of the cam in the receiver acting against the upper part of the barrel nose notch, the rear of the barrel is brought up into locking position and its ribs fit firmly into their slots in the slide.

The trigger, sear, and hammer mechanisms hook up properly and the pistol is ready for the next pull of the trigger.

Special Note

This pistol was the last invention of John M. Browning and was intended as an improved form of pistol along the lines of the Colt .45 Automatic originally designed by him.

Originally manufactured by the Fabrique Nationale, European holder of Browning pistol patents, it was issued in Belgium under the name "The 9mm Browning High-Power Automatic Pistol, 13-Shot," in 1935. It was expected to supplant the standard Browning 9mm Long as the Belgian Army Pistol. When the Germans captured Belgium they put into use all captured pistols of this type because they use the standard German Luger pistol cartridge.

In 1943 the Chinese adopted this pistol as manufactured in Canada.

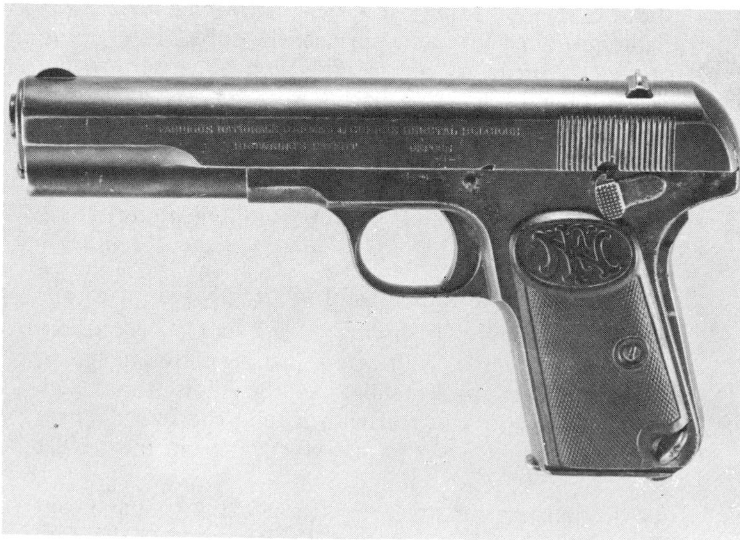

Belgian Browning Long 9mm Automatic Pistol.

Note: This pistol is popularly known in Europe as the F. N., from the initials of the factory where it was originally made. Pistol was manufactured and sold throughout Europe under Browning patents, while pistols of the same design were manufactured and sold under those same patents in the United States by the Colt Patent Firearms Company.

Caliber: 9mm Browning **Long.**
Magazine: Removable box type in handle, capacity 7 cartridges.
Muzzle Velocity: 1110 feet per second.
Weight of Bullet: 110 grains, metal jacket.
Striking Energy: 300 foot pounds.
Barrel Length: 5".
Overall Length of Pistol: 8".
Weight of Pistol: 32 ozs.
Sights: Fixed.
Accurate Range: 50 yards.
Pistol Operated By: Recoil.
Locked: Blowback type, unlocked. Breech is closed during period of high pressure entirely by weight of sliding members and recoil spring.
Type of Fire: Single shot only.
Magazine Release Catch: On bottom of butt at rear.
Position of Slide When Last Shot Has Been Fired: Open. Inserting a loaded magazine and pulling back slightly on the slide will let the action go forward again and load the firing chamber.
Safeties: (a) Automatic safety in grip which disengages when pistol is held firmly in hand. (b) Thumb safety above left stock. Pushing it up into its notch in the slide provides a positive safety.

Loading and Firing

Insert loaded magazine in handle and push until it locks.

Pull slide back to the rear as far as it will go, release it and permit it to run forward driving a cartridge into the firing chamber.

This differs from the customary Colt pocket pistol only in that the slide stays open when last shot has been fired.

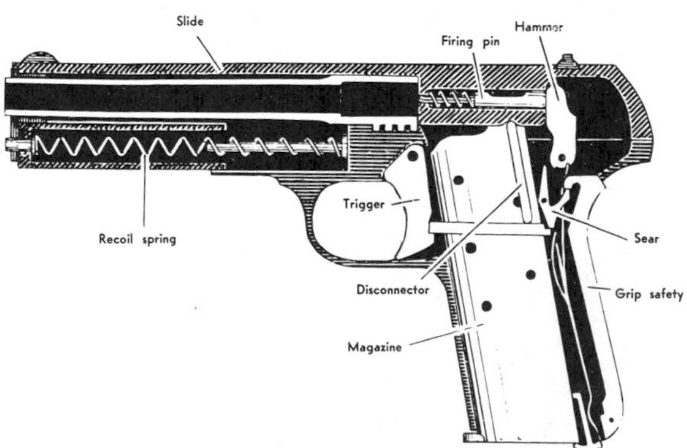

Nomenclature of the 9mm Browning Long.

Note on Ammunition for this Pistol

The 9mm Browning Long is a freak cartridge widely used in Europe but never manufactured in the United States. It cannot be used in any American-made pistols. It is a semi-rim automatic pistol cartridge with ballistics mid-way between the .380 Automatic Colt pistol cartridge (which is a pocket type), and the .38 Automatic Colt pistol cartridge (which is a high velocity military cartridge very popular in Spain and in South America).

Field Stripping

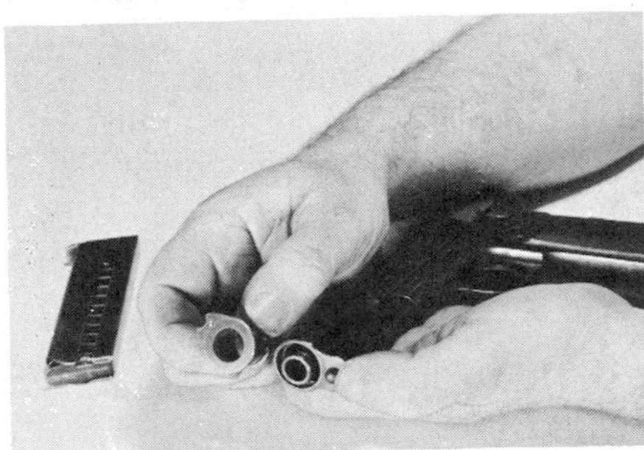

Push in recoil spring guide where it projects from below the muzzle of the barrel. Revolve the barrel bushing and withdraw it from the slide.

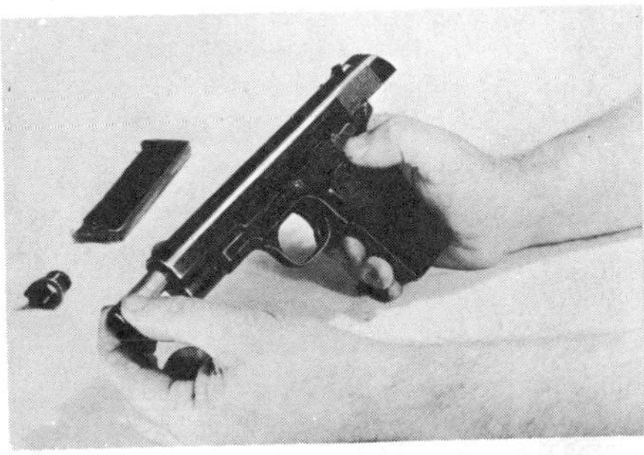

Pull back slide and force the thumb safety up into the second notch to hold the slide open. Note that the first notch is the safety notch. Then twist the barrel one quarter turn towards the ejection port; this will disengage the barrel locking teeth from the corresponding recesses in the receiver.

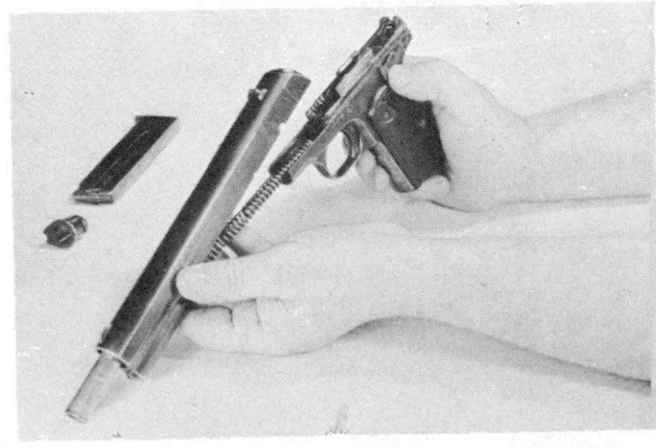

Holding firmly onto the slide, press down the safety and let the barrel, slide, and recoil spring assembly come forward on their guides out of the receiver.

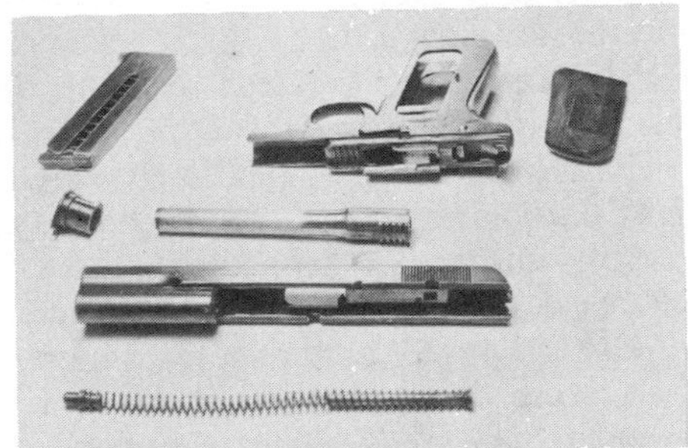

Lift out the recoil spring and its guide. Barrel may be removed from the front.

How the Browning Automatic Pistol Works

The slide being drawn back against the tension of the coil spring under the barrel, its breech end lies over the enclosed hammer which is hit by the exterior shape of the rear of the slide. The hammer is held cocked by the sear. The magazine spring raises a cartridge into line with the breechblock.

The slide being released, the coil spring drives it forward to strip a cartridge into the firing chamber. During the forward motion the disconnector is forced downward preventing the trigger from engaging with the sear until the slide is in its foremost position. Then the disconnector rises to enable the trigger to function.

Note that both the trigger and the grip safety must be squeezed before the sear will release the hammer to strike against the firing pin and fire the cartridge.

The pressure of the recoil spring moving forward, together with the natural inertia of the slide, delay the opening of the breech until the bullet has passed out of the barrel.

Other Calibers of the F. N. Browning

Smaller models of this pistol are also manufactured in 6.35mm (.25 Colt Auto.), 7.65mm (.32) and 9mm Browning (.380 Colt Auto.). These are not military pistols by any accepted standards. But as the F. N. factory has produced over 1,500,000 pistols in the last 35 years, a working knowledge of their models may be considered of military importance. It is to be noted that officers in European armies very often carry small, pocket-type pistols.

BELGIAN SUBSTITUTE STANDARD PISTOLS

More than one hundred forms of elementary blowback pistols were manufactured at one time or another in Belgian factories. All of these types may be encountered by the collector. They vary in weights, lengths, general appearance, and in types of firing mechanisms, slide forms and the like.

However, in general, only the Browning pistols were accepted for limited service use to fill in during shortages of the official models. The standard forms of those Brownings are shown below.

Browning Model 1900. This was the first successful auto pistol designed by John M. Browning. It was commercially manufactured by F. N. in only one caliber, 7.65mm. This cartridge, which was designed for this pistol, is practically identical with the present .32 Colt Auto cartridge. During the early years of manufacture, several minor modifications were made in this design, particularly in the shape and pitch of the grip. Basically all are the same, however.

Pistols of this design were made in Belgium and Spain under a variety of trade names after patents expired. Many of these were of inferior quality. The F. N. name and address on the pistol identifies the genuine.

These (and other) Browning pistols will occasionally be encountered with the Mauser, Steyr, or other trade mark stamped on them. They will also be encountered with Russian characters stamped on. Such pistols, when bearing the Belgian proofs and the name or address of the maker usually represent sample arms purchased by other arms makers for inspection and study, or made by F. N. for special export order as in the case of the Russian.

Identification. Unique slide construction in which recoil spring is housed in a tunnel above the barrel. Striker firing mechanism. Indicator on top of breech shows when pistol is cocked. Pistol is very flat construction.

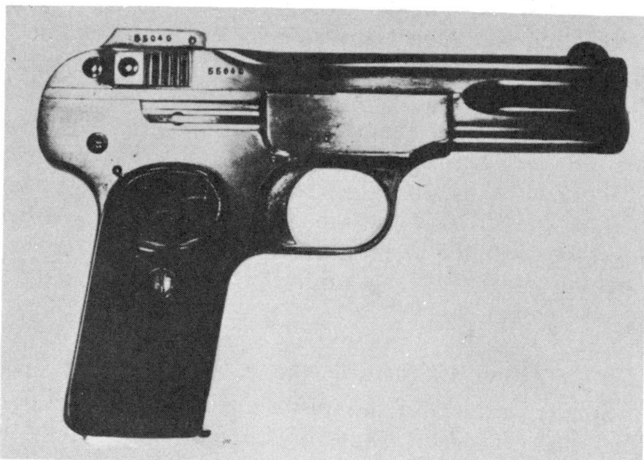

Type A has the following characteristics: Length 7.17″. Barrel 4.75″. Weight 27 oz. Magazine 8 cart.

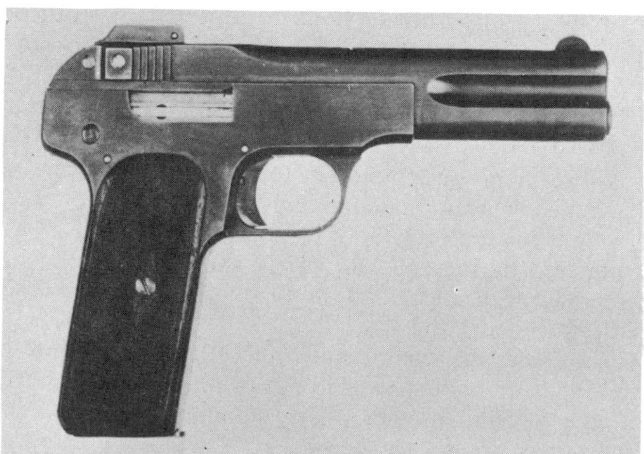

Type B has the following characteristics: Length 6.75″. Barrel 4″. Weight 22 oz. Magazine 7 cart. (Some magazines hold only 6.)

Evaluation. An obsolete form. When in good condition this is still a reliable pistol. Machining and construction both complicated.

Imitations (or copies) as made in Spain are usually poor workmanship, though the materials are sometimes very good. Those of German manufacture, such as the RHEINMETALL, generally are better made than the genuine.

Ammunition. .32 or .380 Colt Auto cartridges, depending on caliber.

Other Pistols. Belgian Pistols bearing the trade mark BAYARD or CLEMENT are generally well made and designed pocket pistols. All are simple blowbacks using U. S. .25 Auto, .32 Auto, or .380 Auto cartridges.

Bayard (or Bergman-Bayard) Military pistols bearing Belgian proofs are similar to the arms under that name shown in chapter 39.

Browning Models 1910 and 1922. These models are the same except as necessary to increase barrel length and magazine capacities. They are blowback pistols with striker firing mechanisms, detachable magazines in handles, recoil springs positioned around barrels and compressed as tubular slides travel back when fired.

Model 1910 has the following characteristics: Length 6″. Barrel 3.5″. Weight 20.5 oz. Magazine (.32 Cal.) 7 cart.; Magazine (.380) 6 cart.

Model 1922 has the following characteristics: Length 7″. Barrel 4.5″. Weight 25 oz. Magazine (.32 Cal.) 9 cart. Magazine; (.380 Cal.) 8 cart.

They are made in both 7.65mm and 9mm Short (.32 and .380) calibers.

At the front end of the slide on the 1922 a slide extension is attached by a bayonet joint lock to enclose the end of the longer barrel. The grip is longer than the M-1910. This is known as the "Police Model."

Browning pistols of these types were also sold with combination barrels specially mated. By changing the barrel the caliber can be converted to either 7.65mm or 9mm Short. Such pistols commonly have both calibers stamped on barrels and the receiver.

Belgian Commercial Pistols

Evaluation. Original F. N. manufactured pistols are good quality materials and workmanship, though finish is seldom as good as in U. S. manufacture. These pistols are reliable and safe, however, being made on Browning's system of forward slide mounting and incorporating an automatic grip safety. Imitations of these designs vary widely.

BELGIAN REVOLVERS

Every conceivable variety of pin fire, rim fire and center fire revolver design and caliber was made in Belgium. These included hinge frame, swing-out cylinder and solid frame models, hammer and hammerless, in hundreds of combinations of designs and barrel lengths. As a rule they bore no marks of identification except when made for some specific export house or Government.

Imitations of S&W and Colt designs in particular are always definitely inferior to the American genuine arms, though as made by Pieper they are sometimes good revolvers. Revolver types shown in chapters 24 and 43 were also made in Belgium; these are representative of the best of the Belgian revolver manufacture.

BELGIAN RIFLES AND CARBINES

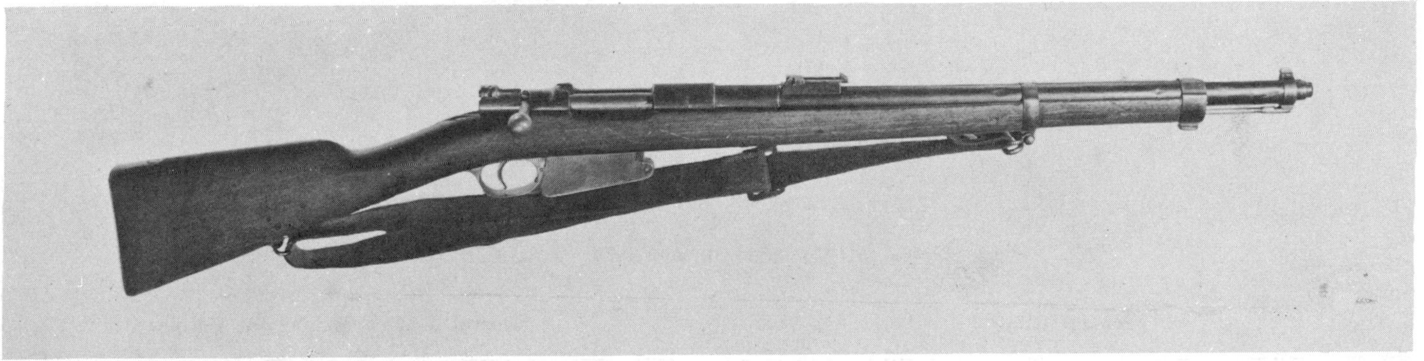

Carbine form of Belgian 1889 Mauser 7.65mm Rifle. Differs from rifle only in length and weight and minor external details. Note barrel jacket and projecting magazine.

This was the first Mauser production rifle to use the solid one piece bolt bored out from the rear. It also introduced the first form of Mauser charger-clip loading. This rifle and the shorter carbine, which is mechanically the same, were still the major Belgian small arms at the beginning of War II. They differ from later Mauser designs in having a single line box magazine which protrudes below the stock, and in the bolt which has two front lugs but no third safety lug. The cocking system also differs from the later patterns in that the mainspring compression is completed as the bolt handle is pushed forward. The flange on the bolt sleeve does not have the broad sweep provided in modern Mausers as a protection against gas back blast in case of a pierced primer.

Caliber: 7.65mm Belgian Service.
Barrel Length: 30.7″.
Overall Length: 50″.
Weight: 8.5 lbs.

Sights: Barleycorn front and graduated rear notch. Graduation 500 to 2000 meters.

Operation: Mauser turn bolt.

Safety: Mauser wing type.

Magazine: Single line vertical box. 5 cartridges. No cutoff.

Loading: Standard for Mauser magazine rifles.

Special Feature: Jacket around barrel.

Identification: The barrel jackets immediately identify these arms when encountered in original condition. The projecting single line box magazine is also characteristic. No rear safety lug on bolt. These arms were made at F.N. and also by Fabrique d'Armes de L'Etate.

Evaluation: Due to the long period of manufacture, the quality of the steels varies greatly. Ballistically the arms changed little. However, the design of bolt, magazine, and barrel jacket are such that converting these arms does not warrant the investment.

Good Features: Mauser type locking, loading, and primary extraction.

Bad Features: Lack of rear safety lug, protruding magazine. Inadequate gas protection on bolt sleeve.

Ammunition: As made in England for sporting purposes it is normally loaded with 35 grs. N.C. and 219-grain bullet or with 46.5 grs. N.C. and 154-grain bullet.

Commercial Pressures: 23,850 to 26,350 foot pounds depending on load. Was commercially made in U. S. before War II, and dealers stocks may be available.

While the Model 89 series was official, the later 1924 and 1924/30 Mauser patterns as made by F.N. were also in service, also in 7.65mm. These patterns and the Belgian Model 1935 were merely minor variants of the official German Kar. 98.

The Model 1936 in caliber 7.65mm was a modernized Model 1889.

Evaluation. All Mauser rifles as manufactured by F.N. under Belgian rule were first quality in materials and workmanship. It is possible that some made during the German occupation may have been deliberately sabotaged, as was unquestionably the case with pistols made at the same factory.

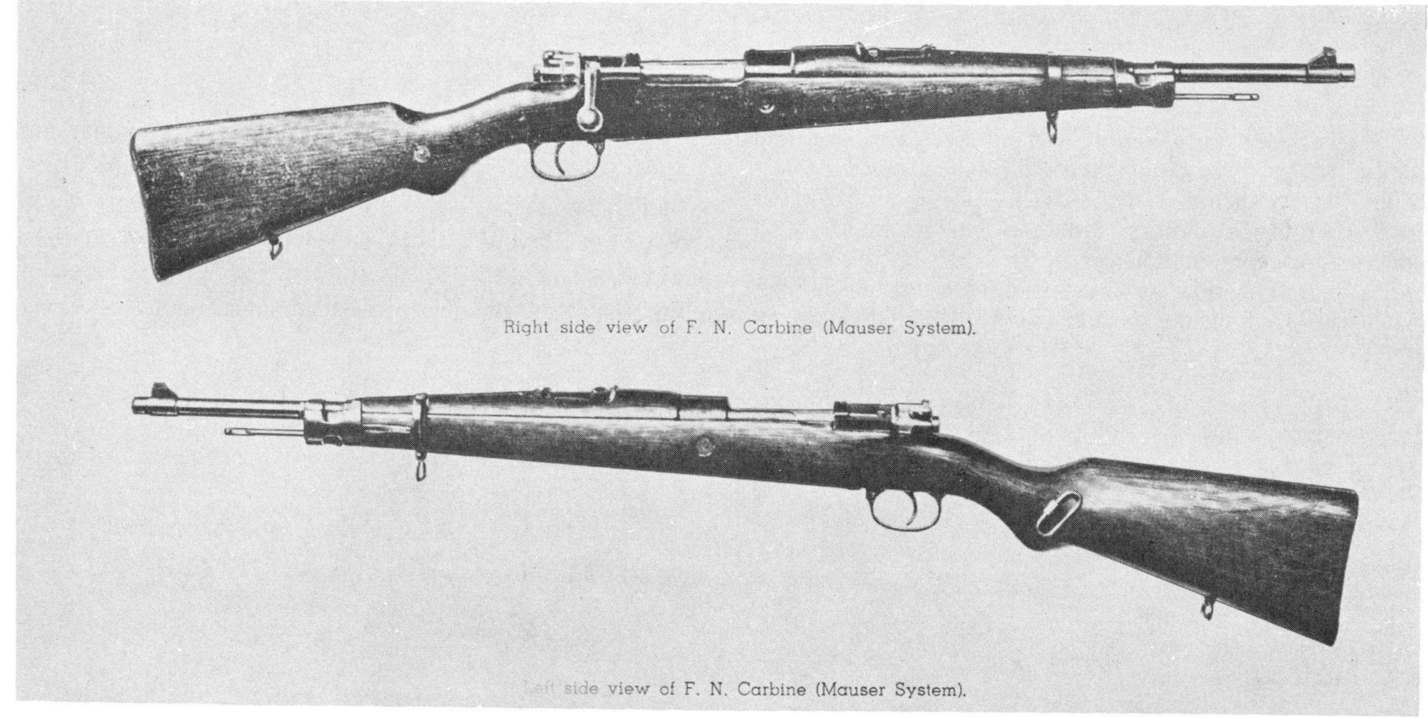

Right side view of F. N. Carbine (Mauser System).

Left side view of F. N. Carbine (Mauser System).

A Typical M1924, 1924/30 and 1930 F. N. Carbine.

General data

Caliber	7mm	7.65mm	7.9mm
Length of rifle without bayonet	1.099 m.	1.099 m.	1.099 m.
Length of rifle with bayonet	1.479 m.	1.479 m.	1.479 m.
Weight of rifle without bayonet (appr.)	3.875 kgs.	3.875 kgs.	3.875 kgs.
Weight of rifle with bayonet	4.350 kgs.	4.350 kgs.	4.350 kgs.
Length of barrel (X)	589mm	589mm	589mm
Length of line of sight	504mm	504mm	504mm
Number of grooves	4	4	4
Direction of twist	to the right	to the right	to the right
Number of cartridges in the magazine	5	5	5
Lowest rearsight graduation in m.	200	200	200
Highest rearsight graduation in m.	2000	2000	2000
Weight of bayonet with scabbard	720 grs.	720 grs.	720 grs.
Weight of bayonet without scabbard	475 grs.	475 grs.	475 grs.
Length of bayonet	516mm	516mm	516mm

(X) The Mauser rifle can be supplied with a barrel of 740mm, the total length of the rifle being in this case 1.250 m.

General data concerning the Carbine

Caliber	7mm	7.65mm	7.9mm
Length af carbine	0.95 m.	0.95 m.	0.95 m.
Weight of carbine	3.300 kgs.	3.300 kgs.	3.300 kgs.
Length of barrel	440mm	440mm	440mm
Length of line of sight	354mm	354mm	354mm
Number of grooves	4	4	4
Direction of twist	to the right	to the right	to the right
Number of cartridges in the magazine	5	5	5
Lowest rear sight graduation in m.	200	200	200
Highest rear sight graduation in m.	1400	1400	1400

These arms were made for South American, African, and Asiatic governments when Belgium took over the German military export market after World War I. The basic design was perfected by German Ordnance.

In every mechanical respect they are duplicates of the German and Czech Service rifles, and the descriptions of mechanisms given for those arms cover the F.N. line as well. Model modifications are minor and deal with externals.

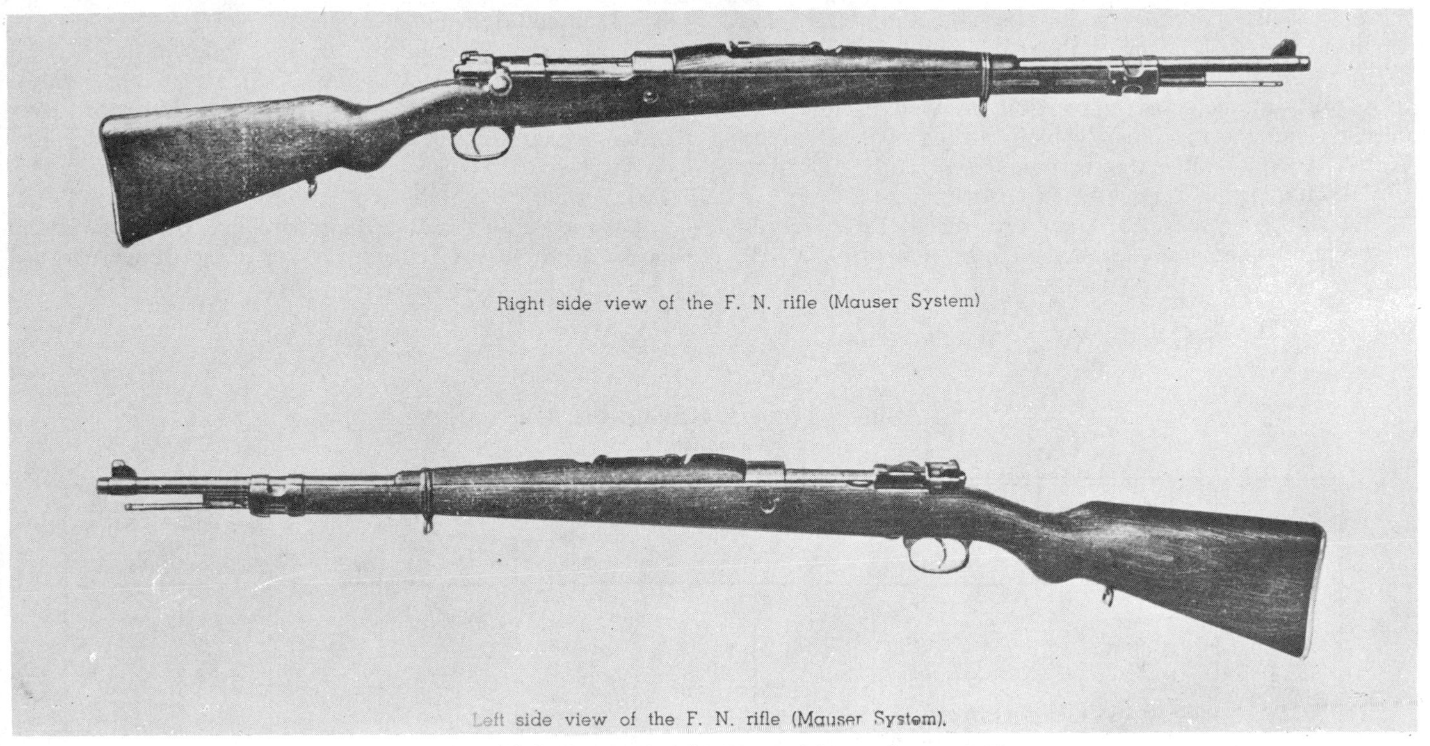

Typical M1924 and 1924/30 F. N. Mauser System Rifles.

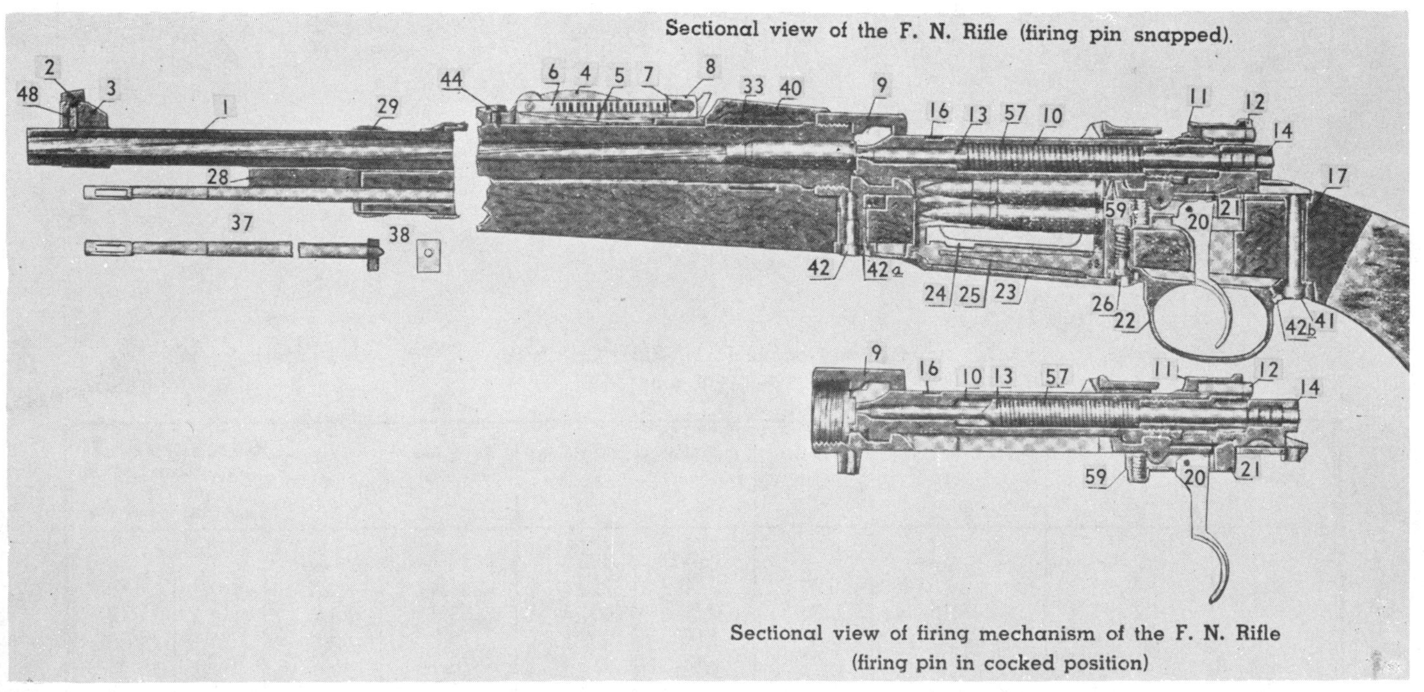

List of component parts of the F. N. Rifle (Mauser System)

1. Barrel.
2. Front sight.
3. Front sight ring.
4. Rear sight bed ring.
5. Rear sight spring.
6. Rear sight tangent.
7. Spring pawl.
8. Sight slide.
9. Body.
10. Bolt.
11. Bolt plug.
12. Safety wing.
13. Firing pin.
14. Cocking piece.
16. Extractor ring.
17. Bolt stop.
20. Trigger.
21. Trigger bar.
22. Triggerguard.
23. Magazine cover plate.
24. Magazine platform.
25. Magazine spring.
26. Magazine cover plate catch.
28. Bayonet attachment.
29. Upper band.
37. Cleaning rod.
38. Cleaning rod stop.
40. Handguard.
41. Triggerguard screw (rear).
42. Triggerguard screw (front).

42a. Check screw of front triggerguard screw.

42b. Check screw of rear triggerguard screw.

44. Rear sight bed screw.
48. Front sight ring screw.
57. Firing pin spring.
59. Trigger bar spring.

Most Mauser military actions are based on the same receiver and bolt. The standard 7mm, 7.65mm and 7.9mm Mauser cartridges were developed by Paul Mauser to permit simplicity of conversion, as well as low cost design. Thus the machinery which in time of peace made 7mm rifles for South America could be readily converted to 7.9mm German Service when needed.

The tables reproduced below are official F.N. records covering all rifles and carbines made by that firm, as well as all ammunition made for them.

These arms were made for the following countries: Abyssinia, Argentina, Belgium (Gendarmerie use only), Bolivia, Brazil, Chile, China, Colombia, Ecuador, Iran, Luxembourg, Mexico, Peru, Turkey, Uruguay, and Yugoslavia. (Note: Mauser pattern rifles as made in Yugoslavia usually have shorter actions than standard.)

They were also sold in commercial export throughout the world for use as, or conversion to, sporting rifles.

Ballistics of the F. N. Rifle, Cal. 7mm

Round nose bullet (11.20 gr.)

Distance	Angle of elevation	Angle of descent	Time of flight sec.	Height of trajectory m.	Remaining velocity m/s.	Remaining energy kgm.	Danger zone h=1m,70	Rectangle of dispersion Zone containing 50 % of shots	
								Height cm.	Breadth cm.
0	—	—	—	—	670	256.3	—	—	—
200	8' 40"	10' 4"	0,33	0,14	540,4	166,7	total	6	4
400	20' 25"	27' 20"	0,75	0,68	433,8	107,4	total	15	10
600	36' 26"	55' 37"	1,26	1,97	355,5	72,2	155	26	17
800	57' 55"	1° 36' 58'	1,87	4,43	306,6	53,7	64	40	25
1000	1° 24' 55"	2° 29' 55"	2,56	8,50	277,8	44,0	38	53	38
1200	1° 57' 42"	3° 32' 55"	3,31	14,51	255,4	37,2	27	—	—
1400	2° 35' 58"	4° 48' 5"	4,13	22,76	236,0	31,8	19	—	—
1600	3° 20' 3"	6° 17' 45"	5,02	33,84	218,4	27,2	12	—	—
1800	4° 10' 30"	8° 5' 30"	5,98	48,22	202,7	23,5	9	—	—
2000	5° 7' 55"	10° 15' 55"	7,03	66,46	188,3	20,2	3	—	—

Muzzle velocity ... ... 670 m/s.
V. 25 ... ... 650 m/s.
Pressure... ... ... 3,000 kg/cm²
Maximum range ... ... 3.250 metres.

Ballistics of the F. N. Rifle, Cal. 7mm

Bullet S. 9 gr.

Distance	Angle of elevation	Angle of descent	Time of flight sec.	Height of trajectory m.	Remaining velocity m/s.	Remaining energy kgm.	Danger zone h=1m,70	Rectangle of dispersion Zone containing 50 % of shots	
								Height cm.	Breadth cm.
0	—	—	—	—	852,9	333,7	—	—	—
200	5' 11"	5' 52"	0,26	0,08	720,8	238,3	total	7	6
400	11' 45"	14' 54"	0,56	0,38	601,4	165,9	total	14	12
600	20' 16"	28' 59"	0,93	1,05	497,9	113,7	total	25	20
800	31' 23"	50' 54"	1,37	2,31	413,4	78,4	151	45	35
1000	45' 58"	1° 23' 22"	1,89	4,49	350,4	56,3	76	65	45
1200	1° 4' 55"	2° 7' 28"	2,51	8,02	308,8	43,7	44	—	—
1400	1° 33' 53"	3° 15' 10"	3,29	14,30	274,2	34,5	28	—	—
1600	2° 11' 50"	4° 40' 20"	4,17	23,76	246,3	27,8	20	—	—
1800	2° 49' 31"	6° 5' 2"	5,02	34,73	228,6	24,0	14	—	—
2000	3° 41' 32"	8° 5' 27"	6,06	51,14	207,1	19,7	10	—	—

Muzzle velocity .... 855 m/s.
V. 25 .... 835 m/s.
Pressure .... 3200 kg/cm2.
Maximum range .... 3.700 mètres.

Ballistics of the F. N. Rifle, Cal. 7.65mm

Light pointed bullet (10 gr.)

Distance	Angle of elevation	Angle of descent	Time of flight sec.	Height of trajectory m.	Remaining velocity m/s.	Remaining energy kgm.	Danger zone h=1m,70	Rectangle of dispersion Zone containing 50 % of shots	
								Height cm.	Breadth cm.
0	—	—	—	—	855	368	—	—	—
200	5' 25''	6' 18''	0,26	0,09	677,4	233,9	total	8	6
400	12' 57''	17' 54''	0,60	0,44	524,6	140,3	total	20	14
600	23' 47''	39' 7''	1,03	1,32	406,1	84,0	total	32	24
800	39' 35''	1° 14' 59''	1,59	3,19	328,1	54,9	87	47	37
1000	1° 1' 34''	2° 6' 4''	2,24	6,59	286,0	41,7	50	63	50
1200	1° 29' 58''	3° 9' 40''	2,98	12,00	258,5	34	31	—	—
1400	2° 9' 15''	4° 37' 40''	3,87	20,64	230,4	27	19	—	—
1600	2° 52' 28''	6° 17' 10''	4,78	31,81	209,8	22	14	—	—
1800	3 52' 11''	8° 44' 20''	5,91	48,58	186,4	18	7	—	—
2000	4° 58' 20''	13° 40' 00''	7,11	71,00	161,0	13	2	—	—

Muzzle velocity .... 855 m/s.
V. 25 .... 835 m/s.
Pressure .... 3.000 kg/cm2.
Maximum range .... 3.700 metres.

Ballistics of the F. N. Rifle, Cal. 7.65mm

Streamlined pointed bullet with tapered base (11.25 gr.)

Distance	Angle of elevation	Angle of descent	Time of flight sec.	Height of trajectory m.	Remaining velocity m/s.	Remaining energy kgm.	Danger zone h=1m,70	Rectangle of dispersion Zone containing 50 % of shots	
								Height cm.	Breadth cm.
0	—	—	—	—	725	301	—	—	—
200	7' 8''	8' 2''	0,30	0,11	615,1	216,9	total	7	5
400	16' 9''	20' 14''	0,65	0,52	518,2	154,0	total	15	10
600	27' 35''	38' 45''	1,08	1,42	436,6	109,3	total	25	17
800	42' 13''	1° 5' 56''	1,57	3,07	372,2	79,4	107	35	25
1000	1° 4' 55''	1° 54' 16''	2,24	6,33	309,7	55,0	51	50	35
1200	1° 30' 13''	2° 46' 26''	2,91	11,12	283,2	46,0	37	—	—
1400	2° 0' 20''	3° 47' 31''	3,65	17,80	263,0	39,7	25	—	—
1600	2° 35' 10''	4° 58' 6''	4,44	26,81	245,3	34,5	18	—	—
1800	3° 14' 53''	6° 20' 30''	5,29	38,40	229,0	30,1	13	—	—
2000	3° 59' 42''	7° 56' 57''	6,20	52,94	213,8	26,2	8	—	—

Muzzle velocity .... 725 m/s.
V. 25 .... 710 m/s.
Pressure .... 3.000 kg/cm2.
Maximum range .... 5.000 metres.

Ballistics of the F. N. Rifle, Cal. 7.9mm

Light pointed bullet (10 gr.)

Distance	Angle of elevation	Angle of descent	Time of flight sec.	Height of trajectory m.	Remaining velocity m/s.	Remaining energy kgm.	Danger zone h=1m,70	Rectangle of dispersion Zone containing 50 % of shots	
								Height cm.	Breadth cm.
0	—	—	—	—	830	351,0	—	—	—
200	5' 37''	6' 27''	0,27	0,09	674,5	231,9	total	6	5
400	13' 10''	17' 34''	0,60	0,44	539,6	148,4	total	14	9
600	23' 33'	36' 30''	1,02	1,27	430,2	94,3	total	26	19
800	37' 55''	1° 7' 21''	1,53	2,94	351 1	62,8	103	42	31
1000	57' 33''	1° 52' 12''	2,15	5,93	302,8	46,7	54	60	44
1200	1° 26' 45''	2° 58' 6''	2,92	11,33	267,9	36,6	32	—	—
1400	1° 59' 20''	4° 9' 15''	3,70	18,62	245,4	30,7	23	—	—
1600	2° 42' 23''	5° 45' 15''	4,62	29,50	221,6	25,0	16	—	—
1800	3° 28' 55''	7° 32' 57''	5,57	43,04	203,8	21,2	11	—	—
2000	4° 31' 8''	10° 8'	6,72	62,60	183,7	17,2	6	—	—

Muzzle velocity .... 830 m/s.
V. 25 .... 805 m/s.
Pressure .... 3.000 kg/cm2.
Maximum range .... 3.700 metres.

Ballistics of the F. N. Rifle, Cal. 7.9mm
Streamlined pointed bullet with tapered base (12.80 gr.)

Distance	Angle of elevation	Angle of descent	Time of flight sec.	Height of trajectory m.	Remaining velocity m/s.	Remaining energy kgm.	Danger zone h=1m,70	Rectangle of dispersion Zone containing 50 % of shots Height cm.	Breadth cm.
0	—	—	—	—	760	—	—	—	—
200	6' 10"	6' 20"	0,28	0,10	660	284	total	8	6
400	13'	14' 20"	0,61	0,40	574	215	total	16	14
600	21' 50"	26' 40"	0,98	1,1	495	160	total	28	23
800	33' 40"	46' 50"	1,43	2,3	426	118	111	40	32
1000	49'	1° 17' 10"	1,96	4,5	367	88	68	60	45
1200	1° 9'	1° 59' 50"	2,56	8,0	322	68	46	—	—
1400	1° 33' 30"	2° 52' 50"	3,23	13,5	293	56	33	—	—
1600	2° 1' 30"	3° 52'	3,94	20,0	274	49	25	—	—
1800	2° 33"	4° 56' 20"	4,70	29,0	259	44	19	—	—
2000	3° 7' 30"	6° 6' 30"	5,51	41,0	245	39	16	—	—

Muzzle velocity .... 760 m/s.
V. 25 .... 740 m/s.
Pressure .... 3.200 kg/cm2.
Maximum range .... 4.700 metres.

Ammunition Characteristics

	Cal. 7 m/m			Cal 7,65 m/m		Cal. 7,9 m/m	
	Round nose bullet	Streamlined pointed bullet w/tapered base	Light pointed bullet	Streamlined pointed bullet w/tapered base	Light pointed bullet	Streamlined pointed bullet w/tapered base	Light pointed bullet
Numerical Data							
Length of cartridge (maximum)	78 mm.	78 mm.	78 mm.	75.4 mm	75,4 mm.	80,4 mm.	80,4 mm.
Weight of cartridge	24 gr.	23,8 gr.	23 gr.	25,35 gr.	23,1 gr.	26.2 gr.	23,5 gr.
Average weight of bullet	11,2 gr.	10,5 gr.	9 gr.	11,25 gr.	10 gr.	12,8 gr.	10 gr.
Average length of bullet	31,0 mm.	35 mm.	30,0 mm.	33,1 mm.	27,0 gr.	35,0 mm.	28,0 mm.
Diameter of bullet (maximum)	7,26 mm.	7,26 mm.	7,26 mm.	7,98 mm	7,97 mm.	8,23 mm.	8,23 mm.
Sectional density	29,1 gr/cm2	28 gr/cm2	23,4 gr/cm2	22,6 gr/cm2	21,8 gr/cm2	26,2 gr/cm2	20,4 gr/cm2
Composition of jacket	steel plated	brass	steel plated	brass	steel plated	steel plated	steel plated
Weight of clip for 5 cartridges	8,6 gr.	8,6 gr.	8,6 gr.	7 gr.	7 gr.	6,5 gr.	6,5 gr.
Approximate weight of powder charge	2,50 gr.	2,70 gr.	2,90 gr.	2,55 gr.	2,90 gr.	2,90 gr.	3,20 gr.
Ballistics							
1. — RIFLE							
Muzzle velocity	670 m/s.	750 m/s.	850 m/s.	725 m/s.	830 m/s.	760 m/s.	855 m/s.
Velocity 25 m. from muzzle	650 m/s	730 m/s.	835 m/s.	710 m/s.	805 m/s.	740 m/s.	835 m/s.
Pressure	3000 kg/cm2	3200 kg/cm2	3200 kg/cm2	3000 kg/cm2	3000 kg/cm2	3200 kg/cm2	3000 kg/cm2
Muzzle energy	256 kgm.	310 kgm	334 kgm.	300 kgm.	351 kgm.	377 kgm.	368 kgm.
Maximum range	3250 m.	5000 m.	3700 m.	5000 m.	3700 m.	4700 m.	3700 m.
2. — CARBINE							
Muzzle velocity	640 m/s	710 m/s	810 m/s.	700 m/s.	800 m/s.	730 m/s.	800 m/s.
Velocity 25 m. from muzzle	620 m/s	690 m/s	790 m/s.	680 m/s.	780 m/s.	710 m/s.	780 m/s.
Muzzle energy	234 kgm.	293 kgm.	301 kgm.	290 kgm.	326 kgm.	348 kgm	326 kgm.

F. N. SEMI-AUTO RIFLE

In 1940 F. N. introduced a new semi-automatic infantry rifle developed to meet the needs for a semi-auto military arm to replace the bolt designs of the general pattern of the Mauser and equivalent to our Garand.

This rifle was originally designed to use the standard group of military rimless pattern cartridges of the type of the U. S. .30 M1, the 7mm, 7.65mm, and 7.9mm Mauser. It is a fully locked breech weapon, gas operated.

In the light of later developments, particularly the adoption by the United States of the new 7.62mm NATO cartridge, it is highly unlikely that this excellent F. N. design will go into future general manufacture to any great degree since, like the Garand, it can be supplanted by superior Belgian short-cartridge rifles.

It must be stressed that this rifle is not to be confused with the later F. N. Full Automatic Rifle with

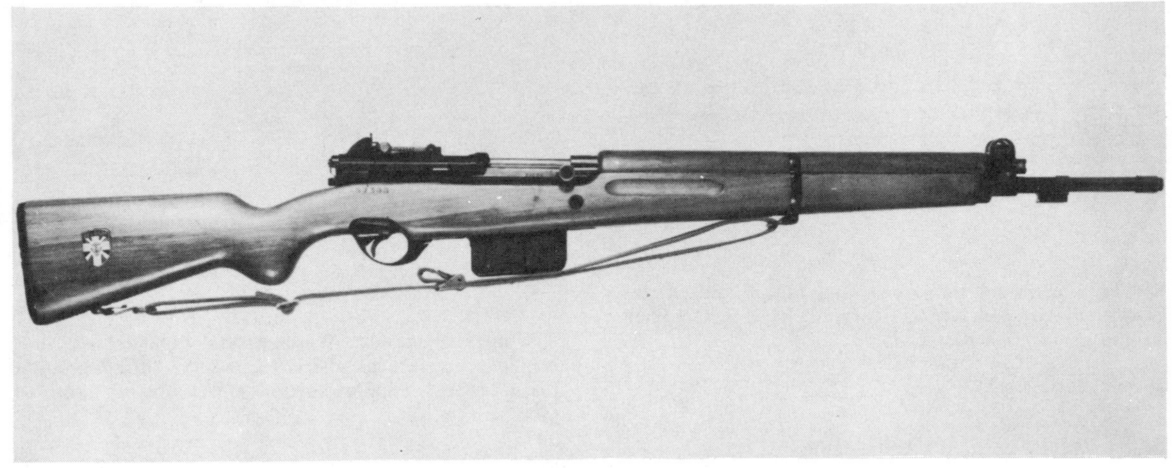

Belgian Semi-automatic Rifle as used by Belgian troops with the UN in Korea. This rifle is chambered for the U.S. .30 M1 and M2 cartridges. The rifle is also made to order for all military rimless cartridges.

which we will presently deal. The new weapon is a modification but also a very considerable improvement in a score of ways over the semi-automatic infantry design here mentioned.

Since this semi-auto F. N. rifle is a basic development, it requires our attention.

The design and operation of this rifle very closely approximates in many respects that of the Russian Tokarev 40 semi-automatic design. As is to be expected, it is far better constructed than the Russian because of the superior technology of the Belgian gun manufacturers.

The basic design factors in the weapon were patented originally by Dieudonné Saive, chief design engineer at the F. N. Works, who was John Browning's mechanic. However, in spite of the patent issued, it must in all fairness be pointed out that the tappet gas principle used for operating the design did appear in considerably earlier models, notably the Italian Cei Rigotti early in the century, while variations of the locking system were early utilized by Paul Mauser, among others.

From the author's own personal contact with and knowledge of the Belgian designer, there is no question in his mind that the Belgian rifle was conceived as an entirely original development. The fact is inescapable, however, to the firearms historian and researcher that all the elements of the design had appeared at earlier times. This is a common experience in design, only the Germans seeming to do research first and design afterwards, in the personal observation of the author.

Caliber: Any rimless military high power such as the .30 U. S. M1, 7mm, 7.65mm, and 7.92mm Mauser.

Magazine: Projecting steel box. Capacity 10 cartridges. Loaded single shot or from 5-shot clip.

Hold Open Device: Action is held open by standard operation through follower acting on hold open device when last cartridge has been ejected.

Ballistics: Standard for cartridges used.

Barrel Length: 23.2 in.

Overall Length of Gun: 43.7 in.

Weight of Gun: 9.48 lbs.

Sights: Front shielded post type mounted in gas cylinder at end of forearm several inches back from muzzle giving short sighting radius. (This design is required to protect the front sight. Since the gas-operating mechanism is on top of the barrel, placing the front sight at the extreme barrel muzzle end as in customary practice would require too great a sight height and resulting fragility.) Rear sight—elevating receiver pattern.

Rifle Operated by: Gas. Port from barrel into gas regulator allows gas to expand into cylinder on top of barrel as in Russian and 1943 German practice.

Gas System: Tappet system as utilized in Russian and German designs. Instead of customary connected piston, the tappet with its individual recoil spring is driven back to strike a sharp blow against the face of the bolt carrier.

Locked: Cammed down breechblock actuated as in Russian 40 Tokarev rifle. Locks firmly into receiver to support cartridge.

Cooled: No cooling device provided.

Operating Rod Handle: Right side near breech face. Gun fires from closed bolt.

Ejection: Up and to the right.

Operation: Tappet driving back through hole in receiver above line of barrel strikes bolt housing and starts it to the rear until pressure has dropped. At unlocking point, the housing is machined to cam the breechblock up a ramp at its rear end, thus allowing the housing and breechblock to travel to the rear with the breechblock carrying the cartridge case in its face, held by the extractor, until it strikes the ejector and is tossed out of the weapon. Recoil springs compressed during this motion start the housing and breechblock forward at the end of the recoil stroke. Upon closing, as the cartridge is chambered and the breechblock face is against the breech face of the barrel, the housing still has continuing forward movement which enables it, through its machined surfaces, to depress the rear of the breechblock into its locking recesses with the rear locking surface at the top of the ramp.

Loading and Firing

Magazine is hand- or clip-loaded. The cocking handle on the right side is drawn back to unlock the action and compress the springs. Releasing the cocking handle permits the springs to drive the mechanism forward to chamber the top cartridge from the magazine and lock the breech. A pull on the trigger fires the cartridge and the gas functions as described above to operate the arm in recoil and energize the springs for the counter recoil stroke. Thus one shot is fired, the empty case extracted and ejected, the weapon cocked, and a new cartridge loaded into the chamber ready for firing on the next

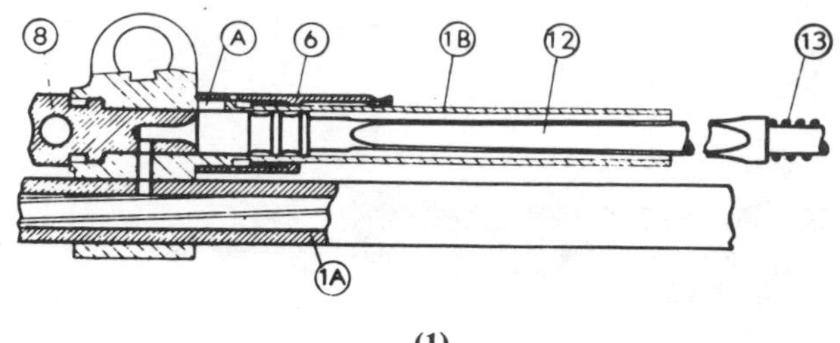

(1)

Gas action. May be sealed off by turning nut. Standard gas point top of barrel bleeds gas into cylinder to drive piston back on tappet principle as for German Kar. 43.

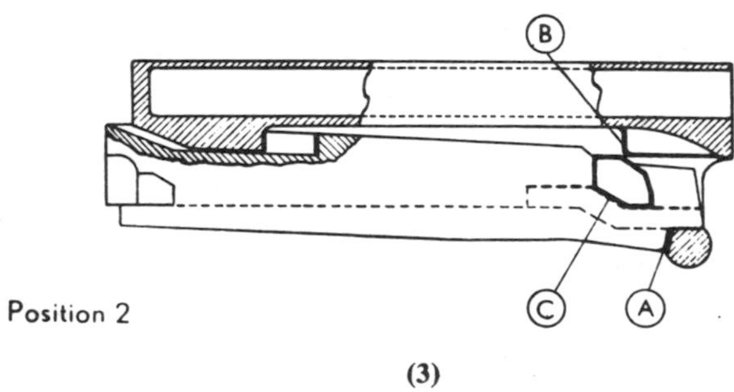

(3)

Cams on slide raise breechblock out of receiver engagement as with Russian Tokarev rifle.

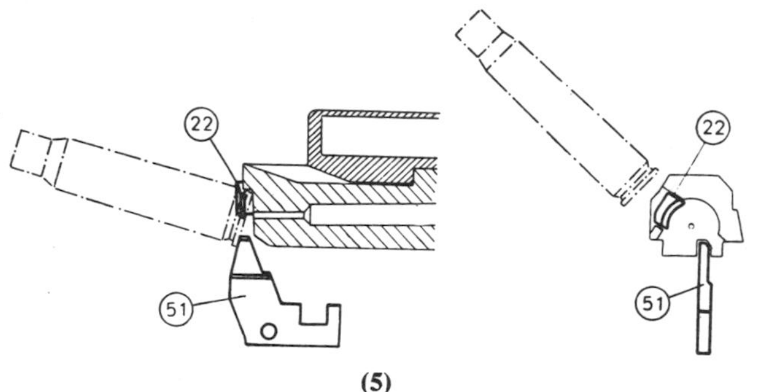

(5)

Near end of recoil stroke the cartridge case held by the extractor hits the ejector and is tossed out of the rifle.

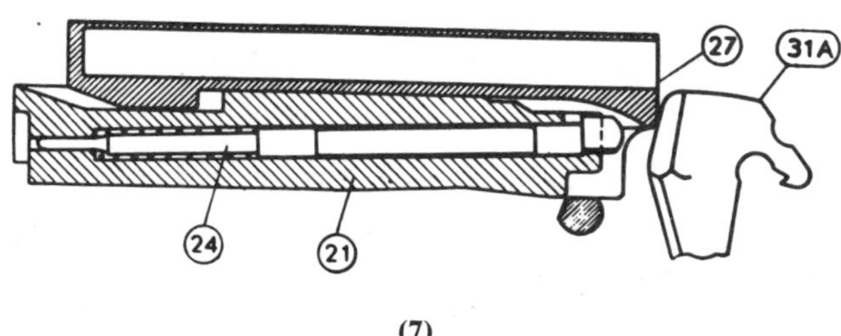

(7)

Safety feature. If action is not locked, hammer will hit slide instead of firing pin.

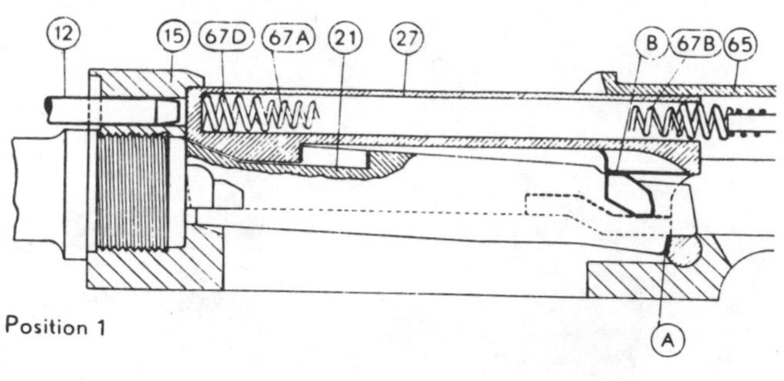

(2)

Unlocking action. Tappet hits breechblock slide starting it back. Spring returns piston to battery. Slide has initial free movement before camming action starts. Breech still locked.

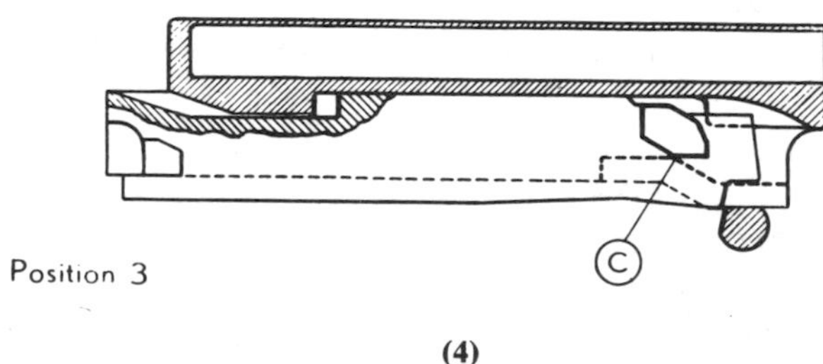

(4)

Slide and block go back. Hammer is ridden down to cock. Recoil spring compressed in standard fashion.

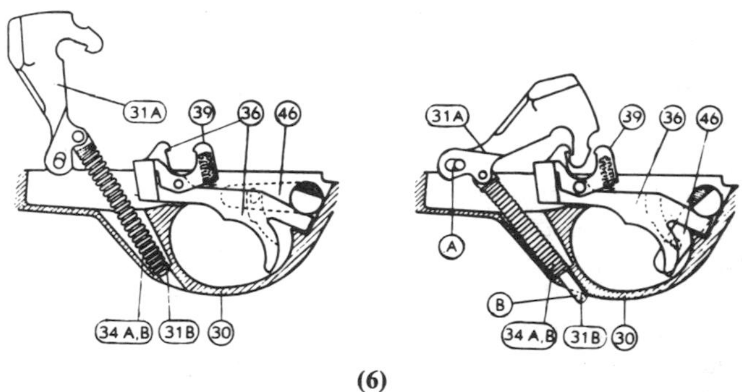

(6)

Left—Hammer and mechanism in fired position. On recoil hammer hook will be engaged Browning style on rear sear to prevent firing until trigger is released. Right—Hammer held by forward sear ready for firing. Mainspring guide pin projects as signal that hammer is cocked. Walther system.

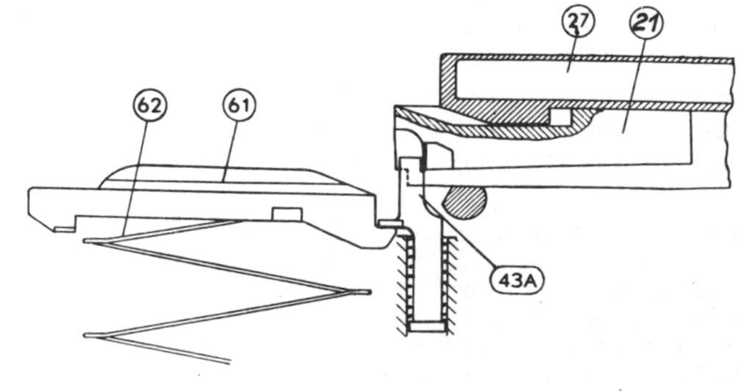

(8)

Magazine follower pushed up plunger to hold breech open when last shot is fired.

Operation of the Belgian Semi-Automatic Rifle

trigger pull. An individual pull is required to fire each shot.

Mechanism

The hammer mechanism in the design is an adaptation of the familiar John Browning hammer hook system as used originally in his automatic shotgun. Variations of this design are encountered in most sporting arms of successful types today, and a minor variant of it is used in the United States Rifle M1 and the Carbine M1. It is not unusual that a modification of it, and in many senses an improvement of it, should be encountered in this Belgian rifle, since its designer Monsieur Saive was a very close associate of John Browning throughout the period of that great inventor's years at the F. N. establishment.

This hammer hook system is so designed that during recoil, the rear upper hook on the hammer is engaged automatically to prevent full automatic fire. When the trigger is deliberately released, the upper hook (or sear) releases, the hammer spring reacts but the forward holding sear, which is at a lower level than the automatic holding one, grips a lower cut or hook in the hammer. One innovation in the design, (which has, however, appeared on German rifles, notably of Walther commercial design), is that the hammer spring guide is designed to protrude slightly below the line of the triggerguard when the hammer is in cocked position. It is remembered that the hammer is concealed in this type of weapon. The F. N. design permits the holder of the weapon to tell by sight or touch if the hammer is cocked as evidenced by the protruding nose of the mainspring guide.

The safety system also includes a variation of the one utilized in the Garand in that the breechblock housing or carrier is so designed that it interferes with the hammer striking the firing pin until both the breechblock is locked and the housing itself is in its full forward position. Thus if the housing is not completely closed, while the hammer may fall it can only strike the rear of the housing and cannot fire the cartridge in the chamber. In such an instance, it is necessary to pull back the cocking handle to recock the arm before it can be fired. The firing pin itself is of the inertia type which is automatically retracted by a return spring after being driven forward to fire.

The breech face of the breechblock is slotted to allow it to travel back over the ejector which also helps to serve as a travel guide. As the proper motion nears the end of the recoil stroke, the ejector is far enough out from the face of the breechblock so that it can pivot the cartridge out of the gun.

The manual safety is on the right side of the triggerguard and is in the form of a turning lever with a half round block which not only locks the trigger to prevent any movement, but also drops its bar down far enough to interfere with the trigger finger being inserted into the triggerguard as a warning that the safety is applied.

While this design was far superior to either the German or the Russian variants, it has already been outmoded by the later F.N.-Saive design developments.

A study of the detail drawings will disclose all the salient features and show the resemblance to the Russian designs in particular. While this is a beautifully constructed rifle, the very nature and quality of the workmanship in it make it a relatively costly one to produce.

Full advantage of all the fine points of construction were incorporated in the later Belgian design.

THE F. N. LIGHT AUTO RIFLE

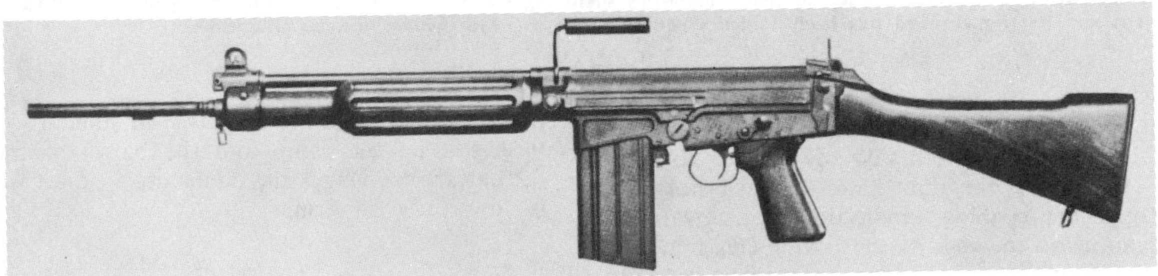

Belgian F.N. Light Auto Rifle Cal. 7.62 NATO, early type.

Description: Weight: 8 pounds 9½ ounces without magazine.
Magazine Weight Empty: 7 and 9/10ths ounces.
Barrel Weight: 1 pound 12¼ ounces.
Overall Length: 39 inches.
Barrel Length: 20 inches.
Method of Operation: Gas.
Feeding: From detachable box magazine, staggered, 20 round capacity.
Ejection: To the right.
Cocking Handle: Left side of receiver.
Sights: Hooded front post. Windage elevating rear in 100 meter steps to 600 meters.
Distance Between Sights: 21.77 inches. (Note: Relatively short sight base is due to the fact that design makes it advisable to mount front sight on top of gas regulator. Placing it conveniently on the muzzle of the barrel would require a high and fragile sight.)
Rifling: 4 grooves, right hand, one turn in 8.66 inches.
Rate of Fire: 650 to 700 per minute. Most of the weapons in service throughout the world are only used as semi-automatic weapons.

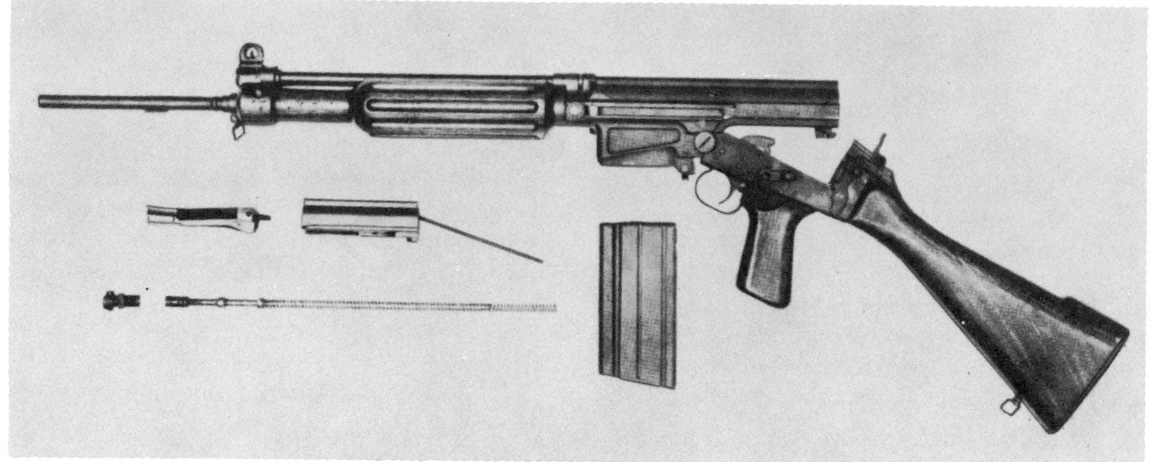

Belgian F.N. Light Auto Rifle. Hinged open. Operating parts removed. Field strip without tools.

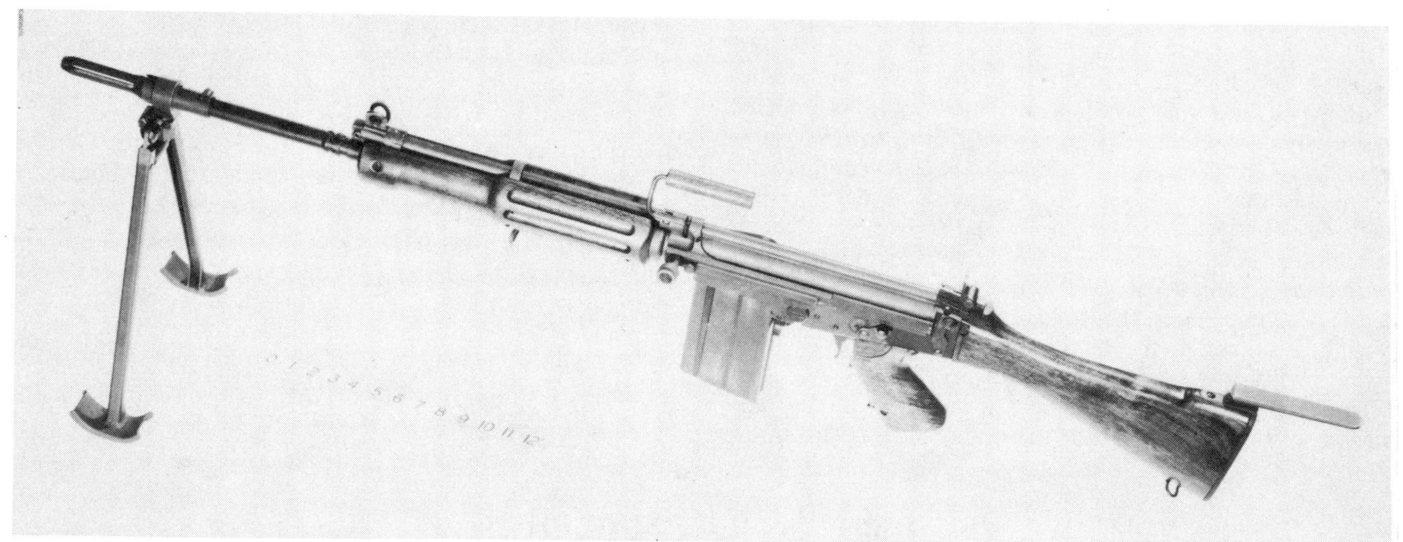

The heavy barrel version of the F.N. light automatic rifle (FAL). This weapon, which is the same as the light rifle except for the weight of its barrel, is now in service in many countries including Canada, Israel, and Peru. The specimen shown has the early type handguards and its triggerguard has been folded down to make use with winter mittens practicable.

Operation

Pull cocking handle on left side of receiver to rear as in BAR. This leaves the right hand on the pistol grip ready for firing. The cocking handle does not move during firing, again as in the case of the BAR. This removes danger to the firer's face and does not interfere with aiming.

At the end of the cocking handle's stroke, the breechblock is held open automatically. A loaded magazine is inserted in the magazine housing and pushed in until the retaining catch secures it.

Pressing the release stud on the left side near the magazine catch releases the breechblock which is driven forward by its compressed return spring.

This return spring is housed in the butt. It acts on the breechblock slide through a rod pivoted at its rear face. As the breechblock moves forward, its feed face strips the top round from the magazine in standard fashion and thrusts it up the ramp into the barrel chamber, where the extractor engages the cannelure in the case. The gun is now ready for firing.

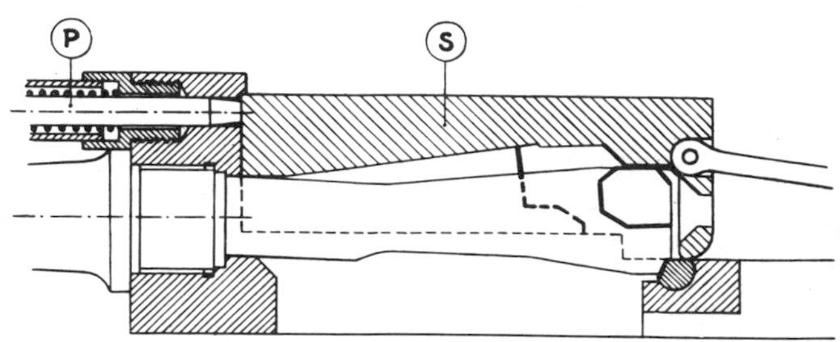

Piston driven back by gas hits movable slide above locked breechblock, driving it back and compressing return spring.

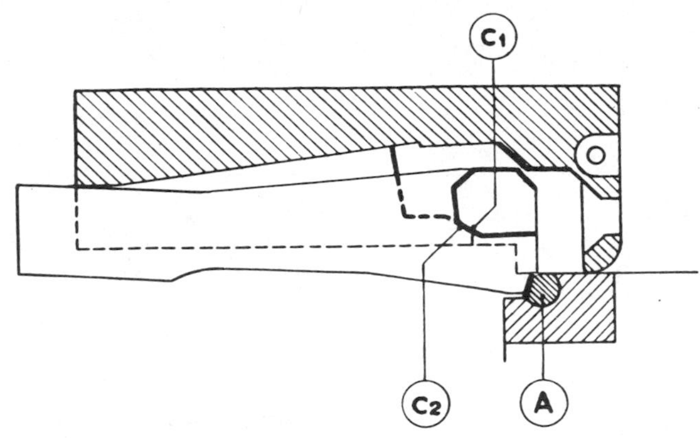

Ramps in the slide engage cam (C1) on breechblock as bullet leaves barrel, thus raising the rear of breechblock out of its locking seat (A) in the receiver.

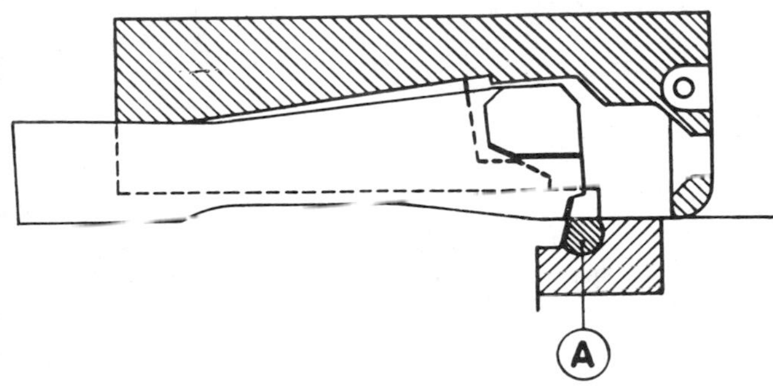

Slide and breechblock travel back togeter. Piston tappet spring returns piston. Breechblock rotates and cocks hammer. Extractor withdraws fired case.

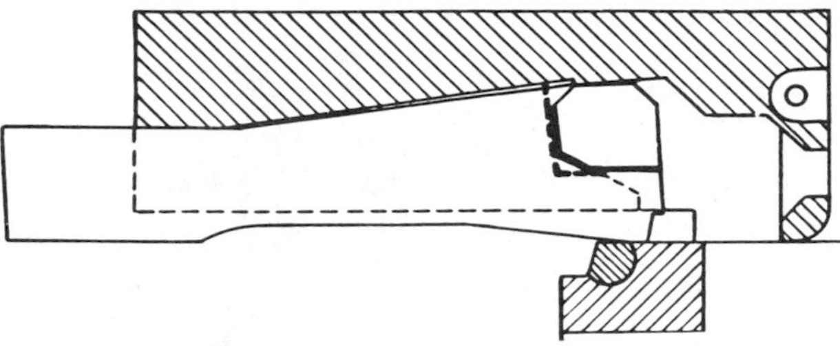

Breechblock and slide reach end of stroke. Case hits ejector. Return spring in butt is fully compressed.

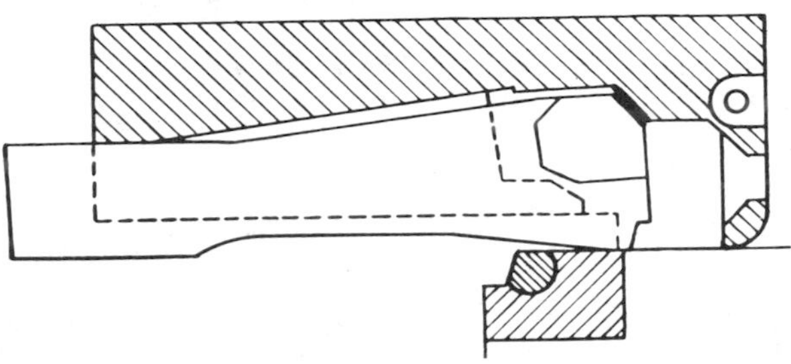

Spring starts slide and breechblock forward. Block picks up top cartridge in magazine and starts it toward chamber.

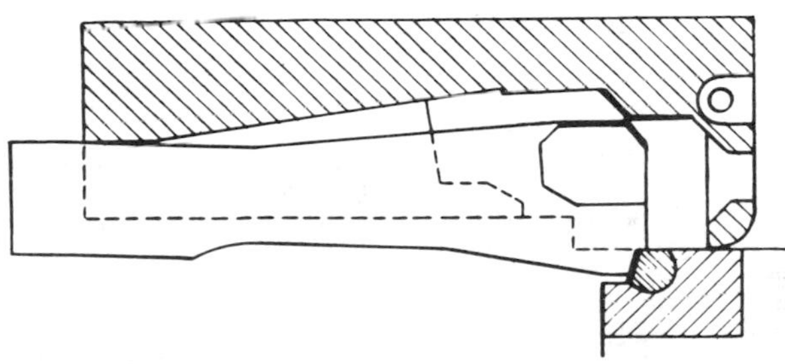

Face of breechblock chambers cartridge. It is stopped against face of barrel. Slide is still driven forward, and it cams breechblock down into locking seat in the receiver.

Firing

The change lever on the left side of the receiver may be set for "Safe," "Single shot," or "Full Automatic" fire. The positions are widely spaced deliberately so that in the dark one can tell by sense of touch the position of the change lever.

If the change lever is set for single shot fire, pressure on the trigger releases the hammer to strike the rear face of the firing pin and fire the cartridge. Since the weapon fires from a closed breech, there is no such disturbance of aim as occurs in weapons like the submachine gun and the Browning machine rifle, where the mass of the breech mechanism moves forward with the pull on the trigger.

The operation is the standard gas system whose reliability has long been established for this type of weapon. Part of the gases following the bullet down the barrel pass through the port into the forward section of the gas cylinder. A gas regulator, previously adjusted, provides sufficient gas to satisfactorily operate the piston which is driven back to function the mechanism. Remaining gas passes to the open air through holes in the gas cylinder.

The piston, acting on the tappet principle, is driven to the rear in its tube on top of the barrel. It strikes the breechblock slide (or carrier) and pushes it to the rear.

Ramps machined into the breechblock slide engage a cam on the breechblock after the bullet has emerged from the barrel and the pressure has dropped to safe limits. The breechblock is cam lifted out of engagement with its locking shoulder in the receiver—this unlocks the action.

The breechblock slide and breechblock now travel together to the rear. They ride down the hammer to cock it.

During rearward motion of the breechblock, the extractor has carried the empty case out of the chamber with it. The case strikes the ejector and is thrown out the right side of the gun.

After the piston tappet strikes the breechblock slide and imparts the necessary impetus to it, during which travel the spring around the piston has been compressed, the spring operates to return the piston to forward (battery) position. The return spring within the butt is fully compressed during rearward movement of the breechblock and slide in standard fashion. At the end of the

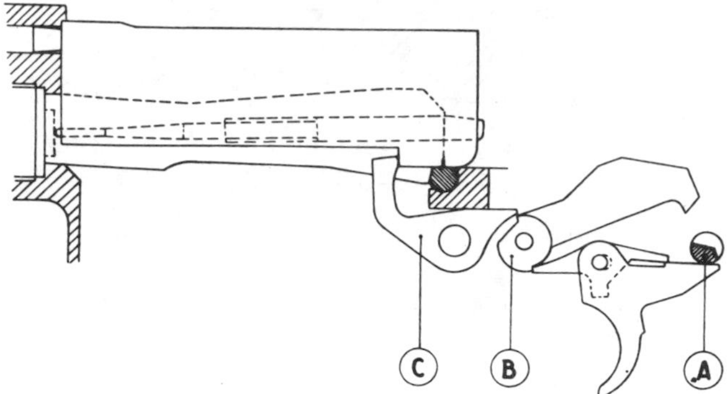

Gun with safety applied. Change lever stud (A) is locking trigger to prevent movement.

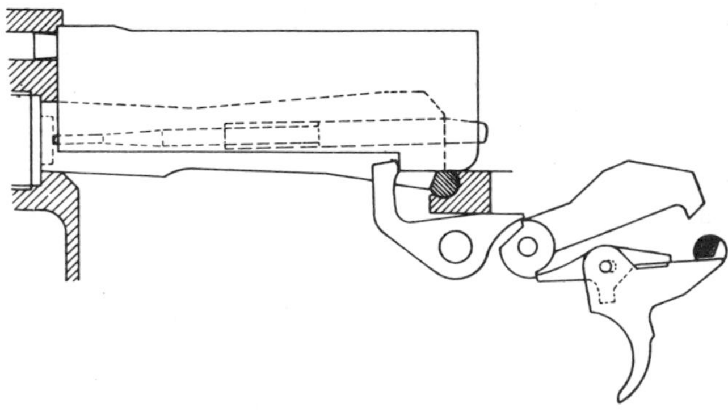

Change lever stud set for single shot fire. Pressure on trigger will free sear from hammer contact, but as rifle action opens safety sear will hold hammer until finger pressure is released.

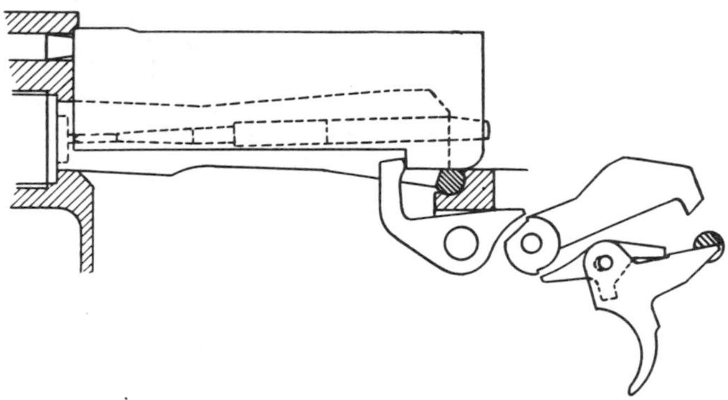

Lever is set for full auto fire. Firing sear is out of engagement except when trigger is released. Safety sear now controls firing to prevent premature discharge.

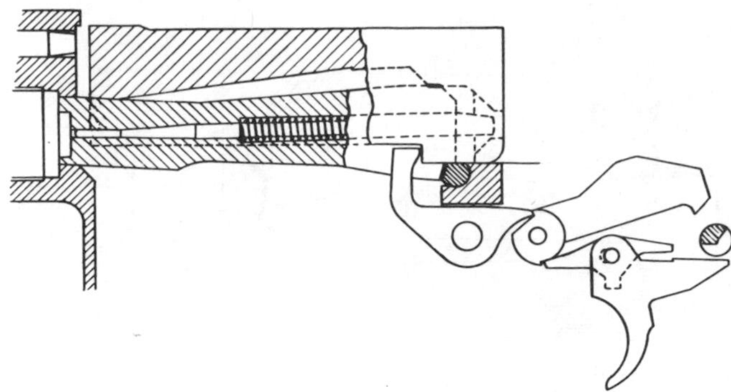

Safety sear mechanism. It is released by blow of the slide as it goes home after breechblock is locked, thus freeing the hammer to fire.

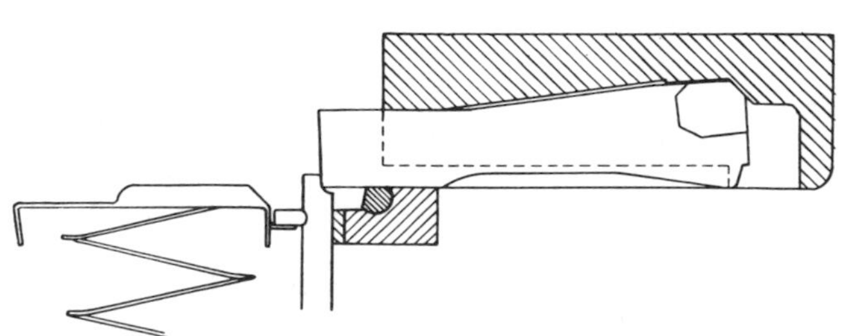

When last shot has been fired, the magazine follower forces a holding plunger up in front of the breechblock to hold the action open.

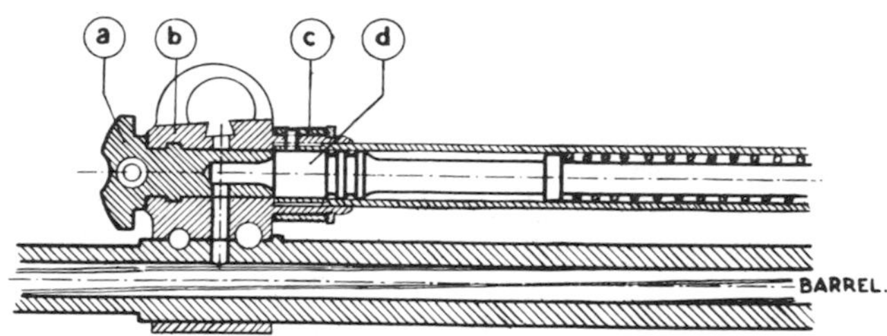

Gas plug (a) is positioned in end of gas cylinder (b). It may be turned to shut off gas when using rifle for grenade launching or as a straight pull rifle. Gas regulator (c) has 3 different size holes. (d) Head of gas piston.

recoil stroke, the compressed spring reasserts itself and working through its connecting rod thrusts the breechblock and carrier forward. The breechblock strips a cartridge from the magazine and chambers it and stops against the face of the barrel. The breech slide, which still has continuing movement under thrust from the recoil spring guide and spring, works through the cam and ramps to force the rear locking end of the breechblock down into its locking recess in the receiver. At the end of the movement of the breechblock slide, it is resting against the return position above the line of the chamber where it is in contact with the rear end of the piston tappet. The extractor, of course, snaps over the cannelure of the cartridge as the bolt chambers the cartridge.

When the change lever is set for automatic firing, the operation is identical with that already described except that the hammer is automatically released to continue fire until pressure on the trigger is released.

Trigger Operation

Turning the change lever on the left side of the receiver to the safe position turns a stud into position at the extreme rear of the trigger to lock it mechanically. In this position, trigger movement is impossible.

When the change lever is set for single shot fire, the stud is turned into position to clear the rear of the trigger and to permit a pull on the trigger to draw the tip of the sear attached to the trigger down out of engagement with the hammer notch to release the hammer for firing. There are actually two sears—the rear or firing sear which connects hammer and trigger during single shot operation; and the front or safety sear. This safety sear performs two functions. It blocks the hammer to prevent it from falling except when the breechblock and the breechblock slide are fully home. It is struck by the breechblock slide at the final movement of closing travel when it releases the hammer so the firing sear may be operated on single shot operation to release the trigger, or so the hammer may fire in full automatic fashion if the firing sear is out of engagement due to the automatic fire control being set on the change lever.

The entire operation is extremely simple mechanically and a study of the drawings accompanying the explanation will clearly demonstrate all the mechanical features involved.

The ejector is mounted in the receiver and serves as a guide in its slot in the lower side of the breechblock. At the end of the recoil stroke, the cartridge case strikes the ejector as the breechblock passes slightly past the nose of the ejector to hurl the empty case out of the gun.

Hold Open Device

The pin to hold the breechblock in rear position when the magazine is empty is mounted in the receiver to the right of the ejector.

It is in the form of a heavy plunger which is elevated by a nib on the rear of the magazine follower through a small pin working in a slot.

In rest position this plunger is held down by its spring. However, when the magazine follower rises as the last cartridge is fired, upward pressure of the heavy magazine spring overcomes the lighter spring attached to the pin and the pin is thrust upwards. The plunger is thereby raised to its complete height and projects into the forward path of the breechblock.

When a full magazine is inserted in the gun, drawing the breechblock slightly to the rear allows the plunger spring to react and lower the plunger, and the breechblock driven by the recoil spring now moves forward to chamber a cartridge.

Gas Regulator

The gas regulator and a gas plug control the quantity of gas permitted to reach the piston. The gas plug A is fixed into the end of the gas cylinder B. This plug has two positions. One permits full access of the gas from the barrel directly to the gas cylinder. The other when turned through 180 degrees blocks off all entry of gas. In this condition the arm will not function automatically. In this condition, however, it can be operated manually as a straight pull bolt action rifle. In other words, pulling the cocking handle back and releasing it will load and cock the gun ready for firing. After firing, another full pull to the rear and release of the cocking handle will eject the empty case and load a new round ready for another trigger pull.

Many American military experts believe that the full automatic feature is entirely too wasteful of ammunition by the average infantryman. This device permits a commander to control the type of fire developed by his troops if he so desires. By putting the gas plug in its closed position, he can have the equivalent of a manually-operated arm in the hands of his personnel to save ammunition. When desired, opening the gas plug gives him the full advantage of either semi-automatic or full automatic fire.

In this closed position the arm may be used as a grenade launcher, since automatic action is not required for such a purpose.

A gas regulator C consists of a shroud around the end of the gas cylinder. It has three different-sized holes. The smaller the hole lined up with the corresponding hole in the gas cylinder, the greater the quantity of gas which is available to act on the piston. The larger holes exhaust increasingly more gas and thereby lessen the amount used for piston operation.

This system of gas regulation by exhaust keeps fouling of the piston to an absolute minimum.

The gas cylinder is placed above the barrel. The center of gravity of the weapon is in line with the axis of the barrel. As a result, the recoil does not tend to pull the weapon upwards as in the case of most semi-automatic rifles. This enables the firer to keep his sights on the target.

The line of sight is extremely low as a result of the mounting of the front sight on the gas cylinder, a feature which enables the soldier to remain close to the ground and protected while firing.

Field Stripping

Stripping and assembling this weapon for normal maintenance and repairs is done without the aid of tools.

With the magazine removed, the release catch at the rear of the top of the receiver is pressed and the body of the gun is hinged exactly as in the case of the familiar shotgun. The entire breechblock and gas operating assembly may now be withdrawn as a unit from the open rear of the receiver. The extractor and firing pin (the normal breakage points in any automatic design) may be withdrawn in a matter of seconds and replaced. All parts are self-contained. There are no loose springs, guides, screws, or pins to be removed during this operation. The recoil spring is retained within the butt when the gun is opened for field stripping. When the assembly is returned to the receiver, the guide rod at the end of the bolt, resting against the compression plug in front of the butt, serves to compress the spring housed within when the action is cocked or in recoil motion.

For all practical purposes, no further stripping of this arm is necessary.

Carrying Handle

A special collapsing carrying handle is provided above and forward of the magazine housing. This handle is placed at the center of gravity to make the arm easy to carry in rapid advances. It may also be used as a carrying handle for marching and general field order. It can be

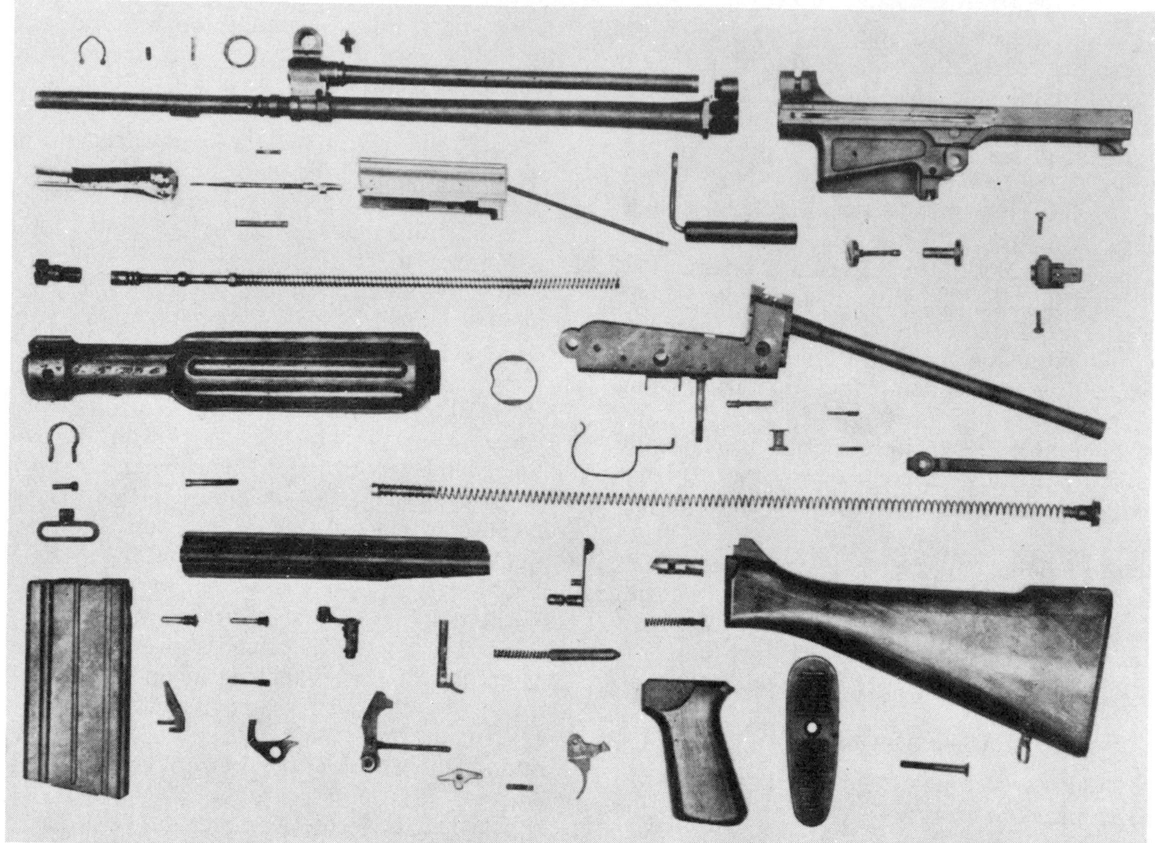

F.N. Light Auto Rifle detail stripped.

quickly turned down out of the line of sight and out of the way.

The grip of pistol type design behind the triggerguard aids greatly in stabilizing fire and, since all operations of loading and cocking and change lever adjusting are done on the left side of the receiver, full control of the arm may be maintained at all times. In addition, of course, this pistol grip gives the weapon the advantage of ease of operation for firing at waist level under appropriate conditions. The forestock is designed for comfort and secure control as a normal left hand hold for shoulder firing or waist firing.

As special accessories, a muzzle brake and flash hider are available. A grenade launcher is also part of the accessory equipment as is a special bayonet and a detachable folding bipod mount.

Further Dismounting

Remove the magazine. Draw the cocking lever to the rear and check that the chamber is empty. Move the cocking handle back to free the breechblock and allow it to go forward to locked closed position.

Push down the butt locking lever on the left rear side of the receiver as far as it will go. Simultaneously push the butt itself downwards. The butt will pivot together with the lower receiver section. This allows the arm to open as in the familiar case of the hinged-frame shotgun.

Pull back the spring rod attached to the breechblock; this will pull the breechblock and slide assembly to the rear out of the gun.

Slide the receiver cover to the rear off the receiver.

Lift the front end of the breechblock while pressing it forward into the slide and continue lifting the front end to raise the rear gently out of slide contact against the pressure of the firing pin spring.

Push out the cross retaining pin while holding onto the rear of the firing pin and the pressure of its spring will force it out of its housing.

Insert the nose of a bullet under the extractor and pry outwards and upwards to withdraw the extractor.

The gas plug can be removed if desired and a rod passed through the gas cylinder to clean fouling.

The gas plug can be turned with the nose of a bullet for removal. This permits removal of the piston and spring from the gas cylinder. While there are very few remaining parts, and additional stripping of the firing mechanism can be done easily, it is not normally done by the average soldier.

Special Note: This weapon is used by more than 30 countries, including Great Britain, Canada, Australia, New Zealand, Israel, Peru, West Germany, Austria, Luxembourg, South Africa, Belgium, Chile, Netherlands, Ireland, Portugal, Syria, Ecuador, and Venezuela.

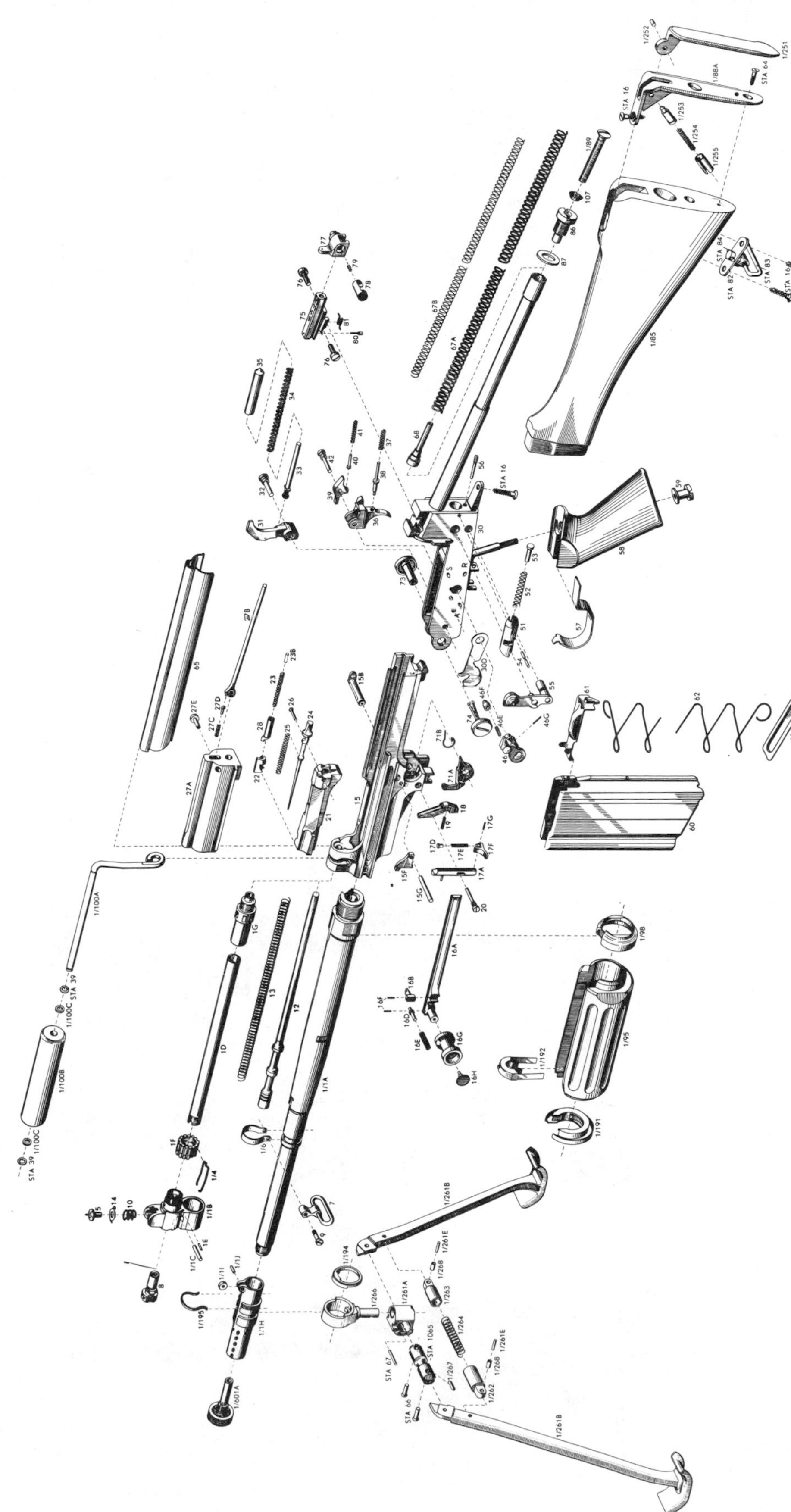

F.N. Heavy Barrel Automatic Rifle 7.62mm as made for South Africa.

Variations Among Some F.N. Light Automatic Rifles Produced at F.N.

	Barrel 1. Smooth muzzle 2. Threaded muzzle 3. Threaded muzzle for combined grenade launcher/flash suppressor	**Flash Suppressor** 1. Without 2. With 3. Combined with grenade launcher	**Bayonet** 1. Flash suppressor type or normal 2. Tubular type 3. Without	**Extractor in** 1. One piece 2. Two pieces	**Butt stock** 1. Without front socket 2. With front socket	**Butt Plate** 1. Without butt trap 2. With butt trap	**Handguard** 1. Wood 2. Metal 3. Molded material	**Bipod** 1. Without 2. With	**Loading** 1. Without charger (Stripper clip) 2. With charger
Austria	3	3	3	2	2	2	2	2	1
Belgium	1	1	1	2	2	1	3	1	2
Cambodia	1	1	1	2	2	1	3	1	1
Chile	2	2	1	2	2	1	3	1	1
Ecuador	2	2	1	2	2	1	3	1	1
Indonesia	1	1	1	2	1	2	1	1	1
Ireland	2	3	2	2	2	2	3	1	1
Israel	1	1	1	1	1	1	1	1	1
Kuwait	1	1	1	2	1	2	1	1	1
Libya	1	1	1	2	2	1	3	1	1
Luxembourg	1	1	1	1	1	2	1	1	2
Netherlands	3	3	2	2	2	1	2	2	1
Paraguay	1	1	1	2	1	2	1	1	1
Peru	1	1	1	2	2	2	1	1	1
Portugal	1	1	1	2	2	1	3	1	1
Qatar	1	1	1	1 & 2	1	2	1	1	1
San Domingo	1	1	1	1	1	1	1	1	1
South Africa	1	1	2	2	2	1	3	1	1
Syria	1	1	1	1	1	2	1	1	1
West Germany	1	2	3	2	1	2	2	2	1
Venezuela	2	2	3	1	1	1	1	1	1

There are other variations as for example, the British produced L1A1 and the Canadians produced C1.

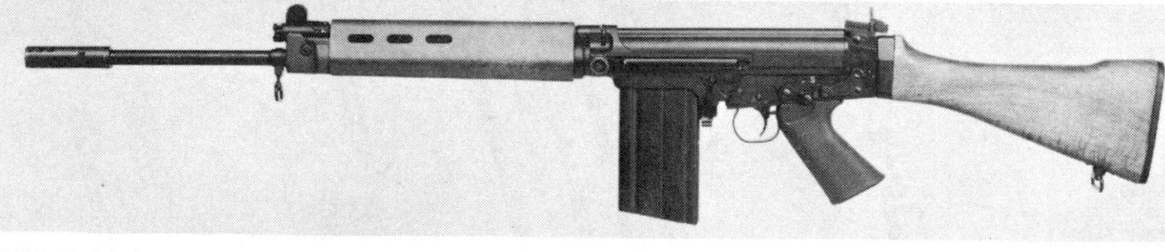

7.62mm F.N. Light Automatic Rifle (FAL), 1962 type.

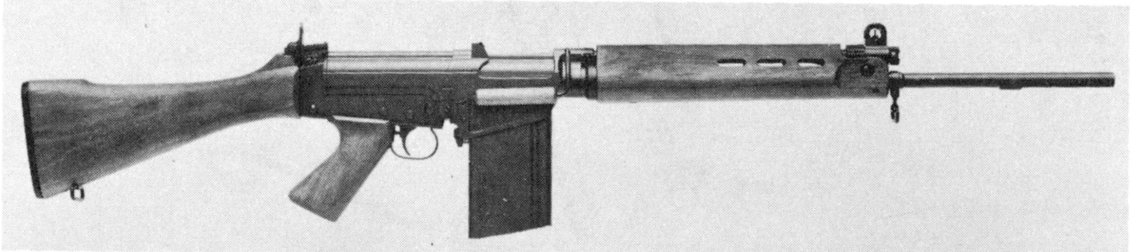

7.62mm F.N. "FAL" Rifle, as used by Belgian Army.

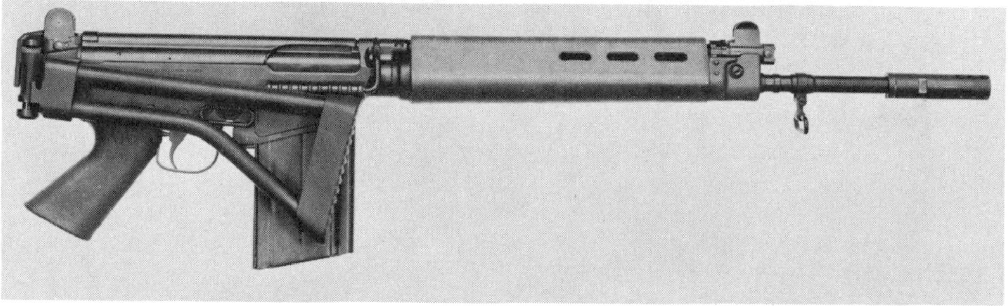

7.62mm F.N. "FAL" Paratroop Rifle.

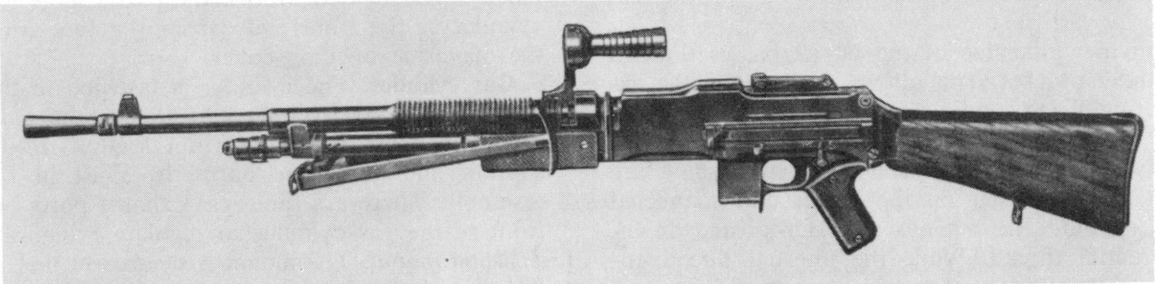

Belgian Type D. Quick removable barrel type. Left side view.

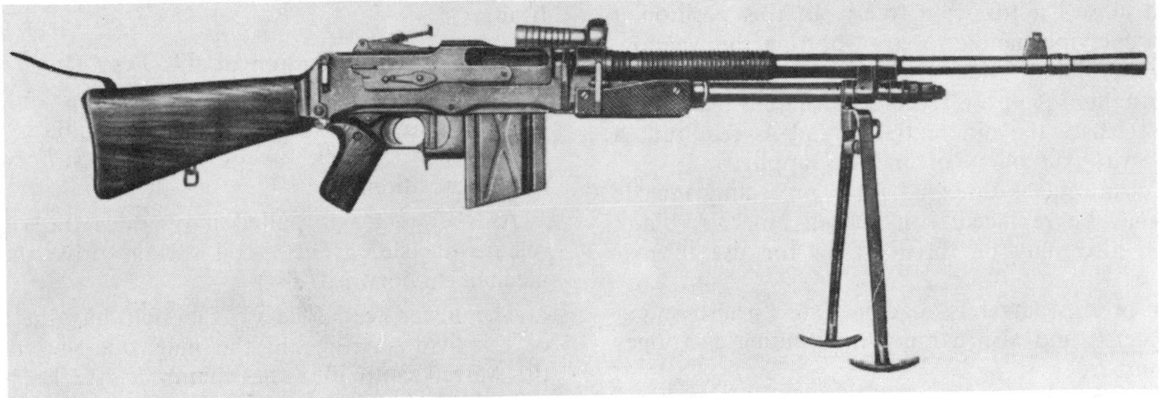

Belgian Type D. Right side view, bipod extended.

BELGIAN F.N. TYPE D MACHINE RIFLE

After World War II the Browning design was further modified along lines suggested by the experience of the military and technical groups associated with F. N. While all the basic original design features were retained, very considerable advances were made, including the introduction of a quick-removable barrel and an alteration to permit removing the breechblock mechanism without completely stripping the gun. Since this gun is available throughout the world in calibers specified by the military purchasers, and since it constitutes a basic machine arm usable as both an automatic rifle and a light machine gun, the Type D F. N. Browning automatic machine rifle must be given special consideration.

Caliber: Any specified rimless military pattern, commonly the U. S. caliber .30 M1 and the Mauser 7mm, 7.62mm, 7.65mm, and 7.92mm.

Magazine: Detachable box. Holding 20 cartridges in staggered line. Magazine positioned directly below receiver.

Muzzle Velocity of Cartridge: As given for specific cartridges.

Weight of Bullets: As for cartridges indicated.

Barrel Length: 19.7 in.

Overall Length of Gun: 41.7 in.

Length of Gun with Flash Hider Attached: 45.1 in.

Weight Without Magazine: 20.3 lbs.

Weight of Magazine: 9 oz.

Sights: Post type front. Elevating graduated rear with windage.

Accurate Range: Dependent upon cartridge. Normally about 600 yards.

Rifle Operated by: Gas escaping through small hole in barrel through gas cylinder and driving piston rearward. The piston unlocks the action, carries the breech mechanism back to extract and eject and compresses the customary return springs. The return springs provide the counterrecoiling motion to load, lock, and fire the arm.

Locked: Browning pattern rising bolt locking into recesses in top of receiver.

Cooled: Air. Barrel flanged at rear breech section for added radiation. Bolt remains open between shots to allow air circulation down barrel.

Detachable Barrel: Held to receiver by a differential nut. This takes up any play or clearance between barrel and receiver. A handle is attached to the barrel for carrying the weapon and to permit quick dismounting when the barrel is overheated.

Cyclic Rate of Fire: Normal rate 600 rounds per minute. Using the special slow down device incorporated in the triggerguard permits the rate to be reduced to as low as 350 rounds per minute.

Position of Operating Handle: Left side of receiver above triggerguard. This position is preferred as it allows cocking the arm without lowering the butt from the shoulder. As in standard Browning practice, the cocking handle operates only when drawn back to cock the action. It is then thrust forward. It does not reciprocate while the gun is firing.

Dust Cover: Unlike American patterns, the Type D utilizes a cover to keep the action closed yet ready for instant firing. Must be manually applied. Opens automatically during firing.

Flash Hider: A slightly belled metal tube extending beyond the muzzle of the weapon. It serves to hide the flash produced by burning powder emerging after the bullet leaves the muzzle.

Mount: Folding bipod.

Gas Regulator: A regulator is provided to control the amount of gas entering the gas cylinder. This makes it possible to regulate the functioning of the weapon to suit various types of ammunition or varying atmospheric conditions.

Hold Open Device: Firing mechanism is automatically held open when magazine is empty. Actuated by rising magazine follower. Inserting a loaded magazine permits immediate resumption of firing.

Description

Barrel group. The barrel has a bedding point at the front end to receive the front sight. It also carries a gas cylinder bracket which forms the housing for the gas regulator.

A hole in the underside of the barrel passes through the gas cylinder bracket. This allows gas to enter the gas cylinder during firing, and provides the energy for operation.

The carrying handle and barrel removal bushing are mounted at gravity center on the barrel and connected with a locking nut. The nut has an external and an internal differential thread. While the internal thread engages the barrel, the external thread engages the receiver. Pulling the handle loosens it from its notch in the locking nut and allows it to swing freely. In this position it is used as a carrying handle for transporting the weapon.

On the other hand, when it is desired to remove the barrel or to tighten it in the receiver, swinging the handle tightens or releases the differential thread as required in accordance with direction of motion applied.

The barrel muzzle is threaded for a protecting muzzle ring. This may be replaced with a flash hider. A blank firing device also may be threaded on for use in maneuvers.

The rear of the barrel is machined to furnish a cut for the extractor and also a ramp for guiding cartridges into the chamber.

The flanges on the barrel provide a greater area for radiation to increase air cooling.

Regulator. This is the exhaust type. It permits adjusting the amount of gas utilized to function the action to meet varying conditions.

When it is screwed in, most of the gas passes into the cylinder giving maximum thrust. As it is unscrewed, the regulator allows progressively larger amounts of gas to escape into the atmosphere and the smaller quantities used for thrust slow down the action correspondingly.

Receiver. This is the heart of the gun. It receives all the mechanism. The rear sight is mounted conventionally at the upper rear end of the receiver. The cocking handle groove guide is on the left side plate. Above it is a push button to free the bolt for quick dismounting.

The left side plate also carries the triggerguard retaining pin. It is stamped with the letter "M" indicating full automatic fire, "R" for automatic firing at slower rate, and "S" for safety. (N.B. Single shot fire is obtained in this design by fast trigger release from the "R" position.)

Ejection is from the right and the port there is fitted with a moving cover. When the gun is cocked or fired, this cover opens automatically. At other times it serves to keep dust and foreign matter out of the receiver.

The magazine opening in the bottom of the receiver is also closed by a dust cover when the magazine is not inserted. To the rear of this is the triggerguard opening. The butt support at the rear of the receiver is secured by a removable axis and axis screw. Two grooves are machined inside the receiver to guide the reciprocating slide. Also machined are an opening for the bolt guide and its spring, locking recess for the breechblock, and recess for the two bolt guides.

An interrupted thread at the forward end of the receiver is provided to lock the barrel in. The gas recess cylinder at the front end carries the fore-arm plate and the magazine opening cover.

Gas cylinder. The cylinder is fastened to the receiver. It is open at its front end to receive the gas regulator. Two wings on the upper front section of the cylinder support and guide the barrel to assist in rapid barrel assembly. There are three gas exhaust ports bored in the front of the gas cylinder to regulate firing rate.

Bipod mount. The mount is secured to the front end of the gas cylinder by an assembly block pinned to a head. The carrying sling swivel is fastened on the bipod mount head.

Operation of the Type D

A magazine is inserted in the bottom and pushed in until the catch holds it. The cocking handle is then pulled to the rear to cock the gun and thrust forward to its normal position.

As the trigger is pulled it operates the right sear to release the slide. The recoil springs drive the operating mechanism forward.

The lower feed face on the bolt hits the upper part of the first cartridge in the magazine and drives it up the barrel ramp into the chamber. As the base of the cartridge case slides up the front face of the bolt behind the extractor, the lower cam surface of the breechblock hits the end of the bolt supports and buckles the breechblock up.

The bolt stops against the rear face of the barrel, but the breechblock continues forward driven upward by its link and by the reciprocating slide. The breechblock is now in its locking recess in the receiver, but the slide continues forward under action of the springs, carrying the hammer with it to strike the firing pin and fire the cartridge. The slide shoulder strikes the rear section of the gas cylinder halting its forward movement.

Recoil Movement

As the bullet passes over the gas opening in the barrel, some of the expanding gases pass through the opening into the gas cylinder and drive the piston and attached slide to the rear.

The slide acting through its link pulls the breechblock down out of the locking recess and as motion continues backward the bolt (which starts very slowly relatively) gains speed when the breechblock is near its completely unlocked position. At this point of complete unlocking, the bolt and breechblock travel the same speed as the slide.

The firing pin is withdrawn during this rearward motion by the action of the slope in the breechblock on the firing pin heel. Meanwhile, the empty case held by the extractor against the front face of the bolt travels back with the bolt until it strikes the ejector and is thrown out the right side through the ejection port.

The rearward movement is limited by the buffer which compresses the return springs. At this point where the recoil movement is complete, the slide and the attached sear catches the slide.

Note: One of the most important features of the Browning action is the two-stage extraction system. As the opening movement begins, the breechblock is started slightly backwards by a progressive movement as its cam comes in contact with the rear section of the bolt guides. This loosens the case from the chamber in very efficient primary extraction. The loosened cartridge case is completely extracted by direct pull only after the breech pressure has been dissipated and the action is unlocked.

This is one of the basic reasons for the reliability of this type of design.

Automatic Fire

When the gun is cocked the change lever is pushed to position "M." In this position the left sear is cut off and does not interfere with the movement of the slide. As a result, when the trigger is pulled, and the action is operated by the gas piston and slide, at the end of the recoil stroke the sear is not in position to grasp the slide. This results in the slide continuing to go forward to fire automatically until the trigger is released to catch the recoiling slide.

Automatic Fire—Slow Rate

Cocking the gun and pushing the change lever to "R" position introduces a relatively new feature in automatic weapon operation. This serves to slow down the normal high rate of full automatic fire. It is not single shot fired and should not be so construed.

In position "R," the slide is held at the rear by the right sear which is somewhat longer than the left one. Pulling the trigger lowers the right sear and releases the slide to be driven forward by the recoil springs, but it is momentarily caught by the left sear which moves slightly forward through the action of its pin travelling in an elongated hole. The left sear moves forward a catch which in turn releases the slowing up device lever. The lever is raised by action of its spring and the movement is slowed by interference of a rack, pinion, and ratchet. This effectively slows down the forward travel of the moving mechanism.

As the lever is raised it swings up the forward end of the left sear and pulls down the rear end of the sear. When this raising movement is completed the sear disengages completely from the notch in the slide releasing it for forward travel. The moving slide depresses the lever which is again caught and held by the latch.

Single Shot Firing

When the gun is cocked and the change lever set at position "R," the rate of fire is slowed down enough that the trigger may be released without difficulty to furnish single shot fire. In effect, the action therefore is one merely of slowing down the automatic operation so that manual tapping of the trigger gives single shot fire, but at the same time the gun may be held in position to allow a burst of automatic fire at a relatively low rate in case of emergency.

Buffer Operation

As the slide is driven back by the attached piston when the gun fires, the opening movement is slowed by the return springs through their spring rods.

When the slide contacts the recoil plug, it pushes back the first friction ring and cone, the first cone pushes the next one, and so on until the final compression of the buffer spring is completed.

These friction rings are split and they open slightly under action of their cones rubbing against the tube containing the buffer. The friction thus engendered, working with the action of the return springs and the buffer spring itself, absorbs the violent recoil of the mechanism.

Gas Adjustment

The gun is first placed in firing position. By use of a special tool provided, the gas shroud is unscrewed until the gas escape holes are very nearly uncovered. The change lever is then set in position "R" and the gun cocked. In this position when the gas adjustment is correct, the mechanism will remain open after each shot and ejection must be normal (meaning an empty case projection of about four to five yards from the gun). If this condition does not ensue, the screw must be further adjusted to achieve it.

To Load the Gun

Pull cocking lever as far back as possible until slide is caught and held by the sear. Push cocking lever forward. Open magazine cover and insert a loaded magazine through bottom of gun. Set change lever at position desired. Gun is ready to fire by pulling the trigger.

Barrel Removal

First check to be sure that the end of the handle is inserted in the groove in the locking nut. Press in the locking lever and turn the handle upward to vertical position. Push forward on handle and remove barrel.

Replacing Barrel

Seize barrel by handle with regulator downward. Insert the rear of the barrel into the receiver, its front end resting on its vee support in the front section of the gas cylinder. Push the regulator into the gas cylinder. Draw the barrel to the rear of the receiver and swing to the left as far as possible on the handle. This will lock the barrel securely to the receiver.

Complete Dismounting

With weapon in firing position on bipod, remove magazine and pull trigger and ease mechanism forward.

Withdraw triggerguard retaining pin and triggerguard.

Pull the butt access pin out to the right. This allows butt to be swung completely downward, the gun being held standing by the bipod and the butt.

Using the recoil spring rod, pull the operating mechanism out the rear of the weapon. (This mechanism carries the slide, piston, bolt, breechblock, link, hammer, and return spring rod.)

Firing pin may be removed from the bolt if desired.

Removing hammer pin allows slide to be separated from hammer and link-bolt breechblock group. Hammer may now be withdrawn from the slide. Return spring rod may now be removed. Punching out link pin permits link to be separated from bolt and breechblock group. Use firing pin to press under head of extractor to disengage and remove it from the bolt. Extractor spring may then be removed.

Reassembling

Replace spring in the extractor and insert assembly in the bolt by pressing head of extractor and pushing completely home.

Use link pin to reconnect bolt and breechblock group to the link. Replace the return spring in the slide followed by the hammer.

Use hammer pin to connect bolt link group to slide and hammer taking care that the head of the pin is on the right side of the slide. The firing pin should now be replaced on the bolt.

The assembled mechanism should then be inserted in the receiver. Care must be taken that the slide is properly started in its housing and the bolt is kept in the upper section of the receiver so it travels in its guide grooves.

The butt is then swung upwards and secured to the receiver by pushing home the axis pin. The triggerguard is then replaced and its retaining pin pushed into position. Replacing the magazine completes the operation.

Operating Recommendations

Very little oil is needed in this gun. It normally should be kept very nearly dry. Only the moving parts should be slightly oiled.

Before any possible combat use, the gas inlet should be checked for proper setting and the barrel for being clear of obstructions and cleaned.

Cartridges should be fed through the magazine and not inserted into the chamber by hand, particularly in case of a hot barrel where "cook-offs" may occur. Feeding a cartridge into the chamber with a loaded magazine in place will jam the gun.

If the gun jams, withdraw the magazine and pull back the cocking handle to clear the action. In the event of a misfire, wait at least three seconds before opening the mechanism. This is extremely important because, if it happens to be a hangfire, the gun may be ruined if the explosion occurs after the gun has been unlocked.

The gun may be carried in complete safety with a loaded magazine in the receiver and the mechanism closed since there is no cartridge in the chamber except at the instant of firing. Cocking the gun is all that is necessary for use under these conditions. At all times when the weapon is not in use, both the magazine cover and the ejection port cover should be kept closed by their dust covers to keep the mechanism free from obstructions.

Pre-war FN Browning Automatic Rifle Model 30.

This weapon was used in the Belgian Army and is still used in many South American countries. It is quite similar to the U. S. M1918 Browning Automatic Rifle. F. N.-Made Browning light and heavy machine guns have a wider distribution.

BELGIAN SUBMACHINE GUNS

Belgium has also adopted a new submachine gun of native design and manufacture, the 9mm Vigneron M2. This weapon is chambered for the 9mm Parabellum cartridge.

The Vigneron is a conventional submachine gun, well suited to mass production. A blowback-operated gun, its method of loading and its functioning are the same as the British Sten or almost any other submachine gun. The bolt handle is mounted on the left side of the gun, and a grip safety is mounted at the top rear of the pistol grip. The grip safety must be squeezed at the same time the trigger is pulled, or the weapon will not fire. The grip safety prevents accidental discharge if the weapon is dropped.

F.N. is now producing the Uzi on license as the F.N. submachine gun. This weapon is undoubtedly one of the best of its type in existence in the world today. Characteristics and other details are basically the same as those given for the Uzi in the chapter on Israel.

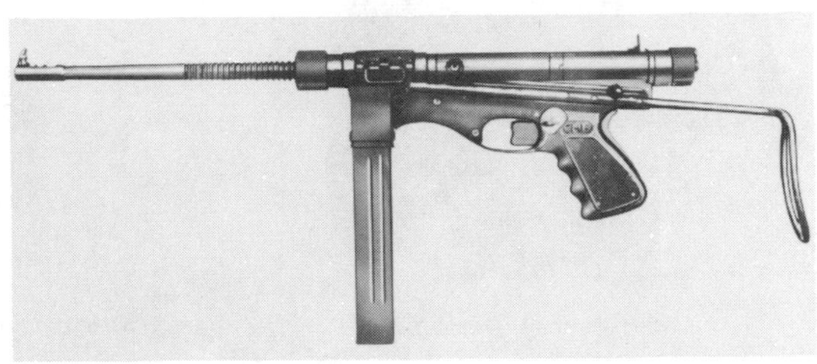

The Belgian 9mm Vigneron M2 Submachine Gun.

System of operation: Blowback, selective fire.
Weight, loaded: 8.74 lb.
Length, overall: 34.9 in. w/stock extended. 24 in. w/stock telescoped.
Barrel length: 12 in.
Feed device: 32-round, detachable, staggered box magazine.
Sights: Front: Blade. **Rear:** Nonadjustable aperture.
Muzzle velocity: 1224 f.p.s.
Cyclic rate of fire: 600 r.p.m.

F.N. 9mm Uzi Submachine Gun.

BELGIAN MACHINE GUNS

The M.A.G. is another development of F.N. and, like most of the products of that concern, it demonstrates first-class engineering ability. The Type M.A.G. has been adopted by Belgium and by Sweden (where it is called the Model 58), and may be adopted by the UK. The gun combines the operating system of the Browning automatic rifle (BAR) with a belt feed mechanism similar to that of the German MG 42. The bolt mechanism of the BAR has been changed in the M.A.G. so that it locks on the bottom of the receiver, rather than on the top as

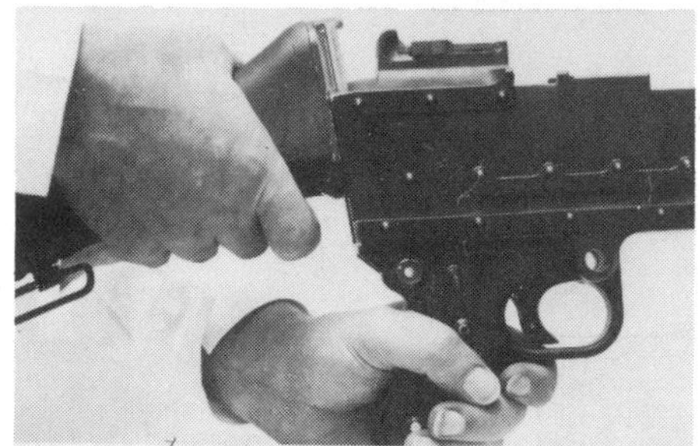
Removing butt assembly.

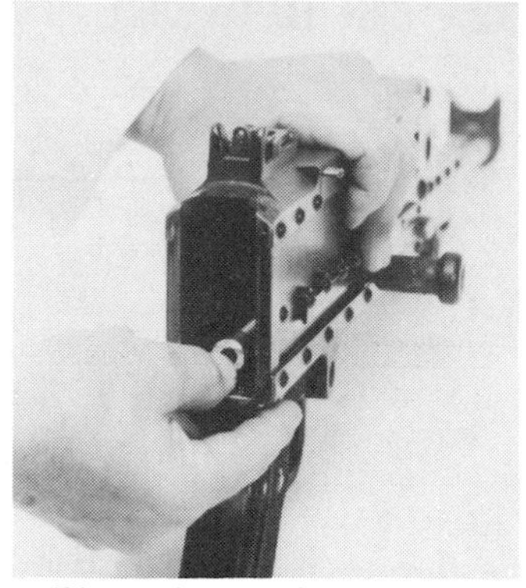
Disengaging recoil spring rod.

Removing recoil spring assembly.

Removing bolt, piston, and slide.

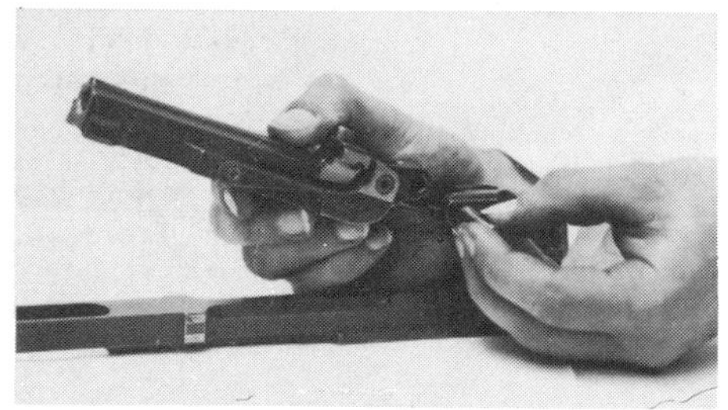
Removing bolt lock and link.

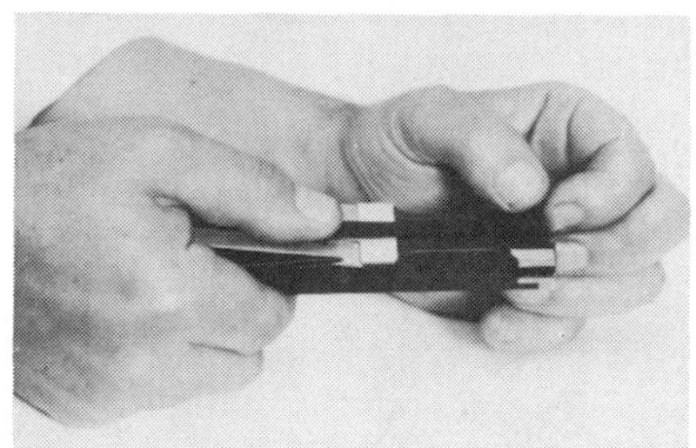
Removing extractor.

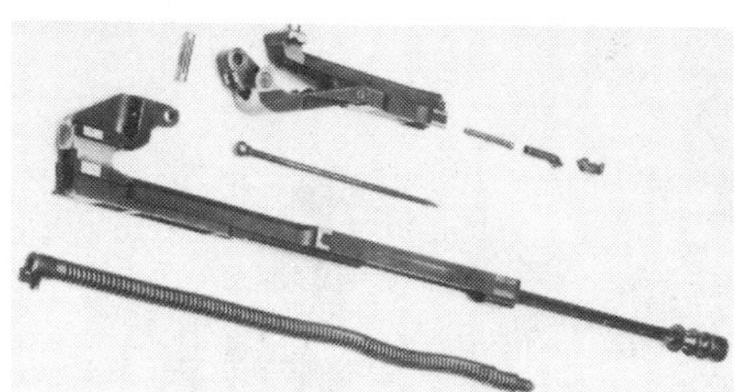
Bolt and slide components.

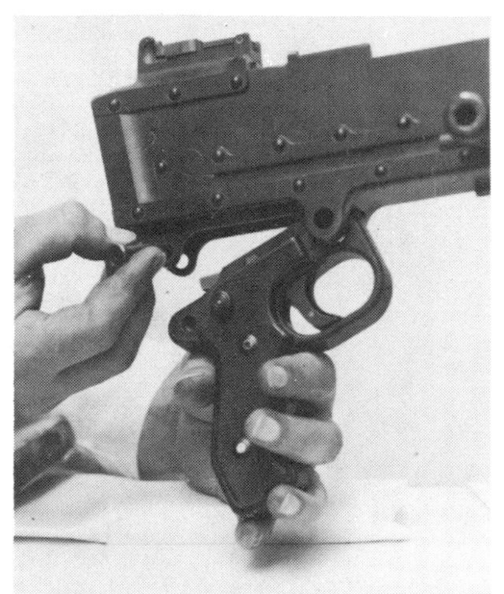
Removing grip-trigger assembly.

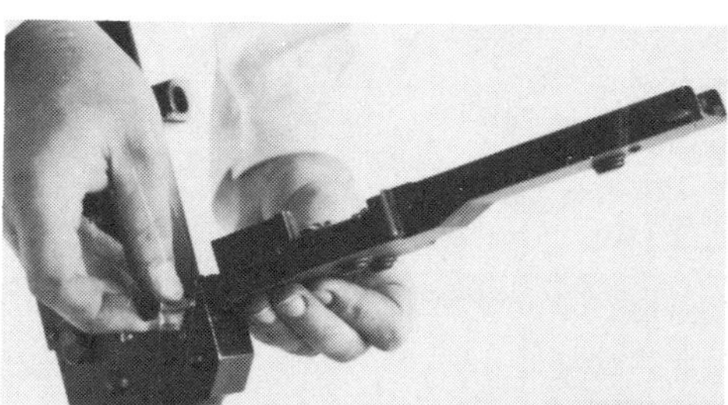
Removing cover.

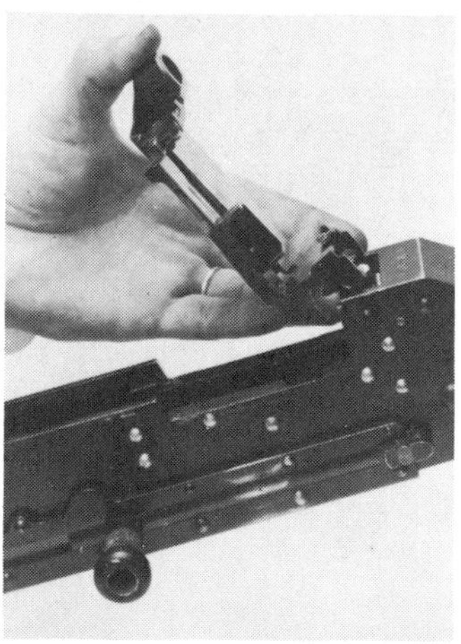
Removing feed plate.

Cover assembly.

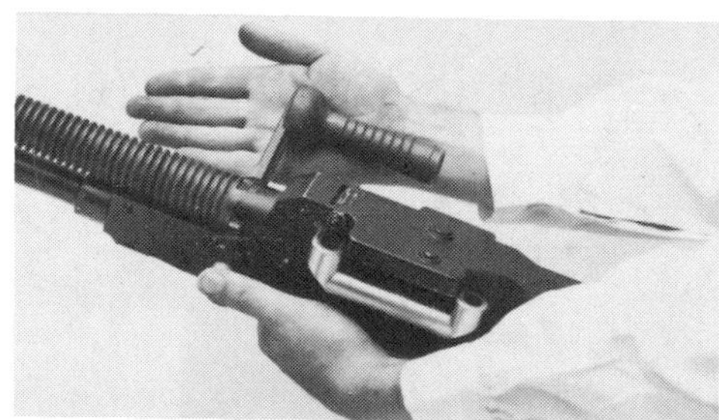
Removing barrel.

Replacing barrel.

Drawing barrel to rear.

Adjusting gas cylinder aperture.

with the BAR. It has a chrome-plated and stellite-lined bore and chamber in its quick-change barrel. The M.A.G., like the German World War II guns and the U. S. M60, is designed to be used on a bipod as a light machine gun and on a tripod as a heavy machine gun. Its rate of fire can be adjusted, through the use of its gas regulator, from a low cyclic rate of 700 rounds per minute to a high cyclic rate of 1000 rounds per minute.

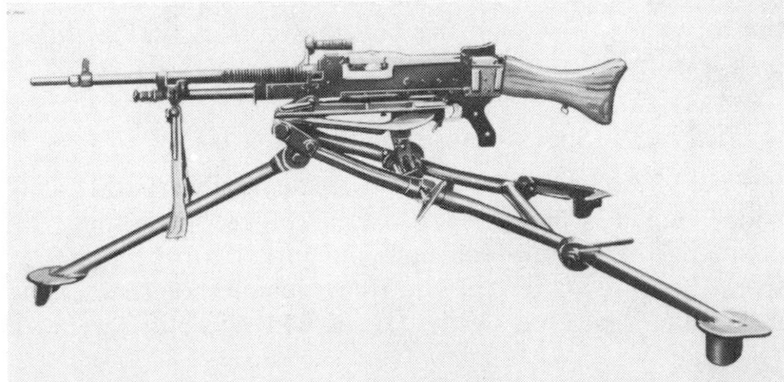

The Belgian F.N. General Purpose Machine Gun Type M.A.G.

Caliber: Has been made in 7.62mm NATO and 6.5 Swedish.
System of operation: Gas, automatic only.
Weight, w/butt and bipod: 23.92 lb.
Weight, w/o butt and bipod: 22.22 lb.
Weight of FN tripod: 22 lb. (constructed of aluminum alloy).
Length, overall: 49.21 in. w/flash suppressor.
Barrel length: 21.44 in.
Feed mechanism: Link belt, (nondisintegrating push-out type links similar to those used on the MG 34 and MG 42 or U. S. M13 disintegrating links may be used).
Sights: Front: Folding type with blade, or type adjustable for height.
Rear: Combined battle-sight peep and leaf with notch; peep adjustable to 600 meters and leaf adjustable to 1400 meters.
Muzzle velocity: 2800 f.p.s. (approx.), 7.62mm NATO ball cartridge.
Cyclic rate of fire: 700 to 1000 r.p.m.

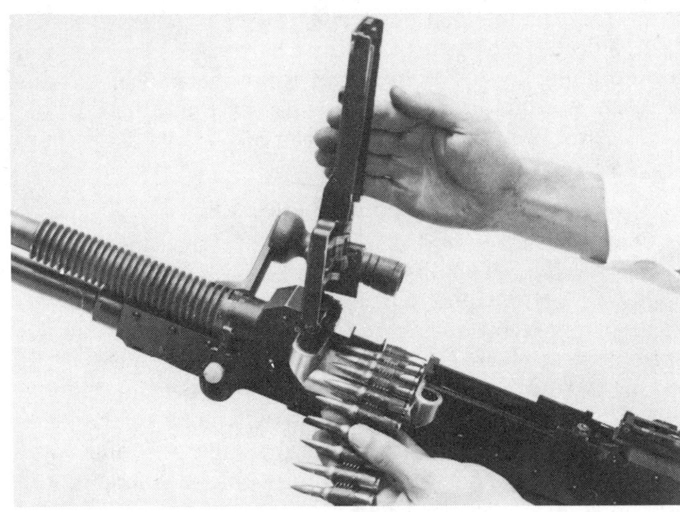

Loading M.A.G.

How to Load and Fire the M.A.G.

Pull the operating handle to the rear; since the M.A.G. fires from an open bolt, the slide and bolt will remain to the rear. Push the button-type safety mounted in the pistol grip from the left side, so that the letter "S" is exposed on the right side. Open cover by pressing cover catch at rear of cover. Lay cartridge belt on feedway so that the first cartridge abuts against the cartridge stop. Close cover securely and push safety button from right to left. Squeeze trigger and the weapon will fire.

How the M.A.G. Works

Essentially, the operation of the M.A.G. is the same as that of the Browning automatic rifle, with the exception of its belt feeding mechanism and bottom receiver locking. A stud mounted on the top of the bolt operates

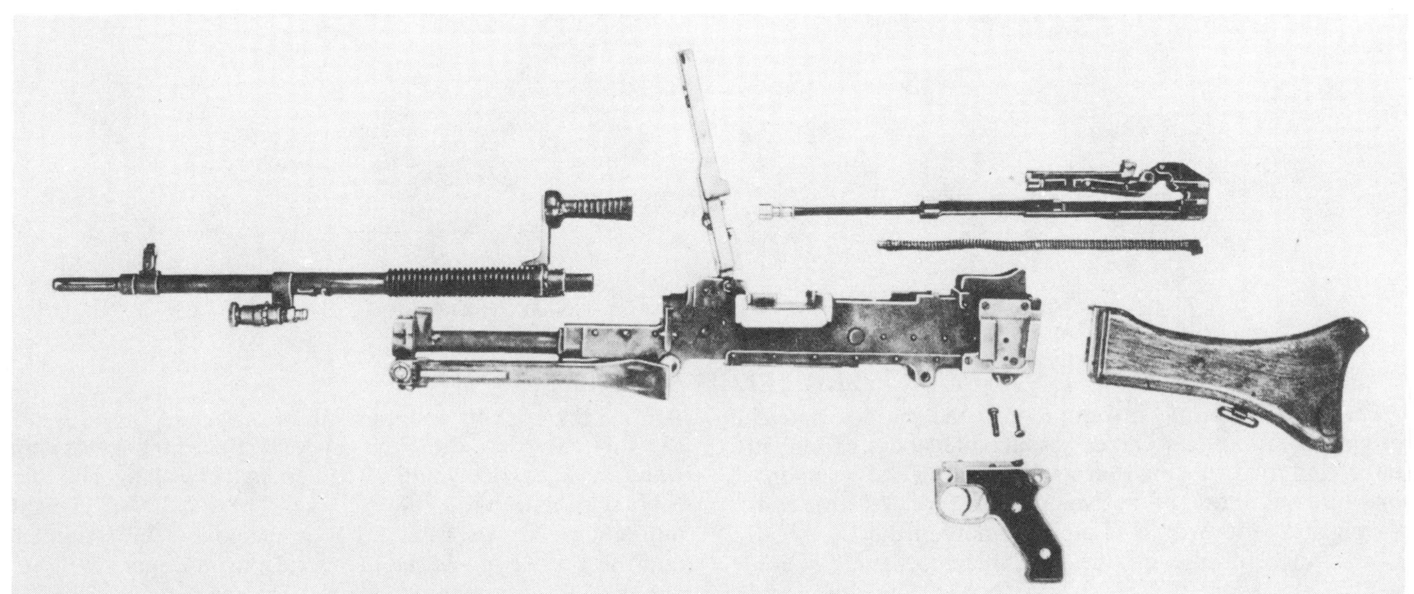

The M.A.G. Field Stripped.

in a track in the belt feed lever, which moves the belt feed slide back and forth, pulling cartridges into position for ramming by the bolt. The trigger mechanism of this weapon appears to be much simpler than that of the BAR. No rate-reducing mechanism is used with this gun.

Field Stripping the M.A.G.

Open the cover and check to insure that the weapon is not loaded. Push in on stock catch located on front underside of butt and slide butt up and off the receiver. Push in on recoil spring rod and disengage it from the bottom of receiver; remove recoil spring assembly (recoil spring and rod are packaged unit). Pull operating handle to the rear and the slide and bolt will move to the rear. Grasp slide and bolt assembly by the slide post and withdraw assembly from the receiver. Remove link pin; the link, bolt lock, and bolt can be removed from the slide. To remove the pistol grip, pull out the retaining pin from the right side. To remove the cover and the feed tray, pull out the cover pin from the right side. To remove barrel, push barrel lock in (barrel lock is located at left front of receiver), move the barrel handle to the left so that it is in the vertical position, and pull barrel straight out. No further disassembly is recommended.

Reverse the above procedure to reassemble the weapon. When reassembling the bolt slide assembly to the receiver, the head of the bolt must be supported so that the forward grooves on the bolt engage the mating ridges on the sides of the receiver.

Special Note on the M.A.G.

The M.A.G. can be used with any military rifle cartridge which is not longer than 3.14 inches, simply by changing the barrel. The butt and bipod can be removed from the gun for use in transport vehicles or tanks. The weapon can be used on the tripod with the butt removed.

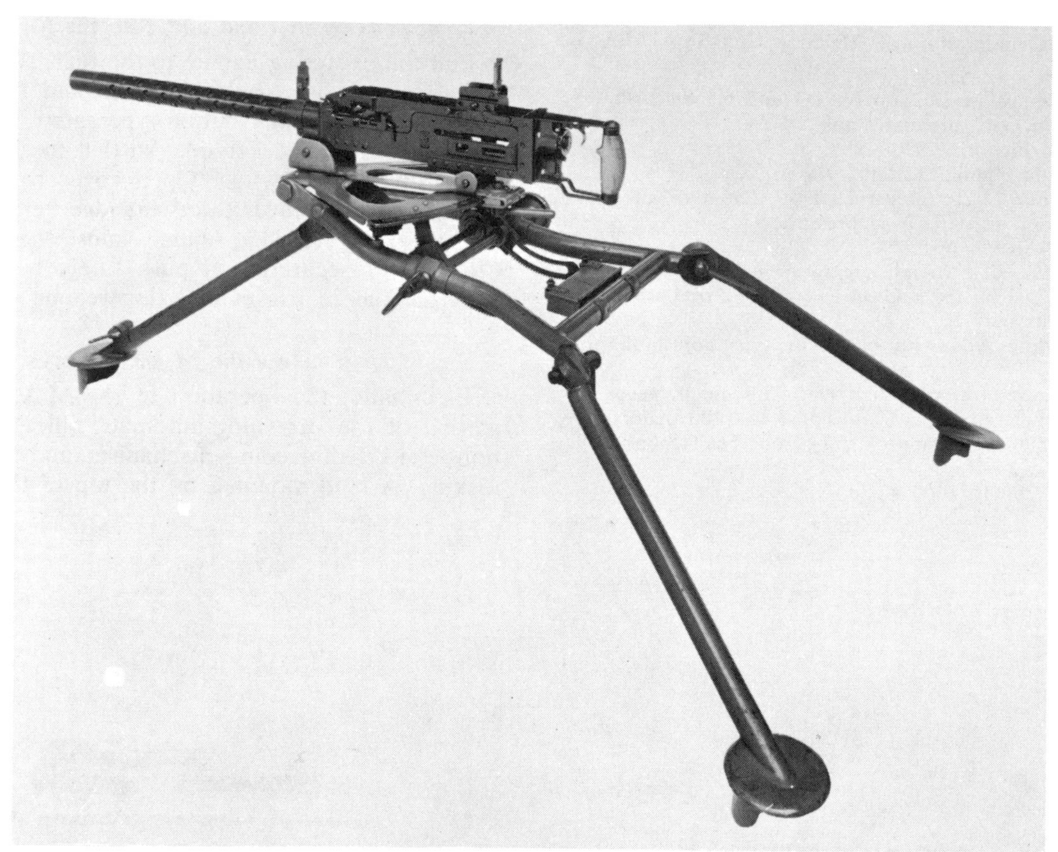

Caliber .30 Browning F.N. Machine Gun as used by Belgian Army.

THE BELGIAN ARMY

The Belgian Army, in addition to the various native-designed weapons, also holds respectable stocks of United States and British small arms. The principal weapons, however, are those of native manufacture. At the conclusion of World War II, Belgium adopted the U. S. cal. .30 cartridge for use in rifles and machine guns; subsequently, she adopted the 7.62mm NATO cartridge, and is now making weapons chambered for that cartridge. Among the cal. .30 weapons still in service in Belgium are the F.N. Mauser, the F.N. Type D Browning automatic rifle, the F.N. Browning aircooled machine gun, and the F.N. semi-automatic rifle M1949. The F.N. NATO light automatic rifle, or FAL, as it is called by the Belgians, and the F.N. Type M.A.G. general purpose machine gun, are the two weapons chambered for the 7.62mm NATO cartridge that are now in service in the Belgian Army.

Chapter 17. The British Commonwealth of Nations

IT IS no longer realistic to attempt to collect under Britain all weapons in use in the British Commonwealth, since many of the member nations of the Commonwealth already have taken an independent course on weapons, and more and more of these nations will tend to do so. This independence in weaponry should not be too surprising, inasmuch as the United Kingdom does not dictate to the member nations of the Commonwealth what weapons they will or will not adopt. In the past these nations have usually adopted the same weapons as the UK, because in most cases (but not all, by any means) they were members of defense treaties with the UK, and because their political, social, and economic orientation would put them on the same side as the UK in any major war. Since World War II, however, the defense arrangements have tended to be more general and to include nations outside the Commonwealth, notably the United States. It is therefore likely that the future will see many United States weapons added to those that are already standard in the member nations of the British Commonwealth.

BRITAIN

NOTE ON BRITISH SMALL ARMS NOMENCLATURE

The model-designation procedures of the UK are somewhat involved and can be confusing. Prior to World War I, British model designations for small arms were comprised of the word Mark followed by a Roman numeral, e.g., Mark I, Mark II. Two exceptions to this form of designation were the Pattern 13, which was an experimental cal. .276 rifle tested in 1913, and the Pattern 14, which was made in cal. .303 as the production version of the Pattern 13.

Between World Wars I and II, rifles and pistols were given number designations in addition to mark designations. Thus the Rifle Mark III SMLE became Rifle No. 1 Mark III SMLE, and the Pattern 14 became the Rifle No. 3 Mark I. Toward the end of World War II, the British began using Arabic numerals for both the number and mark designations. An additional complication was the star symbol (*) which was frequently found tacked to the end of everything else, e.g., Rifle No. 4 Mark 1*. This star indicates a minor modification from the Mark design.

For the last few years, weapons entering the British service have received an L designation, and modifications have been indicated by an A, as in L2A3. The L, in itself, has no particular meaning that the writer has been able to determine. Older weapons that have been considerably modified, such as the Brens rebarreled for the 7.62mm NATO cartridge, also receive an L designation, as do (in most cases) United States weapons adopted as standard or limited standard by the UK.

BRITISH PISTOLS AND REVOLVERS

The UK has adopted the 9mm Browning Hi-Power pistol (see CANADA section) as standard; stocks of the cal. .38 Enfield revolver are being held in reserve. The 9mm Brownings in service were made in Canada during World War II, and their official British (and Canadian) nomenclature is Pistol, Browning, FN, 9mm, HP, No. 1 Marks 1 and 1*, and No. 2 Marks 1 and 1*

Their points of difference are as follows:

No. 1 Mark 1—The butt is machined for a shoulder-stock holster, and a tangent leaf rear sight, adjustable from 50 to 500 meters, is used.

No. 1 Mark 1*—Also machined for a shoulder-stock holster, but the height of the ejector has been increased, and the rear sight (which is similar to No. 1 Mark 1's) has been machined to accommodate the increased height of the ejector.

No. 2 Mark 1—Not machined for shoulder-stock holster; has the smaller ejector and a notched rear sight.

No. 2 Mark 1*—Same as No. 2 Mark 1, except for ejector and extractor.

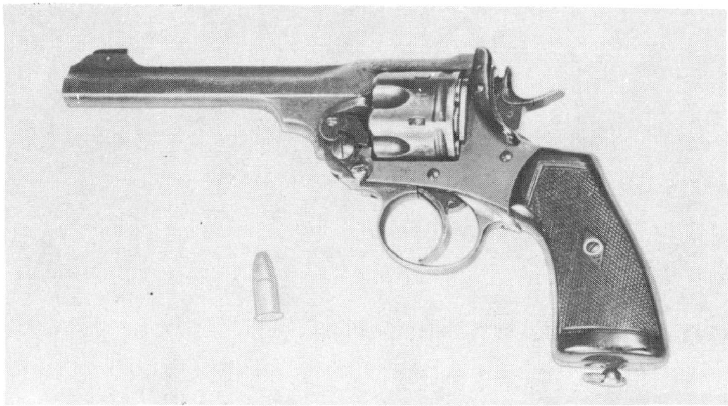

British Webley .455 Pistol No. 1, Mark VI.

Caliber: .455-inch Mark VI.
Cylinder: Capacity, 6 cartridges.
Muzzle Velocity: About 600 feet per second.
Weight of Bullet: 255 grains, metal jacketed. A conical bullet with a long slender point. Note: A cartridge called the Mark II, intended for target use only, has a lead bullet weighing 265 grains.
Muzzle Energy: About 220 foot pounds.
Barrel Length: 6 inches.
Overall Length of Revolver: 11¼ inches.
Weight: 2 lbs. 6 ozs.
Sights: Fixed.
Accurate Range: 50 yards.
Maximum Range: About 800 yards.
Type of Action: Hinged frame.
Double Action: Hammer may be cocked by thumb or may be drawn back and fired entirely by pressure on the trigger.
Safety: (a) There is a projection on the hammer nose which prevents it from striking the cartridge unless the barrel catch is fully in place and the revolver securely locked. (b) When the revolver is in the firing position, the cylinder is securely locked by the pawl which engages against the ratchet on the cylinder. This prevents backward rotation. A solid stop on the trigger bears against the end of a groove at the rear of the cylinder, preventing over-rotation. (c) When a cartridge has been fired and the trigger is loosened to permit it to move forward for the next shot, the hammer rebounds automatically, thus withdrawing the firing pin from the head of the next live cartridge. This action is induced by the inclined base of the short side of the mainspring auxiliary which under the influence of the mainspring bears against the tail of the hammer.

Instructions for Loading and Firing

Push forward on the curved tail of the pivoted barrel catch which is on the left side of the revolver just below the hammer. As the catch is pushed it pivots on its screw drawing the upper latching end back over the barrel

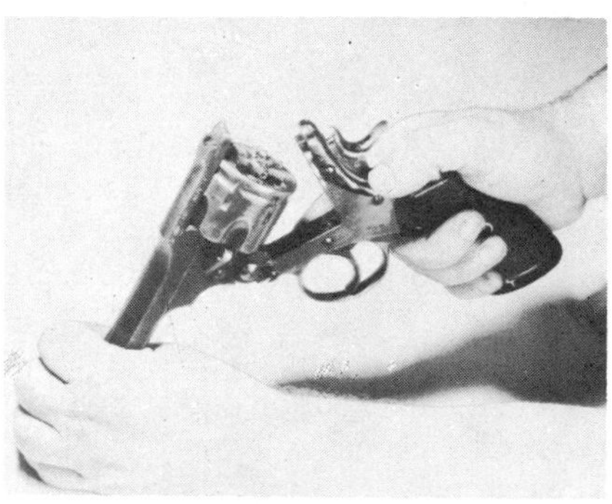

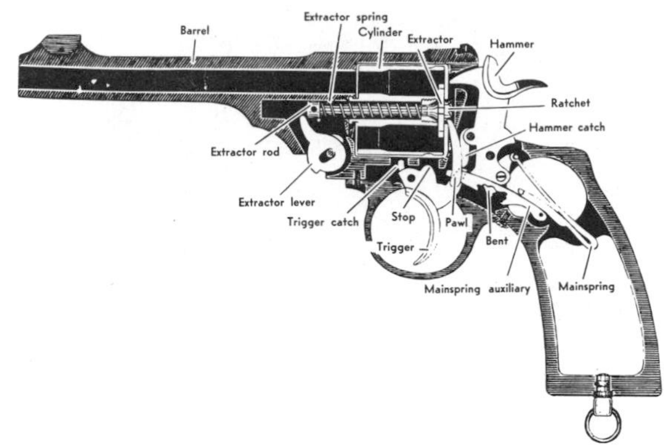

strap, freeing the barrel to be tipped down on its hinge. As the barrel is bent down, the extractor will rise on its stem until the revolver is fully opened, at which point the extractor under the influence of its spring will slip back into its place in the cylinder.

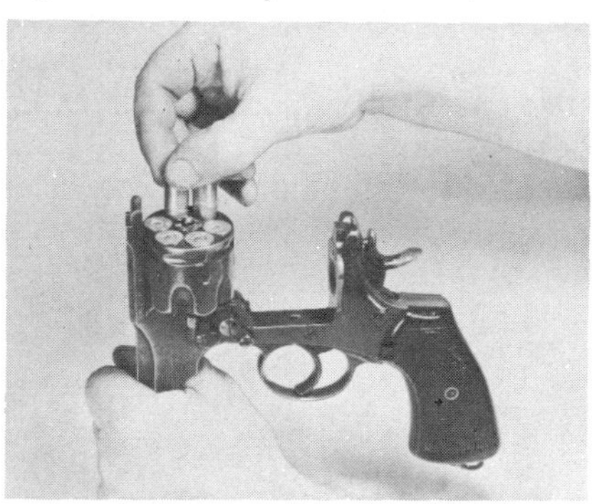

Now load the six chambers. With a little practice this may be done two chambers at a time. If the cylinder is to be only partly loaded, remember that the cylinder revolves clockwise; and that the first cartridge must be to the left of the chamber in direct line with the hammer nose when the weapon is closed. Cocking the hammer automatically turns the cylinder the distance of one chamber.

Now turn barrel and loaded cylinder up to the fullest extent. The heavy catch will automatically be sprung over the barrel strap and lock it securely.

If you have time, and accuracy is desired, always pull back the hammer with the thumb to full cock for each shot. For close quarters or emergency firing, drawing the trigger straight back will raise the hammer to full cock and turn the cylinder and trip the hammer, completing the firing. It is necessary to release the pressure on the trigger after each shot to permit the mechanism to engage for the next shot. Accurate shooting except at close range is difficult when shooting double action.

Field Stripping

The only stripping necessary and recommended for this revolver is removing the cylinder. The bottom screw at the extreme forward end on the left side of the receiver is the cylinder catch retaining screw. Unscrew this. Now push bottom marked "cylinder catch retainer" directly above the screw upwards. This will depress the rear of the catch and permit the cylinder to be lifted out.

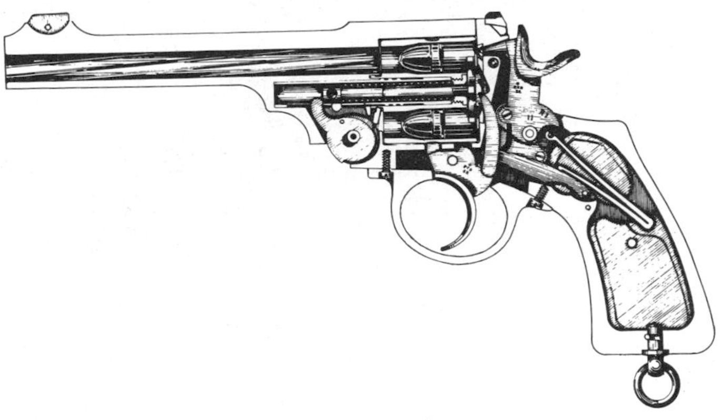

Action closed.

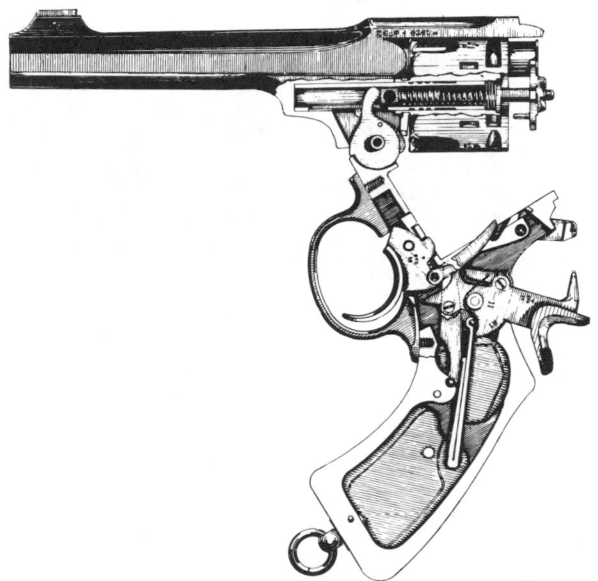

Action open, showing details of extraction and locking.

How the Pistol No. 1 Works

Drawing the hammer back compresses the mainspring. The pawl is moved upward against the ratchet and revolves the cylinder. When the chamber containing the cartridge to be fired next is in line with the barrel, the cylinder stop engages in a notch in the cylinder and prevents further rotation. Simultaneously the trigger catch rises to its peak in the cylinder, holding the cylinder securely so that it cannot turn in either direction. The trigger nose drops into the bent holding the hammer at full cock. The mainspring is fully compressed when its lower arm is raised by the mainspring auxiliary. When the trigger is squeezed, the hammer falls, striking the primer of the cartridge exploding the charge.

Note on the Pistol No. 1

This weapon consists of a single barrel with a cylinder having chambers for six cartridges. It is one of the finest heavy duty military hand weapons ever made. The combination of heavy bullet and comparatively low velocity, gives a tremendous shock force when the bullet strikes. This weapon is not to be confused with the typical small caliber U. S. hinge-frame revolvers intended for low power cartridges. The locking system on this revolver is very much stronger and much more sturdily built than that of the typical American pocket revolver. It is the only hinge-frame revolver in which it is safe to use heavy powder loads. With a little practice, one will be able to push forward the stirrup of the barrel catch with the thumb of the right hand, snap the weapon down, opening and extracting empty cartridges with one movement of the right hand. In the hands of an expert, this revolver is a most formidable weapon. This weapon was declared obsolete by the U.K. in 1947.

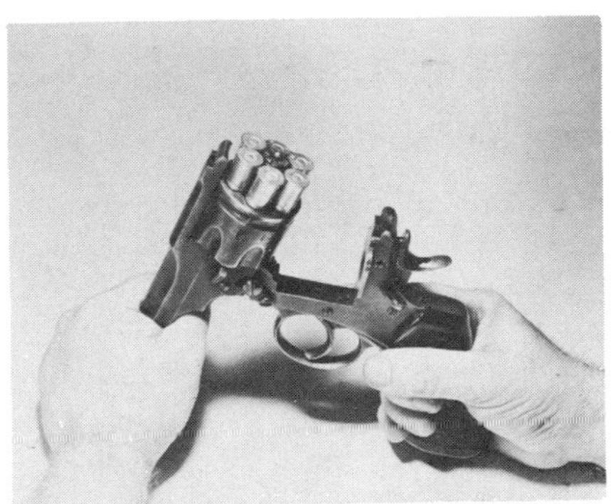

How the Extractor Works

When the barrel catch has been drawn back and the barrel tipped down, the extractor lever tooth catching against the frame is stopped in its movement. The extractor lever arm stops the motion of the extractor rod, and as the barrel and cylinder move down the extractor is forced up out of its seating carrying with it the cartridges, the rims of which have been resting on the base of the extractor. When the barrel nears its completely open position, a corner of the barrel joint passes over the tooth and presses it to the rear. It is thus forced into the groove in the frame. The extractor spring (wound around the extractor stem) which has been compressed during the downward motion of the barrel and cylinder, is now permitted to drive the extractor lever back to its seat in the cylinder.

Note on Use of Revolver: In actual battle use it has been found that the lighter weight, better balance, greater accuracy and lower recoil of the .380-inch has resulted in far more effective use of the revolver as a weapon in the hands of the average man to whom it is issued. The weight of the heavy bullet and the comparatively low velocity produces a shock effect on impact apparently as effective as weapons of larger bore. Also, the effectiveness of the lead bullet as a man stopper is considerably above that of full jacketed bullets of larger caliber. Note: Full metal-jacketed bullets only are now issued for field use. Lead bullets are classed as dum-dums.

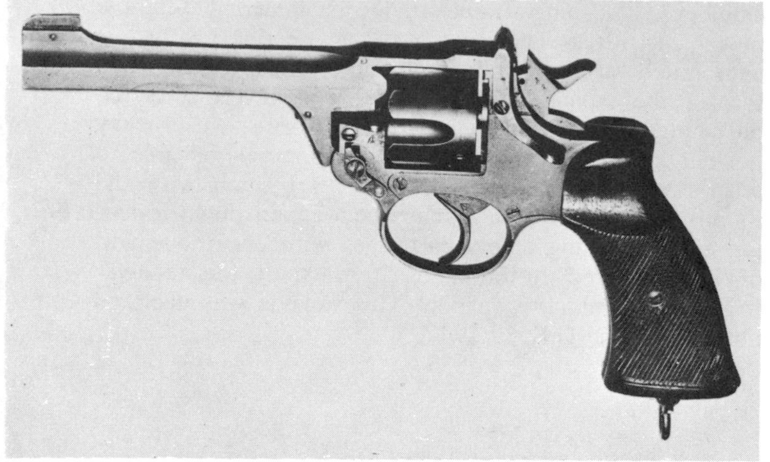

Britisn Enfield .380 Pistol No. 2 Mark 1.

Action closed.

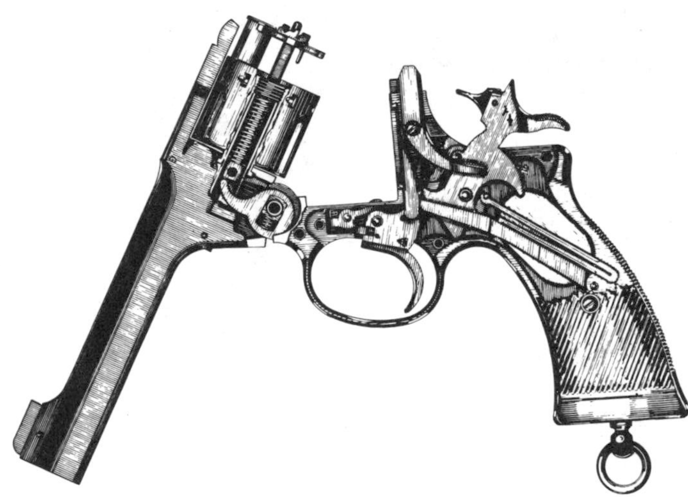

Action open, showing details of extraction and cocking.

These weapons are all considered obsolescent in the U. K. at present.

Caliber: British .380-inch.
Cylinder: Capacity 6 cartridges.
Muzzle Velocity: About 600 feet per second.
Weight of Bullet: 200 grains, lead.
Muzzle Striking Energy: About 190 foot pounds.
Barrel Length: 5″.
Overall Length of Pistol: 10½″.
Weight: 27½ ozs.
Other Data: In general same as for pistol No. 1.
Data on Stripping, Loading, Firing and Operations: All about the same as for pistol No. 1. While it has many points of difference in design, it is operated like the No. 1.

Note: Pistol No. 2 is produced in two Marks. The common form is Mark 1, herewith illustrated. Its design and appearence is very much the same as .455, Pistol No. 1, but many refinements and improvements have been incorporated into its design. The grip is of particular interest. The space behind triggerguard has been made larger to accommodate the second finger of the gun hand comfortably; while the incline of the bottom of the frame has been so designed that the triggerguard is partly taken up by the frame metal, providing better support for the revolver as it is held in the hand.

Note on Ammunition for This Revolver: The ammunition ordinarily issued for use in this revolver is called the British .380 inch. Commercially this cartridge is known as the .38 Webley & Scott Special. However, it will also fire the ordinary .38 Smith & Wesson cartridge with 146-grain lead bullets, commercially manufactured in the U. S. Because of the difference in the weight of the two bullets, however, the points of impact of the bullets are entirely different; and separate front sight blades, which may be changed, are issued with this revolver.

The British have officially adopted Pistol No. 2 as the standard issue for the British Forces. After years of checking and experimenting and after close battle studies of the results of revolvers in action, the 200-grain bullet with comparatively low velocity in caliber .380 has proven to be as effective a man-stopper as the heavier and bulkier .455. The .38 Smith and Wesson cartridge develops a muzzle velocity of 745 feet per second with an approximate muzzle energy of 180 foot pounds.

How These Revolvers Work

Single Action. As the hammer is drawn back it rotates on its axis pin and compresses the main spring. While this is happening, the bent of the hammer bears against the nose of the trigger to rotate the trigger. When the hammer is all the way back, the nose of the trigger is forced into the bent of the hammer by the main spring lever. The hammer is now full cocked.

When the trigger is pressed the nose of the trigger is released from the bent of the hammer and the compressed main spring reacts to drive the hammer forward. The hammer nose inset in the hammer strikes the primer and fires the cartridge.

As the trigger pressure is released, the mainspring lever pushed by the mainspring forces the lower part of the hammer forward a short distance; this withdraws the upper part of the hammer and the hammer nose is brought clear of the cartridge primer. At the same time the mainspring lever pushes the trigger forward again.

Double Action. The action here is the same as for single action with the exception that rotation of the hammer and compression of the mainspring is brought about by pressure on the trigger instead of by the thumb on the hammer.

The trigger nose bears behind the hammer catch to lift the hammer until the nose of the trigger rises high enough to slip over the end of the hammer catch, and allow the mainspring to drive the hammer forward to fire the cartridge.

British Enfield .380 Pistol No. 2 Mark 1*.

This differs from the Mark 1 model in that the comb of the hammer and the bent of the hammer have both been eliminated. As a result, this model will function only as a double action weapon; the hammer cannot be cocked by the thumb, and the revolver can be fired only by pulling straight back on the trigger. This model is intended only for close quarters work and rapid fire double action work. It is of very little real value at over 15 yards range, but for quick firing at close quarters it is extremely effective. A later Model No. 2 Mark 1** has no hammer safety stop.

Cylinder Rotation. The rotating pawl is pivoted to the trigger. Thus when the trigger moves the pawl correspondingly rises and falls. It engages with the teeth of the ratchet on the cylinder; hence an upward movement of the pawl revolves the cylinder. As soon as the trigger is released, the pawl drops to engage behind the next tooth of the ratchet where it is ready to rotate the cylinder once more when the trigger is pressed. In single action, cocking the hammer thus operates the pawl.

Cylinder Lock. When the hammer is at full cock, the trigger has lifted the pawl to its highest possible position. It holds it here against the ratchet. This prevents the cylinder from rotating backwards.

Forward rotation of the cylinder is prevented by the cylinder stop which at this point has risen to lock into one of the recesses in the face of the cylinder. These two engagements hold the cylinder in line so that the chamber to be fired is properly alined to the barrel.

Enfield No. 2, Mark 1.

Loading and Firing

Loading and firing the Enfield Mark 1 are accomplished exactly as in the Webley Mark VI. The Mark 1* is handled in the same manner, except that it can be used only double action. The barrel latch is the same as on the Mark VI.

The .38 Webley Mark 4. Used during World War II; now obsolescent.

Field Stripping

Unscrew cam lever fixing screw. Push barrel catch to open pistol and remove the cylinder.

Unscrew the stock and side plate screws on the left side of the weapon; and remove the stock and the side plate.

All parts are now exposed and further dismounting is not recommended except by a competent armorer, as springs and parts may be injured unless properly handled.

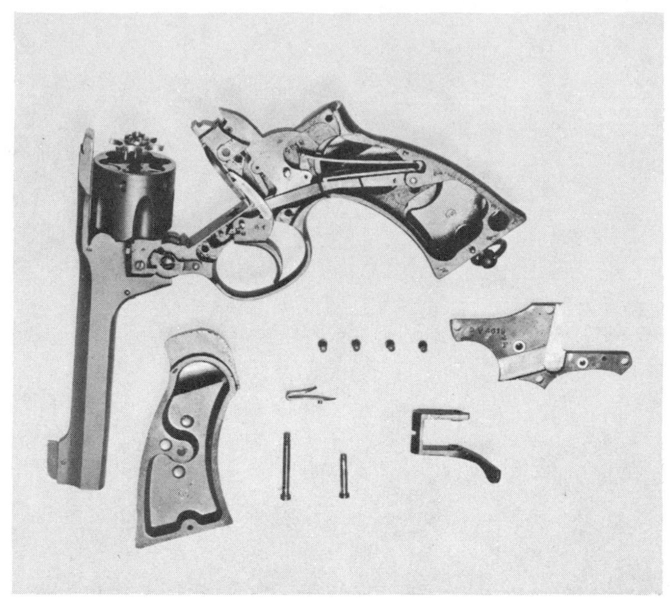

Enfield No. 2. Mark 1*.

British Smith and Wesson .38 Pistol (.38/200).

Caliber: British Service .380 inch. Also .38 S & W, 148- or 200-grain bullet. (Note: British Service Ammunition has metal jacketed bullet.)
Cylinder: 6 chambers.
Muzzle Velocity: About 600 feet per second with British Service Ammunition.
Weight of Bullet: 200 grains, jacketed.
Muzzle Striking Energy: About 190 pounds.
Barrel Length: 5 inches.
Overall Length of Pistol: 10⅛ inches.
Weight: 31 ounces.
Sights: Front, fixed. Rear, square notch.

Other Data: Essentially the same in operation and stripping as the United States Smith & Wesson .45 1917 Revolver.

Note: This revolver was a favorite Commando weapon.

It should be noted that this revolver, which in British terminology is called a pistol, will not handle the .38 Smith & Wesson Special type cartridges. It will handle the shorter and wider .38 S & W type. This cartridge is known in England as the Webley .380 inch. These weapons are considered obsolescent in the U.K. at present.

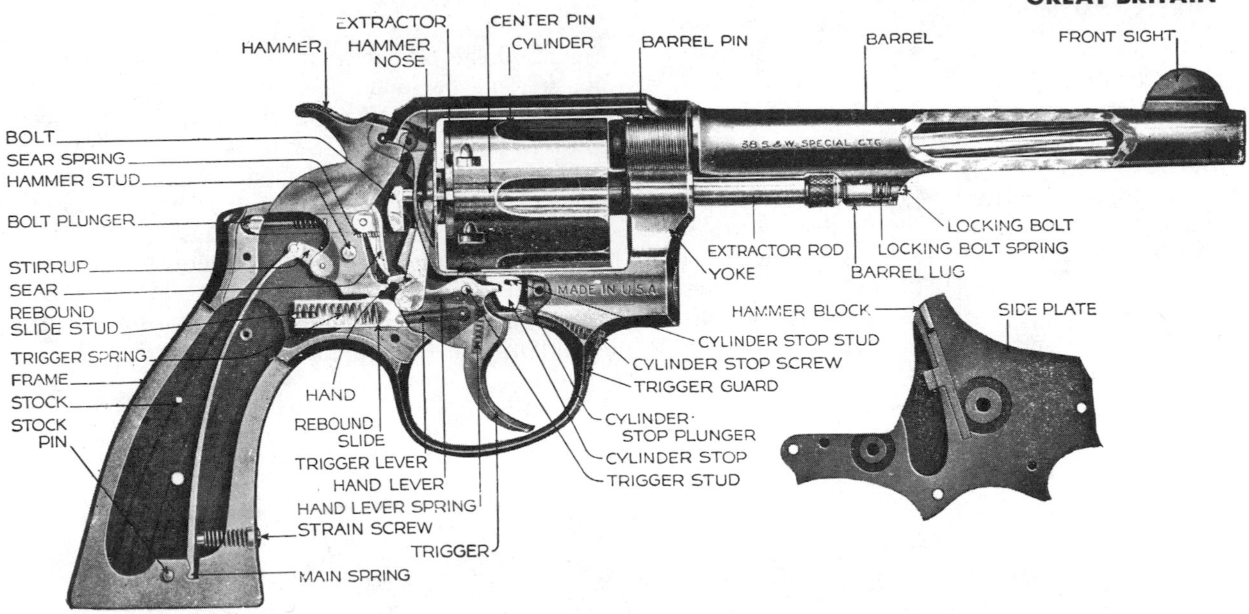

Nomenclature of all S & W Swing-out Revolvers.

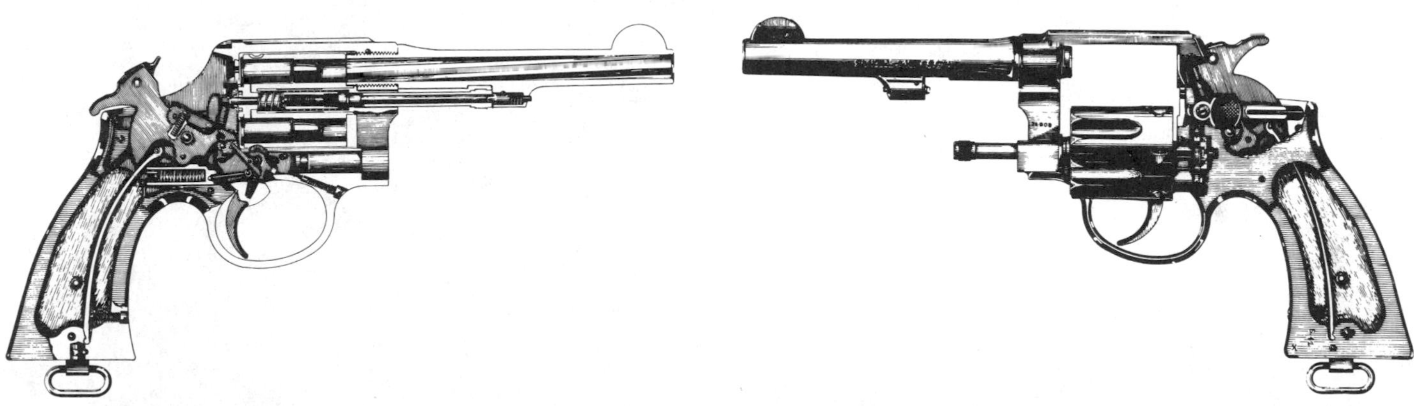

Hammer back, showing details of lock work and cylinder front and rear locking mechanism.

Hammer down, cylinder swung out to show details of extraction. Side plate cut away to show detail of thumb lock.

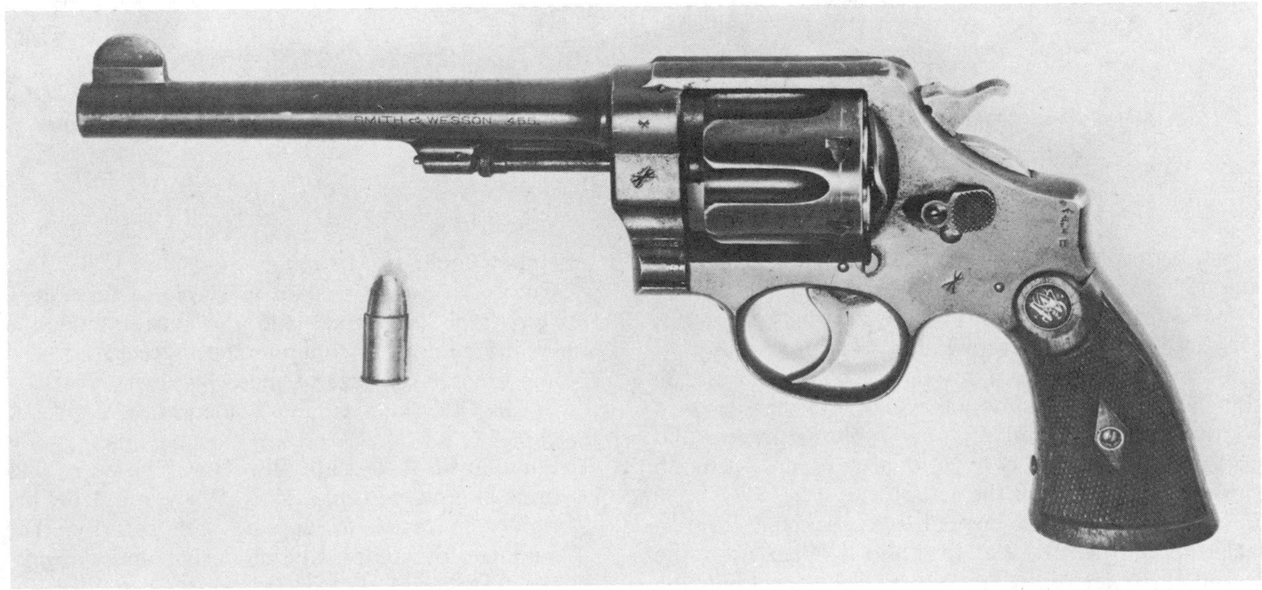

British Smith and Wesson .455 Revolver.

In all essentials this revolver is identical with the United States Revolver Smith & Wesson Model 1917. These revolvers when chambered for the .455 British Service cartridge, will usually be found to have stamped on the barrel ".455 Eley." This cartridge has a bullet weight of 265 grains, a muzzle velocity of about 600 feet per second in the 6½″ barrel model illustrated (some models of this revolver have been manufactured with 5″ barrels). Muzzle energy is about 220 foot pounds and extreme range at 35° elevation is about 1300 yards. Revolvers of this make and caliber are in very common use in Great Britain and Canada. On some models a housing will be found extending forward from the frame under the barrel acting as a protector for the ejector rod.

In common with all Smith & Wesson swing-out cylinder revolvers, the cylinder on this model may be swung out to the left on its crane by pushing forward on the thumb piece mounted on the left side of the revolver. It is fitted with the standard Smith & Wesson locking system with a lock at the rear of the cylinder. Both locks are operated by single pressure on the thumb piece. The cylinder revolves counter-clockwise, from right to left.

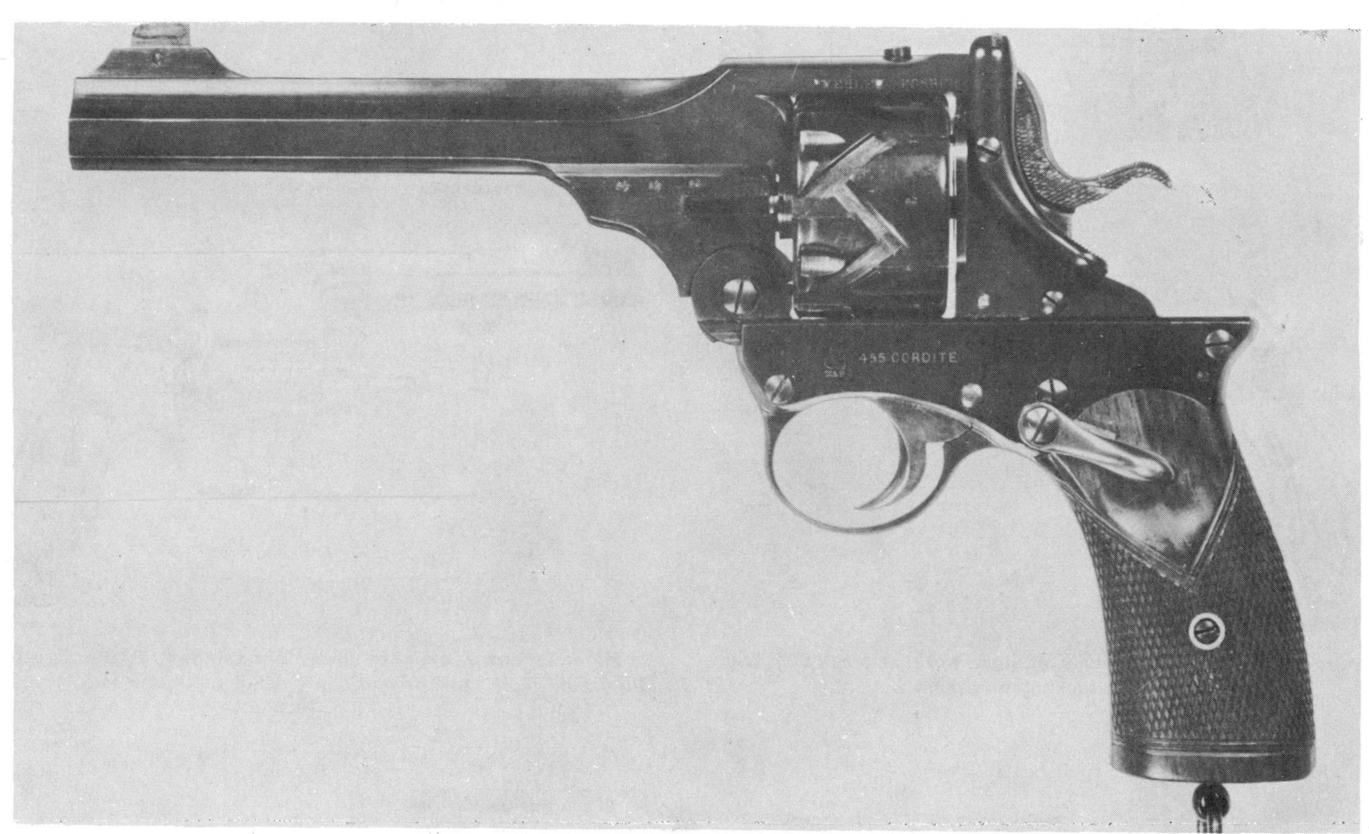

Webley-Fosbery Automatic Revolver. The safety lever is on the side of the frame near the stock frame.

This is an obsolete revolver form never made in large quantity. It resembles the standard Pistol No. 1 Mark VI in external appearance except for the zig-zag cuts in the cylinder walls which effect cylinder rotation.

The barrel, cylinder, and an upper frame can recoil as a unit in a lower frame of which the handle is a part. The arm is locked by a Webley stirrup, and is hinged open to load in conventional manner. A thumb safety lever is mounted on the left side.

The hammer is thumb cocked (or cocked by pushing back the barrel) for the first shot. When fired the barrel and cylinder units recoil, thereby cocking the hammer and causing cylinder rotation to bring a loaded chamber under the hammer.

Empty cases are ejected in standard fashion when the stirrup latch is pushed and the barrel hinged down to open the action and operate the extractor.

Note: A small number of these revolvers were also issued in .38 Colt Auto caliber loaded with a special circular clip.

Evaluation of W-F Auto Revolver. These are finely made arms of the best materials. They must be held fairly rigidly in order to operate satisfactorily. The disadvantages of complexity of design and danger of malfunctions from dirt in frame travel guides and action outweigh any possible advantage of the design.

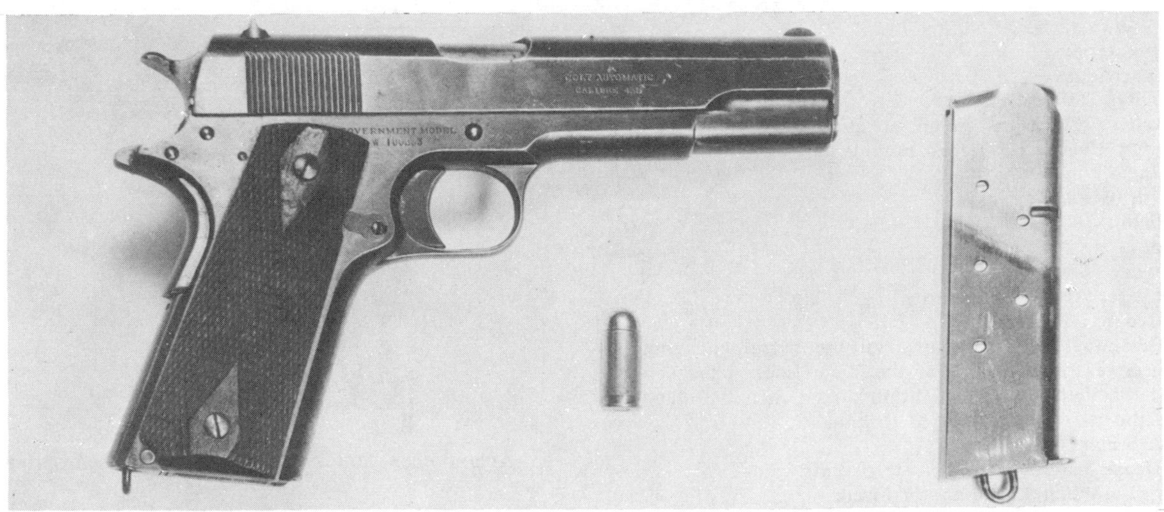

British Colt .455 Automatic Pistol.

Caliber: .455 Webley Self-Loading Pistol Cartridge.
Magazine: Box type, single line.
Capacity: 7 cartridges.
Muzzle Velocity: 750 feet per second.
Weight of Bullet: 220 grains metal jacketed.
Muzzle Striking Energy: 270 ft. pounds.
Barrel Length: 5 inches.
Overall Length: 8½ inches.
Weight: 39 ounces empty.
Sights: Fixed.
Accurate Range: 50 yards.
Maximum Range: 1500 yards.
Pistol Operated by: Recoil.
All Other Data: Same as for United States .45 1911 Automatic Pistol.

Special Note on this Pistol

This is our own 1911 model service pistol modified for use in British and Canadian Armies and adapted to take the cartridge originally designed for the British Webley Naval Pistol.

The cartridge has a semi-rim which makes it rather different than our rimless type. Its bullet is much more conical than that in our .45.

While the practice is not recommended, in emergency the standard United States .45 pistol cartridge may be used in this weapon. However the .455 cartridge will not chamber in our .45 service pistol.

This one way interchangeability of ammunition is occasioned by the fact that the actual bullet diameter of the U. S. .45 Auto cartridge is .4515 inch; while that of the .455 Webley S. L. is actually .455 inch. Thus while the smaller diameter .45 will chamber in the .455, the reverse is not true. The caliber .455 will be found stamped on the right side of the receiver in this weapon. This weapon is no longer in military service.

British Webley .455 Automatic.
This weapon is obsolete in the U. K.

Caliber: .455 Webley Self-Loading Pistol.
Magazine: Box type.
Capacity: 7 cartridges.
Muzzle Velocity: 750 feet per second.
Weight of Bullet: 220 grains, metal jacketed.
Muzzle Striking Energy: 270 foot pounds.
Barrel Length: 5″.
Overall Length of Pistol: 8½″.
Weight of Pistol: 36 ozs.
Sights: Fixed.
Accurate Range: 50 yards.
Maximum Range: About 1500 yards.
Pistol Operated by: Recoil.
Locked: By diagonal inclined planes on the barrel engaging in diagonal grooves on the sides of the slide. Locked barrel and slide recoil together for a short distance, and then the diagonal slots force the barrel down out of locking.
Type of Fire: Single shot only.
Magazine Release Latch: On underside of butt.
Position of Slide When Last Shot Is Fired: Open. Pressing large catch on left side of pistol lets it run forward.
Safety: A safety is provided in the rear of the grip as in the Colt Automatic Pistol. When pistol is held firmly, this grip is pushed in permitting the weapon to be fired.
Special Feature: Magazine is provided with two catch notches in the magazine, one above the other. Push the magazine all the way in and the catch will lock in the lower notch leaving the pistol ready for magazine fire. If the magazine is pushed only part way in so that the catch locks in the upper notch, the pistol can be loaded with single cartridges inserted through the open breech; and action closed by pressing slide release catch. After each shot thus fired the slide will remain open ready for the next cartridge. Meanwhile the magazine remains loaded in the handle held in reserve. To achieve magazine fire it is only necessary to push the magazine in until it catches in the second lock notch.

Instructions for Loading and Firing

Insert loaded magazine in handle, push in as far as it will go.

Grip milled surfaces at rear of slide, pull slide to the rear as far as it will go. Cartridge will rise in line with the breech block. Release the slide and permit the recoil spring to drive it forward pushing a cartridge into the firing chamber.

When last cartridge has been fired: slide will be held open by slide stop. Extract empty magazine, insert loaded magazine, press slide release catch on left hand side of pistol and slide will go forward and load the firing chamber.

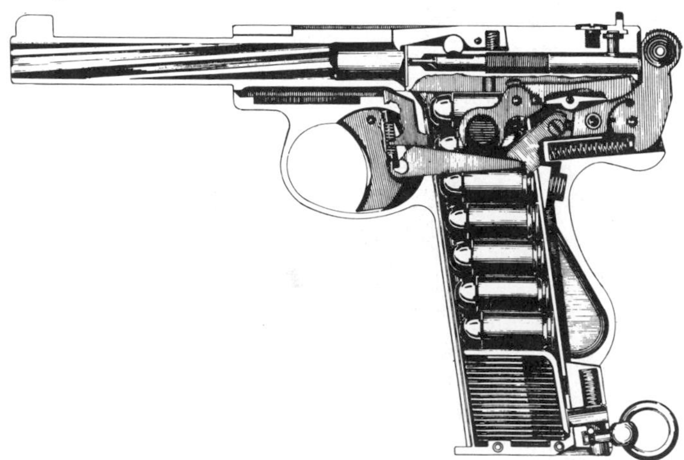

Action closed.

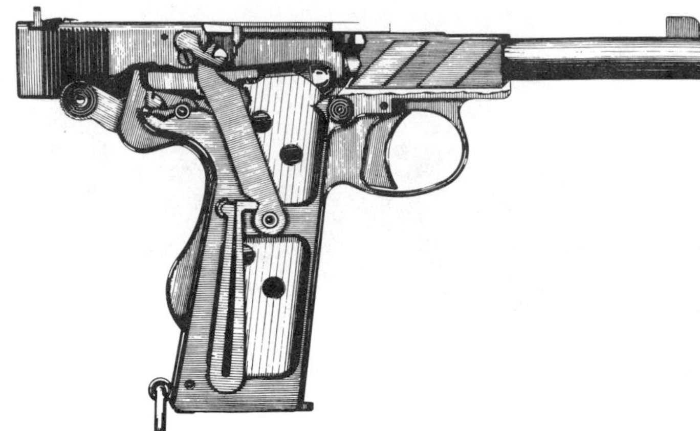

Action open and cut away to show mainspring and sear.

As the cartridge is fired, the locked barrel and slide start backward together. The diagonal inclined grooves on the inside of the slide force the diagonal inclined planes on the barrel down, thus swinging the barrel down out of its locking arrangement with the slide. As the barrel stops, the slide continues to recoil in a straight line, withdrawing the empty cartridge case and ejecting it up and to the front. It rides over and cocks the hammer. At the same time the trigger and hammer action are disconnected, as in automatic pistols generally. In its rearward motion the action compresses the flat spring housed beneath the grips compressing it to provide energy for the forward action of the pistol.

Field Stripping

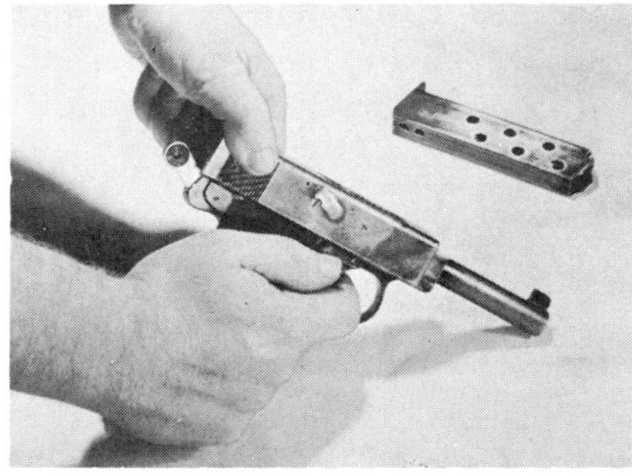

Move slide about ¼″ to the rear and press in recoil lever stop. This is the small milled stud on the right side of the pistol directly behind the trigger. This locks the recoil spring out of action. Now push the slide forward again.

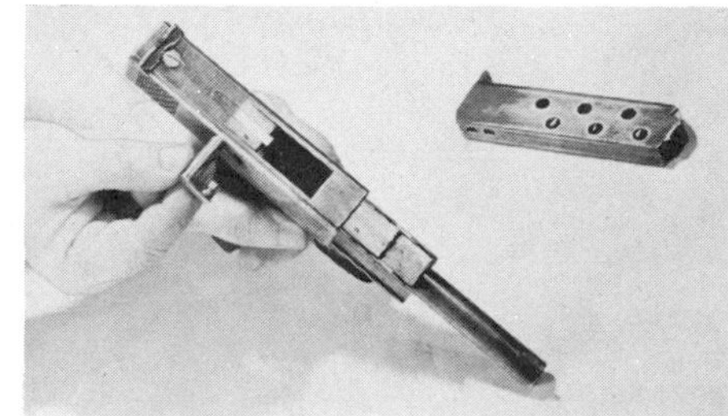

The slide (or breech) stop is now loose as the recoil spring is locked out of action by the recoil lever stop. Pull this out as far as it will go.

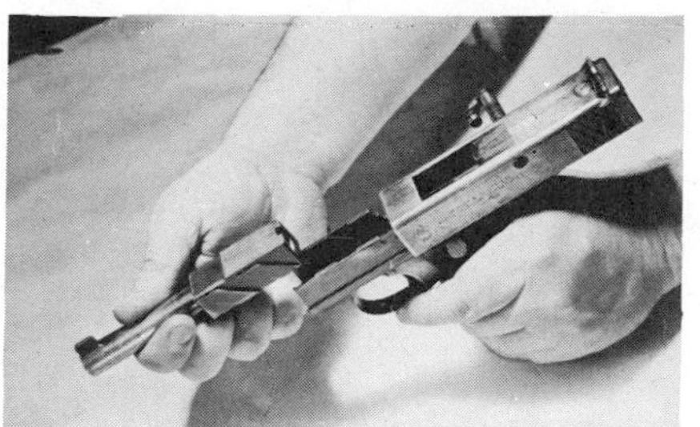

Displacing the breech stop permits the slide to be drawn directly to the rear.

This releases the barrel which can now be lifted out.

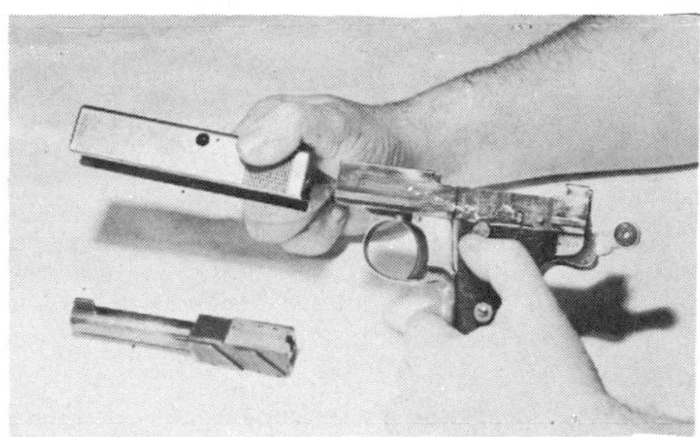

The slide can now be pushed forward off the receiver.

No further dismounting is necessary or recommended.

Note: The recoil spring in this pistol is a flat spring positioned inside the handle under the right hand stock. Its pressure is exerted against a hard steel pin extending transversely through the slide and called the recoil lever bar and breech stop. This spring system is not to be compared for reliability with the coil spring system used in our Colt Automatic Pistols. However, it does permit exceptionally easy dismounting, which is an important factor in giving proper care to any weapon.

BRITISH RIFLES AND CARBINES

THE BRITISH BOLT ACTION MILITARY RIFLES—FROM 1888 TO 1951

The Canadian and British governments have been selling out large stocks of bolt action rifles over the last five or six years. Most of these rifles have been imported into the United States and are being sold for very reasonable prices. Since a large number of models are being sold, and interest in these rifles has increased considerably among gun collectors, a listing of the various types of British bolt action rifles, and photographs of some of the types, are given in this section. Some variants of these rifles have been omitted from the listing, because they were made in such small quantities that the reader is unlikely to encounter them.

Safety Measures and Inspection Criteria

British rifles are usually well made and, if in good condition, are safe enough. Rifles of earlier marks than the long Lee Enfield Mark 1 should not be used with the Mark 7 or other heavily loaded cartridges. The No. 4 and later rifles, if they are in good condition, will safely use any .303 cartridge loaded for rifles. United States commercial ammunition is not loaded too heavily in cal. .303, and will not bother any of the Long Lee Enfield's or later weapons. Wherever there is any doubt about safety, the weapon should not be fired until checked by a reliable gunsmith.

In passing, it is worth noting that the .303 British and .303 Savage are not the same cartridge, and are not interchangeable. The .303 British, as currently loaded by American cartridge manufacturers, has a 215-grain bullet with a muzzle velocity of 2,180 feet per second. This is quite close to the loading of the British Mark 6 cal. .303 cartridge, which had a 215-grain bullet with a velocity of 2,060 feet per second. The Mark 6 cartridge was used with the Long Lee Enfield's and the early No. 1's.

As an aid to gunsmiths and others who will undoubtedly encounter many British Lee Enfield rifles in the future, some of the inspection criteria for the weapons are listed below.

Headspace. Since the .303 is a rimmed cartridge, headspace is measured from the rear face of the barrel to the face of the bolt. The headspace of the .303 rifle should not exceed .074 inches, although—as a wartime measure—a maximum of 0.80 inches was allowed. Minimum headspace is .064 inch.

Barrel gaging. The bore diameter should be from .301 to .304 inches, in a new barrel. To gage a used barrel, plug gages from .303 to .310 inches should be used. The .303 gage should run through the barrel; the .307 gage should not run through the barrel. The .308 gage should not enter the muzzle more than .25 inches, and the .310 gage should not enter the breech more than .25 inches.

Firing pin protrusion. The high for firing pin protrusion for the No. 1's is .055 inches, and the low is .050 inches. The high for the No. 4's and No. 5's is .050 inches, and the low is .040 inches.

Trigger pull. The first pull or slack should be from 3 to 4 pounds. The second pull should be from 5 to 6

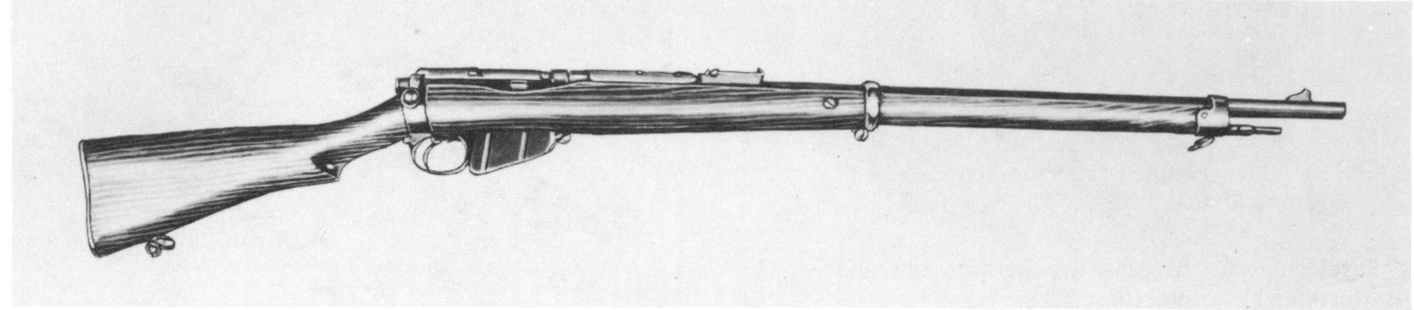

Lee Metford Mark II.

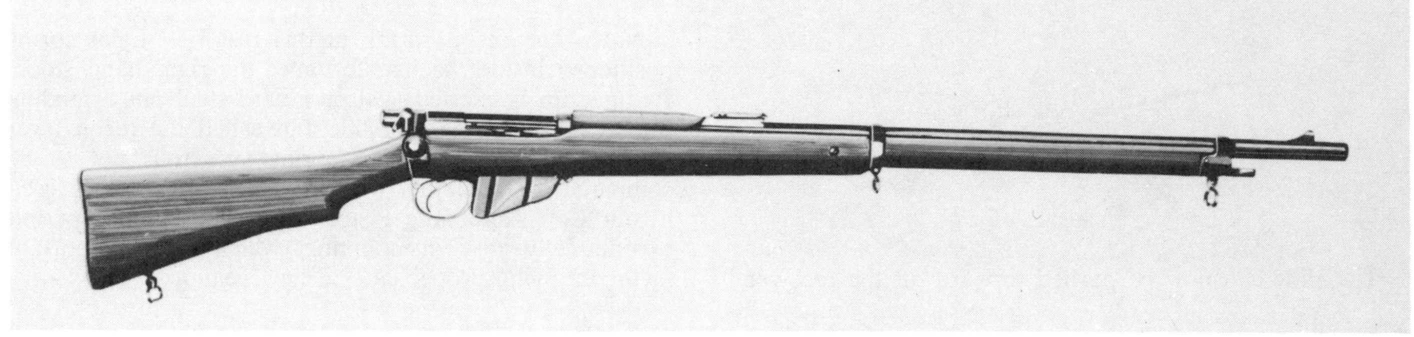

Lee Metford Mark II*.

pounds. To increase or decrease the trigger pull weight, alter the angle of the cocking piece sear notch.

Butt stock lengths. Butts for the No. 1 rifles were made in long and short lengths, and during World War I a special short butt called the Bantam was made. These butts will be marked "L," "S," or "B" on the top of the stock, approximately one inch from the butt plate tang. Butts for the No. 4 rifles come in long, short, and normal lengths.

The Cal. .303 Lee Metford Rifles and Carbines

Rifle, Magazine, Lee Metford Mark I. Adopted December 1888. Was the first British production Lee. Chambered for the Cal. .303 black-powder-loaded cartridge. Had an eight-round magazine and a full-length cleaning rod.

Rifle, Magazine, Lee Metford Mark I*. Adopted January 1892. Was a conversion of the Mark I; the sights were changed from "Lewes" and "Welsh" pattern to barleycorn front and V-notch rear sight.

Rifle, Magazine, Lee Metford Mark II. Adopted April 1892. Was the first of the series to be fitted with a 10-round magazine. The bolt was modified and the outside contour of the barrel was changed. A half-length cleaning rod was fitted to the gun, and the brass marking disk on the butt stock was omitted.

Carbine, Magazine, Lee Metford Mark I. Adopted 1894.

Rifle, Magazine, Lee Metford Mark II*. Adopted 1895. Had a safety catch added to the bolt. (Previous marks had a half-cock notch on the cocking piece as their only safety.)

The Cal. .303 Lee Enfield Rifles and Carbines

Rifle, Magazine, Lee Enfield Mark I. Adopted November 1895. Had the deep Enfield rifling, rather than the shallow Metford rifling used on previous marks. The sights were also modified.

Rifle, Magazine, Lee Enfield Mark 1*. Adopted 1899. Had no cleaning rod mounted in the stock.

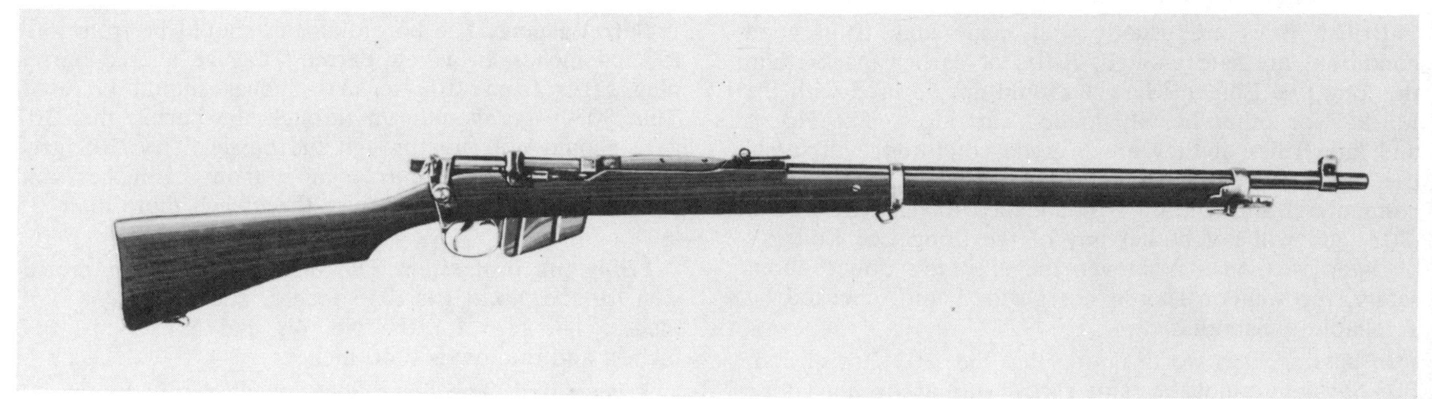

Rifle, Charger Loading, Long Lee Enfield Mark 1*.

BRITISH BOLT ACTION RIFLES AND CARBINES

	Lee Metford Rifle Mark I*	Lee Metford Rifle Mark II	Lee Metford Carbine Mark I	Lee Enfield Rifle Mark I
Caliber	.303	.303	.303	.303
Overall length	49.85 in	49.85 in	40 in	49.5 in
Barrel length	30.19 in	30.19 in	20.75 in	30.19 in
Feed device	8 rd detachable box w/cut-off	10 rd detachable box w/cut-off	6 rd detachable box w/cut-off	10 rd detachable box w/cut-off
Sights: Front	Barley Corn	Barley Corn	Barley Corn w/ protecting ears	Barley Corn
Rear	Vertical leaf and ramp	Vertical leaf and ramp	Vertical leaf and ramp	Vertical leaf and ramp
Muzzle velocity (at date of adoption)	2000 FPS	2000 FPS	1940 FPS	2060 FPS
Weight	10.43 lbs.	10.18 lbs	7.43 lbs	9.25 lbs

	Pattern 14 Rifle (Rifle No 3 MK 1*)	Short Lee Enfield Rifle Mark I (Rifle No 1 SMLE MK 1)	Short Lee Enfield Rifle Mark III (Rifle No 1 SMLE MK 3)	Short Lee Enfield Rifle Mark III* (Rifle No 1 SMLE MK 3*)
Caliber	.303	.303	.303	.303
Overall length	46.25 in	44.5 in	44.5 in	44.5 in
Barrel length	26 in	25.19 in	25.19 in	25.19 in
Feed device	5 rd integral magazine	10 rd detachable box w/cut-off	10 rd detachable box w/cut-off	10 rd detachable box
Sights: Front	Blade w/ protecting ears	Barley Corn w/ protecting ears	Blade w/ protecting ears	Blade w/ protecting ears
Rear	Vertical leaf w/ aperture battle sight, long range side sights	Tangent leaf w/notch long range side sights	Tangent leaf w/notch long range side sights	Tangent leaf w/notch
Muzzle velocity (at date of adoption)	Apprx 2500 FPS	2060 FPS	2060 FPS	2440 FPS
Weight	9.62 lbs	8.12 lbs	8.62 lbs	8.62 lbs

	Rifle No 2 Mark 4	Rifle No 4 Mark 1	Rifle No 5 Mark 1	Rifle No 8 Mark 1
Caliber	.22	.303	.303	.22
Overall length	44.5 in	44.5 in	39.5 in	41.05 in
Barrel length	25.2 in	25.2 in	18.7 in	23.3 in
Feed device	Single shot	10 rd detach-able box	10 rd detachable box	Single shot
Sights: Front	Blade w/ protecting ears	Blade w/ protecting ears	Blade w/ protecting ears	Blade w/ protecting ears
Rear	Tangent leaf w/notch	Vertical leaf w/ aperture battle sight or L type	Vertical leaf w/ aperture battle sight	Vertical leaf w/ aperture battle sight
Muzzle velocity (at date of adoption)	1050 FPS	2440 FPS	2400 FPS	1050 FPS
Weight	9.19 lbs	8.8 lbs	7.15 lbs	8.87 lbs

Characteristics are listed only for the principal models.
Lengths are with normal butt.

Lee Enfield Mark I Carbine.

Rifle No. 1, Mark I.

Carbine, Magazine, Lee Enfield Mark I. Adopted 1896. Had a six-shot magazine.

Carbine, Magazine, Lee Enfield Mark I*.

Rifle No. 1, Short Magazine, Lee Enfield Mark I. Adopted December 1902. Was the first of the short rifles (SMLE). Was stocked to the muzzle and charger loaded. The right side charger guide is on the bolt head, and the left charger guide is on the receiver. Has a V-notch rear sight with adjustable windage and a barleycorn front sight. Was the first of what later came to be called the No. 1 series of rifles.

Rifle, No. 1, Short Magazine, Lee Enfield Mark II. Essentially the same as the SMLE No. 1 Mark I, but was converted from earlier Mark II and Mark II* Lee Metford's and Long Lee Enfield's.

Rifle No. 1, Short Magazine, Lee Enfield Mark I*. A minor variant of the SMLE No. 1 Mark I.

Rifle No. 1, Short Magazine, Lee Enfield Mark II*. A minor variant of the No. 1 Mark II SMLE.

Rifle No. 1, Short Magazine, Lee Enfield Mark III. Adopted January 1907. Was the backbone of the British Army in World War I, and was also used extensively in World War II. Is still in use in many of the areas of the British Commonwealth today.

Rifle No. 1, Short Magazine, Lee Enfield Mark IV. Adopted July 1907. Basically the same as the No. 1 Mark III; converted from Long Lee Metford's and Long Lee Enfield's.

Rifle, Charger Loading, Long, Lee Metford Mark II. Was converted to charger loading in 1907 for use of the Territorial Army, and converted to rifle charger loading Lee Enfield Mark I* in 1909.

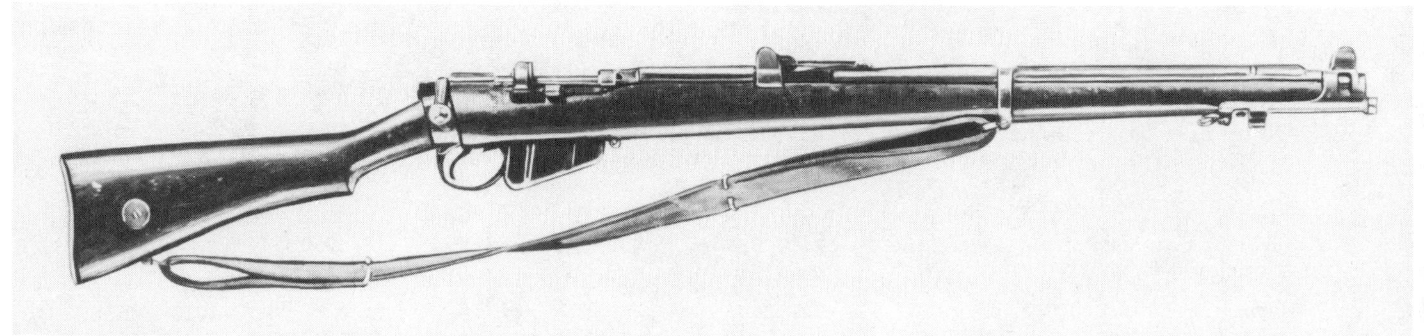

Rifle No. 1, Mark III.

Rifle No. 1, Mark III*.

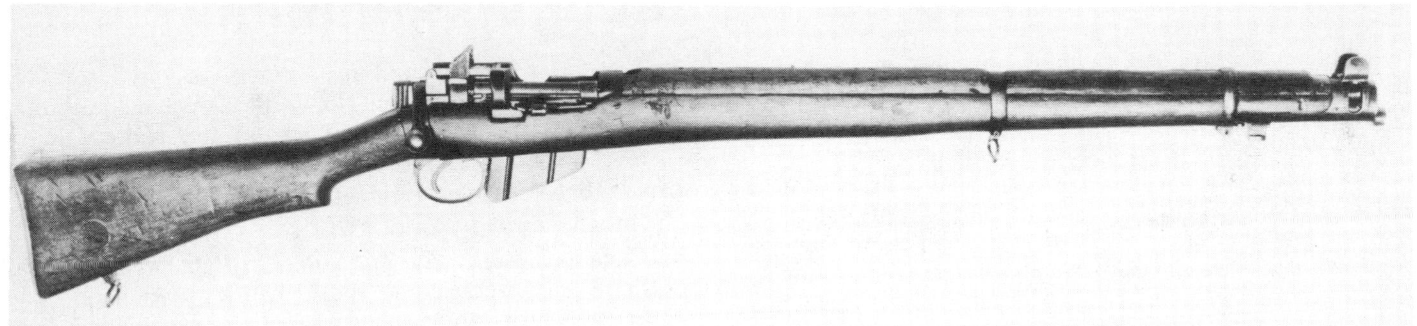

Rifle No. 1, Mark V.

Rifle, Charger Loading, Long, Lee Enfield Mark I. A 1907 conversion of early marks of Long Lee Enfield to charger loading. A Mark I* version also exists. A large number of these weapons were used by British forces in the early days of World War I.

Rifle No. 1, Short Magazine, Lee Enfield Mark III*. Was adopted during World War I, and made in very large quantities. Is still in widespread use throughout the world. Does not have the long-range side sights of the Mark III and earlier marks, and does not have a magazine cutoff.

Rifle No. 1, Short Magazine, Lee Enfield Mark V. Appeared around 1922. The rear sight is mounted on the receiver bridge, and an additional stock band is mounted to the rear of the nose cap. Many of these weapons were used in India.

Rifle No. 1, Short Magazine, Lee Enfield Mark VI. Was developed in the period 1929-1930. Was the forerunner of the No. 4 rifles. Had rear sight on the receiver bridge. Had a lighter nose cap, heavier barrel, and smaller bolt head than the earlier marks.

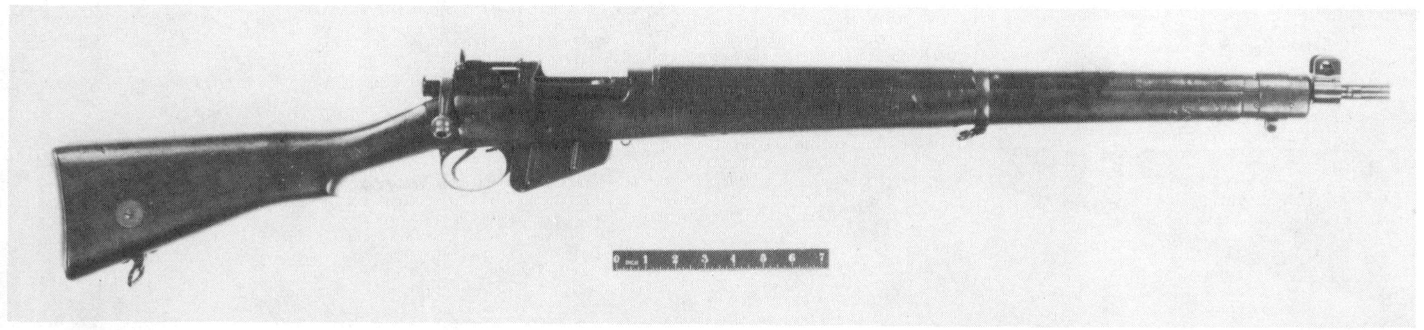

Rifle No. 1, Mark VI.

Rifle No. 4, Mark 1 Stripped.

Rifle No. 4 Mark 1. Originally appeared in 1931. Was finely made, and was generally similar to the No. 1 Mark VI except that some were fitted with a magazine cutoff. Was redesigned for mass production around 1939 and became, with the No. 4 Mark 1*, the British "work horse" of World War II. Stamped bands were used, and various manufacturing shortcuts were taken to increase production. Three different marks of rear sights may be found on this weapon, ranging from a finely machined adjustable leaf to a simple L-type. Many of these weapons are still in service in the British Commonwealth and in former British territories.

Rifle No. 4 Mark 1*. Was the North American production version of the No. 4 Mark 1. The principal difference was that the bolthead catch, which was situated behind the receiver bridge on the No. 4 Mark 1 (and earlier Marks), was eliminated on the No. 4 Mark 1*, and a cutout on the bolt head track was used for bolt removal. Over five million No. 4 rifles were made during World War II in the UK, Canada, the United States (Stevens Arms), and India. Australia did not adopt the No. 4, but continued production of the No. 1 Mark III* at Lithgow during World War II.

Canadian Rifle No. 4 Mark I* (light weight). This weapon was produced at the Canadian arsenal at Long Branch in prototype form. It has a one piece stock, and its trigger is pinned to the receiver. Weight about 6¾ pounds. Barrel length about 23 inches. Overall length about 42½ inches. One piece stock. Receiver wall cut down and stock inletted to reduce weight. Sporting type Hawkins rubber buttplate. Micrometer sights with peep battle sight. Sight adjustable in clicks and 100 meter steps from 100 to 1300 yards. This arm may be used for grenade launching.

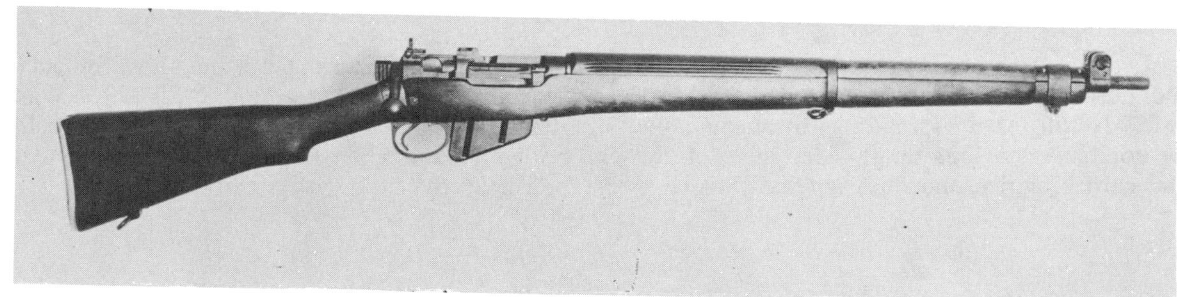

British Rifle No. 4 Mark 1*.

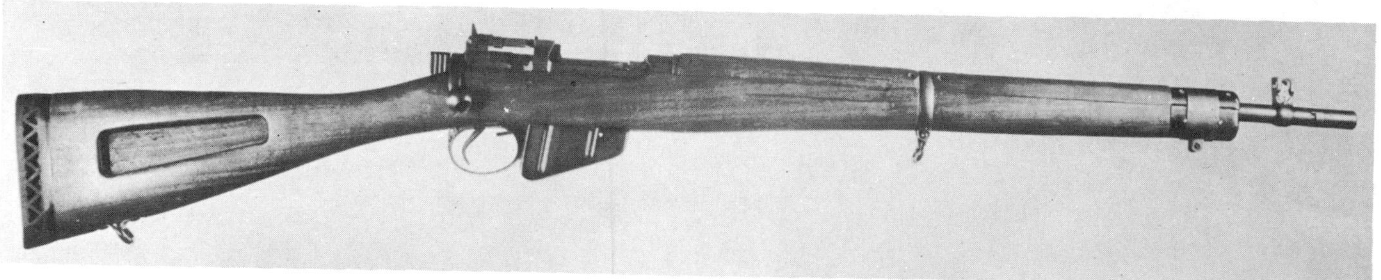

Canadian Rifle No. 4 Mark 1* (light weight).

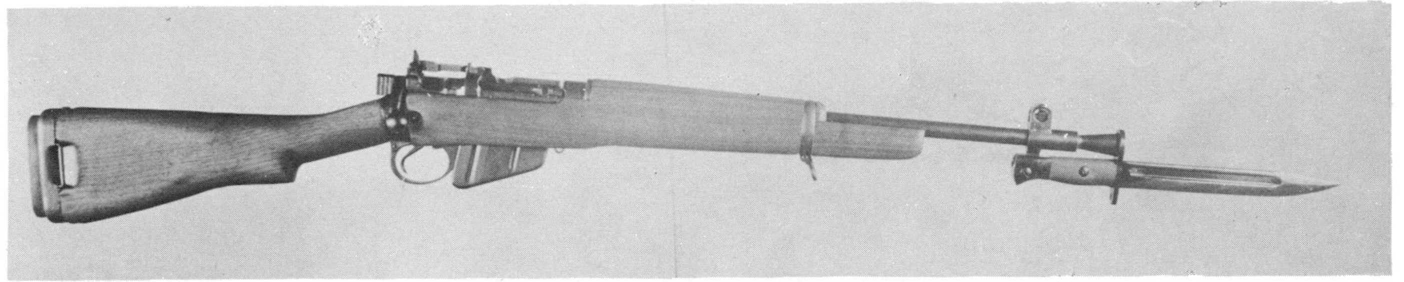

British Rifle No. 5 (Jungle Carbine) Mark 1*.

Rifle No. 4 Mark 2. Was developed at the end of World War II. Differed from the earlier marks by having its trigger pinned to the receiver rather than to the trigger guard.

Rifle No. 5 Mark 1. Appeared toward the end of World War II. Was a lightweight weapon, and was commonly called the jungle carbine. Has a lightened and shortened barrel which is fitted with a flash hider. Fore-end has been cut back and rounded, giving weapon the appearance of a sporting rifle. A rubber recoil pad is fitted to the butt.

Rifle No. 5 Mark 1*. A variant of the jungle carbine.

Rifle No. 4 Mark 1(T) and No. 4 Mark 1*(T). Are the sniper versions of the No. 4. Are fitted with scope mounts on the left side of the receiver, and have a wooden cheek rest screwed to the butt. The No. 32 telescope is used on these weapons. There are also sniper versions of the No. 1 and No. 3 rifles (Pattern 14).

Rifle No. 6. Appeared only as prototype; 18″ barrel version of No. 1.

The Cal. .22 Rifles

Rifle No. 2 Mark IV. Is a conversion of cal. .303 SMLE's to cal. .22. Some have new .22 barrels, and some were "Parker Rifled," i.e., a .22 liner was placed in a bored-out .303 barrel. A special bolt head was made for these rifles.

Rifle No. 2 Mark IV*. A variant of the No. 2 Mark IV.

Rifle No. 7. Developed at Long Branch; single shot version of No. 4 Mark I*. Called Rifle "C" No. 7, .22 in Mark I.

Rifle No. 8. A postwar weapon, adopted in 1951. Sighting equipment is similar to that of the No. 4 rifles. Is a single shot weapon.

Rifle No. 9. Converted to .22 by Parker Hale, from No. 4 rifles, single shot.

Rifle No. 4, Mark 1 (T).

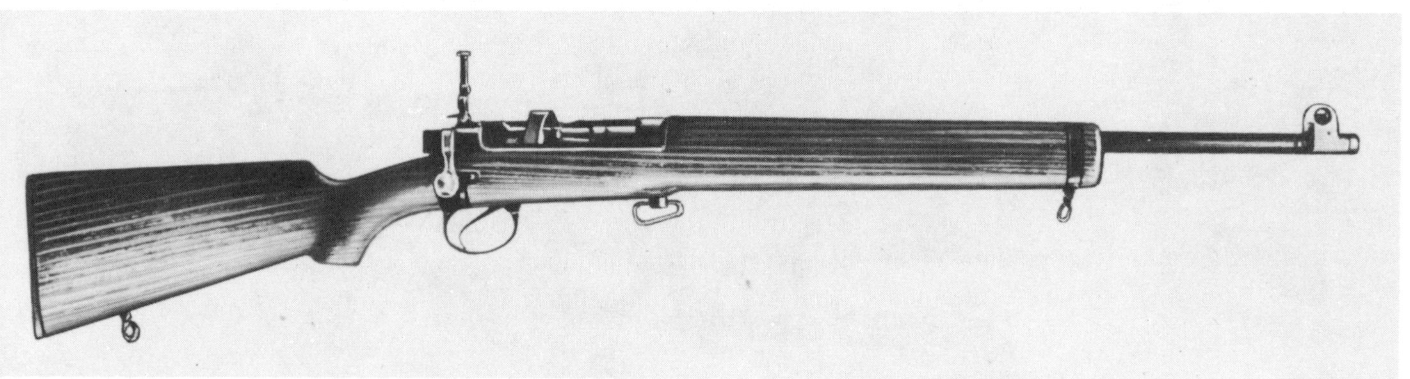

Rifle No. 8, Mark 1.

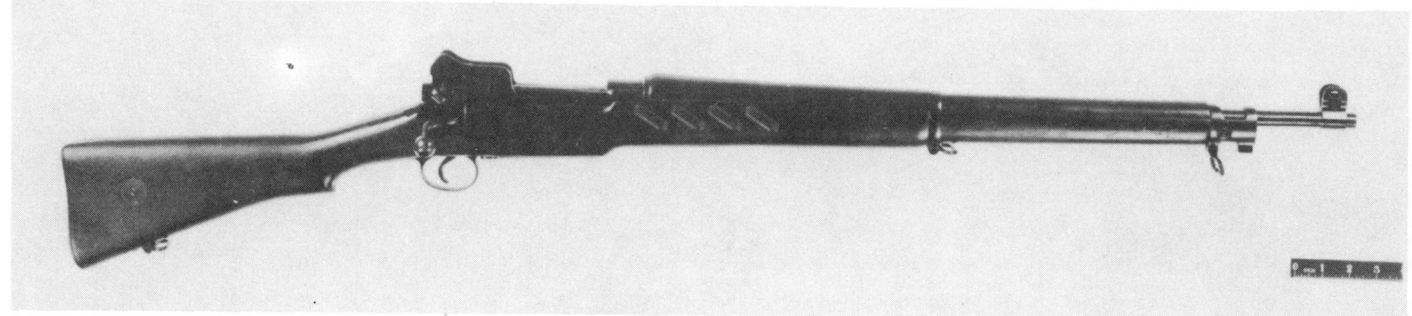

Pattern 13 Rifle.

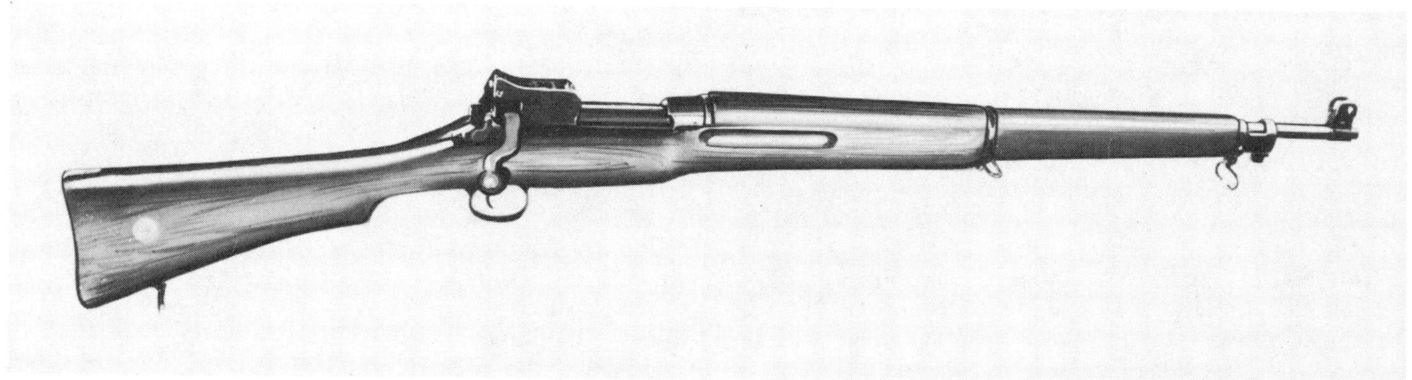

Pattern 14 Rifle.

The Mauser-Type Rifles

Pattern 13 (P-13). Tested in 1913. Was a modified Mauser (it cocked on the forward stroke of the bolt), chambered for a large cal. .276 cartridge. The cartridge was remarkably similar to the Canadian cal. .280 Ross cartridge. The rifle was made in comparatively small numbers for field trials.

Pattern 14 (P-14). Was the production model of the P-13. Was made in the United States in cal. .303 for the UK, during World War I. The weapon was classed as limited standard in the British Army, and, except for sniping, was not too widely used. Upon the entrance of the United States into World War I, the design was changed to U. S. Cal. .30, and the weapon was produced as the U. S. rifle, cal. .30, M1917 and was commonly known as the Enfield. Between World Wars I and II, the British changed the nomenclature of the P-14 to Rifle No. 3 Mark I and Mark II*.

Loading and Firing Bolt Action Rifles

Turn bolt handle up as far as it will go and pull it straight back to the limit of travel.

Insert loaded clip in the clip guide in the receiver and strip the cartridges down into the magazine. Remove the empty clip. Insert a second clip, push these cartridges down and remove clip. This will leave the magazine fully charged with 10 cartridges.

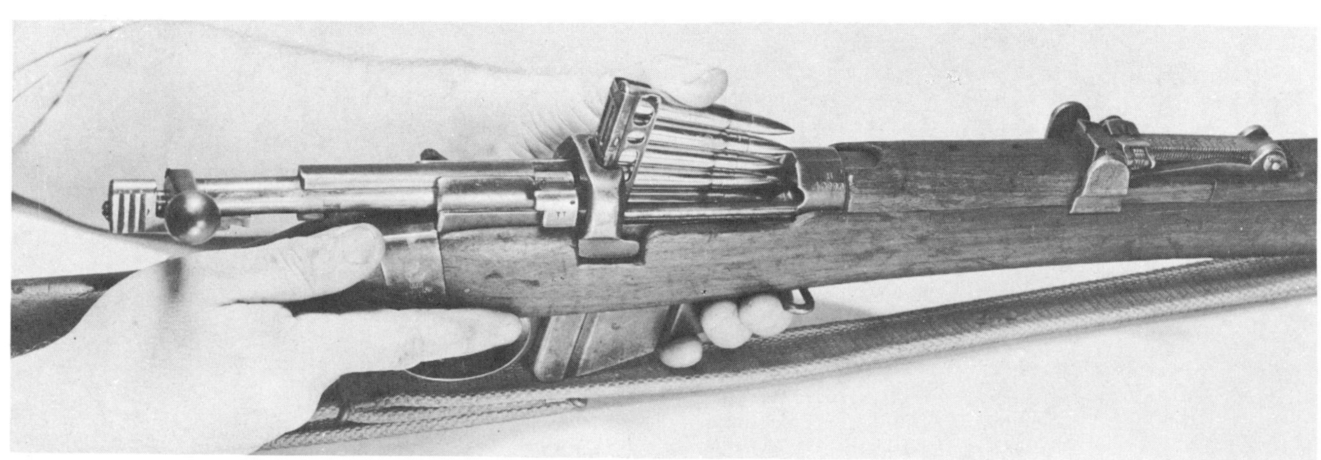

Pushing bolt handle fully forward and down loads the firing chamber, cocks, and locks ready for firing with a pull of the trigger.

Unless weapon is to be fired immediately, pull the thumb rocker on the left rear of the receiver to "Safe."

Field Stripping

Remove magazine. This may be done by pushing in or pulling up, as different rifles may require, the magazine catch located in the forward end of the triggerguard. This will release the heavy sheet steel box which may be withdrawn from the bottom of the receiver.

Removing the magazine follower and its spring is simply done. Hold the magazine, open end up, and push the rear of the magazine follower down inside the casing. This will permit you to ease the front end of the follower up and out of the casing and remove it and the spring.

In order to remove the bolt, it is first necessary to rock forward the safety catch just above the rear end of the triggerguard, on the left side of the rifle. Then turn the bolt handle up and turn it back as far as it will go. Catch your right forefinger under the head of the bolt. While using the right thumb, press down on the top of the clip guide to provide a lever action. Pull the bolt head up until it is released from its spring catch. Then withdraw it straight to the rear.

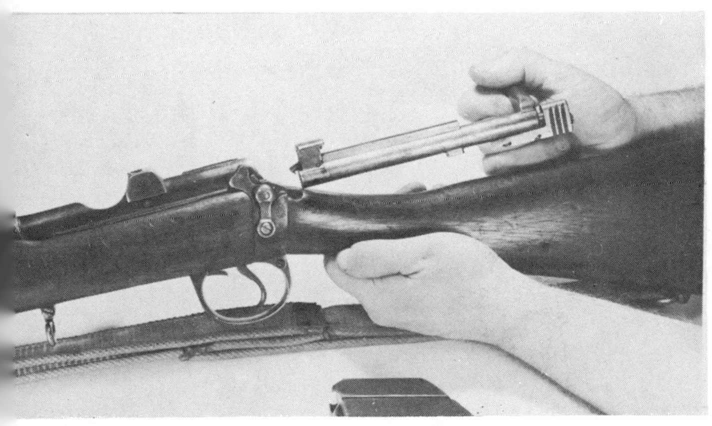

Note on Replacing Bolt. These bolts are not interchangeable and the number on the bolt should always be checked against the number on the rifle when there has been any possibility of substitution of another bolt. Before inserting the bolt, be sure that the head is fully screwed home, and that the cocking piece lines up with the lug on the underside of the bolt. Insert the bolt in the boltway and thrust it forward, and then pull it back as far as it will go until the head touches the resistance shoulders and force the bolt head down over the spring retaining catch. Then push it forward to the forward position. Turn down bolt handle and press trigger.

How the Bolt Action Rifle Works

Starting with the rifle loaded and cocked, the action is as follows: When the trigger is pressed, it draws down the sear until the sear nose reaches the bottom of the full bent. (This provides the first pull or slack, which is a feature of the best military rifles.) As the trigger pressure continues, the upper part of the sear is drawn still further down until the sear nose clears the bent allowing the cocking piece on the striker to be driven forward by the compressed mainspring. The striker nose, or firing pin, passes through a hole in the face of the bolt head and discharges the cartridge in the firing chamber.

Upward Action of the Bolt. Turning the bolt handle up, the rear end of the bolt rib is turned away from the resistance shoulder and the resistance lug travels down in an inclined groove on the left hand side of the boltway. As the extractor is snapped over the head of the empty cartridge case firmly, this action twists and frees the empty cartridge case, to start the movement of extraction. It also pulls the entire bolt back about 1/8″, while the cocking piece stud is forced from a cam groove up into a shorter cam groove and thereby withdraws the firing pin about an eighth of an inch.

As the bolt is pulled back to the rear, the extractor pulls the fired case to the rear until it strikes against the ejector and is thrown out the right side of the gun. Then the extractor spring snaps the extractor back into its place in the bolt head. As the bolt reaches its full rear position, the zig-zag spring in the magazine pushes the magazine follower attached above it directly up and brings the next cartridge into line with the bolt.

As the bolt is thrust forward, it strikes the base of the cartridge and drives it ahead into the firing chamber. The full bent of the cocking piece comes against the sear nose stopping its forward travel. The striker being attached to the cocking piece, the mainspring is compressed between the striker collar and the rear wall of the bolt chamber. As this motion is completed, the bolt head still is about an 1/8″ away from full feeding.

When the bolt handle is turned down, the bolt head, being a separate piece attached to the bolt by screw tension, is held from rotating with the bolt. The bolt itself is turned by a hook on the bolt head extension, traveling along the body rib which snaps over the retaining spring. The rear of the bolt rib turns down over the resistance shoulder while the resistance lug on the bolt itself travels up the inclined groove on the left side of the bolt. These take the shock of discharge when the rifle is fired. Note that this differs radically from the Mauser and Springfield in which the locking lugs are at the forward end of the bolt and turn into recesses in the receiver.

The long cam groove is now brought opposite the cocking piece stud. The short cam groove traveling upward is now able to receive the pin of the safety—the safety has been pulled back, securely locking the action as the bolt handle turns completely down. Meanwhile the upper limb of the sear is held upwards by the long limb of the sear spring whose short end rests against the magazine catch which it holds securely in place.

The magazine holds its 10 cartridges in two columns. The magazine follower is so formed that its left side is higher than its right. Thus as the cartridges are fed up, they come alternately from each column in the magazine, into line with the bolt. The sides of the rear end of the magazine extend slightly upwards and are turned in somewhat to retain the cartridges.

The magazine cutoff works in a slot below the rib on the receiver for the bolt head hook on the right side of the gun. When it is in the shut position, this cutoff holds the cartridges down below the line of the bolt travel, so that the magazine follower cannot rise to bring cartridges up. This keeps the magazine in reserve and permits single cartridges to be loaded directly into the firing chamber and lets the rifle be used as a single shot, while holding the magazine in reserve.

Thumb Safety. This is in the form of a rocker on the left side of the weapon. When it is fully forward, the rifle is ready to fire. When the thumb piece is rocked to the rear as far as it will go, the rifle is on "Safe." The locking pin on the safety catch then protrudes into the short cam slot in the rear of the bolt to prevent the bolt from rotating; while the half moon lug on the safety catch engages in a recess in the cocking piece preventing it from going either forward or rearward, while the safety is engaged.

Special Note on the Enfield System. The locking system on this rifle makes it the fastest operating bolt action rifle in the world. The abrupt turning action of the Mauser system will not permit it to attain a speed of operation possible with the Lee Enfield.

This rifle, since it has no locking recesses cut into the receiver, is much easier to clean than the Mauser type, and functions well under all battle conditions.

However, really accurate shooting at long ranges is difficult with this form of locking: Until recently the sniper rifles used by the British were developed from the Rifle No. 3 (American Enfield 1917 type). The new Rifle No. 4, however, is now issued with an American type sling for support and a No. 32 scope mounted on the left for sniping.

SEMI-AUTOMATIC AND AUTOMATIC RIFLES

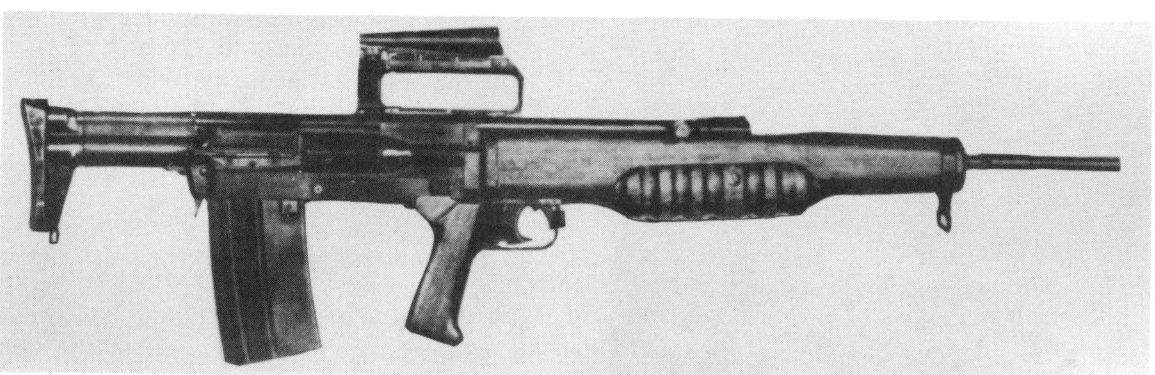

British experimental E.M.-2 full and semi-automatic rifle. Caliber 7-mm short (.280). This rifle on test did not compare favorably with the Belgian and U.S. designs.

Designation: EM-2.

Caliber: 7mm (short) .280.

Operation: Gas through piston operation, conventional.

Overall Length: 45 inches.

Weight: 8 pounds.

Magazine Capacity: 20 rounds, staggered box magazine detachable.

Change Lever Stud: Right hand side above pistol grip.

Cocking Handle: Upper right hand side of weapon above molded forestock, well forward of triggerguard.

Sight: Special optical design, non-magnifying, positioned on top of carrying handle on top of receiver.

Magazine Position: Below receiver. Rear of triggerguard.

Butt: Suppressed straight line type. Very close shoulder support. Molded forestock to protect hand from barrel heat. Pistol grip to rear of triggerguard for right hand support while firing.

Mechanism Design. Unconventional ejection opening at level of firer's face.

Trigger Position: Well forward of magazine, unconventional. (Note: Trigger position being level with barrel produces danger of firer burning forefinger during sustained fire.)

Ejection: Very close to firer's face. Can be fired only from right shoulder.

Length of Cartridge: 2½ inches.

Length of Rifle: 35 inches.

Notes on This Design

This rifle was developed by British Ordnance and scientific experts under the direction of Noel Kent-Lemon of the Ministry of Supply. It was dropped by the British, after much controversy, in favor of the FN light rifle.

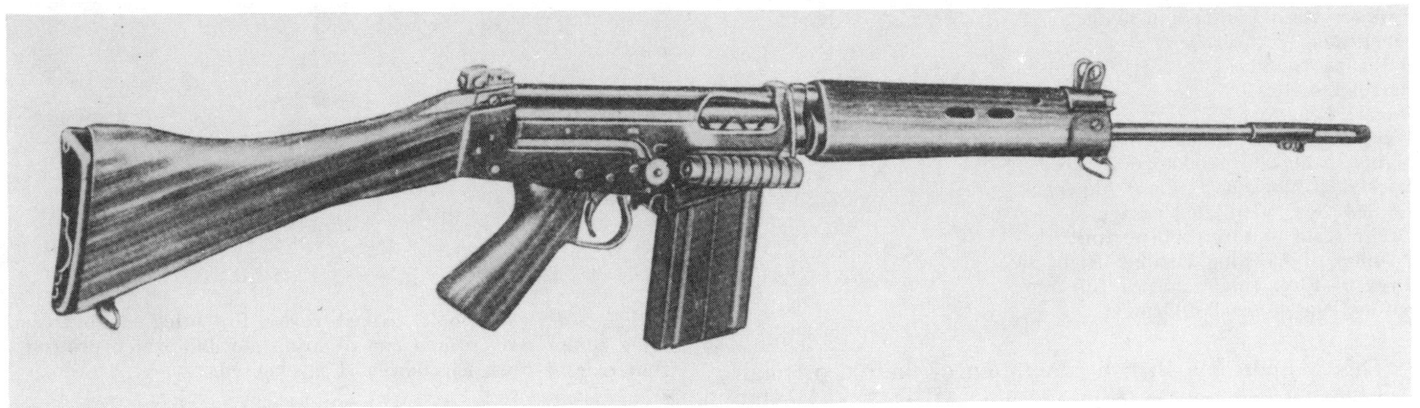

British 7.62mm Rifle L1A1.

The UK has adopted the 7.62mm NATO FN "light automatic rifle" and is producing it locally at BSA and one of the Royal Ordnance Small Arms Factories. The official British nomenclature for the weapon is: Rifle, 7.62mm, L1A1. The rifle is issued in the semi-automatic version; however, by the change of a few parts, it can be made to deliver full automatic fire as well.

The L1A1 is the British-produced version of the FN NATO "light rifle," or "FAL," as it is commonly called in Belgium. The FN design has been modified in a few components, but basically the weapon is the same as that covered in detail in chapter 19. Cuts have been made in the bolt carrier to serve as gathering places for dirt and dust that may enter the action. These cuts are deep enough so that a good deal of foreign matter can accumulate in them without impairing the normal functioning of the weapon. The L1A1 fires the 7.62mm NATO cartridge.

System of operation: Gas, semi-automatic fire only (can be modified to selective fire).
Weight, loaded: 10.48 lb.
Length, overall: 44.5 in.
Barrel length: 21 in.
Feed device: 20-round, detachable, staggered box magazine.
Sights: Front: Post w/protecting ears.
Rear: Aperture, adjustable from 200 to 600 yd.
Muzzle velocity: 2800 f.p.s.

BRITISH SUBMACHINE GUNS

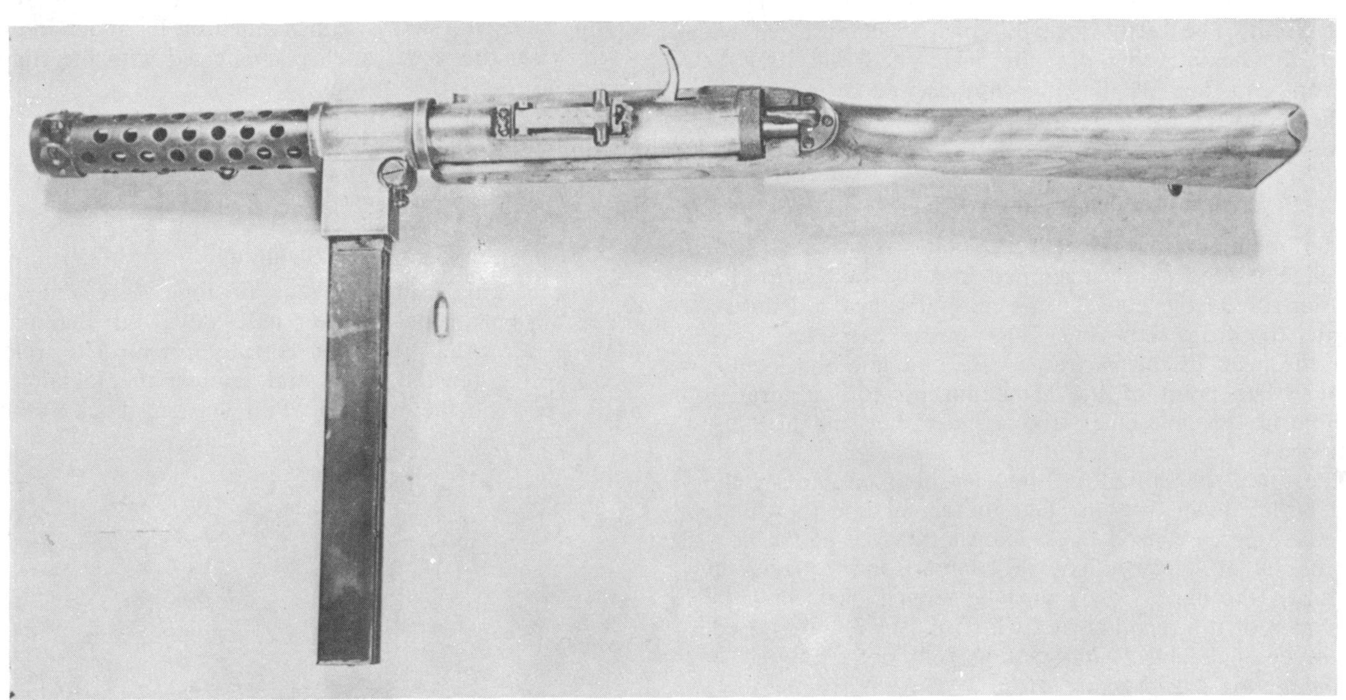

British Lanchester 9mm Mark 1.

Caliber: 9mm Parabellum (Luger).
Magazine: 32 cartridges.
Ballistics: Standard for cartridge used.
Barrel Length: 7.9".
Overal Length: 33.5".
Weight: 9.6 lbs.
Sights: Adjustable 100 to 600 yards.
Locked: Unlocked. Straight blowback.
Cooled. Air. Ventilated casing.
Cyclic Rate of Fire: 600 per min.
Position of Cocking Handle: Right side.
Type of Fire: Single shot or full auto.
Safety: Notch for bolt handle.

This weapon is a British adaptation of the old original German Bergmann machine pistol. It was originally issued as a Navy weapon. It fires the standard 9mm Sten (or Luger) cartridge.

The Lanchester is a standard pattern blowback submachine gun in which the weight of the bolt and other moving parts and the tension of the recoil spring hold the breech closed until breech pressure drops to safe limits after firing.

Loading and Firing

It is loaded and fired quite like the Sten. A loaded magazine is inserted in the magazine housing on the left side of the weapon and pushed in until it locks. The bolt handle on the right side of the receiver is drawn back until the bolt rides over the sear, which is forced up by its spring to catch in its notch in the underside of the bolt. This action of withdrawing the bolt permits the magazine spring to force the top cartridge into line with the bolt. Pulling the bolt handle still further to the rear permits it to be turned up to catch in the safety slot. When the bolt is freed from the safety slot, pressure on the trigger withdraws the sear nose from its notch in the bolt. The recoil spring (which is compressed between the heavy firing pin unit inside the bolt itself at its front end, and the locking cap screwed over the rear of the receiver tube at its rear end) is now free to exert forward pressure.

How the Gun Works

The recoil spring pushes the bolt assembly straight ahead. The feed guide machined into the bolt strips the first cartridge from between the magazine lips and thrusts it into the firing chamber. The spring extractor snaps over the head of the cartridge case and into the locking groove. The point of the firing pin protruding through its hole in the bolt face strikes the primer and fires the cartridge.

The gases generated in the cartridge case push the light bullet down the barrel at the same time they push the cartridge case itself back against the face of the bolt. As the bullet is very light in comparison to the great weight of the parts which must be moved back, and the resistance of the recoil spring which must be compressed, the breech is delayed in opening fully long enough to let dangerous gas pressure drop.

The extractor set in the bolt face guides the empty cartridge case back as the action opens, until the case

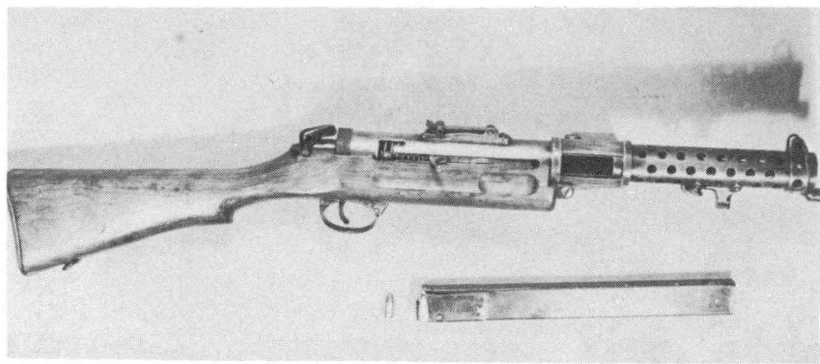

Right side view, bolt cocked ready for firing. Note recoil spring compressed around end of firing pin unit which protrudes from rear of bolt. Ejection port is exposed.

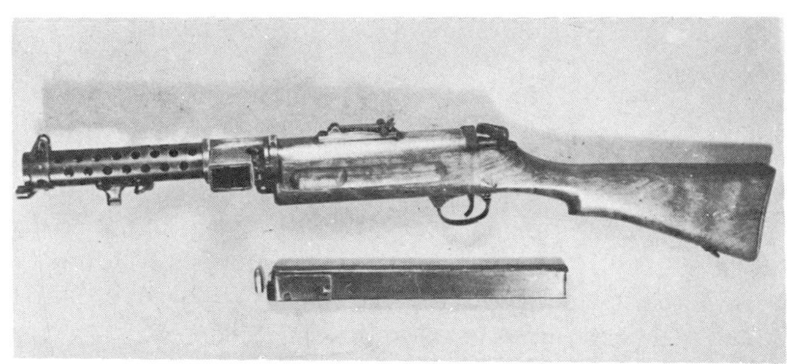

Left side view, magazine withdrawn to show magazine housing. Note that this gun is fitted with a lug to take the standard British bayonet.

strikes against the ejector which pivots it out the right side of the gun.

As the bolt clears the magazine in rearward travel, the magazine spring pushes its cartridge ahead, bringing the first one into line for the next loading stroke of the bolt.

The bolt pushes back the firing pin, and also compresses the recoil spring against the receiver cap. Continuing back, the bolt is so machined on its underside that it runs over the sear (which is connected with the trigger) and compresses the spring.

If the trigger is held, the bolt will run forward to fire continuously. If the trigger is released, the spring will force the sear up to catch in its notch in the bolt and hold it open.

Field Stripping

Turn locking catch at rear of top of receiver and break the barrel and receiver units down on their hinge. Making sure that the bolt is fully forward to release recoil spring tension, twist and remove the locking cap at the end of the receiver. Pull straight back on bolt

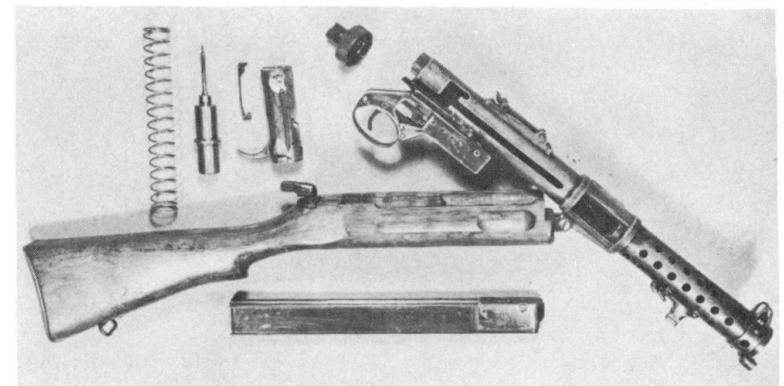

handle to bring recoil spring and bolt assembly out rear of receiver. Tip bolt up and remove firing pin unit. Pry out extractor if necessary. Pressing down on catch permits magazine to be withdrawn. Remove barrel from casing only when necessary.

Special Note on this Weapon

The Lanchester is fitted with a regulation type heavy rifle butt and its construction throughout is much more massive than is necessary for the cartridge it shoots, or for the accuracy obtainable from the weapon. It is fitted with rifle type sights. Like the Russian submachine guns in its class, it lends itself to use as a support weapon. It is a very strongly built weapon and will stand more abuse than many of the lighter weapons of this class. Sights are graduated to 600 yards.

British Sten 9mm Submachine Gun Mark I.

Caliber: 9mm Parabellum (.35).
Magazine: Staggered box type, capacity 32 cartridges.
Weight of Bullet: About 125 grains, round nose with metal jacket.
Muzzle Velocity: About 1280 feet per second.
Muzzle Energy: About 300 foot pounds.
Overall Length: 35 inches.
Weight without Magazine: 7.8 lbs.
Weight of Loaded Magazine: 1½ lbs.
Front Sight: "Barleycorn"—common European type like an inverted V.
Rear Sight: Fixed aperture, set for 100 yards range.
Accurate Range: About 200 yards.
Gun Operated by: Backward pressure of gases against fired cartridge case.
Locked: Simple blowback. Heavy bolt and return spring delay opening of breech until bullet has left barrel.
Cooled: Air. Bolt stays open between shots and air enters through open ejection port.
Cyclic Rate of Fire: 500 to 550 per minute.
Position of Cocking Handle: Right hand side of gun, to rear of ejection port.
Type of Fire: Selective. Single shot per trigger squeeze or full automatic.
Safety: When cocking handle is pulled back almost to end of slot, it can be turned **down** into lock slot.

Note: It is dangerous to carry this weapon with a loaded magazine inserted and the cocking handle in forward position, as a jar may fire it.

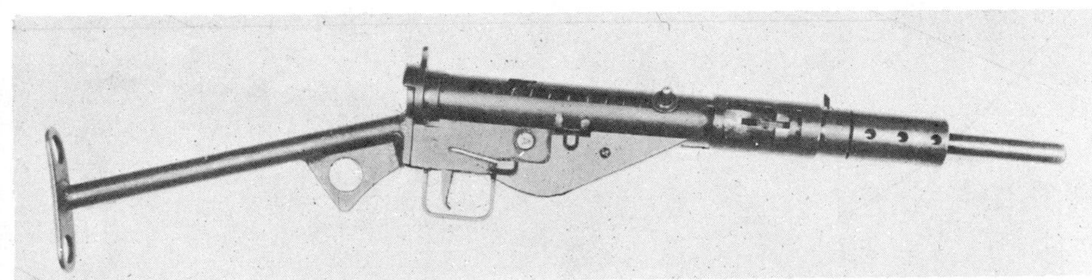

Overall Length: 30 inches.
Weight without Magazine: 6¾ lbs.
All other data same as for Mark I.
View showing gun uncocked, bolt handle forward.

Sten Model Mark II.

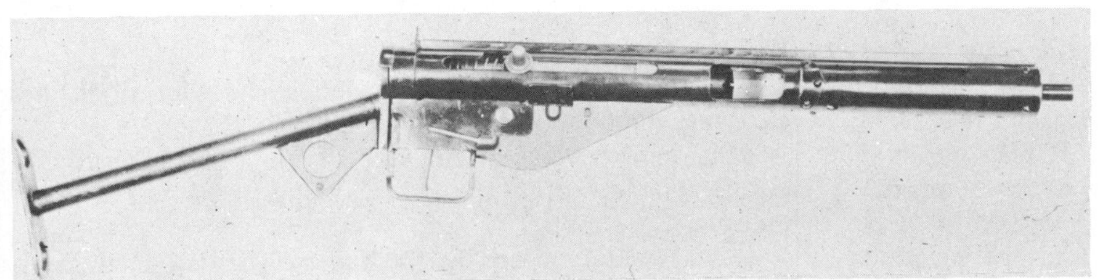

Overall Length: 30 inches.
Weight without Magazine: 7 lbs.
All other data same as for Mark I.
View showing gun cocked, ready to fire.

Sten Model Mark III.

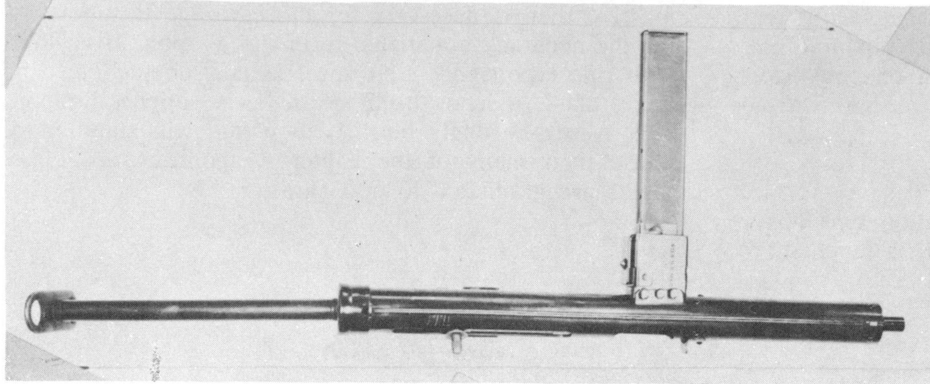

View showing magazine, catch, and housing.

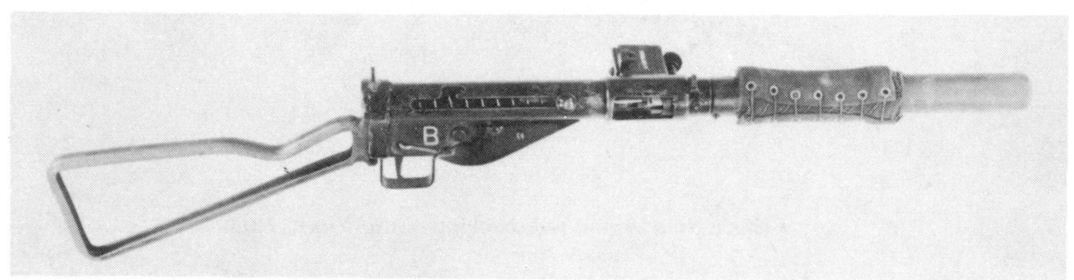

Sten Mark 2S fitted with Silencer.

Sten Model Mark V.

Mechanically this model is practically the same as the Mark II.

It is, however, fitted with a special bayonet which is equipped with a removable metal cover. It also has two rough wooden hand grips somewhat like those on the early Thompsons to facilitate handling and to protect the user from getting his fingers injured in the ejection port or from being burned by an over-heated barrel or barrel casing.

It is also equipped with a wooden shoulder stock and carrying sling.

This model was specifically developed for more accurate placing of shots when being used as a semi-automatic weapon.

It was widely used by the famous British Red Devil troops at Arnhem.

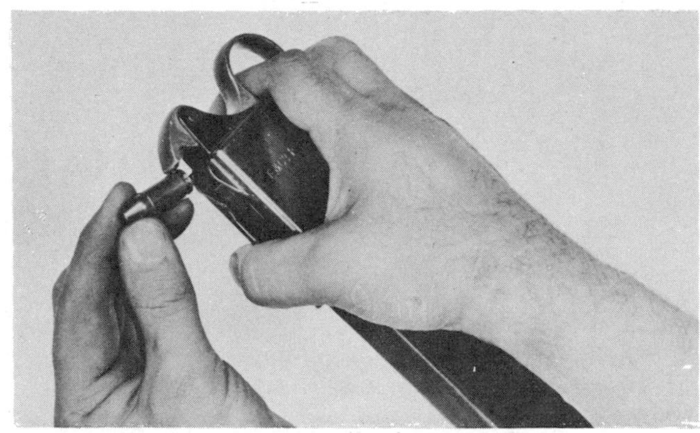

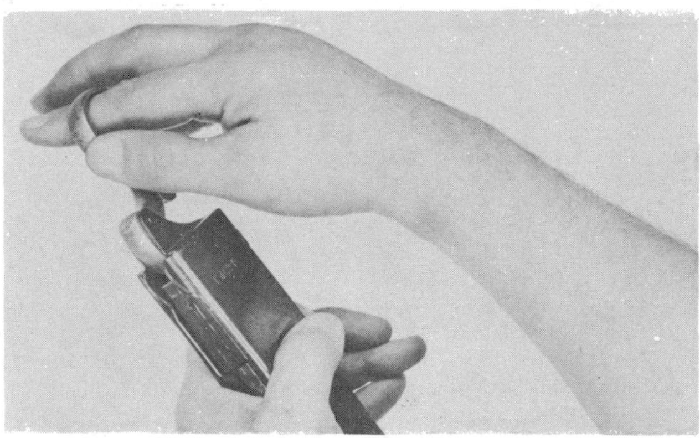

Instructions for Loading and Firing

A small special hand loader is provided as part of the equipment of every Sten gun. This is very helpful as compressing cartridges in this magazine is quite difficult due to the cartridge capacity and heavy spring.

The loader is clamped over the mouth of the magazine. The ring is pulled down as illustrated and a cartridge inserted into the mouth of the loader.

The ring is then lifted up to force the cartridge down and back under the magazine lips. It is then brought down to permit insertion of the next cartridge.

Insert loaded magazine, bullets pointing forward, into magazine housing on left side of gun just ahead of forward end of cocking handle slot. Push in until magazine locks with a click.

Pull back cocking handle and turn down into safety slot if the model is Mark I. (If model is Mark II or III, the safety slot is up—so turn cocking handle up into slot.)

When ready to fire, turn cocking handle out of the safety slot.

Directly under the safety slot is a button passing through the gun from side to side. (a) If you wish to fire one shot with each pull of the trigger, push the button from the left side. (It is marked "R," meaning "Repetition.") (b) If you wish to fire full automatic, push the button through on the right side of the gun where it is marked "A," meaning "Automatic."

Note: To remove magazine press down with the left thumb on the magazine catch (which is at the rear of the magazine housing), and at the same time grasping and pulling the magazine out with the fingers of the left hand.

Sten Mark III showing magazine in place and bolt ready to fire.

Field Stripping

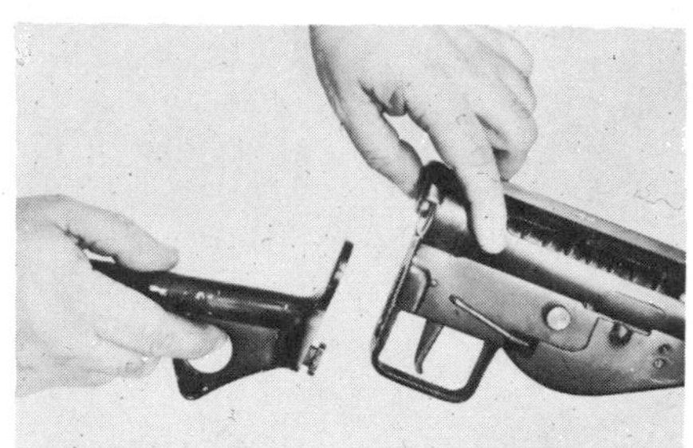

Press in the stud on return spring housing to clear hole and slide butt down out of its slots.

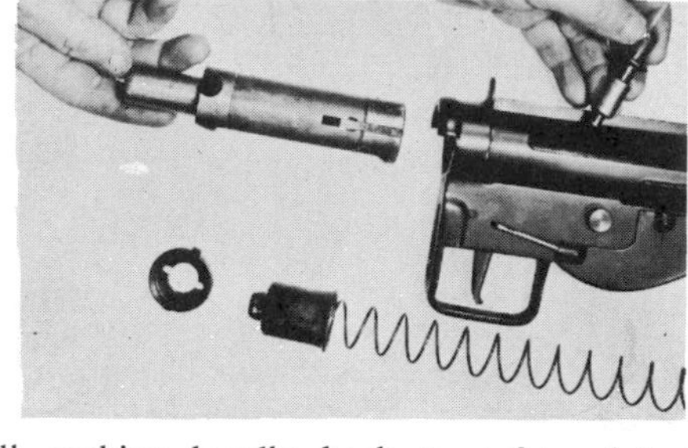

(a) Pull cocking handle back to safety slot. (b) Rotate until it can be pulled out of breech block. (c) Tip up gun and slide out breech block.

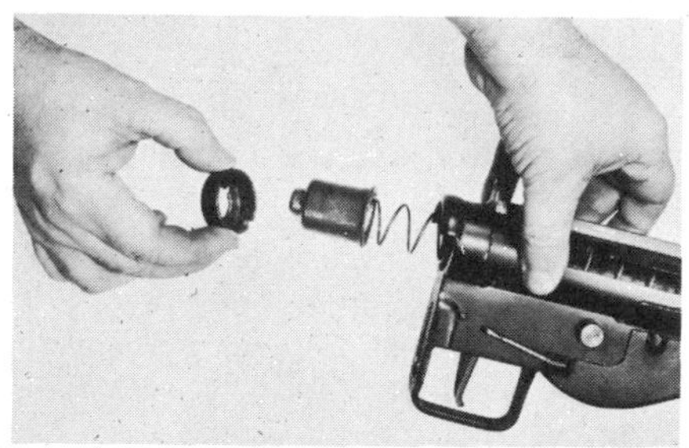

Press in on stud and spring cap and twist to the left to unlock lugs. Ease out spring cap, return spring and return spring housing and remove.

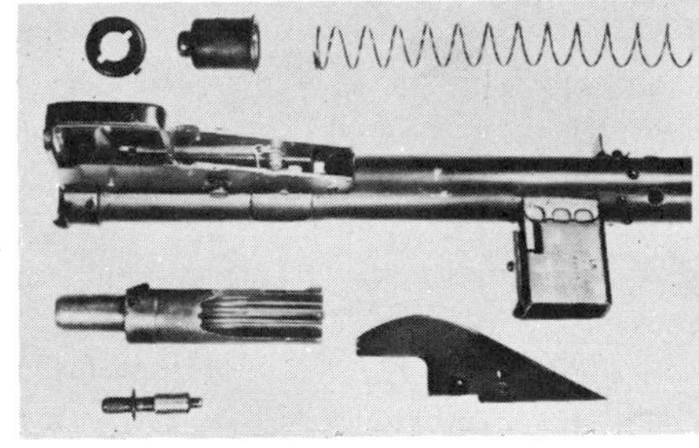

Weapon disassembled showing trigger and feeding mechanism.

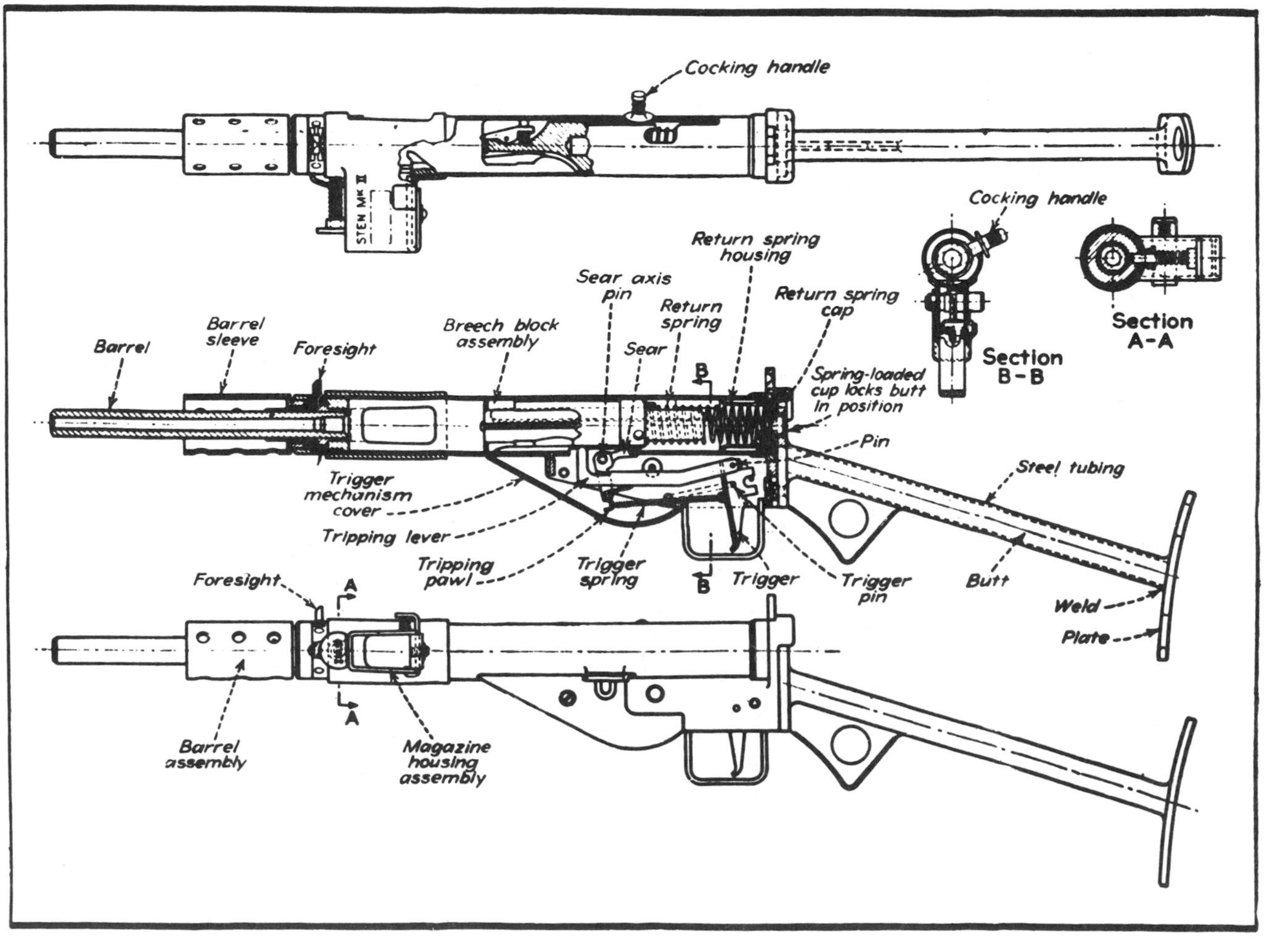

Note on Ammunition for Use in Sten Guns

The 9mm Parabellum cartridge used in the Stens is probably the most widely used cartridge in the world. It is almost universally used among the western powers with the exception of the U.S.

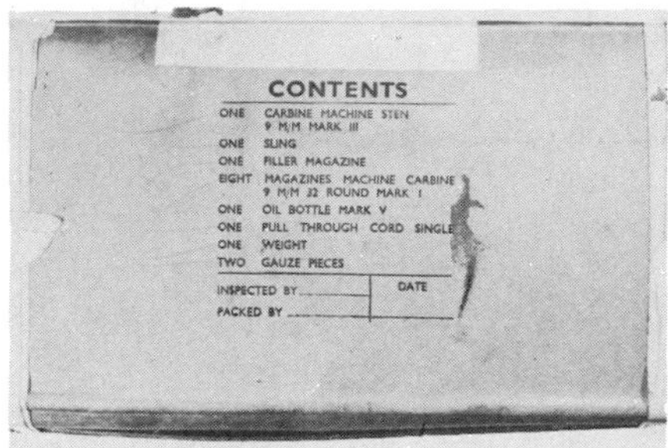

Package markings on Sten guns dropped into occupied countries.

How the Sten Gun Works

A loaded magazine being inserted in the magazine housing until it locks, the cocking handle is then pulled back to the cocked position, compressing the return spring.

When the trigger is pressed, the heavy breech block is freed and driven forward by the return spring. Feed ribs on the breech block strip the top cartridge from between the lips of the magazine and drive it into the firing chamber. The extractor, which is attached to the breechblock, snaps into the cannelure in the cartridge case and the firing pin strikes the cartridge primer exploding the powder.

The inertia of the heavy breech block and spring in forward motion keeps the breech closed until the bullet has left the barrel and the breech pressure has dropped to safe limits.

The remaining pressure drives the empty cartridge case and moving parts to the rear. The case strikes against the ejector and is hurled out of the gun. The magazine spring pushes the next cartridge in line for feeding.

Note: The Mark I, II, II-S, and III are obsolete in the U. K. The Mark V is being replaced by the L2A3.

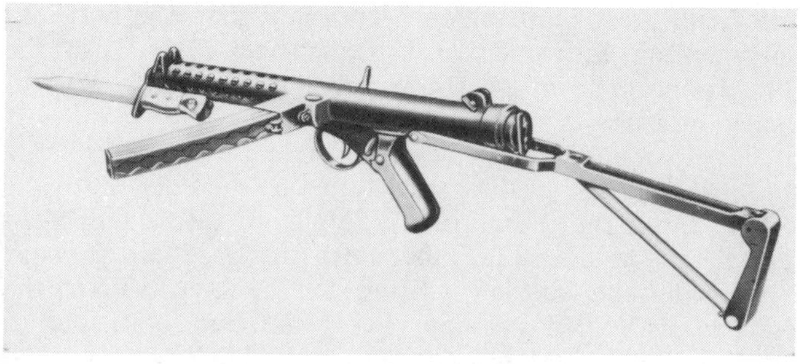

The British 9mm Submachine Gun L2A1.

System of Operation: Blowback, selective fire.
Weight: Unloaded, w/o bayonet: 6 lb.
Loaded, w/bayonet: 8.25 lb.
Overall length: Stock extended: 28 in.
Stock folded: 19 in.
Barrel length: 7.8 in.
Feed device: 34-round, detachable, staggered box magazine.
Sights: Front: Blade w/protecting ears.
Rear: Flip-type aperture, graduated for 100 and 200 yd.
Muzzle velocity: 1280 f.p.s. w/British 9mm service ball.
Cyclic rate: 550 r.p.m.

The 9mm submachine gun L2A3 is now standard in the UK. The L2A3 is sometimes referred to as the Patchett (the name of its designer), or as the Sterling (the name of its manufacturer). This weapon, which is already in extensive use, will completely replace the Sten guns in the British service.

The L2A3 is better made than the Sten guns it replaces, and is therefore less subject to functional and maintenance difficulties. The early Stens might be described as wartime improvisations, and could not be considered satisfactory for long-term service. On the other hand, the L2A3 is a weapon designed to last, and it can also be produced in large quantities at a reasonable cost. The weapon was given extended field trials in Malaya, Kenya, and the Middle East before adoption by the UK. Some minor changes have been made from the original L2A1 (L2A3 is actually the third model). The principal change was the substitution of a new type of front sight. The L2A3 is chambered for the 9mm Parabellum cartridge.

How to Load and Fire the L2A3

Pull the cocking handle to the rear; the bolt will remain to the rear, since the weapon fires from an open bolt. Engage the safety by turning the change lever (located on the left side of the pistol grip) to the letter "S." Insert a loaded magazine in the magazine guide, checking to insure that it locks in place. Move change lever to letter "R" for semi-automatic fire, or letter "A" for automatic fire. Squeeze the trigger and the weapon will fire.

Field Stripping the L2A3

Elementary Stripping. Before stripping, insure that the weapon is not loaded, and remove sling if fitted. Set change lever to "A"; place butt in the folded position and bolt forward.

To Remove Return Spring and Bolt. Press back-cap catch for full depth. Push back-cap forward and rotate counterclockwise until locking lugs disengage from locking recesses. Remove back-cap and draw cocking handle to rear of weapon. Lift cocking handle outward and withdraw return spring assembly from rear of receiver. Remove bolt from rear of receiver. Reassemble in reverse order. The spring-loaded fouling pin will prevent misassembly, since the cocking handle cannot be inserted until this pin is pushed forward by the center pin on the spring assembly. This ensures that the cocking handle must pass through the hole in the center pin.

L2A3 Field Stripped.

L2A3, Stock Folded.

To Remove Trigger Group. With a small coin or the rim of a cartridge, turn the slot in the head of the trigger group retaining pin until it is in line with the word "FREE" on the right side of the pistol grip. With the nose of a bullet or the blunt end of the cocking handle, push the trigger group retaining pin out and remove. Press the trigger, and pull the trigger group toward rear of weapon, disengaging it from the step in underside of barrel case; then swing front of trigger group out and remove from receiver.

Note: Elementary stripping does not include any further stripping of trigger group.

Assembly. Assemble in the reverse order of stripping.

Special Note on the L2A3

It should be noted that the receiver and barrel jacket of the L2A3 are composed of one piece of tubular steel. The Sterling Engineering Co.—the manufacturer of the L2A3—has designed and produced the Lanchester submachine gun, which was adopted by the Royal Navy in World War II. A trigger mechanism suitable for semiautomatic fire only is also made for the L2A3, and the weapon with this trigger mechanism is sold by Sterling as a police carbine.

How the L2A3 Works

The L2A3 is a blowback-operated weapon, and its bolt operation is essentially the same as that of most other blowback-operated guns. The action of the trigger mechanism differs among these weapons, however, and accordingly is described below in detail for the L2A3.

Semi-automatic Fire. When the change lever is set to the single shot position "R," the inner arm of the change lever is located under the tail of the tripping lever.

When the weapon is cocked and the trigger is pressed, the sear cradle is rotated about the sear axis pin, the sear is lowered, and the bolt is carried forward by the pressure of the return spring. During this movement the tail of the tripping lever contacts the inner arm of the change lever, causing the tripping lever to partially rotate. Continued pressure on the trigger causes further rotation of the tripping lever until the upper arm disengages from the step on the sear. At the same time the sear plunger and spring are compressed.

When the round is fired, the sear is held down by contact with the undersurface of the bolt, but as the bolt reaches the end of its rearward movement and is clear of the sear, the sear is forced upward by pressure of the sear plunger and spring. Then, as the bolt is moving forward, the sear engages against the notch on the face of the bolt and holds the bolt in cocked position.

When the pressure on the trigger is released, the rear end of the sear cradle rises, lifting the tripping lever and causing it to rotate about its axis pin until the upper arm of the tripping lever re-engages the step of the sear.

The trigger must be fully released and again pressed for each single shot.

Automatic Fire. With the change lever set at automatic fire position "A" and the weapon cocked, when the trigger is pressed the projection on the upper part of the trigger lifts the end of the sear cradle, rotating it about its axis pin. This action depresses the sear, freeing it from contact with the face of the notch on the bolt, and allowing the bolt to fly forward. The movement of the sear cradle compresses the sear cradle spring.

The weapon will now continue firing until either the trigger is released or the magazine is empty.

When the trigger is released, the sear cradle returns to its former position under the action of the sear cradle spring, and the sear is raised into the boltway where it engages the notch on the bolt, to hold the bolt in the cocked position.

Applied Safety. When the weapon is cocked, and the change lever is set at the safe position "S," the inner arm of the change lever is positioned directly under the short arm of the tripping lever. When the trigger is pressed, the sear cradle and sear cannot be depressed because the short arm of the tripping lever is held immovable by the inner arm of the change lever.

When the bolt is forward, and the change lever is set at the safe position, the weapon cannot be cocked because the sear is engaged in the safety slot at the rear of the bolt, and the sear cannot be depressed because it is held immovable as described in the previous paragraph.

The Butt Mechanism. To open butt, hold the weapon with the left hand near the rear sight, with the barrel pointing toward the ground. Pull the butt plate outward with the right hand to release the butt catch, and swing the butt to the rear of the weapon. With the thumb of the left hand press the back-cap catch and snap the butt into engagement with the lugs on the back-cap. Open the butt frame to form a triangle and the butt catch will engage, to lock.

To close butt, release the butt plate catch and collapse the triangle by pushing the tubular member into the frame. With the thumb of the left hand, press the back-cap catch; at the same time, push the back-cap forward and swing the butt away from the back-cap. Pivot the butt to its folded position, swing the butt plate out to operate the butt catch, to engage in the barrel casing, then fold the butt plate flat to lock in position.

BRITISH MACHINE GUNS

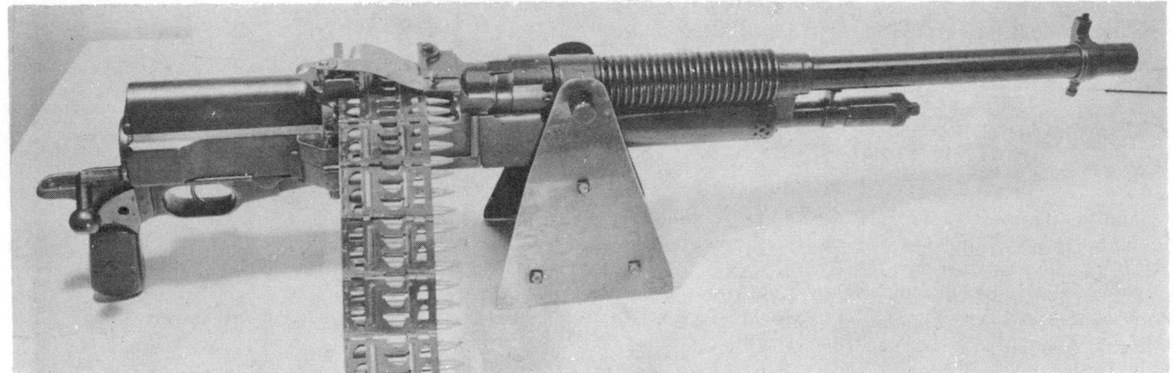

British Hotchkiss .303 Light Machine Gun.

The model illustrated is the Mark I* without shoulder stock intended for tank use. Identical in all other ways with the typical Infantry and Cavalry model. This weapon is obsolete.

Caliber: .303 British Service cartridges.

Method of Feed: Mark I models use tempered metal strips holding 9, 14, or 30 cartridges. This model will not use a belt. Mark I* models will take the metal strips as in the Mark I or will take a metal link belt holding 50 rounds. This belt is in strip form.

Ballistics of Cartridge: Standard for British Service .303.

Barrel Length: 23¼".

Overall Length with Attached Butt Stock: 3' 10½".

Weight: Approx. 27 lbs. with butt, but without mounting.

Weight of Loaded 30-Round Strip: 1 lb. 15 ozs.

Weight of Loaded 50-Round Belt: 3 lbs. 3½ ozs.

Accurate Range: About 500 yards.

Gun Operated by: Gas, escaping through a small hole bored in the barrel as the bullet passes over it into a cupped piston head fitting over a gas nozzle; the gas drives back the piston to work the action. A spiral recoil spring is compressed as the action is forced rearward, storing energy for the return motion.

Locked: By interrupted screw. Two parts of the mechanism (the breech block and the fermature nut) furnish the locking arrangement. The fermature nut which is rigidly supported in the body bears female threads; while the breech block, which enters it, bears male threads. A portion of each thread is removed, so that the breech block can slide into the fermature nut, and then by a partial turn of the fermature nut, the two can be securely locked. This necessary partial rotation is caused by the action of an inclined groove on the rearward moving system working on a stud.

Cooled: Has extra heavy barrel with radiator rings. Barrel is changeable.

Sights: Barleycorn front sights, V notch rear sight adjustable to 1000 yds.

Cyclic Rate of Fire: About 550 shots per minute.

Position of Cocking Handle: Extends back over pistol grip coming out of the lower rear end of the receiver. Must be turned up to the left before pulling back.

Type of Fire: Single shot or full auto. (a) Turning handle up and pulling it to the rear as far as it will go cocks the weapon. Then the cocking handle is thrust forward. When it is fully home, it may be turned over to the right and lined up with lines engraved directly in front of it as follows: (1) "A" for full automatic fire (2) "R" for repetition or rounds, single shot fire and (3) "S" for safe, in which position the weapon cannot be fired.

Gas Regulator: This is positioned at the extreme front end of the gas cylinder. Screwing in this regulator increases the amount of gas and unscrewing it diminishes the amount. The normal setting for the regulator is between 15 and 25 on the indicator. Start testing at 25 and work down or up as the functioning of the gun seems to require.

Feeds: From the right side. **Ejects:** From the left side.

Position of Breech or Bolt on Cease Fire: Open. This gun fires from an open bolt and so the action cannot be eased forward while there is a strip in the gun.

Mounts: A small tripod mount is normally supplied with this machine gun. The weapon may be handled by one man. However, if there is a second one to load, it is possible to achieve at least 400 delivered rounds per minute. This is a very flexible gun and is designed to be fired primarily from a prone position, the weapon being rested on ammunition boxes, sand bags, tree limbs, or other rests or covers.

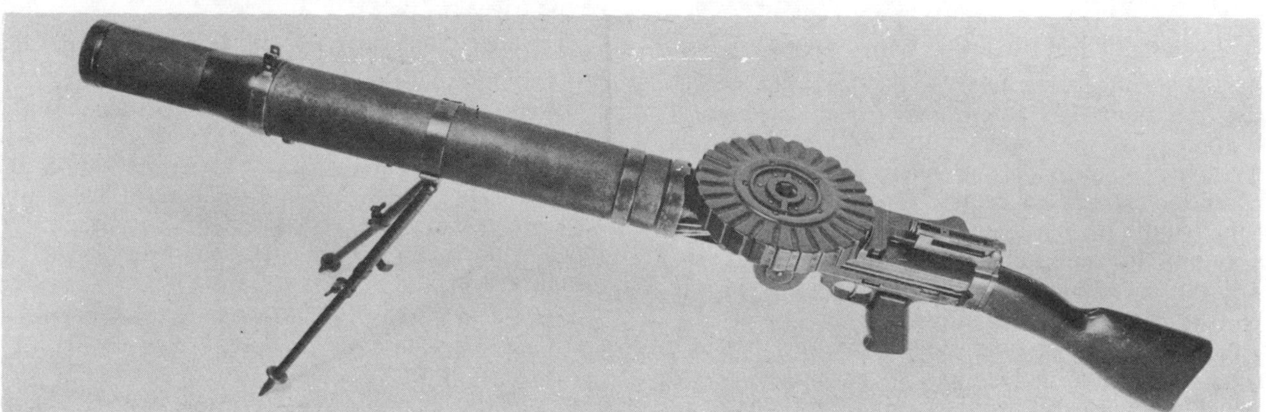

British Lewis .30-06 Light Machine Gun.

This weapon, although developed by a U. S. Army officer, was originally adopted by the British Army for their rim type cartridge, caliber .303. It was later altered and somewhat improved to handle the standard U. S. Government .30-06 cartridge, which is rimless. Differences between the two models are comparatively minor, and will be pointed out where essential.

Weight of Standard Ground Type: 25¼ to 28 lbs., complete.
Caliber: .30-06 in United States Model.
Caliber: .303 British if British model.
Magazine: Rotating pan type, holding 47 cartridges in spirals.
Muzzle Velocities of Cartridges: Standard for cartridges employed.
Weights of Bullet: Standard service cartridge weight.
Barrel Length: 26¼.
Overall Length of Gun: 50½".
Weight of Loaded Magazine: 4⅛lbs.
Gun Operated by: Gas escaping through small port in underside of barrel into gas chamber where it forces back head of piston and drives it back to eject empty cartridge and wind mainspring to provide driving power for forward movement of action.
Cooled: Aluminum radiator and radiator casing surround the barrel. When firing, cool air is sucked from the rear through fins in the open casing around the barrel to help dissipate heat.
Sights: Fixed front, aperture rear, graduated to 2000 yards.
Cyclic Rate of Fire: 500 and 600 rounds per minute.
Locked: By rotating bolt. It is provided with four resistance lugs which lock into corresponding slots in the receiver during the period of high pressure in the barrel. These lugs are revolved out of their slots as the piston travels backwards.
Type of Fire: Full automatic only. No selector device is provided.
Position of Charging Handle: (Called cocking handle in Great Britain.) Normally on the right side of the receiver. However, on the U. S. Airplane type Lewis guns, which have a spade grip and no radiator barrel casings, the cocking handle may be on the left side. On certain types of Lewis guns this handle may be inserted on right or left side.
Safety: On U. S. Models, a long narrow sliding strip of steel is fitted on the receiver, directly below the charging handle slot. When the charging handle is to the rear, meaning the weapon is cocked, a thumb piece on this strip may be pushed, which will force the strip up and let the slot engage with the shank of the charging handle so it cannot go forward. This also disengages the trigger mechanism. Pulling back slightly on the charging handle and pushing down on the thumb piece removes the safety.

Warning: Remember that this gun fires from an open bolt. When there is a magazine in place, if the bolt goes forward it will fire a cartridge. This bolt cannot be lowered while the magazine is in place. Except when ready for firing, the cocking handle should always be in the forward position.

Loading and Firing the Lewis Gun

Put handle on magazine filler in the magazine socket to release the magazine catch and permit the center block to rotate.

Insert cartridges in magazine filler, rim toward outside of pan, bullets toward center.

Turn the handle on the filler from right to left to feed cartridges into the magazine; and be sure that the groove in the base of each cartridge engages in the retaining plate inside the magazine.

If no filler is available, hold magazine with left hand, inserting a finger from below to depress the magazine catch, which must be released to permit rotation, and insert cartridges singly, starting the bullet in the magazine center and revolving slowly so that the cartridges take their proper places between the separators.

Put a loaded magazine into place over the magazine post and press down until the catch engages. The catch should face to the right. Rotate the pan slightly in both directions until the hook of the catch locks inside its recess in the magazine.

Now rotate the magazine from left to right until resistance is encountered.

Draw back the charging handle as far it will go and release it. It will be held in place waiting a pull of the trigger.

Warning: The weapon will now fire when the bolt moves forward.

Special Note on Unloading Lewis Gun. With most machine guns, removing loaded cartridges safely is simply a matter of removing the magazine; or in the belt type, working the operating mechanism back by hand once or twice. However, the feed construction of the Lewis gun is such that it is not feasible to use the ordinary procedure.

For U. S. Caliber .30. Press in magazine release stud and pull magazine off the post. There will still be a cartridge in the feedway.

Grasp the charging handle firmly with the left hand and pressing the trigger with the right to release the moving parts, ease them forward very slowly until the cartridge in the feedway clears the feed arm and drops into the boltway. At that point, pull back the charging handle and push up the safety catch to lock it into place. Then turn the gun over on its right side and shake the cartridge out. The action may now be safely permitted to go forward.

British .303. Push in magazine catch with thumb and remove magazine from post. Use cartridge or screw driver to press against the base of the round held by the feed arm so that the bullet end will rise. Pull the cartridge forward as far as possible. Holding the cocking handle securely, press the trigger to release it and work cocking handle slowly forward and back until the cartridge falls clear or can be pulled out. (Take care not to let the action go forward far enough to chamber the cartridge, as that would fire it.)

Note on Cooling System of Lewis Gun

A very ingenious cooling system is employed in this gun. A barrel mouthpiece is screwed over the end of the barrel and has a cone shaped interior. As the bullet leaves the muzzle, the expanding gases strike against the cone shaped interior of this barrel mouth piece, rebound and strike against the front end of the radiator casing, thus forcing all the air out in front of them. This creates a suction which draws a current of air from the rear of the gun through the rear casing and around the aluminum flanges of the radiator. The aluminum radiator is in contact with the barrel throughout its length and theoretically draws heat from the barrel. Thus while the gun is firing, a constant stream of air is being sucked over the radiator.

While this system is theoretically very valuable, in actual practice the amount of heat so dissipated is not of any particular importance. In other words, the Lewis gun without the cooling device will perform just about as well as it will with it. This fact is generally understood by engineers, but would probably be classed as heresy by the avowed Lewis gun enthusiasts. However, tests speak for themselves.

Special Note on the Lewis Gun

During the war the Lewis gun was used extensively by our Coast Guard units and some branches of the Navy. Both the United States and the British type (which are practically identical) were imitated line for line and piece for piece by the Japanese. Regular ground-type Lewis guns equipped with aluminum radiators and regular rifle-type butts, antiaircraft-type Lewis guns with spade grips and minus the cooling device, and special tripod mounted Lewis guns were in wide use by the Japanese. The British made very extensive use of Lewis guns, particularly aboard small craft. These guns are credited by the British with destroying more low-flying aircraft than any other type of weapon employed by them.

Model 92, 7.7mm Lewis Gun made at Yokosuka Naval Arsenal in Japan.

Stripped-type Lewis guns usually were equipped with antiaircraft sights. They also handled special oversize magazines with a cartridge capacity of 97 rounds. If these magazines are used on the standard type gun, they interfere with the line of sight unless the gun is equipped with special sights.

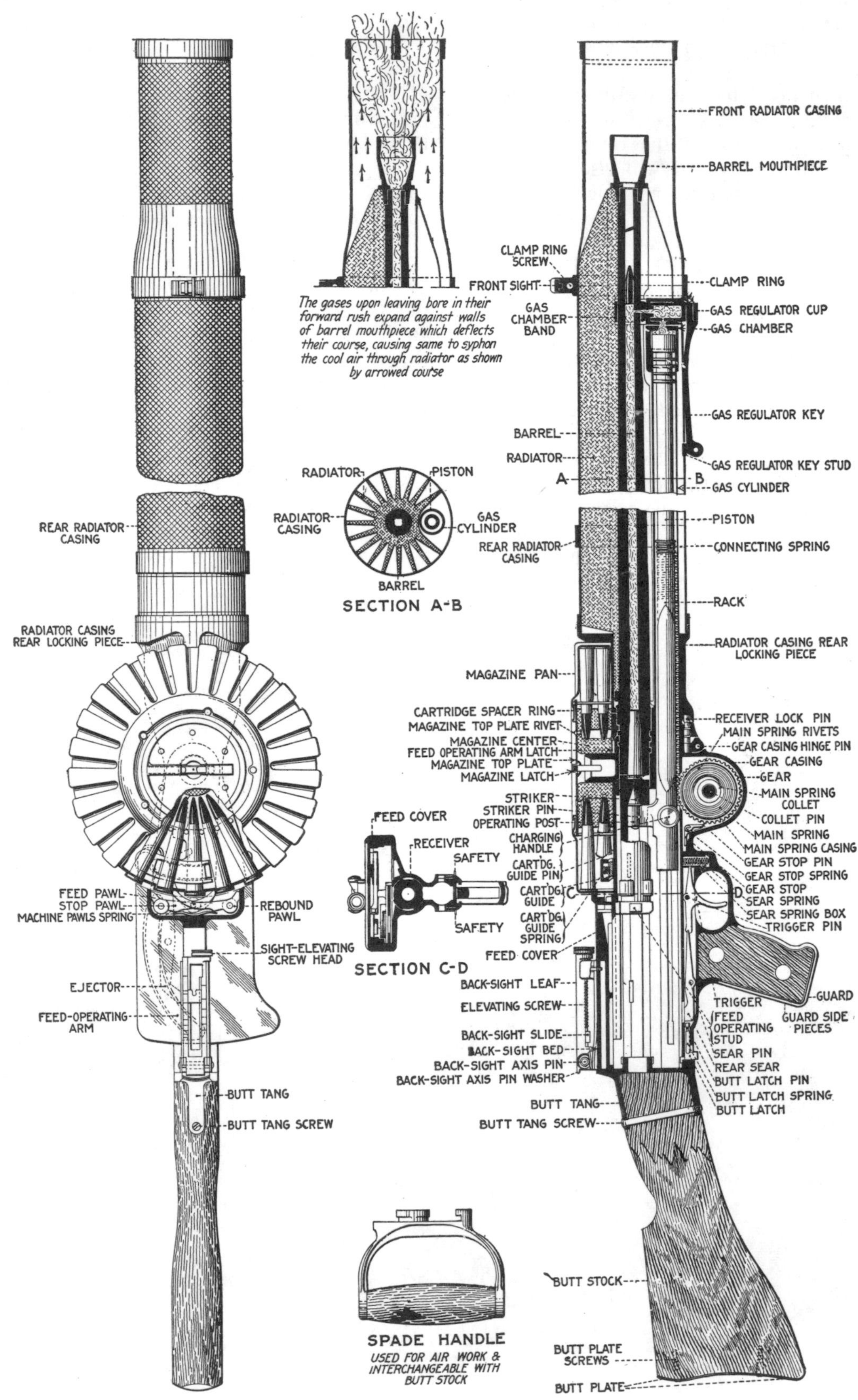

Courtesy McGraw-Hill Book Company

Field Stripping the Lewis Gun

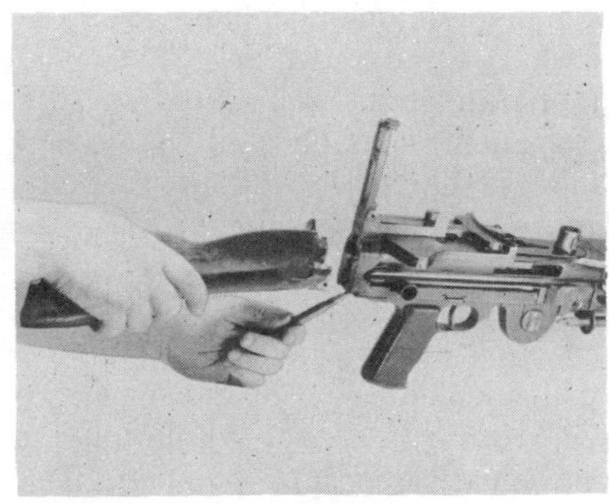

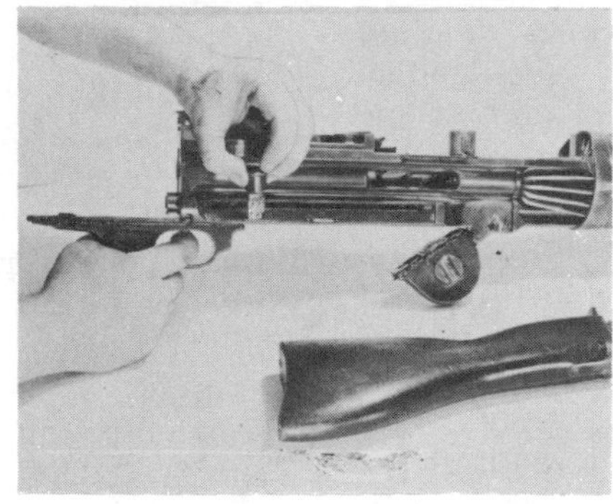

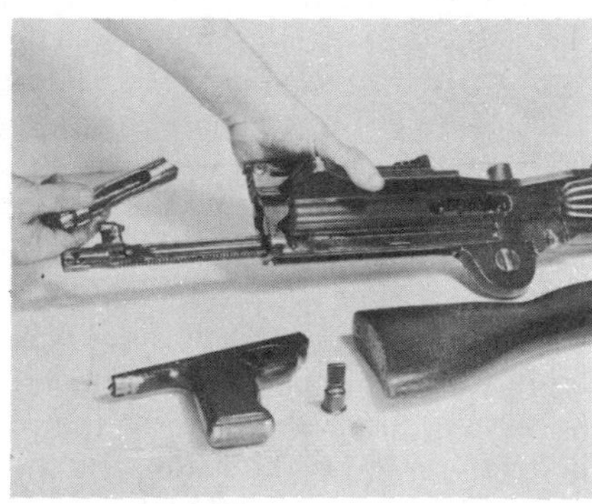

Insert the point of a bullet into the slot below the point of the butt where it joins the receiver. (In some British models there is a latch here which is pushed.) Maintaining forward pressure with the bullet point, twist the butt stock up and to the left and pull it straight back to the rear.

Pull the trigger and draw back the triggerguard until it is a few inches out on the receiver, which will let the pinion casing (which contains the flat coiled mainspring) drop on its hook. This will also permit pulling the charging handle back to the end of the receiver where it can be lifted out of its slot. Now pull out the triggerguard mechanism; and grasping the bolt and piston rod, draw them both back and completely out of the weapon.

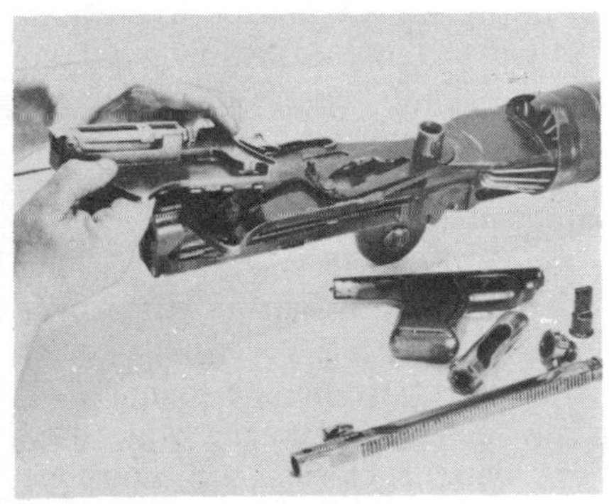

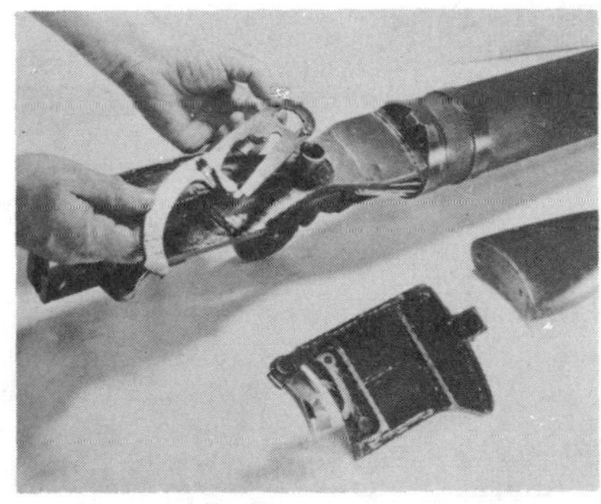

Gripping the feed cover (the flat piece on top of the receiver at the rear on which the rear sight is mounted) draw back about ½" and lift up and off. This exposes all the feed mechanism. Note that the feed arm should be over to the right before the cover can be pulled back.

Turn the feed arm and lift it off the magazine post. (In British guns, there is a latch at the front of the feed arm which must be pushed back before the feed arm can be raised.) Midway along the feed arm is a pawl and its spring; the function of which is to push the magazine a notch as the feed arm moves to the left. These may be lifted off if necessary. Note: In the cover are the stop pawl and the rebound pawl, which lock into the edge of the magazine pan and hold it securely in place at the moment of feeding each cartridge; and a cartridge guide spring. All these may be pried out with the point of a bullet.

Pinion casing (housing the main spring) may be unhooked and removed. Receiver lock pin (at front end of receiver near the barrel) may be pushed with the point of a bullet; which frees the receiver so that it may be twisted up to the left.

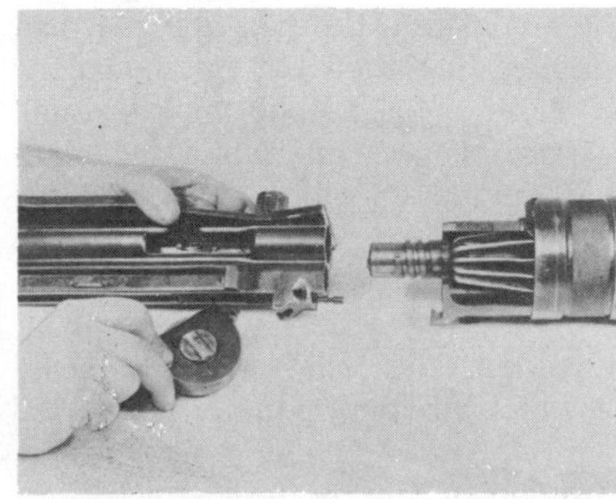

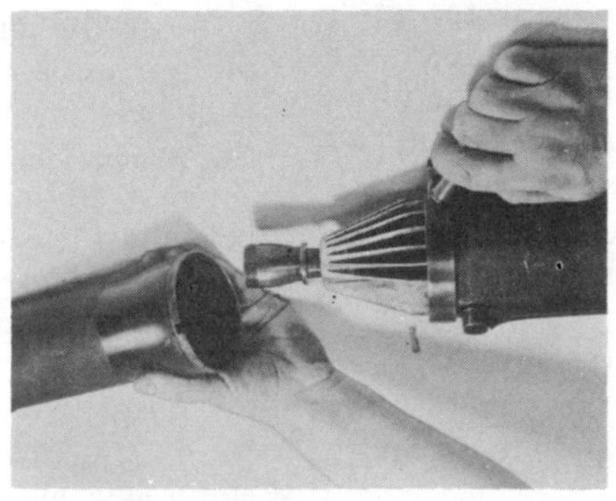

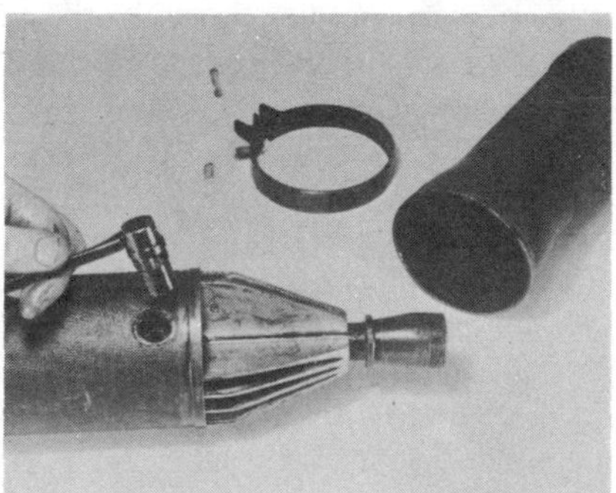

Receiver is then unscrewed completely from the barrel. Note: No further stripping is ordinarily necessary. However, to strip the barrel group for thorough cleaning, the following steps should be taken:

With head of cartridge, unscrew clamp ring screw and lift off the front radiator casing.

Lift up the spring lever end of gas regulator key and unwind it until it can be removed. Slide off the bipod. Now pull out the rear radiator casing. The gas cylinder may now be removed using the piston rod to unscrew it. A wrench must be used to remove the gas chamber and barrel mouth piece. (This mouth piece has a left hand thread.)

How the Lewis Machine Gun Works

Starting with the gun cocked and loaded magazine in place, the action is as follows: The mainspring (or recoil spring) in this weapon resembles a heavy clock spring. It is housed in the pinion casing just forward of the triggerguard under the receiver. It is fitted in a gear box and, on the under side of the piston, teeth are cut to make a rack which engages with this gear.

As the trigger is pressed, the nose of the sear is released from the bent in the rear of the rack on the piston rod and the return spring is allowed to come into play and revolve the pinion. Since the teeth of the pinion are engaged with the teeth on the rack of the piston, the piston rod is driven violently forward. The bolt is mounted over the striker which is attached to the rear of the piston. As it moves forward, the front top edge of the bolt strikes the lower edge of the rim of the cartridge positioned in the feedway, driving it forward and downward into the firing chamber.

As it nears the end of this forward movement, the resistance lugs on the rear of the bolt come out of their guide slots (machined into the receiver) and the projection called the operating post, which is mounted on the piston, continuing to move forward, presses against a curved slot in the bolt, revolving it. As the bolt locks behind the cartridge in the chamber, two extractors slip over the head of the cartridge, grasping it securely.

During this forward movement of bolt and operating rod, the rebound pawl (the small metal arm caught in the outside of the pan) has prevented the magazine from moving.

A stud on top of the bolt, riding in the groove on the underside of the feed operating arm has returned the arm to the right in preparation for picking up the next cartridge.

When the bolt has completely turned into the locked position, and the lugs are securely locked, the striker can continue straight ahead in the bolt slot and the firing pin passes through a hole in the center of the bolt to fire the cartridge. The bolt stays securely locked until after the bullet passes over the gas port in the barrel.

Return Movement of the Action: As the bullet passes over the gas port on its way to the muzzle, a small portion of gas enters through the gas port into the gas regulator cup. Here the gas expands through an aperture in the gas regulator cup and the corresponding aperture in the wall of the gas chamber and comes back with a hammerlike blow against the head of the piston.

As it goes back, the rack on its underside, which is engaged with the gear, winds up the mainspring to provide energy for the next forward motion of the action.

The dual extractors pull the empty cartridge case out of the chamber and it is hurled out of the gun by the ejector, actuated by the feed operating stud striking against its rear end.

The operating post traveling back in a straight line forces against the curved or cam slot in the bolt and rotates the bolt far enough to unlock the lugs and from that point carries the bolt back to the rear.

Meanwhile the feed operating stud, mounted on the bolt riding in the channel on the underside of the curved feed operating arm, moves the arm over to the left, carrying a cartridge from the magazine under the cartridge guide spring and positioning it in the feedway on top of the receiver.

The feed pawl (which is carried by the feed operating arm, and which acts on the outside wall of the magazine pan) pushes the magazine through a part revolution far enough to bring the next cartridge into position. The stop pawl now engages in the wall of the magazine to hold the magazine in this new position while the rebound pawl prevents the magazine from bounding back. This prevents any movement of the magazine while the action is going forward.

The head of the operating rod and the bolt mounted on it strike against the butt tang at the extreme rear end of their movement. If the trigger has been released quickly enough, the sear will catch the piston and hold it to the rear. If the trigger is still depressed, the action will go forward and repeat the firing cycle.

Description of Magazine

For a proper understanding of the operation of the Lewis gun, a knowledge of how the magazine pan works is necessary. A cartridge spacer ring carrying interior separators is fastened by a rivet to the magazine pan. Inside the pan itself is the magazine center; while outside is the magazine top plate, enclosing the magazine latch and the magazine latch spring. The magazine center and the top plate are fastened together by rivets.

The wall of the magazine pan has corrugations which from the outside serve to engage with the stop pawl and the rebound pawl to permit feeding and hold the magazine in proper place. Inside the pan these corrugations provide spaces in which the bases of the cartridges rest.

The magazine center is hollow and provided with a keyway which fits over the magazine post and center key on top of the receiver, providing a locking arrangement.

When the magazine is not in use, the pan and the center are automatically locked together by the magazine latch which engages in a series of notches cut through the inside edge of the spacer ring. Thus when the magazine is to be loaded or unloaded, the latch must be held back to permit the pan to revolve around the magazine center.

The magazine center is locked securely to the magazine post on the gun; and as the pan revolves around the post, the cartridges which are individually supported by the separator pins are forced down and around the spiral and one by one brought in line by the feedway.

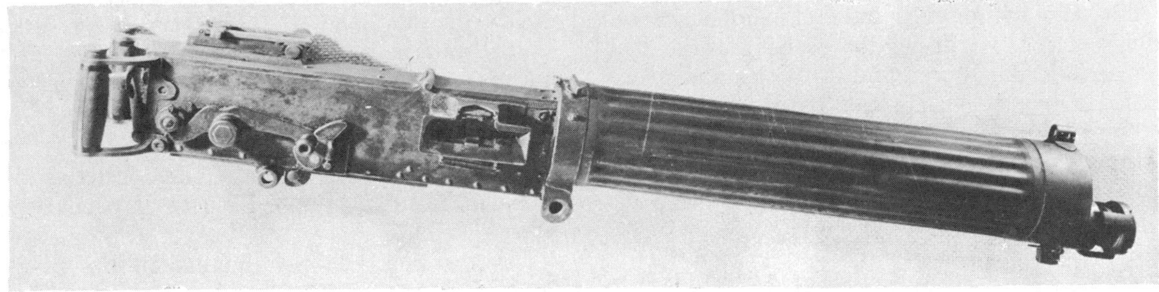

British Vickers .303 Machine Gun Mark 1.

Caliber: .303 British Mark 8z ammunition.
.30 M1 U. S. Ammunition.
(Note: Ammunition not interchangeable.)

Method of Feeding: Fabric belt containing 250 rounds. (When mounted in aircraft, these guns are fitted with belts made of disintegrating steel links.)

Ballistic Data: Standard for .303 British Mark 8z or .30 M1 U. S. Ammunition.

Length of Barrel: 28⅜".

Overall Length of Gun: About 3′ 8″.

Weight of Gun With Water Jacket Empty: About 33 lbs. With jacket filled, about 10 lbs. heavier.

Weight of Loaded Ammunition Belt: With .30 U. S. Ammunition about 15 lbs.

Sights: Blade front sight. Rear sights differ in different guns, but all have calibrated leaf sights. Aperture on the average sight normally used has adjustable plate with five different sized apertures. Adjustable for windage. In American types drift is also allowed for as in the sight on the Springfield rifle.

Elevation Provided For: Varies. 0 to 2400 meters on some sights, 0 to 4000 yards on other sights. Battle sight—400 yards.

Accurate Range: About 1100 yards. Maximum range much greater.

Gun Operated By: Recoil. The barrel and locking mechanism recoil together a short distance; then the barrel is stopped and the recoiling mechanism continues backward to work the weapon. This recoil is insufficient in itself to operate the gun properly; so a device fitted over the muzzle utilizes gas escaping after the bullet has left the barrel. The expanding muzzle gases strike the front cone of the ball firing attachment and rebound violently against the front of a muzzle cup, adding to the backward thrust on the barrel.

Locked: By toggle joint. Barrel, lock, and operating mechanism all move back locked together until bullet has left barrel; then the toggle buckles in the same fashion as a human knee when it bends, drawing the lock straight to the rear, while the barrel is stopped in its backward motion after traveling something over ½".

Cooled: Water; there is watertight jacket fitting around the barrel. This is filled with water and absorbs the heat generated in the barrel; if steam develops it is taken off through a hose attached to a condenser bucket.

Cyclic Rate of Fire: 500 rounds per minute.

Position of Crank Handle and Lock When Weapon is Ready to Fire: Fully forward. In this machine gun the lock and barrel are firmly locked together when the weapon is cocked ready for firing.

Type of Fire: Full automatic only. Should single shot fire be desired for any reason, withdraw alternate cartridges from the cartridge belt. Under this system, the rocker handle must be pulled back to load the weapon after each shot.

Safety: A ring safety catch is provided at the rear of the weapon between the two handles. The trigger is a thumbpiece directly below this ring, and the ring must be lifted by the fingers before the trigger can be pushed in by the thumb.

This gun is normally mounted on a tripod mount. The folding mount weighs 52 lbs.

Firing Procedure: This type of gun is normally fired in bursts of 10 to 20 rounds; 60 shots a minute rated as slow fire; 125 a minute as medium fire, and 250 a minute as rapid fire.

Loading the Gun

Under normal firing conditions, the rear leg of the tripod will be aligned with the target. The gunner sits behind the gun to the rear of this leg with his legs on either side of the tripod. The knees are drawn up slightly so that the elbows can rest on the inside of his thighs while his hands grasp the traversing handle.

Proper Hand Position. Both thumbs are rested lightly on the thumb trigger. The forefingers are wrapped around the top of the handle. The second fingers are placed underneath the ring safety catch. The other two fingers of each hand grasp the traversing handles firmly but without strain.

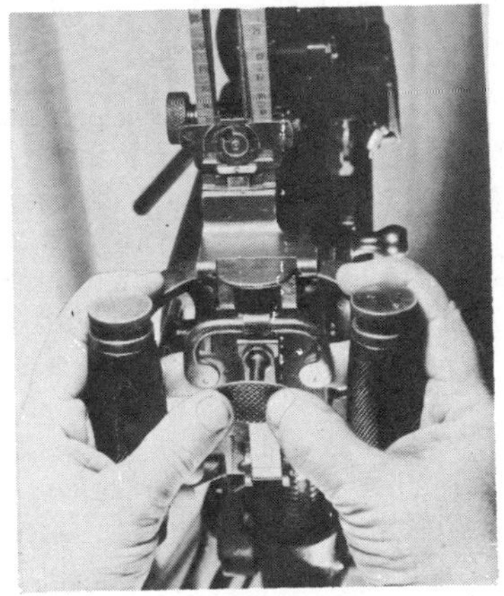

To load. See that ammunition box is placed on right side of gun directly below the feed block.

If the gun is equipped with a shutter, open the shutter.

Pass the brass tag-end of the belt through the feed block from the right side and grasp it firmly with the left hand.

With the right hand pull the crank handle back on its roller as far as it will go, and while holding it in that position, pull the belt sharply through the feed block with the left hand as far as it will go.

Release the crank handle and let it fly forward under the influence of the spring. This action grips the first cartridge firmly between upper and lower portions of a gib at the top of the extractor. Now pull the crank handle back on its roller once again. Give the belt another sharp tug to the left as far as it will go, and again let the crank handle fly forward under the influence of the spring. This action withdraws the cartridge from the belt, places it in the chamber ready for firing and grips the next cartridge by the gib in the upper part of the extractor.

The gun is now cocked and ready to fire, whenever the safety catch is lifted and the trigger pushed in.

Firing the Gun

With forefingers wrapped over the top of the traversing handle, raise the safety catch with the second fingers of the hands, wrap the other fingers around the traversing handles, and with both thumbs press in on the thumb trigger.

The gun will now fire as long as the trigger is kept pushed in and cartridges are fed into the gun. Releasing either trigger or safety will stop the gun.

Remember that this gun is supported by the tripod, and that the hands are intended only for use in firing. Thus no particular effort is required on the part of the gunner.

Note on Unloading

Because of the method of feeding, safely unloading this weapon requires special consideration. Without touching the belt, pull the crank handle back onto the roller as far as it will go and release it.

Again pull the crank handle back as far as it will go and permit it to fly forward. The first motion of the crank handle extracts the cartridge from the firing chamber, and drops or ejects it through the bottom of the gun. The cartridge in the feed block is withdrawn for positioning by this movement, and is fed into the chamber, but as the belt is not moved across, no new cartridge is gripped by the top of the extractor. Thus when the crank handle is run back for the second time, the second live cartridge is dropped through the bottom of the gun, leaving the firing mechanism empty.

With the left hand raise the finger plate of the bottom pawls and simultaneously push down the top pawl by squeezing the pawl grips. Keeping the pawls disengaged, pull the belt out of the block to the right. The pawls hold the belt in position in the feed block, the top pawls being behind the first cartridge and the bottom pawls behind the second. During recoil of the gun the top pawls feed the cartridge into position while the bottom ones prevent any backward lash of the belt; thus it is necessary to release the pawls from their position before the belt can be pulled out of the gun.

How the Gun Works

Starting with the gun loaded and cocked the action is as follows: The safety catch is normally held down by a spring which also holds the firing lever to the rear. This catch prevents any forward movement of the firing lever while it is in safe position. When this catch is raised by the second finger, it clears the way for the thumb-piece of the firing lever to push the lower end of the trigger bar forward. The trigger bar lever is engaged with the trigger bar in the rear cover and as the lever moves back it draws the trigger bar to the rear also.

The forward end of the trigger bar is in engagement with the trigger situated in the lock; and as the trigger moves to the rear, it releases the striker, contained in the lock, from its spring and the striker is driven forward to fire the cartridge in the chamber.

As the cartridge explodes, the bullet is driven down the barrel and the locked barrel and locking mechanism start rearward.

As the bullet leaves the barrel, the gases behind it expand in the muzzle attachment. Some of these gases strike against a cone which surrounds the muzzle and rebound to strike the front face of the muzzle cap cup, fastened over the muzzle.

Thus it will be seen that the rearward action of this gun is brought about by two forces—1: By recoil (the rearward thrust of gases in the barrel against the cartridge case and the lock as the bullet is forced ahead); and 2: By the effect of the rebounding gases after the bullet has left the muzzle, giving an added backward push against the muzzle cup.

On the rear of the left side plate is a protruding metal box. A powerful fusee spring is attached to the front end of this box. The rear end of the box is locked to the body of the gun. At the front end of this box is the fusee which is attached to the fusee spring. The rear of this spring, being attached to the fusee, can be drawn straight backwards, extending the spring and storing up energy to provide the return movement of the action. The recoil forces the tail of the crank handle to roll against its roller and rotate the crank, which is attached to the fusee. This winds the fusee chain and extends the fusee spring while the lock is traveling to the rear. The sharp backward thrust caused by the recoil forces the lock, crank, and crank handle to move back as the crank handle continues to roll against the roller.

While the mechanism is moving backward, a stud on the bottom lever of the feed block located in a recess in a prolongation of the left side plate is forced to the rear, taking with it the bottom lever, which being connected with the top lever carries the bottom one over to the right, thus causing the feed block slide to move over to the right. This movement causes the top pawls in the feed block to drive to the right and slip over and behind the next cartridge in the belt, which is being held in place by the bottom pawl.

Meanwhile the lock had been moving backwards. The extractor attached to it removes the loaded cartridge from the belt at the same time it draws the empty cartridge case from the chamber. Horns on this extractor ride along the top of solid cams in the breech casing sides; and as the cartridge is drawn clear of the belt, the horns clear the ends of these cams. Rims in the rear cover force the extractor downward and bring the live cartridge into line with the chamber. During this downward movement of the extractor, the empty cartridge case usually drops out. If it fails to, it will be ejected during the forward movement of the extractor. The loaded cartridge is held firmly in position in the extractor by the gib which has a bottom projection to prevent the cartridge from slipping down out of the extractor face.

During recoil the backward rotation of the crank moves the connecting rod and side lever head upwards. The side lever head bears on the tail of the tumbler and rotates it, thrusting the firing pin to the rear.

Further rotation of the tumbler in the lock completely withdraws the firing pin as the long arm of the lock spring bears against the projection of the pin. Thus the lock spring is compressed until the trigger nose, forced by the short arm of the lock spring, is pushed over the bent of the tumbler. The firing pin is withdrawn still farther until the sear spring forces the bent of the sear into the bent of the firing pin which thus holds it in cocked position.

It should be noted that in this weapon part of the action attributable to backward movement is actually to start some parts forward. The crank handle, continuing to roll against the roller during recoil movement, actually starts the recoiling portions forward while the lock is still moving backwards.

Return Movement of the Action

The force of the recoil having expended itself, the stretched fusee spring now reasserts itself, unwinds the fusee chain, moves the link to rotate the crank in the forward direction and forces the connecting rod and side lever head to drive the lock forward.

The stud of the bottom lever of the feed block is carried forward in its recess in the prolongation of the side plate, moves the bottom lever of the feed block forward, thus causing the top lever and the slide to move over to the left. As the pawls move and are gripping the next cartridge in the belt, the loaded cartridge is moved into position against the cartridge stops, ready to be gripped by the extractor on the next rearward movement.

As the lock is driven forward, the extractor supported by the gib is carrying the cartridge into the firing chamber.

The extractor is now raised and its levers are pushed by the side levers; the gib is depressed against its spring, thus letting go its hold of the cartridge as the round is chambered and the gib is forced back into the face of the extractor.

The upper end of the extractor slips up around the rim of the cartridge in the feed block and the gib is pushed forward by its spring to grip the head of the cartridge to place it in proper position in the extractor when the next rearward motion of the lock will draw it out of the feed block. Springs located in the side plates engage in slots in the side of the extractor to hold it in its highest position to prevent it from falling should there be no cartridges left in the belt.

If the empty cartridge case has not dropped off the extractor face, it is ejected as the extractor rises during the forward movement by striking against the ejection feeding in the barrel casing.

When the lock approaches its fully forward position, its side lever head is forced slightly below the horizontal by the connection rod. It now depresses the sear, disengaging it from the firing pin, and allowing the firing pin to move forward slightly so that the trigger nose engages the bent in the tumbler.

If pressure on the thumb-pieces is maintained for automatic fire, the trigger nose is held clear of the bent in the tumbler. The firing pin is free to spring forward under compression of the lock spring when the sear is depressed by the side lever head. However, it should be noted that the depression of the sear is so arranged that the firing pin cannot possibly be released until the lock is fully home and in firing position.

Locking Principle

This gun is locked securely at the moment of firing by a toggle joint. This is the principle developed by Hiram Maxim. The Vickers gun is a modification of the Maxim gun. This locking principle is used in Maxim guns throughout the world, notably in Germany and in Russia.

The simplest way to explain this principle is to compare it with the human knee.

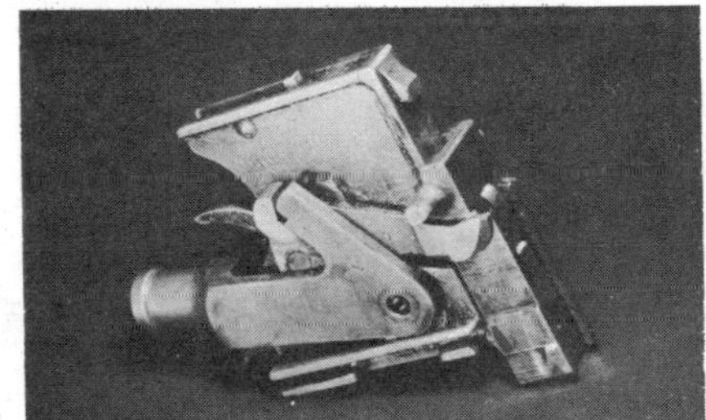

Vickers Lock.

When in firing position, the lock on the Vickers gun fits securely against the firing chamber. Now picture the human foot with the heel held firmly in the position of this lock against the head of the cartridge. Pivoted to the lock is the connection rod, a heavy metal bar, thrust straight forward. This connection rod is like the lower part of the leg but it can buckle at the ankle where it joins the foot. The crank is attached to the connection rod by a hinge pin and extends to the rear. This crank forms a bending knee where it joins the connection rod; it resembles the upper part of the human leg. However, the knee in this mechanical device is actually below the line of the connection rod and crank.

This crank is rigidly supported from below by the inside plates of the weapon and pressure applied to it by the side levers, during the opening movement of the recoil, merely presses the crank down harder on the plates.

Attached to the crank is a crank handle which travels back with it and after the gun has recoiled far enough to permit the bullet to leave the barrel, the tail on the lower side of this handle is forced back in contact with a roller which causes the crank handle to rotate upwards. This raises the axis of the crank pin and permits the knee-like joint to buckle. (Thus, as the human foot is driven backwards, pressure applied to the underside of the knee will buckle the knee but draw the foot straight back.)

The connection rod is locked securely by a twisting

motion inside the side lever head, which projects beyond the lower rear end of the lock. As the connection rod buckles, it naturally raises the side lever head with it, and this raises a tumbler which cocks the lock.

Field Stripping

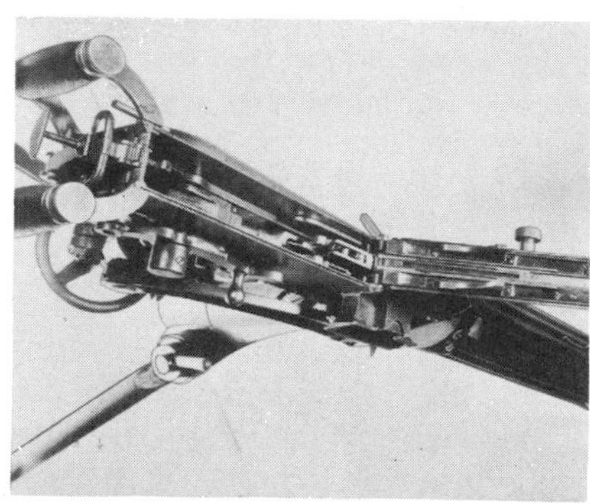

At the rear of the gun above the safety is the rear cover catch. It is held in place by a spring. Push up on the catch and raise the cover up as far as it will go.

Now pull back the crank handle

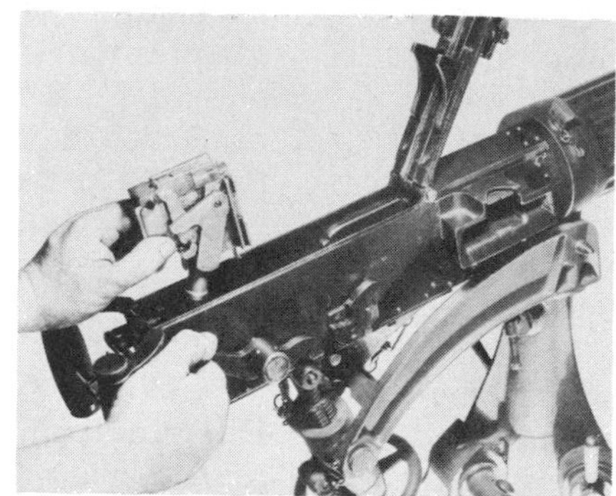

against the tension of the fusee spring. Hold it firmly. Reach inside the gun and lift out the lock which is fastened to the connection rod.

Now twist the lock on the connection rod about one-third of a turn to

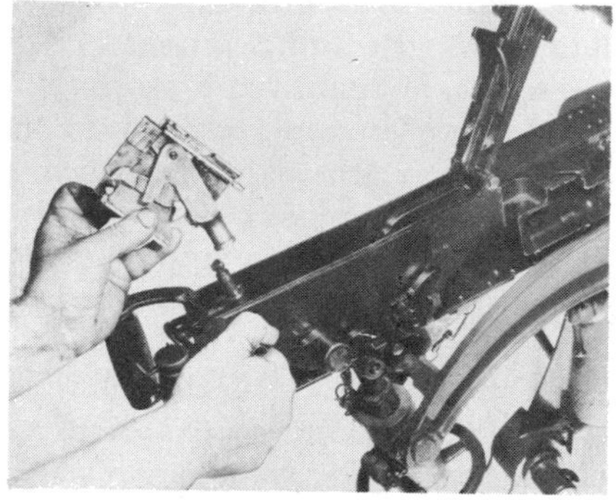

the right, to release it from the connection rod, which in its turn is connected to the crank. Lift the lock out, ease the crank handle home under the tension of the fusee spring. Then close the cover.

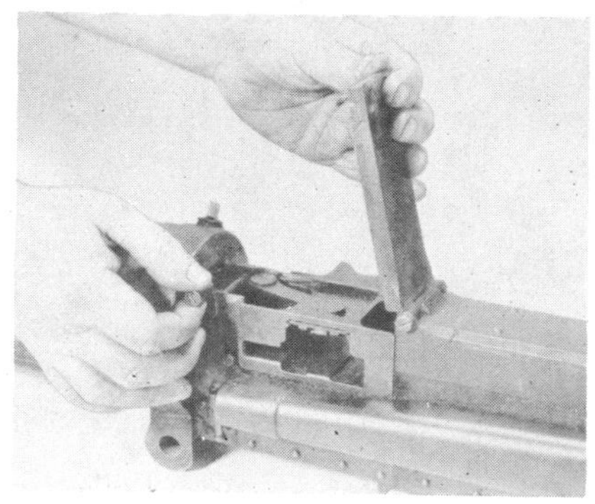

Turn the cover latch (on the forward end of the cover on the left side of the gun) up to the left as far as it will go. This releases the front cover which should now be raised as high as it will go.

Now lift complete feed block directly up and out of the gun.

Go to the forward end of the gun. Pull out the split pin and twist the outer casing through about one-sixth of a turn. It can now be pulled off to the front. The muzzle cup and the front cone may also be unscrewed and removed. (The gland and packing should be removed only if absolutely necessary.)

Grasping the front end of the spring box with the left hand, push forward on the rear end with the right hand until the hooks which fasten the box at front end and rear can be sprung out of their studs. Disconnect the box from the gun and unhook the fusee spring from the fusee. The fusee may now be turned until its lugs are free and then it can be withdrawn with its chain from the left.

Now lift the rear cover and unscrew the large key pin protruding from the left side at the rear of the gun. Pull this pin out to the left, and it will permit the handles and their enclosed mechanism to be swung down to a horizontal position.

Slides which travel in the body at the rear may now be pulled straight out. The right slide carries the roller with it.

Now pull the crank handle stem directly to the rear which will withdraw the crank, together with the right and left inside plates and the barrel.

Disconnect the right and left side plates from the crank and the barrel. This completes field stripping.

Further Notes on Stripping

As this is one of the world's basic mechine gun types, a more detailed explanation of stripping should be of value. An understanding of the Vickers is particularly helpful in understanding all the German and Russian type Maxim Guns.

Stripping the Lock. The lock is cocked as it comes out of the gun. Should it not be, due to having been snapped when withdrawn, it may be cocked by raising the side lever head.

A split pin with a bushing fastens the combined side lever head and side levers to the lock casing. Force these out. The side levers, and the extractor and extractor levers may now be removed.

The tumbler, the finger-like projection protruding from the locked casing just above the side lever, is fastened by an axis pin. Push this lever out and remove the tumbler. Now push down the tail of the sear which will release the lock spring.

Push out the trigger axis pin (the tip of the trigger protrudes from the top of the lock) and the trigger and lock spring may be removed.

Push downward on the sear and remove the firing pin and the sear and sear pin.

The gib may be removed by pushing out its spring cover and removing spring and gib.

To Assemble the Lock. First insert the sear with spring downward, making sure that the sear jaws engage with the sear pivot.

Next insert the firing pin in its groove. Then replace the tumbler and fasten it with its tumbler axis pin.

Insert the trigger, fasten it by the trigger axis pin.

Replacing the gib and its spring and cover in position on the extractor, slide the assembled extractor from the bottom up in the guides in the locked casing.

Replace the extractor levers and side levers and fasten with the bushing and pin.

With sear held down by side lever head, pull back the trigger and press down the tumbler. Now insert the lock spring with its long arm facing toward the extractor and force it down and home.

The firing pin must be released only when the extractor is up in the casing as far as it will go; as only at this point is it lined up so that it will pass through the hole in the extractor. The pin will be injured if it strikes against a solid steel surface in the extractor.

Stripping the Feed Block. The split pin holds the top and bottom block together and this must be forced out to permit separating the top and the bottom levers.

Pull out the slide with the top pawls and springs. They may be removed from the slide.

Now pull out the bottom pawl axis pin, which will permit removal of the bottom pawl and spring.

Assembling the Feed Block. Reverse the above procedure.

Adjusting the Gun

The most important adjustment on a machine gun of this type is the head space. This is the correct space between the head of the cartridge in the firing chamber and the face of the lock. Should this space be too great, the head of the cartridge will not be held firmly during the moment of high breech pressure. This may bulge the cartridge case so that extraction will be extremely hard, or it may rip the head completely off the cartridge case, resulting in an even more serious jam.

On the other hand, if there is insufficient head space, the lock cannot go forward completely and as a result the side lever head on the lock will not push the sear down far enough to permit the gun to fire.

To Adjust Head Space. Remove the lock and the fusee spring.

Place crank handle in vertical position. Put the No. 1 washer on the outer face of the adjusting nut, making sure that the nut is tight. Now replace the lock in the rear position.

Reach up from below the breech and insert a dummy round or the correct armorer's gauge in the extractor over the firing pin hole, and raise the extractor to its highest point with the fingers. (Use a live cartridge only under suitable range conditions as this is a dangerous operation.)

Make sure that recoiling portions are all locked fully forward and guide the round or gauge into the firing chamber.

Rotate the crank handle forward while guiding the cartridge into the chamber.

Aside from the pressure necessary to compress the sear, a slight check will be felt when the crank handle reaches the check lever if the connecting rod is adjusted to the proper length to give the correct test space.

If no check is left, separate No. 1 or No. 2 washers should be added as required to the outer face of the adjusting nut to provide the correct length.

When the correct length has been ascertained, the washers are assembled permanently on the shoulder of the connecting rod and secured by its nut. (This is done by unscrewing and removing the nut with a combination tool, placing the washers on the connecting rod, and replacing and screwing up the adjusting nut on the washer.)

Tests should be made to be sure that adjustment has been done correctly before completing assembly.

Water Glands. To prevent the cooling water from leaking out of the casing, glands are provided at the muzzle end and oiled asbestos packing wound in a cannelure cut around the breech end of the barrel.

If water leaks at the rear or breech end, empty the casing and then strip the weapon to remove the barrel. A piece of oil soaked asbestos string is then wound into the cannelure of the barrel; and pressed in with the point of a screw driver until the cannelure is full. Now oil this packing and smooth it down until it is flush with the barrel, then reassemble the weapon.

Should water leak at the muzzle, stand the gun up on its traversing handles and remove the muzzle attachment together with the cup and unscrew the muzzle gland.

Remove the asbestos string packing, reoil it, and wind it loosely around the barrel, pushing it in with a punch or piece of wood. Then screw the gland on as tightly as possible by hand.

This should stop the leakage and yet permit the recoiling portions to move freely.

Cooling System. Whenever it is at all possible, the barrel casing should be kept full during the firing period. The water will boil after firing two belts. It evaporates at the rate of one and a half pints for every 500 rounds, or two belts, if fired continuously. If 2000 rounds are fired, casing will require refilling.

Weighing the Recoiling Portions. Remove the fusee spring and put the crank handle in almost vertical position. Now place the loop of the spring balance on the crank shaft and draw it slowly to the rear. The weight should not exceed 4 lbs. If more than 4 lbs. is required to remove the recoiling portions, it indicates that the packing is pressing too hard on the barrel and the gland nut must be removed and one or two strands taken out of the asbestos.

To Check Weight of Fusee Spring. Remove the lock and place the loop of the spring balance over the top of the crank handle. Stand to the left of the gun and press down the check lever with the left hand; and with the right pull the balance vertically upwards. When the crank handle begins to move, the weight should be between 7 and 9 lbs.

If necessary to adjust it, wind the vice pin at the forward end of the fusee spring box on the left side of the gun. Six clicks turning from right to left increases the weight one pound; while six clicks turning from left to right decreases the weight one pound.

Improper adjustment of the fusee spring will jam the weapon.

Special Note on Vickers Gun

During World War I, Colt's in the United States were manufacturing Vickers Guns for the Russian Government when the United States entered the war. Some of this machinery was adapted to producing Vickers Guns to shoot the standard United States Army ammunition. The intention was to use the Vickers as a supplemental United States Service weapon because the Browning could not be manufactured in sufficiently large quantities to fill the need during that emergency.

Since that time the Browning model 1917 became the standard Service weapon of this class in our service. Large stores of these guns in caliber .30 U. S. as well as the standard British .303 were sold or lease-lent to Great Britain during World War II. As a result, Vickers Guns are in use in Great Britain and throughout the world. China and many nations had stores of these guns purchased from English manufacturers before the War. The British paint all the .30 U. S. (or as they term them .300) Caliber Guns with a 2″ band of red paint across the front body cover; while the mouth of the feed block and the side lever head are also painted red. This is done to prevent confusing the non-interchangeable parts with the .303 British issue. No caliber .30 Vickers guns are in use in the U. K. today.

British Besa 7.92mm Machine Gun Marks 1, 2, 3, and 3*. The Besa MG is a British modification of the Czech Heavy MG Model 37.

Caliber: 7.92mm British or German manufacture.
Feed: Metal belts, holding 225 rounds.
Muzzle Velocity: About 2650 feet per second.
Barrel Length: 2′ 5″ including Flash Hider.
Overall Length of Gun: 3′ 7½″.
Weight Without Belt: 47 lbs. for the Mark 1, 48 lbs. for the Mark 2, 54 lbs. for the Mark 3, and 53.5 lbs. for the Mark 3*.
Weight of Loaded 225-round metal belt: about 18 lbs.
Sight: Telescopic.
Maximum Range: 1500 yards with telescopic sight.
Gun Operated By: Gas. This is an unusual design. The recoil drives the breech block, piston, barrel extension, and barrel to the rear locked as one unit, while some gas escaping through barrel vent into gas cylinder then drives the piston back to unlock, eject, and prepare the gun for the forward motion.
Locked: Securely locked by breech block at moment of discharge.
Cooled: Air. Weapon is fitted with a heavy barrel and a radiator casing. This gun fires from an open bolt which permits circulation of air through barrel during cessation of fire.
Cyclic Rate of Fire: This gun is fitted with a special accelerating device. When this is set at "L," rate is 450 to 550 per minute. When accelerator is set at "H," rate is 750 to 850 rounds per minute. The Mk 3 and Mk3* fire at only one rate—450-550 r.p.m.
Type of Fire: Full automatic. Empty belt is ejected from the gun.
Flash Hider: A wide mouth extension is added to the front end of the barrel serving to hide the flash of unburned powder which ignites as it leaves the barrel.

These guns are widely used in armored vehicles by the British. They do not use the standard British .303 cartridge. They were specially developed for a 7.92mm cartridge, and the standard German rifle and machine gun ammunition may be used in them. Mark 1 indicates that the gun is converted from a ground pattern. Mark 2 indicates that it is a specially manufactured gun for armored vehicle use.

Differences are comparatively minor. The mounting base on the Mark 2 is integral with the body while that on the earlier model is a shoe riveted to the underside of the body. In the Mark 2 the triggerguard catch housing is integral with the body; while in the Mark 1 the catch is housed in a blanket riveted to the rear of the gun. Different triggerguard catches are used, as the cover and triggerguard of the Mark 1 are larger than those of the later model. Trigger catch in the Mark 1 is held by a screw in the body, while that in the Mark 2 is held by a stop pin in the return spring guide. The accelerator arms in the two models are different. Mark 2 barrels, cover catches, flash eliminators, and return spring guides may be fitted directly to the Mark 1 guns.

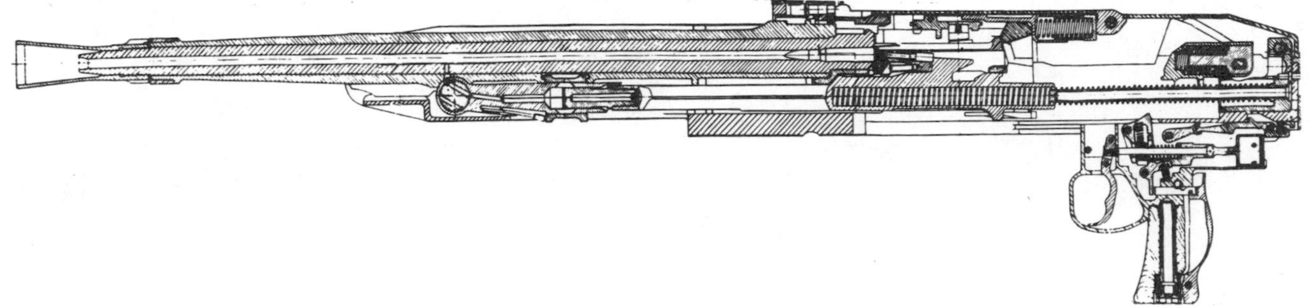

Loading and Firing

The triggerguard is part of a heavy steel unit called the triggerguard body. Press forward the cocking catch thumbpiece which is mounted on the left side of the triggerguard body to disengage the cocking catch which is in a recess in the underside of the receiver. Be careful not to touch the trigger.

Push the triggerguard body forward and the sear will click into engagement in a bent in the piston extension.

Still keeping the finger away from the trigger, and holding firmly to the pistol grip, pull the triggerguard body back with a quick motion. This withdraws the working parts and compresses the return spring. The operating parts will be held to the rear by the sear which is now engaged in the bent of the piston extension. The cocking catch engages in a recess in the underside of the receiver and locks the triggerguard in firing position.

Push the tab-end of the belt through the feed block from the right side and pull through to the left as far as possible. This places the first cartridge in line with the chamber, bullet pointing downwards. The weapon is now ready to fire.

The pistol grip of the triggerguard body in this weapon is fitted with a grip safety somewhat like the one on the Colt .45 automatic. With finger on trigger, compress the hand to push in the safety catch lever. This will rotate the safety catch to the rear until it clears the underside of the sear; as the trigger is pressed, the sear is pulled out of the bent of the piston extension permitting the return spring to force the working parts forward. The gun will fire as long as the trigger is held back and the safety catch lever is kept depressed. The gun will stay open between shots when trigger is released.

Note: When the belt is emptied, it is expelled from the gun; but the action will go forward to close on an empty chamber.

Unloading

Release feed pawl depressor lever which will free the feed pawl from engagement with the belt. Open cover to release retaining pawl which permits engagement with belt links.

Lift out the belt. Close the cover, lower the depressor lever, and ease the working parts forward.

Field Stripping

See that the gun is cocked.

Pull the barrel retainer carrying handle up about half an inch and push it forward until it rests on the ramp.

Press in the cover catch, push the carrying handle straight forward, then strike the handle with the palm of the hand to bring it to the upright position.

Lift the rear of the barrel until it clears the barrel extension, then ease it forward. This frees the slides on the barrel sleeve from their guides in the body and permits the barrel to be pulled out.

Remove the body cover. Pull the cover locking pin out as far as it will go, press in on the cover catch, and lift the cover. Raise it until it can be lifted out of the body (receiver).

Press in the catch on the belt guide and lift it out of the receiver. Lift out the feed block and remove the feed slide.

The breech block may now be lifted out.

Now pull the exposed accelerator arm and plunger cap outwards, pull up the crank arm, and lift out the accelerator.

Maintain downward pressure on the barrel extension with the left hand and ease the working parts forward. Pull the triggerguard to the rear.

Push the return spring guide block ahead until it clears the guides in the receiver, then lift it up. The guide lock and return spring may now all be removed.

Grasp piston with the right hand and the rear end of the barrel extension with the left and lift both pieces out, then slide out the piston.

The feed lever may now be inclined inward and lifted out of the weapon.

At the rear of the receiver is the triggerguard catch. Raise this, and press the triggerguard easily to the rear to its fullest extent. Then release the trigger, jerk back on the triggerguard till it clears the gun, and then lower the catch.

Field Assembly

Reverse the stripping procedure. Start by replacing the triggerguard, and make sure that it is in its normal position. In replacing feed lever, check that the upper arm is slightly to the right so it will engage correctly its stud with the groove in the piston.

In assembling barrel extension and piston, take care that the upper flange on the piston engages in the lower groove in extension. Work piston backwards and forwards when inserted to be sure that stud on lower arm of feed lever is properly engaged with piston extension groove.

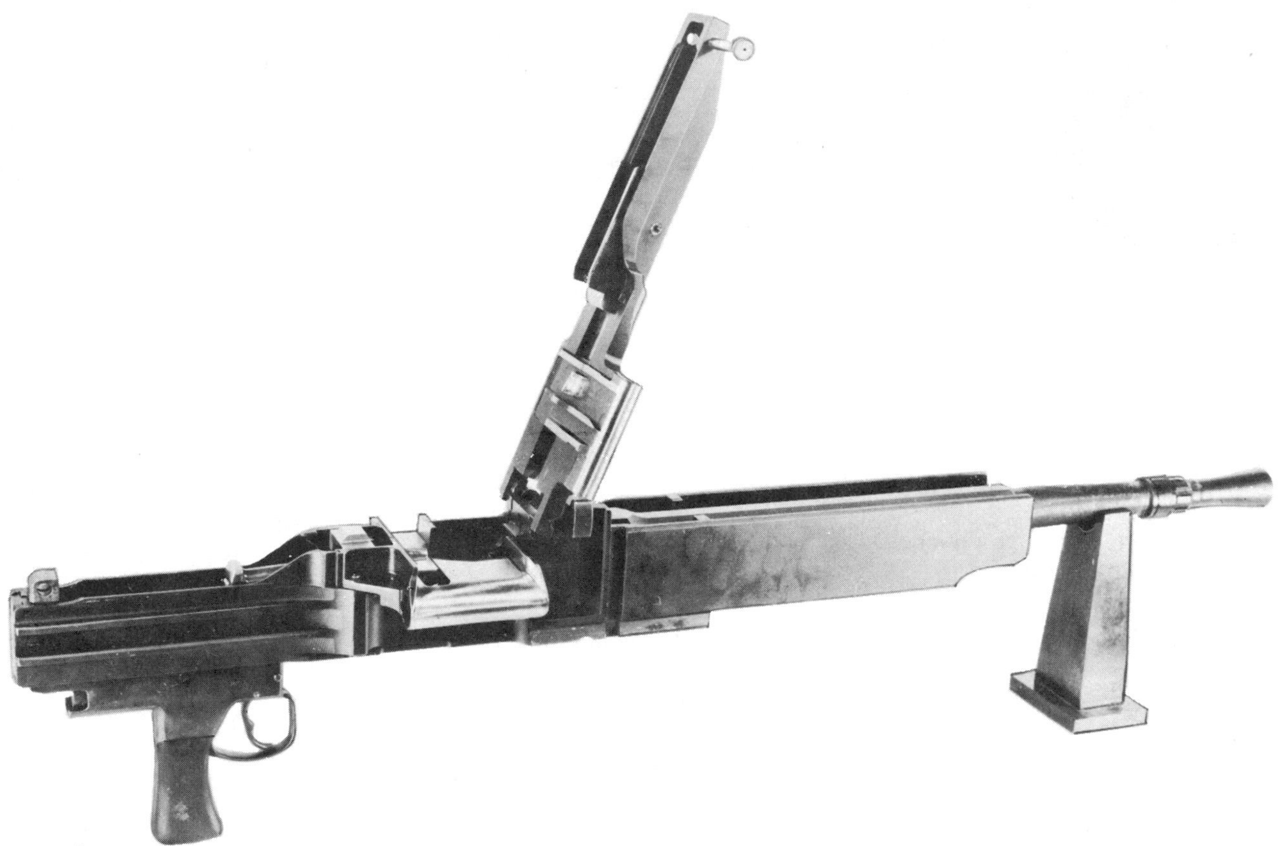

Place return spring in piston, and while holding the spring firmly, place the guide rod in the spring, push forward until the rod enters the piston extension. Then press the guide lock down into the receiver and release the pressure. This will permit the spring to position the guide lock properly.

Hold the barrel extension down with the left hand while cocking the gun with the right and replace accelerator, breech block, feed block body, and feed slide asesmbly. Be sure that the stud on the feed slide engages in the slot of the upper arm of the feed lever belt guide.

When replacing the body cover, check that the cover bearings engage properly with the body trunnions.

Barrel Replacement

Keeping rear end of the barrel elevated, insert the slides on the barrel sleeve in the guides on the body. Then draw the barrel to the rear until the flanges at the breech end of the barrel are just above the grooves in the barrel extension. Then lower the barrel into the barrel extension, push the carrying handle over to the right until it rests on the ramp, strike it back sharply with the palm of the hand and push the handle down to lock the barrel.

How the Besa Gun Works

Starting with the gun loaded and cocked, the action is as follows: As the safety catch lever is squeezed in, the trigger is free to engage with the sear, drawing it out of the bent in the piston extension and permitting the return spring to start the piston and moving parts forward.

As the piston and piston extension move ahead, the extension acts to move the breechblock ahead, a projection on the front of the block strikes the rim of the cartridge in front of it, strips it out of the belt, and chambers it.

The extractor rides up over the cannelure of the cartridge during the closing movement of the breechblock and snaps into engagement.

As the rear end of the breechblock is lifted, it disengages from the shallow stop in the piston extension by engaging with projections in the barrel extension. It rides up an inclined plane and engages with a resistance face on the barrel extension.

As the breechblock locks, the piston extension carrying the piston post against the firing pins discharges the cartridge.

Also during the forward movement, the piston extension acts on the lower arm of the feed lever moving the upper arm and the feed pawl over to the right permitting the feed pawl to be depressed by the belt and cartridge and engage in the link of the third round in the belt.

The retaining pawl is engaged behind the link of the cartridge just stripped into the firing chamber and holds the belt stationary during the movement.

Return Movement of the Action

As the cartridge in the chamber is exploded, the bullet moves down the barrel and the rearward thrust of the recoil bearing against the cartridge case forces the breechblock, piston, barrel extension, and barrel to the rear as a unit. The barrel extension presses against the recoil spring in the cover easing the rearward motion; and after the initial shock the barrel extension and barrel are forced forward by the action of the recoil spring.

Gas Action

As the bullet passes over the gas vent in the barrel, some gas escapes through and into the gas cylinder, then through the gas regulator to strike a sharp blow against the piston head.

This sudden thrust drives the piston and its extension to the rear, and the inclined ramp on the piston post bearing against the breechblock lowers the rear end of the block out of engagement with the resistance space at the rear of the barrel extension, unlocking the weapon.

Further rearward motion of the piston extension pulls the breechblock clear of the barrel. The extractor draws the fired case out of the chamber until the base of the empty cartridge case strikes the ejector, which is a fixed projection on the belt guide. This snaps the case free from the breechblock, permitting the extractor to snap back into place, and the empty is hurled through a slot in the piston extension and out the ejection opening in the bottom of the receiver. Also during the backward movement of the piston extension, the return spring is compressed between its place in the extension and the return spring guide lock.

If the trigger has been released, the sear spring will reassert itself and push the nose of the sear into engagement with the bent of the piston extension holding it to the rear. If the trigger is kept depressed, on completion of rearward motion the return spring will drive the piston and other moving parts forward and the cycle of firing will be repeated.

The Accelerator

When the accelerator is set in its high position, the rear of the piston extension will not make contact with the accelerator and the gun will fire at its normal rate of 450 to 550 per minute.

If, however, the accelerator is set in its low position, the complete backward motion of the piston extension is halted by the rear of the extension striking the front face of the accelerator. This forces the accelerator casing to the rear, thereby compressing the heavy accelerator springs. Thus, when the forward movement starts, the operating parts are forced forward not only by the return spring, but also by the accelerator springs. This extra spring action speeds up the forward movement of the working parts and the rate of fire is increased to 750 to 850 shots per minute.

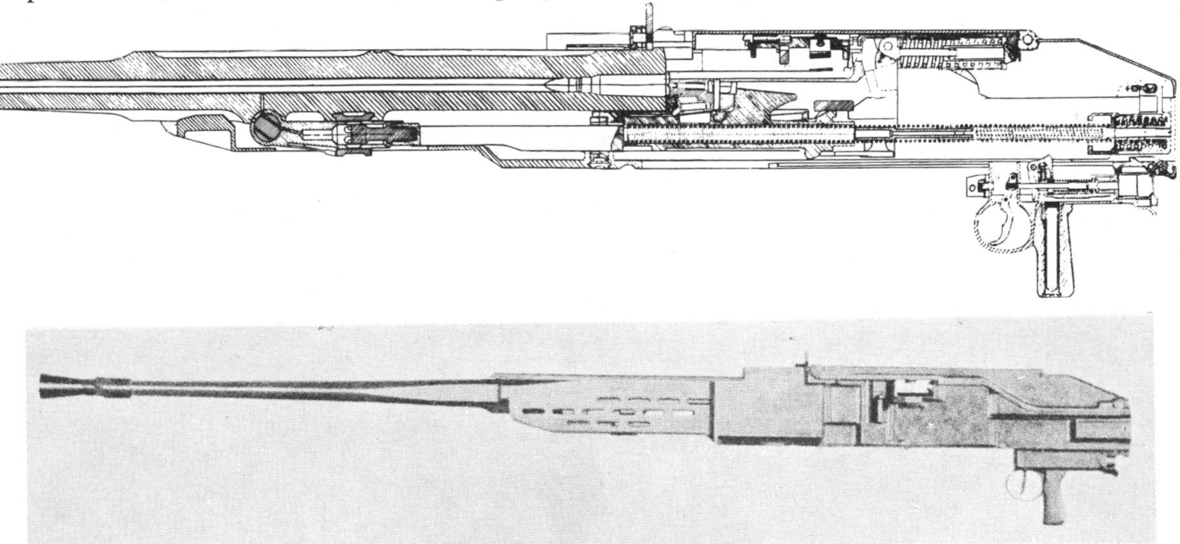

British Besa 15mm Machine Gun Mark 1.

This is a heavy model of the original Besa Machine Gun developed for use in armored vehicles. Its handling and functioning are much the same as the smaller caliber. It is not equipped with an accelerator, but it is fitted with a change lever device permitting single shot or full automatic fire.

Caliber: 15mm Mark 1.
Feed: Metal belt holding 25 cartridges.
Muzzle Velocity: Approximately 3,000 feet per second.
Barrel Length: About 57″ including the flash hider.
Overall Length of Gun: About 81″.
Weight: 125½ lbs.
Barrel Weight: About 48 lbs.
Weight of Filled Belt: About 12 lbs. 4 ozs.
Sight: Telescopic, maximum range limit 1800 yards.
Gun Operated By: Gas. Same as lighter model.
Locked: Rising breechblock, same as small model Besa.
Cooled: Air. Fires from open bolt.
Cyclic Rate of Fire: 400 to 500 per minute.
Cocked: Same as the lighter gun. Cocking catch to triggerguard body is pressed forward. Then the triggerguard assembly is pushed forward as far as it will go. Pulling triggerguard to the rear smartly until it is held back completes the cocking of the gun.
Type of Fire: Single shot or full automatic. Move the change lever to the right as far as it will go for full automatic fire. When change lever is in center position, weapon is "Safe." When change lever is pushed to the left as far as it will go, trigger must be pressed for each shot.
Special Note on Besa Guns: These guns were originally adapted from the Czech 15mm ZB 60, (Model 38).

Barrel Removal

Removing the barrel on this model is a two-man job. While one man holds the barrel, the other raises the carrying handle of the barrel retainer a half-inch and pushes the handle forward until it can be turned up. About 13″ from the breech-end a special slot is provided to permit this action.

Second man now raises the rear end of the barrel until it clears the barrel extension, then both ease it forward and lift it out. Slides on the barrel are freed from the guides of the body by this forward motion.

British Bren .303 Light Machine Gun Mark 1.

CALIBER .303 BREN GUNS

	Mark 1	Mark 2	Mark 3	Mark 4
System of operation ...	Gas, selective fire	Gas, selective fire	Gas, selective fire	Gas, selective fire
Overall length	45.5 in	45.6 in	42.6 in	40.9 in
Barrel length	25 in	25 in	22.25 in	22.25 in
Feed device	30-round box or 100-round drum	30-round box or 100-round drum	30-round box	30-round box
Sights:				
Front	Blade w/ears	Blade w/ears	Blade w/ears	Blade w/ears
Rear	Aperature w/radial drum	Leaf w/aperture	Leaf w/aperature	Leaf w/aperture
Muzzle velocity w/MK 7 ball	2,440 fps	2,440 fps	Apprx 2,400 fps	Apprx 2,400 fps
Cyclic rate	500 rpm	540 rpm	480 rpm	520 rpm
Weight of barrel	6.28 lbs	6.46 lbs	5.09 lbs	5 lbs
Weight of gun	22.12 lbs	23.18 lbs	19.3 lbs	19.14 lbs

Accurate Range: About 800 yards.

Gun Operated by: Gas escaping through hole in under side of barrel into gas cylinder and forcing piston to the rear to operate the mechanism and compress the return spring which supplies power for the forward motion of the action.

Locked: By rear end of breechblock rising and locking into recesses in the top of the receiver.

Cooled: Air cooled. Action remains open between shots. Bolt stays back permitting circulation of air through ejection port and barrel.

Position of Cocking Handle: On right hand side of receiver. It is drawn straight back to cock the weapon, then pushed forward so that the action will not have to carry it forward, and in the Mark 1 type it is then folded against the receiver. In the Mark 2 model it does not fold.

Type of Fire: Either single shot or full automatic. A change lever is mounted on the left side directly above the trigger. Push this lever forward to the letter "A" and the weapon will fire full automatic as long as the trigger is held back. Set the lever in the center at the letter "S" and the weapon is locked and cannot be fired. This is the safety. Turn the lever back to the letter "R" (this is the position normally used) and the rifle will fire one shot for each pressure of the trigger. "R" stands for repetition or rounds, the British designation for single shot fire.

Flash Hider: As in the Browning automatic rifle, a sleeve extending forward beyond the muzzle of the barrel hides the flash of powder burning after it leaves the muzzle of the barrel.

Tripod: A tripod weighing 30 lbs., and having an elevation limit of 19° with a traverse of 42°, is sometimes furnished with this weapon to convert it to a medium machine gun.

Ejection: This weapon ejects through the bottom.

Mark 2 Bren. Stock and sights changed from Mark 1.

Loading and Firing

To load the magazine by hand: The magazine is rested on the thigh, or on a solid object, and cartridges placed in the magazine as for ordinary automatic pistol. They should be inserted with the right hand, and pressed down into place with the thumb of the left hand. Unlike our United States cartridge, the British service cartridge has a rim. In inserting cartridges in magazine, therefore, care must be taken to see that the rim of each cartridge is placed in front of the round already in the magazine. If rim gets behind rim, jams will inevitably result.

Magazine Filler. Push the magazine into the mouth of the filler, and swing the filling lever as far as it will go to the left. Fill the hopper and push the filling lever over to the right and back to its limit 6 times; this will put 30 rounds into the magazine. If the filler is the small hand type, push magazine in until the magazine catch engages, and then insert a loaded cartridge charger (or clip as it is called in the United States) into the mouth of the filler over the head of the magazine. See that the tip of the operating lever is against the topmost cartridge and push down slowly and firmly with the operating lever.

Note: While the magazine capacity is 30, it is better practice to use 27 or 28 cartridges so as not to strain the magazine spring.

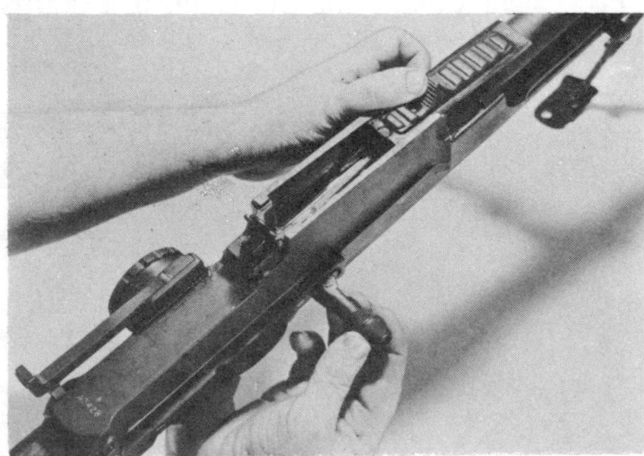

The magazine opening on top of the receiver is fitted with a sliding cover; push this opening cover forward as far as it will go.

Holding the magazine mouth downward in the right hand, insert the lip at the front end into the magazine opening and hook it there; then press downward the rear of the magazine until the magazine catch engages on the magazine rim.

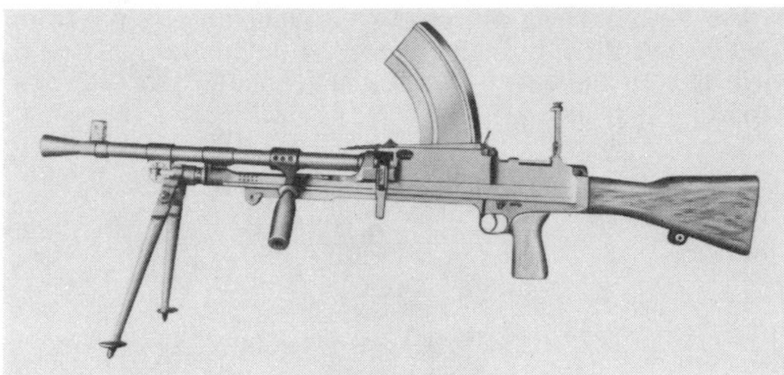

Mark 3 Bren.

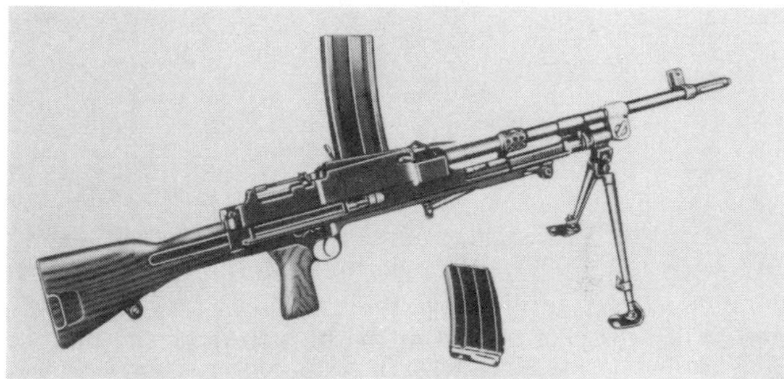

L4A2 Bren. 7.62mm NATO.

Draw the cocking handle back as far as it will go to cock the action and push it forward again. If weapon has a folding cocking handle, fold it over.

Set the change lever on the left side of the receiver at the desired position of "Automatic," "Safe," or "R" for single shot.

Note: A cover over the ejection opening will automatically spring open when the trigger is pulled to permit ejection of empty cartridge case.

Caution: Always remember that gun fires from an open bolt. The bolt should never be permitted to go forward while there is a magazine in the gun unless you intend it to fire. The magazine must be removed first, and the action eased forward second in unloading the weapon.

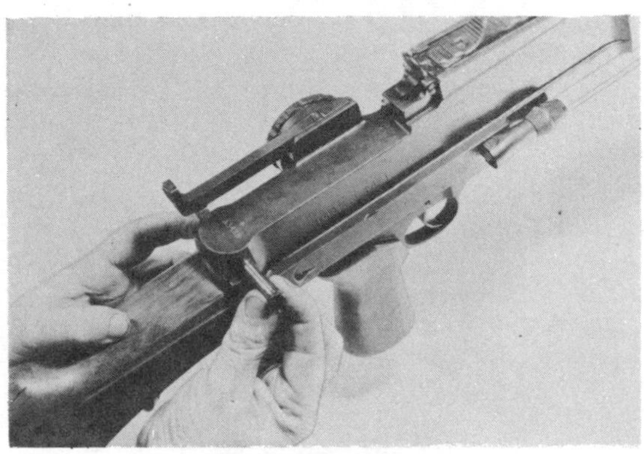

Field Stripping

Be sure there is no magazine in the gun and all moving parts are forward.

The body locking pin passes through the receiver from right to left directly under the aperture of the rear sight. Push it with the point of a bullet from the left side and withdraw it from the right.

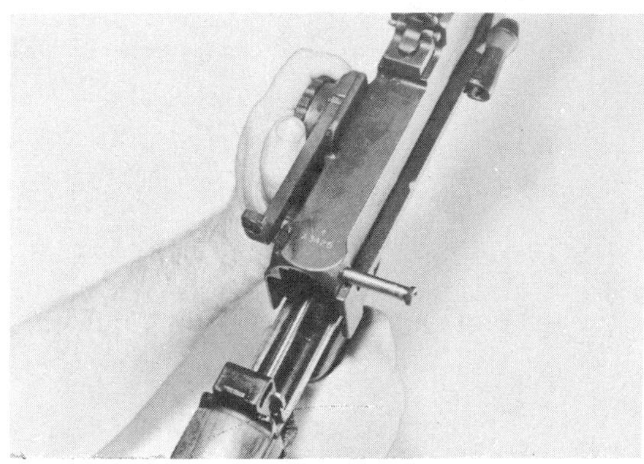

Grasp the back sight drum firmly with the left hand, and with the right pull back the butt group as far as possible. The return spring rod, which is housed in the butt, will now protrude from the butt through the buffer.

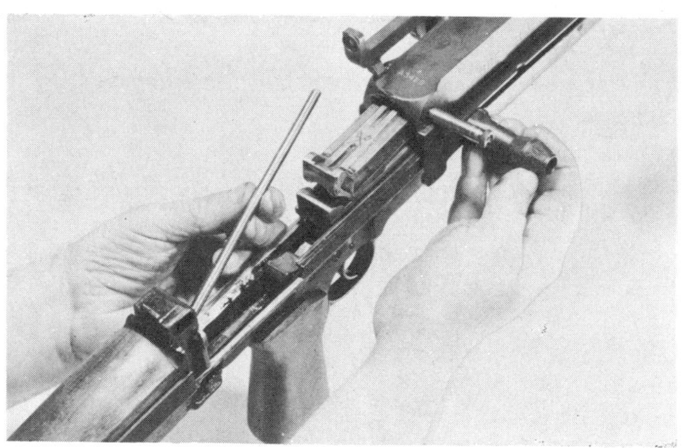

With the thumb and forefinger of the left hand pull the return spring rod to the left out of line with the piston; and with the right hand pull the cocking handle back with a rapid motion. The piston and breechblock will now come out of the receiver and may be removed from the gun.

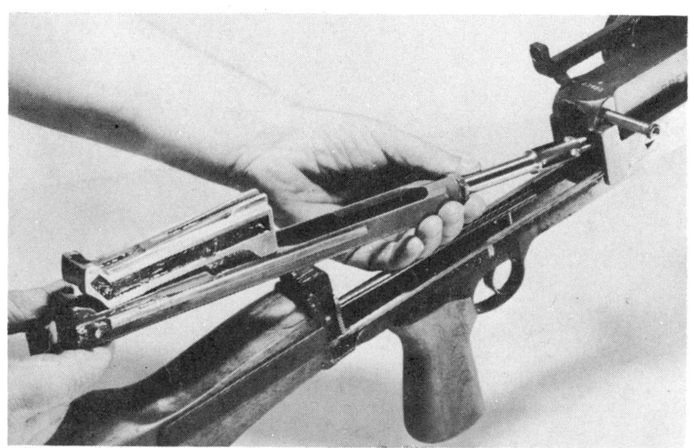

The claws at the front end of the breechblock are in engagement with grooves on the piston, and if the breechblock is slid to the rear it can be lifted out of this engagement and removed.

The barrel nut catch lies on the side of the barrel just ahead of the magazine opening. Force in the spring catch on its underside and lift the barrel nut catch as far as it will go; which will free the barrel for removal.

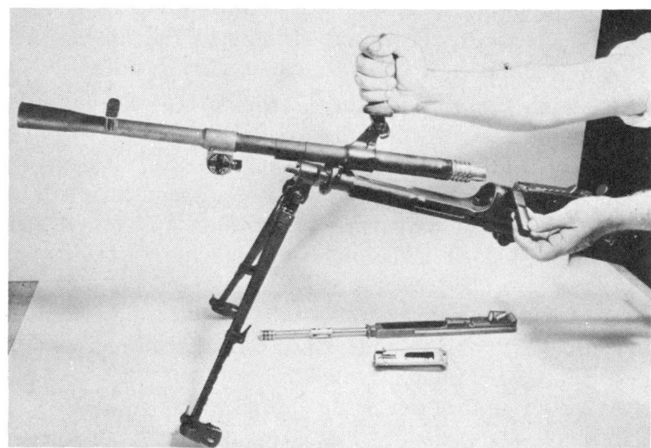

Holding the wooden carrying handle with the right hand, push forward on the barrel while holding firmly to the back sight drum with left hand. The barrel will now come forward and may be lifted out.

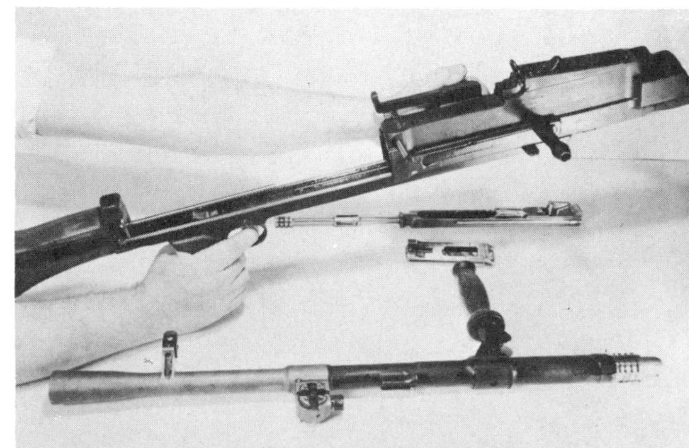

Grasp the rear sight drum firmly with the left hand and with the right hand pull directly back on the butt. The entire butt group may now be removed.

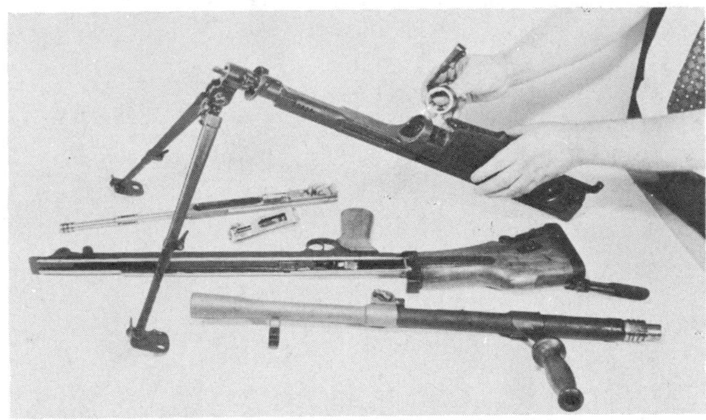

The barrel nut may be removed by lifting the catch as far as it will go and pushing down the small stud in front of the magazine opening cover. The barrel nut is then lifted out vertically.

Now lift the front of the body with the right hand and with the left pull the left leg of the bipod as far forward as possible—slide bipod sleeve off the front end of the gas cylinder.

Notes on Assembling

Reverse the stripping order.

In replacing bipod take care the mount is fully home.

In Mark 1 guns check that the stop on the left of the forward end of the butt group is in front of the barrel nut catch before lowering the catch.

In replacing barrel on Mark 1, make sure the long groove underneath between gas block and carrying handle engages properly with stud on top of receiver.

Be sure the barrel nut catch is fully locked and catch has engaged on rib in the body or receiver.

When replacing breechblock on piston, slide the claws down into the groove as far forward as possible and then let the tail of the breechblock drop.

When inserting the assembled breechblock and piston, make sure that the breechblock is fully forward and that the two are pushed into the receiver before attempting to push forward the butt group.

Be sure that the return spring rod engages in a recess for it in the end of the piston when the butt group is being pushed forward.

Gas Regulator

The gas regulator is mounted on the barrel near the muzzle. It faces to the left. The correct setting is usually the No. 2 size. There are four different ports. Lifting the retainer pin permits the gas regulator to be turned to increase the size of the port. Should the gun become sluggish in action, the gas regulator is altered to the next larger hole to increase the amount of pressure available.

How the Bren Gun Works

Starting with the gun loaded and cocked the action is as follows: If the change lever is set at "R" pressing the trigger pulls a connecting tripping lever, which in its turns draws down the sear out of engagement with the pin on the piston. This action also compresses the coil sear spring. The compressed return spring, situated in the butt, pushes the rod forward, and this in turn pushes against the seat in the piston driving the piston forward, carrying with it the locking and firing mechanism. Meanwhile the sear spring pushes the sear back into place. The breechblock mounted on the top of the piston is carried forward, and the feed piece strikes the base of the first round in the magazine and forces it forward out of lips of the magazine and into the chamber, with the extractor slipping over the rim. The rear end of the breechblock is cammed up into a locking recess in the top of the receiver as the cartridge is properly chambered; in its final move the piston post drives the firing pin against the primer of the cartridge, exploding it.

Showing Change Lever for Safe, Automatic, or Single Shot Fire.

As the bullet passes over the small gas vent cut in the barrel, a short distance from the muzzle, a small amount of gas under high pressure passes through the vent and through the gas regulator (where the size of the port selected determines the amount of gas to be let in) and escapes into a well where it expands with a hammerlike thrust against the piston. As the piston is driven back in its cylinder, the gas can now escape through holes provided for it.

Meanwhile the sudden thrust on the piston drives it back and forces the return spring rod back into the butt where the return spring is compressed; this action being finally stopped by the piston buffer.

The empty cartridge case, gripped by the extractor and carried to the rear on the face of the breechblock, strikes its face against the base of the ejector and is hurled downward through the ejection slot in the piston and out of the weapon. During this rearward action the upper locking surfaces of the breechblock are forced down into line, so that in its final movement, the piston and breechblock travel together in a straight line.

Note: The buffer spring is in the butt below the line of the return spring.

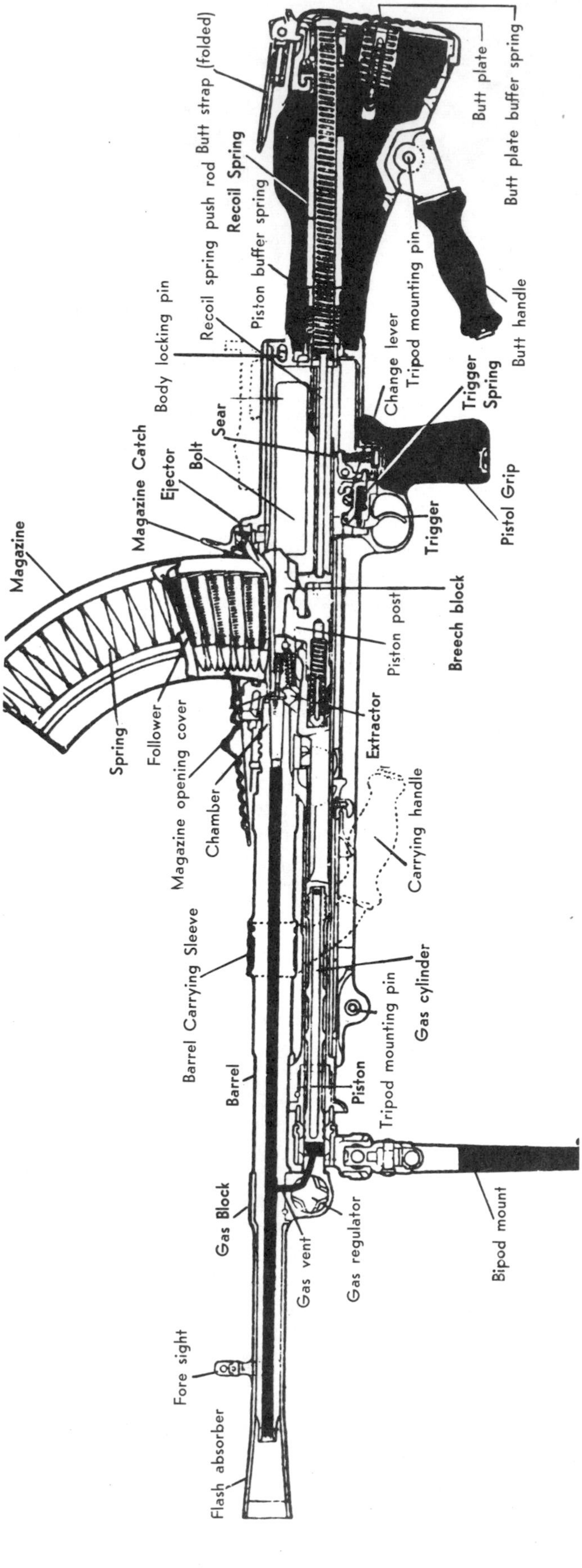

Showing Details of Tripod Mount.

Special Note on the Bren Gun

This is one of the finest light machine guns ever developed. Originating from the Czech ZB26, it was further engineered and developed in England and gets its name from the combination of Brno and Enfield. As mentioned before, while this weapon is essentially a one-man machine gun intended to be used from a bipod mount, or fired from the hip while moving in action, it may quickly be converted into a heavy machine gun firing from a solid tripod mount, or a very effective antiaircraft machine gun against low-flying planes. The normal rate of automatic fire is 5 bursts of 4 or 5 rounds each, averaging about one magazine a minute. In emergencies, it may be fired at the rate of 4 magazines a minute. A very fast operator can deliver 150 shots or 5 magazines in a minute. For all general purposes, however, it is intended to be fired one shot for each pull of the trigger, as an automatic rifle. This procedure saves ammunition and conceals from the enemy the fact that a machine gun is in operation against them.

A spare barrel is issued with each gun and the ease and rapidity of barrel change is a very important feature of the weapon. As the magazine is mounted on top of the receiver, the sights have to be set off to the side of the barrel so that the line of sight will not be interfered with.

The Japanese made very extensive use of Bren guns captured in the Far East from the British. The Chinese produced Brno-type guns, manufactured in crude Chinese factories, and used guns originally made for them in Czechoslovakia. Brno guns made in captured Czech factories were used by the Germans in caliber 7.92mm.

AA Mounting. The tripod is issued with a special attached device which permits it to be quickly converted into an antiaircraft mount. On the tripod mount, the gun is locked at front below gas cylinder and at rear below butt; on the AA mounting, it is fastened near the muzzle on a mounting pivot, giving complete flexibility to the gunner.

LATEST BRITISH MACHINE GUNS

The British 7.62mm Light Machine Gun L4A2 is basically similar to the later Brens, except that it has a flash suppressor rather than a flash hider and is chambered for the 7.62mm NATO cartridge. The British have started converting some of their cal. .303 Bren guns to 7.62mm NATO caliber.

At this time it seems quite likely that the FN-designed 7.62mm Type M.A.G. general purpose machine gun will be adopted as a replacement for the watercooled Vickers Mark 1. Since the M.A.G. is suitable for use as either a light or heavy machine gun, it could also be used as a replacement for the Bren, if so desired.

Although some Besa tank machine guns are still in service, the UK has adopted the U. S. Brownings and the M37 for rifle-caliber tank guns, and the U. S. Cal. .50 M2 HB for a heavy-caliber tank machine gun. It is possible that the UK will adopt the new U. S. 7.62mm M73 and the cal. .50 M85 at a later date.

7.62mm F.N. M.A.G. Machine Gun as made for Great Britain.

AUSTRALIA

Australia has adopted and is manufacturing (at Lithgow) the 7.62mm NATO FN rifle. Australia has announced her intention to adopt United States weapons as standard, whenever possible, and has adopted the U. S. 7.62mm M60 machine gun.

AUSTRALIAN SUBMACHINE GUNS

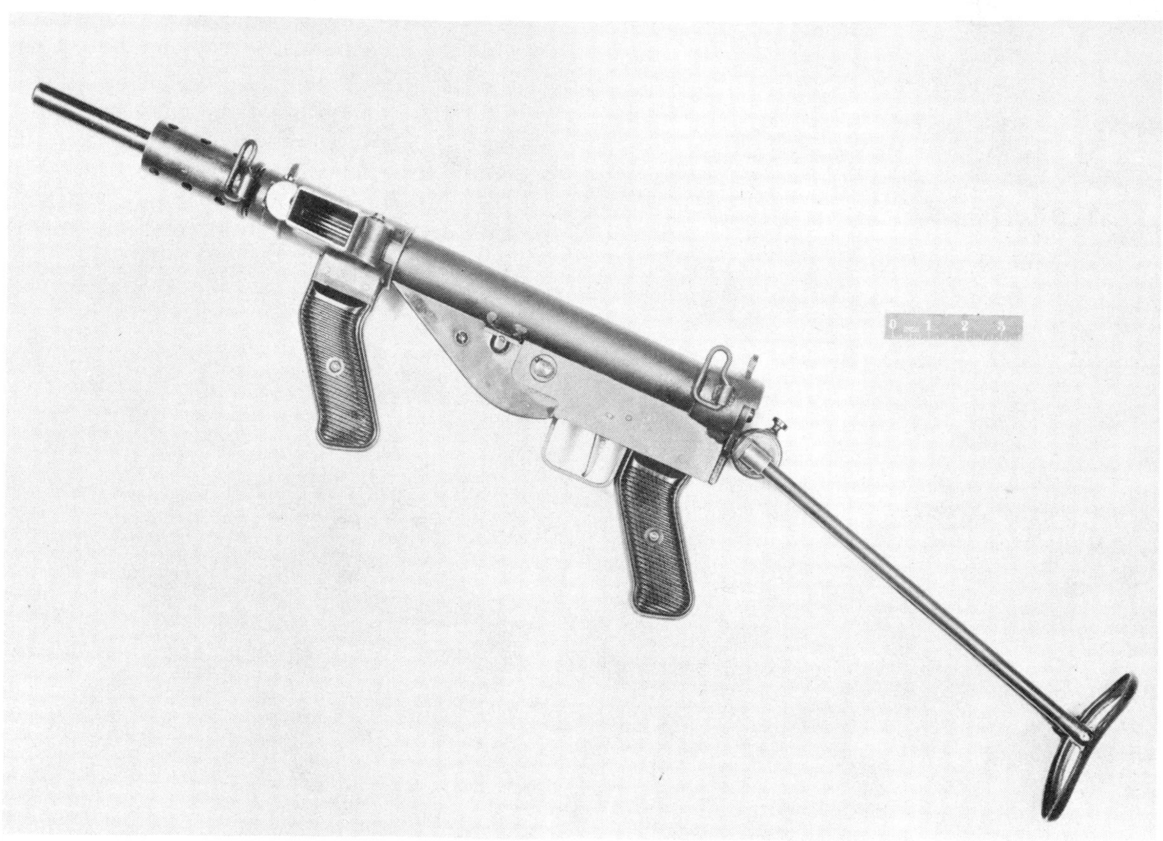

Australian 9mm Austen Mark I Submachine Gun, no longer being made.

Caliber: 9mm Parabellum, ball, tracer, or semi-armor piercing ammunition of the Luger type.
Magazine: Box type holding 32 cartridges. Positioned in housing on left side of receiver.
Ballistics: Standard for cartridges used. (Varies from 1050 to 1500 FPS, depending on type and makes of ammunition.)
Barrel Length: 7⅞″.
Overall Length of Gun: 33¼″ with stock open. 22″ with stock closed.
Weight, Without Magazine: 8¾ lbs.
Weight of Magazine: ½ lb. empty.
Front Sight: Barleycorn type.
Rear Sight: Aperture, set for 100 yards.
Gun Operated By: Rearward pressure of gas in firing chamber against the base of the fired cartridge which passes thrust on to the bolt.
Locked: Simple blowback. The weight of the recoiling parts and the inertia of the forward motion is sufficient to keep the weapon closed until the bullet is safely out of the barrel and the period of high breech pressure has dropped.
Cooled: Air. Bolt stays open between shots permitting circulation of air down barrel; barrel is also fitted with a half-length barrel casing which is ventilated.
Cyclic Rate of Fire: 500 to 550 per minute.
Position of Cocking Handle: Right side of gun.
Type of Fire: Single shot or full automatic. A button passes through the frame of the gun above and ahead of the front of the triggerguard. If it is pushed from the right side where the button is marked "A," it will fire as long as the trigger is held back and there are cartridges in the magazine. If the button is pushed through from the left where it is marked "R," it will fire one shot each time the trigger is pressed.
Safety: When the gun is cocked, the bolt may be drawn back and turned up so that the bolt handle locks in a slot cut in the top of the receiver. It cannot be fired until the cocking handle is pulled back and turned out of the slot.

Instructions for Loading and Firing

Load magazine exactly as for automatic pistol. Magazine will hold 32 cartridges, but gun will function better if about 28 are used.

Insert magazine in housing on left side of receiver and push forward until it clicks.

Pull the cocking handle back as far as it will go. It will be held back by the sear, and is now ready for firing when the trigger is pressed.

The folding skeleton stock may be opened by pushing down on the release plunger and pulling back the stock.

How the Austen Gun Works

Starting with the gun loaded and cocked the action is as follows:

When the trigger is pressed it moves the sear down out of its contact with the bent of the bolt. The compressed recoil spring in the telescoping tube is now free to drive the bolt forward. The firing pin is seated inside a hole in the bolt and protrudes through its hole in the front face of the bolt. It is blocked by the heavy extractor from striking the cartridge until the weapon is in full forward position. Feed ribs are cut in the side of the bolt and these strip the top cartridge from between the cutaway lips of the magazine and push it into the firing chamber.

As the cartridge is chambered, the heavy extractor cams up over the base of the cartridge, and its hook snaps, under the tension of the extractor spring, into the cannelure of the cartridge case. At this point the firing pin is free to strike the primer and explode the cartridge.

As the powder explodes, the bullet is driven down the barrel. The rearward action starts at the same time, but since the weight and inertia of the recoiling parts is very much greater than that of the bullet, opening the breech is delayed long enough to assure that the moment of dangerous breech pressure passes before it opens.

As the bolt starts back, the extractor draws the empty cartridge case with it; this case is struck against the ejector and pivoted out the right side of the gun and then the extractor spring snaps the extractor back into its place. As the bolt in its rearward travel passes the mouth of the magazine, the magazine spring forces the next cartridge into line ready to be picked up on forward motion.

The rear buffer end of the recoil spring tube is firmly supported by the cap and retaining ring through which it passes. Hence as the bolt goes back, it telescopes the heavy steel sections, one over another, compressing the spring inside.

If the selector has been set for single shot fire, the bolt rides over the sear nose which springs up and catches in the bent of the bolt holding it open for the next press of the trigger. If the selector has been set for full automatic fire, it is not retained and the bolt is free to move forward to fire the next cartridge.

Special Note on the Austen Gun

This submachine gun (or machine carbine as the British termed it) is one of the most remarkable developments of World War II. It combines all the best features of the famous British Sten and the almost equally famous German Schmeisser submachine guns. The Sten Gun was originally adopted by the British to provide a very cheap submachine weapon which would be simple, absolutely reliable and accurate.

However, the Sten Gun has several faults: the weapon cannot be fired except with the shoulder stock attached; the recoil spring is subject to kinking under some conditions of firing; and it has a front-end design which makes it possible for the fingers to be injured or burned under some conditions of action.

The Australians combined the best features of the Sten with the best features of the Schmeisser and added several entirely unique details to make this remarkably fine weapon. While the German Schmeisser skeleton stock was adopted, it was fitted with an improved lock which makes it very rigid when used as a shoulder weapon. The Schmeisser type of bolt and telescoping recoil spring tube (probably the simplest of all such systems) was adopted, but they were fitted in the Sten-type receiver which permits easier cleaning and dismounting than does the German. The magazine was mounted on the left side as in the case of the Sten Gun, which permits the weapon to be used from a prone position with much more ease than does the bottom positioning of the magazine. A simplified form of barrel removal was developed, which permits the barrel to be speedily changed when it is overheated, or if it is to be replaced or cleaned.

It will further be noted that this weapon is chambered to handle cartridges available in almost every corner of the world. It can use Italian-type ammunition, and all the other forms of 9mm ammunition generally used under the name of Parabellum in Europe.

This cartridge with different powder loads was used by the Germans.

The Mark II Austen

A later version of the Austen machine carbine was also introduced. This design, known as the MARK II, resembles the original in outward appearance, but differs radically in construction.

The receiver consists of two pieces of cast aluminum, and represents an endeavor on the part of the designers to speed up production and at the same time provide a sturdy weapon.

The receiver may be separated when stripping the weapon by pushing a Schmeisser-type button just ahead of the front hand grip on the left side; then pulling back on the rear grip. The rear section of the receiver containing the trigger mechanism will come straight back out of its joint with the front section.

The barrel rests in the front section of the aluminum receiver, while a cylindrical steel bolt travel-piece acts as a barrel extension. It is attached to the barrel, but extends back into the rear section of the aluminum receiver. Both the barrel extension and the rear of the receiver are cut away to permit travel of the cocking handle to be unimpeded. Note that the bolt travels back and forth in this steel barrel extension—at no time does it come in touch with the aluminum receiver shell. The customary Sten-type push through button is provided to give single shot or full automatic fire.

As the tube in which the bolt travels is of heavy steel and is partly enclosed in and cushioned by the aluminum receiver, injury to or deformation of the travel tube is not as likely to occur as in submachine guns made from straight steel stampings. The bolt and recoil spring tube, as in the Mark I Model, follow the Schmeisser design.

Field Stripping

Push down on stock locking plunger and bend the stock down out of line with the rear of the gun.

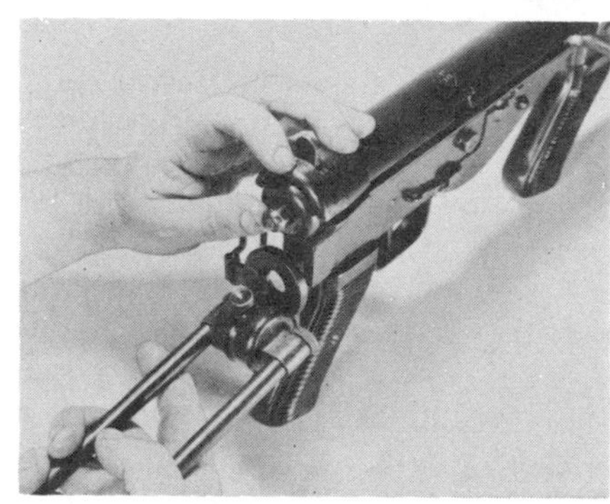

With the left thumb press in on the head of the spring tube protruding through the back of the gun. With the right hand grasp the stock firmly and

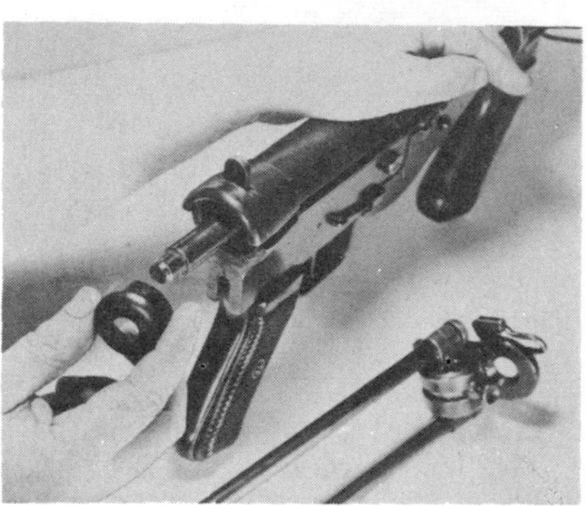

slide it down out of its locking groove in the rear of the receiver.

Lift out the buffer cap.

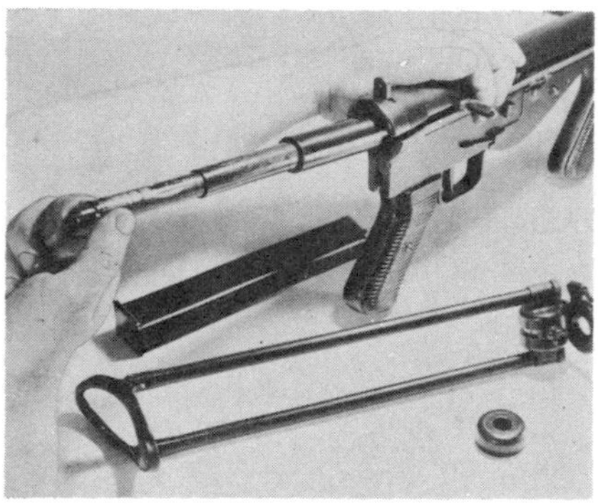

Pull back the cocking handle which will bring the recoil and buffer spring tube back and pull the telescoping tube out of the receiver.

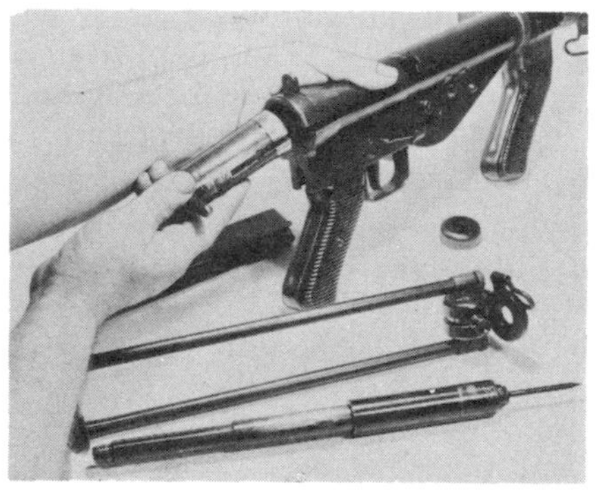

Now pull the bolt back out of the gun. The extractor may be punched out of the bolt if necessary.

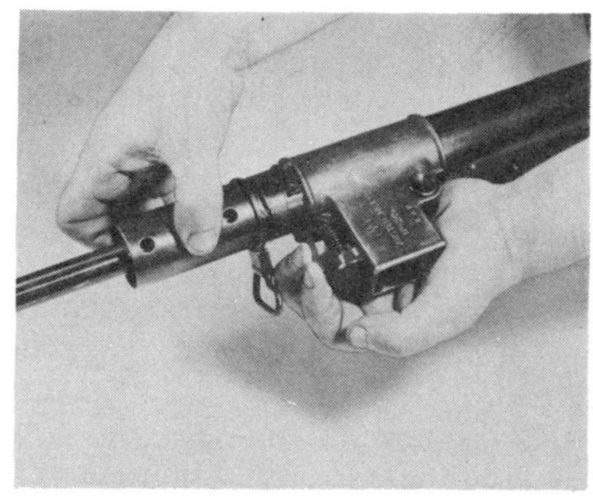

With the fingers of the left hand, pull back the barrel nut catch against its spring tension (It is at the front end of the magazine housing on the left side of the gun) and with the right hand unscrew the barrel casing and barrel nut to the right.

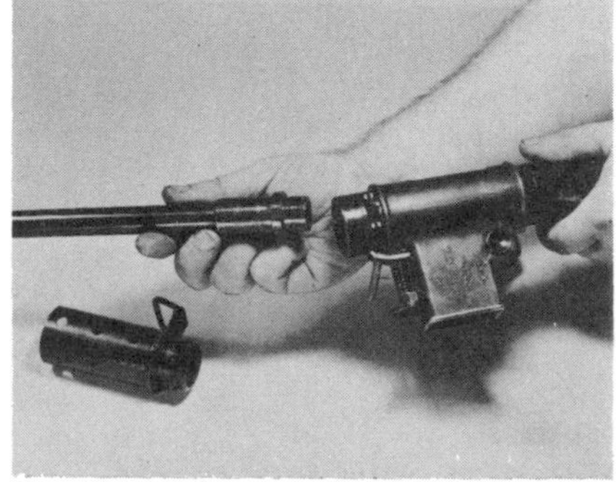

Pull the barrel nut and casing forward out of the receiver. Pull barrel straight forward out of the receiver.

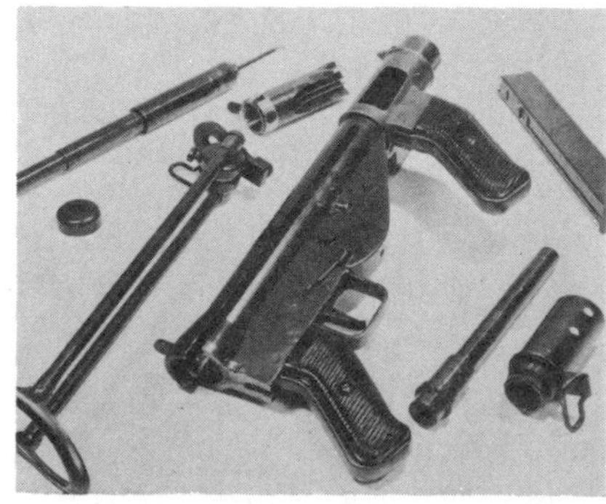

This completes field stripping.

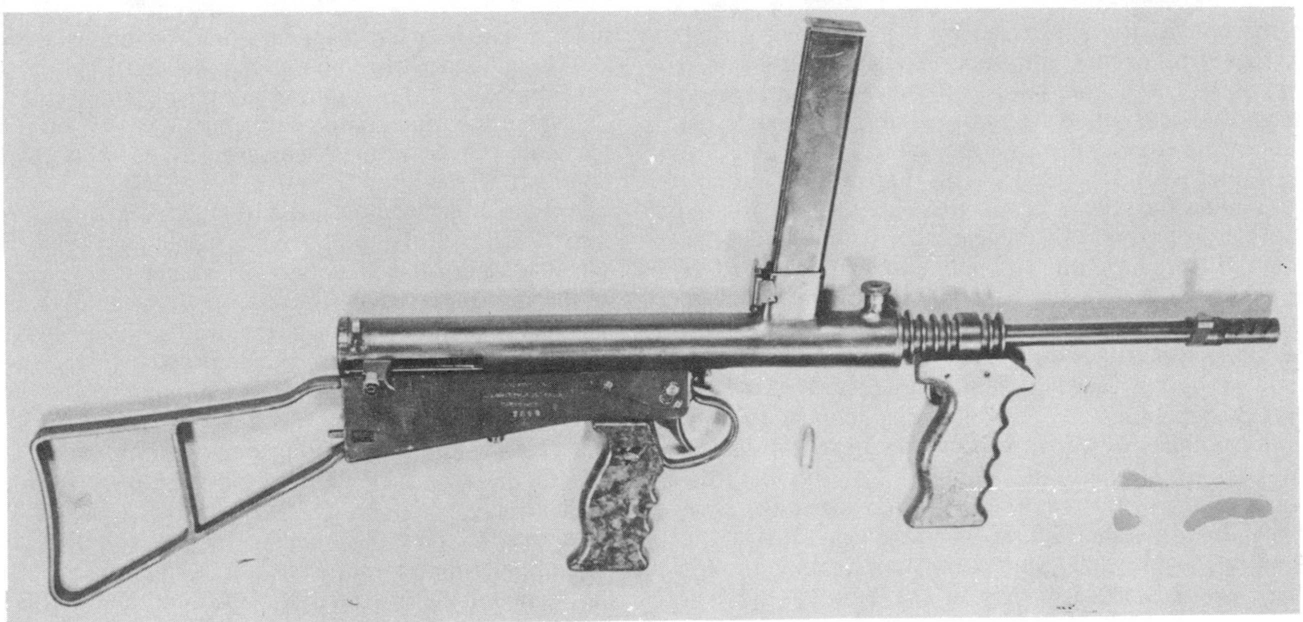

Owen 9mm Submachine Gun, no longer being made.

Caliber: 9mm Parabellum (Luger).
Magazine: 33 cartridges.
Ballistics: Standard for cartridges used (1375 f.p.s with Australian issue ammunition).
Barrel Length: 9.87".
Overall Length: 32" with butt; 24" without butt.
Weight: 10 lbs. 3 oz. with and 9 lbs. 4 oz. without butt. Magazine empty.
Sights: Fixed for 100 yards. Offset.
Gun Operated By: Recoil.
Locked: Unlocked. Blowback.
Cooled: Air. Fires from open bolt.
Cyclic Rate of Fire: About 600 per mniute.
Position of Cocking Handle: Right side.
Type of Fire: Single shot or full auto. Change lever on left.
Safety: Part of change lever.

The Owen was one of the most unusual of all the machine carbines (or submachine guns, as we class them) to be used in the war. It is so small, light, and toy-like in appearance that its deadliness is hard to appreciate. While it is cheap to manufacture and generally reliable in action, it costs more (about $30) than its cheaper but heavier brothers—the Sten and the Austen.

This is a straight blowback weapon using the 9mm Luger type of cartridge. Among its unusual features are the top-mounted magazine which requires that the sights be offset on the side of the weapon to permit sighting, its quick change barrel, and detachable stock.

When a loaded magazine is inserted in the housing on top of the receiver and pushed in until it locks, pulling the cocking handle back until the bolt is caught and held by the sear leaves the gun ready for firing. The gun may be set to fire a shot for each pull of the trigger; or for full automatic fire as long as the trigger is held and cartridges feed.

It will be noted that the barrel is equipped with a compensator at the muzzle to help hold the gun down when firing, and with ring cooling surfaces near the breech end. The barrel catch releases the barrel and front grip for speedy removal under favorable conditions; but in use the barrel may heat so rapidly that it tends to freeze in the receiver and thus make removal somewhat difficult.

The recoil spring and guide are mounted in standard fashion in the head of the bolt and within the receiver tunnel, where they are retained by the cap at the rear.

The metal skeleton stock is easily removed by pressing the spring held catch mounted within its forward section.

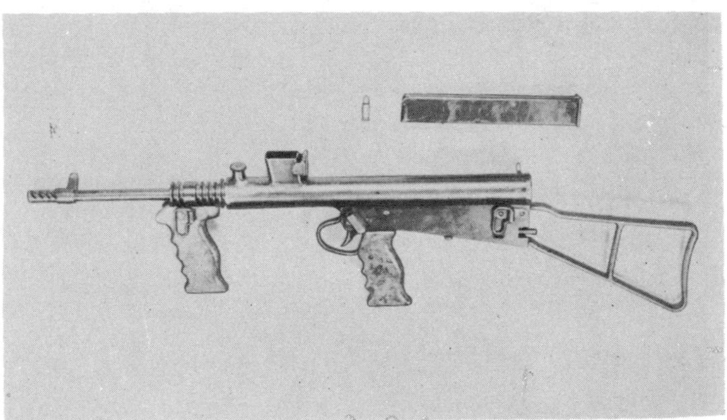

How the Gun Works

When a loaded magazine is in position and the bolt is withdrawn to its fullest extent, if the change lever is set for single shot fire, pressure on the trigger forces the rear end of the sear out of contact with the bolt. As the operating spring starts to drive the bolt forward, the bent on the front end of the sear slips over the bent on the trigger permitting the sear to return to its former position under action of the sear spring. This leaves it free to engage and hold the bolt when it is blown to the rear by the force of the explosion.

As the bolt is driven forward by the operating spring, either the right or the left upper feed piece machined in the bolt strikes the base of the first cartridge in the magazine and drives it straight ahead through the opening in the front end of the magazine lips.

The bullet nose is guided by the barrel feed into the firing chamber as the rear of the cartridge clears the lips of the magazine. As the cartridge enters the firing chamber, it lines up with the bolt enabling the head of the cartridge to seat in the base of the bolt head recess, in which the firing pin is machined.

The cartridge comes to rest when the front end of the case stops against the square shoulder at the front end of the chamber. As the cartridge comes to rest, the bolt continues forward to drive the firing pin against the primer and discharge the cartridge. At this time the extractor is sprung over the groove in the cartridge case.

The gases generated in the cartridge case drive the light bullet forward and exert rearward pressure through the base of the cartridge case to the base of the bolt head. The bolt starts to the rear but in view of the much greater weight of the moving parts and the spring tension in relation to the comparatively light bullet weight, the action does not open appreciably until the bullet has left the muzzle. By this time the breech pressure has dropped to safe limit.

When the bullet emerges from the muzzle, the gas behind it expands in the compensator.

The pressure wave thus created thrusts downward against the solid lower half of the compensator while the gases expanding upward strike against the inclined surfaces cut into the compensator to result in a forward and downward thrust at the muzzle end. This tends to hold the muzzle down during automatic fire.

(Note that the compensator merely acts to stabilize the gun. It has nothing whatever to do with the functioning of the weapon itself.)

As the bolt starts to the rear, the empty cartridge case is held in the bolt face gripped by the extractor. When it clears the chamber far enough, the upper face of the cartridge strikes the ejector (which in the Owen is a part of the rear magazine wall). The empty shell is hurled out the ejection opening which in this weapon is in the lower part of the receiver tube.

The bolt continues to travel to the rear in a straight line pressing the main spring or operating spring behind it until the rear face of the bolt is stopped against the receiver plug.

In this weapon the cocking handle and the cocking bolt are permitted to travel still further to the rear in the slotted hole provided for the bolt pin in the head of the cocking bolt. This action prevents a sudden shock on the bolt pin.

At this point the main spring is at practically full compression and it halts further rearward movement.

The sear spring forces the sear up to catch in the underside of the bolt, holding it ready for the next shot.

Trigger action. There are three projections on the trigger in the Owen which can engage with the sear. The upper projection locks the sear from rising if the change lever is set at the safe position. The central projection forms a bent which is accurately located from

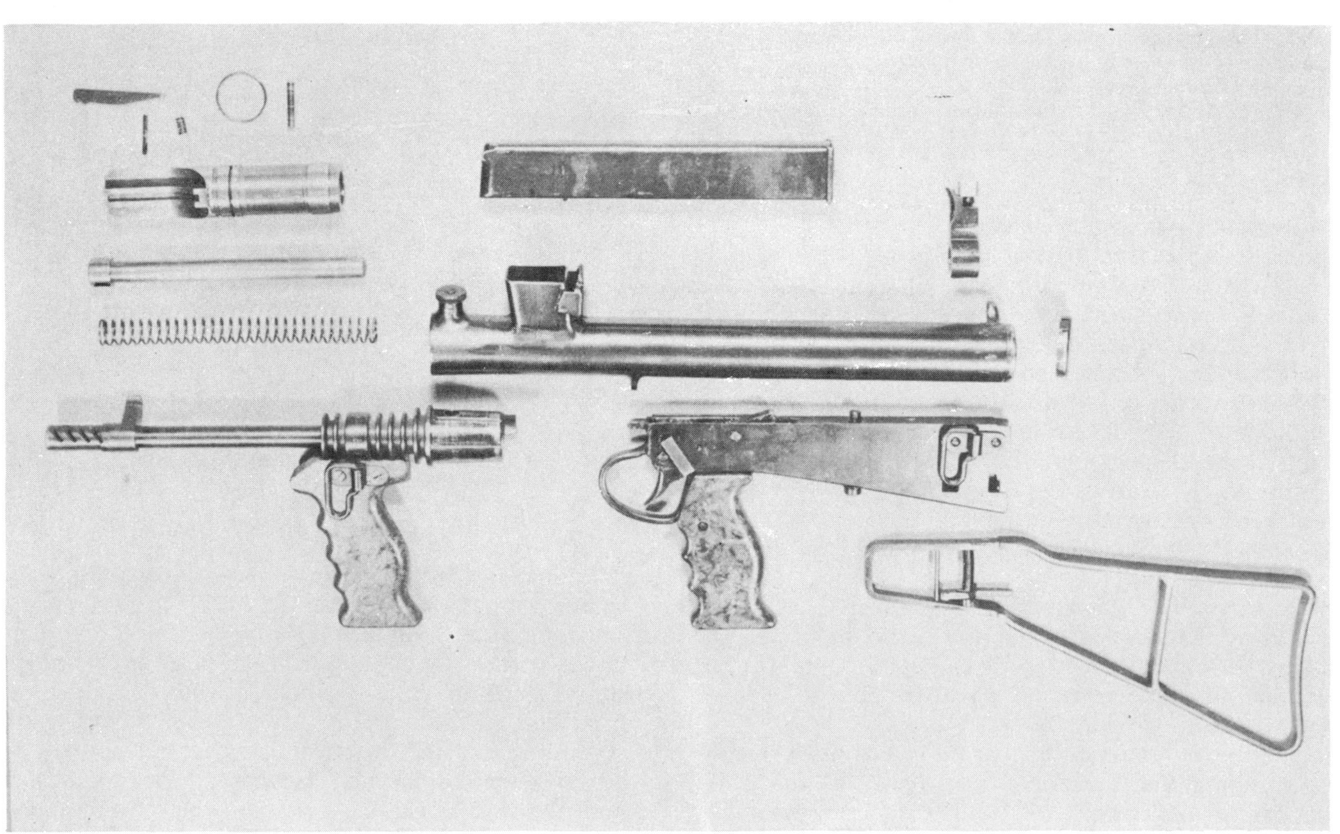

the trigger axis. When the change lever is adjusted to the single shot position, the rise of the trigger is strictly limited assuring that the sear will hold the bolt back on its first rearward movement. The lower projection engages the underface of the sear and carries one end of the trigger spring. It permits continuous fire.

The three surfaces on the change lever are in a circle and in turn engage the top of the trigger to limit the distance of rise. Thus on "safe" the trigger is locked; on "single shot" the rise of the trigger being limited, only one shot can be fired until the trigger is released and pulled back again; and on "rapid" or automatic fire the trigger is permitted full movement which permits the bolt to shuttle back and forth so long as cartridges are fed into the firing chamber and the trigger is kept depressed.

Special Note on the Owen

Two other varieties of this gun were issued. The first is called the "Mark I Wood Butt" type. This is a lightened version of the Mark I in which some of the metal is cut away from the receiver behind the rear grip and which is provided with a wooden butt. With the butt attached and the magazine empty this type weighs nine pounds and thirteen ounces, while without the butt and with the magazine empty it weighs eight pounds and fourteen ounces.

The second type of Owen is the Mark II. In this type the shape of the receiver to the rear of the rear hand grip is still further modified resulting in a weight with butt and empty magazine of only eight pounds and three ounces while without the butt it is only eight pounds. The trigger assembly differs from the Mark I.

9mm Submachine Gun (Aust) X3

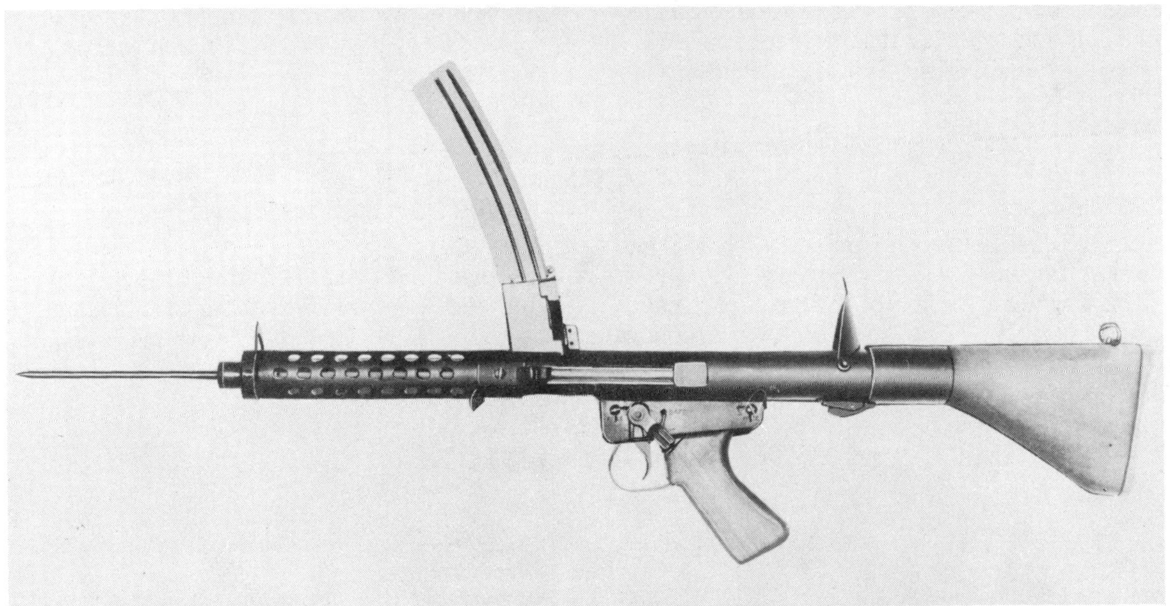

Left side view of the 9mm Submachine Gun with bayonet fixed.

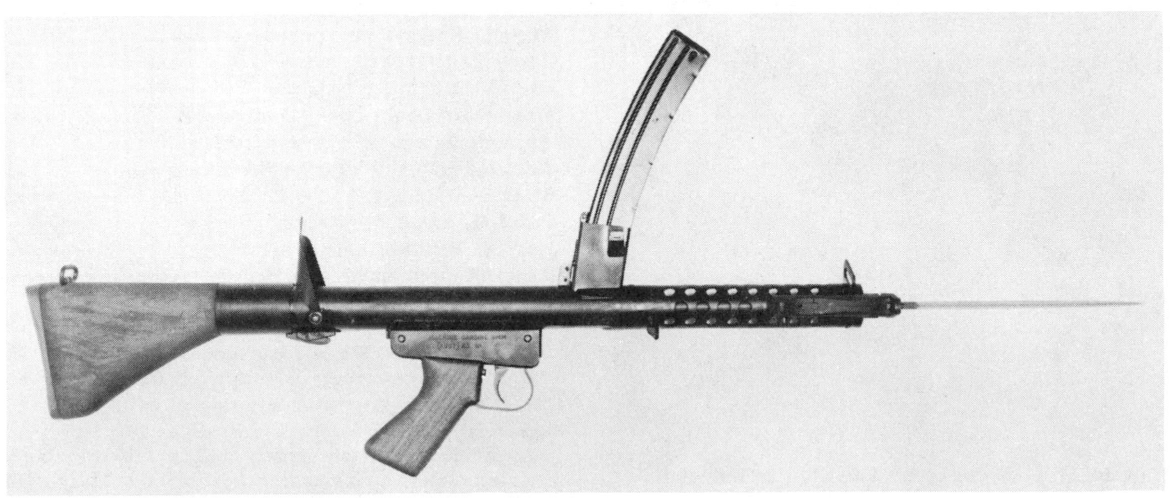

Right side view of X3 Submachine Gun with bayonet fixed.

Australia has been the most prolific designer of submachine guns among the Dominions of the British Commonwealth and all of the Australian designs have been eminently practical. In a desire to secure a weapon with the reliability of the Owen, but of lighter weight, lower rate of fire, and easier to produce, the Australians designed the X3.

Caliber: 9mm Parabellum.
System of Operation: Blowback, automatic fire only.
Weight, Loaded with Bayonet: 9.88 lbs.
Length, Overall: 28.12 in.
Feed Device: 34-round staggered detachable box magazine.
Sights: Front: Blade mounted on the right side of magazine guide.
Rear: Aperture in stamped leaf type sight.
Muzzle Velocity: Approx. 1300 f.p.s.
Cyclic Rate: 600 r.p.m.

The X3 has a separate cocking handle and cover which do not reciprocate with the bolt during firing. The pistol grip and butt plate are the same as those used on the Australian-made F.N. L1A1 rifle. The top loading magazine of the X3 is the same as that used on the British L2A3 and the Canadian C1 (the Sterling or Patchett submachine gun). The weapon has a bayonet lug on the left side.

Loading and Firing

Pull cocking handle to the rear. Insert a loaded magazine in the magazine guide on top of the receiver. Press trigger and the weapon will fire. To put the weapon on safe, push safety catch located on the left side of the pistol grip, to down position, word "Safe" will be exposed.

Australian Small Arms Developments

Since the establishment in 1912 of the Australian government rifle factory at Lithgow Australia has had the capacity to produce and design its own small arms. As with other members of the British Commonwealth, Australia has, on occasion, taken an independent tack in the development of small arms. The development of the X3 submachine gun is an example of this as was the nonacceptance by Australia of the rifle No. 4. Australia continued to manufacture the Rifle No. 1 Mark 3*, SMLE, through World War II and also developed some prototype light weight versions of that weapon during World War II.

CANADA

Canada was the first country to put the FN rifle into mass production (at Long Branch Arsenal, in Ontario Province). The Canadian version of the weapon is called Rifle, 7.62mm FN (C1). The heavy-barrel version of the FN NATO rifle is used by Canada as the squad automatic weapon and is called Automatic Rifle, 7.62mm F.N. (C2).

Canada has modified the British L2A3 submachine gun and is producing it as Submachine Gun, 9mm, C4. The U. S. Cal. .50 Browning machine gun is extensively used by Canada.

CANADIAN PISTOLS

9mm Browning FN Hi-Power of Canadian manufacture.

Used also by British and Chinese Forces.

Caliber: 9mm Ball Ammunition, flat point or round point (Cal. .35). Luger type.
Magazine: Box type, double line staggered. Capacity 13 cartridges.
Muzzle Velocity: 1040 to 1500 feet per second depending on type and manufacture of ammunition.
Weight of Bullet: Variable.
Muzzle Energy: 365 pounds average.
Barrel Length: 4.64 inches.
Overall Length: 7.34 inches.
Weight of Pistol: 2.06 pounds empty.
Accurate Range as a Pistol: About 50 yards.
Accurate Range with Shoulder Stock: About 200 yards.
Maximum Range: About 1200 yards.
Pistol Operated by: Recoil.
Locked: Parallel ruler system.
Type of Fire: Single shot only. Has positive disconnector.
Magazine Release Catch: Button on left side near trigger. Pressing it will eject magazine from handle.
Position of Slide When Last Shot is Fired: Open. Step on magazine follower forces slide stop up into locking notch in slide.
Safety. Thumb safety on left side of pistol.

Special Note: This pistol is issued in two types. (1) As a standard pistol with fixed sights, and a lanyard ring. (2) With a shoulder stock attachment similar to the Mauser Pistol. In this type the pistol is carried in a hollow inside the stock. Sights on this model are graduated to 500 meters.

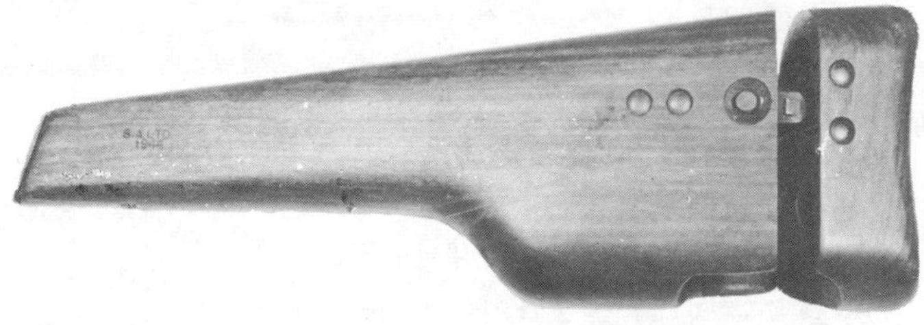

The shoulder stock attachment, also used as a holster with Pistol No. 1, Mark 1 and Mark 1*.

7.62mm Automatic Rifle F.N. C2

Caliber: 7.62mm NATO.
Weight Loaded (30 round magazine): 15.25 lbs.
Overall Length (normal butt): 44.75 in.
Barrel Length: 21 in.
Feed Device: 20 or 30 round box magazine.
Sights, Front—Protected post.
Rear—Tangent w/aperture graduated from 200-1000 yds.
Muzzle Velocity: 2800 f.p.s.
Cyclic Rate of Fire: 675-750 r.p.m.

The C2 is the heavy barreled selective fire version of the Canadian semiautomatic F.N. rifle C1. The method of operation and field strip of the C2 are similar to that of the C1. C2 like C1 has a prong type flash suppressor and can be fitted with a bayonet or grenade launcher. The bipod legs are fitted with wooden strips allowing the bipod to be used as a fore-end when in the folded position. Differences between the C2 and C1 rifles other than noted above are as follows:

a. The rear sight of C2 is different.
b. C2 has a bipod.
c. C2 has no hand guard.
d. C2 change lever has 3 positions safe, semiautomatic and automatic fire.
e. C2 gas block assembly includes a mounting for the bipod.

This weapon is the Canadian squad automatic weapon and has the advantage of using most of the components of the basic rifle including magazines.

C2 is, like C1, made at the Canadian government small arms plant at Long Branch, Ontario.

Ross Rifles

	Mark II	**Mark III**
Caliber:	.303	.303
Overall Length:	47.81 in.	50.5 in.
Barrel Length:	28 in.	30.5 in.
Feed Device:	5-round box magazine	5-round box magazine
Sights:		
Front:	Hooded blade	Hooded blade
Rear:	Tangent or leaf	Leaf
Muzzle Velocity: (at date of adoption)	2060 f.p.s.	2060 f.p.s.
Weight:	8.31 lbs.	9.75 lbs.

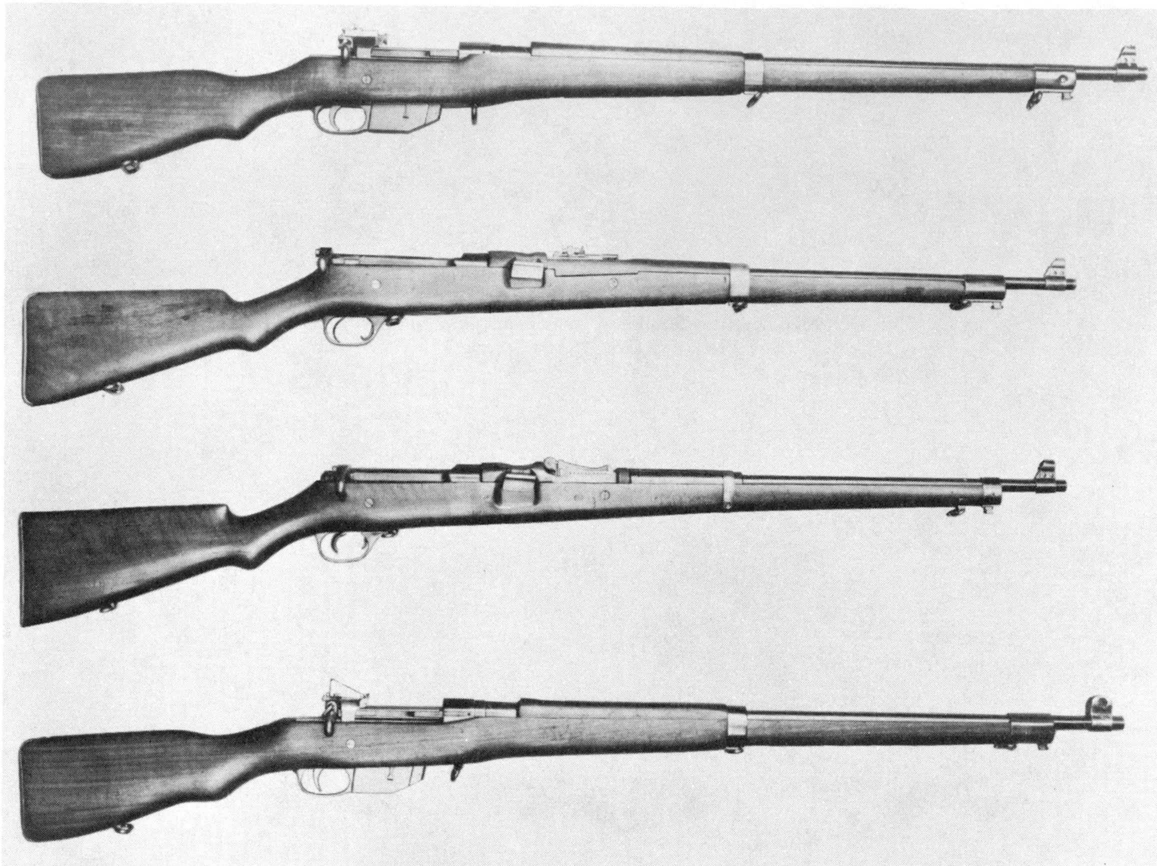

Top: Rifle, Ross, Mark III*, Cal. .303, Canada.
Upper center: Rifle, Ross, Mark II, Cal. .303, Canada.
Lower center: Rifle, Ross, Mark II*, Cal. .303, Canada.
Bottom: Rifle, Ross, Mark III, Cal. .303, Canada.

Canadian Rifles

Although these rifles have not been used as first line weapons since mid-World War I, there are still a fairly large number of them in circulation among collectors and sportsmen. There are two basic variations of the .303 Ross and a number of minor variations to the basic types; all are straight pull bolt actions. The Mark II, which is frequently called the Model 1905, has solid bolt locking lugs and the Harris type magazine. This magazine, which is flush with the stock, cannot be loaded with chargers. There is a magazine lifter thumb lever on the right side of the rifle ahead of the receiver. The Mark II may be found with tangent type sight or with leaf type sight. A cut-off projects into the forward part of the trigger guard. The Mark III has several variations in rear sights and front sights. The Mark III is frequently called the M1910. It is easily distinguished from the Mark II by its magazine which protrudes below the stock. The Mark III magazine can be loaded with a charger and the Mark III cut-off is mounted at the left rear of the receiver in the same position as that on the U.S. Springfield M1903. It also functions the same as that of the Springfield. The Mark III has locking lugs with interrupted screw thread.

Field Stripping. Mark II—Push down piece at left rear of receiver and remove bolt by pulling straight to the rear. The bolt is very difficult to disassemble and is best left alone since it can be assembled improperly with possible *fatal* results.

Mark III—Push cut-off into mid position and remove bolt by pulling straight to the rear. Remarks about Mark II bolt apply to Mark III as well.

Loading and Firing. Mark II—Pull bolt to the rear, press down on magazine lifter thumb lever with right thumb. Drop individual cartridges into magazine insuring that rim of upper cartridge is ahead of lower cartridge —rifle will jam badly if cartridges are not properly placed. Cut-off should be in top position if it is desired to use the rifle as a magazine loader. Push bolt forward and rifle is loaded. The safety is a knob mounted in bolt handle; when pushed to the left it locks the rifle on safe.

Mark III—Pull bolt straight to rear. Insert rear edge of charger in charger guide and press down on mid section of top cartridge with left thumb. Cartridges should strip into magazine and charger will fall from rifle. If cut-off is up, cartridge will feed into chamber when bolt is pushed forward and rifle will be loaded. Rifle can be loaded with single cartridges, observing precautions given under Mark II. The safety is a lever mounted on the bolt handle; when rotated forward, the rifle is on "safe."

Special Note on the Ross Rifles

The Ross rifles are well made of good materials, but they had several serious design defects which caused their abandonment as an infantry weapon by Canada in 1916. The action is suitable for sporting rifles, but was found eminently unsuited for the mud of Flanders. In an attempt to make up for the poor extracting qualities of these weapons when dirty, the chamber was relieved slightly. This makes the Ross a rather poor rifle for a hand loader since cases are badly stretched on firing.

The most serious problem with the Ross for the modern shooter is the fact that on most models the bolt can be reassembled wrong and yet put in the weapon and may fire a cartridge in an unlocked condition with resulting *serious injury, if not death* to the shooter. The bolt is assembled wrong if the distance between the bolt head and the bolt sleeve is less than one inch when the bolt is withdrawn from the rifle (bolt in unlocked posture). The bolt is exceedingly difficult to disassemble and reassemble and it is best to take it to a gunsmith if in doubt.

INDIA

During the period between World Wars I and II, the Indian Army, then a semi-autonomous branch of the British Army, adopted the cal. .303 Vickers Berthier Light Machine Gun Mark III. This weapon is still in use in India. It is quite similar in construction and external appearance to the Bren. The main differences between the Bren and the Berthier lie in the breechblock, the feed, the holding-open device, the gas cylinder arrangement, the barrel change, and the sights.

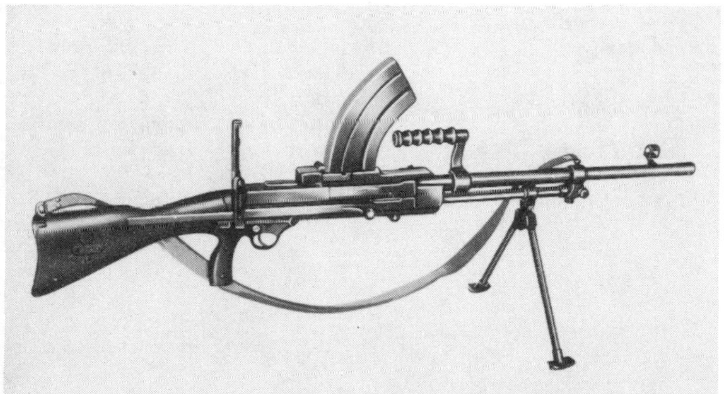

Cal. .303 Vickers Berthier Mark III.

Caliber: .303 British.
Weight, loaded: 24.4 lb.
Overall length: 45.5 in.
Barrel length: 23.9 in.
Feed mechanism: 30-round, detachable, staggered box magazine.
Sights: Front: Hooded blade.
Rear: Leaf.
Muzzle velocity: 2400 f.p.s. w/Mk 7 ball (approx).

NEW ZEALAND

The Lithgow Small Arms factory in New South Wales, Australia, is making FN NATO rifles for New Zealand as well as for Australia. New Zealand has adopted the L2A3 submachine gun.

OTHER COMMONWEALTH MEMBERS

Other major members of the Commonwealth, such as Pakistan and South Africa, are mainly equipped with British weapons of World War II origin. United States weapons, however, are being furnished to some of these countries—notably Pakistan—under defense agreements. Insofar as small arms are concerned, the United States weapons are usually confined to cal. .30 Browning and cal. .50 Browning machine guns mounted on armored vehicles.

Chapter 18. Chile

Chile has adopted the F.N. 7.62mm light and heavy barrel rifles as standard. In addition they have purchased SIG weapons, German 7.62mm MG42/59s and have a quantity of U. S. cal. .30 M1 rifles and cal. .30 carbines. They also have a number of 7mm Madsen machine guns.

Chilean Rifles

As a result of Chile's adoption of the F.N. rifle, United States arms dealers have purchased quantities of Chilean Mausers which are now in this country in quantity for the first time.

Special Note on Chilean Mausers

The Chilean Mausers are generally similar to the Spanish M1893 Mauser. The specimens imported into the United States are all of German manufacture, and are of good finish and materials. Loading, firing, field stripping and functioning is the same as other bolt action Mausers. It should be noted that the Chilean M95, as the Spanish M1893, does not have a bolt sleeve lock. Therefore in field stripping, the bolt sleeve assembly will turn off easily when the bolt is withdrawn with safety in the middle position (straight up).

There is also a Chilean M95 short rifle which falls between the rifle and carbine in length and weight.

	M1895 Rifle	M1895 Carbine
Caliber:	7mm	7mm
System of Operation:	Manually operated bolt action.	Manually operated bolt action.
Weight:	8.9 lbs.	Approx. 7.5 lbs.
Length, Overall:	48.5 in.	37 in.
Barrel Length:	29.06 in.	18.25 in.
Feed device:	5-round, non-detachable staggered box magazine.	5-round, non-detachable staggered box magazine.
Sights: Front	Barleycorn.	Barleycorn.
Rear	Leaf.	Leaf.
Muzzle Velocity:	Approx. 2700 f.p.s.	Approx. 2600 f.p.s.

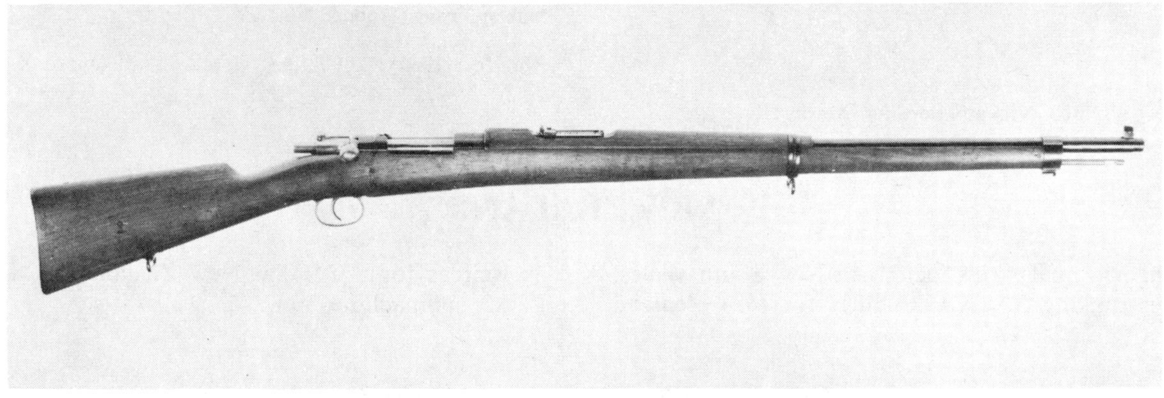

Chilean 7mm M1895 Rifle. Specimens with turned down bolts also exist.

Chilean 7mm M1895 Carbine.

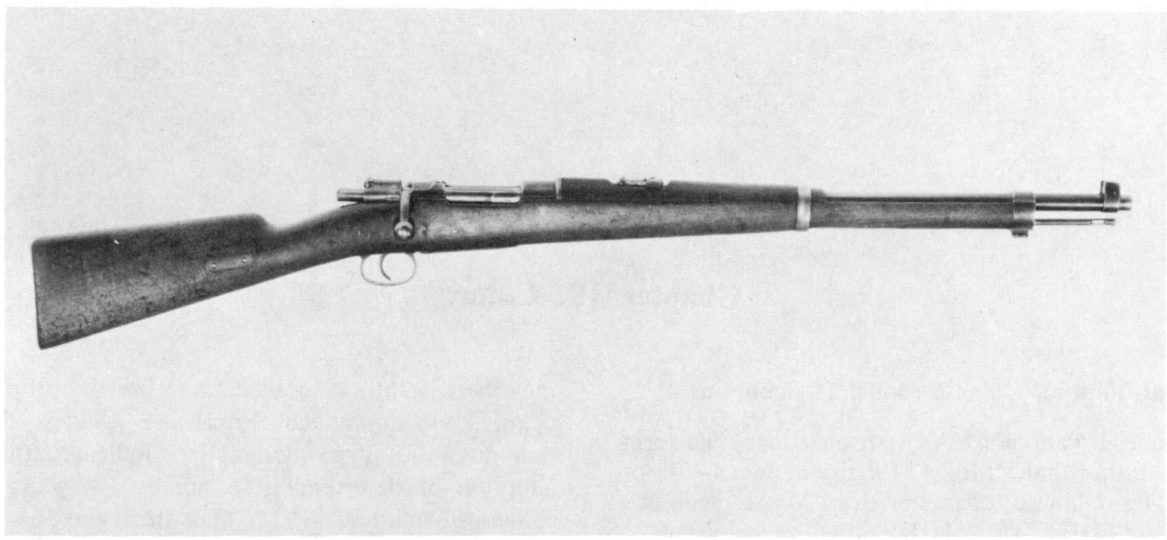

Chilean 7mm M1895 Short Rifle.

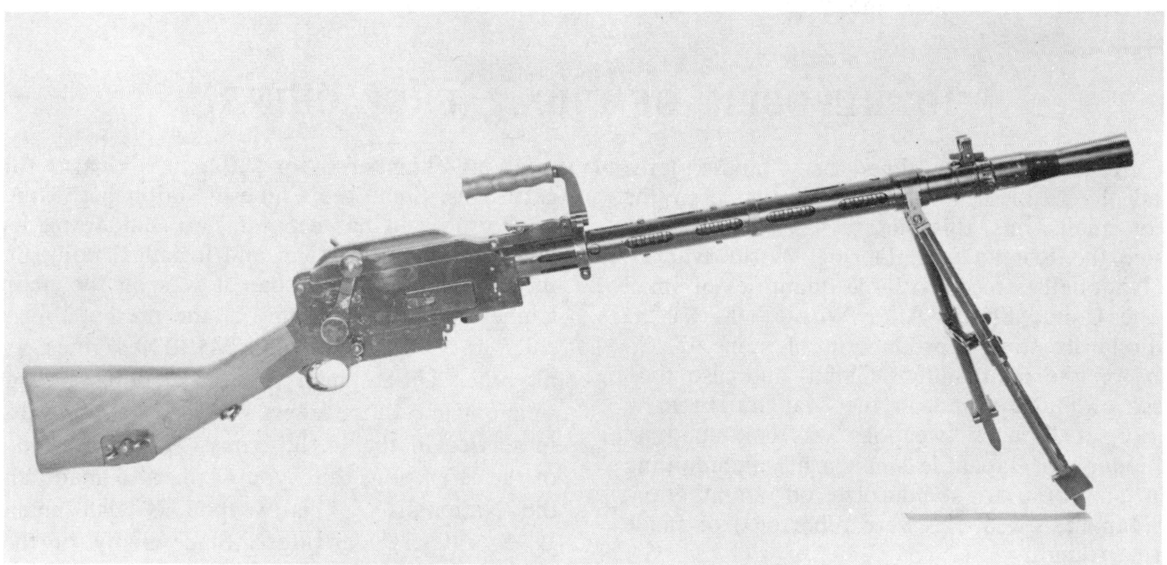

Chilean 7mm Madsen Machine Gun.

Chapter 19. China

Special Note on Chinese Model Designations

THE Chinese Nationalist Army usually uses the term "Type" rather than "Model" for the nomenclature of weapons. The Chinese character for "Type" can be translated as "SHIH" or "SHIKI" and is the same as that used by the Japanese. Since a type designation may be followed by a model designation to indicate a modification (as with the old Japanese system, for example, the Type 34 Model 1), Chinese markings on weapons must be carefully examined to secure the proper nomenclature. On many (but not all) Chinese Nationalist weapons, the Type designation indicates the date of adoption of the weapon in number of years since the Chinese revolution—1911. Thus the Type 36 submachine gun was adopted in 1947, the Type 41 light machinegun was adopted in 1952. The Chinese Communists, however, use the calendar year designation, i.e., 51 for 1951, etc.

THE REPUBLIC OF CHINA (FREE CHINA)

Although for a period of time the Chinese (free Chinese) and the Chinese Communist armies used the same types of small arms, this picture has changed considerably since the Korean war. During World War II, the Chinese Nationalists received large quantities of small arms from the United States. After World War II, the Chinese Nationalists started production of some U. S.-type weapons on the mainland of China, and also took over Japanese ordnance plants in the Manchurian area. The production of Japanese weapons was continued, as was the production of Japanese small arms ammunition. However, in an effort to standardize on ammunition, some of the Japanese weapons were rebarreled or made for 7.92mm cartridges.

Thus, at the time the Chinese Nationalists were forced to leave the mainland, they had some of their earlier weapons chambered for the 7.92mm cartridge, American weapons chambered for U. S. cartridges, and Japanese weapons chambered for 7.92mm and also for Japanese cartridges. Since the Chinese Nationalist Army has been on Formosa, it has been able to standardize its weapons, and is, from a technical and logistical point of view, immeasurably better off than it was on the mainland. The Chinese Nationalist Army at the present time uses U. S. cal. .30 M1, M1903, and M1903A4 rifles. It also uses all other U. S. small arms, excepting 7.62mm NATO weapons and those others which are not as yet completely in service in the U. S. Army. A Chinese-modified copy of the Bren gun, the Type 41, is also made and used by the Nationalists. This weapon is also chambered for U. S. cal. .30 cartridges. Since many of the Chinese-made or Chinese-modified weapons are still in being (although not accepted as standard anywhere), a short description of these weapons, and illustrations of some of them, are included in this section.

CHINESE PISTOLS

As with all other small arms, the Chinese had a wide collection of pistols. The Mauser in 7.63mm was a great favorite, and Chinese-made copies of the Mauser in cal. .45 have been encountered. During World War II, the United States supplied the Chinese with cal. .45 M1911A1 automatics, Colt and Smith & Wesson M1917 revolvers, as well as some cal. .38 revolvers. The Canadians supplied the Chinese with the 9mm Browning Hi-Power pistol made by John Inglis in Toronto.

CHINESE RIFLES

The pre-World War II Republic of China had many rifles in service. The oldest was probably the Type 88 or Hanyang rifle as it was called from its place of manufacture. This weapon is a copy of the German M1888 rifle, large quantities of which were sold to China by Germany after the Germans adopted the Model 98 rifle. This rifle is chambered for the old 7.92mm x 57mm rimless cartridge, and has a .318 bore rather than the .323 bore of the 98 and later 7.92mm weapons. Therefore, this weapon should not be used with 7.92mm x

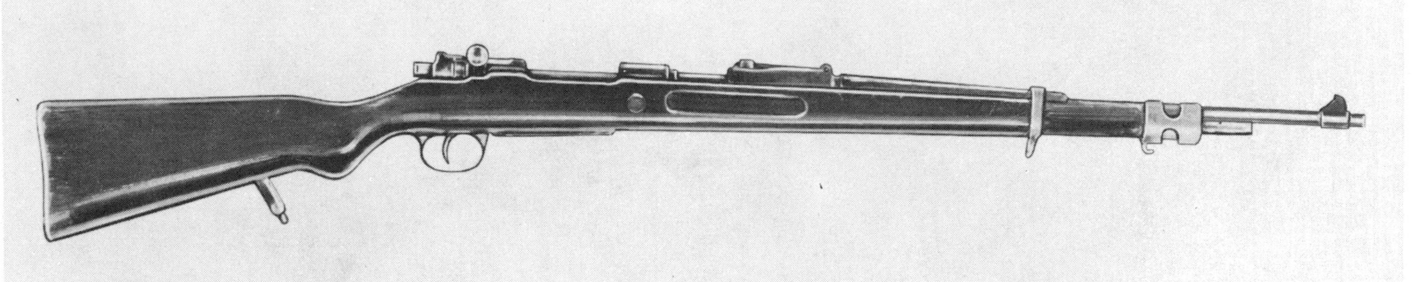

Chinese-Made "Chiang Kai Shek" 7.92mm Rifle. This weapon is a copy of the "Standard Model" Mauser.

57mm IS (sometimes called JS) ammunition. The Chinese issued a special conical-nosed ball cartridge for this weapon. It should also be noted that Chinese weapons of pre-World War II manufacture are widely variable in quality of materials and construction. Chinese weapons manufactured since World War II are, so far as can be determined, made of first-class materials and show fine workmanship. Other Chinese rifles of this period are:

7.92mm Belgian FN M1924 and M1930 rifles, and Chinese copies.

7.92mm Czechoslovak Brno M1924 rifles, and Chinese copies.

The Mauser 7.92mm "Standard Model," a Mauser export model which was copied by the Chinese and is called the "Generalissimo" or "Chiang Kai Shek" model. All of the above weapons were encountered in the hands of Chinese Communist troops in Korea.

CHINESE SUBMACHINE GUNS

The most common submachine guns in the Chinese Army prior to and during World War II were:

All the models of the U. S. Thompson in cal. .45 (frequently called 11mm by the Chinese) plus a Chinese-made copy of the 1921 Thompson.

The U. S. M3 and M3A1, and a Chinese copy of the M3A1 called the Type 36, in cal. .45, and Type 37 in 9mm Parabellum.

British Stens chambered for the 9mm Parabellum cartridge. The Chinese also made some copies of these.

The Thompson, the M3A1, and the Type 36 are still in use in the Chinese Nationalist Army.

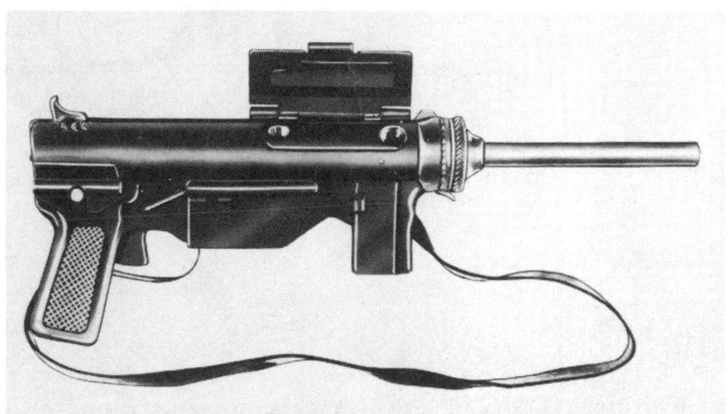

Type 36 Submachine Gun. A caliber .45 Chinese-made copy of the U. S. M3A1 submachine gun. Similar weapons in 9mm Parabellum were made by the Chinese.

CHINESE MACHINE GUNS

The Chinese used a wide variety of machine guns prior to and during World War II. Most of these weapons again appeared in Korea during the early stages of the Chinese Communist commitment. The most common weapons were:

The Chinese-made Type 24 heavy machine gun. This 7.92mm weapon is a modification of the German Maxim Model 08, (MG 08).

Czechoslovak- and Chinese-made 7.92mm ZB 26 and ZB30 light machine guns. These weapons were called Type 26 and Type 30 by the Chinese.

Swiss SIG-made KE 7 light machine guns in 7.92mm caliber.

Danish Madsen-made 7.92mm light machine guns.

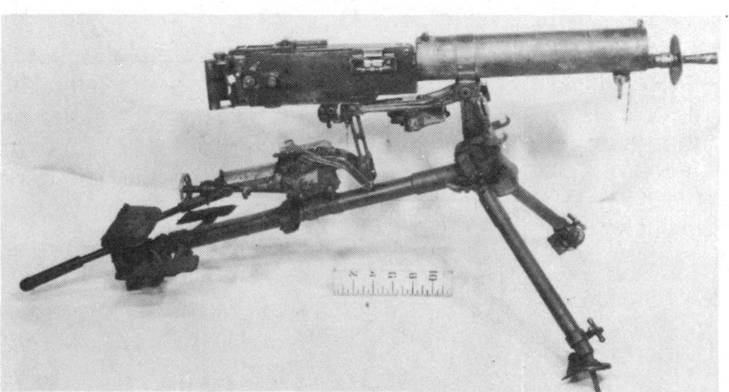

Chinese-made Type 24 Heavy Machine Gun. A 7.92mm weapon similar to the German 08 Maxim gun.

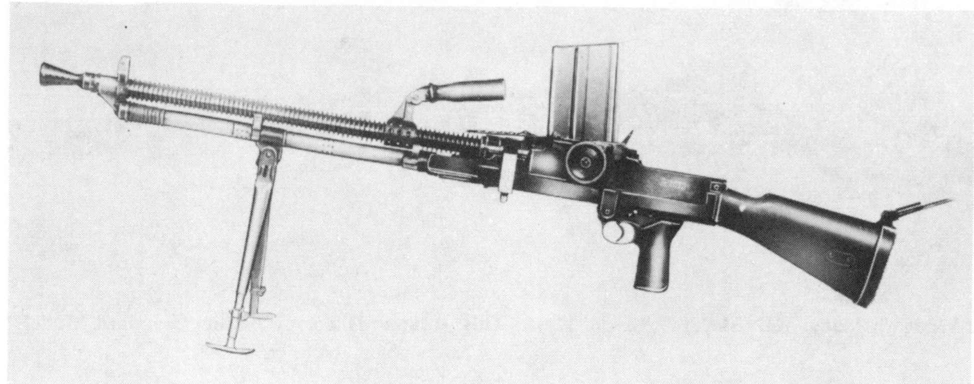

Chinese-made 7.92mm Type 26 Light Machine Gun. A copy of the Czech ZB26.

Chinese-made Type 41 Light Machine Gun. Bren modified for U. S. Caliber .30 cartridge.

Colt and FN-made Browning automatic rifles, also chambered for the 7.92mm cartridge. There apparently were not too many of these.

Colt and FN-made Browning watercooled machine guns in 7.92mm. These were also apparently in short supply.

7.92mm Bren guns Mk. 2, made in Canada for the Chinese during World War II.

The list given above is by no means complete. When one considers purchases, Lend-Lease, war booty, etc., the Chinese Army was a gun collector's paradise and an ammunition supply officer's nightmare. All the standard United States machine guns and most of the standard British machine guns were in wide use before the end of World War II.

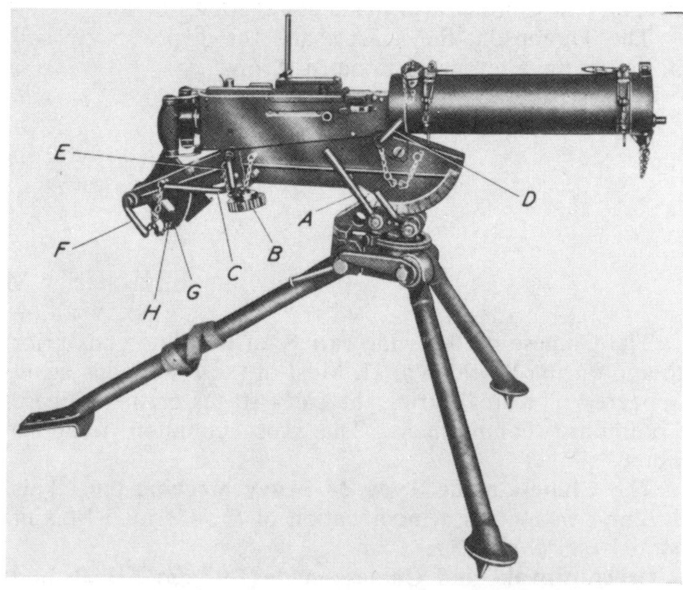

Colt Model 38B Machine Gun. Modified Browning M1917A1. Supplied to China in 7.92mm before World War II.

COMMUNIST CHINA

At the conclusion of World War II, the Chinese Communists inherited large quantities of Japanese weapons from the Soviets, who had taken them in Manchuria. During the Chinese civil war, they captured respectable quantities of materiel from the Chinese Nationalists, in-

7.62mm Chinese Tokarev Pistol Type 51, a copy of Soviet TT M1933 Tokarev.

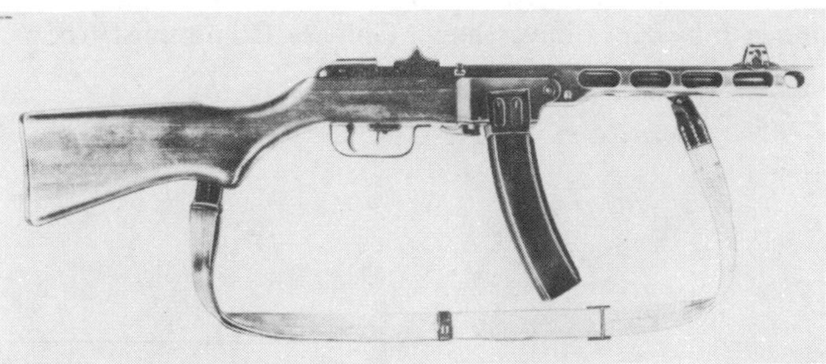

Type 50 7.62mm Submachine Gun. A copy of the Soviet PPSh M1941.

cluding quantities of U. S. weapons. When the Chinese Communists entered the Korean War, they had far more Chinese, Japanese, and U. S. materiel in the battle area than Soviet materiel. However, battle losses, breakages, and probably the impossibility of fighting a war of attrition like the Korean War with their crazy-quilt weapons system, resulted in the Chinese Communists ending the Korean War with far more Soviet equipment than any other type.

The Chinese Communists used all the Soviet pre-World War II and World War II weapons in Korea. They also put some of these weapons into production, using their own year of adoption as their model designations. The Soviet 7.62mm PPSh M1941 submachine gun was produced by the Chinese Communists as the Type 50. This weapon is basically the same as the Soviet weapon covered in chapter 43. The major difference between the Chinese- and the Soviet-made guns is that the former will not accommodate the drum magazine; it is made for the box magazine only. The Soviet 7.62mm TT M1933 pistol was adopted and put into production as the Type

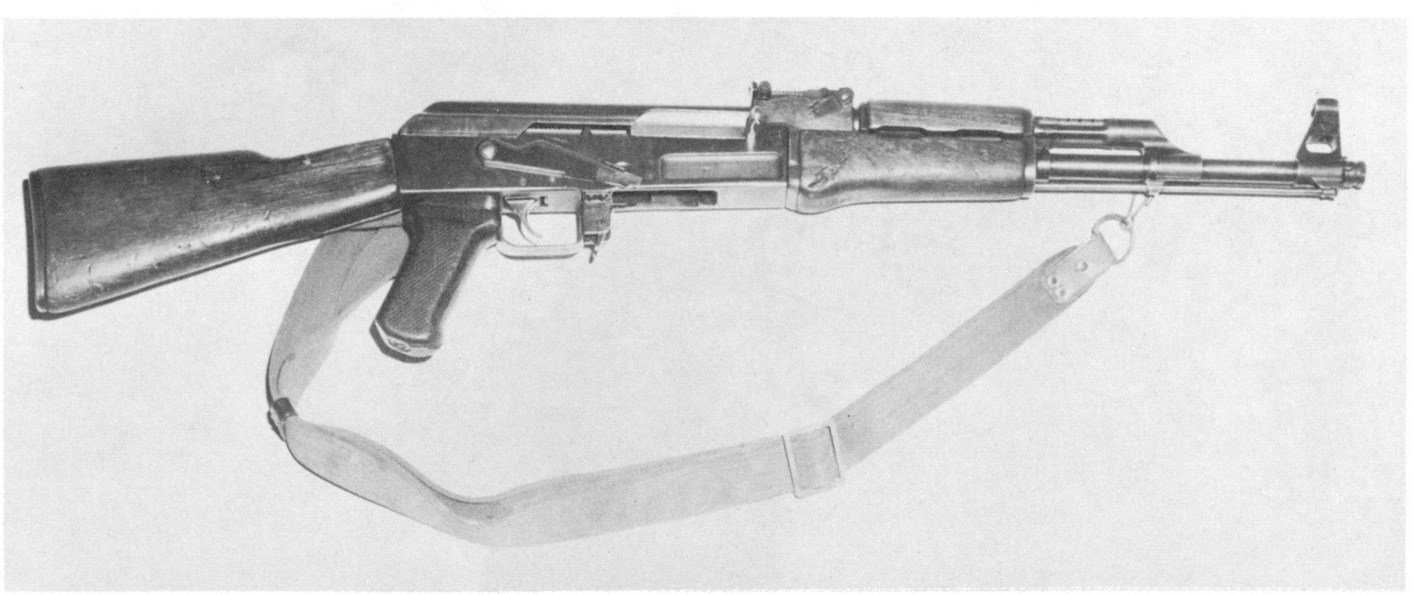

Chinese Communist-made 7.62mm Type 56 (AK) Assault Rifle.

51, and the Soviet M1944 Mosin Nagant carbine was put into production as the Type 53.

Within the last year, photographs in Chinese Communist magazines have shown Chinese Communist troops armed with the postwar Soviet weapons, the AK, RPD, and SKS, which are called Type 56 in China. It is considered likely that the Chinese Communist Army will be, in time, standardized on all the new Soviet small arms.

Cuba

Cuba is currently reported to have the largest Army in the Western Hemisphere barring that of the United States. It is therefore appropriate that the coverage of this book be broadened to include Cuba. The Cuban Army was, prior to the seizure of power by Fidel Castro, mainly equipped with U.S. small arms. The U.S. caliber .30 M1903 Springfield rifle and the U.S. caliber .30 M1 rifle were used as were U.S. Browning machine guns. Purchases were made of Belgian 7.62mm NATO "FAL" F.N. Rifles and 7.62mm NATO M.A.G. machine guns prior to the western nations' embargo on arms shipments to Cuba.

Cuba has been receiving arms shipments from the Soviet bloc on a very substantial scale for the past several years. Soviet bloc small arms displayed in parades and newsreels by the Cubans include the following: Czech 7.92mm Model 37 machine guns, Czech 12.7mm Quad DShK M1938/46 machine guns, Soviet 7.62mm DP, DT, and DTM machine guns, Soviet 7.62mm SG-43 Goryunov machine guns, Czech 9mm Model 23 and 25 submachine guns and Czech 7.62mm Model 52 rifles. It should be noted that little of this equipment is considered to be the latest or best of the Bloc's small arms. The multiplicity of types and calibers of weapons currently in use in Cuba presents them with a very large logistical headache from the point of view of weapon maintenance and ammunition supply. Although Cuba has the capability to produce limited amounts of spare parts it is not economically or industrially feasible for them to produce spares for all the weapons types they have.

All the weapons mentioned above are fully covered in the chapters on their countries of origin.

Chapter 20. Czechoslovakia

SINCE the country was founded at the conclusion of World War I, Czechoslovakia has been a prolific producer of small arms and of new designs in small arms. Since World War II, the Czechoslovaks have developed a new family of small arms. Although these weapons do not have any revolutionary features, they do show, in some cases, very thorough design work.

The Czechoslovaks introduced a new 7.62mm cartridge, the Model 52. This cartridge, like the new Soviet M1943 rimless cartridge, is intermediate (that is, between the United States rifle and carbine cartridges) in size. The Czechoslovak M52 cartridge, however, is not interchangeable with the Soviet M1943 or any other 7.62mm cartridge. (Inasmuch as Czechoslovakia is a Soviet satellite and a member of the Warsaw Pact, her use of a cartridge which is not used by the Soviet Union was rather peculiar. The Czechoslovak Model 52 cartridge has a 132-grain bullet which attains a muzzle velocity of 2440 feet per second with the Model 52 rifle. In 1957 the Czechs adopted the Soviet 7.62mm M43 cartridge.

The Czechoslovaks have also adopted the Soviet 7.62mm pistol cartridge, which they use in a submachine gun and a pistol. They also are making and using the Soviet Goryunov machine gun, which is chambered for the older Soviet 7.62mm rimmed cartridge, and the Soviet 12.7mm DShK M1938/46 heavy machine gun.

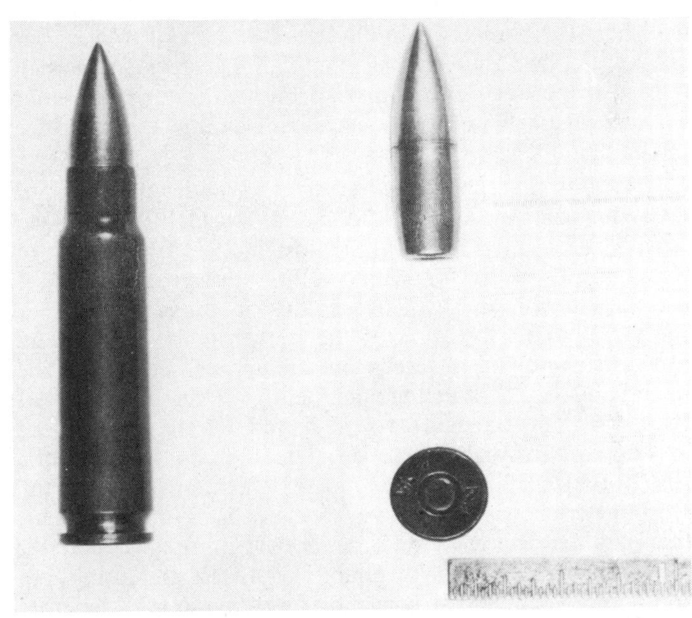

Model 52 7.62mm Czech Cartridge.

CZECHOSLOVAK PISTOLS

Caliber: 9mm Parabellum.
Magazine Capacity: 8 cartridges.
Ballistics: Standard for use of this cartridge in pistol.
Barrel Length: 4.63 inches.
Weight: 2.09 pounds.
Locked: Short-recoil, swing-down barrel, Browning pattern system with top lugs engaging in slide recesses.
Safety: No manual safety provided.
Magazine: Detachable straight line box in butt. Catch at bottom of grip.
Special Features: Mechanical double action hammer firing only. Hammer actuated by trigger and springs for all shots, not by slide recoil as in standard semi-auto practice.

This pistol is a locked modification of the earlier design listed variously as the CZ-37Z and the CZ38, the elementary unlocked blowback arm. The unlocked blowback used the 9mm Browning (or .380 Colt automatic pistol) cartridge.

Czech CZ-47 self-loading pistol. Locked breech. Mechanical double action firing at all times.

The firing mechanism and the general lines of the original pistol have been followed to a considerable degree in the new model, though the use of the powerful 9mm Parabellum cartridge made the addition of a locked breech mechanism advisable. The pitch of the grip and the stocks have also been modified to improve them.

Operation

Loading is standard. The magazine is loaded and then inserted in the butt. The slide is manually drawn to the end of the recoil stroke and released to chamber the first cartridge. The small exposed hammer cannot be thumb cocked. There is no holding sear. It has only a double action lever hookup to the trigger. This system gives extreme simplification of mechanism, but results in an extremely heavy and entirely too long pull for any degree of accuracy except at very close quarters.

When the trigger is pulled, the attached trigger bar rotates the hammer to the length of its stroke and then slips it to permit the hammer spring to drive the hammer forward against the firing pin and discharge the cartridge in the chamber.

The barrel recoils locked to the slide in standard Colt-Browning practice. After about ¼ inch of rearward travel, the slotted lug on the underside of the rear of the barrel, as in Browning High Power practice, is cammed down, in this case against a cross member in the frame. This lowering of the barrel at the breech end draws the locking surfaces on the upper section of the barrel out of their engagement cuts in the underside of the slide. The barrel travel is halted by the cross piece in standard Browning practice. The slide continues to the rear to extract and eject in normal fashion, carrying the hammer back with it. However, there is no holding sear; the hammer follows the slide down in forward counter recoil movement, but is unable to reach the firing pin for continued firing. Each shot fired requires a separate trigger pull.

The design does not require a disconnector in the standard sense of short-recoil weapons, since the hammer is not held back. Instead, when the trigger is released, springs react to bring the trigger bar once again into position to grip the cocking spur on the hammer to rotate it back to its release limit for the next shot.

The pitch of the grip has been modified from earlier designs, obviously influenced by the P-38 German design.

Sights are fixed and of conventional design. Extraction and ejection are conventional.

Dismounting

Pull down the locking catch at upper left hand side of triggerguard. Thrust slide assembly forward about ¼ inch and raise. This will lift the slide and barrel assemblies out of the receiver. Barrel, recoil springs, and bushings may then be withdrawn. Removal of stocks affords access to trigger mechanism.

This is distinctly a close quarters weapon, the trigger pull making accurate shooting at any considerable pistol range all but impossible. This factor, in the opinion of most qualified military observers, completely nullifies the advantages of the mechanical simplification of the firing system employed. This weapon is not used by the Czech Army and is not in wide use anywhere.

Catch lowered and magazine withdrawn to permit slide and barrel assembly to lift out.

Czech Model 1927 Service Pistol.

Characteristics: This is an elementary blowback pistol for the 7.65mm Browning (.32 Colt Auto) cartridge. It is a composite design using the Colt-Browning system of barrel mounting and a form of Mauser pocket pistol firing mechanism adapted to use of a small external hammer. There is no grip safety. The manual safety is similar to that of the German Mauser Pistol Model 1910. Pushing down a lever on the left side to the rear of the trigger sets the safety. Pressing a button below the lever releases the safety.

Length 6.3″. Weight 25 ounces. Magazine 8 rounds.

Identification: Mauser 1910 safety with small external hammer. Special dismounting piece above triggerguard on left. Mauser type left side plate. Military models are commonly 1927. All are the same mechanically.

Evaluation: Well made of excellent materials. From a design standpoint they are inferior to American type in being more complicated, having no automatic grip safety, and relatively easier to jam through dirt entering mechanism. Safe and sturdy within their limitations.

Ammunition: .32 Colt Auto ammunition.

Czech 9mm Model 22 Pistol.

Model 22, Model 24, and Model 26 are locked breech pistols, chambered for the Czech 9mm M22 (.380 ACP) cartridge.

This pistol breech lock is a variant of the Steyr 1911 pistol. The barrel has lugs just ahead of the chamber. Two lugs on opposite sides lock into the slide. A cam lug on the bottom of the barrel travels in a cam cut in a special removable block positioned in the receiver extension. A stop lug is provided to halt barrel travel when the cam lug running in its cut turns the barrel enough to disengage the locking lugs from the slide. The slide then travels back by itself to eject and compress the recoil spring. The magazine is the standard detachable box. On forward movement of the slide, as the barrel is forced slightly ahead, the barrel cam lug is compelled to follow its cut in the block and turn the barrel until the locking lugs engage.

The firing mechanism in general follows the 1927 Model, being a Mauser system adapted to a small exposed hammer.

Evaluation. This is a well-made pistol constructed of the best materials. By American standards it is of complicated design. Its chief failing is found in the fact that the cartridge is not powerful enough to require a locked breech. The recoil spring is necessarily light. By the time the pistol has unlocked, residual pressure in the barrel is not always sufficient to blow the slide fully back. This results in poor ejection or feeding jams. At times, the light spring will fail to completely close the action, particularly if ammunition is dirty or is not up to standard.

Ammunition. 9mm Browning Short—.380 Colt Auto.

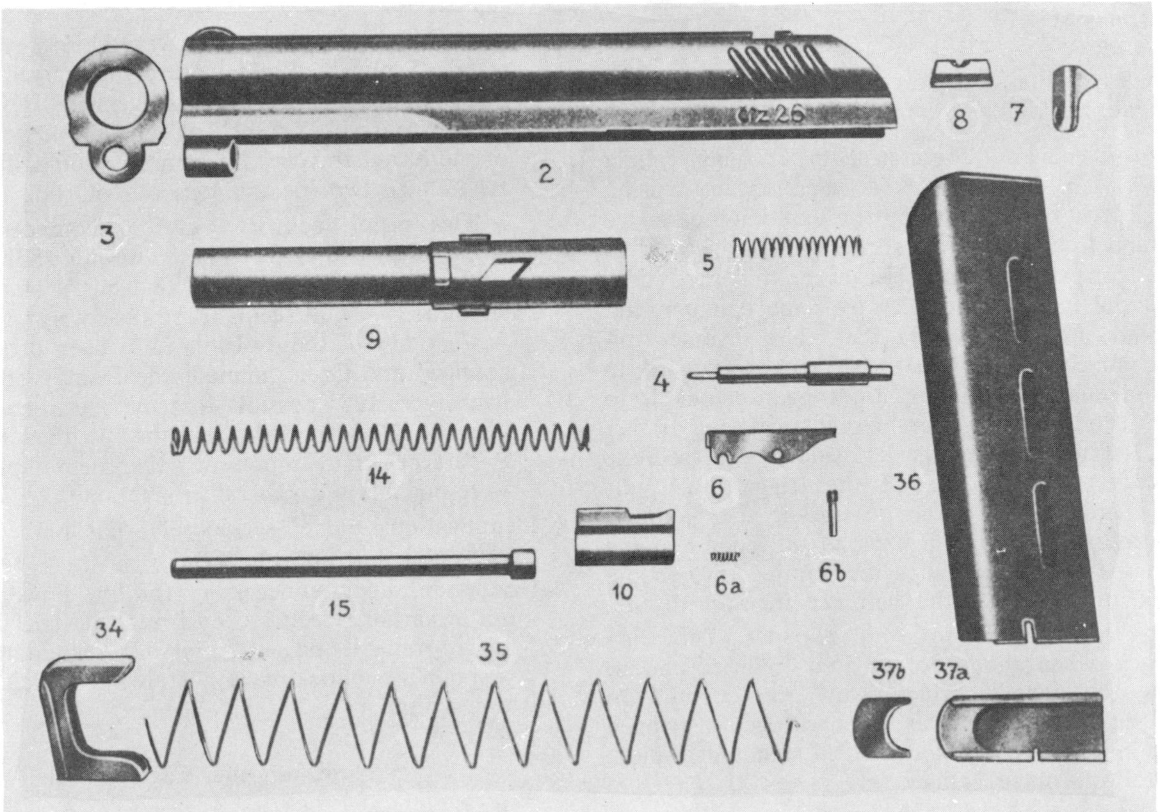

Details of slide and magazine components. No. 10 is a removable block which is placed in the receiver extension above the trigger. The guide lug on the barrel rests in a cam cut on top of this block to compel the barrel to turn.

Czech M1938 Double Action Pistol.

This pistol as commonly encountered is a blowback arm in which the small exposed hammer follows the slide down after every shot. Each shot is fired by a pull on the trigger which raises and drops the hammer as in double action revolver fire.

Early specimens, which may be experimental only, may have hammer which is held cocked when slide goes forward. Experimental pistols of the same external construction are also encountered with locked breech on revolving barrel system.

Three types of this design are known. All look alike on the outside, but differ in construction.

Type 1. This is the most common form. Common caliber is 9mm Czech. It resembles a standard auto pistol, and its slide is blown back by the exploding cartridge to eject and to compress the recoil spring which drives the slide forward to load. However, this slide does not cock the hammer. It rides over the hammer, but there is no standard holding sear. The hammer follows the slide down as the slide moves forward to reload the chamber. Pulling the trigger causes it to pivot on its pin and to exert a pull on a long trigger bar which extends along the left side of the receiver. A hook on the rear end of the trigger bar pulls against a projection on the bottom of the hammer. The hammer is thus drawn back to full cock and the hook on the trigger bar slips the hammer projection. The mainspring rotates the hammer forward to fire.

This is a blowback form of reloader. The slide blows back when the pistol is fired to eject and to compress the recoil spring below the barrel. On forward slide movement the top cartridge is stripped from the magazine and chambered in standard fashion. The barrel, of course, is fixed.

This pistol is held open when empty as the magazine follower catches the slide. When the magazine is withdrawn the slide moves forward. It must be manually pulled back to reload the chamber when a loaded magazine has been placed in the handle.

The slide mountings and take down are unique. A stud on the left side of the receiver above the trigger is pushed forward to unlock the slide and barrel assemblies. The muzzle of the barrel is supported in a hinged mounting against which the front of the slide abuts, the unit being hinged to the extreme front end of the receiver extension. Hence the slide and barrel can be raised as a unit when unlocked. The slide may be drawn back off the barrel. The barrel itself remains pinned into the hinged stop, but can be cleaned as easily as though removed in standard practice.

Identification. Small external hammer will not stay cocked when slide is pulled back and released. Raising slide will disclose if barrel is pinned at front end.

Evaluation. Excellent materials and workmanship. Excellent takedown. Heavy and clumsy for the power of its cartridge. This hammer design is favored for cavalry use in some European quarters, since there is less danger of squeezing off an accidental shot if the horse shies. For American use, the trick trigger pull is too long and unsatisfactory.

Ammunition. 9mm Browning Short; pistol will use .380 Colt Auto cartridge.

Type 2. Identical in every respect to Type 1 except for a holding sear. Trigger bar and projection pull hammer from full cock when slide closes and trigger is pulled.

Type 3. Externally this design very closely resembles the standard blowback. However, the barrel, instead of being pinned in to prevent movement, is free to slide in the front yoke. A helical cam lug on the underside of the barrel travels in a cam cut, compelling the barrel to turn two locking lugs out of slide engagement.

This pistol lock is a curious composite of early Roth-Steyr and later Czech turning barrel designs. An earlier type stamped 1928 using a standard single action trigger pull seems to be the forerunner.

Very few of these pistols have been brought to this country, and Czech manuals deal only with the blowback type. It is possible that the specimens examined, like the Mauser HSV and the Walther Hammerless P-38 types, may represent experimental pistols which were not put into general production.

Identification. Barrel set loosely, not pinned. Locking, cam, and stop lugs on barrel.

Evaluation. Lock unnecessary for low power cartridges. As in earlier Czech locked breech designs, functioning is not reliable because pressure remaining in barrel at point of unlocking is not always sufficient to function action.

Note on Other Czech Pistols

6.35mm Czech pistols use .25 Colt Auto cartridges.
7.65mm Czech pistols use .32 Colt Auto cartridges.
9mm Br. Short pistols use .380 Colt Auto cartridges.

Czechoslovak 7.62mm Model 52 Pistol.

Caliber: 7.62mm pistol cartridge.
System of operation: Recoil, semi-automatic fire only.
Weight, loaded: 2.31 lb.
Length, overall: 8.25 in.
Barrel length: 4.71 in.
Feed device: 8-round removable box magazine.
Muzzle velocity: 1600 f.p.s.
Sights: Front: Blade.
Rear: Square notch.

The Czechoslovaks have used several types of service pistols since the conclusion of World War II. The 7.65mm M1950 is a modified copy of the Walther PP, and is no longer regarded as a service weapon. The 7.62mm Model 52 is the current service weapon.

The Model 52 pistol is a native Czechoslovak design which has borrowed its locking system from the German MG42 machine gun. The pistol is chambered for the Czechoslovak-made version of the Soviet 7.62mm Type P pistol cartridge, which the Czechoslovaks call the Model 48. The Soviet and Czechoslovak cartridges are interchangeable with the 7.63mm Mauser, but are considerably hotter loadings than are the United States commercial loadings of this cartridge. For this reason, the functioning of Soviet and Czechoslovak weapons with commercially loaded 7.63mm cartridges is, at best, marginal. The Czechoslovak cartridge has a particularly heavy loading, being about 20% heavier than the Soviet.

How to Load and Fire the Model 52 Pistol

Remove the magazine by forcing to the rear the magazine catch, which is located at the bottom rear of the grip. Load the magazine with eight cartridges; insert magazine in well in pistol grip. Draw slide smartly to the rear, and release; the weapon is now loaded. With the safety in the "fire" position, squeeze the trigger and the weapon will fire; after the trigger is released, it can be squeezed again to fire the pistol. This sequence can be repeated until the weapon is empty. The slide remains to the rear on the last shot. The slide cannot be released from the outside of the weapon as can that of the United States M1911A1 automatic pistol. The slide must be drawn to the rear before it will release. The Model 52's safety is mounted on the left rear of the receiver and has three positions; the lowest position is "fire," and the middle and topmost positions are "safe." The Model 52 is not a double-action automatic. The hammer, if it is in the down position with a cartridge in the chamber, must be manually cocked before the weapon can be fired.

Field Stripping the Model 52 Pistol

The slide-dismounting catches at the front of the trigger guard are pulled down, and the slide assembly is pushed forward until it can be drawn straight up, to the rear, and off the receiver. With the slide in an upside down position, the barrel can be removed from the slide by pushing the roller cam and barrel forward so that the rollers clear their locking recesses. (To force the barrel forward, a screwdriver or a punch must be inserted in the hole in the roller cam.) Then the breech end of the barrel can be swung upward, clear of the slide, after which the barrel can be removed toward the rear of the slide. This process is very difficult and must be performed carefully, because the barrel, while being withdrawn, is under the pressure of the partly compressed recoil spring.

How the Model 52 Pistol Works

Loading. A loaded magazine is inserted in the magazine well in the grip of the receiver. The slide is drawn to the rear, cocking the hammer, and then released. As it moves forward, the slide forces a cartridge out of the lips of the magazine, up the bullet ramp, and into the chamber. The claw of the extractor, which is mounted on the right side of the slide behind the ejection port, slips over the rim of the cartridge.

Firing. Pulling the trigger to the rear draws forward the trigger bar, which is pinned to the trigger. If the slide is now in battery position (locking the weapon), the trigger bar pulls the sear ahead, allowing the hammer to snap forward under the pressure of the mainspring. The hammer strikes the firing pin and then rebounds to a position out of contact. The firing pin in turn strikes the primer of the cartridge and causes the cartridge to explode.

Operation of the slide group. Both the barrel and the slide, which are locked together by the roller bearings, move to the rear for three-sixteenths of an inch. During this period, the roller bearings are locked in their recesses in the slide and in the barrel lug (located under the barrel) by the thick center section of the roller cam. The roller cam, a sleeve-like piece which encircles the barrel ahead of the barrel lug, has a tongue-shaped section which extends through a longitudinal groove cut in the underside of the barrel lug. The roller cam is kept from going to the rear by another lug which is located in the mid-section of the receiver, forward of the bullet ramp. When the narrowed section of the roller cam tongue lines up with the roller bearings and their locking slot in the barrel lug, the roller bearings are cammed completely into the cutout portion of the barrel lug by the edges of the roller bearing recesses in the slide. The gun is now unlocked.

When the barrel and slide have traveled three-sixteenths of an inch to the rear, the barrel is stopped by the abutment of the barrel lug against the forward edge of the bullet ramp of the receiver. The slide continues to the rear and compresses the recoil spring, which is mounted on the barrel between the roller cam and the front of the slide.

The cartridge case, which is held by the extractor, goes rearward with the slide until it hits the ejector. The ejector, mounted on the sear pin on the left rear side of the receiver, then throws the case out the ejection port.

The lower front of the slide abuts against the receiver, and the compressed recoil spring forces the slide back into battery position. As the moving slide picks up the next round from the magazine and pushes it into the chamber, the extractor claw slips over the rim of the cartridge and engages the extractor groove. The roller bearings are cammed out of their position in the cutout of the barrel lug and into the locking recesses of the slide. They are then held in the locked position (i.e., half in the slide and half in the cutout of the barrel lug) by the wide central portion of the roller cam.

If the trigger is pulled again, the process is repeated. After the last shot is fired, the slide is held to the rear by the slide stop, which is mounted on the left side of the receiver, and which engages a cutout on the underside of the slide.

Operation of the receiver group. The spur-type trigger is attached to the trigger bar, which disengages the sear from the hammer when the trigger is pulled to the rear. On the top side of the trigger bar, near the center, is a lug which serves as a means of disconnection. When the trigger is pulled, this lug rises into a cutout portion in the right rear underside of the slide. If the weapon is not fully locked, however, the trigger bar lug will strike the underside of the slide rather than the cutout portion; thus prevented from rising, the trigger bar will be unable to contact the sear, and the weapon will not fire.

Pulling the trigger also causes an arm of the sear to rise and force up the spring-loaded firing pin lock, which is mounted in the feed rib of the slide. A portion of the firing pin lock is seated in a semicircular notch cut in the inertia-type firing pin, near its head, and both locks the firing pin and cams it back from the primer when the slide and barrel start to move to the rear. The forcing of the firing pin lock upward by the sear arm allows the firing pin to move forward when struck by the hammer. Rearward movement of the slide disengages the firing pin lock from the sear arm, allowing the firing pin lock to come down, under the pressure of its spring, and to cam the firing pin rearward out of engagement with the cartridge primer.

The hammer is the rebound type. The sear engages the rebound notch of the hammer, which then cannot move forward to strike the firing pin unless the trigger is pulled to the rear.

The safety, which is mounted on the left rear side of the receiver, in a location similar to that of the safety lock of the United States cal. .45 M1911A1 pistol, has three positions. Its lower position is "fire"; in this position, the safety does not engage the hammer or the trigger mechanism. Its central position, indicated by a red dot, is "safe"; when pushed upward to cover the red dot, the safety blocks rearward movement of the trigger bar and engages the rebound notch of the hammer, preventing its forward movement. With the safety in this position, not only can the hammer be locked, but the slide can be drawn to the rear, permitting the unloading of the chamber. With hammer cocked, the safety may be pushed all the way up to its top position, which also is a "safe." The hammer will fall, but, restrained by the safety stud which enters the rebound notch, cannot strike the firing pin.

The mainspring is mounted on the mainspring strut, which is positioned to the rear of the magazine well of the receiver. The mainspring exerts pressure upon the hammer when the hammer is cocked. It also presses against the magazine catch, mounted at the bottom rear side of the receiver, in the rear of the magazine well, thus enabling the catch to hold the magazine firmly in place.

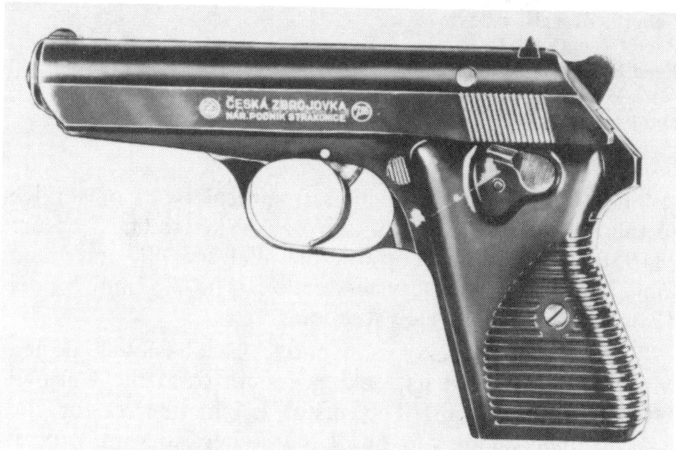

Czechoslovak 7.65mm M1950 Pistol.

System of operation: Blowback, semi-automatic fire only.
Weight, unloaded, w/magaine: 1.5 lb.
Length, overall: 6.8 in.
Barrel length: 3.8 in.
Feed device: 8-round removable box magazine.
Muzzle velocity: 919 f.p.s.
Sights: Front: Blade.
Rear: Round notch.

The M1950 is no longer used as a service pistol in Czechoslovakia, but is probably still used as a police weapon. It is chambered for the 7.65mm automatic pistol cartridge (cal. .32 ACP). Specimens have been examined, and appear to be of good quality manufacture, but there is nothing unusual about the design of the weapon.

How to Load and Fire the M1950 Pistol

Remove magazine from pistol grip by depressing the release button on left side of receiver and pulling magazine out. Fill magazine with eight cartridges. Insert magazine in the well in pistol grip. Draw slide smartly to the rear, and release. With the safety off, the trigger may now be squeezed and the weapon will fire; when the trigger is released, it may be squeezed to fire again. This process may be repeated till the weapon is empty.

The safety of the M1950 operates like that of the Walther PP and PPK. The M1950 is a double action pistol; with a cartridge in the chamber and the hammer in the down position, pulling the trigger to the rear will cause the hammer to rise and fall, firing the weapon.

How the M1950 Pistol Works

In its functioning, the M1950 pistol is generally similar to the Walther PP and PPK.

How to Field Strip the M1950 Pistol

The dismounting button is pushed, and the slide is pulled to the rear as far as it will go. The rear end of the slide is then drawn upwards, and the slide is pushed forward and off the weapon. The recoil spring which encircles the barrel can be removed. The barrel is fixed to the receiver and should not be removed. No further disassembly is recommended. Reverse the procedure to reassemble the weapon.

CZECHOSLOVAK RIFLES

The former Czechoslovak service rifle, the 7.92mm Model 24, is covered in great detail in this chapter. Before the adoption of the present service rifle (the semi-automatic Model 52), the Czechoslovaks made another Mauser for service use; this 7.92mm weapon is a very slightly modified version of the German World War II service rifle, the Kar 98K. Some quantities of these Czechoslovak weapons, as well as the earlier Model 24, have come into this country lately as the result of the Sinai fighting in 1956.

Czechoslovakia exported Mauser rifles and 7.92mm ammunition to various Middle Eastern countries in the period between World War II and the Korean War; the Israeli government has sold some of these weapons to various commercial arms dealers in the United States. In general, it can be said that these arms are well made and—if in good condition—make fine, reliable weapons.

Czech Copy of German Kar 98k Rifle.

In 1924 Czechoslovakia adopted the Model 24, a Mauser type short rifle practically identical with the F. N. Mauser of that year. The factory was government subsidized. Rifles were made to fine tolerances, and the steels used were among the best ever developed—Poldi and Skoda. The official caliber was 7.9mm German Service.

Minor modifications of this design were made in 1933. In 1940 the Germans adopted this 18-inch barrel model with slight changes, as the Model 33/40.

Czech Mausers in various calibers were sold throughout the world. In general the ammunition data for F. N. Mauser (see chapter 16) applies to the Czech forms.

Since description and technical data on these rifles is for all practical purposes the same as the late model German types, the official Czech data is limited below in free translation. This data covers more factory information than has ever before been pubiished concerning Mauser specifications.

Identification. Except for minor matters of stock and sight accessories these can be identified from German and F. N. Mausers only by markings and proofs. They may be found with any African, Asiastic, or South American national markings. They were also made for Yugoslavia.

Evaluation. These were among the world's finest rifles before the war. Poldi steel was the most highly prized barrel steel in Europe. While many of the business heads of the Czech arms industries were pro-German, the rank and file were ardent patriots. It is possible that some sabotage of these arms may have occurred during the German occupation. All specimens personally examined, however, have been first class Mausers.

Ammunition. 7mm Mauser as made in the U. S. 7.65mm Mauser as made here or as made in England and 7.9mm (called 8mm Mauser also) as made by U. S. cartridge manufacturers are the commonly obtainable calibers.

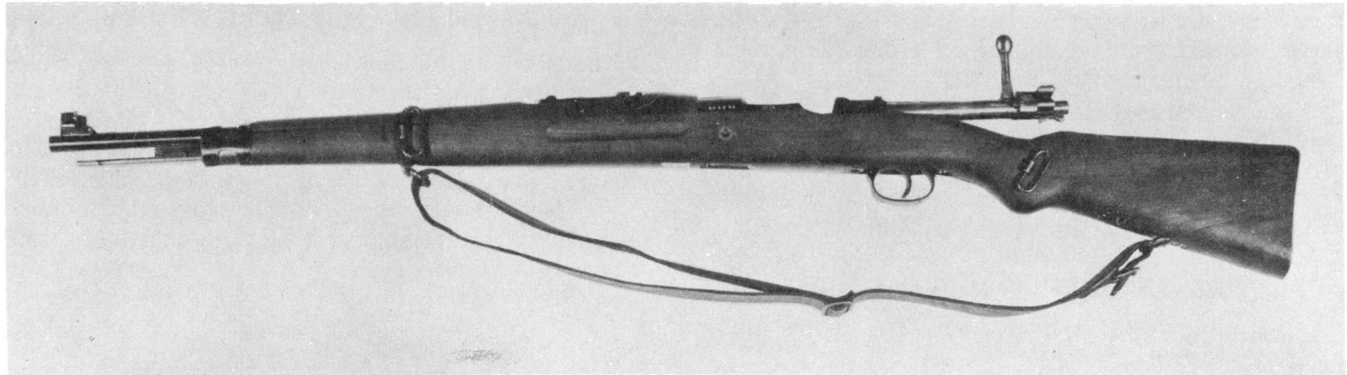

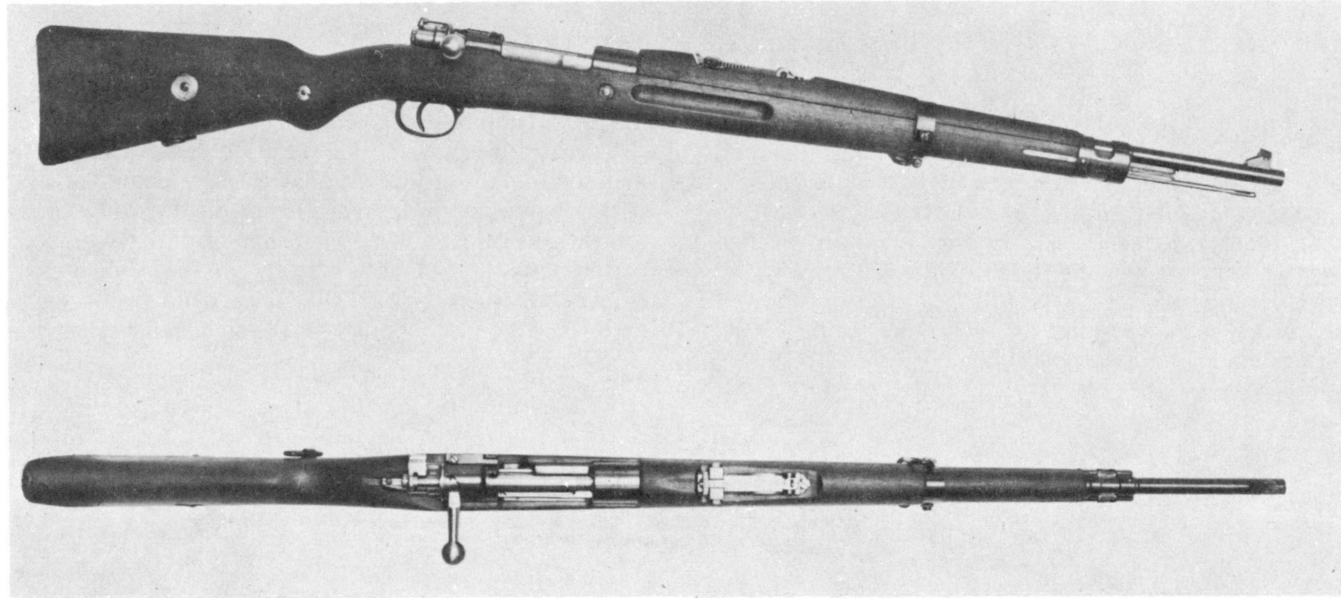

Czech 7.92mm Model 24 (VZ 24).

Caliber: 7.92mm.
Number of grooves: 4.
Depth of grooves: 0.15mm.
Twist: right hand.
Length of one turn: 240mm.
Length of rifled part: 534mm.
Length of barrel: 590mm.
Length of rifle: 1100mm.
Length of rifle with bayonet: 1410mm.
Distance between foresight point and backsight notch: 504.8mm.
Range scale: From 300m, always by 100m, until 2000m.
Weight of rifle: 4080 gr.
Weight of rifle with bayonet: 4484 gr.
Weight of bayonet: 404 gr.
Weight of scabbard: 192 gr.
Muzzle velocity of bullet: 810 m/sec.
Weight of bullet: 10 gr.
Length of bullet maximum: 28.4mm.
Diameter of bullet maximum: 8.24mm.
Weight of cartridge: 21 gr.
Weight of clip for 4 cartridges: 10 gr.
Weight of powder: 3.06 gr.
Length of cartridge maximum: 80mm.

Since these rifles were also made to special order, sporters may be encountered in any European caliber, most of which are unavailable in the U. S.

The design of the 1924 Model Short Service rifle is based on the Mod. 98 Mauser rifle. The cartridges are held in position in the chamber and against the recoil of the powder charge by two symmetrical lugs solid with the bolt. The magazine is fed by a clip. The cartridges are staggered in the magazine positioned below the bolt.

The rifle consists of the following main parts:

Barrel with rearsight and band from sight block, Bolt, Magazine, Stock, Fittings and Receiver.

Barrel. The bore of the Mod. 24 Short Service Rifle is 7.92mm. The rifling grooves formed in this bore are 0.15mm deep, and 4.3mm wide. They are made in spiral, and one turn is 240mm long. The whole length of the barrel is 590mm, the length of the rifling 534mm. The chamber is of the same shape as the standard cartridge of 7.92mm caliber, the first conical part being 43.35mm long, 12mm in dia. at the rear end, and 11mm in dia. at its front, the second conical part backing the cartridge is 2.85mm long with a slope of 18° 30′ passing into a cylindrical part 9.1mm in dia. recessed on 54.35mm of the barrel front face. The chamber is manufactured with precision, so that any deformations or cracks of the cartridge case during firing are almost impossible.

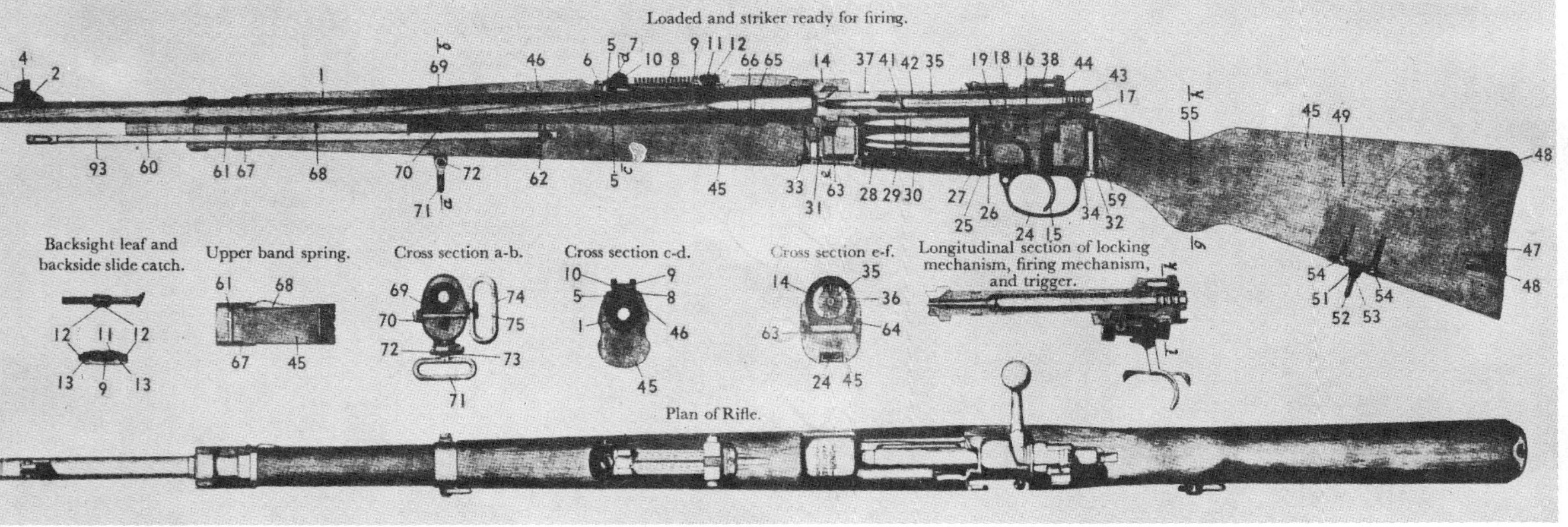

LIST OF COMPONENT PARTS

1) barrel
2) band foresight block
3) band foresight screw
4) front sight
5) backsight base
6) backsight base screw
7) backsight cheeks
8) backsight spring
9) backsight leaf
10) backsight leaf pin
11) backsight slide
12) backsight slide catch
13) backsight slide catch spring
14) receiver
15) trigger
16) trigger pin
17) sear
18) sear pin
19) sear spring
20) bolt stop
21) bolt stop screw
22) bolt stop double spring
23) ejector
24) magazine
25) magazine catch pin
26) catch pin spring
27) catch pin split pin
28) magazine bottom plate
29) magazine platform (follower)
30) magazine spring
31) front coupling screw
32) rear coupling screw
33) front set screw
34) rear set screw
35) bolt
36) extractor
37) extractor collar
38) bolt sleeve
39) bolt sleeve lock
40) pressure bolt spring
41) striker
42) main spring
43) cocking piece
44) safety catch
45) stock
46) hand guard
47) butt
48) butt screw
49) plate
50) plate screw
51) butt swivel plate
52) lower swivel
53) lower swivel pin
54) butt swivel plate screw
55) lower side swivel pin
56) lower side swivel nut
57) lower side swivel
58) side swivel plate pin
59) stay
60) bayonet lug
61) bayonet lug pin
62) cleaning rod nut
63) stock sleeve
64) stock sleeve nut
65) hand guard spring
66) hand guard spring screw
67) upper band
68) upper band spring
69) lower band
70) side screw of the lower band
71) upper swivel
72) lower band screw
73) lower band nut
74) upper side swivel
75) upper side swivel pin
76) bayonet blade
77) bayonet handle
78) bayonet handle pin
79) bayonet guard
80) bayonet guard pin
81) bayonet catch
82) bayonet catch nut
83) bayonet catch spring
84) bayonet grip
85) bayonet grip nut
86) bayonet grip nut pin
87) scabbard
88) scabbard knob
89) scabbard hook
90) scabbard spring
91) scabbard mouthpiece
92) scabbard mouthpiece pin
93) cleaning rod

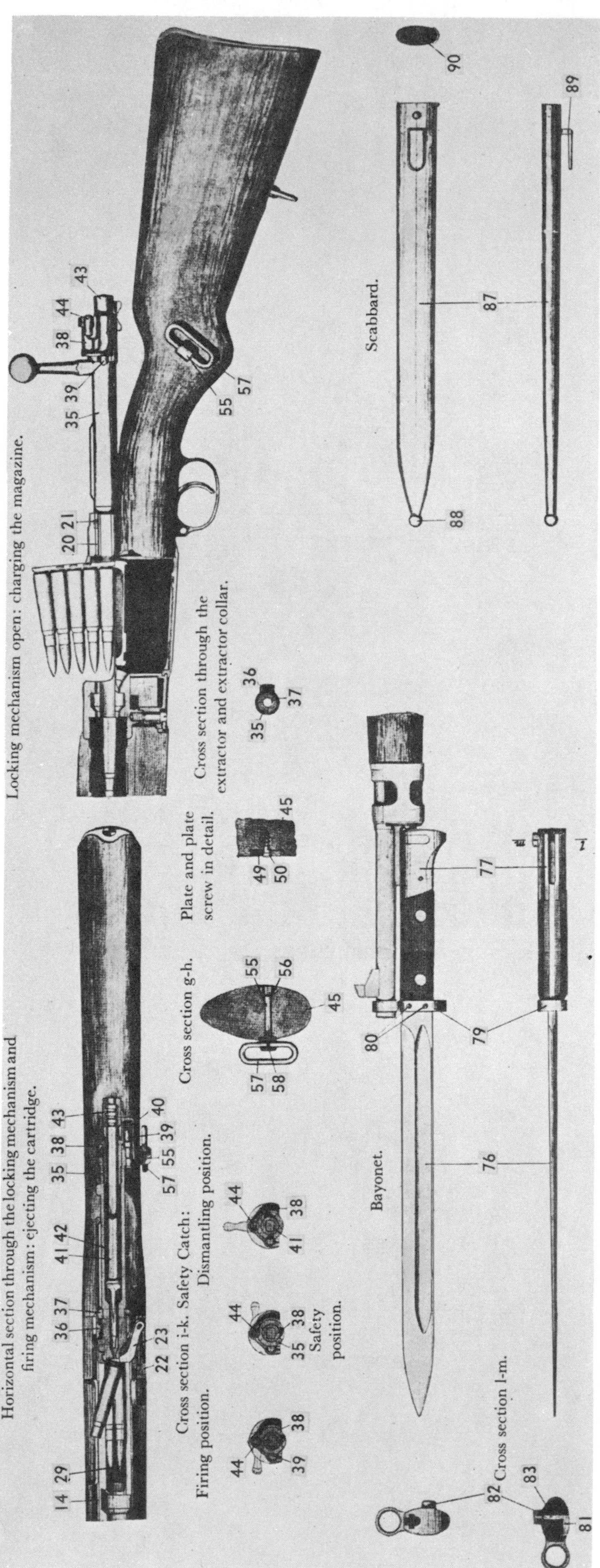

Horizontal section through the locking mechanism and firing mechanism: ejecting the cartridge.

Locking mechanism open: charging the magazine.

Cross section i-k. Safety Catch: Dismantling position. Firing position. Safety position.

Cross section g-h.

Plate and plate screw in detail.

Cross section through the extractor and extractor collar.

Bayonet.

Scabbard.

Cross section l-m.

The barrel is threaded on its rear end, and screwed into the receiver. The barrel has a symmetrical shape, with neither lugs nor recesses, so that when re-barreling it is not necessary to select a special barrel; each barrel fits every receiver.

On the first cylindrical section of the barrel, the sight is welded on by tin. The exact position of the sight is assured by an adjusting screw entering in a small recess of the barrel drilled after connecting with the receiver. In the same way the band foresight block (2) is mounted on the second barrel section. The backsight base (5) is provided with a notch, in which the backsight cheeks with curvature (7) are inserted.

The "curvature" forms an entirely exchangeable part. It is well annealed, and gives the rifle a superior quality in comparison with other models. In the event of any modification of the ballistic data, other backsight cheeks can be installed without being obliged to use any special tool or having to return the rifle to the armory.

The backsight slide (11) sliding on the backsight leaf (9) is supported by the curvature. It is retained on the leaf by two slide catches (12) pressed against the grooves of the leaf by the slide catch springs (13). The leaf swinging round a pin is provided with a range scale up to 2000m. The leaf is pressed against the slide by the backsight spring (8) dovetailed by one end together with the backsight cheeks, and with the other end pressing against the leaf. The band foresight block (2) is dovetailed with the foresight (4). When the rifle is being sighted in, the deviation is corrected by regulating the position of the foresight in the dove tail of the foresight block, the vertical deviation is corrected by exchanging the foresight for one of greater or smaller height. The distance between the backsight notch and the foresight point is 504.8mm.

Bolt and Receiver. The action consists of the following parts:

Receiver (14),
Locking mechanism,
Extractor,
Firing mechanism,
Safety catch,
Trigger.

The locking mechanism moves in the receiver (14) screwed on the barrel. The receiver is bored out on its entire length to 18mm in dia. On both its sides there are grooves into which the bolt lugs (35) engage. The grooves are terminated by a circular recess, the bottom of which forms a supporting face to absorb the pressure caused by the powder charge. When locking the cartridge in the chamber, and turning the bolt lever into its horizontal position, the bolt lugs come into a vertical position, whereby they slide on the helicöidal ramps in the receiver at the passage from the grooves, and form the bed plate. By this movement the cartridge is securely locked into the chamber. One of the grooves is prolonged up to the contact face of the rifle, and serves at the same time

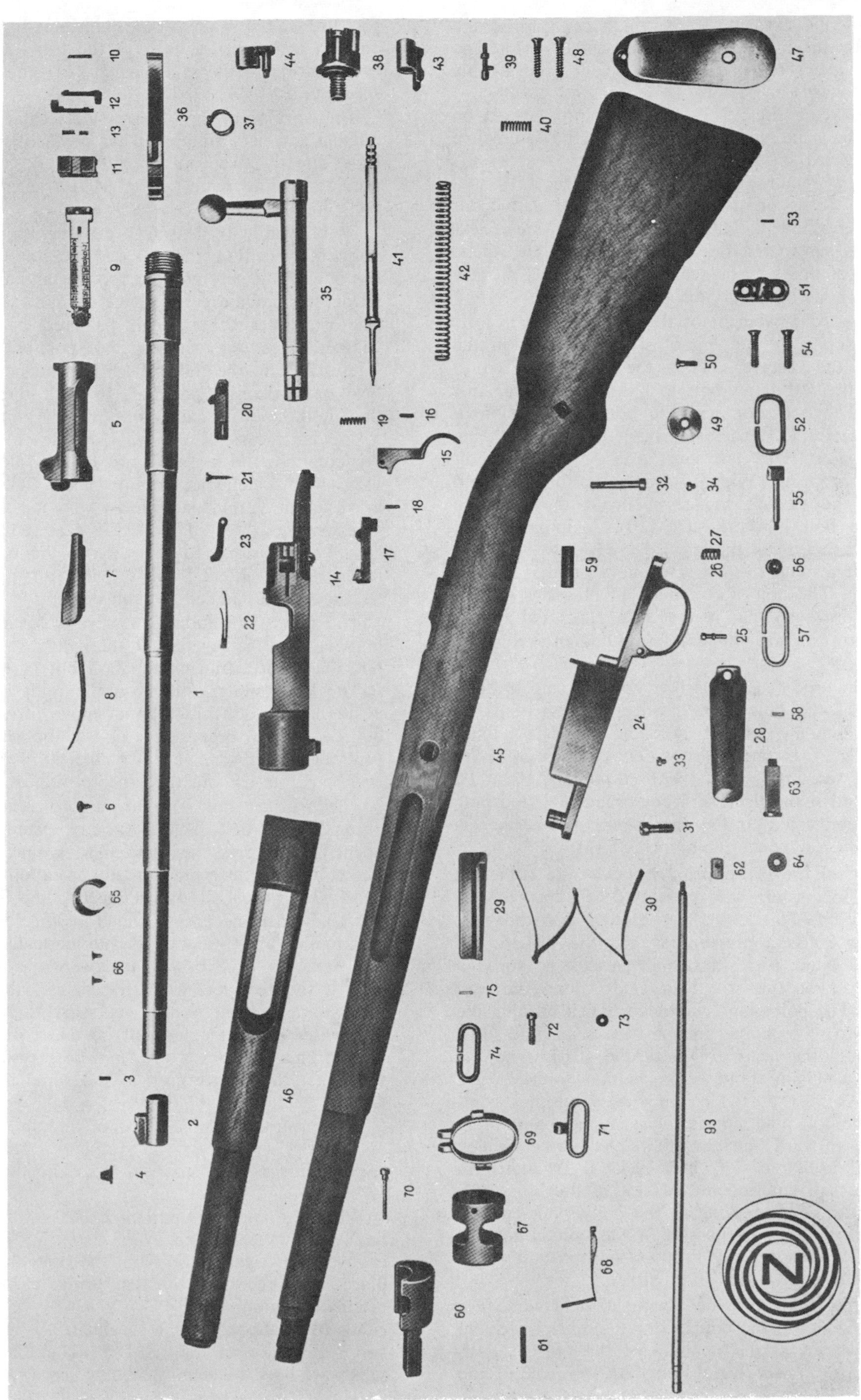
10 12 13 11 9 5 7 8 6 65 66 3 2 4
36 1 46
44 37 38 43 35 20 21 23 22 14
39 48 47 40 41 42 19 16 15 18 17
45 53 51 54 50 49 52 32 34 55 59 27 26 56 25 57 24 58 28 33 63 31 62 64
29 30 75 72 73 74 69 71 70 67 68 60 61 93

for guiding the extractor (36) which can turn round the bolt by means of the extractor collar (37). The extractor always remains in the receiver groove, only moving forwards or backwards. It does not turn.

The extractor engages in the cannelure formed on the cartridge, and presses the latter at the same time against the lug on the opposite side in front of the bolt. The extractor grips the cartridge securely and, since it is elastic on its whole length, any fatigue or fracture is excluded. This design of the Mauser extractor has shown itself to be superior to all others, and proof of this may be seen in the fact that all new designs of bolts have adopted this type.

A backward movement of the bolt is prevented by the bolt stop (20), the lug of which engages in the groove of the receiver. When the bolt is moved to the rear, the left hand bolt locking lug runs against this lug. The bolt stop and the bolt lug are slotted, and the ejector (23) passes through these slots, being pressed against it by the short arm of the dual bolt stop-ejector spring. When drawing the bolt (35) to the rear, the ejector engages beneath the cartridge before the bolt hits the stop (20). It imparts from beneath a thrust to the cartridge-case, so that the latter turns around the extractor hook, and is ejected to the side. The bolt stop can be pivoted out around the stop screw, so that its lug disengages out of the receiver groove, and the bolt may be removed from the receiver.

The firing rod (41) or striker rod, passing through the bore of the bolt stem, has on its fore end the striker, which in relaxed position protrudes about 1.5mm. The rear end is provided with three dovetailed recesses, into which the bolt plug (43) can be inserted, and if the firing rod be turned 90°, the plug is firmly connected to the firing pin. The striker is pressed forward by the main spring (42).

One end of the main spring is held by a collar on the firing rod, while the other end is supported by the face of the bolt lock (38) screwed into the bolt. The spring exerts a pressure against the striker, and pushes the latter forward, which in passing through the flat hole of the bolt lock pulls along the bolt plug (43). The bolt plug is retained, when pushing the bolt forward to lock the arm, by the sear head (17), which causes the firing rod with the striker and the bolt plug to remain about 12mm behind its discharged position. As soon as the cocking mechanism is compressed, the bolt plug stop is released, the main spring imparts a forward movement to the striker which causes the discharge. The bolt lock is terminated in front by a cam entering into a slot of the bolt. This cam prevents firing, as long as the bolt is not entirely locked, i.e., as long as the slot of the bolt is not opposite the bolt plug. Any firing when the bolt is incompletely closed is thus impossible.

The safety cam provided with a helicoidal face slides on the slot of the bolt having a similar helicoidal face, and serves at the opening of the bolt to push back the firing rod with the bolt plug, overcoming the pressure of the main spring. The bolt lock serves not only as a supporting face to the firing rod, but also as a bearing to the safety catch (44) and to the pressure bolt (39).

The working of the Mauser safety catch (44) is very reliable and very simple. It has no auxiliary spring, as it is directly fixed in its different positions by the pressure of the main spring (42) transmitted by the bolt plug.

If the wing of the safety cam be brought into its horizontal position, the recessed part of the safety rod no longer engages into the groove, and the bolt plug encounters no more resistance to move forward. The rifle is unlocked, and can be fired by pulling the trigger. From this position it is possible to turn the safety catch to the right, the firing rod being in a vertical or horizontal position. In both these positions, the safety catch is fixed, for the bolt plug enters into a circular recess of the wing of the safety cam. At this rotation, the recessed part of the safety rod, provided with a helicoidal ramp, causes the bolt plug to move about ½mm backwards, whereby the sear (17) is disengaged. As soon as the recessed part of the safety rod has barred the way of the bolt plug, the latter is prevented from moving forward, and the trigger can be handled without danger.

The vertical position is used only for removing the bolt (it is necessary to put the safety catch into this position before drawing the bolt out of the receiver).

The horizontal position on the right is the locked position. The bolt plug cannot move forward, nor the bolt be opened, because the end of the safety rod prevents the turning movement of the bolt which is, however, possible in both the other positions.

The pressure bolt (39) prevents any accidental rotation of the bolt lock (38), e.g., when the bolt is opened. The pressure bolt engages into a notch of the bolt, and thus prevents the rotation of the bolt lock against the bolt. When pushing the bolt forward, this rotation is necessary, therefore the locking of the bolt lock against the bolt is automatically released as the pressure bolt moves backwards, when running against the receiver, which disengages the bolt lock. The disengagement is also necessary for dismounting, otherwise the bolt could not be taken out of the receiver. This is done by pressing the pressure bolt with the finger, and in turning at the same time the bolt lock.

The firing mechanism is mounted in the receiver, and comprises the trigger (15), the sear (17), the trigger pin (16), the sear pin (18), and the sear spring (19).

When the trigger is pulled, it bears first against the first point, then against the second point, and disengages the trigger nose from the bolt plug. A spring placed in a recess of the sear brings it back into the original position.

Feeding Mechanism. The magazine (24) is secured by two set screws in the receiver. These screws themselves are fixed by small fastening screws thus preventing loosening. In its central part the magazine forms the well, a square cavity, where the cartridges are placed when charging; the bottom plate is maintained by the magazine catch pin (25). The magazine bottom plate may be removed by means of a cartridge, by pressing the catch pin into the magazine with the bullet point and pulling the bottom plate to the rear to remove it out of the grooves of the magazine.

The magazine bottom plate (28) has a dovetailed groove to insert the magazine spring (30). This latter exerts a continual pressure upwards against the magazine platform (29). The magazine being full charged, its platform bears against the bottom, and after each round and repetition, the magazine spring, being in a state of compression, pushes the cartridges upwards, so that the upper one is ready to be introduced into the chamber. The cartridges are placed in fives into a clip, whence they are passed by a thrust of the thumb into the well of the magazine. There they are automatically arranged in two rows, so that one cartridge from the left side and then another from the right side feeds into line with the bolt for chambering.

Stock. The stock (45) and the handguard (46) are made of walnut. They cover the barrel on its whole length, so that there is no danger of the hand of the rifleman being burned by the heat of the barrel.

The symmetrical covering of the barrel affects accuracy at quick fire, for if the barrel were not symmetrically covered by the wood, the naked part would cool more rapidly than the covered one. Experience shows that on account of the resulting barrel deformation the mean trajectory is moved upwards. All the parts of the bolt and the magazine are so surrounded by wood, that, save the bolt handle, no metallic part exceeds the contours of the wooden cover.

The handguard is held in its position by the hand guard spring (65) fixed by two screws to the hand guard. With its front end the latter is joined to the stock by the upper band (67) and in the middle by the lower band (69).

In the central part, the stock is drilled out so that all receiver parts and the magazine are exposed. The barrel with the receiver is bedded from above, the magazine from below, into the stock. The magazine is connected with the receiver by the front coupling screw (31) and the rear coupling screw (32).

The front coupling screw is guided by a socket directly formed on the magazine. The rear coupling screw has a special bushing placed into the stock, called a stay (59). After tightening both these screws, they are secured in their positions by the front set screw (33), and the rear set screw (34). In its thickest part the stock is surrounded by the stock sleeve (63) of rectangular section, and the tang of the receiver bears against one of its faces. At this point the recoil pressure is transmitted to the stock, thus preventing longitudinal splits of the stock, which might be caused by recoil pressure. The stock is protected at its rear end from shocks and against other damage by the butt (47), secured to it by two butt screws (48).

Fittings. On the front end of the stock, there is mounted the bayonet lug (60) used with its cylindrical opening as a bearing for the front section of the barrel. This bayonet lug is secured against slipping from the stock by a bayonet lug pin (61) traversing the stock. The bayonet lug bears the upper band (67) connecting the barrel to the bayonet lug. The upper band is protected against any gliding of the lug by the upper band spring (68) engaging with a cylindrical tenon from inside into the upper band hole. The former can be brought home into a groove of the stock, when it is necessary to remove the upper band. The spring has at its end a tenon strongly fixed into the stock. The lower band (69), coupling the stock with the hand guard, is secured by the lower band screw (72) and the lower band nut (73), and carries two swinging swivels.

The upper side swivel (74) swings directly on the lower band, the upper swivel turning round the lower band screw (72). The lower band is secured against gliding off by the side screw of the lower band (70) traversing the stock.

The stock is drilled out parallel to the barrel axis, to a certain length to place the cleaning rod (93). One of the rod ends passes through a hole on the bayonet lug, the other threaded end is screwed into the cleaning rod nut (62) placed in the stock. The cleaning rod bypasses at the front end the bayonet lug which permits the arms to be stacked. Any two rod parts may be screwed together, in order to form a long rod to clean the barrel, when hemp is fixed thereon.

The lower side swivel (57) swings around the lower side swivel pin (55). The pin traversing the stock is secured on the other end by the lower side swivel nut (56). The lower swivel (52), swinging around the butt swivel plate (51), is fixed to the stock by two butt swivel plate screws (54). The rifle has, therefore, two side swivels and two ordinary ones; the sling can be, consequently, fixed either to the side swivels or to the ordinary ones. For this reason it may be used as a common arm both for infantry and cavalry. For cavalry a short barrel was adopted.

Bayonet and Scabbard. The bayonet blade (76) has a steel band, on which there is hard welded the bayonet handle (77) and the bayonet guard (79), secured in its position by two bayonet guard pins (80). The bayonet guard is provided on one end with a barrel hole, through which the barrel passes, when fixing the bayonet. The bayonet handle has on its whole length a groove in T shape in order to glide easily on the bayonet lug (60). Moreover, the handle has a recess for the bayonet catch (81) pressed against the handle by the bayonet catch spring (83). The lug of the bayonet catch enters, on fixing the bayonet, into a slot of the bayonet lug, by which the bayonet is firmly held on the barrel. To remove the bayonet from the barrel, press home the bayonet catch nut (82) exerting at the same time a pull forward. The bayonet handle is provided with a large aperture, through which the cleaning rod passes, when fixing the bayonet.

The scabbard (87) is made of steel sheet, and has on its smaller end a scabbard knob (88) welded on. The scabbard hook (89) is welded on the scabbard. In the mouth of the scabbard there is fixed a double scabbard spring (90), which prevents the bayonet slipping off. The pressure of the spring requires a pull of 4 kg to unsheath the bayonet.

Operation of the Mechanism

The bolt handle is raised to vertical position, then pulled back to expose the magazine.

The clip, with five or less cartridges, is put in the clip guides in the receiver. On pressing down the top cartridge with the thumb, all the cartridges are forced into the magazine. The magazine platform, being raised by the flat magazine spring, has the top cartridge always ready for loading into the chamber. As the bolt starts ahead the extractor glides underneath the edge of the cartridge case so that its hook engages in the cannelure of the cartridge case. By pushing and turning the handle of the bolt to return it to its horizontal position, the cartridge is loaded into the chamber, and the arm is ready for firing.

The sight is adjusted by pressing on both sides the slide catches, and moving the slide on the range scale.

The trigger can be pulled lightly until certain resistance is felt. As soon as this is overcome (about 3½ kg) and the movement continued, the trigger nose descends, thus releasing the bolt plug. The firing pin is thrown forwards by the main spring, the striker strikes the cartridge cap, firing the cartridge. The empty cartridge case is drawn back out of the chamber by the extractor. During the backward movement of the bolt the ejector strikes the bottom of the cartridge case and ejects it to the right of the receiver. This happens before the bolt is checked by the stop.

Dismounting and Assembling the Bolt

Before removing the bolt from the receiver, turn the safety catch into its central position between its safe and unsafe position, i.e., with the wing turned upwards. The bolt can be removed from the receiver only when the bolt stop (20) is moved to the side with a slight pressure, whereby the groove in the receiver is (fig. 1) opened to permit bolt passage.

Turn the bolt lock to the left, then the latter with the safety catch, the bolt plug and the firing rod may easily be separated from the bolt. While removing these parts the main spring is still in a state of compression (fig. 2).

For further dismounting put the striker with its point turned downwards against a convenient bearing (for this purpose a hole is provided in the stock sleeve) (fig. 3).

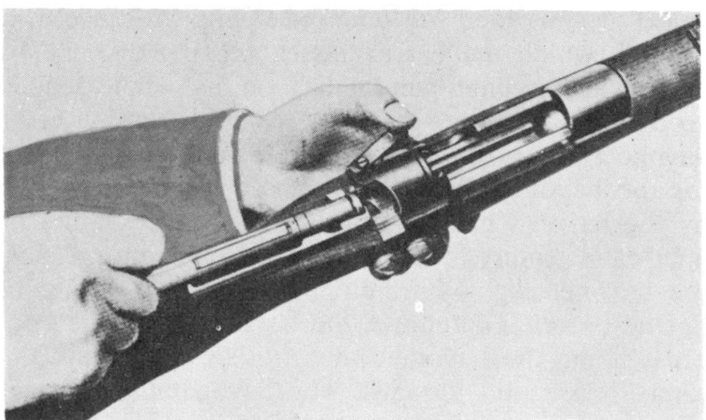

Figure 1.

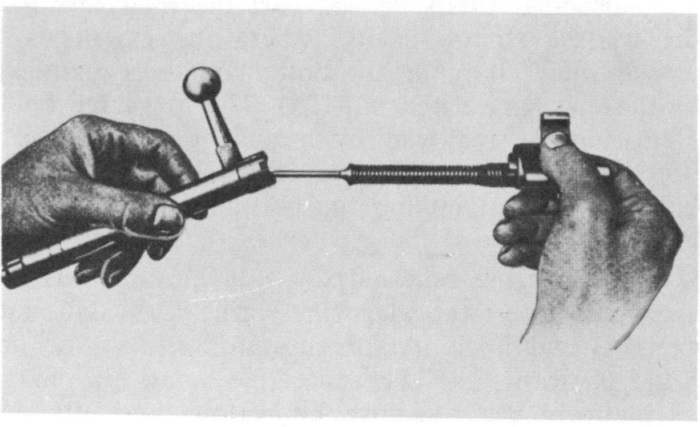

Figure 2.

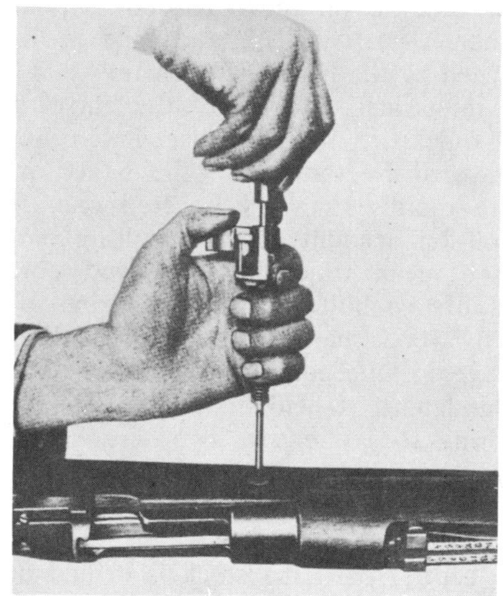

Figure 3.

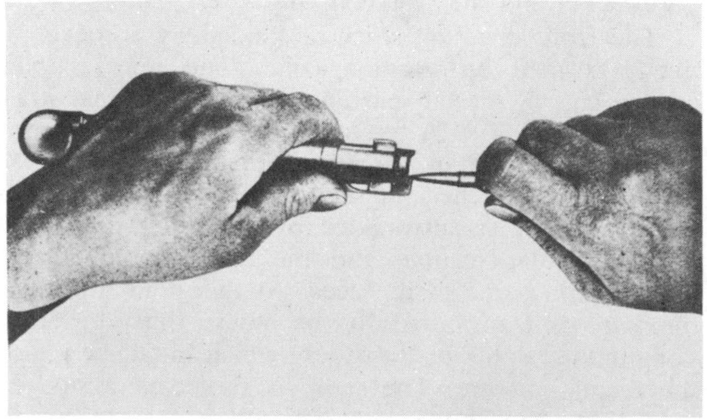

Figure 4.

RANGE TABLE FOR THE MOD. 24 MAUSER SHORT SERVICE RIFLE.

Weight of bullet 10 *gr.* Muzzle velocity 810 *m/sec.*

Range *m*	Elevation	Angle of descent	Distance of vertex of trajectory *m*	Height of vertex of trajectory *m*	Time *sec.*	Remaining velocity *m/sec.*	Kinetic energy in *kgm*
0	—	—	—	—	—	810	334
100	0°2′40″	0°2′40″	50	0·025	0·1305	714	260
200	6′20″	7′10″	108	0·11	0·297	645	212
300	10′20″	12′20″	166	0·24	0·442	575	169
400	14′40″	19′40″	224	0·49	0·626	511	133
500	19′40″	29′00″	282	0·84	0·830	455	106
600	25′40″	41′00″	342	1·37	1·066	406	84
700	33′20″	56′00″	402	2·17	1·323	366	68
800	42′30″	1°16′00″	464	3·32	1·62	334	57
900	53′20″	40′30″	525	4·90	1·95	308	49
1000	1°06′40″	2°08′30″	586	7·15	2·31	287	42·5
1100	22′00″	43′10″	646	9·91	2·69	269	38
1200	38′40″	3°20′00″	704	13·31	3·09	252	32·5
1300	57′00″	4°00′40″	761	17·33	3·52	238	29
1400	2°17′00″	47′30″	819	22·00	3·98	225	26
1500	40′00″	5°39′20″	880	27·94	4·45	213	23
1600	3°05′40″	6°38′00″	943	34·70	4·95	201	20
1700	36′00″	7°44′40″	1007	43·50	5·50	191	18
1800	4°14′40″	9°12′00″	1072	55·30	6·1	179	16
1900	59′20″	11°22′40″	1160	70·40	7·0	165	14
2000	6°00′00″	14°06′40″	1280	91·90	7·9	152	11·5

COORDINATES OF TRAJECTORIES OF THE MOD. 24 MAUSER SHORT SERVICE RIFLE.

Weight of bullet 10 *gr.* Muzzle velocity 810 *m/sec.*

Range in meters	Laying the sight to (Ordinates of trajectories in meters)																		Dangerous zone for 1 *m* of height of target *m*
	300	400	500	600	700	800	900	1000	1100	1200	1300	1400	1500	1600	1700	1800	1900	2000	
100	0·22	0·35	0·49	0·67	0·89	1·16	1·47	1·86	2·31	2·79	3·33	3·91	4·58	5·32	6·21	7·33	8·63	10·40	100
200	0·23	0·49	0·78	1·13	1·57	2·10	2·73	3·51	4·40	5·37	6·44	7·60	8·94	10·43	12·20	14·44	17·04	20·57	200
300	0·00	0·39	0·80	1·34	2·00	2·80	3·74	4·90	6·24	7·71	9·31	11·06	13·06	15·30	17·95	21·32	25·22	30·51	300
400	-0·50	0·00	0·58	1·28	2·17	3·24	4·50	6·05	7·83	9·77	11·91	14·23	17·01	19·99	23·52	28·02	33·22	40·28	400
500	-1·36	-0·73	0·00	0·87	1·99	3·32	4·90	6·83	9·06	11·49	14·15	17·06	20·40	24·13	28·54	34·16	40·66	49·48	500
600		-1·92	-1·05	0·00	1·34	2·94	4·83	7·15	9·83	12·74	15·94	19·43	23·44	27·92	33·22	39·97	47·77	58·37	125
700				-1·56	0·00	1·87	4·07	6·79	9·91	13·30	17·03	21·11	25·79	31·01	37·19	45·06	54·06	67·51	70
800					-2·13	0·00	2·52	5·62	9·19	13·07	17·33	21·99	27·34	33·31	40·37	49·37	59·77	73·90	48·5
900						-2·84	0·00	3·49	7·51	11·88	16·68	21·92	27·94	34·66	42·61	52·73	64·43	80·31	34·5
1000							-3·88	0·00	4·46	9·31	14·64	20·46	27·15	34·61	43·44	54·69	67·69	85·34	23·5
1100								-4·90	0·00	5·34	11·20	17·60	24·96	33·16	42·86	55·23	69·53	88·95	20
1200									-5·82	0·00	6·40	13·38	21·41	30·36	40·96	54·46	70·06	91·24	17
1300										-6·94	0·00	7·56	16·26	25·96	37·43	52·05	68·95	91·90	14
1400											-8·15	0·00	9·36	19·80	32·16	47·90	66·10	90·81	12
1500												-10·03	0·00	11·19	24·44	41·31	60·81	87·29	10
1600													-11·94	0·00	14·13	32·13	52·93	81·17	8·5
1700														-15·00	0·00	19·13	41·23	71·23	7·3
1800															-20·23	0·00	23·40	55·17	6·1
1900																-24·68	0·00	33·52	4·9
2000																	-36·37	0·00	4

Press home the main spring till the bolt plug can be turned 90°, remove the latter and, in releasing the pressure of the spring, take out the firing rod. The safety catch may easily be dismounted by turning the wing to the right side.

To remove the pressure bolt, pull it into a position of 90°, where its spindle can be turned in the notch of the bolt lock.

To remove the extractor (36), pull it to the side with the help of a solid object (for instance with a cartridge), till it disengages the dovetail before the bolt lug (fig. 4). Then turn it to an angle of 90°, and, holding it against a table edge, draw it out of the groove of the extractor ring (37) (fig. 5).

The extractor ring of the bolt should not be dismounted. The extractor and the pressure bolt should seldom be removed.

The assembling is done in the opposite order. Mount the extractor on the extractor ring, until it can be turned and engaged in the groove of the bolt. Put into the bolt lock the pressure bolt spring, then the pressure bolt itself, and turn 90°. Place the main spring on the firing rod, place the safety catch into the bolt lock, and compress the main spring, just enough to insert the bolt plug, and turn 90°. The bolt lock, thus assembled, is screwed on the bolt. Now the bolt can be pushed into the receiver. When doing so, it is not necessary to push aside the bolt stop, for it disengages itself by the pressure on the bolt.

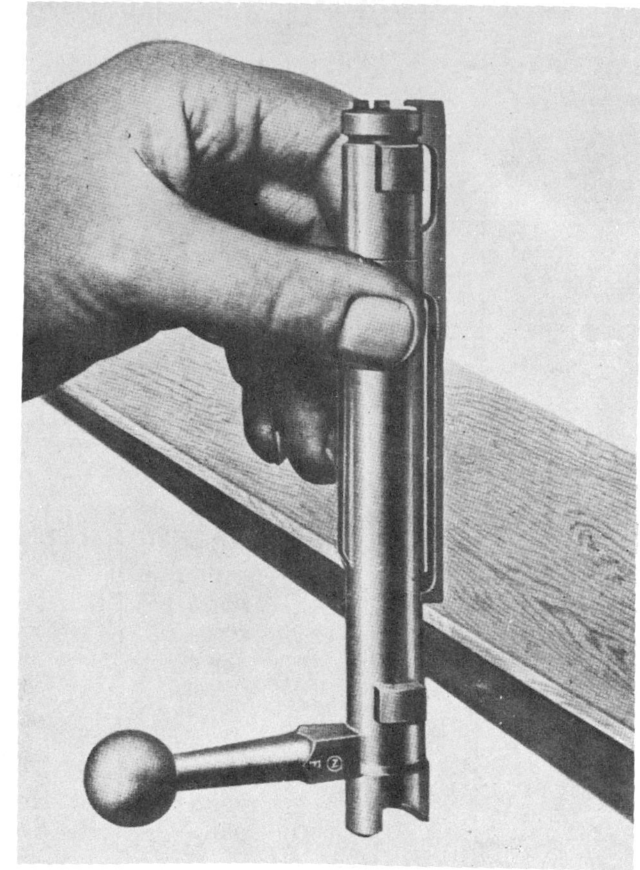

Figure 5.

The Czech Model ZK-420S 7.92mm Rifle.

Caliber: 7.92mm German.
Magazine Capacity: 10 cartridges.
Magazine: Staggered Box.
Ballistics: Standard for cartridge.
Overall Length: 41.73 inches.
Barrel Length: 21.65 inches.
Weight: 10.58 pounds.
Operation: Gas through gas cylinder and piston or conventional.
Locked: Rotation of lugs into recess by cam slots in bolt carrier. Dual lugs directly behind chamber reminiscent of our Garand.
Sights: Conventional post front and tangent rear leaf. Ranges in 100-meter steps from 300 to 2,000.
Unlocking: Operating rod extension of piston rotates bolt to unlock, somewhat as in Garand.

The weapon was designed and manufactured at the factory where the original Brno machine gun, the forerunner of the famous Bren, was developed. This is the Zbrojovka Brno Works.

Note. This weapon appeared in prototype form only. It was never produced in quantity. Its weight is relatively high, being somewhat over 10½ pounds. The rifle was actually produced as a design prototype to counter the Garand.

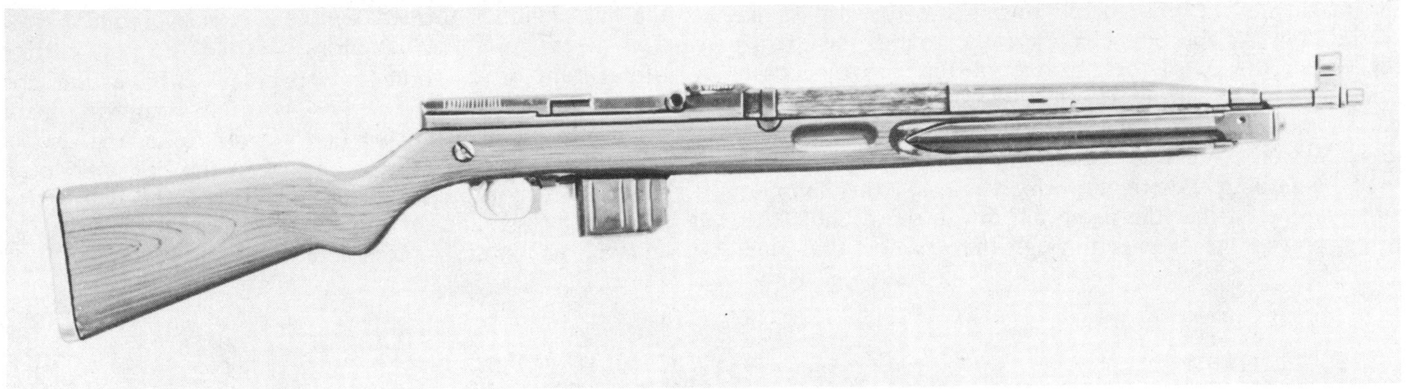

Czechoslovak 7.62mm Model 52 Semi-automatic Rifle.

Caliber: 7.62mm, Czechoslovak Model 52.
System of operation: Gas, semi-automatic fire only.
Weight, loaded: 9.8 lb.
Length, overall: 39.37 in.
Barrel length: 20.66 in.
Feed mechanism: 10-round, double staggered-row, detachable box magazine (loaded with 5-round chargers).
Sights: Front: Hooded blade (removable hood).
Rear: Notched tangent with curved ramp.
Muzzle velocity: 2440 f.p.s.

The Model 52 is chambered for the Czechoslovak 7.62mm Model 52 cartridge. Its design is a combination of several older designs added to a few native ideas. The gas system is generally similar to that of the German MKb 42W and some of the earlier Walther commercial semi-automatic rifle designs. The trigger mechanism is similar to that of the United States M1 rifle. The bolt appears to be a native design; it is somewhat unusual in that it is a tipping bolt design with frontal locking lugs. For the first time the Czechoslovaks have put a nondetachable bayonet on one of their rifles, possibly as a result of Soviet influence. The Model 52 makes fairly extensive use of stampings, but, all in all, the design is hardly revolutionary and in some respects is not too remarkable considering the date it appeared—1952.

The Czechs have issued a slightly modified version of the 52 rifle called the Model 52/57 and chambered for the Soviet designed 7.62mm M43 cartridge.

How to Load and Fire the Model 52 Rifle

Pull the operating handle all the way to the rear; since the weapon has a bolt-holding-open device, the bolt and carrier will remain open. Insert the end of a five-round charger in the charger (clip) guide at the front of the receiver cover and force the cartridges down into the magazine with the thumb of the left hand. Repeat this process with another five-round charger; then draw the operating handle slightly to the rear and release. The bolt and carrier will run home, chambering a cartridge. The weapon is now loaded and, with safety off, the trigger will cause it to fire. The trigger must be released after each shot. The safety is similar to that on the United States M1 rifle. When the safety is forward the rifle will fire; when the safety is drawn to the rear, the weapon is on "safe."

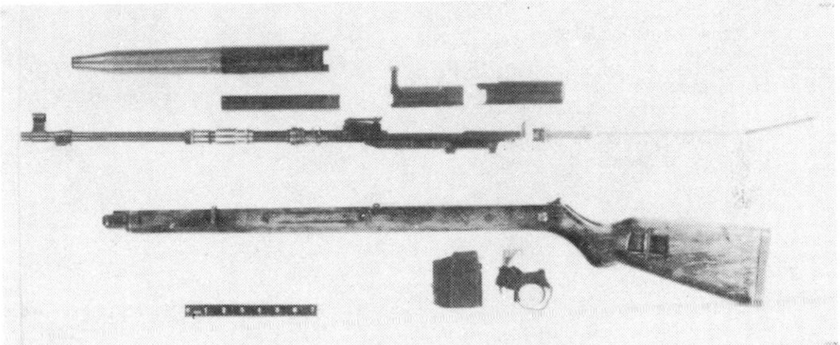

Model 52 Field Stripped.

Field Stripping the Model 52 Rifle

The magazine is released by pressing forward on the magazine lever. After clearing the weapon to assure that the chamber is empty, disassemble the receiver cover—carefully, as the driving spring is always compressed. Push the receiver cover forward until the side rails are out of the receiver slots. Lift the cover slightly and slide back along the top of the receiver until the driving spring snaps down. Hold bolt carrier to the right and slide it to the rear until it reaches the disassembly notch. Remove bolt carrier and bolt. To remove bolt from bolt carrier, slide bolt to the rear and press down the front end until it is disengaged from the bolt carrier.

Slide the bolt forward out of the carrier. After applying the safety, remove the trigger housing group by forcing the rear of the triggerguard back and rotating it downward. (Disassembly is difficult, as the rear of the triggerguard is hard to grasp and pull to the rear to disengage guard from housing.) Slide the trigger housing group forward and downward. Remove the handguard over the barrel by depressing ears on each side of the stock, at the rear end of the handguard. If the barrel and receiver assembly is to be removed from the stock, depress plunger visible through hole in bayonet, and slide the barrel sleeve forward. Assemble in the reverse order.

How the Model 52 Rifle Works

The magazine is loaded and the operating handle is pulled to the rearmost position, compressing the driving spring, and released. The driving spring drives the bolt carrier and bolt forward. The top round is stripped from the magazine and chambered during the forward stroke of the bolt. As the bolt chambers the round, the extractor enters the extractors groove of the cartridge case. Locking occurs during the last 0.3 of an inch of bolt carrier travel, when the bolt locking lugs are cammed down into the receiver locks. The weapon can now be fired by pulling the trigger, which releases the hammer. The hammer strikes the firing pin to fire the round. After firing, powder gases pass through the gas port and enter the gas chamber formed by the gas sleeves and barrel. The gases cause the actuator to strike the bolt carrier. Momentum of the bolt carrier unlocks the action and carries the bolt to the rearmost position, compressing the driving spring. During the bolt recoil stroke, the extractor pulls the cartridge case back with the bolt until ejection occurs as the ejector strikes a lug in the rear of the receiver recess. The driving spring returns the bolt carrier and bolt to battery to complete one cycle of fire.

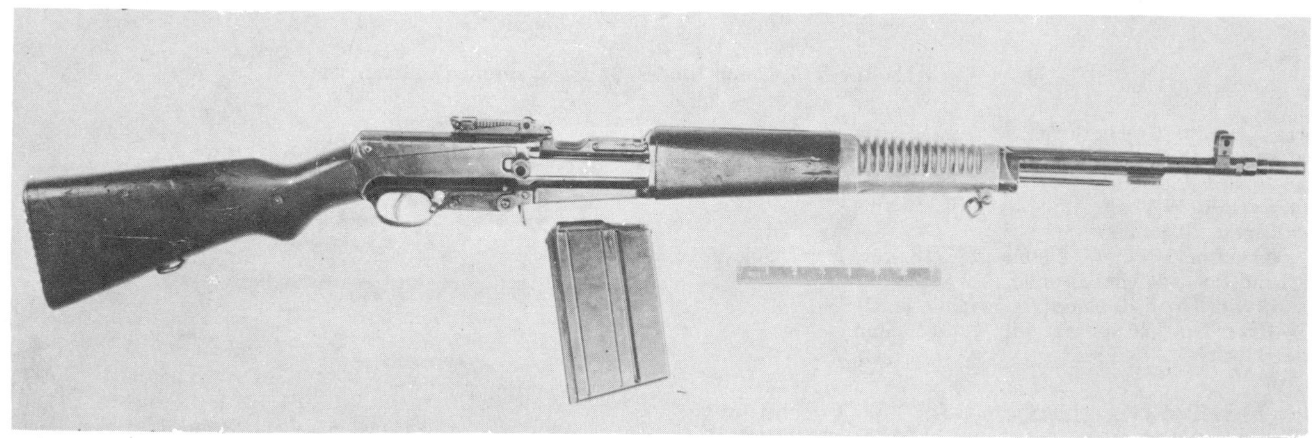

Czech ZH 29 Semi-automatic Rifle.

This rifle was manufactured in limited numbers. Most of these weapons are semi-automatic only. Specimens were distributed very widely to Government heads who might be able to swing contracts to the manufacturers. Specimens bearing the insigne of the Lion of Judah, King of Abyssinia, were brought to this country from the Middle East. At least one with the insigne of the King of Siam was returned from the Far East.

These rifles are beautifully made of the finest materials. Caliber is 7.9mm German Service.

Characteristics. Length 45.5″. Barrel 21.5″. Weight about 10 lbs. Magazine 10 cartridges. (Some are 15 shot.)

These rifles are gas operated. Gas passing through a barrel port expands against the head of a piston-operating rod below the barrel. As the rod is driven back its rear contacts the breechblock, forcing it out of locking engagement in the receiver, then carrying it straight back to eject and compress the recoil spring. The magazine is a detachable box mounted from below. The magazine may be loaded through the top with two 5-shot Mauser clips if desired. Rear sight has a wind gauge and is adjustable from 100-1400 meters.

Normal fire requires a single pull for each shot.

Identification. Projecting box magazine. Special side camming breechblock. Aluminum cooling jacket. Sporter type appearance.

Evaluation. One of the finest light rifles ever built, from the standpoint of materials and manufacture. As a military rifle it is too complicated and too susceptible to stoppage by dirt in action. If converted to a legal rifle by removal of the full-auto feature, it is a fine sporter within its limitations.

Ammunition. German Service 7.9 mm. Made in the U. S. as 8mm Mauser. Because standard commercial ammunition for hunting is usually less powerful than military charges, gas port adjustment may be necessary for proper function. This can be done without tools.

Czech 7.62mm Model 58 Assault Rifle

Caliber: 7.62, uses Czech copy of Soviet M1943 rimless cartridge.
System of Operation: Gas, selective fire.
Weight, Loaded:
- **Wooden stock version:** 8.75 lbs.
- **Metal stock version:** 8.75 lbs.
- **Weight, empty:** 7:31 lbs.

Length, Overall:
- **Wooden stock version:** 33 in.
- **Metal stock version, stock folded:** 25 in.
- **Metal stock version, stock fixed:** 33 in.

Barrel Length: 15.8 in.
Feed Mechanism: 30 round, staggered column, detachable box magazine.
Sights:
- **Front**—Protected post.
- **Rear**—Tangent leaf, adjustable in 100-meter increments from 100 to 800 meters.

Cyclic Rate: 700-800 R.P.M.
Muzzle Velocity: 2300 f.p.s.

The Czechs have adopted a new selective fire weapon which may, in time, replace the Model 52/57 semi-automatic rifle and their submachine guns chambered for pistol cartridges.

The light weight of this new weapon indicates that some components may be made of light weight alloys. The weapon has a superficial external resemblance to the Soviet AK-47. A short knife type bayonet is used with this weapon.

Czech 7.62mm Model 58 Assault Rifle.

Czech 7.62mm Model 58 Assault Rifle with folding metal stock.

Czech 7.62mm Model 58 Assault Rifle with metal stock folded.

CZECHOSLOVAK SUBMACHINE GUNS

The Czechoslovaks have come out with a large number of submachine gun designs since World War II. Most of these designs appeared only in prototype form and were intended for oversea sales. Among these were the ZK466, CZ247, ZB47, and ZK476. These weapons are not used by the Czechoslovak Army. Before the Communists took over Czechoslovakia, her army used the 9mm Parabellum as the service cartridge for pistols and submachine guns. Two submachine guns chambered for that cartridge were adopted by the Czechoslovak Army: the Model 23 and the Model 25 submachine guns. After the adoption of the Soviet 7.62mm pistol cartridge by the Czechslovaks, two weapons similar to the Models 23 and 25, but chambered for the 7.62mm pistol cartridge, were produced. These are the current Czechoslovak service weapons.

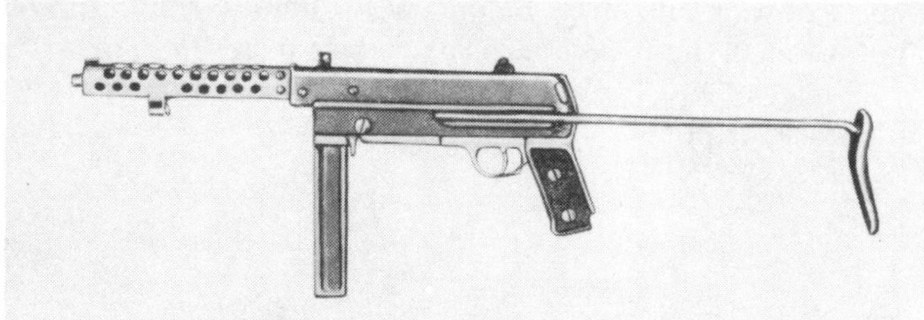

ZK466 9mm Submachine Gun.

Czechoslovak 9mm Model 23 Submachine Gun.

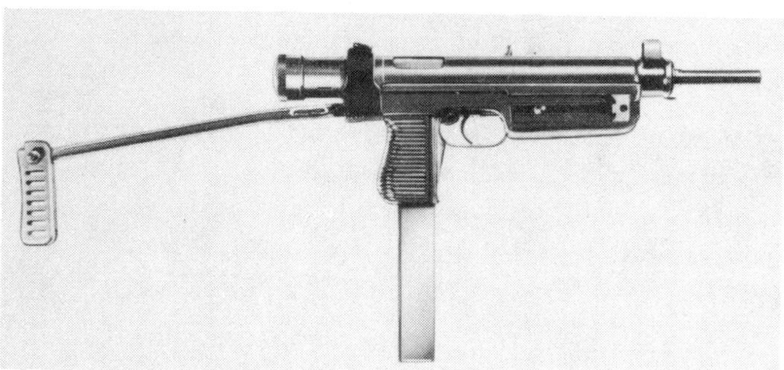

Czech 9mm Model 25 Submachine Gun.

Caliber: 9mm Parabellum.
Weight, M23, loaded: 8 lb., with 24-round magazine. 8.4 lb., with 40-round magazine.
M25, loaded: 8.7 lb., with 24-round magazine. 9.0 lb., with 40-round magazine.
Length, overall: 27 in. for Model 23 and Model 25 with stock extended; 17.5 in. for Model 25 with stock folded.
Barrel length: 11.2 in.
Feed mechanism: 24-round or 40-round detachable, staggered, box magazine.
Sights: Front: Hooded barleycorn.
Rear: V-notch on rotary base; adjustable for 100, 200, 300, and 400 meters.
Muzzle velocity: 1470 f.p.s.
Cyclic rate of fire: 600-650 rounds per minute.

The Model 23 and Model 25 are basically the same weapon, but the Model 23 has a wooden stock and the Model 25 has a folding metal stock. The weapons have several outstanding features and are good examples of modern submachine gun construction. They share most of their unusual features with the Israeli Uzi submachine gun. Among these features are:

The magazine well is in the pistol grip. This gives the magazine far better support than is normally obtained with a submachine gun.

The guns have a very short overall length in comparison to their barrel length. This is made possible by

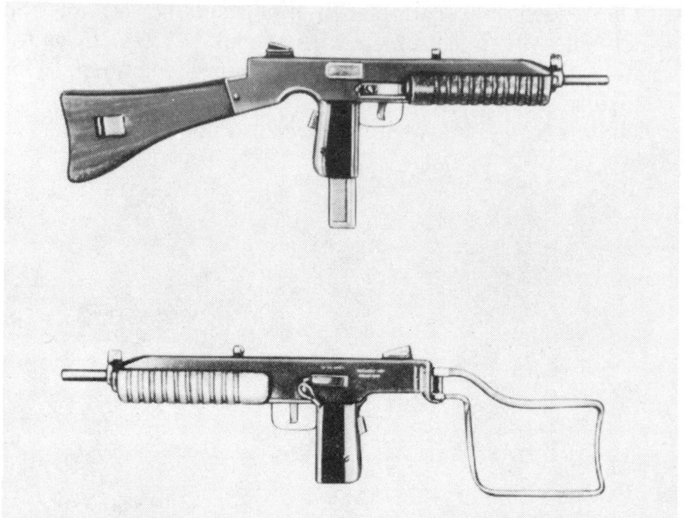

ZK476 9mm Submachine Gun.

a hollow bolt, which telescopes the rear 6⅛ inches of the barrel. Only a 1⅞-inch length of the 8-inch bolt is solid; the remainder is hollowed out to telescope the barrel.

The trigger mechanism on the Czechoslovak weapons is so designed that a short pull on the trigger gives semi-automatic fire, while pulling the trigger all the way to the rear gives full automatic fire.

The ejection port is closed at all times to the entry of dirt, except when the weapon is ejecting.

These weapons also have an unusually simple method of disassembly and assembly.

How to Load and Fire the Model 23 and Model 25 Submachine Guns

Draw the operating handle to the rear. The weapon fires from an open bolt, and therefore the bolt will remain to the rear. Insert a loaded magazine in the well of the pistol grip. Squeeze the trigger. If the trigger is pulled about halfway to the rear, the weapon will fire single shots with occasional doubles. If the trigger is pulled all the way to the rear, the weapon will fire automatically until it is empty or until the trigger is released. To remove the magazine, pull the magazine catch (located at the bottom rear of the pistol grip) to the rear, and pull the magazine down and out of the weapon. The safety blocks the rear of the trigger, and also locks the bolt. To put the weapon on SAFE, push the safety lever to the right.

How the Model 23 and Model 25 Submachine Guns Work

Chambering. With the bolt in rearward position, the trigger is pulled. This depresses the sear, releasing the bolt. The operating spring drives the bolt forward. The lower edge of the bolt face strips a round from the magazine and forces it forward into the chamber.

Locking. No locking step takes place, since the weapon is of the straight blowback type.

Firing. Firing occurs when the operating spring drives the bolt forward against the chambered round, and the fixed firing pin strikes the primer.

Extraction. The extractor engages in the extraction groove of the round as it is chambered. When blowback drives the bolt rearward, the extractor pulls the cartridge case out of the chamber.

Ejection. When the cartridge case (held by the recoiling bolt) clears the chamber, it strikes the tip of the stationary ejecting rod and pivots to the right. Simultaneously, the ejection ports of the bolt and receiver move into alinement, allowing the cartridge case to be thrown clear of the weapon.

Cocking. Since the gun fires only from an open bolt, it is cocked by moving the bolt rearward until the sear engages the sear notch in the bolt, thus holding the bolt to the rear against pressure of the operating spring. Cocking may be accomplished either manually or, when firing, by blowback.

Semi-automatic fire. The sear assembly is pivoted at the front and contains a spring-loaded plunger extending to the rear. The trigger, which is pivoted at the rear, has a forward projection which rests on the sear plunger. As the trigger is pulled, its projection bears against the sear notch in the bolt. The bolt then moves forward to chamber and fire the round. As the trigger is pulled beyond the point at which the bolt is released, the trigger projection rotates out of engagement with the sear plunger, thus allowing the sear to rise under pressure of the sear spring. Upon firing, the bolt is blown back to the rear until the sear engages the sear notch in the bolt.

NOTE. Since no positive disconnector is provided, a slow squeeze on the trigger can result in short bursts.

Full automatic fire. In full automatic fire the trigger is pulled all the way to the rear, beyond the semi-automatic fire position. A projection on the trigger now engages the sear directly, disengaging it from the bolt and allowing full automatic fire until the trigger is released or the magazine emptied.

Field Stripping the Model 23 and Model 25 Submachine Guns

Disassembly of weapon. Remove magazine. Push forward on button in center of receiver barrel jacket cap; at the same time, turn cap ⅛ turn to right or left and remove to the rear.

Slide bolt assembly rearward by means of the operating handle.

Pull trigger, and slide bolt assembly to the rear, out of receiver/barrel-jacket assembly.

Use bolt assembly as tool to loosen barrel locking nut. Place bolt assembly around barrel, with slots at front of bolt engaging lugs of barrel locking nut. Unscrew locking nut by turning bolt counterclockwise.

Pull barrel forward from receiver/barrel-jacket assembly.

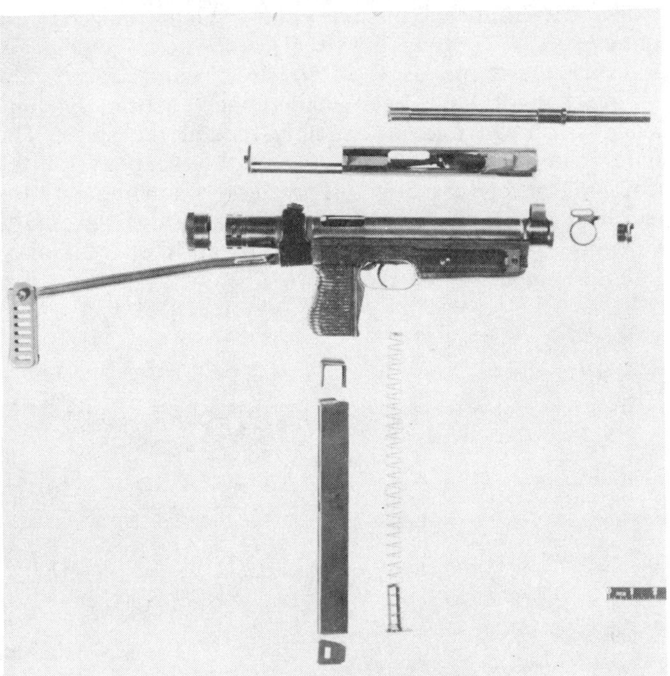

Model 25 Field Stripped.

To unfasten stock, remove screw holding the metal neck of stock to the stock support. To remove from receiver/barrel-jacket assembly, pull stock to the rear and left.

Use same procedure for Model 23.

Disassembly of magazine. Through the rectangular opening in magazine base, depress flat metal stop; slide flat metal base cover to the rear, thereby releasing magazine spring. Withdraw spring and cartridge follower through bottom of magazine.

Assembly. Assembly is accomplished by performing the steps for disassembly in reverse order.

Czechoslovak 7.62mm Submachine Gun.

System of operation: Blowback, selective fire.
Length, overall: 27 in.
Barrel length: 11.2 in.
Feed mechanism: 32-round detachable, staggered-box magazine.
Sights: Front: Hooded blade.
Rear: Square notch on rotary base, adjustable for 100, 200, 300, and 400 meters.
Muzzle velocity: 1800 f.p.s.
Cyclic rate of fire: 600-650 r.p.m
Weight, loaded: 8.8 lbs.
Note that only the weight and overall length with stock folded will be different for the version with metal stock.

The 7.62mm submachine gun which replaced the 9mm Models 23 and 25 in the Czechoslovak Army are basically the same as the Models 23 and 25. A few minor changes have been made, but function, loading, firing, assembly, and disassembly remain the same. The major change is the chambering of the weapons for the 7.62mm pistol cartridge. The heavy loading of the Czechoslovak-made 7.62mm pistol cartridge gives the weapons a velocity which falls in the class of the United States M1 and M2 carbines.

Special Note on Czechoslovak Submachine Guns

The Czechoslovak 9mm Models 23 and 25 submachine guns, as well as the 7.62mm submachine guns, have a magazine filler built into the right side of their plastic fore-ends. The ammunition for these weapons is packed in 8-round chargers (clips). The charger is laid base down in the guide slot of the magazine filler, with the weapon on its left side. The empty magazine is then pushed down the guide, mouth forward (toward the muzzle of the weapon), and the cartridges are stripped into the magazine.

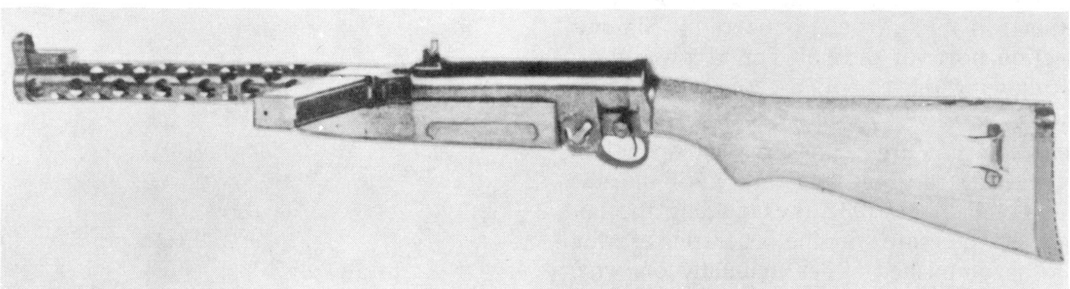

Czech Submachine Gun Model ZK-383-P.

Caliber: 9mm Parabellum.
Magazine: Detachable box, staggered, capacity 40 rounds.
Ballistics: Average for cartridge employed.
Weight: About 8 pounds excluding magazine.
Magazine Positioned: Horizontally to left.
Sights: Rear adjustable leaf. Post front.
Gun Operated By: Straight blowback. Projection of spent case.
Locking: Strictly unlocked. Only weight and inertia of breechblock plus recoil spring supports breech closure at instant of firing, as in common submachine gun practice.
Cooling: Heavy ventilated barrel.
Cyclic Rate of Fire: 500 to 700 per minute, rate can be regulated.
Regulator: Removable bolt weight to allow fire increase by lessening inertia.
Type of Fire: Semi or full automatic.
Selector System: Actuated through short or long pull on trigger.
Cocking Handle: Right side.

Note: While this model is an elementary blowback, it has several unusual features. The regular military model is fitted with a detachable barrel and equipped with a bipod mount. With supporting bipod to fire from prone position, continuous fire may be maintained for a considerable period through changing barrels when overheating develops.

A police model is available under the designation ZK-383-P. Intended for normal police use where sustained fire is seldom required, it has a fixed barrel and is minus the mount. These guns were manufactured at Brno, home of several Czech pistol designs. This weapon has not been used extensively.

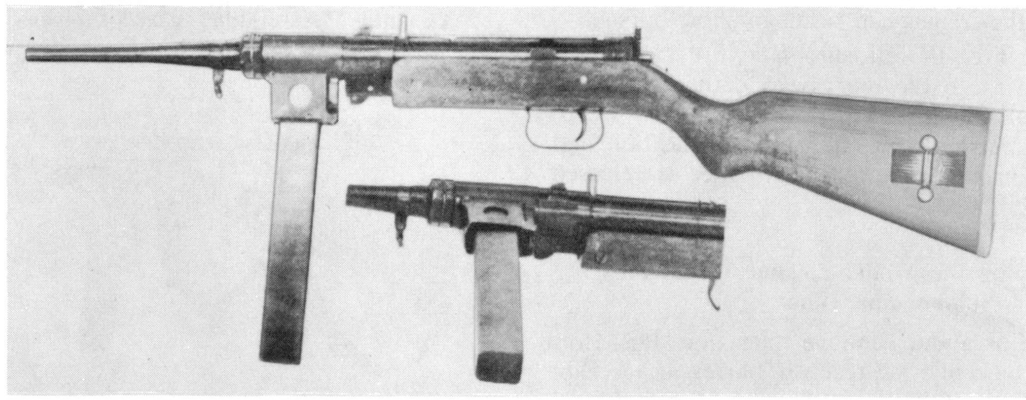

Czech CZ-47 Submachine Gun.

Caliber: 9mm Parabellum.
Magazine: Detachable box, staggered, capacity 40 rounds.
Ballistics: Average for cartridge.
Magazine Positioning: Vertically below OR horizontally to the left on special rotary nut.
Overall Length: 30.9 inches.
Weight Without Magazine: 6.4 pounds.
Gun Operated by: Blowback. Projection of the spent case.
Locked: By inertia only, standard blowback. No formal lock required.
Cooled: Heavy tapered barrel only.
Cyclic Rate of Fire: 560 per minute.
Bolt Position When Firing: Open, standard practice.
Type of Fire: Semi or full automatic.
Selector: Operates through trigger. Initial pressure fires semiautomatically.

Continuing further pull on trigger produces full automatic fire until trigger is released.

Ejection: To the right.
Cocking Handle: Right side.

Note: This gun is an entirely different design than the ZK-383. It is made by a different factory, the Strakonice plant. It is not used by the Czech Army.

CZECH MACHINE GUNS

Czechoslovakia has been a prolific producer of machine gun designs since the early twenties. The famed ZB26 (Model 26 light machine gun) is still used extensively throughout the world, as is the ZB30 and ZB53 (Model 37 heavy machine gun). The British Bren was developed from the ZB series of light machine guns, and still has an excellent reputation as a light machine gun. Since World War II, the Czechoslovaks have come out with a new gun which borrows considerably from their older designs, but has some very interesting innovations. The Model 52 light machine gun, a very versatile weapon, has replaced the Model 26 in the Czechoslovak Army. The Model 37 heavy machine gun has been replaced by the Soviet Goryunov, and the 15mm Model 38 (ZB60) has been replaced by the Soviet 12.7mm DShK M1938/46, for which the Czechoslovaks have produced a quadruple antiaircraft mount.

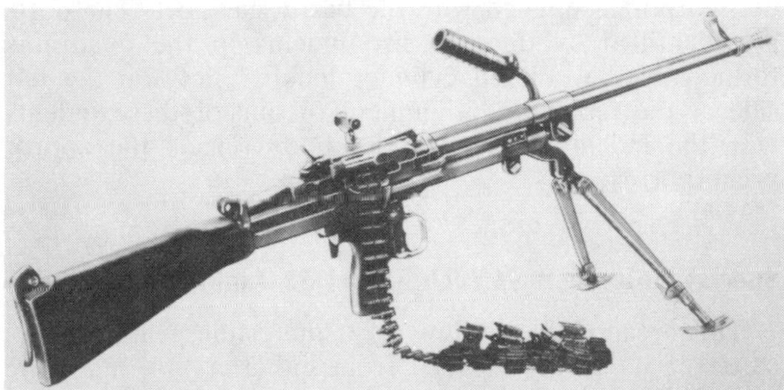

Czechosolovak 7.62mm Model 52 Light Machine Gun.

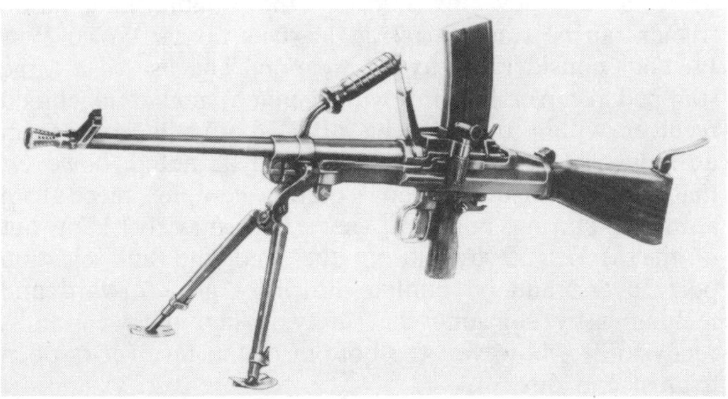

Czech Model 52 with Box Magazine.

System of operation: Gas, selective fire.
Length, overall: 41 in.
Barrel length: 21.3 in.
Feed mechanism: 25-round box magazine, or 100-round non-disintegrating link belt (push-out type link).
Sights: Front: Blade with removable hood.
Rear: U-notch, adjustable for elevation and windage, graduated from 200 to 1200 meters.
Muzzle velocity: 2450 f.p.s.
Cyclic rate of fire: 1140 r.p.m. with belt, 900 r.p.m. with box magazine (approx.).
Weight without belt or magazine, with bipod: 17.6 lb.

The Model 52 light machine gun is also chambered for the Czechoslovak 7.62mm Model 52 "intermediate-sized" cartridge. The weapon can be fed from a belt or a box magazine without changing feed covers. When fed from the belt, the feed is similar to that of the Czechoslovak Model 37 heavy machine gun; when fed from the magazine, it is similar to that of the ZB26. The weapon makes extensive use of stampings and is, all told, a very sophisticated weapon. Possibly its greatest shortcoming is that it may be too sophisticated; in general, it can be said that the simplest weapons give the best performance in the field. Although the Model 52 is a well-designed weapon, it is not particularly simple.

A slightly modified version of the model 52 light machine gun, chambered for the Soviet designed 7.62mm M43 cartridge, was adopted in 1957 as the Model 52/57.

How to Load and Fire the Model 52 Light Machine Gun

Cock the gun by pressing down on the lug which protrudes from the safety (on top left side of pistol grip) and pulling pistol grip to the rear. The bolt will remain to the rear since this weapon fires from an open bolt. If the pistol grip is in the rearward position, press down on the lug and push the pistol grip forward until the slide is engaged by the sear; then pull the pistol grip rearward until the pistol grip catches on the rear lock.

To load the gun with a belt of ammunition, push upward on the feed-way cover. Lay the first cartridge in the belt between the belt holding pawls, and close and lock the cover. The link ejection port cover must be in its raised position or belt movement will be blocked.

To load the gun for magazine fire, press forward on the magazine feed port latch, allowing the cover to spring forward. Invert the magazine and insert it in the magazine opening until the latch engages the magazine. The belt feedway cover and the link ejection port cover should be closed. Pressure on the bottom half moon of the trigger will produce automatic fire; pressure on the top half moon of the trigger will produce semi-automatic fire. To put the weapon on safe, push the safety lever (located on top left side of the pistol grip) down.

How the Model 52 Light Machine Gun Works

When the gun is fired, gas from the barrel is bled through a port into the gas cylinder and into the gas chamber at the front of the receiver housing. The expanding gas operates on the gas piston to force the bolt carrier rearward in recoil. For a short distance, the bolt carrier travels alone. This short period is followed by an unlocking period, during which the rear of the bolt rotates downward out of engagement with the receiver locking abutments. Upon completion of unlocking, the bolt is carried to the rear by the carrier, the spent cartridge is extracted from the barrel, and the case is ejected forward.

Upon completion of recoil, the residual energy of the bolt and bolt carrier is absorbed by a recoil plate at the rear of the receiver housing, and the bolt carrier moves forward under the force of the compressed driving spring in the stock. If the gun is being fired semi-automatically, the sear will engage the carrier and hold it until the trigger is again pressed. When the trigger is pressed, the carrier will move forward; as the rear of the carrier clears the sear, it will depress the disconnector, releasing the sear so that it can again be in position to engage the carrier.

Feeding takes place on the counterrecoil stroke of the bolt and bolt carrier. The cartridge to be fed is held in the center of the feedway by the belt holding pawl or by the pressure of the magazine spring, depending upon the type of feed being used. The forward-moving bolt strikes the lower edge of the cartridge rim, stripping it from the belt link or magazine lips. The nose of the cartridge is depressed by a ramp in the receiver breech ring, and, as the bolt continues forward, the ramp depresses the rear of the cartridge, seating the rim between the extractor claws.

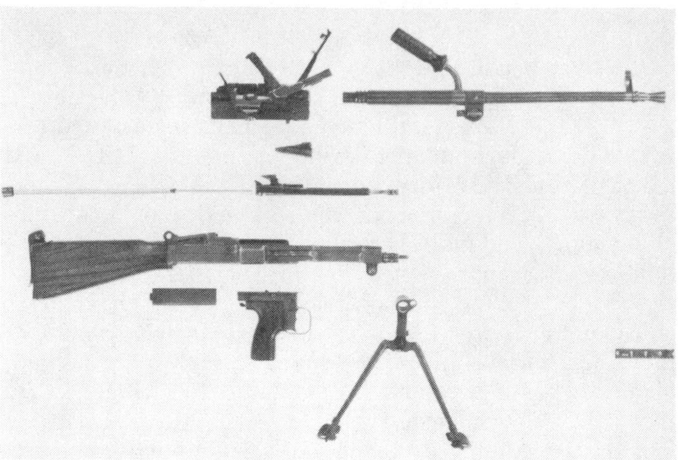

Model 52 Field Stripped.

Field Stripping the Model 52 Light Machine Gun

Driving spring and rod. The driving spring is retained by a cap with internal bayonet-type slots that engage projections of the spring tube within the stock. To remove the spring assembly, press in on the cap, turn it counterclockwise to disengage the slots, and withdraw the spring and rod from the stock.

Barrel and bipod. Press forward on the magazine feed port latch, allowing the cover to spring open. Using the cover as a handle, turn the barrel lock clockwise and draw the barrel forward out of the receiver. Turn the bipod assembly to disengage its key, and remove the bipod from the weapon housing.

Receiver assembly, bolt carrier, and bolt. The receiver, bolt carrier, and bolt are removed simultaneously. Draw the bolt carrier rearward so that the piston is located slightly to the rear of the gas chamber in the receiver housing. Lift up on the front end of the receiver and remove the receiver, bolt carrier, and bolt from the weapon. Remove the bolt carrier and bolt through the rear of the receiver.

Trigger mechanism assembly. Depress the pistol grip lock lever and push forward on the pistol grip. Slide the trigger mechanism assembly out of the front end of its slot in the weapon housing. Unhook the dust cover from the rear of the trigger mechanism housing.

Reassembly. Reassemble the weapon by reversing the procedure described above.

Adjustment of gas cylinder. There are four gas port openings that may be selected to vary the power of the weapon. To change the port setting, the barrel must first be removed from the gun as described above. To change port setting, turn the gas regulator until the desired port is aligned with the barrel gas port. The ports are identified by different-size indents in the quadrants formed by the crossed cylinder locking slots on the left side of the regulator. Alignment of one of these indents with the indent in the cylinder body selects the appropriate port size.

Special Note on the Czech Model 52 Light Machine Gun

This weapon has many very interesting features. Because of its ability to feed from either a box magazine or a belt, without changing feed components, it has a great deal of tactical flexibility. Its trigger mechanism, while hardly new in concept (the double half moon trigger can be traced back at least as far as World War I), adds considerably to the weapon. The use of a large stamped receiver housing with a much smaller machined receiver within the housing also is advantageous from an industrial point of view. It should be noted, however, that the machined receiver is quite a complex piece from a manufacturing point of view. Dirt may be kept out of the Model 52 by closing the feed and link ejection port covers, and by pulling the pistol grip forward and locking it by engaging the safety. When the weapon is ready to fire, however, the bottom of the receiver is open to dust and dirt.

The bolt is carried on a post on the slide/piston assembly in a fashion similar to that of ZB26 or the Bren gun, but it does not lock like these guns. The two locking lugs on the rear of the bolt ride in cut-outs in the receiver and are locked in the side of the receiver.

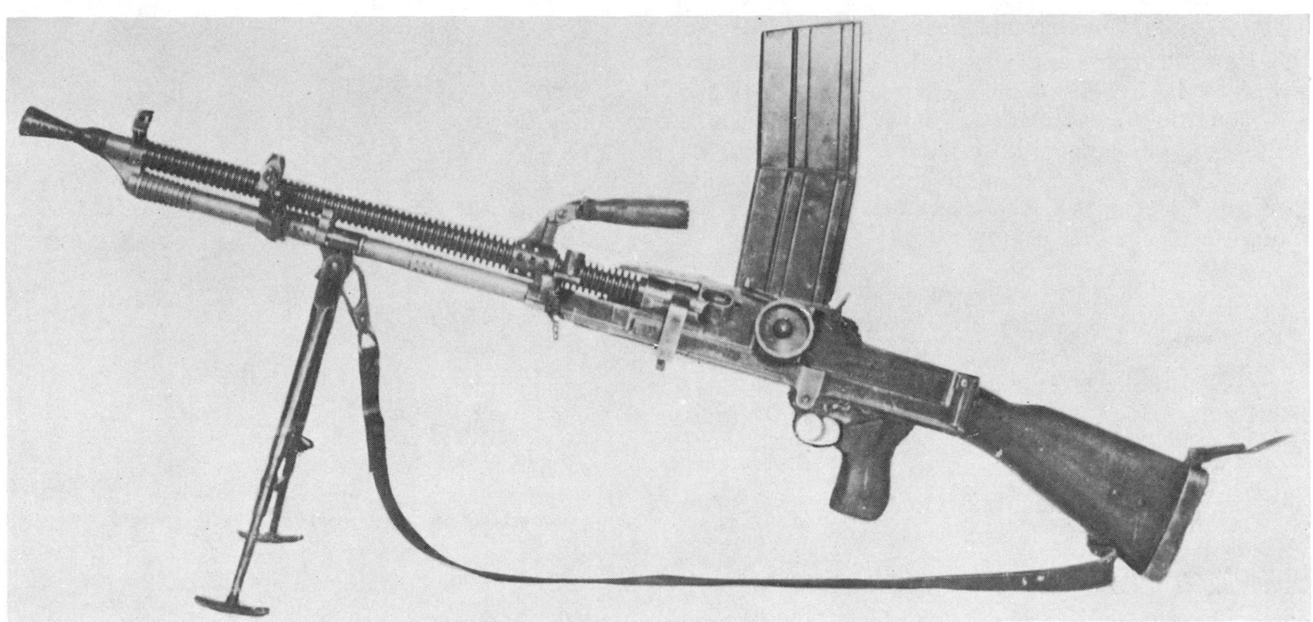

ZB26 (Brno) LMG. The magazine is a special oversize one.

The Brno light machine weapons are world famous. In several modifications they have been used in Europe, Asia, and South America. The British Bren Gun was modified from the Brno.

The Besa Heavy Machine Guns used by the British, are also of Czech design.

Special features include the carrying handle with wooden grip mounted around barrel near breech end; perforated flash hider and folding bipod mount. The large number of cooling rings around barrel is common in guns of this design.

These arms were also made in Czechoslovakia for South American countries in various calibers.

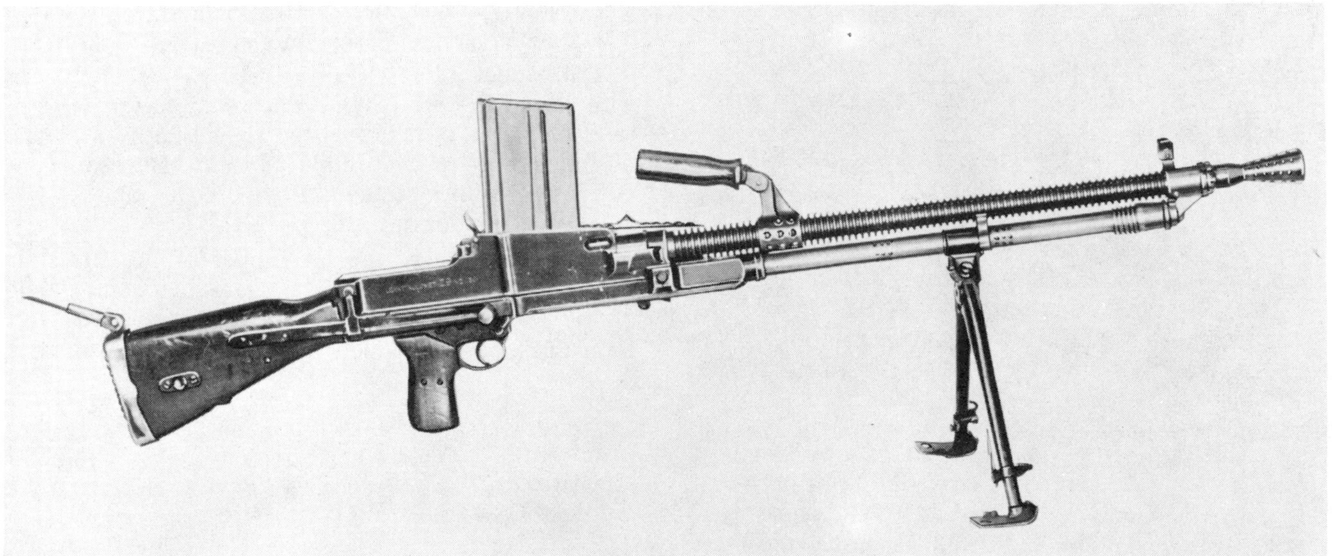

7.92mm ZB30 Light Machine Gun. Czech and Chinese manufacture.

Caliber: 7.92mm German type ammunition.
Magazine: 20-round detachable box.
Overall length: 46.1″.
Weight loaded: 21.3 pounds.
Ballistics: Standard for cartridge.
Barrel Length: 24 inches.
Barrel Removal: General Brno type.

Special Note on ZB26 and ZB30

The ZB26 was the forerunner of the famous British Bren Gun. Originally manufactured in Czechoslovakia it was sold throughout the world. In recent years it was manufactured in Chinese arsenals. It was the standard light machine gun of the Czech Army and has been used by many other countries as well.

Loading and Firing

Pull back the bolt handle to cock the bolt and then push the handle forward. Pull back magazine cover and insert loaded magazine mouth end first. Push down until it locks. For semi-automatic fire move the selector on the left side of the trigger group to the rear; for full auto fire, push it forward. When the selector is in the vertical position, it acts as a safety.

Field Stripping

Push out receiver locking pin and withdraw the frame group. The slide, bolt, and gas piston will now come out the rear of the receiver.

Release the barrel nut catch and lift up to the right as far as it will go. This releases the barrel which may now be slid off to the front.

Push the butt plate catch and remove the two buffer springs.

Differences Between the ZB26 and ZB30

Outwardly, the two weapons are almost identical in appearance. The bolt of the ZB26 does not ride on the piston post as does that of the ZB30 (and the Bren). It is cammed into the locked position by a built-up rear section of the piston/slide assembly, but does not "sit" on the post. The ZB30J is similar to the ZB30, but has a knurled section on its barrel to the rear and just in front of the carrying handle.

Czechoslovak 12.7mm Quad DShK M1938/46 Heavy Machine Gun.

This weapon consists of four Czechoslovak-made (but Soviet-designed) DShK M1938/46 heavy machine guns on a Czechoslovak-designed, two-wheeled antiaircraft mount. The weapon is therefore generally similar in purpose to the United States M45 quad cal. .50. The Czechoslovak mount, however, lacks powered operation and also suffers from having magazines with a very limited capacity (fifty rounds for each gun).

The weapons are the same as the Soviet DShK, which is covered in detail in chapter 43. The weight of the complete equipment is 1411 pounds, and the mount is capable of 360-degree traverse and 90-degree elevation.

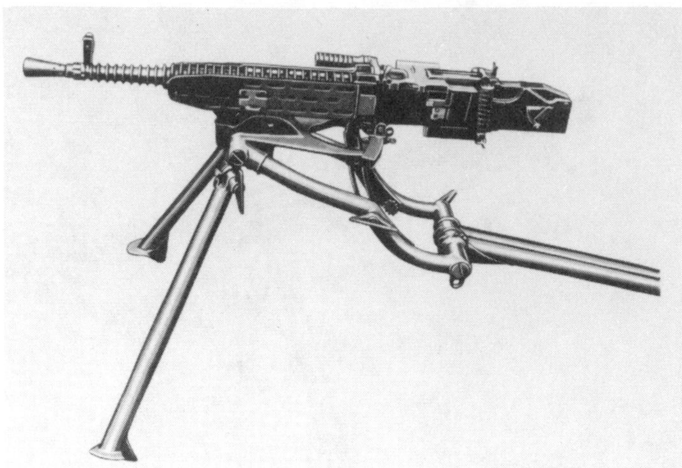

Czechoslovakian Heavy Machine Gun Model 37 (ZB 53).

Caliber: 7.92mm.
System of operation: Gas operated, two cyclic rates of fire.
Weight: 41.8 lb.
Length, overall: 43.5 in.
Barrel length: 26.7 in.
Sights: Front: Blade with guard.
Rear: Folding, leaf, graduated from 300 to 2000 meters in 100-meter increments, fixed 200-meter battle sight.
Cyclic rate: 450-550 r.p.m. or 700 r.p.m.
Feed device: Metallic link belt, 100- or 200-round capacity.
Muzzle velocity: 2600 f.p.s. (approx.).

The Model 37 heavy machine-gun has been manufactured for export in calibers from 7mm to 8.5mm. The military designation for the gun is Model 37 (ZB 37); the commercial designation is Model 53 (ZB 53).

The Model 37 is an air-cooled, gas-operated weapon with selective slow (500 r.p.m.) and fast (700 r.p.m.) rates of fire. It is fed from the right side by a metal belt of either 100- or 200-round capacity. By use of an attachment to the Model 45 tripod, it can be quickly adapted to antiaircraft fire.

This weapon was the forerunner of the British-made Besa tank machine gun. The main functioning features of the Model 37 are the same as those given for the Besa machine gun, which can be found in chapter 17.

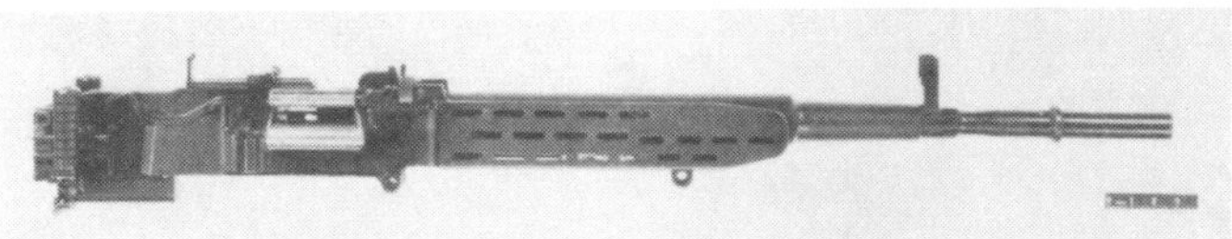

Model 37 with Smooth Barrel.

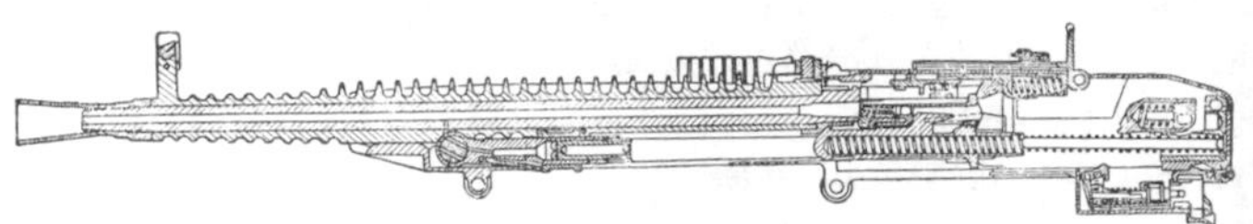

Section View of Model 37.

Chapter 21. Denmark

The Madsen Company

Except in the field of military intelligence, very little attention has ever been given to the Danish Military Small Arms Industry. Yet it has for many years been a factor of very considerable world importance. Its influence is steadily growing today as it adapts U. S. production tools and techniques to its manufacture.

The interested reader is referred to chapter 9 of this book dealing with the subject of machine guns with specific reference to the Madsen products. The developmental and manufacturing work done there by the Arms Syndicate (operating under various names since its inception), has had far greater world significance than is generally recognized.

The prime manufacturer today is the Dansk Industri Syndikat, Compagnie Madsen, A-S, Copenhagen.

Since the close of World War II this organization has done a degree of developmental and experimental work of considerably greater intensity than ever in the past, remarkable though its past performance has always been.

As a matter of record, the following background on the distribution of the Madsen Machine Gun alone may be of interest: Considered alphabetically, the following models have been made for the following countries:

Argentina—Madsen machine guns Models 1910, 1925, 1926, 1928, 1931 and 1935. Most in calibers 7.65mm Argentine Mauser.

Bolivia—Model 1925. Caliber 7.65mm Mauser.

Brazil—Models 1908, 1913, 1916, 1925, 1928, 1932, 1934, 1935 and 1936, in calibers 7mm Mauser and 1946 Model machine gun in caliber 7.62mm (.30 U.S.).

Bulgaria—Models 1915 and 1927. Caliber 8mm Bulgarian.

Chile—Models 1923, 1925, 1926 water cooled, and 1928 and 1940. Most in caliber 7mm Mauser. Model 1946 in caliber 7.62mm (.30-06 U.S.).

China—Models 1916, 1930 and 1937. All in the standard caliber 7.92mm Mauser.

Czechoslovakia—Models 1922 and 1923. Caliber 7.92-mm German.

Denmark—Models 1904, 1916, 1919, 1924, 1939 in caliber 8mm Danish and Model 1948 in caliber 7.62mm.

El Salvador—Models 1951 in caliber 7.62mm and Model 1934 in caliber 7mm Mauser.

Esthonia—Models 1925 and 1937 in caliber .303 British.

Ethiopia—Models 1907, 1910, 1934 and 1935. All in caliber 7.92mm.

Finland—Models 1910, 1920, 1921 and 1923. Most in caliber 7.62mm.

France—Models 1915, 1919, 1922 and 1924. All in caliber 8mm Lebel.

Germany—Models 1941, 1942 in caliber 7.92mm.

Great Britain—Models 1915, 1919, 1929, 1931 and 1939 in caliber .303 British.

Holland—Models 1919, 1923, 1926, 1927, 1934, 1938 and 1939. All in caliber 6.5mm Dutch.

Honduras—Models 1937 and 1939 in caliber 7mm Mauser.

Hungary—Models 1925 and 1943 in caliber 7.92mm German.

Indonesia—Model 1950 in caliber .30.

Italy—Models 1908, 1910, 1925 and 1930 in caliber 6.5mm Italian.

Lithuania—Model 1923. Caliber 7.92mm German.

Mexico—Models 1911 and 1934, Caliber 7mm Mauser.

Norway—Models 1914 and 1918. Caliber 6.5mm Norwegian Mauser.

Pakistan—Model 1947. Caliber .303 British.

Paraguay—Model 1926. Caliber 7.65mm Mauser.

Peru—Model 1929. Caliber 7.65mm Mauser.

Portugal—Models 1930, 1936 and 1952. Caliber 7.7mm. Also in Portugal, Models 1936, 1940 and 1947 in caliber 7.92mm.

Russia—Models 1904 and 1915 in caliber 7.62mm Mosin-Nagant.

Spain—Model 1907 and 1922 in caliber 7mm Spanish Mauser.

Sweden—Models 1906, 1914 and 1921. Caliber 6.5-mm Swedish Mauser.

Thailand—Models 1925, 1930, 1934, 1939, 1947 and 1949. Caliber 8mm and Model 1951 in caliber 7.62mm.

Turkey—Models 1925, 1926, 1935 and 1937. Caliber 7.92mm German.

Uruguay—Model 1937. Caliber 7mm Mauser.

Yugoslavia—Various in caliber 7.92mm.

In addition to infantry type machine guns, the Madsen organization has consistently produced very large quantities of aircraft pattern machine guns for many of these various countries. Work on the aircraft designs began at what was then the Danish Recoil Rifle Syndicate in 1923. Their Technical Director, Haubroe, redesigned the infantry gun to adapt it to aircraft use. A muzzle booster and powerful spring buffer were the major mechanical alterations. Cyclic rates were upward of 1000 rounds a minute. These guns can be synchronized for fixed installations, yet are flexible enough for swinging type mounts. After World War I, the German-controlled Junkers Aircraft Plant in Sweden mounted tremendous quantities of various Madsen weapons in aircraft produced by them in both Danish and Swedish assembly plants. These were sold throughout the world. In 1926, 11.35mm machine guns were also introduced. Belt feeds and disintegrating links are common to most of these aircraft alterations.

Much of the machinery and the tooling in this Danish plant is of American design or procurement. In many ways American high production methods are utilized. In general, quite naturally, the basic liaison has been Scandinavian and German.

At the present time a line of post-World War II equipment is under production, running from submachine guns to tank and A.A. guns. We shall proceed to deal with the important items in this new production as they relate to the field of small arms.

The Danish Army

The Danish Army currently uses the following arms:

Common Nomenclature	Danish Nomenclature	Covered Under
9mm F.N. Browning Hi Power Pistol	9mm P M/46	Belgium
9mm SIG Pistol 47/8	9mm P M/49	Switzerland
9mm Suomi Submachine Gun	9mm Mp M/41	Finland
9mm 37-39 Suomi Submachine Gun	9mm Mp M/44 (37)	Sweden
9mm Hovea Submachine Gun M/49	9mm Mp M/49	Denmark
.30 cal. Rifle M1	7.62mm G M/50	U.S.A.
.30 cal. Rifle M1917	7.62mm G M/53 (17)	U.S.A.
7.62mm Madsen M48 Machine Gun	7.62mm Mg M/48	Denmark
.30 cal. SIG M50 Machine Gun	7.62mm Mg M/51	Switzerland
.30 cal. M1919A4 Machine Gun	7.62mm Mg M/52-1 (19)	U.S.A.
.30 cal. M1919A5 Machine Gun	7.62mm Mg M/52-11 (19)	U.S.A.
.50 cal. M2 Browning Heavy Barrel	12.7mm Mg M/50	U.S.A.
7.62mm NATO MG 42 (MG 42/59)		Germany

The characteristics for the M48 Madsen machine gun are basically the same as those for the M1950, given later in this chapter. Operating characteristics are the same.

The Danes have adopted the SIG Model 47/8 9mm pistol as the Model 49, and recently Danish Model 1910/22 Bergmann Bayard pistols have been showing up the the hands of arms dealers in the United States.

Dansk Industri Syndikat, or Madsen Company, as it is commonly known, has brought out a new edition of its very successful postwar submachine gun. This weapon is called the Model 53 by Madsen. These Madsens are very well designed submachine guns and have been purchased in fairly large quantities since their development.

Madsen has developed several new "Assault Rifles" or, if you will, light rifles. The first of these weapons was originally developed around a 7mm cartridge which was quite similar to the British cal. .280 cartridge. A new weapon of different design chambered for the 7.62mm NATO cartridge is now being produced.

The Madsen Company has brought out two new machine guns: the Madsen Saetter rifle-caliber machine gun, and the Madsen Saetter cal. .50 machine gun. These are gas-operated weapons which incorporate all the sophistications found on postwar weapons. The bolts of the two weapons use locking flaps similar in principle, if not in form, to those of the Soviet Degtyarev-series weapons. The bolt systems however, are considerably more sophisticated than the Degtyarev's, particularly that for the cal. .50 gun. Degtyarev was far from the first to use this system of locking flaps (or butterfly wings, as they are sometimes called). Locking flaps were used in the Kjellman Friberg and on early Mauser semi-automatic rifles many years before they appeared in the Degtyarev DP light machine gun.

As a matter of interest, the following information on the basic models of these now-obsolete weapons is given:

Rifle Model 1889 is the basic model and is illustrated later in this chapter.

Infantry Carbine Model 1889 is a shortened M1889 with a turned-down bolt handle.

Artillery Carbine Model 1889 is also a shortened Rifle M1889, but it has a wooden handguard instead of the tube which surrounds the barrel of the rifle.

Engineer Carbine Model 1889 is like the artillery carbine.

Sniper Rifle Model 1928 has a very heavy barrel, micrometer rear sights, a turned-down bolt handle, and a shortened stock. It looks like a sporting-type target rifle, and is just that, for all practical purposes.

All these weapons were chambered for the Danish 8mm rimmed cartridge. The M1889 cartridge had a round-nosed bullet with a velocity of 1968 feet per second. The M1908 ball cartridge used a spitzer-pointed bullet with a velocity of 2460 feet per second.

DANISH PISTOLS

Only one Danish pistol is considered. It is a locked breech high-power pistol with exposed hammer, left side manual safety, short-recoil action, detachable magazine positioned ahead of the triggerguard. The breechblock is a separate unit which travels in the receiver extension as in the case of the military Mauser Pistol. The locking system differs, however. The breechblock passes through a hollow locking block, and the block is cammed down and up in the receiver to lock and unlock into a breechblock and receiver cuts. The action does not open until the barrel has reached the end of its rearward stroke.

Length 10″. Barrel 4″. Weight 36 oz. Magazine capacity 6 or 10. Magazine may be loaded through top of open action from a clip, or by inserting a loaded box magazine from below.

Identification. Unusually thick grip. Detachable box magazine. Locking system. If pistol was made in Belgium, barrel and receiver extension are a single forging. If made in Germany, grip differs in shape and barrel is screwed into extension.

This pistol was also an official Spanish side arm for some time.

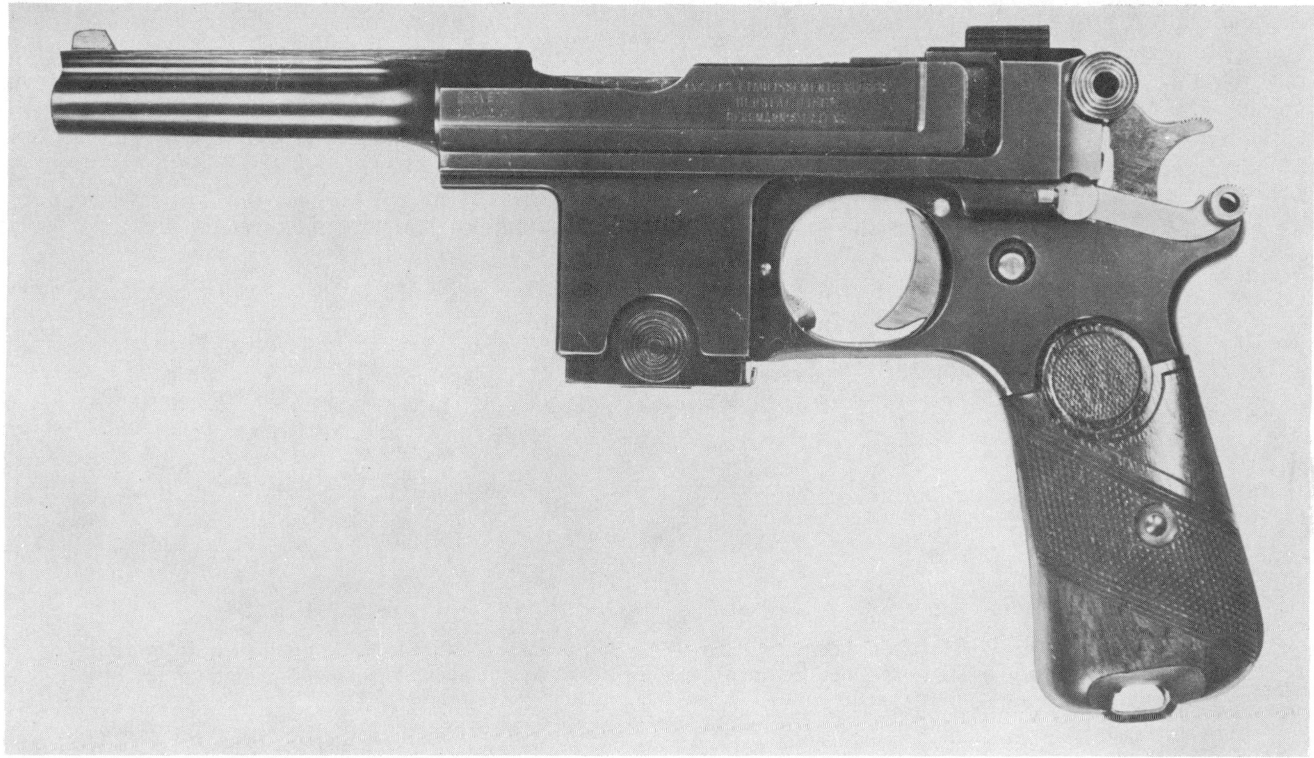

Danish Model 1910/22 Pistol.

Evaluation. One of the strongest and most powerful pistols ever made. Good materials and fine workmanship. Positive lock. However, design is clumsy and bulky and should be considered obsolete.

Ammunition. 9mm Bayard ammunition is not made in the U. S.

DANISH SERVICE RIFLES

The standard Danish rifle was the Krag-Jorgensen, 8mm Danish. This arm somewhat resembles the familiar American Krag (which evolved from the Danish model) in its basic design. It is loaded through a hinged side gate which projects from the right side of the receiver, but the gate hinges forward instead of downward as in our type. The bolt has the customary single front locking lug.

There are several minor modifications of this design, notably in 1910, which introduced a manual safety on the receiver behind the bolt handle and did away with a half cock notch.

The 1928 modification uses a heavy barrel without the barrel jacket found in other models. The stock has only one band instead of the familiar two. Special peep and globe sights are standard. This model was issued for snipers (sharpshooters).

Four minor modifications of carbine forms are also known. Mechanically all are the same, however.

Danish 8mm Krag-Jorgensen Model 1889-10. Note barrel jacket.

Caliber: 8mm Danish Service (rimmed).
Barrel Length: 33".
Overall Length: 52.7".
Weight: 9.75 lbs.
Sights: Barleycorn front; rear tangent adjustable 300-1900 meters.
Operation: Krag-Jorgensen turn bolt. Single front locking lug.
Safety: On late models. Hook behind bolt handle.
Magazine: Horizontal box loaded through right side gate.
Loading: With single cartridges or special clip.
Special Features: Jacket covering barrel in all early standard types. Cutoff. No jacket on barrel of M-1928.

Identification. Magazine gate containing feeding mechanism is hinged at front end. Gate must be pushed out to right to load. Special safety hook identifies late models. Single locking lug on bolt. Barrel jacket on early models.

Evaluation. Excellent materials and workmanship. Clumsy magazine design. While in theory the single locking lug is undesirable, in actual practice the locking system is entirely satisfactory with the cartridges used. The Model 1928 in particular is capable of precision shooting and is highly regarded in Europe for its accuracy, even though the standard military cartridge is relatively poor from a ballistic standpoint. If converted to U. S. caliber, pressures should be held to about 40,000 ft/lbs.

Ammunition. Not manufactured in the U. S.

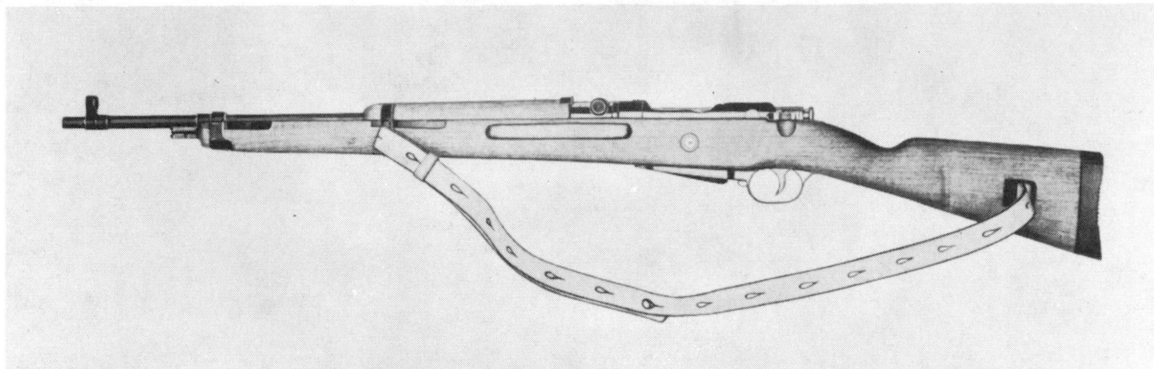

Madsen Light Weight Bolt Action Military Rifle. Turnbolt lock. Fixed magazine loaded from charger (clip). Made for any military cartridge, rim or rimless to order. Weight about 7½ pounds. Designed specifically for soldiers of comparatively small stature.

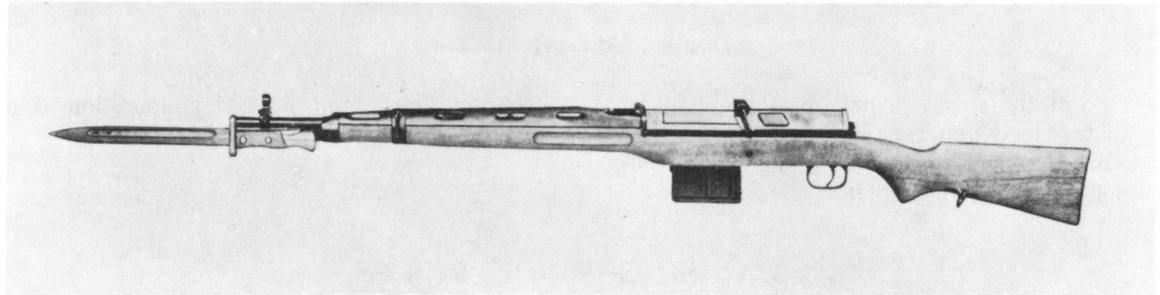

Madsen-made Ljungman Semi-auto military rifle; made as a prototype only.

Special Note: This rifle is an improved version of the official Swedish Army rifle discussed in chapter 40.

Caliber: Any rimless military cartridge specified. (Can be adapted to rim cartridges but is not advisable.)
Magazine: Detachable steel box projecting from bottom of receiver.
Overall Length: 45.66 inches.
Weight: 9.92 pounds without bayonet.
Ballistics: As for cartridges specified.
Magazine Capacity: 10 rounds rimless. Loadable through top of action with two 5-shot clips.
Magazine type: Detachable staggered box.
Operation: Gas through simple communicating cylinder, Ljungman system.
Locking: Dual retracting lugs in bolt actuated through bolt housing, as in German Kar .44 practice.
Sights: Protected blade front on barrel near muzzle.
Rear: Tangent at receiver above chamber.
Cocking Handle: Top right side of housing.
Stock Design: Military. Upper forestock pierced for cooling.

This is a gas-operated semi-automatic rifle. Gas is taken off about half way down the barrel. The gas cylinder is of unusual design. Instead of the long straight tube normally encountered, the tube is wound about the barrel from the middle section. This (theoretically at least) produces a delay in actuation of the lock sufficient to permit holding the breech closed until pressure has dropped to safe limits. In actual gas practice, of course, residual pressure in the chamber is necessary to actuate an arm of this type after the unlocking has commenced, a most important design factor. This may account to some extent for the fact that the Madsen design has been considered as not too successful, attempted gas simplification resulting in trouble from ammunition variables.

It might be mentioned in passing that this arm is also adaptable to rimmed cartridges, though when so produced the magazine is made to carry only 5 cartridges. Sights are graduated in 100 meter steps from 1 to 800 meters. The practical rate of deliverable fire is estimated at 30 rounds per minute. Muzzle brake is built in.

The locking system of this design is based on the very early developments discussed in chapter 7. It is actuated somewhat as in the case of the German World War II semi-automatic rifles, by action of gas passing through a hole in the receiver to a cylinder above the line of the chamber, and striking the breechblock carrier. The carrier has a short free movement during which the breechblock within it stays firmly locked to the receiver.

When the pressure drops to safe limits, cam faces on a slide in the carrier, working against corresponding faces on the internal sections of the retractable locking lugs within the breechblock, cam the lugs out of their seats in the receiver and withdraw them inside the breechblock. From this point on the carrier and the breechblock assembly travel to the rear together to compress the firing spring and recoil springs, to clear the magazine to allow extraction and ejection, and to allow a new cartridge to come up into chambering line.

On the counter-recoil stroke, the cartridge from the top of the magazine is picked up and chambered at the end of the breechblock travel. The carrier and actuating members still have free travel during which the reverse cam action forces the locking lugs through their slots in the outer side of the breechblock walls and into their corresponding locking recesses in the walls of the receiver. The disconnector mechanism requires that the trigger be released before it can engage again for the next shot to be fired.

Madsen Light Automatic Rifle

Madsen 7.62mm NATO Light Automatic Rifle with wooden stock.

Madsen 7.62mm NATO Light Automatic Rifle with tubular steel stock.

Caliber: 7.62mm NATO.
System of Operation: Gas, selective fire.
Weight W/loaded Magazine: 10.6 lbs.
Length, Overall: 42.3 in.
Barrel Length: 21.1 in.
Feed Device: 20 round detachable, staggered box magazine.
Sights: Front—Hooded blade.
Rear—Aperture, graduated from 100 to 600 meters.
Muzzle Velocity: Approx. 2650 f.p.s.
Cyclic Rate: 550-600 rounds per minute.

This weapon currently exists in prototype form only. Extensive use is made of light weight materials in its construction. Aluminum alloy is used in the receiver, receiver cover, trigger guard, rear sight, magazine, and bipod.

How to Load and Fire the Madsen Light Automatic Rifle. Insert a loaded magazine into the magazine port and push home until locked by the magazine catch. Cock

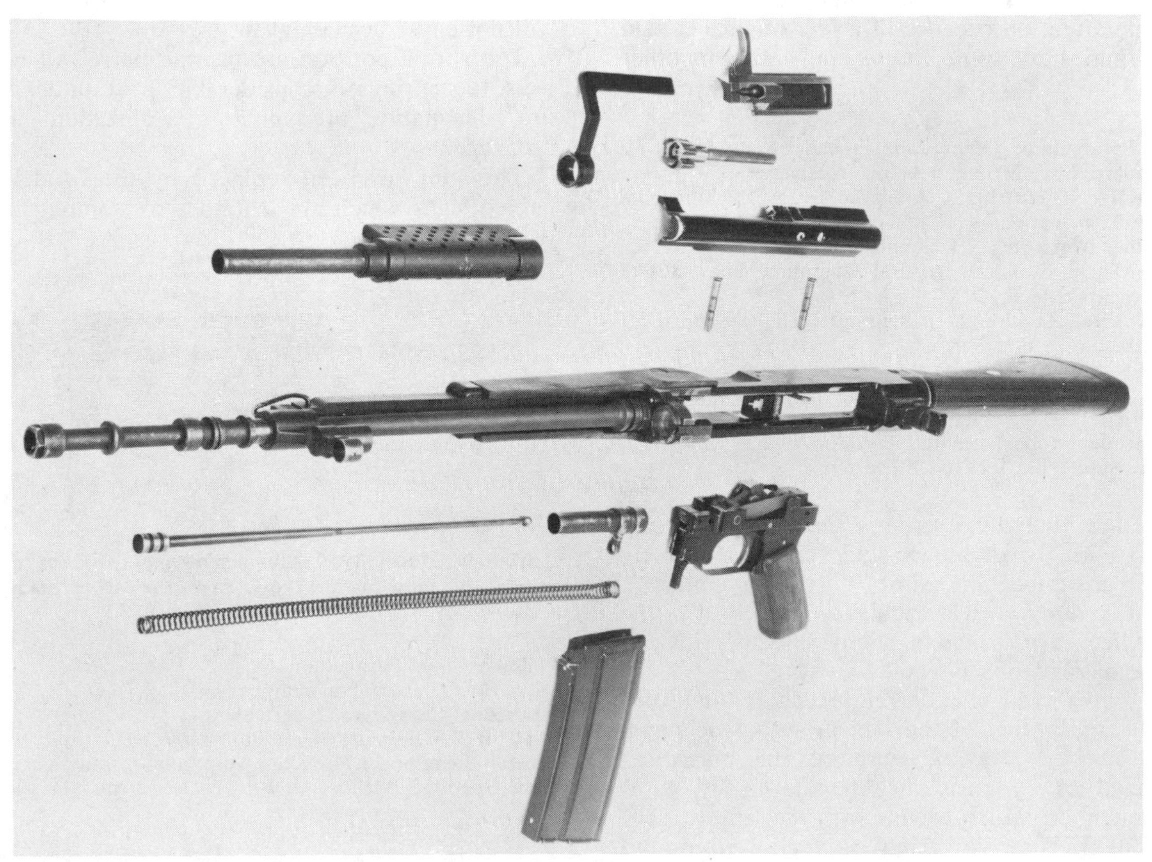

Madsen 7.62mm NATO Light Automatic Rifle field stripped.

the weapon by pulling the operating handle to the rear as far as it will go, release the handle, and let it run forward. The weapon is now cocked and ready to fire. The safety selector lever can be set on safe, semi-automatic, or automatic, as desired.

Special Note on the Madsen Automatic Rifle. The Madsen has its return spring mounted above the barrel and circles the piston rod, thus it pulls the bolt forward into battery position rather than pushes it forward as with most weapons. The bolt is similar to that of the Soviet AK-47 in that it rotates to lock and is rotated by means of a lug on the bolt operating in a cam in the bolt carrier. However the piston rod of the Madsen is not permanently attached to the bolt carrier as with the AK. The piston rod of the Madsen has a ball-shaped end which fits in a cut-out in the bolt carrier. The trigger mechanism of the Madsen is similar to that of the AK. The Madsen has a grenade launcher built into the end of the barrel. It can also be easily fitted with a bipod and a telescopic sight. There are two versions of the weapon: one with a tubular metal stock and one with a wooden stock.

DANISH SUBMACHINE GUNS

Danish Madsen submachine gun Model 1945.

Special Note: While this gun has been rendered obsolete by the improved 1946 and later patterns, it is worthy of some attention because of a few original design factors which may have some future application in other arms.

Caliber: 9mm Parabellum. Other calibers can be produced.
Magazine: Standard box. Mounted below receiver.
Magazine Capacity: 50 cartridges. Achieved by overly long box.
Overall Length: 31.5 inches.
Weight, Excluding Magazine: 7.1 pounds.
Operation: Blowback. Standard general operation but unusual inertia movements added.
Cyclic Rate of Fire: About 800 per minute. High, because of light weight recoiling member.
Firing Pin: Movable. Striker release possible only on trigger pressure.
Safety: Conventional. Triggerguard pattern.
Type of Fire: Semi or full automatic.
Special Feature: Safety pin lock on firing pin.

Despite the fact that this arm uses a rifle type wooden stock and fore-end, the designers achieved the extremely light weight for a submachine gun of only 7.1 pounds.

The weight reduction was achieved largely by the attempt to utilize springs and a sliding member instead of heavy bolt mass to offset recoil.

A cocking cover over the barrel breech in the form of a slide (not unlike that of the typical automatic pistol design) has serrated sides forward of the magazine. Cocking, instead of by customary handle, is by withdrawing this member, which travels with the true breechblock in recoil. The recoil spring is positioned around the barrel below this sliding cover member. Utilization of this spring position, together with the sliding cover, were used to supplement the inertia and mass of a light breechblock, to thereby achieve minimum weight. However, because of this weight reduction, the firing rate is excessively high and gun control is quite difficult. Sights had to be mounted quite high, the front sight being weak because of its height and exposure.

In an endeavor to produce a safety factor to overcome accidental discharge during slamming of the breechblock when the gun is dropped or violently put aside, a sear interrupter was introduced in this model. The striker can move forward through the breechblock to fire only when the trigger is depressing the sear. Dropping the weapon will not cause accidental firing.

The spring position around the barrel, of course, subjects the spring to considerable heat under continuous fire, inevitably producing crystallization and spring breakage.

This gun has been replaced by the Model 1946 and later designs which are triumphs of stamping engineering design.

Madsen Model 1950 submachine gun. One of the finest examples of modern low cost, fast production stamped designs. (Also made in Brazil in caliber .45 A.C.P.)

Caliber: 9mm Parabellum.
Magazine: Detachable straight line box.
Magazine Capacity: 32 cartridges.
Weight: 7.6 pounds, excluding magazine.
Overall Length: 30.71 inches with folding butt extended.
Gun Operated By: Recoil. Blowback system. Standard projection of spent case operation.
Cooled: Barrel radiation only.
Cocking Handle: Top of gun as for Thompson, early 1928 Model.
Firing: Full auto only. No selector provided.
Cyclic Firing Rate: 460 per minute.

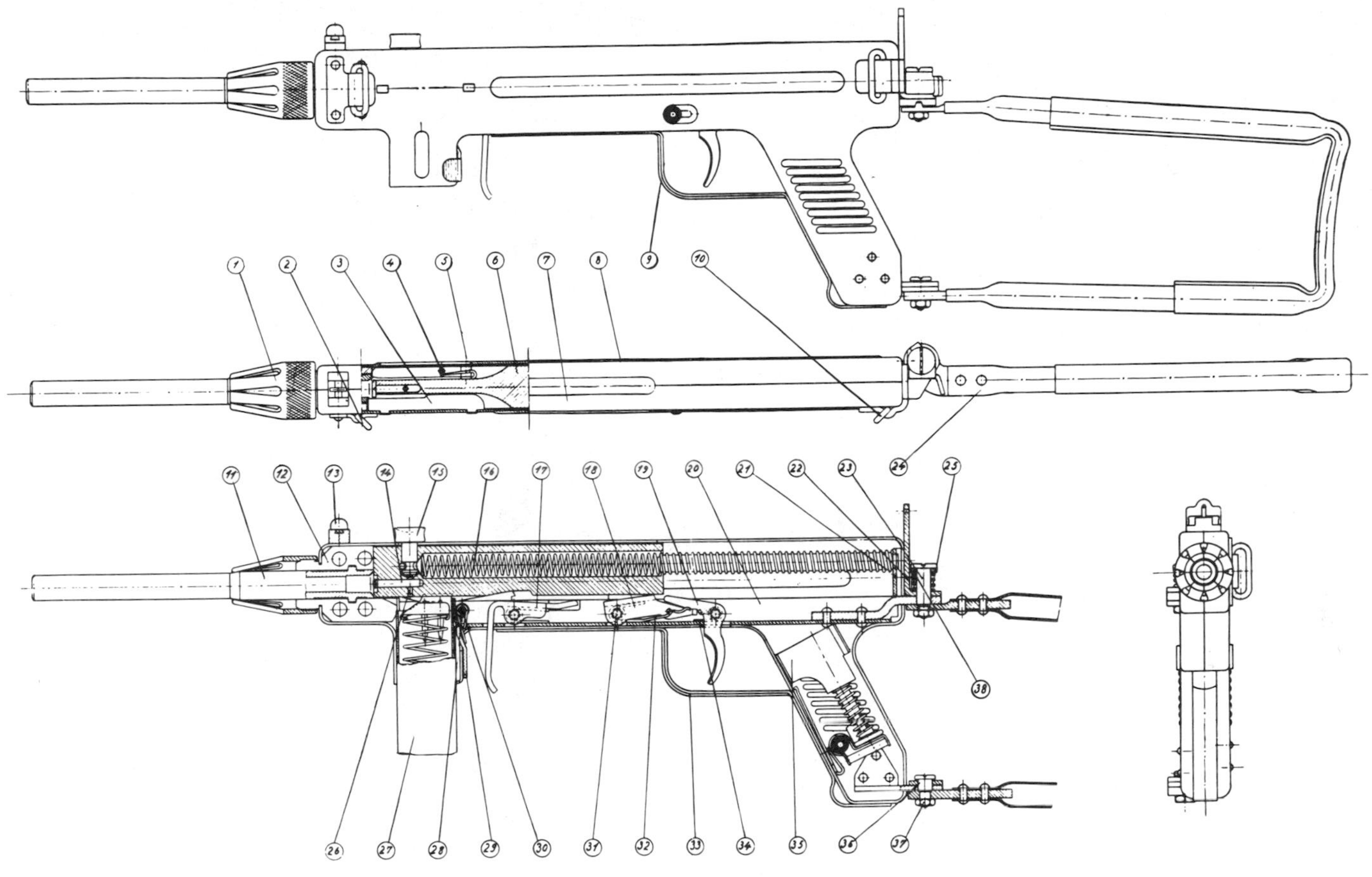

Detail drawings showing construction and parts of the Madsen Model 1950 Submachine Gun.

1 Barrel-bearing nut
2 Sling swivel
3 Ejector
4 Extractor pin
5 Extractor
6 Breech block
7 Frame half (left)
8 Frame half (right)
9 Safety catch
10 Sling swivel
11 Barrel
12 Barrel bearing
13 Corn
14 Firing pin
15 Cocking handle
16 Return spring
17 Breech block retainer
18 Trigger rod
19 Trigger
20 Trigger plate
21 Return spring guide (complete)
22 Rear sight plate
23 Shoulder piece bolt (upper)
24 Shoulder piece
25 Sholder piece spring
26 Firing pin rivet
27 Magazine
28 Magazine catch pin
29 Magazine catch
30 Magazine catch spring
31 Trigger rod pin
32 Trigger rod spring
33 Trigger guard
34 Trigger spring
35 Magazine loading apparatus
36 Shoulder piece bolt (lower)
37 Shoulder piece bolt nut
38 Shoulder piece lock

Special Features: Extremely simple take down through folding hinged receiver.

Safety: Unusual automatic squeezer pattern to rear of magazine prevents firing except when gripped in firing position. Mechanically applied safety provided on left side sliding button to lock trigger rod.

Construction and Design

This is one of the most unusual submachine gun designs ever produced. It incorporates all the desirable features of extremely low cost production of the best German, Russian, and U.S. M3 submachine gun designs. At the same time, it has desirable elements considerably in advance of any of these previous ones.

The gun is designed to lend itself to high speed production at extremely low cost. This is the type of weapon which could be manufactured in American automotive or similar plants equipped with heavy duty punch presses at a fraction of the cost of a typical submachine gun of the Thompson M1A1 design.

Because of its basically revolutionary design, we will consider it here in considerable detail. The construction itself is most ingenious. The receiver (or frame) is flat. It is divided vertically in longitudinal section and is hinged at the rear. The pistol grip and magazine guide are a simple stamping.

The barrel is fastened to the receiver by a locking nut which when unscrewed and thrust forward permits the entire left side of the receiver to be folded back exposing the right side in which all the moving parts are housed. The barrel may be lifted out for immediate replacement or for cooling. While this system of design has been applied in Europe to revolvers in the past, this is the first production example of the application of the design principle to the submachine gun. It permits not only simplified manufacture but extreme ease of fitting and assembly. The photographs and drawings herewith will establish in clear detail all the manufacturing and operational factors of importance which are involved.

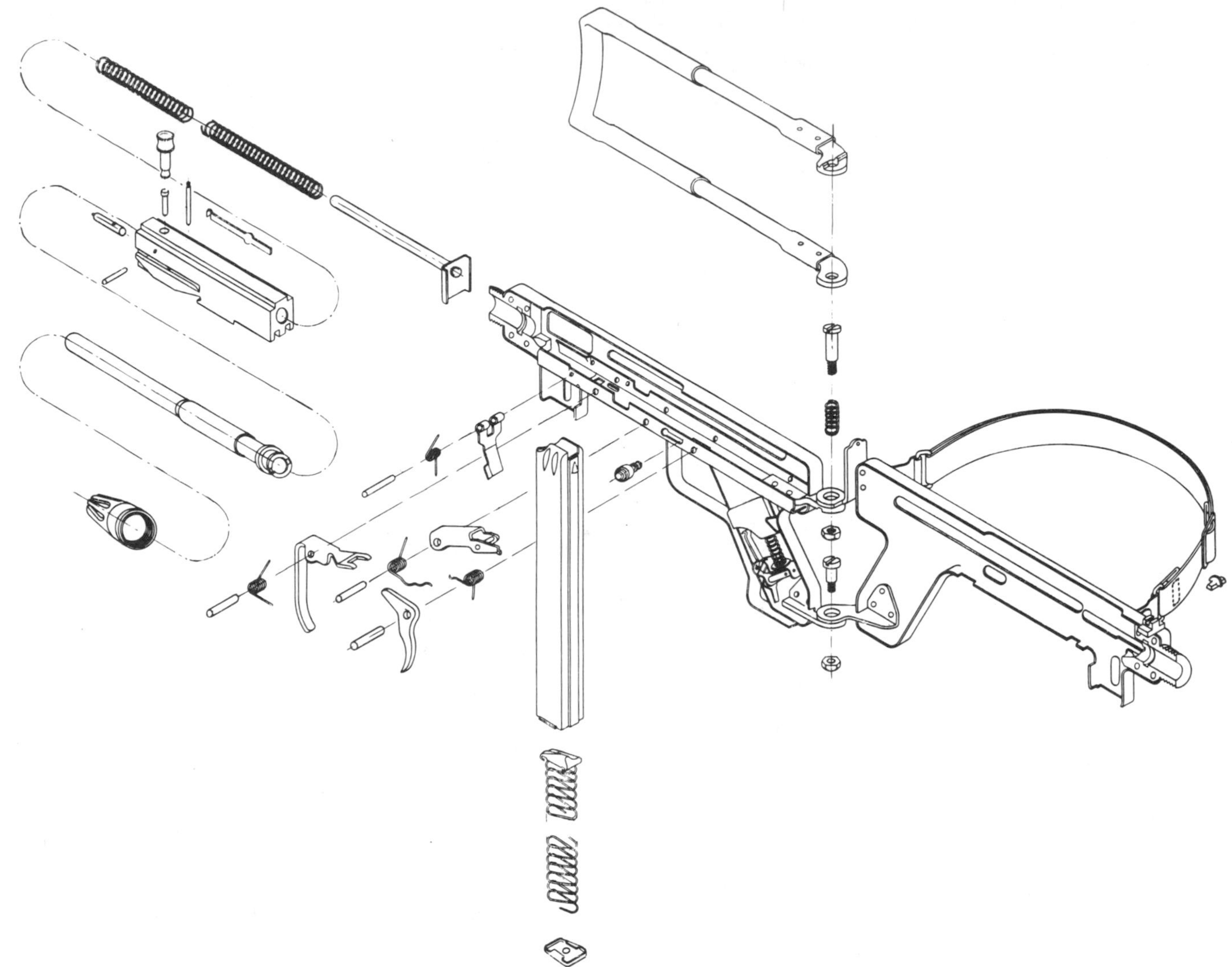

Detailed exploded view of the Madsen Model 1950 Submachine Gun as made in Denmark and Brazil.

The stock is a folding metal skeleton design permitting the gun to be used easily either from the shoulder or from the hip.

The stock when folded does not interfere with access to the trigger. The sling swivel positions on the left side of the gun are designed to permit the weapon to be slung across the chest for immediate use at a moment's notice.

A very unusual factor, yet one of extreme simplicity, is the special automatic safety provided. This is a lever positioned to the rear of the magazine housing. When firing, the normal manner of gripping an arm of this type is with the right hand about the firing grip and the left hand around the magazine or magazine housing. In this position, the firer's left hand in this new design also embraces the safety lever. Should he release this grip at any time, or should he stumble and lose control of it, the lever automatically blocks the path of the breechblock so that it cannot chamber a cartridge from the magazine for firing. Pulling the cocking handle all the way back will put the gun back in readiness for operation.

Construction

The gun consists of the following units: Receiver or frame. Barrel. Breechblock with inserted cocking handle. Recoil spring. Trigger mechanism. Safety device. Magazine. Folding shoulder stock.

The receiver is composed of two nearly identical sections of stamped sheet steel. The pistol grip and magazine housing are formed as sections of these individual halves of the receiver. The two frame sections are hinged at the rear. At the front they are secured to the barrel by the barrel bearing nut.

The left side of the receiver serves as an actual cover for the right section in which the moving members are housed. The sling swivels and sights are on the left hand half. The front sight is positioned at the forward end of the receiver instead of on the barrel, thus eliminating need for accurate barrel positioning, since barrel locking ridges are cylindrical. It is a standard blade design. May be adjusted laterally for windage. The rear sight positioned at the rear of the receiver section is a fixed aperture

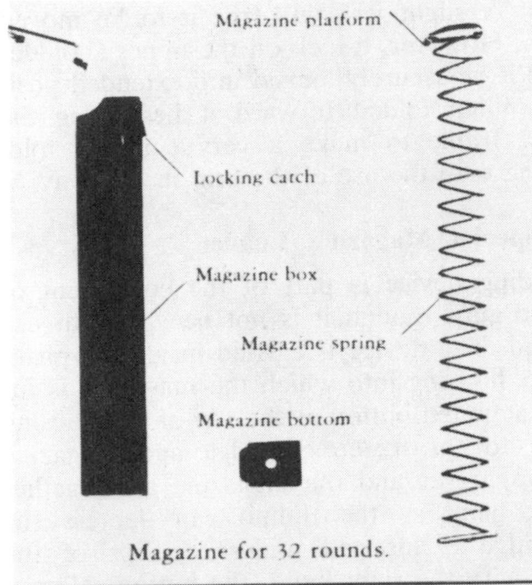

Magazine for 32 rounds.

SAFETY

The breech block retainer serves to prevent a round from being fired accidentally owing to an incomplete cocking motion or as a result of a shock to the gun if dropped or laid down hard. It does not require any attention, however, to release the breech block retainer, because the correct grip for firing the gun, whether kneeling, standing, sitting or prone, is with left hand firmly round the magazine housing, the thumb in the most natural way pressing against the downward lever of the breech block retainer, and with the right hand round the pistol grip.

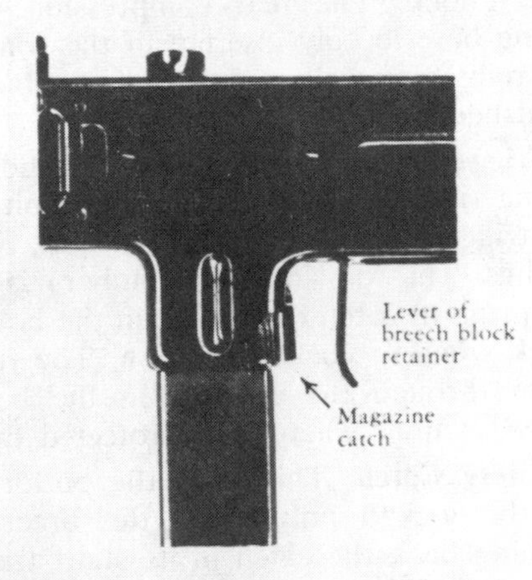

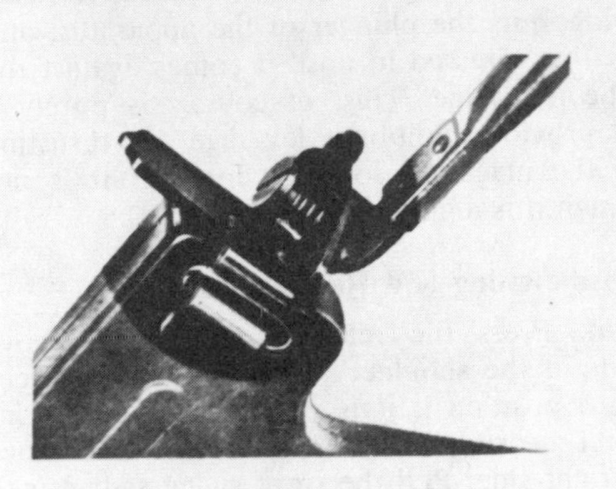

Upper shoulder piece hinge with lock.

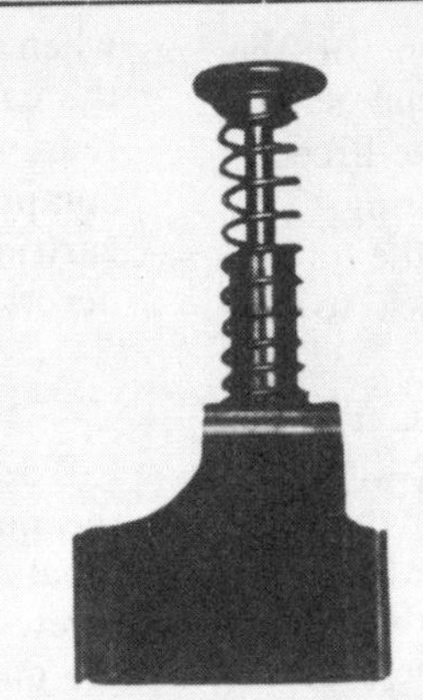

Magazine loader. Standard equipment. Kept in pistol-grip.

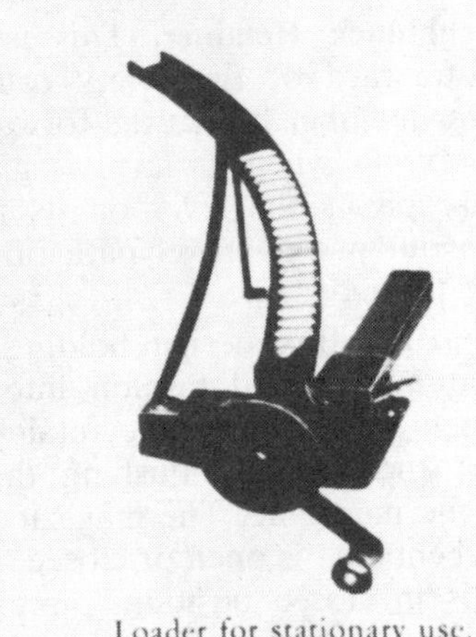

Loader for stationary use.

Details and accessories. Danish Madsen Model 1950 Submachine Gun.

sight. The gun is sighted in at a practical hundred meters range. This is an entirely sensible sighting range and system for the caliber and design. While the sighting radius is relatively short, it is still adequate. The positioning of the front sight is determined by the fact that if it were placed forward on the barrel muzzle to give maximum sight radius, its height would be too great, resulting in possibility of damage to it. Moreover, barrel positioning would require closer tolerances and increased manufacturing costs.

The receiver is smooth finished on the outside. The jointure of the parts gives a dustproof fit.

A projecting rib at the forward end of the left section of the receiver serves as the ejector. The right side of the receiver is pierced for the ejection port.

Except for the barrel, which is detachable by merely unscrewing its nut, all the other operating parts are housed in the right hand side of the receiver.

The Barrel. No radiating rings or cooling flanges are provided. The barrel is a smooth taper screw machine or lathe-turned unit and is quite light. Because of interchangeability factors, the heavier barrel is not considered essential, though for hard military usage a heavy or flanged barrel could readily be provided.

The breech section of the barrel is housed in the forward breech section of the receiver. It is furnished with an external rib which fits into corresponding grooves in both frame halves to prevent the barrel from moving forward or rearward. A groove cut in the rear of the chamber section of the barrel mates with the ejector rib in the left section of the receiver. This positively prevents any barrel rotation when assembled.

Breechblock. This rectangular unit reciprocates inside the receiver on the flat bottom wall of the right receiver section. The firing pin is an integral part of the breechblock for complete simplicity. The extractor at the front right side section of the breechblock is secured with an elementary vertical pin.

Cocking Handle. This is a separate member which is inserted in the top of the breechblock and is fastened by a cross pin. It travels in a slot in the top of the frame between the two halves. While this may be considered militarily objectionable, as in the case of the original Thompson 1928 model, the system could be subject to side operation as in the case of the later Thompson modification the M1A1 if desired.

Recoil Spring. This is positioned in a pilot hole in the breechblock. The rear compression point is against a spring base loosely inserted in the frame receiver against the right rear wall. A protruding tubular spring guide is furnished.

Trigger Mechanism. This is positioned at the bottom of the right receiver section. The unit consists simply of the trigger and arm, the trigger rod, and their respective springs. The rod (or sear member) is thrust upwards by its spring to catch in a notch in the bottom of the breechblock when in cocked position. The trigger arm projects down through the opening in the bottom of the right frame section, where it is protected by the triggerguard.

Safety Catch. This is at the bottom of the frame. It can be locked only when the breechblock is cocked. Pushing back the catch in its short travel slot in the left side of the frame effectively locks the trigger rod in position to prevent any movement of the breechblock.

Breechblock Retainer. This is in the bottom of the frame forward of the safety catch. This special safety squeezer member blocks the forward travel of the breechblock, except when its lever is gripped when firing. The pressure pivots the lever on its pin to lower the upper surface out of the travel path of the breechblock to the rear of the magazine.

Magazine. Box design holding 32 cartridges. This is inserted in standard fashion into the magazine housing from below. The magazine retaining catch is in the rear wall of the housing. Pushing the catch backwards releases the magazine. The magazine may be inserted when the breechblock is open or closed. However, if the breechblock is in closed position, more force must be applied to insert the magazine as it must be thrust up enough for the top cartridge (which presses against the underside of the breechblock) to be thrust further down into the magazine itself.

Butt Stock. This is a skeleton folding butt of steel tubing partly leather covered for comfort. It is hinged to the rear end of the right section of the receiver, its lower hinge being behind the pistol grip. In both open and closed positions the stock is held by a notch and a lug in the hinge. A slight jerk will free it to be moved to either position. However, a lock on the upper shoulder piece bolt allows it be securely locked into extended position if desired. When folded forward it lies along the right side of the frame to make a very compact fold, without interfering with the use of the arm in any way.

Special Magazine Loader

A special loading device is part of the equipment of these submachine guns though it is not necessary to use it in order to load. The device is carried inside the pistol grip. It is a short housing into which the magazine is inserted. A spring actuated button at the top of the housing is pushed down to thrust the cartridge and magazine spring in. The apparatus and the magazine are together held in the left hand so the thumb can depress the button. A cartridge is inserted under the lips of the magazine mouth with the right hand, the button released when the cartridge hits the plunger of the apparatus, and the cartridge is then pressed in until it comes against the rear wall of the magazine. This, of course, is purely a compressor to provide additional leverage for thrusting cartridges into the magazine for easy loading. It is not necessary although it is a great convenience.

Dismounting and Reassembling

To Dismount. Press the release catch and remove the magazine. Fold the shoulder piece. Ease the breechblock to forward position if it is not already there. Unscrew the barrel bearing nut and slide forward. Place the gun on its right side. Pull the front swing swivel with the right hand while holding the left hand pressing against the barrel. This will raise the left receiver section, freeing the barrel. Withdraw the barrel.

Press the base of the return spring forward and upwards. This will allow it to be withdrawn from the breechblock. Lift the breechblock up and out. No further disassembly is normally required. The magazine bottom may be slid out to remove the spring and follower, although this too is not commonly necessary. Reassembly is merely reversal of this procedure.

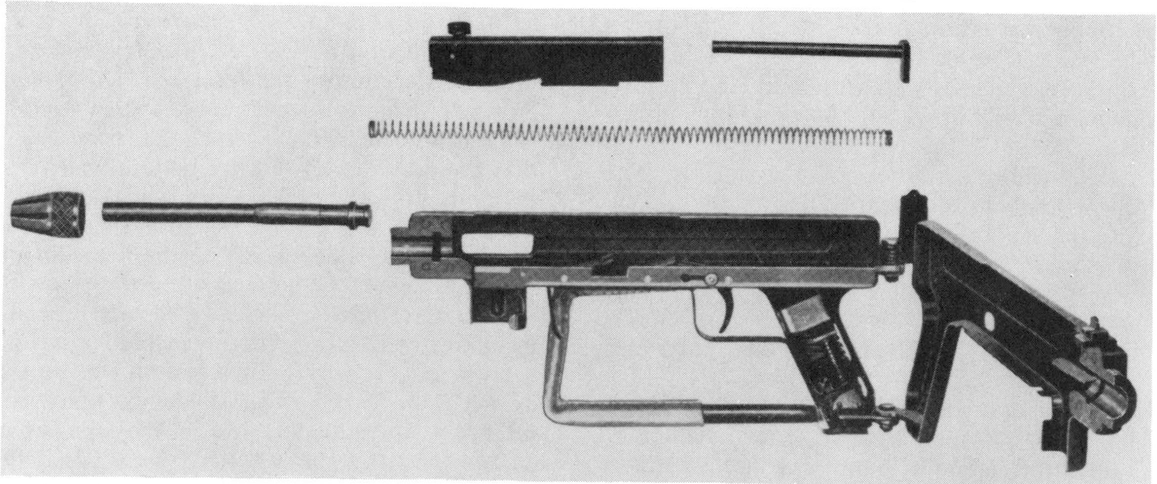

Madsen Model 1950 submachine gun field stripped without tools. This gun represented probably the most advanced manufacturing and design techniques since the introduction of the German Schmeisser in 1938.

Brazilian Cal. .45. Similar to the Danish Madsen Model 1946 except for caliber. Presented to Gen. J. Lawton Collins, then Chief of Staff, U.S. Army by the Brazilian Minister of War.

This gun is in all essentials except caliber identical with the Madsen Model 1946 described herein. Manufacture was tooled by the Danish Madsen firm.

Special Note. This gun in Caliber .45 U.S. Govt. is currently being made in Brazil under Madsen license. Many of the design and manufacturing features lend themselves readily to application to other small arms designs.

Operation

A magazine is inserted in the housing and thrust in until the magazine catch secures it. The cocking handle on top of the breechblock is drawn to the full rear position to compress the recoil spring. At the end of the stroke the trigger rod spring thrusts the rod up to catch in its notch in the under side of the breechblock. The safety catch may be pushed to lock the rod into the breechblock if desired. Otherwise the weapon is now ready to fire on pull of the trigger.

Firing. Pressing the trigger causes it to pivot and its forward arm moves the attached trigger rod down out of contact with the breechblock. The compressed recoil spring drives the breechblock ahead. If the left hand is not supporting both the magazine housing and the safety lever behind it, the breechblock will be halted before striking the cartridge in the magazine lips.

Assuming that the supporting hand is pressing in the safety catch towards the magazine housing, the breechblock impelled by the recoil spring is free to move ahead; since the upper section of the safety lever is not in its path. Its feed face strips the top cartridge from between the lips of the magazine and drives it into the chamber. The nose of the bullet is guided by the barrel feed section of the breech into the chamber as the rear section of the cartridge clears the magazine lips. When the cartridge enters the chamber, it lines up with the firing pin which is fixed in the face of the breechblock. The firing pin strikes the cartridge primer while still moving forward. At the same time the extractor on the right side of the breechblock springs over the cannelure in the cartridge case.

In this quite standard practice for submachine guns, the heavy breechblock and spring members are still moving forward at the actual instant of firing before the chambering is really complete. This serves as an additional inertia factor to offset the recoil of the discharge.

Recoil Movement. The gases developed inside the cartridge case on firing drive the bullet forward and force the cartridge case against the side walls and back against the face of the breechblock in standard blowback practice. The breechblock starts to the rear under this thrust. However, since the breechblock weight and return spring tension are far greater than the comparatively light bullet, the opening movement is barely started when the bullet leaves the muzzle. The breech pressure drops rapidly to safe limits but the residual pressure in the bore continues to exert a backward force against the case head which in turn passes it on to the breechblock in a continuing thrust.

The breechblock moving to the rear, its cartridge extractor draws the empty case back with it. When the case clears the chamber, the left side hits the ejector, pivoting the case through the ejection port opening on the right.

The breechblock continues its rearward travel and as it clears the top of the magazine, the magazine spring pushes the next cartridge up against the lips of the magazine ready to be picked up on the counter-recoil motion. The recoil spring is compressed between its seat in the breechblock in the rear of the frame as the breechblock travels in the tracks provided for it in the frame walls. The travel slot for the cocking handle is greater than the distance of travel of the breechblock in order to prevent sudden halting shock. If the trigger is still retained, the breechblock will continue forward to fire in full automatic cycle. This firing continues as long as the trigger is depressed, the safety lever depressed, and there are cartridges in the magazine.

If, however, the trigger is released, the springs will reassert themselves to thrust the trigger rod up into the breechblock notch to hold it back ready for the next forward motion.

The gun is normally cocked with the left hand. Accidental discharge is almost impossible. Should the trigger be accidentally pulled when the safety is not being thrust in for firing, or should the breechblock be jarred loose under any conditions when the left hand is not gripping the safety, the breechblock, as we have pointed out, cannot complete its forward travel. In this position, it is necessary to pull back the cocking handle to recock the arm before it can be fired.

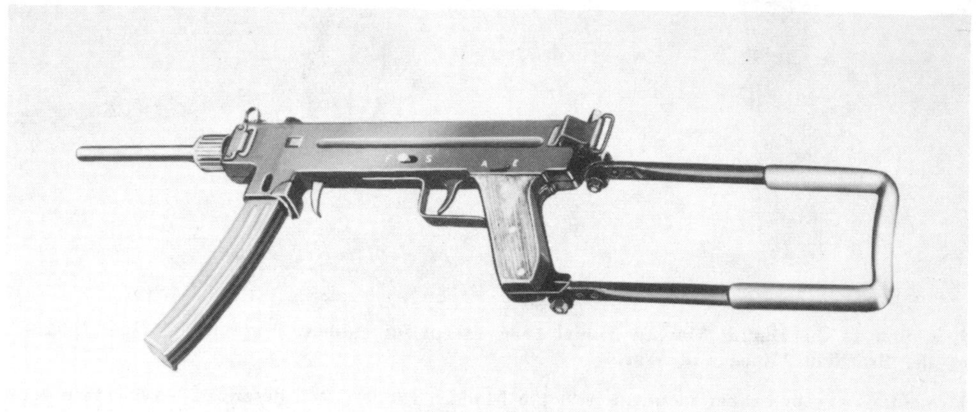

Danish Madsen Model 1953 9mm Submachine gun.

This is a newer model of the submachine gun Model 1946. This weapon was changed in 1950, and again in 1953. This model is called the M53.

The M53 is very similar to the 1950 Model, but it has incorporated several improvements. The most noticeable, at first glance, is the design of the magazine, which is curved instead of being straight as on the 1946 and 1950 models. The curved magazine is considered a better design for feeding purposes.

Another new feature in the M53 submachine gun is that the barrel bearing nut now screws onto the barrel, rather than onto the front of the receiver as on the M46 and M50 models. This feature gives the M53 added strength and stability for the barrel. The bolt has also been streamlined to aid in better functioning.

If desired, the weapon can be supplied with a removable barrel jacket to which a special short bayonet can be fixed. All the Madsen models can be made with or without selection-fire features.

The characteristics and field stripping are the same for this weapon as for the 1950 model pictured in this chapter.

9mm M49 Submachine Gun

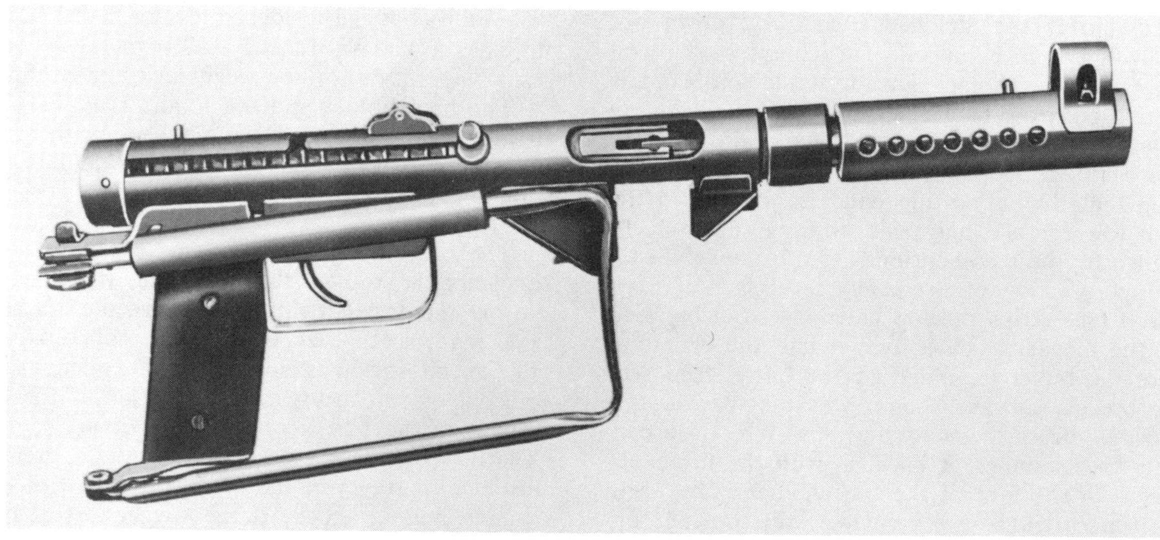

Caliber: 9mm Parabellum.
System of Operation: Blowback.
Weight: 8.9 lbs. (loaded).
Length, Overall: 31.8 in. (w/stock extended).
Barrel Length: 21.6 in.
Feed Device: 35 round detachable, staggered, box magazine.
Sights: Front—Hooded posts.
Rear—L type with setting for 100 and 200 meters.
Muzzle Velocity: 1263 f.p.s.
Cyclic Rate: 600 r.p.m.

This weapon, commonly called the Hovea, was developed by Husqvarna in Sweden. It is similar in construction to the Swedish M45 submachine gun. Functioning, disassembly, and assembly are similar to that described under the Swedish 9mm M45 submachine gun.

DANISH MACHINE GUNS

Danish Madsen 8mm Light Machine Gun.

Originally this was a Danish gun of 8mm caliber. However, Madsen guns have been widely used for years in Holland, the Dutch East Indies, England, Germany, and Japan, as well as in several South American countries. Moreover, Dutch Madsen guns captured by the Japanese were found in use by our troops in the Solomons. In view of these facts, it would seem that some general understanding of the Madsen gun might be of interest.

Caliber: 8mm (.315 inch). Caliber varies in different countries. 6.5mm, 7.7mm and 7.92mm are common.
Magazine: Arc shaped. Containing 25 or 40 cartridges. It is mounted on top of the receiver. **Note:** Magazines of 30 capacity are also known. The caliber will to some extent determine the maximum capacity which will usually be 40.
Barrel Length: 18¾″ and 23⅛″. These lengths are of the Danish gun. Shorter and longer models are in use in other nations.
Overall Length: Usually 40″ to 45″ depending on barrel length.
Mounting: In the infantry type these weapons are usually provided with a stock rest at the rear and the bipod mount in front. Weight is about 2 lbs. Special cavalry types of mounts are also issued weighing about 1½ lbs. Tripod and A.A. mounts also used.
Sights: Barleycorn front and open V rear sighted to 1000 meters.
Gun Operated by: Recoil.
Closed: By hinged block. Breech block and barrel are held closed during the moment of high pressure. As pressure drops and parts recoil, a stud working in a groove pulls the breechblock down out of contact with the barrel.
Cooled: Air cooled. The weapon stays open between shots permitting circulation of air through breech and down barrel. Barrel is also surrounded by ventilating casing.
Cyclic Rate of Fire: About 450 a minute.
Position of Cocking Handle: Right rear of receiver.
Type of Fire: Single shot or full automatic. On the left side of the receiver is a selector device. One of the stops on this device is a safety. This device can only be set when the gun is cocked. This gun ejects through the bottom. A cover springs open when the weapon is cocked. It should be closed after firing.

Loading and Firing

Like the Chatellerault and the Bren guns, the Madsen uses a top loading magazine. This requires the sights to be set off to the side of the gun. The magazine is arc-shaped, as necessitated by the use of rim-type cartridges which cannot lie flat on top of each other.

Pull the cocking handle back as far as it will go and release it.

Put the forward end of the magazine into the forward end of the magazine opening and lower the rear end down into place, snapping it down until it locks. Now set the selector on the left side of the receiver above the trigger in the fire position. **Note:** Remember that this weapon fires as the bolt goes forward and no attempt should ever be made to let the action go forward while there is a magazine mounted on top of the gun.

How the Madsen Gun Works

This gun fits into a subdivision of functioning principles known as the "long barrel recoil type." In the short recoil types, the barrel moves backward only a fraction of an inch, which means that extraction and ejection of empty cartridge cases and feeding loaded cartridges requires special attention. This design is necessarily more complicated than the long recoil type.

In the long recoil type the breech has to move back far enough to permit feeding up the entire cartridge in one operation. This is done by the barrel going forward while the lock is held back until the cartridge has partly entered the chamber. In this type of action, the rate of fire is much lower than in the short recoil.

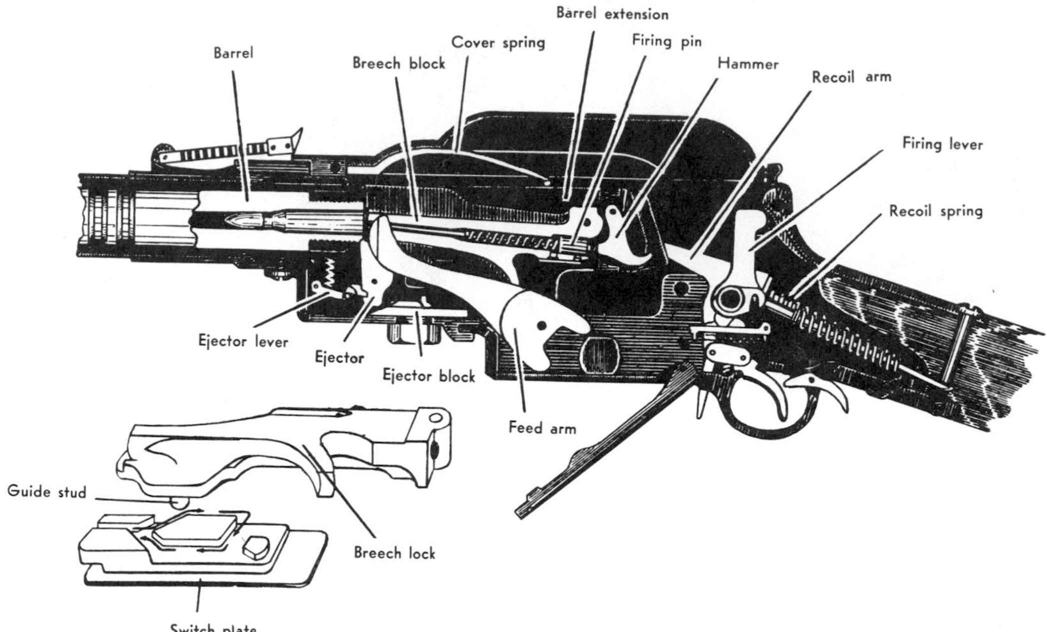

Starting with the gun cocked and in firing position the action is as follows: As the trigger is pressed, the spring below it is compressed while the trigger nose is pulled down out of the bent of the recoil lever. This permits the recoil spring in the butt to force the lever downward, and, as it is engaged in the rear of the breech mechanism, it thrusts the recoiling parts forward. As the recoiling mechanism nears forward position, the recoil arm is still up somewhat. The hump on the recoil lever now bears on the side of the sear and forces the sear downward. The nose of the sear is thus relieved from the bent of the firing lever, and compresses the sear spring. The firing lever is now forced downward by its spring and strikes the tail of the hammer. The front of the hammer drives the firing pin forward to explode the cartridge in the firing chamber. A coiled spring around the firing pin, which is compressed by the hammer movement, pulls the firing pin back into the face of the breech block as the cartridge is fired.

As the recoiling parts are thrust forward by the recoil lever spring, a circular stud in the lower part of the breech block, working in the guide grooves of a switch plate which is fitted to the non-recoiling portion of the receiver, strikes the rear of the center block in the plate and so guides the breech block downward, leaving the chamber ready for the cartridge to be inserted. As the stud continues forward, it strikes the lower cam surface of the switch plate causing the breech block to rise and close the breech. Now the stud is lined up with the horizontal slot in the switch plate, down which it travels during the final half-inch forward motion, securely locking the breech.

Also during the forward thrust of the recoiling parts, an arm is forced up by a cam on the left side of the receiver, forcing outwards the distributor against the tension of its spring and permitting the first cartridge from the magazine which was resting on the distributor to drop into the magazine opening.

Meanwhile the front surface of the rear claw of the feed arm engages with the rear surface of the feed arm actuating block, thus rotating the feed arm forward. The arm strikes the head of the cartridge in its seat against the left flange of the breech block, pushing it ahead into the chamber. The rear claw of the feed arm rises up to the rear surface of the feed arm actuating block and travels along its upper surface. The bottom of the rear claw, now being above the feed arm actuating block, moves the cartridge in the chamber to allow the breech block to rise. It also prevents any rebound of the feed arm.

As the forward action starts, the ejector is positioned alongside the rear of the ejector block. As the recoiling parts go forward a stud on the ejector lever rides down the sloping cam and forces an ejector downward on its spring, thus bringing the lever in contact with the tail of the ejector. As soon as the breech block starts to rise, the tail of the ejector is clear of the ejector block and it is raised in position by its lever. As the breech closes, the ejector is able to rise to the vertical under the influence of the ejector lever spring and falls in place just below the chamber with its hook below the rim of the cartridge.

Note that in this type of gun, the cartridge is not set into the chamber by the breech block; and until the front of the breech block rises to a complete locking position, the hammer, firing pin, and cartridge are not in alinement and so there can be no accidental discharge.

Return Movement of the Action

At the breech, the barrel is joined to the breech block casing in which are the hinged breech blocks. These three units recoil together, with the breech remaining closed and locked for about ½″. This sudden rearward thrust forces the firing lever up as it is struck by the rear of the breech mechanism, and frees it from the hammer, which permits the hammer to pivot back and the firing pin to be withdrawn by the firing pin spring. The guide stud is now passed out of the horizontal groove and travels up the upper cam of the switch plate which pivots the breech block upwards at its nose to permit ejection. The extra stud travels along the top of the cam and the cover spring then forces the front of the breech block downward, compelling the stud to drop out of the rear stud of the switch plate.

Note: This gun has no individual extractor. The ejector pulls the empty cartridge out of the chamber and hurls it from the gun.

With the first movement to the rear, the inclined slope in the front of the ejector block raises the ejector which is held in vertical position by its lever which is engaged in a recess in the bottom of the ejector. From the influence of this separate movement, a hook on the ejector catches the rim of the empty cartridge case and the bottom of the ejector lies on top of the front flats of the ejector block.

Now the stud on the ejector lever runs up the sloping cam on the left of the ejector block to compress the ejector lever spring. This also disengages the ejector lever from the ejector, allowing the ejector tail to be tripped forward by the step on the ejector block, and as the ejector is pivoted about its center, the tripping motion of the tail forces the hook to the rear, pulling the empty cartridge case out and hurling it from the bottom of the gun.

An ejection guide on the breech block guides the empty cartridge case as it is hurled out. The ejector lever stud now rests above the sloping cam holding the ejector levers upwards and free of the ejector, which lies on top of the rear flap of the ejector block beneath the breech block. During the recoil movement, the distributor arm rides down its cam and rotates the distributor inwards and downwards under the influence of the spring. This places the cartridges in the feedway against the left flange of the breech block. Meanwhile, the rear surface of the front feed arm claw engages with the front face of the feed arm actuating block, and rotates the feed arm backwards. The bottom of the front claw now rides along the top of the feed arm block, preventing rebound of the feed arm.

Further Note on Recoil System. Some Madsens are fitted with a so-called "recoil increaser" which forms a choke at the muzzle. By reversing the two parts of the increaser, the rear portion forms a collar which forces the gases escaping at the muzzle to rebound onto the barrel and give an additional thrust to the rearward action. This speeds the gun up greatly.

When the gun is cocked, the claws of the feed arm automatically open the ejector cover. It must be closed by hand on cease fire.

Field Stripping

Remove magazine from gun and ease recoiling parts forward.

Lift the locking bolt lever into vertical position and withdraw it to the left.

Push the butt to the right front while gripping the receiver with the left hand; and then remove the butt.

Holding forefinger of right hand ahead of feed arm axis bar, with the hand draw back barrel and breech mechanism.

Now pull out the barrel. Remove barrel very carefully as it is easy to damage the front end ring. This barrel ring is one of the weak points in the weapon. Handle it carefully.

Now remove the breech block bolt.

Pull feed arm to the rear. Lift the front and lower the end of the breech block, and then pivot the front up to vertical position, when the feed arm may be eased forward and lifted out of the block.

Further dismounting need not be attempted.

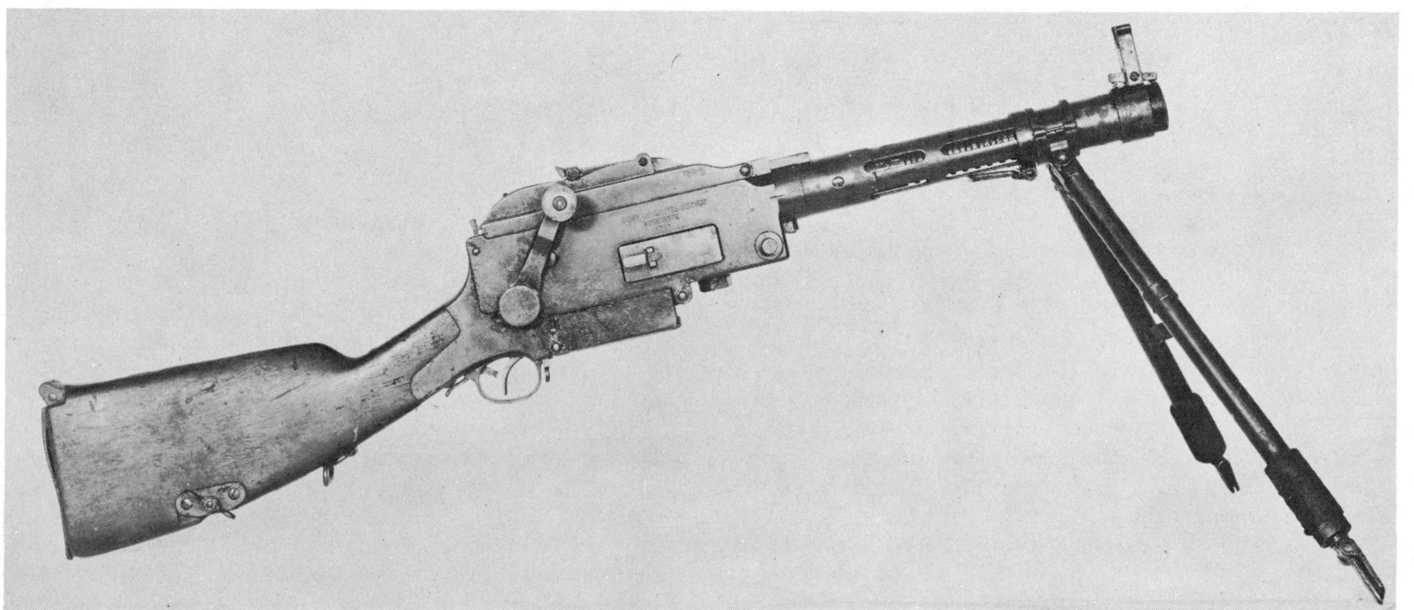

Madsen Gun Made for Dutch East Indies Forces Captured and Used by Japanese.

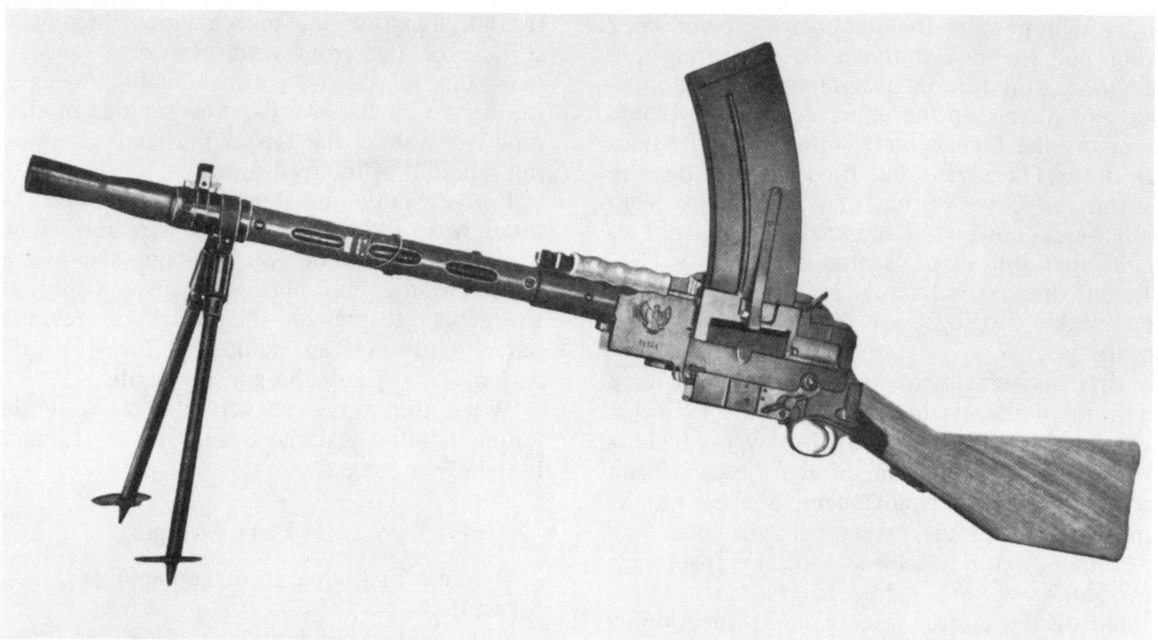

Danish Madsen Model 1950 mounted on bipod, with flash hider and top mounted magazine.

Caliber: Any military caliber specified, rimmed or rimless.
Type of Feed: Madsen box. Capacity, 30 cartridges customarily. (Note: Belt modifications possible.)
Length of Barrel: 18.8 inches.
Weight of Barrel: 3.9 pounds.
Weight of Gun: 20 pounds. With bipod 22.4 pounds.
Overall Length: 45.7 inches.
Rifling: Four grooves, depth .005 inch. Twist 1 turn in 9.5 inches.
Rate of Fire: 600 per minute, approximate.
Deliverable Rate of Fire Including Magazine Time Change: About 350 per minute.
Type of Fire: Semi-automatic and full automatic.
Sights: Standard. Rear graduated leaf from 200 to 1,800 meters in 100 meter steps.
Sight Radius: 16.6 inches.
Tripod Mount: Weight 30.8 pounds to convert to medium machine gun.
Special Feature: Rapid barrel change without tools and without removal of component parts. Twelve seconds installation.

Quick barrel change. Note that this system was developed by Germany and Czechoslovakia and is now used by such diverse makers as the Belgian F.N. and the Mexican Mendoza.

Special Note: The operating characteristics of the Madsen machine gun, except for minor variations as required by feed alterations in some instances, are the same as described for the light machine gun.

This model, while recoil operated on the Madsen principle, is a rather considerable modification of the earlier production. The particular new design is in the nature of a quick change barrel. This may be removed without the use of tools or without removing any component parts.

This Madsen may be fired from muzzle rest of bipod design with or without the shoulder stock. It may also be fired from a light tripod which is convertible to an antiaircraft high angle fire mount. In addition, it may be fired from the shoulder by the rifleman in kneeling, standing, or prone positions.

The Madsen machine gun mounts its arc shaped magazine on top of the receiver to the left of the line of sight. It features a heavy barrel and a perforated cooling jacket. A flash hider and muzzle booster at forward end of jacket are conventional standard equipment.

In the new line of Madsen weapons is the Madsen/Saetter machine gun. This weapon is belt fed and gas operated. It is usually mounted on a light field tripod,

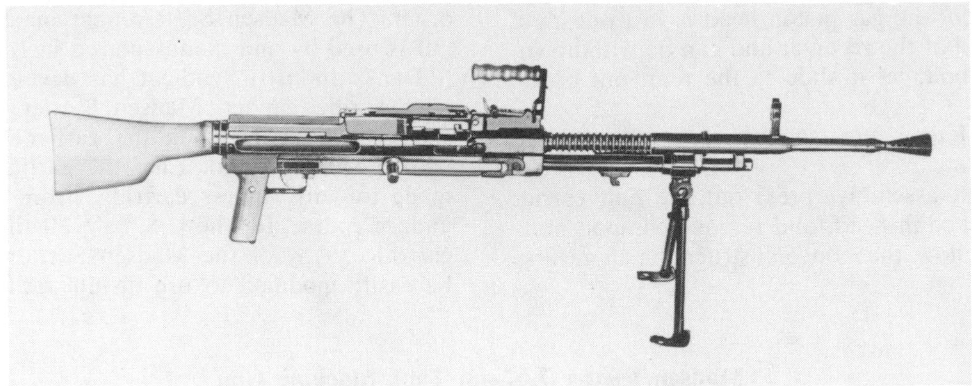

The Danish Madsen/Saetter Machine Gun (Rifle Caliber).

but can be fired from a bipod or from the hip. The gun is, in appearance and design, a modern weapon, embodying all the experience gained during the last few years in the development of machine guns. The component parts are easily mass produced by punching, turning, and precision casting without detracting from reliability and durability.

The Madsen/Saetter machine gun has gone through three changes. These three models are the Mk I, Mk II, and Mk III. The Mk III was not completely developed until 1959. The Mk III is more reliable and shorter than the Mk I or Mk II. Madsen also makes a tank machine gun model which has no buttstock, no bipod, and no sights. The return spring is placed round the gas piston. A special "lightweight" tripod is made for this weapon for use outside the tank.

Caliber: Any military rimless cartridge from 6.5mm to 8mm.
System of Operation: Gas operated, full automatic fire only.
Weight: 25.6 lb., w/heavy barrel.
Weight of Tripod: 36.2 lb.
Length, Overall: 48 in.
Barrel Length: 26 in.
Feed Device: By non-disintegrating metallic belts of 50 rounds, which can be joined to any desired length. The weapon can also be supplied with two box magazines that fasten to the receiver directly below the action; one magazine holds 50 rounds, and the other holds 100 rounds, in metal link belts. The feed system used on this weapon is a copy of the German MG42.
Sights, Front: Barleycorn front sight.
Rear: Open, with graduations up to 1200 meters.
Muzzle Velocity: Standard for ammunition employed.
Cyclic Rate: 700 to 1000 r.p.m.

Field Stripping the Madsen/Saetter

Insure that the chamber is empty by opening the feed cover, and pull back the cocking handle.

To remove the buttstock, seize the pistol grip with one hand, and, with the thumb, press the trigger gear housing latch. The buttstock, now released, should be turned 90 degrees with the other hand, and pulled to the rear.

To remove the triggerguard housing, the cocking handle should be pulled fully back, and then pushed forward again. This brings the bolt carrier to the rear. The triggerguard housing can now be turned downward and taken out of engagement.

To remove the gas piston: when the bolt assembly is in

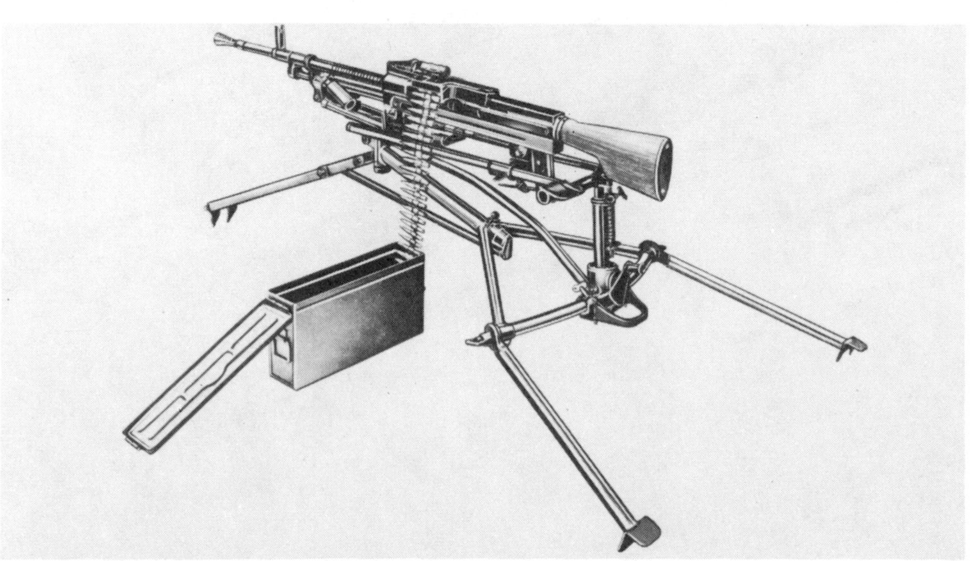

Danish Madsen/Saetter 7.62mm NATO Machine Gun on Tripod.

its rearmost position, the gas piston head is just outside a clearance at the end of the receiver and can be withdrawn.

To remove the bolt, let it slide to the rear, out of the receiver.

To remove the barrel, turn the barrel handle forward until it is free.

To strip the bolt assembly, press out the bolt carrier pin, pull back the action head, and remove components.

To assemble, follow the above instructions in reverse order. The Madsen/Saetter light machine gun in caliber .30 is used by and manufactured in India.

Dansk Industri Syndicat has developed a new version of the rifle caliber Madsen/Saetter. The Mark IV is shorter and lighter than the earlier Marks and is used with a lighter tripod. Like the earlier Marks, it can be made for any rimless cartridge from 6.5mm to 7.92mm and, of course, for the U.S. cal. .30 rifle and machine gun cartridge. Any of the Madsen/Saetter machine guns can be easily modified to use disintegrating metallic links.

Madsen/Saetter 7.62mm Tank Machine Gun

Caliber: 7.62mm NATO (can be made in other calibers).
System of Operation: Gas.
Weight: 22.3 lbs.
Length, Overall: 38.2 in.
Barrel Length w/flash hider: 22.2 in.
Sights, Front: Protected blade.
Rear: Tangent with V-notch.
Feed Device: Non-disintegrating 50 round metallic link belt which can be joined to other belts.

The weapon can be built to use disintegrating links of the M13 (U.S.) type. Belt is normally contained in a box attached to left side of receiver.

Muzzle Velocity: 2800 f.p.s.
Cyclic Rate: 7-800 r.p.m.

This is a version of the rifle caliber Madsen/Saetter made specifically for use on tanks and armored vehicles. It can also be used as a ground gun on a tripod. The arrangement of the gas cylinder and piston is interesting. As with the Soviet RPD light machine gun, there is a definite air gap between the gas cylinder and piston when the gun is cocked. This gap serves a useful purpose during functioning—a good deal of the gas which is bled through the gas port into the gas cylinder is dissipated into the atmosphere after it has served to force the piston to the rear. This has several advantages in that it results in less build-up of carbon in the gas cylinder and piston tube and, of special importance in a tank machine gun, it cuts down the amount of "operating" gas which filters back into the receiver and thereby into the tank.

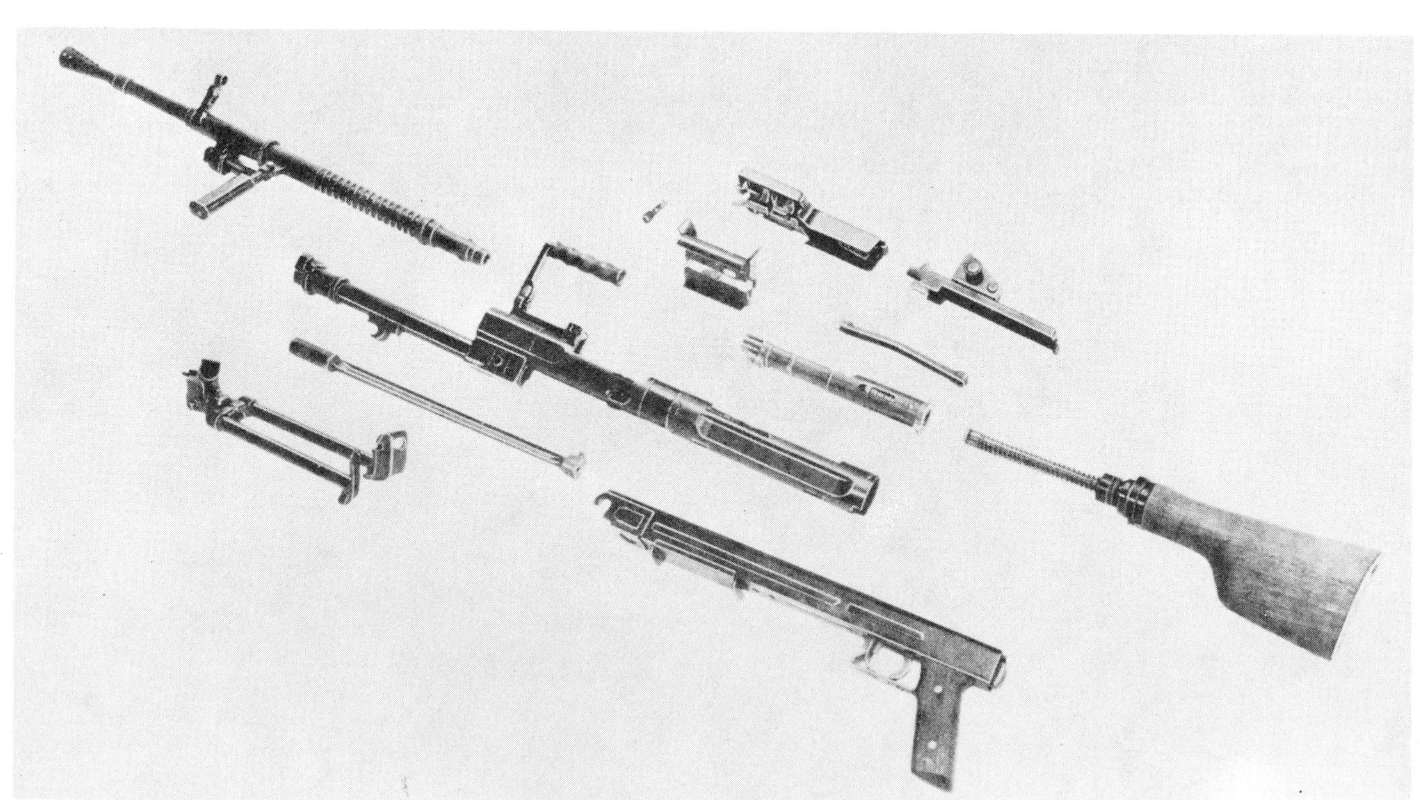

Stripped View of Early Model 7.62mm Madsen/Saetter.

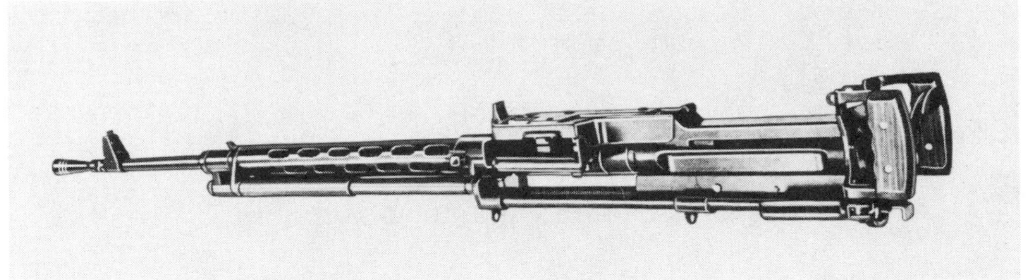

The Danish Madsen/Saetter Cal. .50 Machine Gun; exists in prototype only.

This cal. .50 machine gun utilizes the same basic system and design features as the Madsen/Saetter rifle-caliber machine gun, with the exception of the mounting. The cal. .50 weapon can be adapted for special mounts, for use in armored cars and tanks, or for antiaircraft or antipersonnel use.

There are two types of mounts for this weapon. One serves a dual purpose, as it can be set up for antiaircraft fire, or, with the addition of rubber wheels, can be towed and used against troops on the ground. This mount is generally similar in principle to that of the Soviet DShK M1938/46 heavy machine gun mount, which serves the same dual role.

The other mount used is a light tripod for use on the ground or on armored vehicles.

Caliber: Cal. .50 (12.7mm).
System of Operation: Gas operated, full automatic fire only.
Weight: 61.7 lb.
Length, overall: 64 in.
Barrel Length: 39.4 in.
Feed Device: 50-round non-disintegrating metallic link belts; box magazine holding 50 rounds may be attached to left side of receiver.
Sights: Open sights for ground use; special antiaircraft sights are used when set up for antiaircraft fire.
Muzzle Velocity: Standard for cal. .50 ammunition.
Cyclic Rate: 1000 r.p.m.

Chapter 22. The Dominican Republic

Cal. .30 Automatic Carbine Cristobal Model 2.

The Dominican Republic manufactures an automatic carbine chambered for the U. S. cal. .30 carbine cartridge. This weapon is called the automatic carbine Cristobal Model 2 by the Dominicans. The weapon is produced in a plant which has been run with the help of technicians from P. Beretta of Italy and Hungary; it is, therefore, not too surprising that the Model 2 has some striking similarities in outward appearance to the Beretta submachine guns. Internally, however, there are some significant differences. The Beretta Model 38-series submachine guns are blowback operated; the Model 2 Cristobal carbine is a delayed blowback.

Caliber: Cal. .30 (U.S. M1 carbine cartridge.)
System of Operation: Delayed blowback, selective fire.
Weight, w/o Magazine: 7.75 lb.
Length, Overall: 37.2 in.
Barrel Length: 16.1 in.
Feed Device: 25- or 30-round, detachable, staggered-row box magazine.
Sights, Front: Hooded blade.
Rear: Notch with elevator.
Muzzle Velocity: 1875 f.p.s.
Cyclic Rate: 580 r.p.m.

How to Load and Fire the Cristobal Model 2

Insert a loaded magazine in the magazine well. Pull the handle on the right side of the receiver to the rear. The bolt will remain to the rear, since this weapon fires from an open bolt. Push the handle forward—it does not reciprocate with the forward and rearward movements of the bolt. If the forward trigger is pulled, the weapon will fire single shots; if the rear trigger is pulled, the weapon will produce automatic fire. To put the weapon on safe, pull the lever mounted on the left side of the receiver to the rear. The safety blocks the sear and the triggers, and prevents rearward movement of the bolt. This weapon has no bolt-holding-open device, and therefore the bolt must be pulled to the rear every time a new magazine is loaded.

How to Field Strip the Cristobal Model 2

Remove the magazine by pushing the magazine catch forward. Press in the receiver cap lock and turn the receiver cap, removing it from the rear of the receiver. The recoil spring and the bolt can now be removed from the receiver. The bolt can be disassembled by removing the cross pin at its forward part, and slipping off the inertia lock. No further disassembly is recommended. To reassemble the weapon, perform the above steps in reverse order.

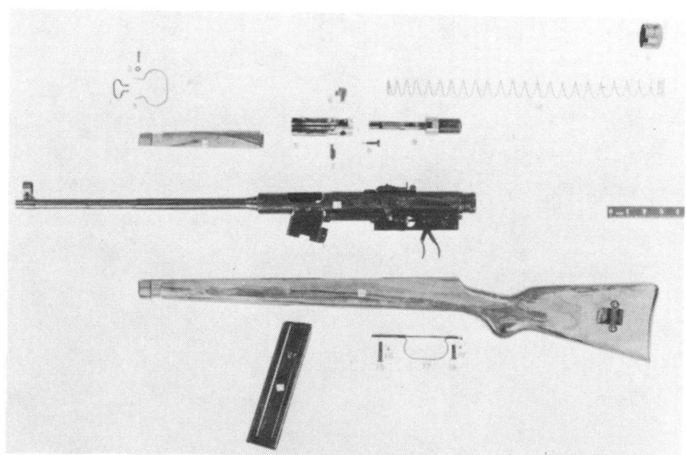

Cristobal Carbine Stripped.

How the Cristobal Model 2 Works

The trigger mechanism of this weapon is similar to that of the Beretta Model 38-series of weapons. The bolt consists of two main parts: the bolt body, and a heavy part called the striker. These parts are joined by a two-armed inertia lever which is seated in the rear end of the bolt proper. The upper long arm of the movable inertia lever engages the striker, and lower short arm of the lever projects down from the bolt. When the bolt is closed, the short arm of the inertia lever stands before a stationary shoulder which is firmly attached to the bottom of the

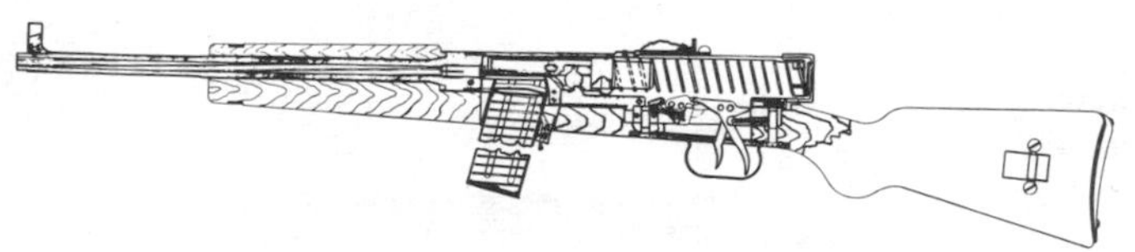

Section View of the Cristobal Model 2.

receiver. When a round is fired, the gases thrust rearward on the cartridge case base, which pushes back against the face of the bolt. Before the bolt can open, however, its inertia must be overcome. When the bolt begins to move rearward, the lower arm of the inertia lever (which could be called an inertia lock) bears against the bottom shoulder of the receiver. The rearward movement of the bolt then causes rearward rotation of the inertia lever, swinging the bottom arm up and out of engagement with the receiver, and forcing the upper arm back against the heavy striker. It is claimed that this system of delayed opening offers as great a resistance to the cartridge thrust as that of a bolt three to five times heavier than the one used with this weapon. During the closing of the bolt, another lateral arm of the inertia lever slides on the receiver wall, and retains the inertia lever and the striker in a cocked position long enough for the bolt to run fully home. When the bolt is fully closed, the lateral arm of the inertia lever moves above a slot in the receiver wall, permitting forward rotation of the lever by the striker and the firing of the round. The inertia lever therefore prevents the weapon from firing before the bolt is fully closed.

Dominican Cal. .30 Cartridges

The Dominican Republic also manufactures its own cal. .30 rifle and carbine cartridges. These are loaded with Berdan primers, rather than the Boxer type used in the United States and Canada.

Cal. .30 M1962 Automatic Carbine

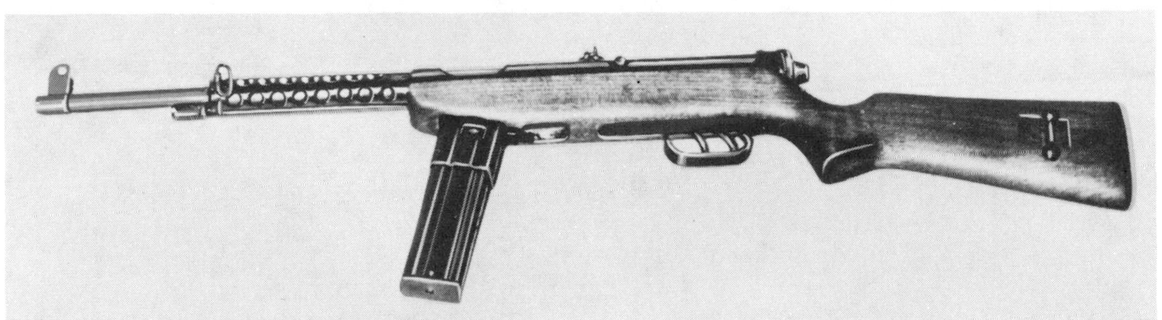

Dominican Cal. .30 Automatic Carbine Model 1962.

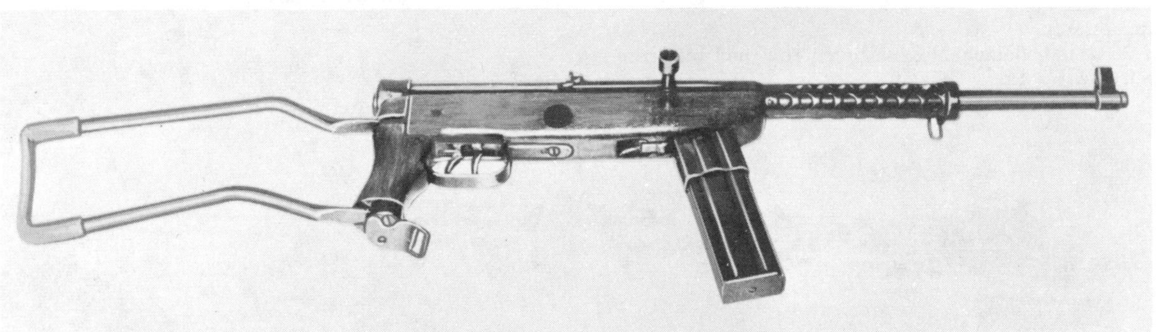

Dominican Cal. .30 Automatic Carbine Model 1962 with folding metal stock.

Caliber: Cal. .30 (U.S. M1 carbine cartridge).
System of Operation: Delayed blowback, selective fire.
Weight, Loaded:
W/wooden Stock—8.7 lbs.
W/folding Steel Stock—8.2 lbs.
Length, Overall:
W/wooden Stock—34.1 in.
W/steel Stock Extended—37 in.
W/steel Stock folded—25.6 in.
Barrel Length: 12.2 in.
Feed Device: 30-round, detachable, staggered-row box magazine.
Sights, Front: Protected blade.
Rear: L type.
Muzzle Velocity: 1870 f.p.s.

A new model of the Cristobal carbine has been introduced. The Model 1962 Automatic carbine may be found either with a fixed wooden stock or a folding metal stock. Its loading, firing, field stripping and functioning are the same as those of the Cristobal Model 2. The main difference in construction, other than the folding steel stock, is the use of a perforated metal barrel jacket on the Model 1962 weapons. Wooden handguards have a tendency to char and smoke on automatic weapons which have been heated by the consecutive firing of a number of rounds. This is probably the reason for the adoption of the metal barrel jacket for the Model 1962.

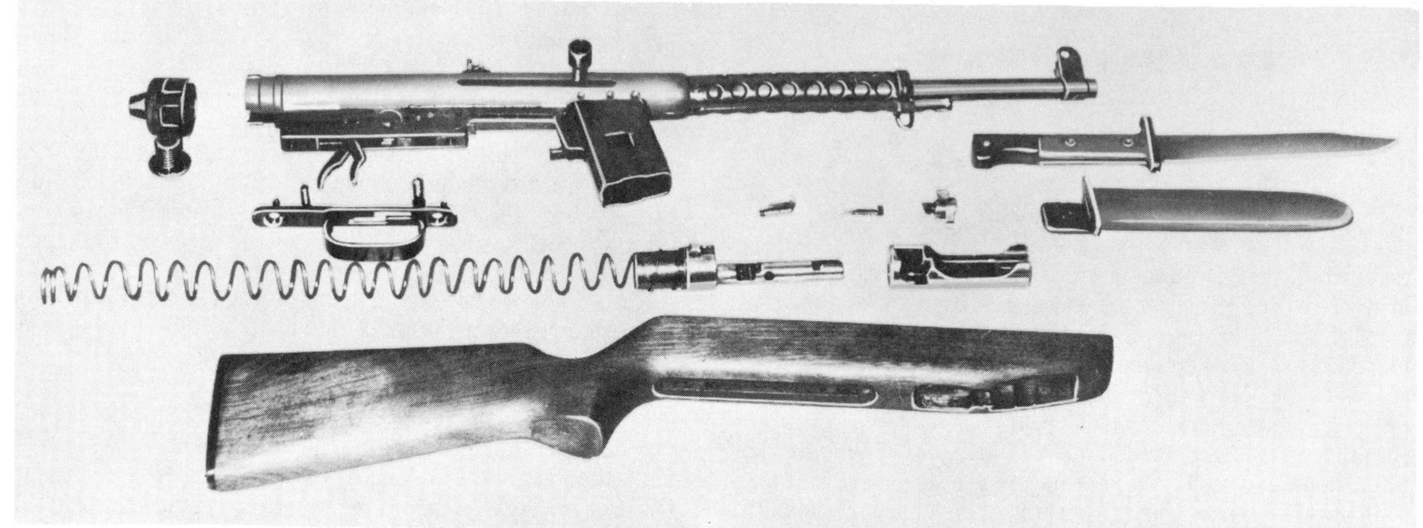

Dominican Cal. .30 Automatic Carbine Model 1962 field stripped.

7.62mm Model 1962 Automatic Rifle

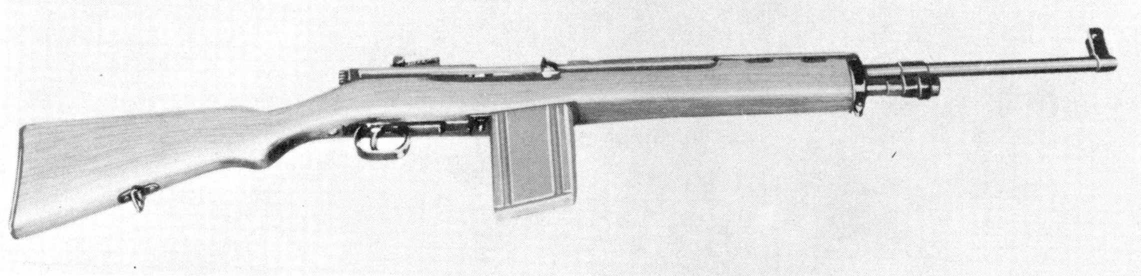

Caliber: 7.62mm NATO.
System of Operation: Gas, selective fire.
Weight Loaded: 10.4 lbs.
Length, Overall: 42.5 in.
Barrel Length: 21.3 in.
Feed Device: 20-round, detachable, staggered row box magazine.
Muzzle Velocity: 2700 f.p.s.

The Model 1962 automatic rifle combines the gas system of the U.S. M14 rifle with the bolt mechanism of the F. N. light automatic rifle.

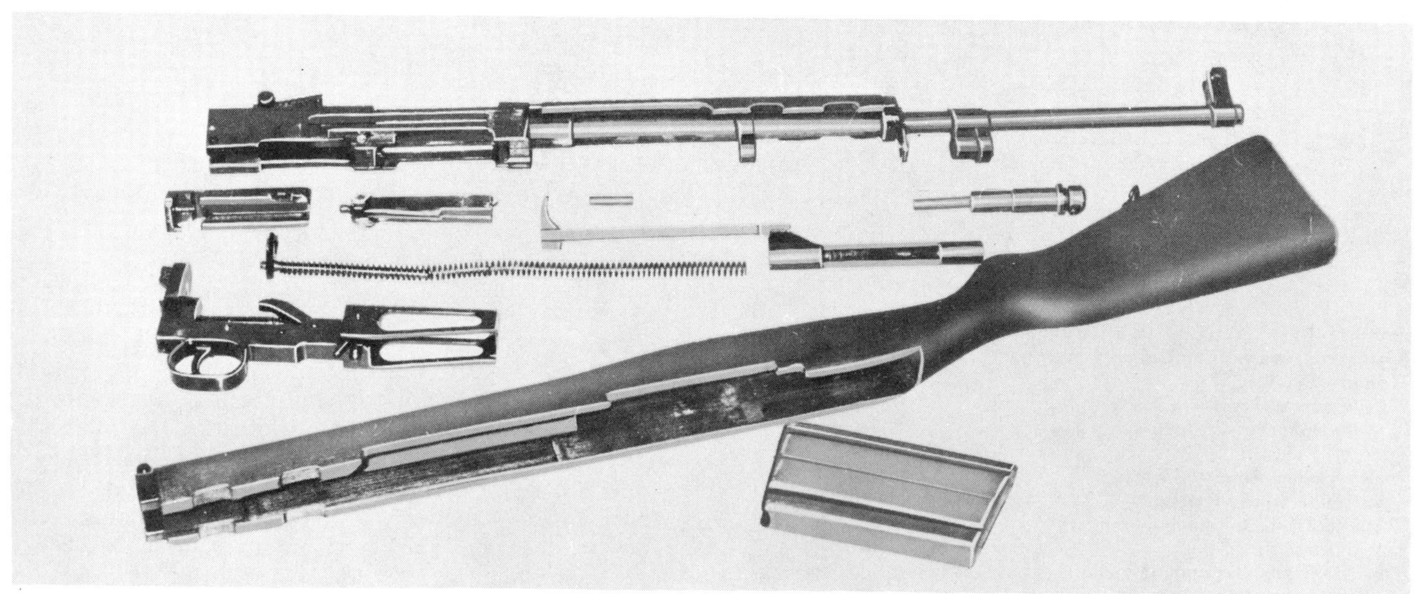

Dominican 7.62mm Automatic Rifle Model 1962, field stripped.

Chapter 23. Finland

Finland has adopted the Soviet 7.62mm M43 "intermediate" sized cartridge and two weapons chambered for that cartridge: an assault rifle and a light machine gun. In the past, the Finns have customarily used the same rifle and machine gun cartridge as the Russians. This was mainly because Finland was a part of Imperial Russia prior to World War I, and apparently inherited a number of Russian weapons along with her independence. The Finns have produced several weapons of native design which were considered outstanding at the time they were introduced. These included the Suomi submachine gun and the Model 26 Lahti Saloranta light machine gun, but both of these weapons are somewhat outdated at present.

FINNISH PISTOLS

Finnish 9mm Lahti Pistol

The Finns use the 9mm Parabellum Lahti pistol Model L-35 and the 7.65 mm Model 23 pistol. The Model 23 is a Luger. The Lahti pistol is covered in detail in chapter 40, where it is known as the Model 40 pistol.

FINNISH RIFLES

Former Finnish service rifles were all based on the Russian 1891 Mosin Nagant action. The Finnish models of the Mosin Nagant vary from the Russian mainly in sights, stocks, fittings, etc. In general it can be said that the Finnish-made weapons are of higher quality manufacture than the Russian weapons. Various Finnish service rifles chambered for the 7.62mm rimmed cartridge are the Model 91 Carbine, Model 27 Rifle, Model 28 Rifle, Model 28-30 Rifle, Model 30 Rifle, and the Model 39 Rifle.

Model 39 7.62mm Rifle.

Finnish 7.62mm M60 Assault Rifle

Caliber: 7.62mm uses copy of Soviet M43 rimless.
System of Operation: Gas, selective fire.
Weight, Loaded: 9 lbs.
Length, Overall: 36 in.
Barrel Length: 16.5 in.
Feed Device: 30 round detachable, staggered box magazine.
Sights: Front—Hooded post.
Rear—Tangent w/aperture.
Cyclic Rate: 650 r.p.m.
Muzzle Velocity: 2362 f.p.s.

This weapon is a modified copy of the Soviet AK-47. Loading and firing, field stripping, and functioning are the same as described under that weapon in the chapter on the U.S.S.R.

The fore-end and pistol grip of the M60 are made of plastic and the weapon has a tubular steel stock. The rear sight is mounted on the receiver cover rather than on the receiver, as on the AK. An unusual feature of the weapon is that it does not have a full trigger guard; a post protrudes downward from the receiver and blocks the trigger from the front. This allows easy use of the weapon with heavy winter mittens. The bayonet of the M60 and its manner of mounting are different from that of the Soviet AK-47.

Finnish 7.62mm M60 Assault Rifle field stripped.

FINNISH SUBMACHINE GUNS

Finnish Suomi 9mm Submachine Gun.

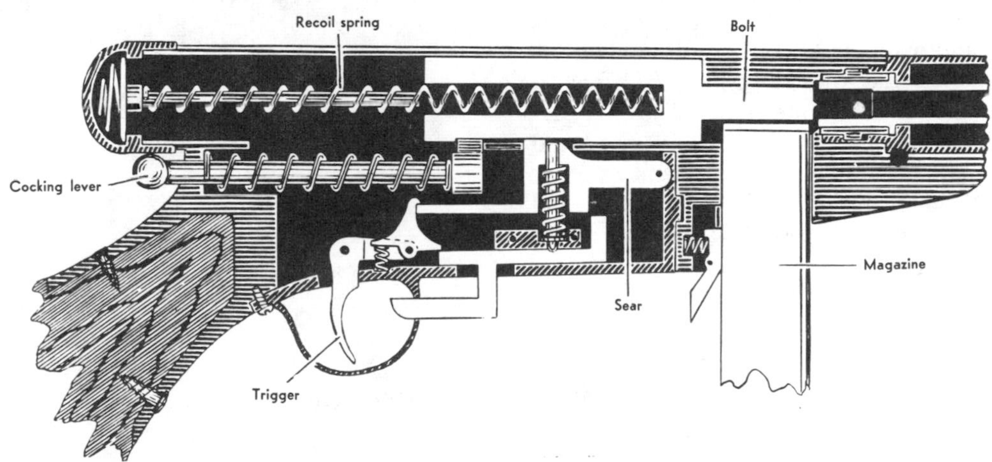

Nomenclature of the 9mm Suomi.

Note: This weapon is one of the most remarkable developments of World War II. Its simplicity, ruggedness, reliability, and ease of operation are all outstanding in machine pistol construction. The Russians made wide use of a modification of this weapon.

Caliber: 9mm Parabellum. (This is also the pistol cartridge of the Finns.)
Magazine: (a) Box type usually holding 25 and 50 cartridges. (b) Drum type containing 70 cartridges.
Position of Magazine: Directly under receiver, positioned from below.
Magazine Catch: Behind magazine, released by pushing forward.
Sights: Open, adjustable to 300 meters.
Cocking Handle: Positioned at end of receiver, directly under milled recoil spring cap. Drawn back with thumb and forefinger of right hand, it cocks the bolt. Its spring automatically returns it to its seat.
Cyclic Rate of Fire: 780 rounds per minute.
Type of Fire: Single and full auto.
Safety: A lever bar directly in front of triggerguard.
Operated: By recoil.
Locked: Blowback type.
Unlocked: Bolt held closed during moment of firing by inertia of moving parts and heavy recoil spring.
Firing Pin: Stationary in bolt but removable.
Cooling: Slotted barrel casing surrounding barrel serves as ventilator.

Loading and Firing

A loaded magazine is inserted below into the magazine housing and pressed up until it locks. The cocking handle protrudes from the rear of the weapon under the milled recoil spring cap. Grip it firmly, pull back to the rear to compress the bolt spring and cock the bolt, and allow to run forward under the influence of its own spring. Pressure on the trigger will now fire the weapon. The bolt will stay back between shots. When a continuous burst of fire is required, maintain a firm stiff pressure.

Field Stripping

At the rear of the receiver is a heavy milled cap. Unscrew this cap and ease out the housing recoil spring guide, and recoil spring.

Drawing back on the cocking handle will now pull the bolt back for removal from the weapon.

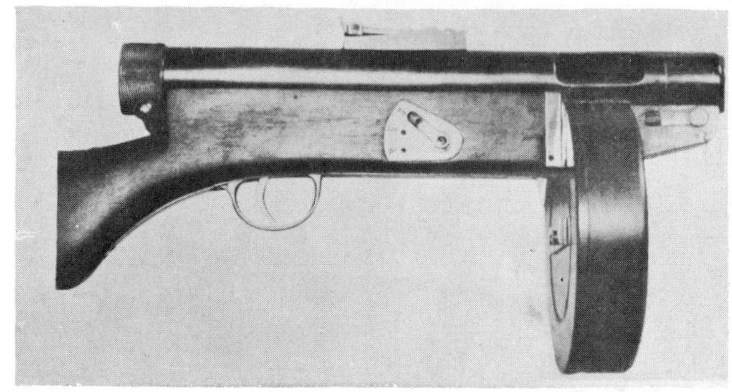

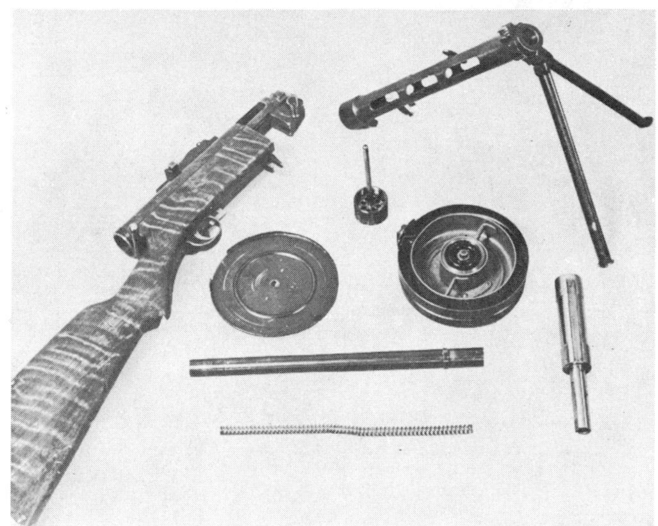

Special Note on the Suomi Submachine Gun

The Suomi is used in two models by Finland, both chambered for the 9mm Parabellum cartridge. Their model designations are Model 31 and Model 44. This weapon is also used in Sweden, where it is known as the Model 37-39 and Model 37-39F, and in Switzerland, where it is called the Model 43/44. It has also been manufactured in both of these countries. A delayed-blowback Suomi "assault rifle" was produced before World War II. This weapon was chambered for a rimmed 7.62mm "intermediate-sized" cartridge, and used a drum magazine and a bipod. The weapon is not in service.

FINNISH MACHINE GUNS

7.62mm M60 Light Machine Gun

Caliber: 7.62mm uses copy of Soviet M43 rimless.
System of Operation: Gas.
Weight: 16.8 lbs.
Feed Device: 100 round non-disintegrating metallic link belt.
Sights: Front—Hooded post.
Rear—Tangent leaf.
Cyclic Rate: 1050 r.p.m.

The M60 is used on a bipod or on a light weight tripod. The weapon has a prong type flash suppressor and a tubular steel stock. Like the M60 Assault rifle it has a bar in front of the trigger in lieu of a conventional trigger guard. The ammunition container is hung on the left side of the receiver allowing easy movement of the gun with ammunition by one man.

Finnish 7.62mm Model 32 Heavy Machine Gun.

The Finns use three 7.62mm heavy machine guns. Apparently, all are Maxim types; their model designations are Model 09, Model 21, and Model 32. The light machine gun formerly used was the Model 26 Lahti Saloranta. Although this weapon was developed for international sale and was advertised as being suitable for any service caliber, so far as known it has only been made in 7.62mm caliber for the Finnish Army.

Finnish 7.62mm Model 26 Lahti Saloranta Light Machine Gun.

The Model 26 was one of the first of the post-World War I "true" light machine gun types. It was considered a noteworthy gun at its time of development and, although somewhat lacking in adaptability as compared with the post-World War II guns, is still a basically sound weapon.

Caliber: 7.62mm rimmed.
System of Operation: Recoil, selective fire.
Weight, w/loaded 20-rd. magazine: 23 lbs.
Length, Overall: 46.5 in.
Feed Device: 20-round box, or 75-round drum.
Cyclic Rate: 500 r.p.m.
Muzzle Velocity: 2625 f.p.s.

How to Load and Fire the Model 26 Lahti Saloranta

Pull the operating handle to the rear, insert a loaded magazine in the magazine port (when using the box magazine) and set the selector on the type of fire desired. Squeeze the trigger and the weapon will fire. The Model 26 fires from an open bolt. To attach the 75-round drum magazine to the gun, remove the magazine support and push the magazine up into position until the holding latch clicks. To remove the barrel, turn the lever 180 degrees. This releases the catch holding the butt to the receiver. Lift the receiver cover and the barrel, barrel extension, and bolt can be lifted out as a unit. Usually the complete unit is replaced.

How the Model 26 Lahti Saloranta Works

Two distinct feed systems are available with this gun. A spring loaded clip which holds 25 cartridges may be used. The alternate is a flat drum magazine mounted below the gun with a capacity of 75 rounds.

Maximum rate of fire is normally set at 500 per minute.

In the Lahti the bolt is automatically held to the rear after the trigger has been released. The effect of this is to keep the action open to prevent a round in the chamber cooking off. This also, of course, permits air circulation through the barrel for cooling purposes.

A quick-change barrel is provided which can be withdrawn by turning the dismounting lever 180 degrees to release the catch which holds the buttstock to the receiver. The receiver cover is lifted, and the barrel extension together with the barrel and bolt are then pulled out to the rear in a manner not unlike that of the Swiss Furrer.

When using the flat 75-shot drum, the magazine support is removed and the drum is pushed up until its holding catch snaps into place. The operating handle on the right is pulled all the way to the rear. The spring-loaded sear rises to catch the notch in the bottom of the bolt and holds it back. The arm is now cocked and ready to fire. Setting the selector from safe to automatic fire prepares it for action.

As the trigger is pulled the sear is freed from the bolt. The bolt is driven ahead by the compressed operating

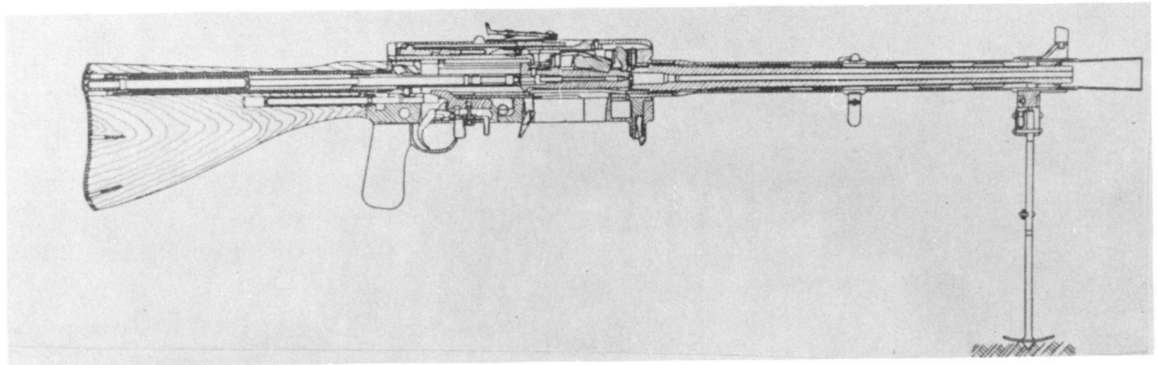

Section view of Lahti.

spring. A feed rib machined into the top of the bolt pushes the first round out of the lips of the magazine and toward the chamber.

The bolt seats behind the cartridge when about one-half inch from final position and the claw extractor snaps over the case.

Simultaneously the bolt locking piece is cammed downwards into its locking notch in the bolt. This releases the holding catch which has been preventing the barrel and extension from moving forward.

The locked barrel with its extension and the bolt start the final movement ahead. When it nears complete battery position, a pivoting pin in the bolt body which has been blocking the firing pin hits a ramp in the receiver and is pushed up out of the way to permit the firing pin to be released and go forward to fire the cartridge.

Again rather on the Furrer principle, we find the timing such that the recoil starts before the forward moving locked parts strike the receiver. This buffing action eases the recoil and makes for smoother functioning.

During the recoil stroke the parts are locked together for about one-half inch of travel. At that point the stud on the bolt lock engages a cam in the receiver to lift it out of its locking recess there.

The bolt is allowed a rearward motion of a few thousandths of an inch before complete unlocking sets in, thereby permitting the extractor to loosen the cartridge before the gas pressure affects it directly. (This allows the extractor to break the gas seal. The cartridge is thereby entirely loosened in primary extraction at this point.)

As the gun fires, energy is transferred from the recoiling barrel to the bolt through an accelerator which pivots to speed the bolt to the rear while the extractor withdraws the empty cartridge case until its rim hits the solid ejector and is knocked out the ejection port to the right.

The firing pin is withdrawn during the initial recoil movement. The firing pin sear in the top of the bolt drops in front of a circular projection over the body of the pin. As the bolt is released from locking, the barrel and barrel extension are held rearward by the holding catch. The compressed operating spring is ready at the end of the stroke to return the members if the trigger is on full automatic.

Chapter 24. France

The French Army has adopted a new family of small arms since World War II. Some of the older equipment is still in limited use, and one of the pre-war weapons is apparently being retained—the 7.5mm M1924 M29 automatic rifle. A new pistol, a new submachine gun, and several new rifles have been put into service, as well as a new general purpose machine gun.

FRENCH PISTOLS AND REVOLVERS

The French captured large numbers of German Lugers and Walthers at the end of World War II. They were also supplied with U. S. cal. .45 M1911A1 pistols, and with some British pistols. In 1950, France introduced a new pistol into service, the 9mm M1950. This is the current standard French pistol, and is a considerably better weapon than those used by the French prior to World War II. The 7.65mm M1935A and M1935S are in limited police use at present, but are not seen in photos of French Army troops.

The 9mm M1950 Pistol.

The M1950 pistol is similar in most respects to the U.S. cal. .45 Colt automatic. It incorporates a few improvements over that weapon, but in loading, firing, and functioning is essentially the same as the cal. .45. It is a much better made and more lethal weapon than any of the earlier French pistols.

Caliber: 9mm Parabellum.
System of Operation: Recoil, semi-automatic fire only.
Weight: 1.8 lb.
Length, overall: 7.6 in.
Barrel length: 4.4 in.
Feed device: 9-round, single-column, detachable box magazine.
Sights, Front: Tapered post.
Rear: U-notch; the top of the slide has a matted ramp.
Muzzle Velocity: 1156 f.p.s.

How to Load and Fire the M1950 Pistol

The M1950 pistol is loaded and fired the same as the U.S. M1911A1 cal. .45 automatic pistol. However, it cannot be fired with the magazine removed. A loaded-chamber indicator is mounted in the slide.

How to Field Strip the M1950 Pistol

Field stripping is the same as for the U.S. .45, with the following exceptions:

There is no barrel bushing and recoil spring plug; the recoil spring is dismounted after the slide has been removed from the receiver.

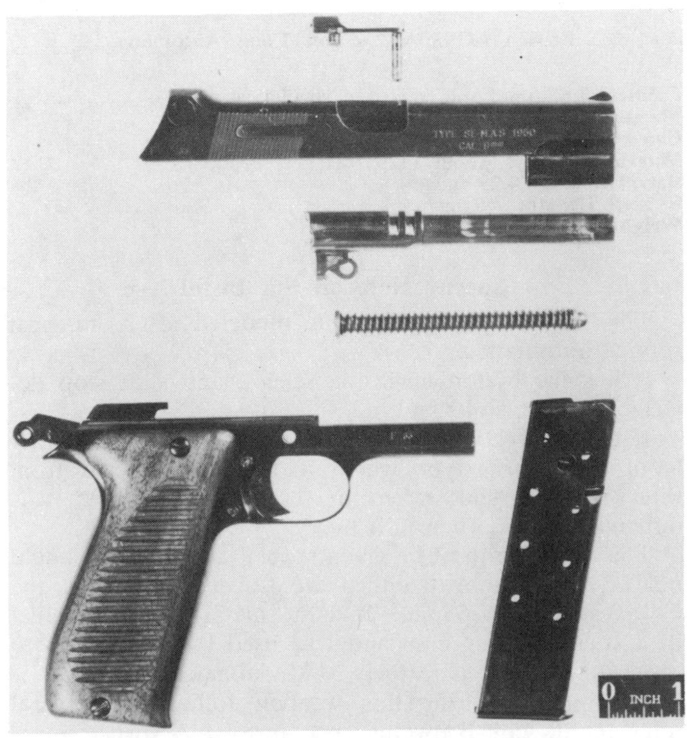

M1950 Field Stripped.

The hammer, its spring and lever, and the sear assembly are contained in a housing which can be lifted out as one piece when the slide is removed.

How the M1950 Pistol Works

The functioning of the M1950 pistol is essentially the same as that of the U.S. service automatic.

Special Note on the M1950 Pistol

The M1950 pistol incorporates some features of earlier French pistols, and has a few changes borrowed elsewhere. The safety on the slide was used in the M1935A and M1935S; it blocks the hammer from the firing pin. The packaged hammer unit is used in the Soviet Tokarev. The internal mounting of the recoil spring is used on practically all the Browning and modified Browning-design pistols in service today except the U.S. cal. .45 and those pistols which are direct copies of the U.S. cal. .45.

French M1935A 7.65mm Long Automatic.

Caliber: 7.65mm Long (this is a special cartridge).
Magazine: Box type, single line.
Capacity: 8 cartridges.
Muzzle Velocity: About 1120 feet per second.
Barrel Length: 4.29 inches.
Overall Length: 7.6 inches.
Weight: 25.7 ounces.

Special Note on this Pistol

This, in many respects, was modeled after our own service automatic.

It has the button magazine release and slide stop devices of our pistol.

It does not however have a grip safety. The hammer is of the "burr" type which is largely protected from injury by the slide when in the down position. It is difficult to cock when in a hurry.

The cartridge must be given special attention. It should not be confused with either the Luger 7.65mm or the Colt-Browning 7.65mm. It is a metal jacketed bullet in a specially long case and was used by the French to some limited extent in their MAS submachine guns.

Loading and firing this weapon follow the general rules of all Colt-Browning type pistols. A loaded magazine is inserted in the handle until it locks into place.

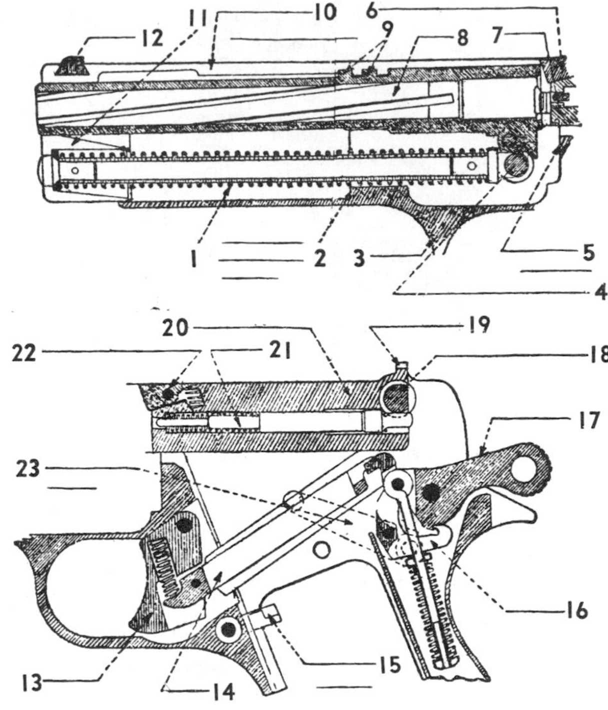

French Pistolet 1935A.

(Drawing from French Manual)

1. Recoil spring.
2. Receiver stop.
3. Receiver.
4. Barrel pivot pin.
5. Barrel stop.
6. Loading indicator.
7. Face of breechlock.
8. Barrel.
9. Duel barrel locking lugs.
10. Slide-breechblock unit.
11. Front of slide.
12. Front sight.
13. Trigger.
14. Trigger bar.
15. Magazine catch.
16. Sear.
17. Hammer.
18. Manual Safety.
19. Rear sight.
20. Breech section of slide.
21. Firing pin.
22. Loading indicator and tor.
23. Magazine safety.

The slide is then drawn back manually to its full length and permitted to run forward to load the first cartridge into the firing chamber. Pressing the trigger will fire the cartridge and the recoil will eject the empty cartridge case, recock the hammer and feed a new cartridge into the chamber. Only one shot can be fired for each pull of the trigger, as this weapon has a safety disconnector. A modification of this weapon, the M1935S, also exists. This weapon also uses the 7.65 mm long cartridge.

French 7.65mm M1935S Pistol.

French-made Walther PPK Cal. .380.

This pistol was made by Manhurin in France before Walther post-war resumption of manufacture. It was not used as a French service pistol and is no longer being made in France. It is currently manufactured in Germany.

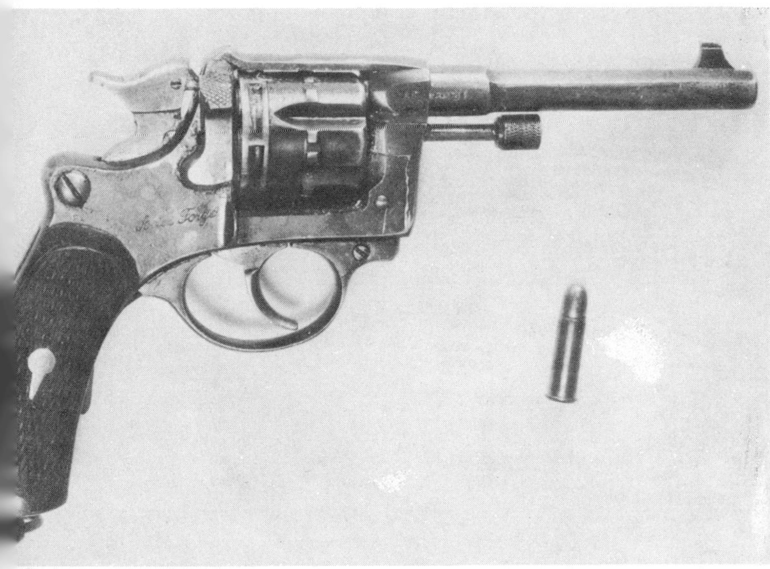

French Modele d'Ordonnance 1892 Revolver.

Caliber: 8mm, .315 inches.
Cylinder: 6 shots.
Muzzle Velocity: 625 feet per second.
Weight of Bullet: 102 grains lead.
Muzzle Striking Energy: 104 foot pounds.
Barrel Length: 4″.
Type of Action: Double action. Hammer may be cocked by the thumb or the entire firing action may be produced by pulling straight back on the trigger.
Cylinder Release Catch: This is a thumb piece on the right side of the revolver. It is swung directly back and down on its pivot. The cylinder then may be swung out to the right.
Extraction: Pushing on extractor rod unloads revolver in exactly the same manner as the Colt revolver. All chambers are ejected simultaneously.
Note on Ammunition: This a freak cartridge somewhat resembling our .32-20. Bullet is copper jacketed and cartridge loaded with black powder. This cartridge is popularly called the 8mm Lebel.

Stripping

With a screwdriver, turn the large dismounting screw on the right side plate above the grip. This will force out the hinged plate on the left side of the revolver

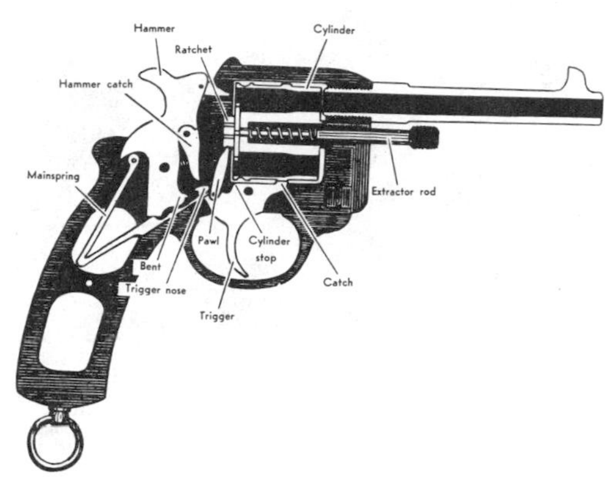

Nomenclature Drawing, French Service Revolver.

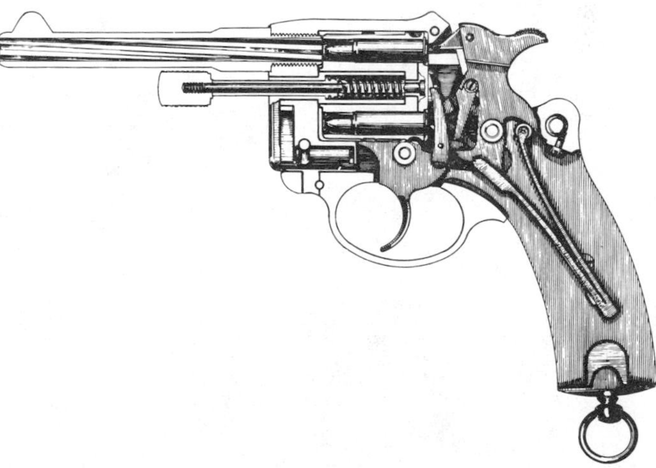

Action Closed.

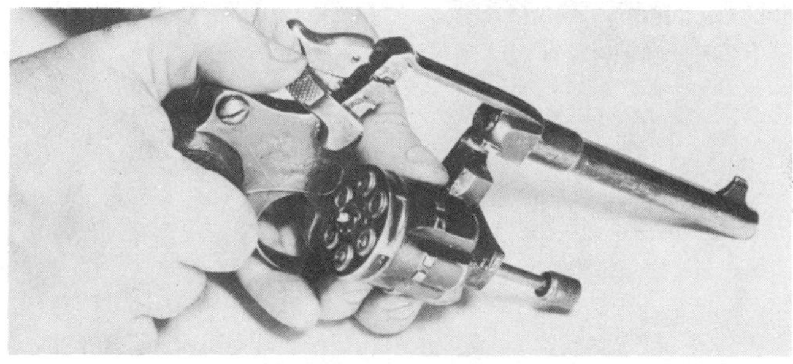

extending from the grip forward to the under side of the frame.

With cylinder swung out to the right, the entire working mechanism of the pistol is now available for cleaning or repair.

Note: This was the official French Service Revolver and is commonly referred to as the Lebel. It is now obsolete.

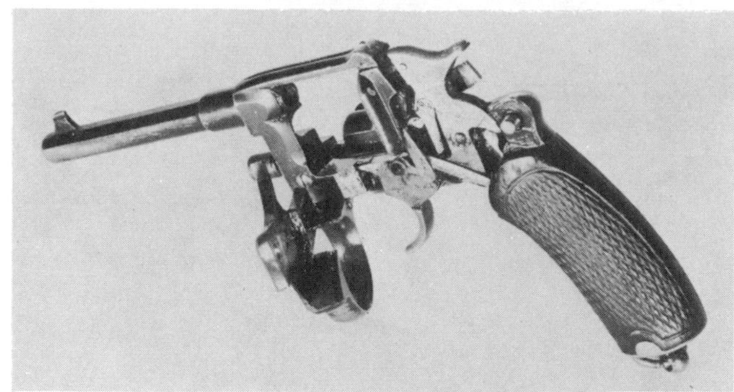

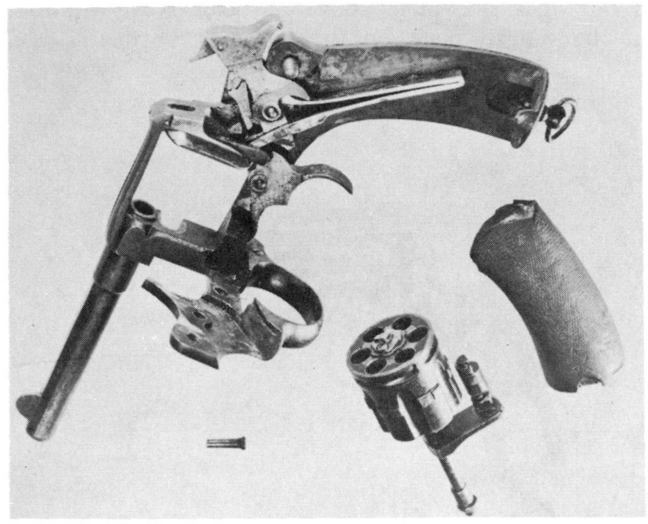

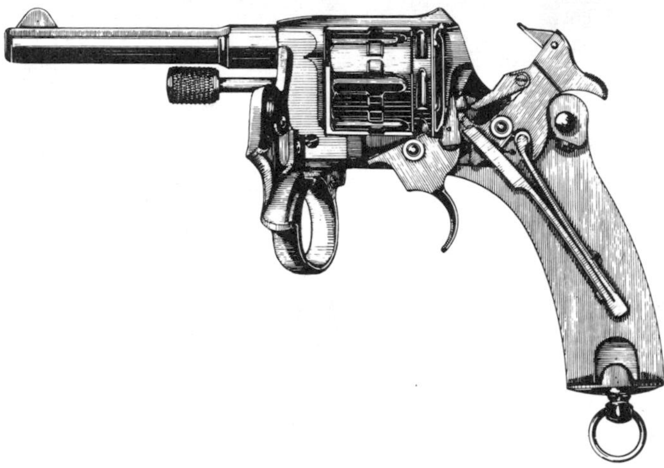

Action Open and Side Plate Swung Out.

Obsolete But Common 11mm M1873 Revolver.

French Model 73. This is an obsolete solid frame revolver with rod ejection similar to the Colt single action principle. Length 9.16″. Barrel 4.37″. Weight 2.64 lbs. Caliber 11mm (.429). Cylinder capacity 6. System, double action.

Miscellaneous. Spanish and Belgian imitations of Smith & Wesson Military and Police Models and of Colt .38 Army Special revolvers. These were made for the French in the standard 8mm French revolver caliber, but were also made in .38 special American calibers.

Evaluation. Models 1873 and 1874 are obsolete black powder types. These arms should be considered collector's pieces and should not be generally altered to any modern U. S. ammunition.

Spanish and Belgian Colt and S&W imitations are impossible to classify on a group basis. In general they are inferior in workmanship and materials to the U. S. originals. Some types are encountered which are made of steels which seem able to take more punishment than the average American revolver. An inspection of the finish, the fitting, and the materials is the best guide as to whether to use these revolvers. As made for the French Army they were adequately proofed by French standards.

Ammunition. Models 1873 and 74. Cal. 11mm French 73/90. Not made in U. S.

FRENCH RIFLES AND CARBINES

The older French rifles are still commonly encountered in Middle Eastern areas and among collectors in the United States. Therefore, coverage on them has been expanded to include a table of characteristics of the various models, and a few words have been added to explain the major differences among the various categories of these weapons.

Basically the bolt action French rifles and carbines can be broken down into three categories:

The 1886 (commonly called the Lebel), which uses the tubular-type magazine; and its modifications. These weapons are chambered for the 8mm M1886 rimmed cartridge.

FRENCH RIFLES AND CARBINES OF PRE-WORLD WAR II DESIGN.

Weapon	System of Operation	Overall Length	Barrel Length	Feed Device	Sights	Muzzle Velocity	Weight
Rifle: 8mm M1886 M93	Manually operated 2-piece bolt	51.3 in.	31.4 in.	8-rd tubular magazine	Front: Notched blade Rear: leaf	2380 f.p.s.	9.35 lb.
Rifle: 8mm M1886 M93R35	Manually operated 2-piece bolt	37.64 in.	17.7 in.	3-rd tubular magazine	Front: Notched blade Rear: leaf	2080 f.p.s.	7.84 lb.
Carbine: 8mm M1890	Manually operated 2-piece bolt	37.2 in.	17.7 in.	3-rd Mannlicher-type, integral, in-line magazine	Front: Blade Rear: Leaf	2080 f.p.s.	6.83 lb.
Mousqueton 8mm M1892	Manually operated 2-piece bolt	37.2 in.	17.7 in.	3-rd Mannlicher-type, integral, in-line magazine	Front: Blade Rear: Leaf	2080 f.p.s.	6.8 lb.
Rifle: 8mm M1902 "Indo-China Model"	Manually operated 2-piece bolt	38.6 in.	24.8 in.	3-rd Mannlicher-type, integral, in-line magazine	Front: Blade Rear: Leaf	2180 f.p.s.	7.9 lb.
Rifle: 8mm M1907 "Colonial Model"	Manually operated 2-piece bolt	52 in.	31.4 in.	3-rd Mannlicher-type, integral, in-line magazine	Front: Blade Rear: Leaf	2380 f.p.s.	8.6 lb.
Rifle: 8mm M1907/15	Manually operated 2-piece bolt	51.42 in.	31.4 in.	3-rd Mannlicher-type, integral, in-line magazine	Front Notched blade Rear: Leaf	2380 f.p.s.	8.38 lb.
Rifle: 8-mm M1916	Manually operated 2-piece bolt	51.42 in.	31.4 in.	5-rd Mannlicher-type, integral, in-line magazine	Front Notched blade Rear: Leaf	2380 f.p.s.	9.25 lb.
Carbine: 8mm M1916	Manually operated 2-piece bolt	37.2 in.	17.7 in.	5-rd Mannlicher-type, integral, in-line magazine	Front: Blade Rear: Leaf	2080 f.p.s.	7.17 lb.
Rifle: 7.5mm M1907/15 M34	Manually operated 2-piece bolt	43.2 in.	22.8 in.	5-rd integral, staggered-row, box magazine	Front: Blade Rear: Leaf	2700 f.p.s.	7.85 lb.
Rifle: 7.5mm M1932	Prototype of M1936, made in limited quantities						
Rifle: 7.5mm M1936	Manually operated 1-piece bolt	40.13 in.	22.6 in.	5-rd integral, staggered-row, box magazine	Front: Barley-corn w/guards Rear: Ramp w/aperture	2700 f.p.s.	8.29 lb.
Rifle: 7.5mm M1936 CR39	Manually operated 1-piece bolt	Stock extended 34.9 in. Stock folded: 24.3 in.	22.6 in.	5-rd integral, staggered-row, box magazine	Front: Barley-corn w/guards Rear: Ramp w/aperture	2700 f.p.s.	8 lb. (approx.)

The M1890 carbine (sometimes called the Mannlicher Berthier), which uses the Mannlicher-type feed system (requiring a special clip which functions as part of the magazine); and the many later rifles and carbines which use this system. These weapons also are chambered for the 8mm cartridge.

The M1932 and its production model, the M1936, which use a 5-round Mauser-type magazine and a one-piece bolt. These weapons are chambered for the 7.5mm rimless cartridge.

The 7.5mm M1907/15 M34 is a variant; this is the M1907/15 rifle cut down and rebarreled for the 7.5mm cartridge. This weapon also was fitted with a Mauser-type 5-round magazine.

The early models have so many variants—Gendarmerie models, Artillery models, etc.—that it would be impossible to list them all here. An interesting point about the early rifles is that many of their parts are interchangeable; with a good supply of parts, and a vivid imagination, anyone can make up a weapon that would keep the collectors guessing for a long time.

A postwar version of the M1936, the 7.5mm M1936 M51, has a rifle grenade launcher built into the muzzle end of the barrel.

Post-World War II French Rifles

The French had considerable quantities of U.S. M1, M1903, and M1917 rifles at the conclusion of World War II. France still apparently makes use of many of these weapons; they appeared in the hands of French troops in the fighting in Indo-China. The French arsenal at Saint Etienne designed a gas-operated rifle called the MAS 44, for the 7.5mm French cartridge. This weapon, in a modified form, was produced as the 7.5mm Rifle M1949 (MAS 49).

A word of explanation about the MAS designation and other French arsenal designations: The French government owns and operates three small arms plants: Saint Etienne, Tulle, and Chatellerault. They are called Manufacture Des Armes by the French. Thus the plant at Saint Etienne is MAS, the plant at Tulle is MAT, and the plant at Chatellerault is MAC. Frequently the French tack this plant identification on a weapon, presumably to give credit to the plant where the design originated.

	M1949	M1949/56
Caliber:	7.5mm French M1929 cartridge, for both models.	
System of operation:	gas, semi-automatic fire only, for both models.	
Weight:	10.4 lb.	8.6 lb. w/o magazine.
Length, overall:	43.3 in.	43.4 in.
Barrel length:	22.8 in.	20.7 in.
Feed device:	10-round, detachable, staggered-row box magazine, normally loaded with 5-round chargers: for both models.	
Sights, Front:	Blade w/protecting ears, for both models.	
Rear:	Ramp w/aperture, for both models.	
Muzzle velocity:	2705 f.p.s.	2700 f.p.s.

These gas-operated weapons show considerable designing skill. They are relatively simple in operation and are very easy to strip and clean. They use a tilting bolt system, and have no moving parts in the gas system. The forward part of the barrel is used as a grenade launcher on

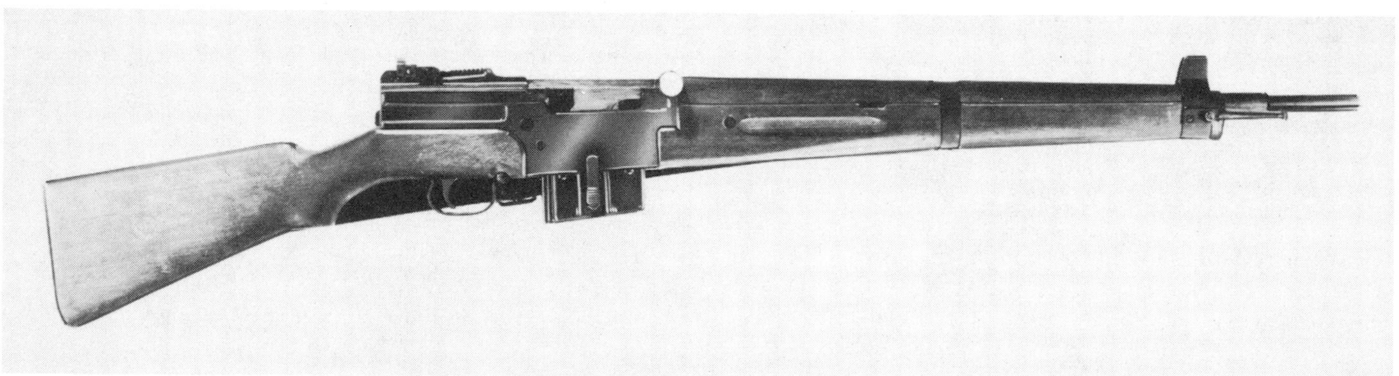

French 7.5mm Rifle M1949 (MAS).

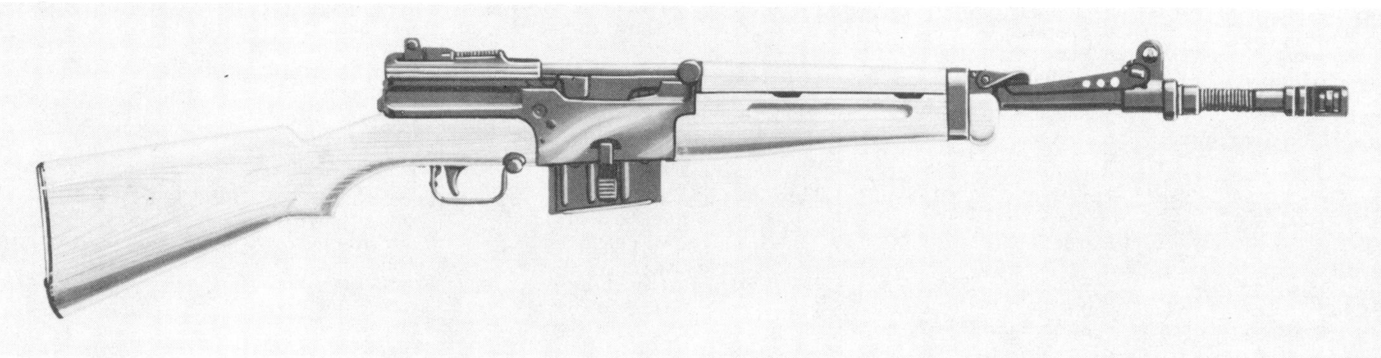

French 7.5mm M1949/56 Rifle.

both models and both have built-in grenade launcher sights. On the M1949 the grenade launcher sight is on the left front side of the fore-end; on the M1949/56, the grenade launcher sights are on top of the barrel, to the rear of the front rifle sight. Both of these weapons have two-piece stocks, as did the M1936 series of weapons. The M1949 does not use a bayonet, but the M1949/56 does.

How to Load and Fire the M1949-Series Rifles

The weapon can be loaded by pulling the operating handle to the rear and filling the magazine, using chargers (clips) in a manner similar to that used with the U.S. M1903 rifle; or the magazine may be removed (note that the magazine catch is a part of the magazine, not of the weapon), and then filled by hand. If chargers have been used, the bolt should go forward of its own accord when the magazine is filled, or it may require a short rearward jerk. If the magazine has been removed and the bolt is to the rear, replace the magazine in the magazine well and the bolt will go home, chambering a cartridge, and the weapon is ready to fire. If the bolt is forward, it will have to be pulled to the rear and released. The safety is located at the right front side of the trigger-guard. Upon firing the last shot, the bolt will remain open.

M1949 Field Stripped.

How to Field Strip the M1949-Series Rifles

Remove magazine by depressing magazine catch on right side of magazine and pulling magazine down and out of the receiver. Release receiver cover by depressing the latch, located at the rear of the receiver; push the cover forward slightly and lift it from its grooves in the receiver. **CAUTION:** The bolt must be in the forward position before attempting to remove the receiver cover. (When the bolt is to the rear, the recoil spring, which is housed in the receiver cover, is compressed.) The bolt and bolt carrier can now be lifted out of the receiver. No further disassembly is recommended.

To reassemble the weapon perform the above steps in reverse.

How the M1949-Series Rifles Work

When a cartridge is fired, propellent gas is tapped off through the gas port in the barrel. This gas blows back through the gas tube directly into a hole in the top face of the bolt carrier. The gas tube protrudes a small distance, so that a portion of it actually enters the bolt carrier. The bolt carrier moves to the rear and, after a slight "dwell" time, the bolt is cammed up and out of its locked position in the bottom of the receiver, and starts to travel back with the bolt carrier. The ejector is a pin type that protrudes from the face of the bolt like that of the U.S. M1 rifle; it ejects the spent case when the case mouth clears the face of the barrel. The trigger mechanism is quite similar to that of the U.S. M1 rifle, and operates in a similar fashion. The bolt and bolt carrier compress the recoil spring, which decompresses at the end of their travel and returns the bolt and carrier to the battery position. On the return of the bolt and its carrier, the bolt strips the top cartridge from the magazine and feeds it into the chamber. The bolt carrier cams the lugs of the bolt down, and the rear end of the bolt is brought down into engagement with the locking bar in the bottom of the receiver. The weapon is ready to fire again.

Special Note on the M1949-Series Rifles

The gas system of the M1949-series rifles is similar to that of the Swedish Ljungman Model 42. Its tilting bolt (or propped breech, as it is sometimes called) has been used in a great number of systems, e.g., the Tokarev, the FN, the Ljungman, and so on. These weapons are an illustration of the fact that a good modern weapon can be produced by selectively choosing from proven past designs and modifying them to suit the need.

Both of these weapons have mounting grooves, cut on the left side of the receivers, for the mounting of telescopic sights.

The French MAS 1936 Rifle

The M1936 is a 7.5mm caliber rifle with modified Mauser magazine. Action is shown ready for trigger pull. Note that dual locking lugs are engaged in recesses within the receiver bridge directly above the trigger. Placing the lugs this far back from the chamber permits a short bolt stroke but results in a rifle locking design weaker than the conventional Mauser front-lug type.

This turn bolt rifle has a modified Mauser magazine with quick removable bottom plate. Primary extraction is by action of bolt handle extension working against a cam in the receiver bridge.

The breech locking system of this rifle is somewhat different than the Mauser. Dual lugs at the rear of the bolt body turn into seatings in the receiver bridge as the handle is turned down. No manual safety.

Locking lugs are on rear of bolt cylinder near handle knob; they lock into receiver bridge to rear of magazine. Note cam shape of left face of receiver bridge which

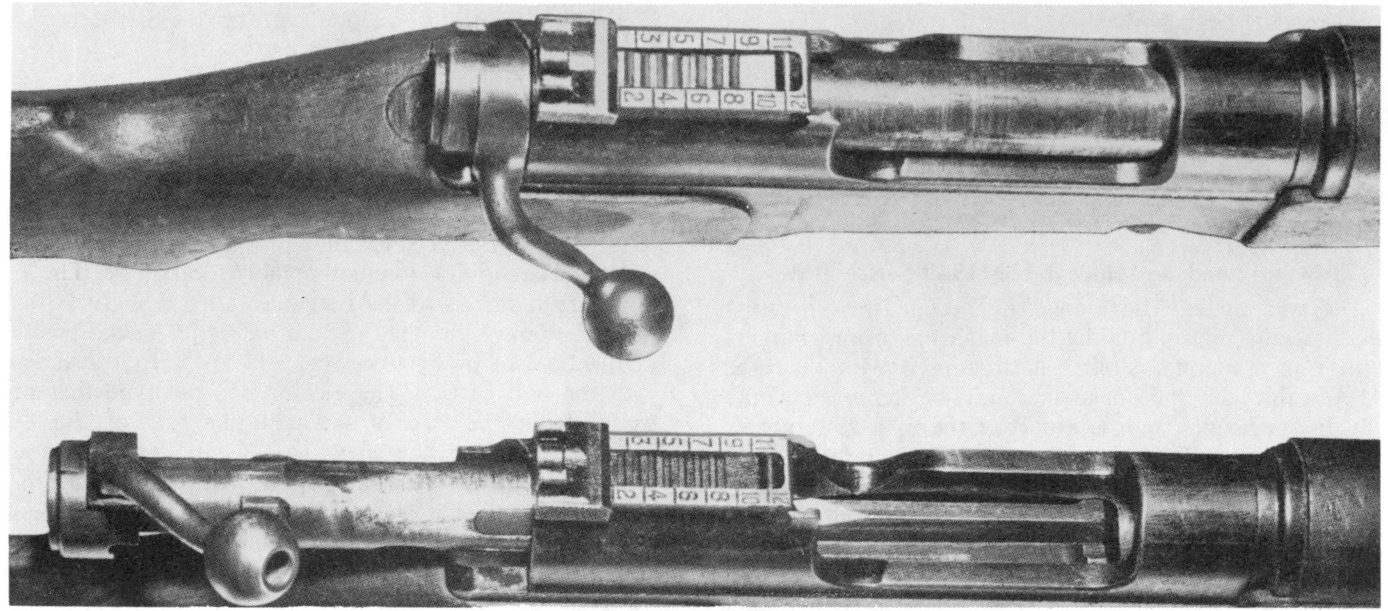

French MAS 1936 Rifle, Action Closed and Open.

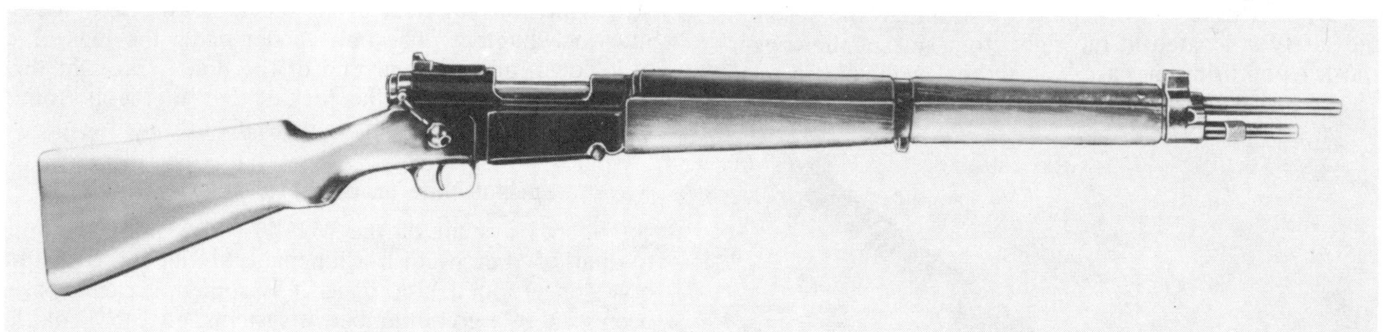

French 7.5mm MAS 1936 Rifle.

affords leverage for primary extraction cam on modified Mauser system. Rifle is loaded with Mauser-type charger clip. Note cuts in receiver for finger pressing cartridges into magazine. This is necessary because of large bolt diameter.

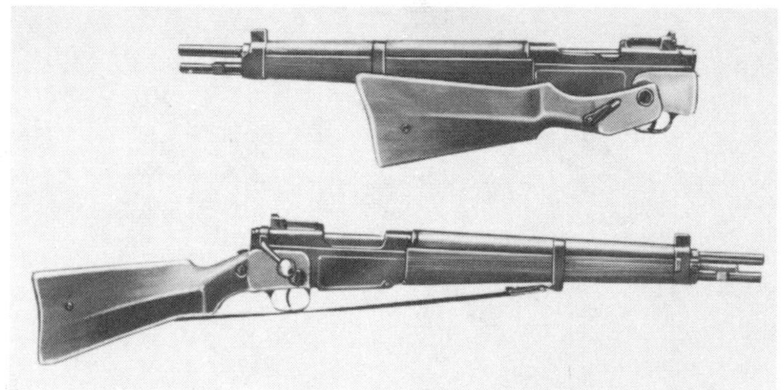

French 7.5mm M1936 CR39 Rifle.

Identification. Side button floor plate release, Bayonet, skewer type, carried reversed in tube below barrel. Lugs lock into receiver bridge cuts. The CR39 modification has a folding aluminum stock.

Ammunition. Not manufactured in U. S. French 7.5mm M1929.

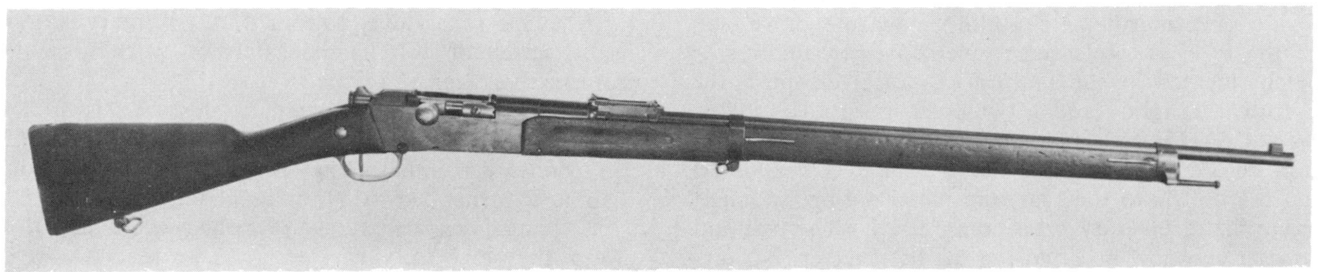

French 8mm Rifle Model 1886 M93.

This rifle was introduced in 1886 to use a new 8mm cartridge loaded with the then revolutionary smokeless powder of Paul Vielle. It is the parent of all modern small bore military rifles. It was slightly modified in 1893, by which time Austrian and German designs had already rendered the French rifle obsolescent. In spite of this fact, it was still in service in War II, while numerous modified rifles were built around many spare parts of the old 86/93.

This is a turn bolt action rifle of individual design. The magazine is a tube in the forestock below the barrel, being loaded through the open action. The bolt is a freak two-piece design with a long detachable bolt head which carries the dual locking lugs.

To remove the bolt, the action must be opened. A holding screw is then removed from a projecting strap on top of the bolt body. The bolt body can then be pulled out of the receiver, leaving the bolt head in the boltway ahead of the receiver bridge. The head can then be picked out of the boltway. Primary extraction is given as the bolt handle is lifted by the projecting bolt strap working against a cam face in a long overhang on the top of receiver.

As the bolt is withdrawn it operates an elevator which raises a cartridge in its trough and lines it up with the bolt. A hook on the bottom of the elevator trough blocks the cartridge in the magazine tube at this point. When the cartridge is chambered, the bolt motion lowers the elevator trough, permitting the magazine spring in the tube to force the next cartridge into the trough ready to be raised on the following rearward bolt stroke.

Modification—1886 M93 R 35. This carbine modification was issued in 1935. It is merely a shorter form with different furniture. Model number is on receiver. Magazine tube holds 3 cartridges, 8mm. Sights are ranged from 200-2000 meters.

Length 37.4″. Barrel 17.5″. Weight 7.82 lbs.

Identification. Tube magazine in forestock. Cal. 8mm. Two-piece bolt with top locking screw. Rifle magazine holds 8 cartridges. R 35 carbine holds 3 cartridges.

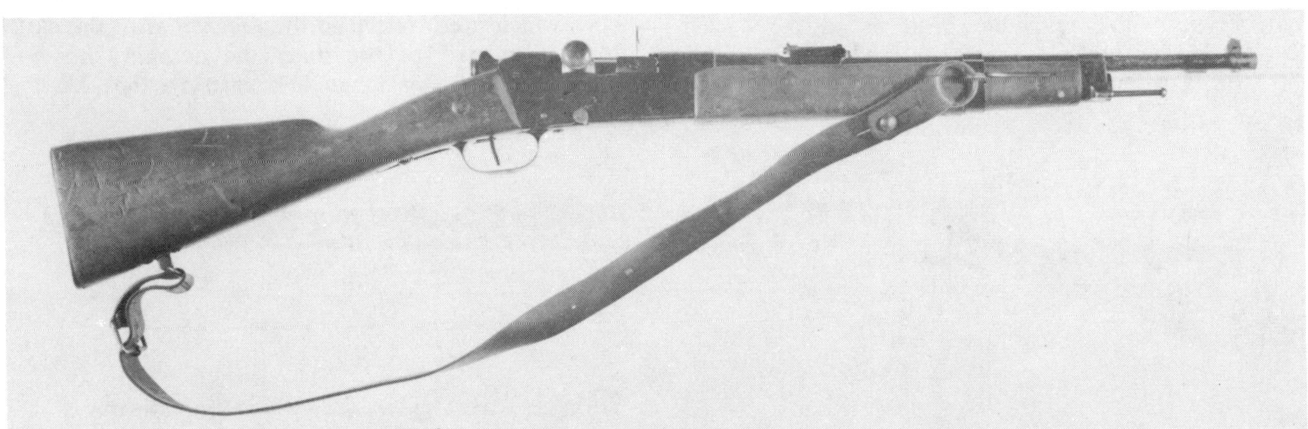

French 8mm M1886 M93 R35 Carbine.

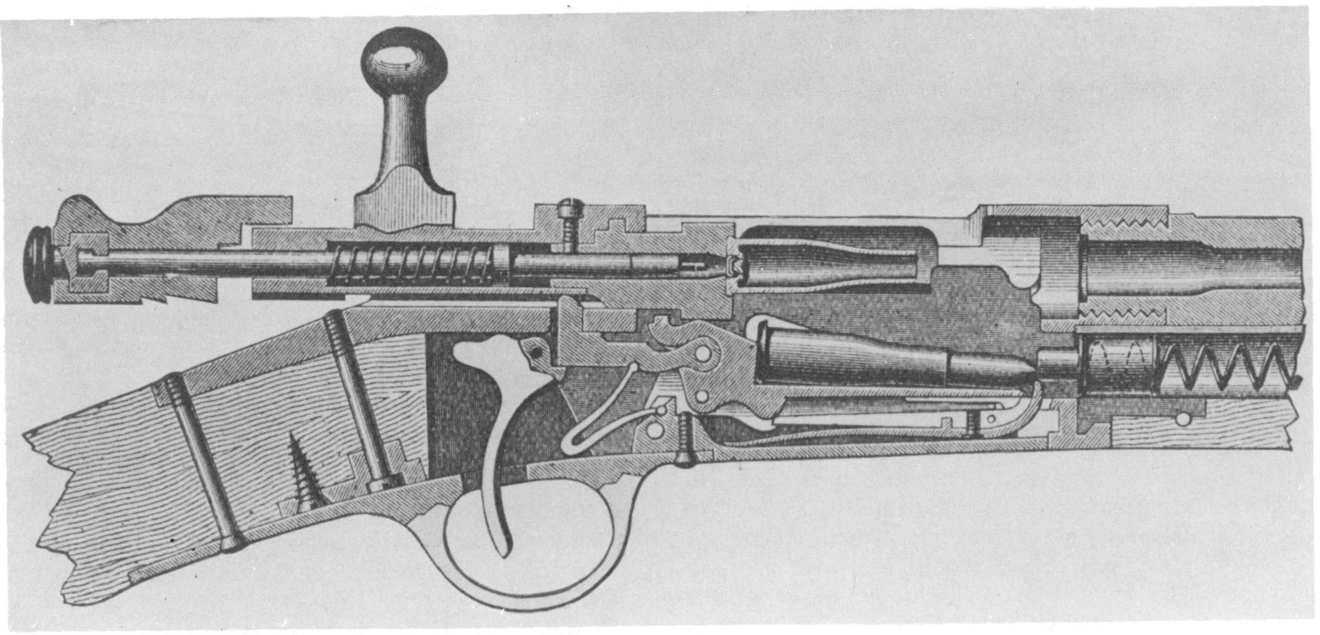

Sectional View. Completing rear bolt pull will eject empty and raise elevator under cartridge.

Evaluation. Obsolete. Tube magazine can be dangerous with pointed bullets since point rests on primer of cartridge ahead of it.

Ammunition. Lebel 8mm. It is currently manufactured in U. S.

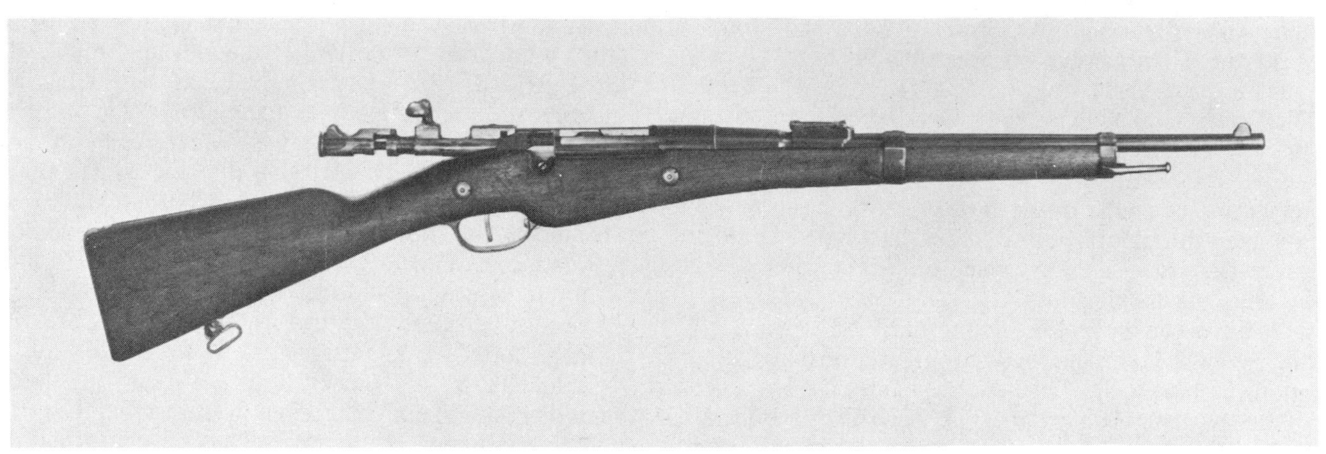

Typical M1892 Carbine as Modified in 1927.

These are the so-called "Berthier" arms. Bolts are two-piece type with removable head as in the earlier Lebel tube loader (1886). They are modified, however, to feed from a Mannlicher-type fixed box magazine.

Cartridges for these arms come in Mannlicher-style clips which are inserted in the receiver with the cartridges to form a part of the magazine action. Clips fall out bottom of receiver when last cartridge has been chambered.

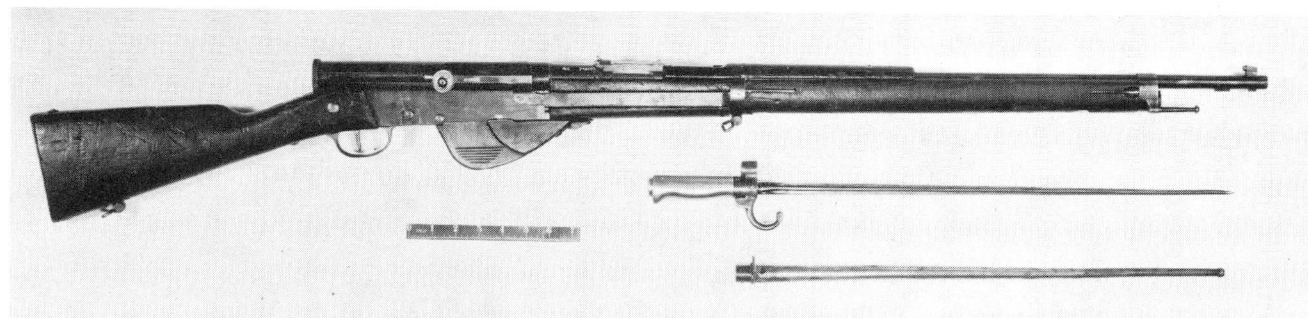

French 8mm Semi-automatic Rifle Model 1917.

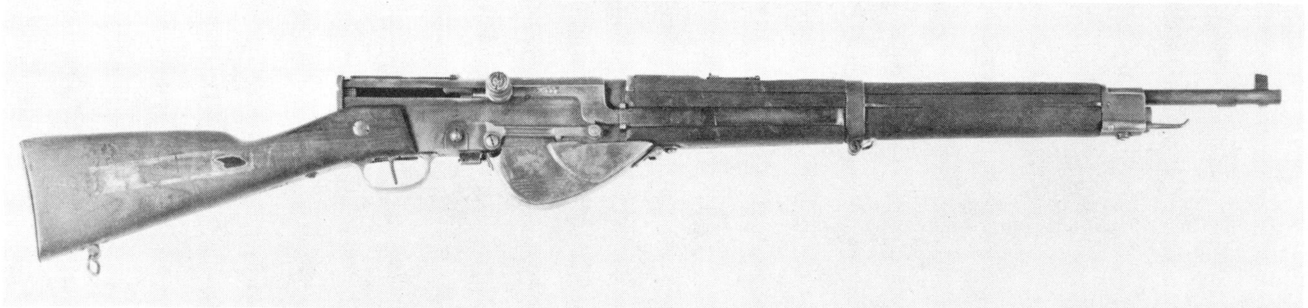

French 8mm Semi-automatic Rifle Model 1918.

French M1917 and 1918 8mm Semi-automatic Rifles. These were the first semi-automatic rifles used in significant quantity in war by any country. They are commonly called Saint Etienne after their arsenal of origin. Both are gas operated and fed with 5-round magazines. The M1918 has an improved action and is shorter than the Model 1917. Quantities of these weapons were modernized in 1935 and are called M1917-1935 and M1918-1935. These weapons are obsolete and are unlikely to be found in service in any country at present.

Characteristics. Semi-auto action. One shot for each pull of trigger. Magazine housing is hinged at bottom for loading.

Identification. Gas operation. Distinctive loading type.

Ammunition. 8mm Lebel. It is currently made in U. S.

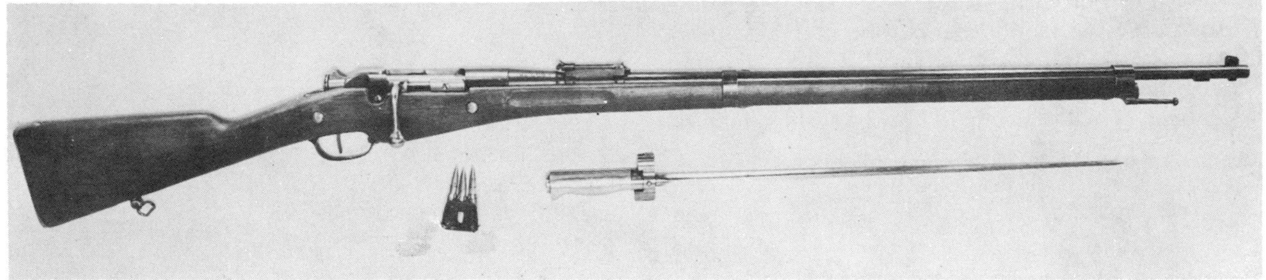

Fusil 1907/15.

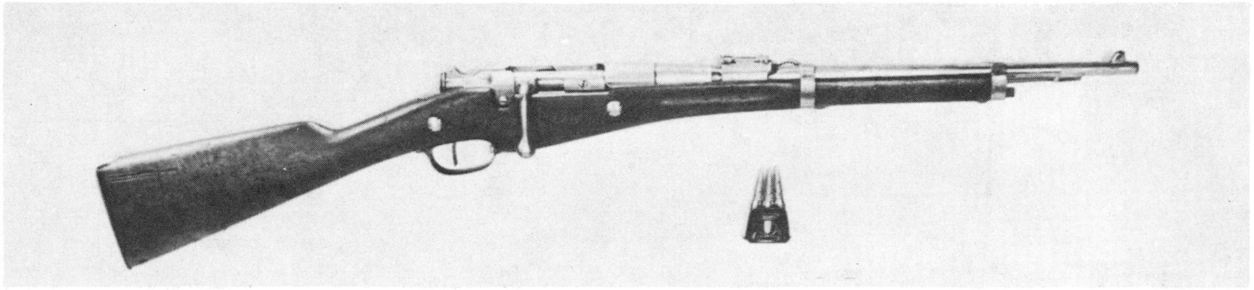

Mousqueton (Carbine) M1892.

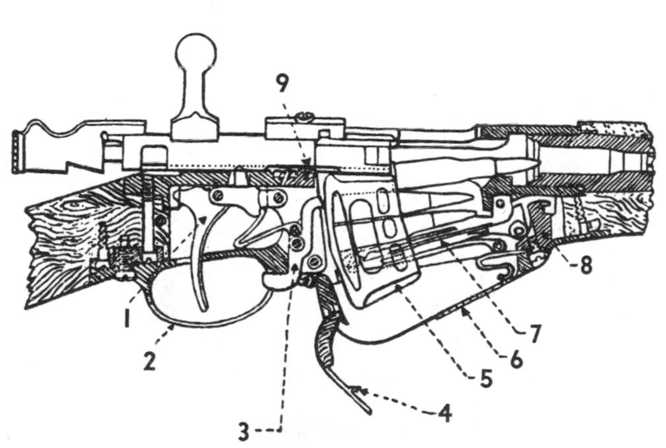

All the Mannlicher Berthier carbines (1890, 1892, 1916) were modified in 1927. Modification consisted of removing cleaning rods and adding a stacking swivel.

FRENCH FUSIL 1916
(Drawing from French Manual)

1. Trigger
2. Triggerguard
3. Clip catch
4. Magazine plate
5. Mannlicher-type clip
6. Magazine bottom
7. Follower
8. Follower support
9. Ejector

French drawing showing details of Fusil (Rifle) 1916. The hinged magazine plate (4) is opened to show how clip is dropped out of magazine when empty. Bolt has been thrust forward far enough to strip cartridge out of clip and guide bullet into chamber. This is a turn bolt rifle. This design uses the Mannlicher-clip loading system.

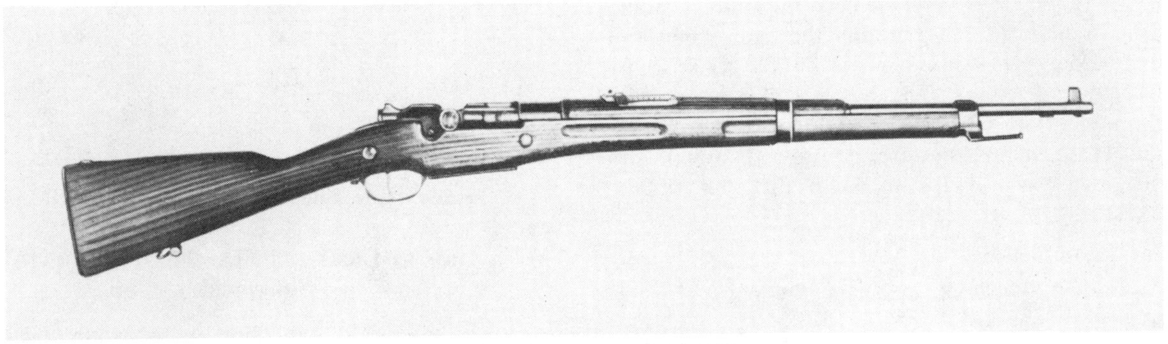

7.5mm Model 07/15 M 34 Rifle.

The 07/15 design was modified in 1934 to handle the 7.5mm rimless cartridge developed in 1929 for light machine guns. The changeover included replacing the old Mannlicher type magazine with a standard 5-shot Mauser type. Cartridges may be loaded into the magazine at any time, staggering from side to side in regular Mauser fashion. The barrel was shortened to 22.62″. Sights are ranged from 200-900 meters.

Identification. Old French two-piece bolt with top securing screw Mauser type fixed box magazine.

Evaluation. While the bolt is clumsy and complicated, this design is perhaps the best of the French rifles.

The detachable bolt head locks with two heavy lugs into a solid receiver section behind the cartridge head, giving a much more effective support than in later French designs. The Mauser magazine permitting the use of cartridges without clips is an important feature.

Ammunition. 7.5mm M 1929 French. Not made in U. S.

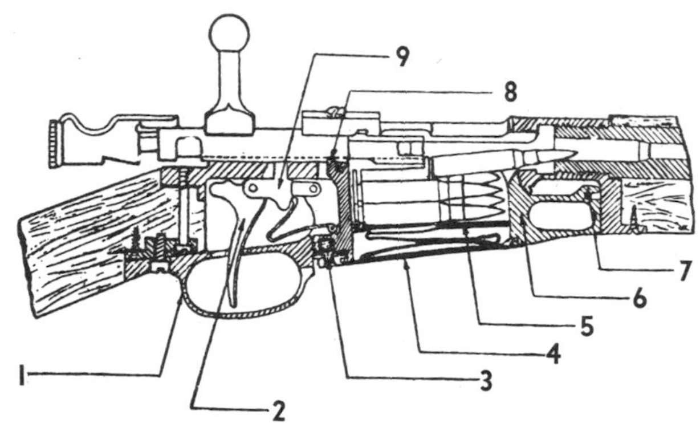

FRENCH FUSIL 07/15 M 34.
(Drawing from French Manual)

1. Triggerguard
2. Trigger
3. Magazine plate lock
4. Bottom plate
5. Follower
6. and 7. Forward magazine section
8. Ejector
9. Sear

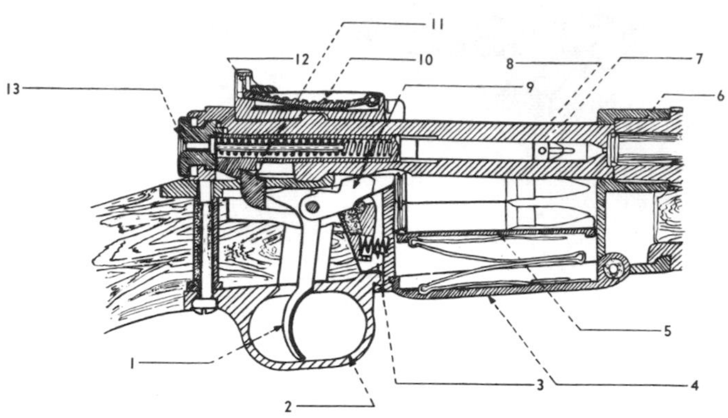

French Fusil 1936
(Drawing from French Manual)

1. Trigger.
2. Triggerguard
3. Sear spring
4. Magazine bottom plate
5. Magazine follower
6. Barrel
7. Bolt
8. Firing pin
9. Ejector & Bolt stop unit
10. Receiver bridge
11. Sear
12. Peep sight
13. Cocking piece head

FRENCH SUBMACHINE GUNS

After World War II, the French held large quantities of U. S. and British submachine guns, as well as captured German guns. Limited quantities of the French M1938 were available, but France changed from the 7.65mm Long cartridge (the design of which was incidentally, based on the cal. .30 M1918 Pederson) to the 9mm Parabellum. The M1938 (MAS 38) was apparently relegated to police duties, and a new weapon, the 9mm submachine gun M1949 (MAT 49), was adopted.

The M1949 submachine gun, which has seen extensive service in Indo-China and Algeria, is well made and of excellent design. It has a very good reputation with French troops. It has a telescoping steel stock, and magazine which folds up under the gun when not in use; this makes the weapon very handy for use by armored or airborne troops. The M1949 also has a grip safety and an ejection port cover. The grip safety prevents the gun from firing when accidentally dropped, and the ejection port cover helps to keep dirt out of the internal mechanism of the gun.

Caliber: 9mm Parabellum.

System of Operation: Blowback, automatic fire only.

Length, overall:
Stock Extended: 28 in.
Stock Retracted: 18.3 in.

Feed Device: 32-round, detachable, staggered-row box magazine.

Sights, Front: Hooded blade.
Rear: L-type w/apertures for 100 and 200 meters.

Muzzle Velocity: 1237 f.p.s.

Cyclic Rate: 600 r.p.m.

Weight, Loaded: 9.41 lb.

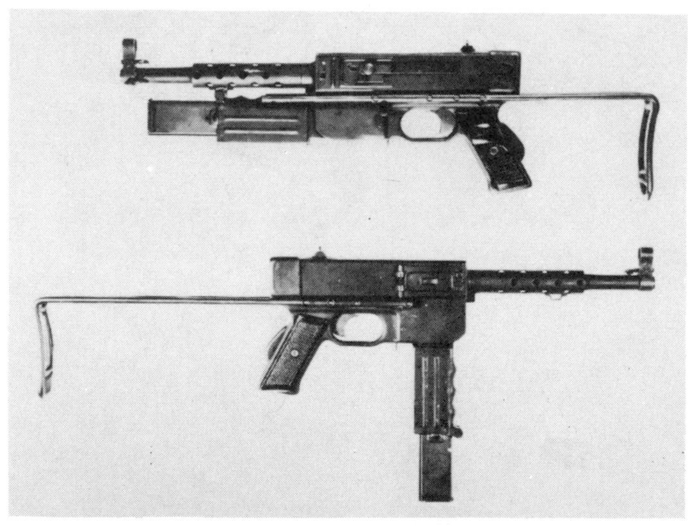

French 9mm Submachine Gun M1949 (MAT 49).

How to Load and Fire the M1949 (MAT 49) Submachine Gun

Insert a loaded magazine in the well of the magazine housing; if the housing is in the horizontal position, pull it down to the vertical, making sure that the lock located on the underside of the trigger housing engages the magazine housing. Pull the cocking handle, located on the left side of the receiver, to the rear. The bolt will remain to the rear, since this weapon fires from an open bolt. Push the cocking handle to its forward position. Squeeze the grip safety with the rear of the hand, pull the trigger, and the weapon will fire. To remove the magazine, engage the magazine catch located at the bottom rear of the magazine housing. To lift the magazine housing and magazine into the horizontal position under the barrel, depress the lock located on the underside of the trigger housing and swing the magazine up till the lug at the forward end of the housing engages the clip on the underside of the barrel jacket. To change the position of—or remove—the stock, depress the catch located on the left side of the trigger housing.

How to Field Strip the M1949 (MAT 49) Submachine Gun

Rotate the magazine housing forward slightly to permit the trigger housing lock to be moved to the rear. When the trigger housing lock is disengaged, the housing can be rotated in a clockwise direction and removed from the receiver. The operating spring assembly and the bolt can then be removed from the back of the receiver. No further disassembly is recommended.

To reassemble the weapon, perform the above steps in reverse order.

Special Note on the M1949 (MAT 49) Submachine Gun

The M1949 submachine gun is composed mainly of steel stampings. Since its functioning is basically the same as that of any other blowback-operated submachine gun, no extended coverage on functioning is given. The ejection port cover is automatically opened by the forward or rearward movement of the bolt.

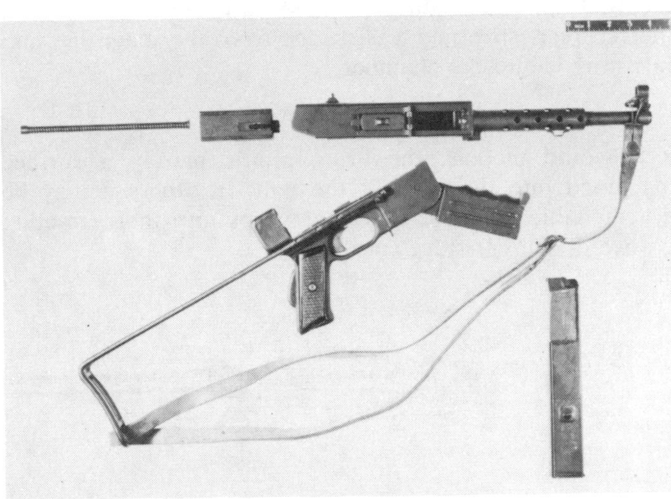

M1949 Field Stripped.

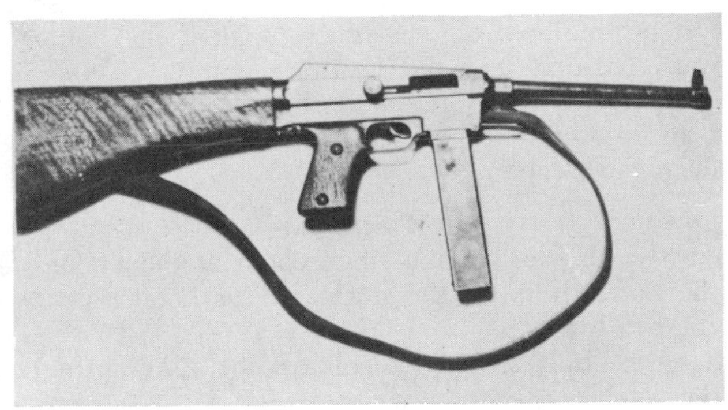

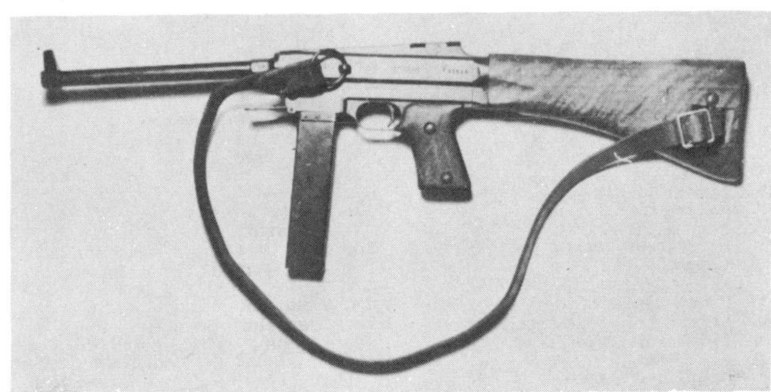

7.65mm Model 38 MAS Submachine Gun.

This French submachine gun, the most common model of which is the 38 though other models with minor modifications such as separate firing pins are known, was the official standard French submachine gun at the beginning of World War II.

This weapon was designed to shoot the model 1935 French service pistol cartridge, a weak 7.65mm long. This is not to be confused with the standard 7.65mm which is identical with the .32 Colt Automatic Pistol cartridge. The case is longer and the cartridge somewhat more powerful.

This is a straight blowback type of submachine gun in which no locking device is employed but which has a number of unusual design features. A version of this weapon with a tubular steel stock also exists.

How the MAS Model 38 Operates

A hinged cover seals the mouth of the magazine housing in the bottom of the receiver in this weapon when the magazine is withdrawn. Pushing this forward on its hinge opens the mouth of the housing and permits insertion of a loaded magazine from the bottom. The magazine is pushed in until it locks in standard fashion.

When the bolt handle on the right side of the receiver is pulled to the rear, it draws the bolt back and presses the recoil spring behind it which extends from the rear of the receiver down into a steel tube inside the shoulder stock. When the bolt has been drawn back far enough, it rides over the sear which is then forced up by its spring to catch in the bent or notch in the underside of the bolt and hold it open ready for firing.

Pressure on the trigger will now withdraw the sear from the bolt and permit the compressed recoil spring to drive the bolt up the slightly inclined surface machined into the receiver, stripping a cartridge from the magazine and thrusting it into the chamber.

Notes on this Weapon

In some models, the firing pin is merely a surface machined into the front of the bolt. In others it may be a detachable pin. The extractor snaps into the extracting groove of the cartridge case.

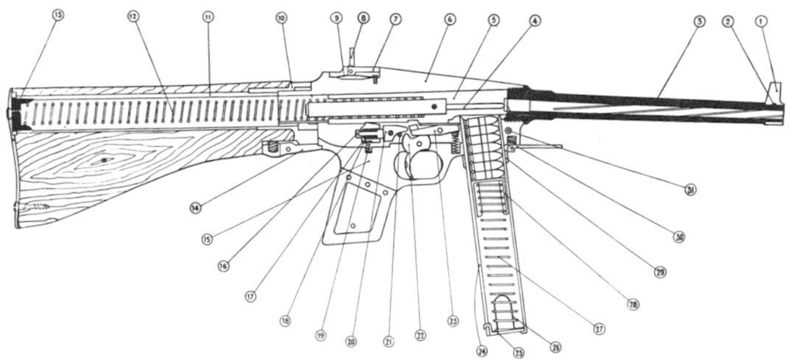

Nomenclature.

1. The barrel, which is screwed into the receiver. Note that the magazine housing cover is open. The cocking handle has been pulled back far enough to expose the ejection port. 2. Butt stock. The spring-held unlocking catch is at the forward end of the stock. 3. Receiver. 4. Bolt assembly. This includes a projecting rod which acts as a seating and guide for the forward end of the recoil spring, the extractor, and a machined or removable firing pin. 5. Recoil or operating spring. 6. Grip and trigger mechanism. This unit slides into tracks prepared for it in the underside of the receiver. 7. Magazine.

MAS 1938 Submachine Gun.
(Drawing from French Manual)

1. Front sight.
2. Fixing pin.
3. Barrel.
4. Striker.
5. Breechblock (bolt).
6. Receiver.
7. Rear sight leaves.
8. Rear sight leaves.
9. Spring.
10. Recoil spring tube bridge.
11. Recoil spring tube.
12. Recoil (or operating) spring.
13. Tube butt cap.
14. Takedown lever.
15. Grip.
16. Sear nose.
17. Sear.
18. Sear spring seat.
19. Sear spring.
20. Sear bar.
21. Pin.
22. Trigger.
23. Safety lever.
24. Magazine.
25. Floor plate.
26. Spring guide.
27. Spring.
28. Follower.
29. Magazine catch.
30. Opening plate (used to close magazine opening when magazine is withdrawn).
31. Magazine release.

The bolt is not a true cylindrical piece moving in a straight line as in most submachine guns. It has a somewhat tilted face to permit it to bring up flush with the head of the cartridge as it is chambered, while the main body of the bolt is at an angle to the bore; this tends to give the effect of a hesitation action.

Just how practical this system is is open to question, in view of the fact that even with a low-powered cartridge and a comparatively light bolt, the recoil action is somewhat stiff. The bolt not only travels to the rear in the receiver, but actually passes down the tube inside the stock itself. During rearward movement, the extractor withdraws the empty case and strikes it against the ejector which is part of the fastening pin to which the forward sling swivel is attached. The empty case is ejected from the port on the right hand side of the receiver.

The sliding cover over the bolt opening or ejection port should be pulled further to the rear after the weapon has been cocked so that it will not have to be carried forward by the bolt in forward travel. This is a full automatic weapon in which the action will continue to function so long as the trigger is held back. When the trigger is released, a spring will force the sear up to catch and hold the bolt to the rear. The weapon fires from an open bolt.

The sights are rough and are of a rather impractical design. The rear sight consists of two separate leaves which fold down into the top of the receiver. One aperture is for one hundred meters and the other is for two hundred meters. The front sight is offset to the left and is too clumsy to permit of anything but typical submachine gun burst fire.

Note that this weapon cannot be fired when the shoulder stock is removed. Additional travel of the bolt inside the tube in the stock is necessary to function the weapon.

Magazine. The magazine catch which is pressed in to release the magazine for withdrawal from the receiver is on the left side of the housing. The magazine itself may be dismounted by pushing the protruding rib at the lower front end of the box. This will tilt the floor plate so that it can be slid out rear end first. The zigzag spring and the follower may be withdrawn from the magazine box.

Design. An unusual safety is incorporated in this weapon. When the trigger is pushed forward it folds up and hence cannot be pressed. Thus, if the bolt is cocked, the weapon cannot be fired until the trigger is deliberately unfolded. On the other hand, if the bolt is in forward position and the chamber empty, pushing the trigger forward will force a catch up into a hole in the bolt and prevent the bolt handle from being pulled back to open the weapon.

Field Stripping

Push in the spring butt-stock catch at the under side of the forward end of the stock and, as it releases, twist the butt to the right.

Ease the butt and the recoil or operating spring out of the receiver.

Pressing the trigger will lower the sear and permit the triggerguard unit to be withdrawn from its guide in the receiver.

Pull back the bolt handle which will bring the bolt to the rear when it and the recoil spring may be withdrawn from the receiver.

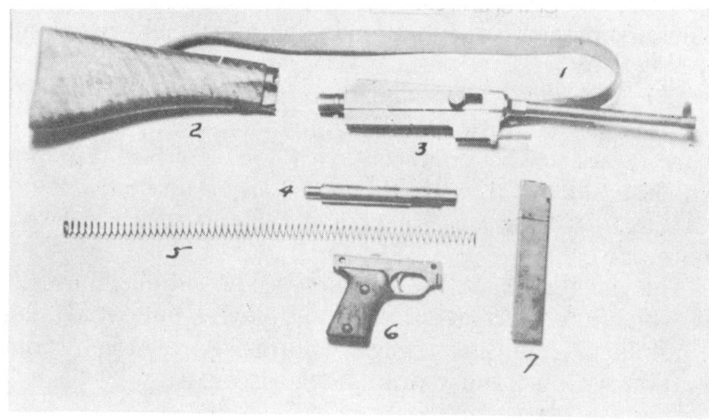

FRENCH MACHINE GUNS

The French used U.S. Brownings, British Brens and Vickers, and some German machine guns after World War II. They had a comparatively small quantity of some of the older French guns left, judging by the scarcity of French machine guns in photos of that era. One of the French guns, the 7.5mm tank and fortress machine gun M1931A, was adapted for use on the U.S. cal. .30 M2 tripod. This weapon is still in use on French-made armored vehicles. Since it is likely to be encountered by some of the readers of this book, it will be covered in detail even though it is not a postwar weapon.

The M1931A machine gun is the tank and fortress version of the French 7.5mm M1924 M29 light machine gun (commonly known as the Chatellerault). The weapon was adapted to the U.S. M2 mount after World War II, but is only likely to be encountered on French armored vehicles these days. A French tripod mount, the MAS M1945, was also used with the gun. The weapon has a very heavy barrel, since it is designed for a high rate of sustained fire and does not have a quick-change barrel. Two magazines can be used with the gun—a box type or a large drum which fastens to the side of the gun.

How to Load and Fire the M1931A Machine Gun

Cock the gun by pulling the operating handle to the rear. If the box magazine is to be used, rotate it into the feed fixture on the right side of the gun, so that the lug on the magazine engages in the recess in the fixture. Then pull the magazine toward the rear of the gun, so that the rear of it is locked in place in the feedway. Pull the trigger and the weapon will fire. This weapon fires from an open bolt and has no safety. To load the drum-type magazine, fit the magazine on the projection of the receiver which is just ahead of the feedway. A stud to the rear of the projection serves as an index when assembling the magazine to the gun. Firing is carried on in the same way with the drum as with the box magazine. To remove the box magazine, engage the magazine catch and swing the magazine forward and out. To remove the drum magazine, apply pressure to the handle on the outside of the drum, and pull the magazine straight off. When this gun is unloaded, using either magazine, there will always be a round in the feedway, unless all the rounds have been fired. To clear the gun, the round must be pushed forward so that it falls free inside the receiver and out the bottom of the gun. USE EXTREME CARE IN UNLOADING THE GUN! DO NOT ALLOW ANYONE TO GET IN FRONT OF THE GUN!

French 7.5mm Machine Gun M1931A on U.S. M2 Tripod.

Caliber: 7.5mm M1929 French rimless.
System of Operation: Gas, automatic fire only.
Length, Overall: 40.5 in. w/flash hider.
Weight, Empty: 27.48 lb.
Weight of Mounts:
Tripod M2: 16.22 lb.
Tripod M1945: 32.15 lb.
Barrel Length: 23.5 in.
Feed Device: 36-round, detachable, staggered-row box magazine, or 150-round drum magazine.
Sights, Front: Blade.
Rear: Tangent leaf w/open notch.
Muzzle Velocity: 2750 f.p.s.
Cyclic Rate: 750 r.p.m.

How to Field Strip the M1931A Machine Gun

Check to see that the weapon is not loaded. Depress the spring-loaded catch in the rear of the backplate. Rotate the lock 90 degrees, and remove the recoil spring and guide. Remove the screw at the lower rear of the receiver; a lever attached to the screw assists in its removal. Remove the backplate; the trigger housing and recoiling parts can then be removed. No further disassembly is recommended.

To reassemble the weapon, perform the above steps in reverse order.

How the M1931A Machine Gun Works

The piston and gas cylinder are similar to those on the M1924 M29 light machine gun. However, because the M1931A ejects through the bottom of the receiver, the piston assembly is cut away to permit cases or complete rounds to pass through. The operating spring is positioned at the rear of the piston assembly, with only a small portion of it inside the piston. Locking is accomplished in the same manner as on the M1924 M29 light machine gun. A spring-loaded lever, positioned in the right side of the bolt, engages the base of the cartridge case for feeding and firing. The ejector operates in a groove in the top of the bolt. The firing pin operates inside the bolt, but is held rigidly to a projection on the rear of the piston assembly.

Special Note on the M1931A Machine Gun

The M1931A cannot be considered an up-to-date machine gun for use either as a tank gun or as a ground gun. It probably will be replaced by the M1952 machine

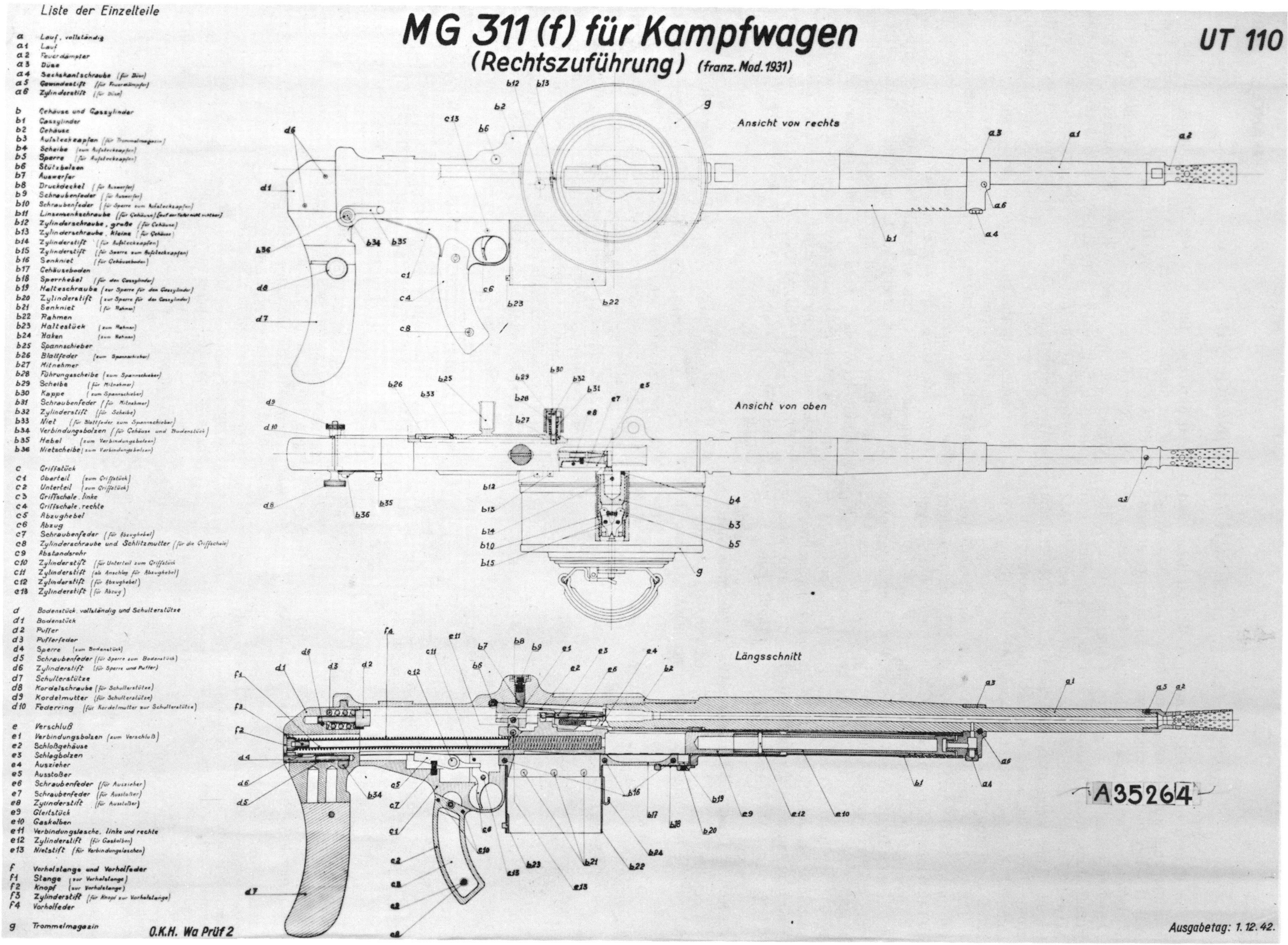

MG 311 (f) für Kampfwagen

(Rechtszuführung) (franz. Mod. 1931)

UT 110

Liste der Einzelteile

a Lauf, vollständig
a1 Lauf
a2 Feuerdämpfer
a3 Düse
a4 Sechskantschraube (für Düse)
a5 Gewindestift (für Feuerdämpfer)
a6 Zylinderstift (für Düse)

b Gehäuse und Gaszylinder
b1 Gaszylinder
b2 Gehäuse
b3 Aufsteckzapfen (für Trommelmagazin)
b4 Scheibe (zum Aufsteckzapfen)
b5 Sperre (für Aufsteckzapfen)
b6 Stützbolzen
b7 Auswerfer
b8 Druckdeckel (für Auswerfer)
b9 Schraubenfeder (für Auswerfer)
b10 Schraubenfeder (für Sperre zum Aufsteckzapfen)
b11 Linsensenkschraube (für Gehäuse) (auf der Tafel nicht sichtbar)
b12 Zylinderschraube, große (für Gehäuse)
b13 Zylinderschraube, kleine (für Gehäuse)
b14 Zylinderstift (für Aufsteckzapfen)
b15 Zylinderstift (für Sperre zum Aufsteckzapfen)
b16 Senkniet (für Gehäuseboden)
b17 Gehäuseboden
b18 Sperrhebel (für den Gaszylinder)
b19 Halteschraube (zur Sperre für den Gaszylinder)
b20 Zylinderstift (zur Sperre für den Gaszylinder)
b21 Senkniet (für Rahmen)
b22 Rahmen
b23 Haltestück (zum Rahmen)
b24 Haken (zum Rahmen)
b25 Spannschieber
b26 Blattfeder (zum Spannschieber)
b27 Mitnehmer
b28 Führungsscheibe (zum Spannschieber)
b29 Scheibe (für Mitnehmer)
b30 Kappe (zum Spannschieber)
b31 Schraubenfeder (für Mitnehmer)
b32 Zylinderstift (für Scheibe)
b33 Niet (für Blattfeder zum Spannschieber)
b34 Verbindungsbolzen (für Gehäuse und Bodenstück)
b35 Hebel (zum Verbindungsbolzen)
b36 Nietscheibe (zum Verbindungsbolzen)

c Griffstück
c1 Oberteil (zum Griffstück)
c2 Unterteil (zum Griffstück)
c3 Griffschale, linke
c4 Griffschale, rechte
c5 Abzughebel
c6 Abzug
c7 Schraubenfeder (für Abzughebel)
c8 Zylinderschraube und Schlitzmutter (für die Griffschale)
c9 Abstandsrohr
c10 Zylinderstift (für Unterteil zum Griffstück
c11 Zylinderstift (als Anschlag für Abzughebel)
c12 Zylinderstift (für Abzughebel)
c13 Zylinderstift (für Abzug)

d Bodenstück, vollständig und Schulterstütze
d1 Bodenstück
d2 Puffer
d3 Pufferfeder
d4 Sperre (zum Bodenstück)
d5 Schraubenfeder (für Sperre zum Bodenstück)
d6 Zylinderstift (für Sperre und Puffer)
d7 Schulterstütze
d8 Kordelschraube (für Schulterstütze)
d9 Kordelmutter (für Schulterstütze)
d10 Federring (für Kordelmutter zur Schulterstütze)

e Verschluß
e1 Verbindungsbolzen (zum Verschluß)
e2 Schloßgehäuse
e3 Schlagbolzen
e4 Auszieher
e5 Ausstoßer
e6 Schraubenfeder (für Auszieher)
e7 Schraubenfeder (für Ausstoßer)
e8 Zylinderstift (für Ausstoßer)
e9 Gleitstück
e10 Gaskolben
e11 Verbindungslasche, linke und rechte
e12 Zylinderstift (für Gaskolben)
e13 Nietstift (für Verbindungslaschen)

f Vorholstange und Vorholfeder
f1 Stange (zur Vorholstange)
f2 Knopf (zur Vorholstange)
f3 Zylinderstift (für Knopf zur Vorholstange)
f4 Vorholfeder

g Trommelmagazin

Ansicht von rechts

Ansicht von oben

Längsschnitt

A35264

O.K.H. Wa Prüf 2

Ausgabetag: 1. 12. 42.

German WWII Training Chart on M1931A.

gun in armored vehicles, as well as in the ground role.

The M1952 is called the Arme Automatique Transformable (AAT) by the French, since it is designed to be used as both a heavy and light machine gun. The weapon can be used as a light machine gun with a light barrel, a bipod, and a butt support. It can also be used as a heavy machine gun on a U.S. M2 tripod with a French adapter.

How to Load and Fire the M1952 (AAT Mle. 52) Machine Gun

Pull the operating handle to the rear, cocking the weapon. Push the cover catch forward and open the cover; lay the belt on the feedway, so that the first cartridge in the belt is positioned against the cartridge stop. Close the cover and press the trigger; the weapon will fire. An alternate method is to feed the loading tab of the belt into the feed port on the left side of the gun, and pull it through to the right until a cartridge clicks into position. Then pull the charging handle to the rear and fire. The weapon fires from an open bolt.

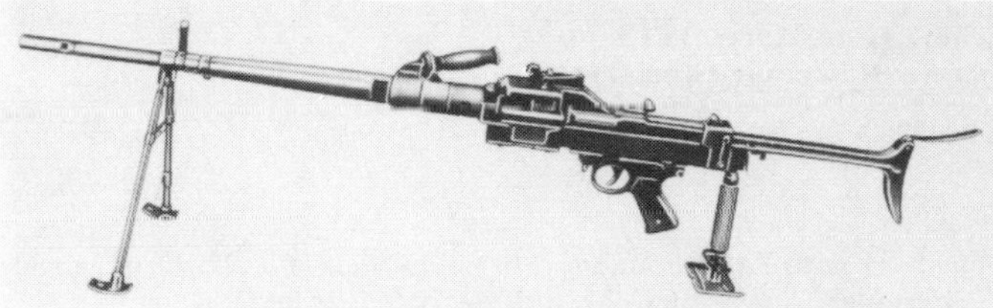

French 7.5mm General Purpose Machine Gun M1952 (AAT MLE. 52) on Bipod.

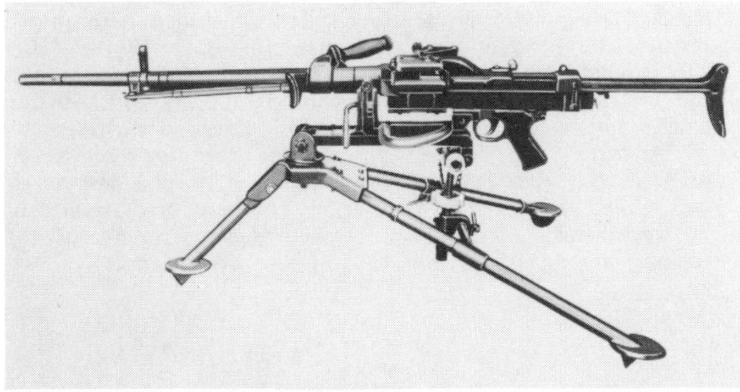

French 7.5mm Model 1952 on U.S. M2 Tripod.

Caliber: 7.5mm French M1929 rimless.
System of Operation: Delayed blowback, full automatic fire only.
Length, Overall:
Stock Extended: 45.9 in.
Stock Retracted: 38.6 in.
Barrel Length (Quick-Change Barrel):
Heavy Barrel, w/o Flash Hider: 23.6 in.
Light Barrel, w/o Flash Hider: 19.3 in.
Feed Device: 50-round, metallic, nondisintegrating link belt; when used as a light gun, a box containing one link belt section is hung on the side of the receiver.
Sights, Front: Barleycorn.
Rear: Tangent leaf w/U-notch.
Muzzle Velocity: 2690 f.p.s.
Cyclic Rate: 700 r.p.m. (approx.).
Weight, w/Light Barrel: 21.7 lb.
w/Heavy Barrel: 23.28 lb.

How to Field Strip the M1952 (AAT Mle. 52) Machine Gun

With the stock in the extended position, press down on the stock bolt lever to remove the two stock bolts; then pull the butt to the rear and remove. Unscrew and remove the assembly pin. Pull back the bolt assembly by swinging it up. Pull the cocking handle to the rear. Remove the recoil spring and the recoil spring guide; then remove the bolt assembly by sliding it out the rear. Remove the triggerguard retaining pin and disengage the

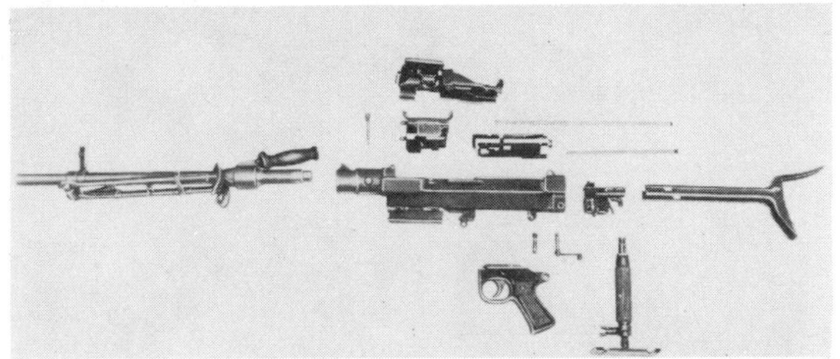

M1952 Field Stripped.

triggerguard from the receiver. Pull back the barrel catch with the left hand and, with the right hand, twist the carrying handle 1/6th turn to the right; then pull the barrel forward. Put the cover and the feed plate at a 90-degree angle from the receiver and remove the cover pin. Separate the bolt head by moving the head forward and up. Remove the firing pin and the bolt lock from the bolt.

To reassemble the weapon, perform the above steps in reverse order.

How the M1952 (AAT Mle. 52) Works

The delayed-blowback bolt system of the M1952 machine gun is similar in principle to that of the Spanish CETME assault rifle and the Swiss Model 57 assault rifle. The bolt is in two pieces—a head and a body; the head is much smaller than the body. Instead of using two roller bearings for locks, as do the Spanish and Swiss weapons, the M1952 employs a locking lever. The bolt head cannot move to the rear until the pressure is high enough to cause the locking lever to start opening and, in turn, force back the bolt body and firing pin. This weapon also uses a partially fluted chamber, to make up for its lack of slow initial extraction. The feed system appears to be quite similar to that of the MG 42.

Special Note on the M1952 (AAT Mle. 52)

The M1952 machine gun is quite an interesting design; it represents a great departure from pre-World War II French practice. It is considered likely that this machine gun will eventually replace the M1924 M29 as the squad automatic weapon, since the French refer to the gun as a "fusil Mitrailleur" (automatic rifle) when it is used in the light role on a bipod. The only other major power that uses a belt-fed gun for a squad automatic is the USSR (RPD light machine gun). On the subject of squad (or "section," as the British call it) automatic weapons, it is interesting to note that the U.S., Belgium, France, and Sweden call their squad-level guns "automatic rifles." Most other countries call them "light machine guns"—e.g., the Bren, the RPD, etc.

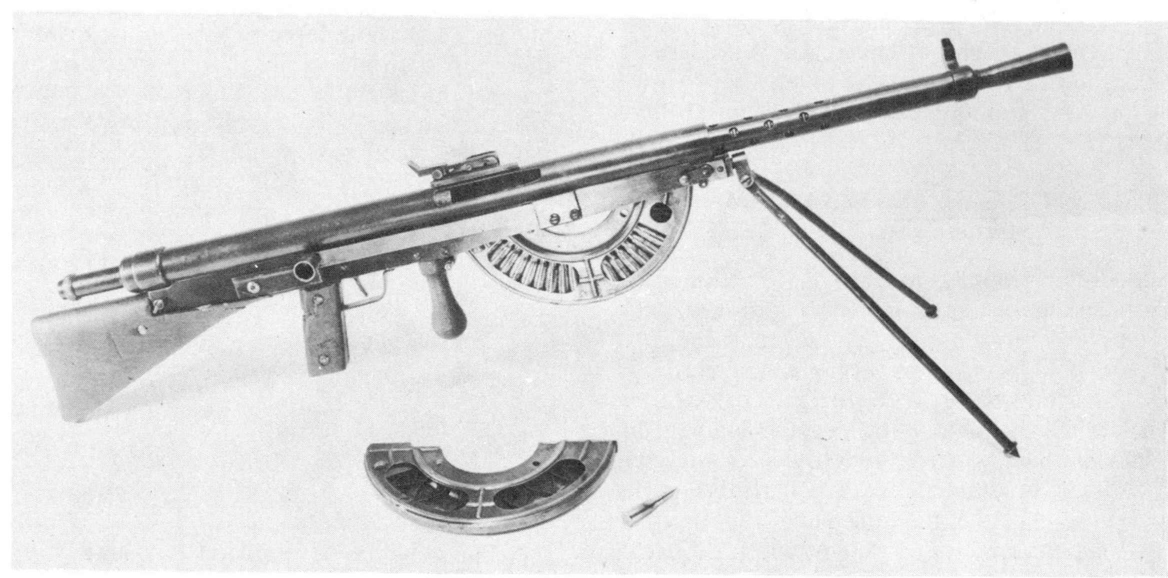

French Chauchat 8mm Light Machine Gun Model 1915. (Called Fusil Mitrailleur Chauchat-Suterre Ribeyrolle-Gladiator.)

This weapon, although obsolescent, was in wide use by the French and the Belgians when World War II started. In England it is called the Chauchard.

Caliber: French 8mm Belgian Caliber 7.65mm. Also modified in U. S. during last war for standard United States service cartridge.

Ballistics: Average for cartridges employed.

Weight of Gun: 18 pounds. Fitted with a tripod mount.

Sights: Graduated to 1200 meters. This is an inaccurate weapon at best.

Gun Operated By: Long recoil. Gas expands in space between front sight cone and barrel and is thrown back against barrel nut thus helping recoil drive the barrel to the rear.

Locked: Barrel and bolt securely locked by locking lugs.

Cooled: Air. Barrel is heavy and has radial flanges, is also enclosed in a barrel jacket.

Cyclic Rate of Fire: About 400 per minute.

Type of Fire: Single shot or full automatic. A lever is provided on left side of receiver which may be set for single shot or full automatic or for safe. ("C" is single shot. "S" is safe. "M" is automatic.)

Flash Hider: Extension on muzzle to hide the flash of powder burning as it leaves the muzzle of the rifle.

Position of Bolt Between Shots: Open. Bolt mechanism travels forward when trigger is pressed to fire cartridge.

Note on This Weapon: This is one of the most poorly constructed weapons ever developed. It is included here merely because large quantities were used in both World Wars. The French types use a crescent shaped magazine because the cartridges have rims. Magazine is loaded with 20 cartridges and inserted in gun from below. Exposed cartridge side of magazine faces to the right. Pulling back the bolt handle prepares the weapon for firing. The recoil in this gun is excessive and the accuracy very poor. This weapon is poor both in workmanship and design. Deactivated specimens of this weapon are on sale in the U.S. at the present time.

Note on Stripping

Press magazine catch forward and remove magazine. Ease operating handle forward.

Push down spring guide latch and unscrew spring tube plug (at rear of receiver).

Withdraw plug, mainspring, and recoil spring. Bushing will fall out.

Pull back operating handle, turn front assembling bolt arm down, and push rear assembling bolt to the left to clear eyelet.

Lift radiator casing and breech housing clear of frame.

Turn radiator casing upside down and draw operating handle to rear. Lift out feed piece assembly.

Grasp bolt stem and draw out bolt assembly.

Withdraw barrel, barrel nut, radiator, breech casing, and barrel sleeves out of breech casing.

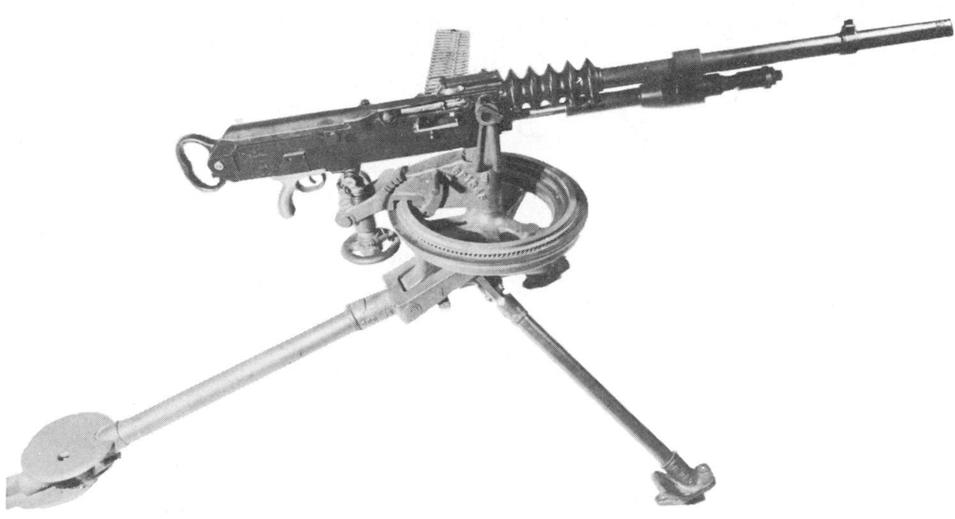

French 1914 Hotchkiss 8mm Machine Gun.

This weapon is obsolete in the French Army.

The Hotchkiss was a basic weapon. The French type is heavy and unwieldy. A modification of this model was the basic heavy machine gun of the Japanese. The light improved weapon of this type was widely used in Great Britain. It was also found in use in Spain in caliber 7mm. This gun was also found chambered for the 7.92mm German service cartridge in China.

Caliber: 8mm French Service Cartridge.
Type of Feed: Metal strip, holding 30 cartridges and feeding from the left hand side of the gun. Paper maché feed strips are sometimes used with this gun.
Muzzle Velocity of Cartridge: 2291 feet per second.
Weight of Bullet: About 198 grains.
Barrel Length: 30½".
Weight of Gun: 54 pounds.
Mounting: A 60-lb. tripod mount, M1916, was provided for this gun.
Sights: Open. Barleycorn front and V rear.
Gun Operated By: Gas. As bullet travels down barrel, a small portion of gas escapes through a hole tapped in the under side of the barrel and expands in a cup-shaped piston fitting on a gas nozzle. This imparts a hammerlike blow which drives the action backwards.
Cooled: Air; has extremely heavy barrel with five thick radiating rings near the breech.
Position of Cocking Handle: A large handle on the left side of the gun directly behind the feed. It is pulled back to cock gun which fires from open bolt, and then pushed forward to relieve the action of strain.

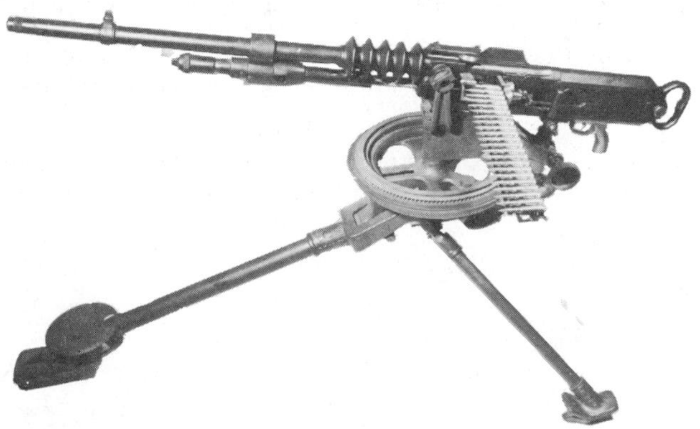

Loading and Firing

Pull cocking handle as far as it will go to the rear to compress recoil spring and cock gun. Bolt will stay open. Now insert cartridge strip in heavy brass feed block on left side of gun and push in as far as it will go. Be sure that all cartridges are properly lined up in the strip. This feed is very susceptible to jams.

Pressing trigger in triggerguard below frame will now fire the weapon. The gun will fire as long as there are cartridges in the strip and trigger is held back.

Field Stripping

Unscrew and pull out the massive cross bolt which passes through the receiver holes and the back plate holes. A groove in the center of the bottom of this cross bolt is held by the rearward extension of the recoil spring guide. Push in the guide where it protrudes into the lower part of the grip. This will disengage the guide from the bolt and relieve the pressure of the spring against the back plate. The bolt can be pulled out and the spring will push the back plate to the rear for removal.

Pull out the feed block retaining key which passes through the lower edge of the feed block at the right side of the receiver. Drive the block out from the left side of the gun.

When it gets too hot, the barrel can be removed with the use of a special spanner.

How the Gun Works

Starting with the gun loaded and cocked, the action is as follows: The trigger being pressed, the sear is permitted to free the breech lock which flies forward carrying with it the firing pin. The feed rib on the breech block strips the cartridge from the strip and feeds it into the firing chamber. As the bolt closes behind it, a hump on the under side of the piston which rides with the breech block comes into contact with the hinge link on the breech block, forcing the lower end of the link down into a recess where it engages in front of resistance shoulders on the body, locking the breech block securely. As this locking takes place, the striker pin is free to go forward and fire the cartridge in the chamber.

Return Movement of the Action. As the gas passes over the gas port, a small amount passes through the port and into the chamber where it expands against the head of the piston, driving it backward. Thus the bullet is well out of the barrel before the action starts to open. This rearward action of the piston raises the locking pin away from the resistance shoulders, leaving the breech block free to be carried to the rear by the piston, while the empty cartridge case is gripped firmly by the extractor in the face of the breech block. The empty cartridge case strikes the ejector and is hurled out of the gun. If the trigger is released fast enough, the trigger and sear will engage to hold the weapon open. If the trigger is held depressed, the gun will continue to fire.

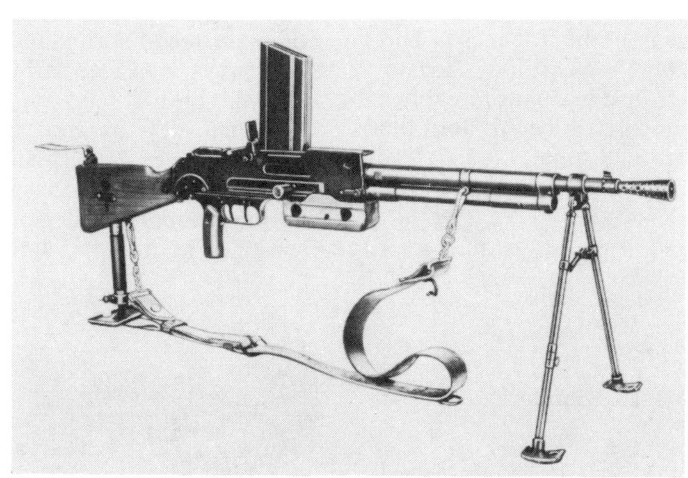

French Chatellerault 7.5mm 1924 M29 Machine Gun.

Caliber: 7.5mm French M1929 Rimless.
Magazine: Vertical box type, mounted on top of gun, holds 25 rimless cartridges.
Barrel Length: About 19½″.
Weight: Approximately 20 lbs. with bipod mounting.
Mounting: Bipod type attached to the barrel. Legs fold to the rear.
Sights: Adjustable foresight on left side of barrel. Radial rear sight on receiver.
Gun Operated By: Gas. Gas escapes through port into cylinder where it strikes against a piston head forcing piston back, compressing spring and opening the action.
Locked: Breech block securely locked during moment of high pressure by a rising type of bolt locking in shoulder in top of receiver.
Cooled: Air cooled.
Cyclic Rate of Fire: 550 rounds per minute.
Type of Fire: Single shot on first trigger or full automatic on second trigger.
Position of Bolt When in Firing Position: Open. When trigger is released entire bolt and operating mechanism will go forward.
Ejection Port: On right side of receiver.
Note: An earlier weapon, the M1924, used the 7.5mm M1924 cartridge. This cartridge was longer than the 7.5mm M1929.

Field Stripping

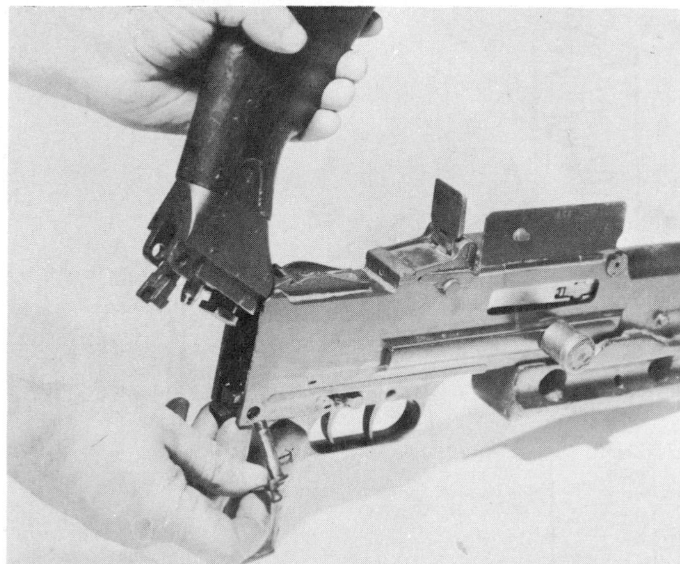

At lower right side of receiver is a retaining pin. Remove it; this permits the rear of the buttstock to be hinged up and back, when it can be lifted out of receiver.

Triggerguard assembly will now swing forward on hinge. Pushing first in, then out, unhook front end and remove.

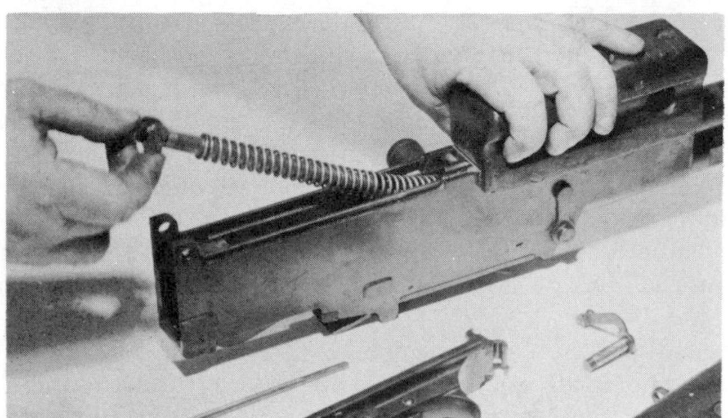

Pulling head of ejector out of its slot will permit it to be removed from the rear. Remove recoil spring and guide.

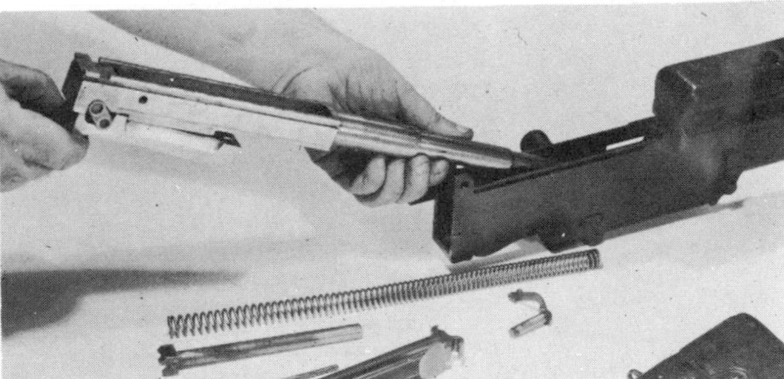

Withdraw bolt and piston with slide out of receiver.

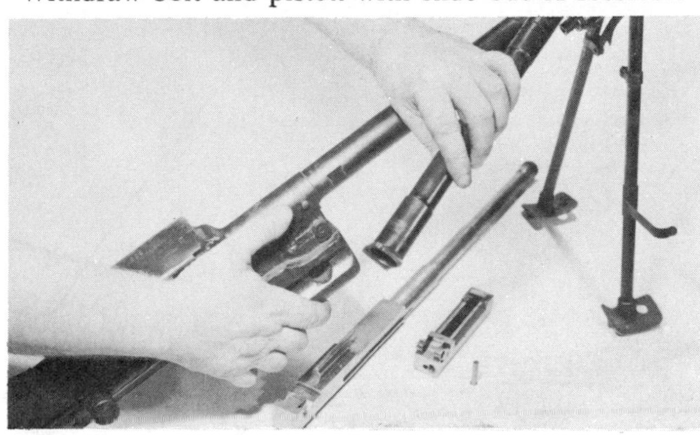

Gas cylinder tube lock is at lower front of receiver. Turn it to "O" mark on receiver, then raise rear end of tube. Tube can now be pulled out of receiver. Barrel lock is on upper front of receiver. Turn it to "O" and unscrew barrel to right.

Loading and Firing

A loaded magazine is inserted vertically in the top of the gun. The magazine opening is fitted with a dust cover which must be hinged up and forward to expose the magazine opening. The magazine release catch is positioned at the rear opening. Pressing it forward will release the magazine to be lifted out with the hand which is operating the catch.

Pull back the cocking handle to cock the weapon and compress the mainspring. Safety lever on the triggerguard may be used to lock the weapon in this position.

If front trigger is pulled, pressure will be exerted on the sear to release the bolt to fly forward and fire the cartridge stripped out of the magazine by the bolt in its forward travel. If the second trigger is pulled, the sear will not engage as long as the trigger is held back, and the weapon will continue to fire full automatic.

How the Gun Works

Starting with the gun loaded and cocked the action is as follows: If the first trigger is pulled, it pushes up the forward tip of the sear, bending down the rear end against the tension of the sear spring and pulling it out of the bent in the slide. The slide carries the striker in the front of its face. The slide and piston form a single unit; the bolt is fastened by a swinging link pin to the rear end of the slide. As the slide goes forward, pulled by the compressed recoil spring, carrying the moving

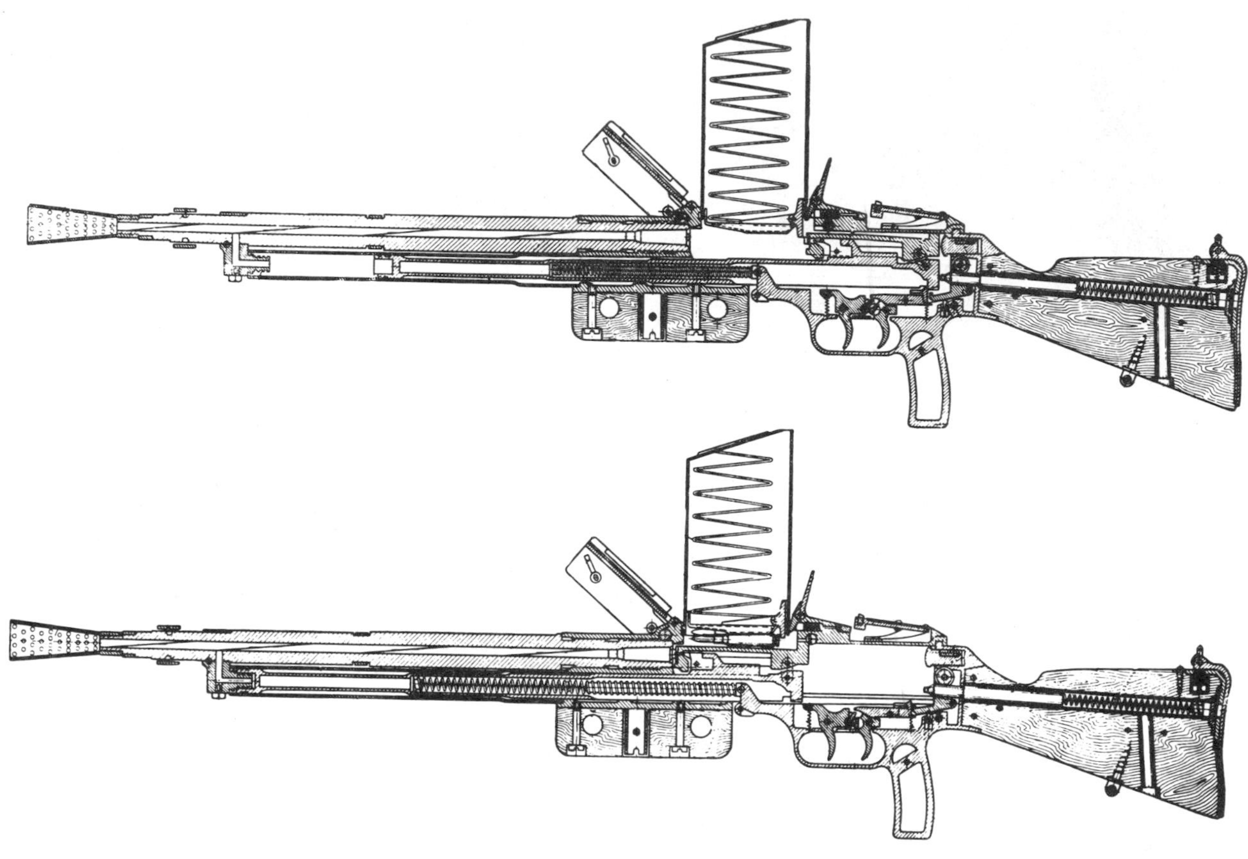

Section View of French 7.5mm M1924/29 Machine Gun.

components with it, the feed rib on top of the bolt passes between the lips of the magazine and strips a cartridge out. The extractor is forced over the base of the cartridge by the magazine spring, bringing the cartridge to proper feeding position in the bolt face.

As the forward motion nears its completion, the front end of the bolt stops against an abutment in the receiver. The rear end of the bolt, fastened on a rotating link to the slide, is now lifted up as the forward-moving slide rotates the link about the pins, and locks firmly in locking recess in the top of the receiver (somewhat like the Browning Automatic Rifle).

The slide, which carries the striker, continues to move ahead during the period of link rotation and the pin passes through its hole in the face of the bolt and strikes the cartridge now locked in the firing chamber.

Return Movement of the Action

Gas escaping through the port as the bullet passes over it (a short distance from the muzzle) passes through the gas cylinder and expands violently against the cup end of the piston in standard Hotchkiss fashion. As the piston starts back under the impact of the thrust, the gas escapes through slots in the gas cylinder tube. The piston, slide, and link go back while the bolt is still securely locked.

Then as the dangerous period of pressure is passed, the rearward moving slide pulling on the bottom of the swinging link rotates it down, drawing with it the locked rear end of the bolt. As the movement continues, the bolt moves back in straight line with the other parts, carrying the empty cartridge case in the extractor. This case strikes the ejector and is expelled from the gun.

In semi-automatic fire, the rearward movement is completed as the end of the slide strikes the buffer sear release attached to the sear mechanism, causing a rebounding action which catches the sear in the side to hold it back; while the back end of the bolt strikes the buffer which absorbs shock through a coil spring. In automatic fire, of course, the sear cannot engage; and the slide goes forward immediately.

An interesting development in this weapon is an actuator in the buttstock which is used to check the rate of fire.

A plunger rod rides in a tube with a spring behind the rod. The front end of this rod passes through a hole into the receiver in line with the slide, and touches a sear trip attached to the sear mechanism. This device adds resistance to recoil and increases the time between shots, as the sear is held in engagement longer than usual.

Chapter 25. Germany

EAST GERMANY

As a satellite of the USSR, East Germany has been forced to follow the dictates of the Soviets on small arms as on all other affairs. The East German Army is equipped at the present time with Soviet-designed and, for the most part, Soviet-made small arms. Before the Army was officially acknowledged to be an Army (that is, when it was a State Security force and a border patrol), it was equipped to a large extent with German World War II weapons and some Soviet World War II weapons. When it officially became an army it was equipped, initially at least, exclusively with weapons of Soviet World War II manufacture. Since that date, some of the newer Soviet weapons are in issue (AK, SKS, and RPD). Although the German arms plants in the Suhl area are apparently back in production (they are exporting arms), little can be looked for from East Germany along the line of original small arms development, unless the political situation changes considerably. The AK and SKS are being produced in East Germany.

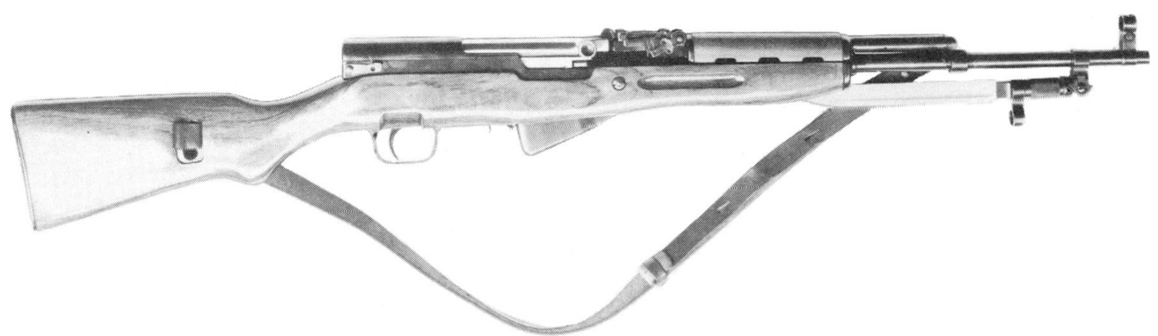

East German 7.62mm Copy of Soviet SKS Carbine. Note that sling is mounted similar to Kar 98k and that no cleaning rod is carried under barrel.

WEST GERMANY

The West German Army was initially equipped mainly with United States small arms of World War II origin. For the past several years, however, the West Germans

West German 9mm P38 of current manufacture. The P-1 of the West German Army.

7.62mm FN Rifle G1. Note metal handguards.

have taken an independent tack in the small arms field. The 9mm Walther P-38 has been put back into production at the Walther plant in Ulm, and the MG 42, in 7.62mm NATO, is now the standard machine gun and is called MG 1. The F.N. 7.62mm NATO light rifle was used in large quantities. This weapon is called the 7.62mm F.N. G1 by the Germans. Recently, West Germany adopted the Spanish CETME assault rifle as standard. This rifle is called the G3 by the Germans.

West Germany has adopted the Israeli 9mm Uzi submachine gun; it is described in the chapter on Israel.

Rifle 7.62mm G3

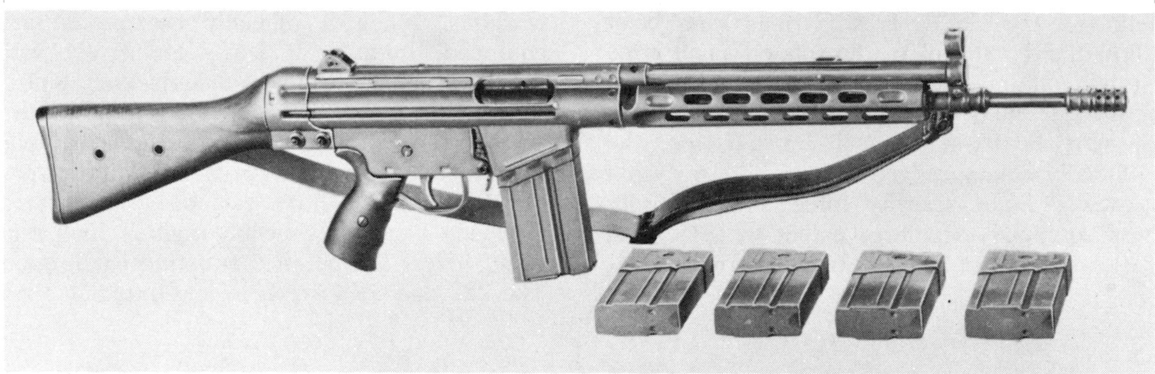

Caliber: 7.62mm NATO.
System of Operation: Delayed blowback, selective fire.
Weight (loaded w/o bipod): 9.9 lbs.
Length, Overall: 40.2 in.
Barrel Length: 17.7 in.
Feed Device: 20 round, detachable, staggered-row box magazine.
Sights, Front: Hooded post.
Rear: L type.
Muzzle Velocity: 2624 f.p.s.
Cyclic Rate: 500-600 r.p.m.

This weapon is basically an improved version of the Spanish CETME Model 58 assault rifle which is covered in full under Spain. Loading, firing, field stripping, and functioning are covered in full under that weapon. One of the principal differences between the G3 and the Spanish Model 58 CETME is in the construction of the bolt head. The G3 bolt head is designed to function with full power NATO cartridges, that of the Spanish M58 is designed to function with a reduced power NATO cartridge used for rifles in Spain. By change of a few components, it can be used with the full power NATO cartridge. The G3 can be used with a bipod, a scope sight, and an infra-red snooper scope, and has a combination flash hider and grenade launcher built into the barrel. This grenade launcher accommodates the more or less standardized rifle grenades, those with a tail boom internal diameter of 22mm, in use in the free world today.

G3 is mainly made of steel stampings; only the barrel and bolt components are machined. Hand guards on first production were plastic; the latest production has wooden hand guards. It has been adopted in 7.62mm NATO, by Portugal as Rifle 7.62mm M1961.

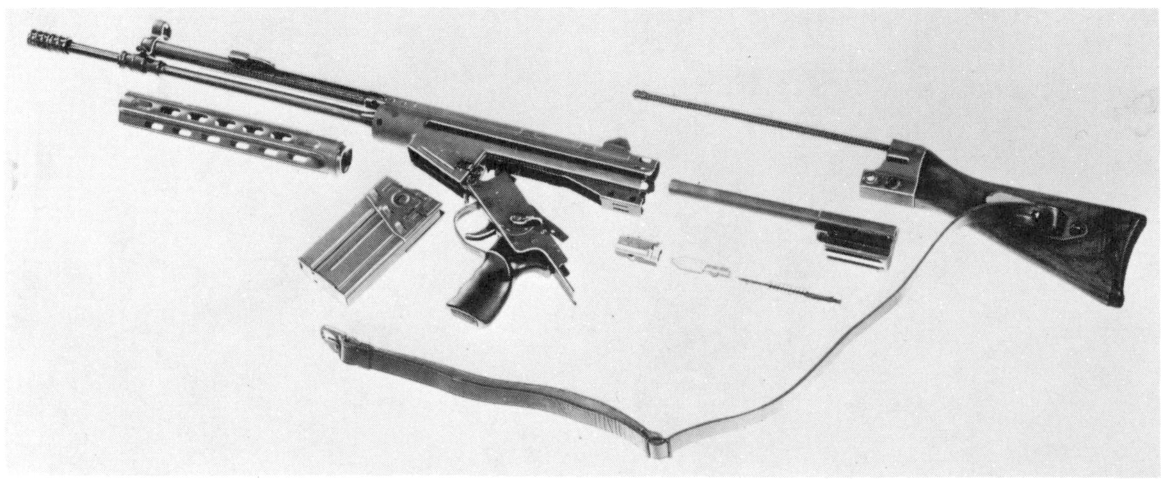

West German 7.62mm NATO Rifle G3 field stripped.

Chapter 26. German World War II Materiel

GERMAN PISTOLS AND REVOLVERS

There were no **official** German revolvers in World War II. All types of revolvers were to some extent used, however, representing captured or seized equipment.

The official service pistols fall into two general classifications, standard and substitute standard. Standard pistols were the Model 38 (Walther 9mm double action locked breech) and the Model 08 (Luger 9mm with short barrel and locked breech). Substitute standard included earlier and special barreled varieties of the Luger in both calibers 7.65mm and 9mm; Mauser Military models in caliber 7.63mm and 9mm Mauser and in 9mm model 08 (Luger).

Pocket model Sauers, Mausers, Walthers, Ortgies, and others in calibers 6.35mm, 7.65mm and 9mm Browning were also pressed into service.

Literally dozens of types of experimental pistols were brought back by our soldiers. None were made in quantity.

P-38. The P-38 derives directly from the commercial Walther HP (Heeres Pistole—Service Pistol). The P-38 adopted in 1938 was adapted to mass manufacture at a cost much lower than the Luger.

Identification. External hammer. Double action trigger. Rising and falling locking block housed in barrel

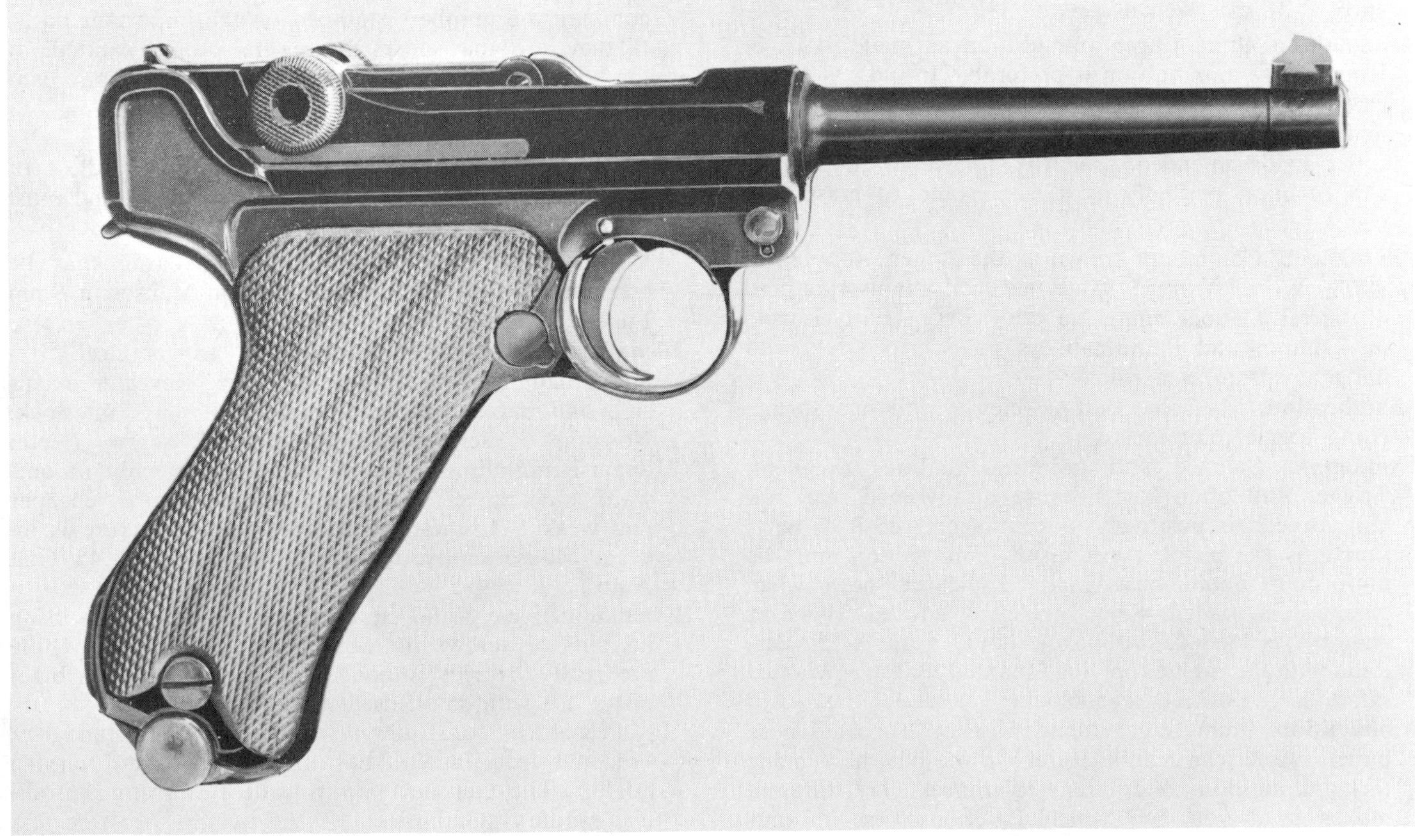

7.65mm Luger.

forging below breech. Round head on firing pin. Firing pin locked by turning thumb lever on slide. Locking takes place forward of firing pin head. Applying safety when hammer is cocked automatically drops hammer.

Evaluation. An advanced design which has forced changes in American manufacture, particularly with relation to the double action feature. Hammer is automatically dropped from full cock on firing pin head when safety is applied. This feature has been reported on one or two occasions as firing cartridge in chamber due to crystallization and breaking of safety lug which normally locks firing pin against movement before dropping hammer.

Another potential danger is that pistol can be fired without locking block, usually resulting in injury to light slide.

It is not advisable to use safety lever to lower hammer on loaded chamber in view of the potential danger. Slide should be retracted to check that white metal locking block is in place before using.

The original commercial Walther HP does not suffer from the potential firing pin threat. The pin head is differently shaped, and cuts in the turning safety lug are arranged to pull the pin itself inside the breechblock before locking it. Thus as the safety lever is turned it removes the head of the pin entirely out of the path of the hammer, then locks the pin inside the slide, then trips the sear.

The shape of the projecting firing pin head identifies the truly safe design, which is found on some early P-38's as well as on the HP.

Ammunition. 9mm Luger ammunition as made in U. S. Round nose ammunition is preferable to old style truncated nose bullets because of pitch of grip. (All German Service 9mm in WW II was round nose.) While super loads intended primarily for submachine guns will function perfectly as a rule, standard brass case pistol types are preferable.

PISTOL 08. Commonly known as the Luger. Adopted in 1908. World War II form had coil mainspring and 4″ barrel. Caliber 9mm. No grip safety. (Early Lugers in 7.65mm and 9mm calibers have grip safety and flat mainspring as a rule.

Identification. Magazine button release, coil mainspring, rising toggle joint lock.

Evaluation. Balance and pointing qualities excellent. Trigger pull often bad because of involved sear system. Breech is positively locked. Short recoil of parts functions the pistol. As a result, ammunition must be uniform to obtain best results. Indicator shows when chamber is loaded. Since striker is cocked whenever chamber is loaded, this pistol should never be so carried without first applying manual safety. Manual safety is a positive sear block.

Ammunition. 9mm Luger round nose or truncated nose bullets. American manufacturers in the past have made this ammunition to different tolerances. Try different makes until you find which functions best in your pistol.

Original ammunition was designed to permit action of pistol by recoil of moving parts; but modern loads are often pressured up to a point where pressure in barrel after unlocking is great enough to further speed up the action.

NOTE ON LUGERS: The original Luger had a flat mainspring. Grip safeties were standard on most pre-World War I types, particularly commercial models.

Lugers have been production made in only two calibers, 7.65mm bottle neck Luger and 9mm Luger. A few were made for early U. S. tests in Caliber .45 Colt Auto, but these are collector's pieces.

Conversions have been made transforming Lugers to .22 caliber; and special insert conversion units in .22 caliber were made and used in Germany and Switzerland.

Very few changes have been made in Luger design. Thumb safeties at different periods have been pushed or pulled to set the safety, and a magazine safety is occasionally found which makes it impossible to fire the pistol when the magazine is withdrawn. Essentially, however, the arm is fundamentally the same today as when it was introduced.

Evaluation. Lugers when commercially made by DWM and Mauser rate among the world's fine pistols. As made in times of peace in German arsenals they are always good quality military arms. As made in times of war they vary in Germany just as they do in every other country—workmanship is comparatively crude and inspection is not up to standard.

A reasonably effective check on these arms is to compare the numbers stamped on the important parts. If they are the same, they were properly fitted. If they vary, you may have a pistol made from cannibalized parts which may mean poor functioning.

Ammunition. 7.65mm or 9mm Luger.

Note: Lugers fitted with shoulder stocks, regardless of barrel length, are listed as machine weapons and must be federally registered.

MAUSER MILITARY PISTOLS. These arms may be encountered in 7.63mm Mauser, 9mm Mauser or 9mm Luger (P 08) calibers.

Identification. Magazine forward of triggerguard. Exposed hammer. Almost straight grip. Receiver extension and barrel a single forging. All parts interlock. No pins or screws except the stock screw. (Note: Spanish imitations resemble the genuine only in outward appearance. Mechanical construction is cheaper and weaker. Chinese and Japanese manufacture is an exact Mauser copy, though caliber may be .45 Colt Auto.)

Evaluation. Heavy and clumsy. Exceptional design using no pins or screws in mechanical construction. These are really hybrids intended for combination carbine-pistol use with stock used as holster.

Peacetime construction to the highest standards. Wartime manufacture has always produced varying quality. The Germans never made this pistol an official military standard.

Ammunition. Cal. 7.63mm uses .30 (7.63mm) Mauser

pistol ammunition which was made in the U. S. before World War II.

Cal. 9mm Mauser uses 9mm Mauser pistol ammunition. Currently not made here. Essentially this caliber was made for South American and Asiatic export. Cartridge is longer than 9mm Luger.

Cal. 9mm Luger (P 08). There were World War I Mauser conversions to take the standard Luger ammunition. Mauser Military pistols for this cartridge commonly have the figure "9" painted, cut, or burned into the stocks. 9mm Luger caliber ammunition is standard production in U. S.

German Walther 9mm Model 38 Automatic.

Caliber: 9mm Parabellum (Pistol 08).
Magazine: Detachable box type in handle, capacity 8 cartridges.
Ballistic Data: Same as for Parabellum (Luger pistol).
Barrel Length: About 4¾".
Overall Length of Pistol: 8½".
Weight of Pistol: 34 ozs.
Sights: Fixed. Inverted V front, open V-notch rear.
Accurate Range: German manuals give 125 yards, but very few men equipped with a pistol can do accurate work at such a range; 25 yards is the maximum range for average use of a pistol.
Pistol Operated By: Recoil.
Locked: By a locking piece swinging up from below as in the Mauser military pistol.
Barrel and Slide Assembly: Firmly locked together during the first quarter-inch of recoil.
Type of Fire: Single shot only, this weapon is fitted wtih a positive disconnector preventing more than one shot being fired with each press of the trigger.
Position of Slide When Last Shot Is Fired: Open.
Magazine Release Catch: At rear of the bottom of the butt. Must be pushed back to release magazine.

Safeties: 1. Thumb catch on left rear of slide. Pushed down it exposes the letter "S" making the pistol safe. When this lever is thumbed up, the letter "F" is exposed and the pistol is ready to fire.

2. When firing chamber is loaded, a small pin will be seen to protrude from the rear end of the slide. If this pin is flush with the slide, the firing chamber is empty.

Special Features. This weapon is of very unusual design. It is fitted with a double-action movement. In the ordinary automatic pistol, the hammer must always be kept at full cock if the pistol is to be ready to fire on a moment's notice. In the Walther Pistol, once the slide has been drawn back and allowed to go forward over a loaded magazine to load the firing chamber, the hammer may be safely lowered and the pistol carried in that position. Then when you are ready to fire, you may either thumb-cock the hammer, as in the case of the Colt .45 Automatic under similar conditions, or you may simply draw straight back on the trigger as in the case of a double-action revolver, and the hammer will come to full cock and fall, striking the firing pin. From that movement on, however, the action is standard for auto pistols, and the hammer is cocked by the slide which rides back over it.

Warning: Applying the thumb safety when hammer is cocked automatically locks the firing pin and then drops the hammer on it. In case of a defective or crystallized safety, the pistol may fire accidentally. It is not advisable to use this hammer lowering device on a loaded chamber unless the pistol is the early (H. P.) type in which the safety draws the firing pin inside the slide before dropping the hammer.

Loading and Firing

Load and insert magazine in handle as is customary in all automatic pistols of this general design.

Draw back the slide, which will ride over the head of the hammer and cock it, meanwhile compressing the recoil springs and permitting a cartridge in the magazine to rise in line with the breechblock. Release the slide and let it go forward under the influence of the recoil springs.

If the safety catch has been in the "Fire" position during the backward movement of the slide, then the hammer will remain at full cock and the pistol is now ready for immediate firing.

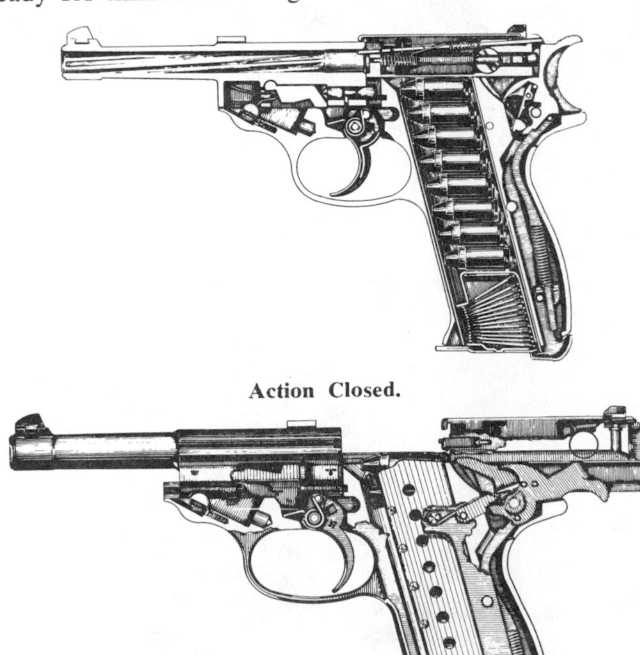

Action Closed.

Action Open.

If the safety catch was in the "Safe" position when the slide was retracted, then the chamber will load but the hammer will go forward safely to its resting place. The pistol cannot be fired now as the safety is locking the firing pin. However, if you now move the safety catch, the hammer may be cocked by the thumb, or the pistol may be fired by pulling straight back on the trigger bringing the double action factor into play.

Field Stripping

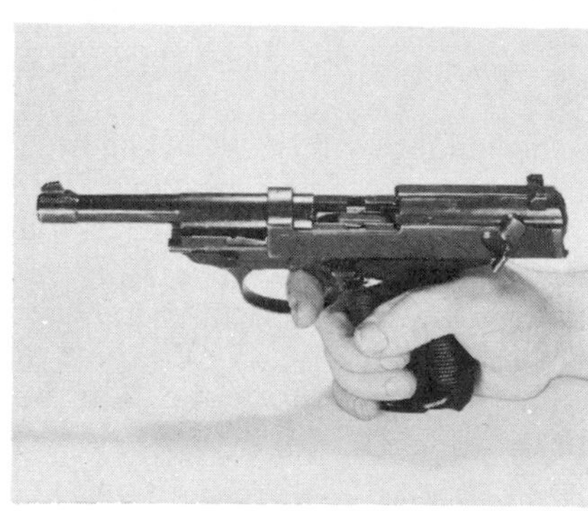

Set the safety catch in the "Safe" position and pull the slide back over the empty magazine, so that the inside catch on the slide stop will be forced up by the magazine follower and hold the slide open. Then remove the magazine.

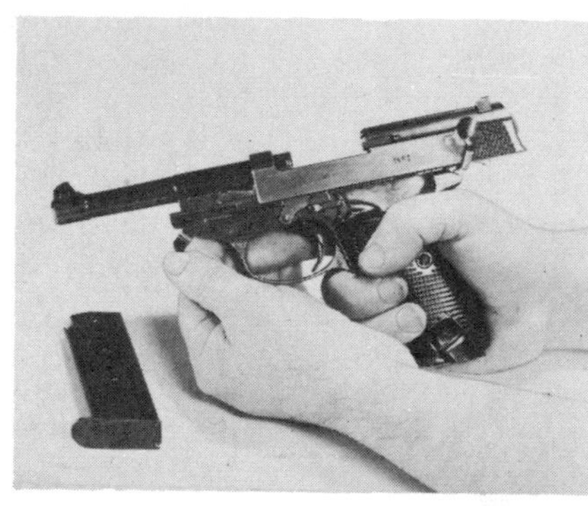

At the front end of the frame below the receiver is a lever-type locking pin. Turn this down and around as far as it will go.

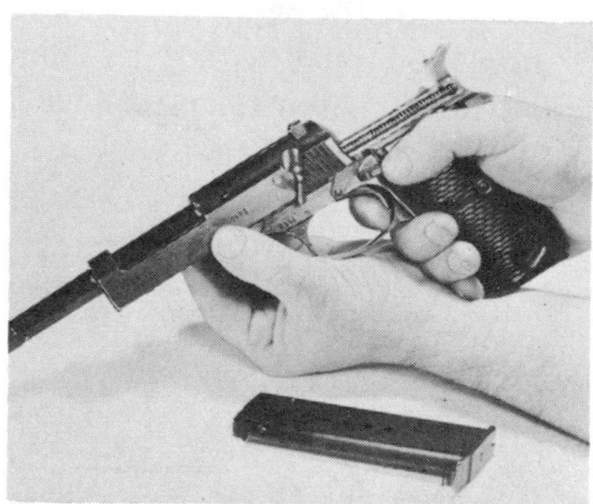

Hold the slide under control with the left hand and with the right thumb push down the slide stop. Now press the trigger and pull the barrel and slide directly forward in their runners on the receiver, sliding them out of the guides.

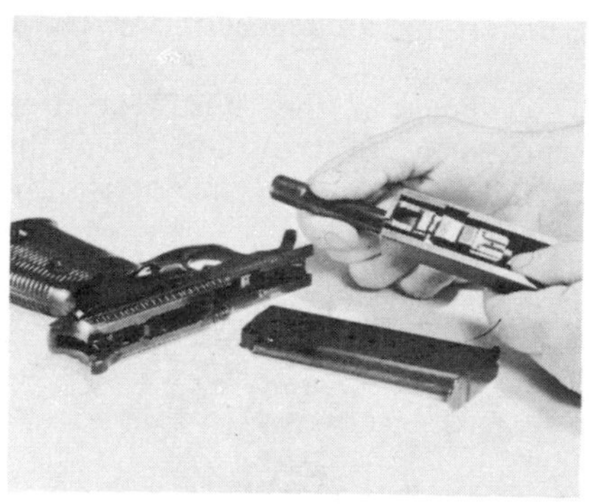

Now turn barrel and slide upside down. A small locking plunger will be seen at the rear of the barrel assembly. Push the plunger and spring out the white metal locking cam block.

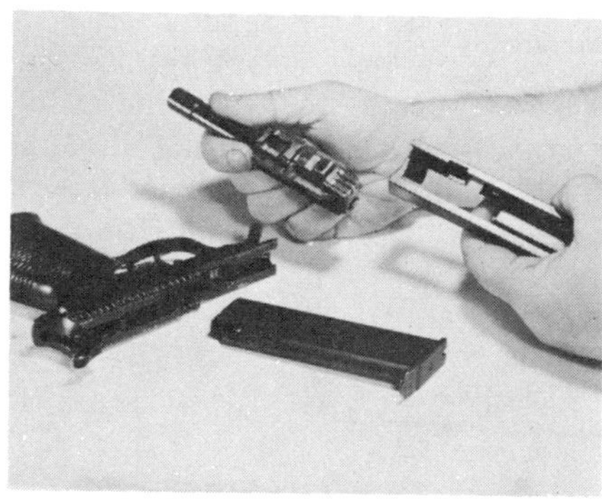

Now slide barrel directly ahead out of slide. Lock will come forward with barrel.

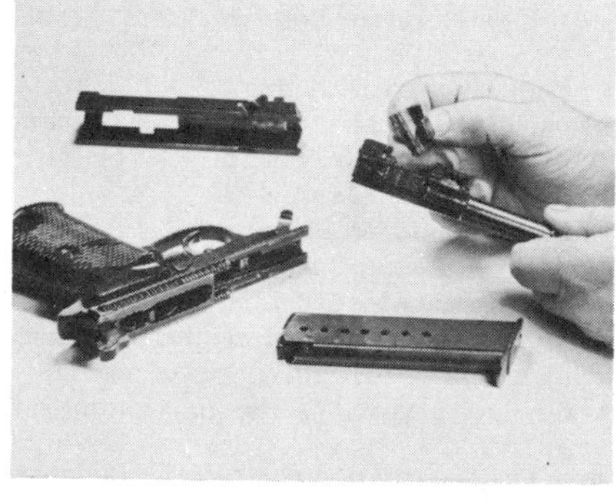

Push forward and up on locking cam block and lift it out of its recess. This completes field stripping.

Top to bottom, left: Slide, barrel, lock, magazine.
Top to bottom, right: Receiver, stock.

Note on Assembly

Reverse stripping procedure.

When replacing locking block, be sure that its lugs are in line with the wide ribs on both sides of the barrel.

Insert barrel assembly as far as it will go into slide, then push the locking block into its locked position.

Hammer must be uncocked, and the ejector and the safety mechanism levers pushed down to prevent them from catching on the rear end of the slide.

With safety catch at "Safe" position, hold the locking block in the locked barrel position, and push the slide and barrel onto the receiver in the guide. Force the slide all the way back against the tension of the springs and raise the stop to catch and retain the slide in the open position.

Turn the locking lever around on its pin as far as it will go to its original position. Press the slide stop and permit the slide to run home. Insert magazine.

Special Note on the Pistol

It has all the good points of the old Luger and does away with practically all the bad ones. The grip, balance, and hang of the pistol are as fine as in the Luger. This weapon is not muzzle heavy as are most automatic pistols. It also incorporates a fine, positive locking system on the general type of the Mauser automatic pistol with the locking block swinging up from below. Its general design, with the short slide running back on guides in the receiver, gives it the sturdiness of our own Colt automatic pistols. The position of the locking catch for the magazine is not good, and magazines cannot be extracted and inserted as rapidly as in the Colt and Luger.

In most military automatic pistols (Colt, Beretta, Steyr, etc.) when the firing chamber is loaded, the hammer is at full cock; and if it is eased down on the firing pin, must be drawn back by the thumb before the first shot can be fired. In the Walther, simply pulling the trigger will raise the hammer and drop it on the firing pin.

In the event of a light hammer blow, or a defective primer in the ordinary automatic pistol, it is necessary to draw the slide back by hand to eject the round from the firing chamber, or to recock the pistol by hand. A second or third pull on the trigger will very often fire a cartridge. In the Walther it is possible to do this without shifting position of hand or taking attention away from the target.

When the pistol is loaded with a cartridge in the firing chamber, a floating pin protrudes from the slide above the hammer. A glance or (in the dark) a touch will always tell whether the chamber is loaded, making it unnecessary to pull back the slide as in other pistols.

The P-38 has been adopted as standard by the West German Army.

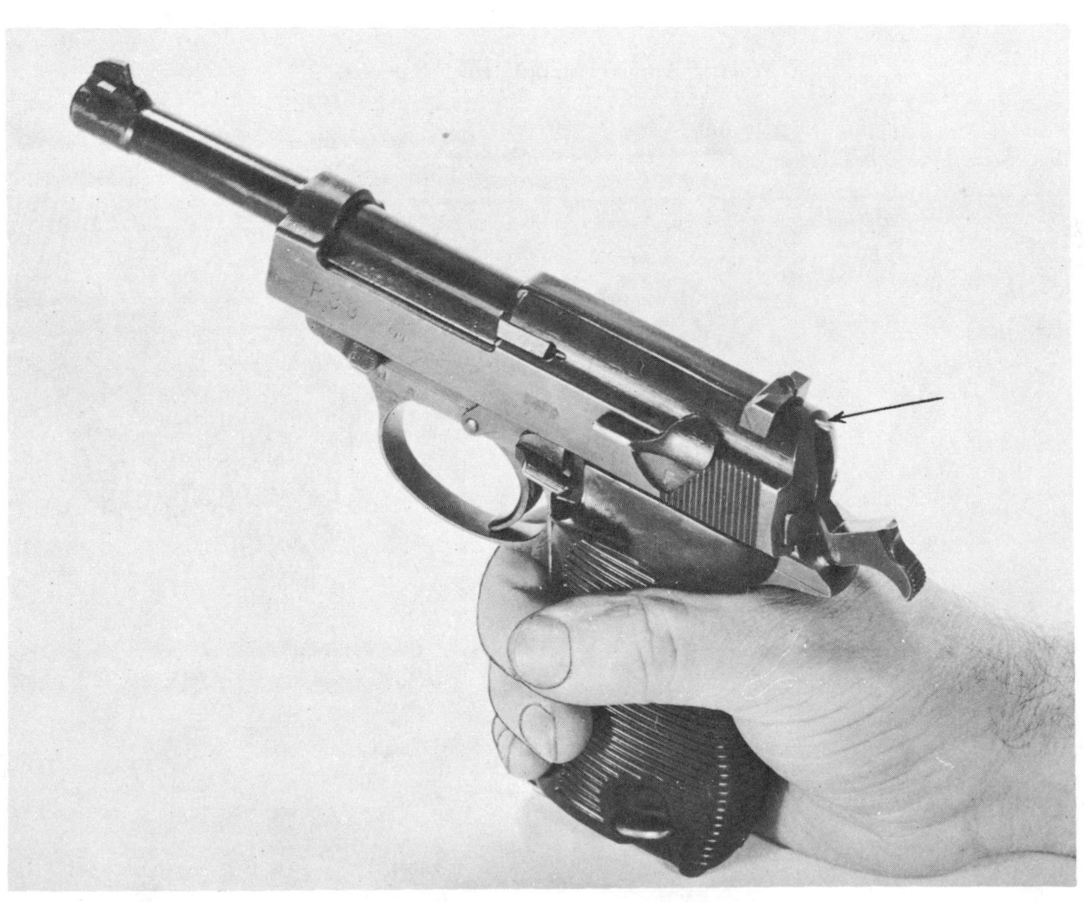

Walther Armee Pistol, Internal Hammer.

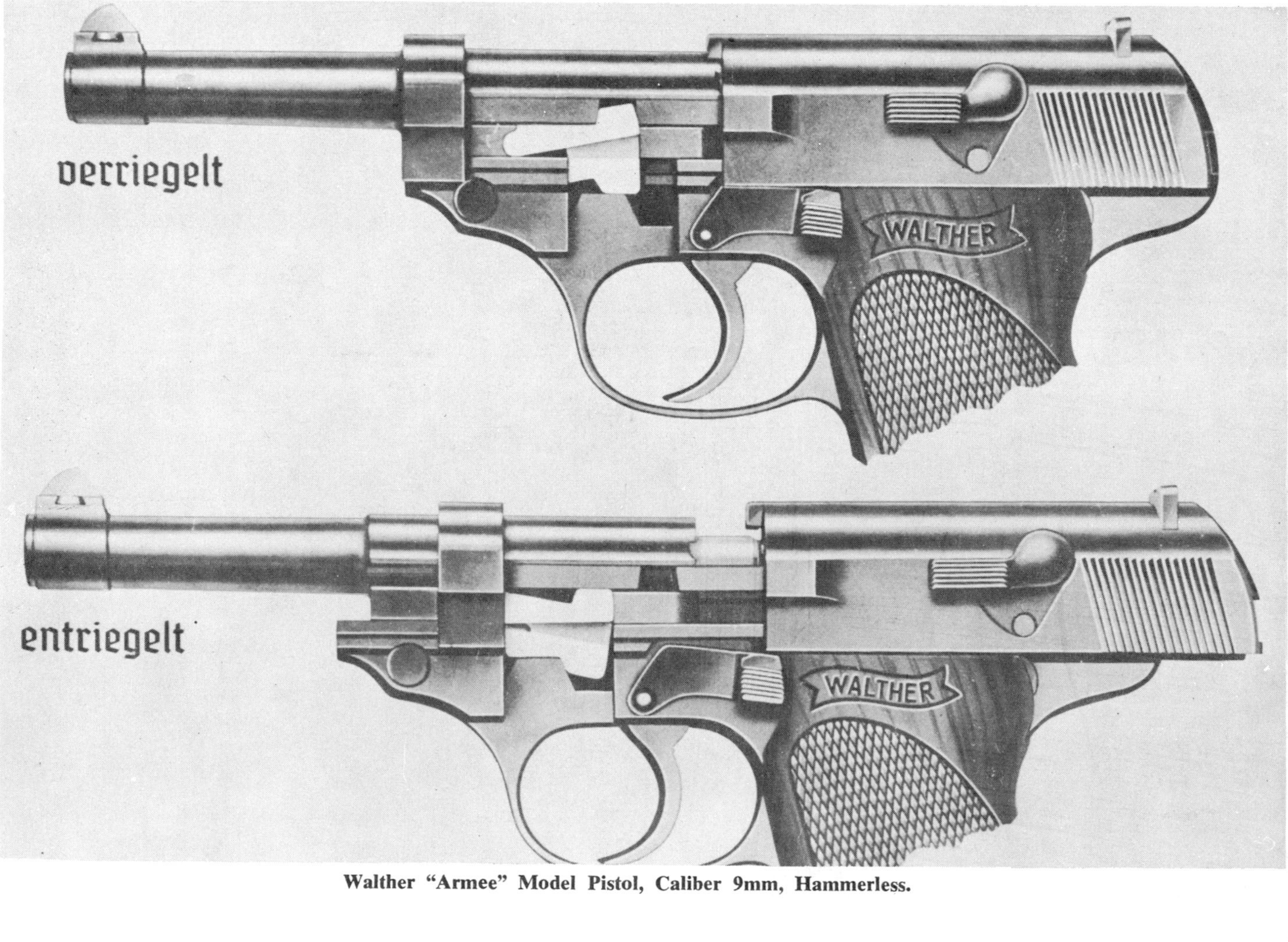

verriegelt

entriegelt

Walther "Armee" Model Pistol, Caliber 9mm, Hammerless.

The pistol on the left has a special safety feature not embodied in the P-38, though otherwise the pistols are much alike. The P-38 is the mass production version of the Walther HP. Firing pins of the pattern pictured in the left photo are commercial safety types. In these the pin is retracted to prevent the hammer from reaching it when the safety is applied.

Pistols with firing pins as shown in the right photo are common to the service model P-38. In this pattern the firing pin is mechanically locked when the safety is applied but can be struck by the falling hammer. This is occasionally dangerous because of crystallization.

The two pistols are shown from the rear with the slide locked fully back.

For the hammerless model:

Top view: Pistol with side cut away to show white metal locking block in place, pistol ready to fire.

Lower view: Barrel is halted at end of recoil stroke, at which point locking block is cammed down into receiver recess and out of slide engagement. Slide is still traveling back drawing empty case gripped by extractor. At end of slide stroke, empty will have been ejected, hammer cocked and dual recoil springs within slide loaded up to compel return loading stroke of action.

Note: While this is essentially an enclosed hammer version of the Walther HP model, its parts are not interchangeable and some differ considerably in construction. Very few of these pistols were made. Some are built with duralumin slides and receivers.

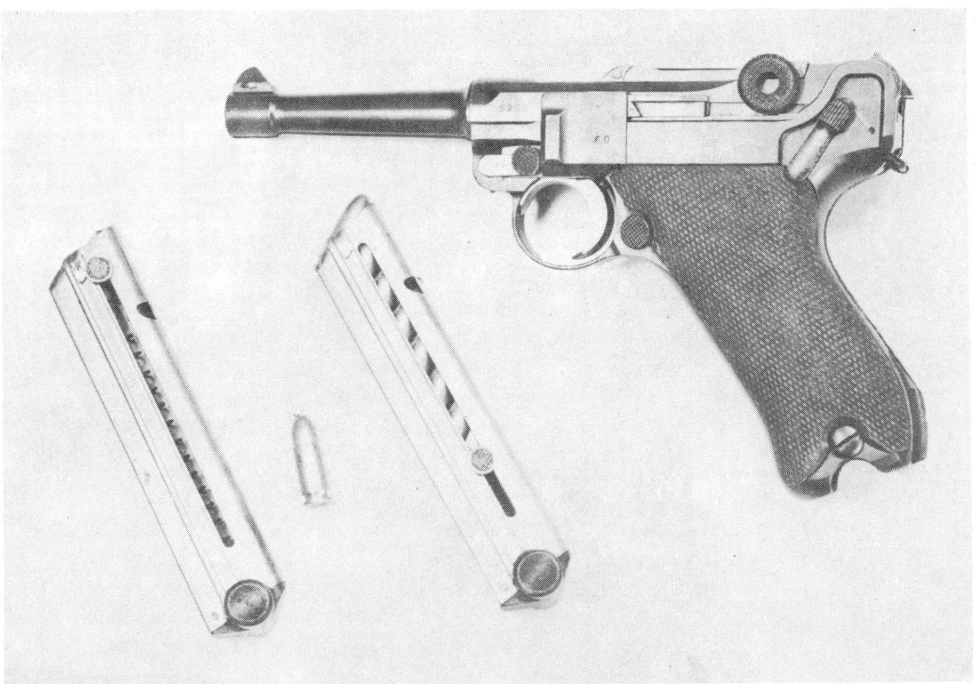

German Luger (Parabellum) 9mm 08 Automatic (Called Luger in U. S.; and Parabellum in Europe).

Caliber: 9mm Ball Ammunition, flat point or round point. (Cal. .35).

Magazine: Box type, single line, capacity 8 cartridges. Note: magazine follower is fitted with special sliding stud to permit easy loading of magazine.

Muzzle Velocity: 1040 to 1500 feet per second. Note: The customary M.V. of the German manufactured ammunition is 1040 F.P.S. but cartridges for this weapon are manufactured in the United States with a M.V. of 1150 F.P.S.; while German ammunition manufactured mainly for machine pistols, but usable in the Luger, develops 1500 F.P.S.

Weight of Bullet: 125 grains, lead with metal jacket, or lead with steel jacket. Note: High velocity cartridges for machine pistols (submachine guns) used bullets of sintered (compressed powdered) iron. These bullets weigh about 110 grains.

Muzzle Striking Energy: 320 to 460 Foot Pounds (365 with U. S. Ammunition).

Barrel Length: 4″. Note: Special 6″, 8″, and 10″ barrels are provided for special purpose weapons.

Overall Length of Pistol: 8¾″.

Weight of Pistol: 30 oz.

Sights: Inverted "V" blade front sight; open "V" notch rear sight. Fixed.
Accurate Range: About 75 yards.
Maximum Range: About 1200 yards with lowest-powered cartridges.
Pistol Operated by: Recoil.
Locked: By Maxim-type toggle joint.
Type of Fire: Single shot only.
Magazine Release Catch: Button on left side, similar to Colt .45 Automatic.
Position of Breech When Last Shot Is Fired: Open. Toggle joints are buckled up.
Safety: Thumb piece on upper left hand side of receiver. To apply this Safety, pull back and down. The German word "Gesichert" is now exposed. To fire pistol, push this catch up and forward.
Special Features: When the firing chamber is loaded, the extractor rises above the base of the breechblock exposing the word "Geladen," indicating loaded.
Special Note: While the 9mm is the official German Army caliber, this weapon may be found in .30 caliber (7.65mm). This model shoots a bottle necked cartridge with a 93-grain bullet, developing a M.V. of 1250 feet per second and a striking energy of 323 foot pounds. Magazine capacity of this caliber is 8 cartridges. It is manufactured in barrel lengths ranging from 3¾" to as much as 16".

Field Stripping

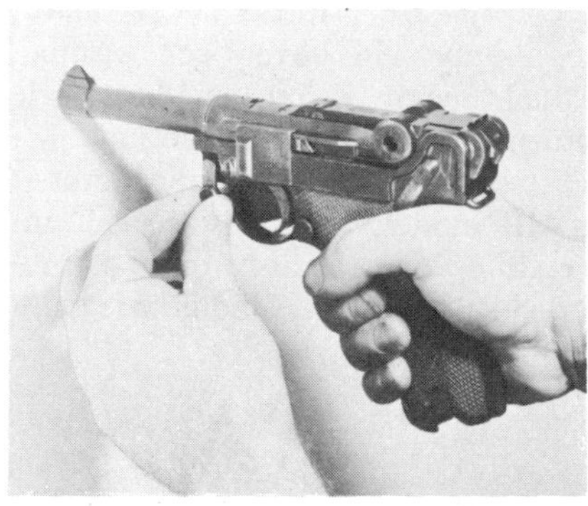

Holding pistol in right hand press muzzle down firmly on a hard surface about ½ inch to release tension on the recoil spring. With the tension removed, the thumb catch on the side plate may now be turned down to a vertical position.

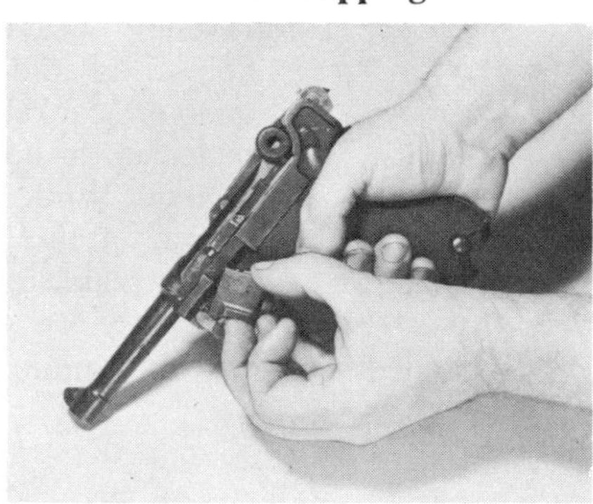

Now lift out the side plate.

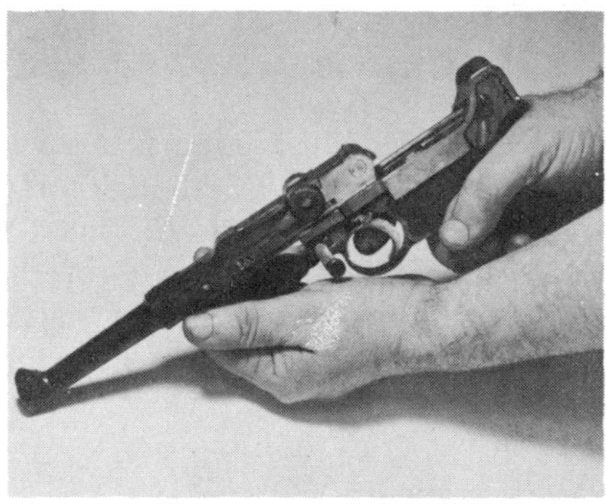

Slide the complete barrel and toggle assembly directly to the front and out of the receiver.

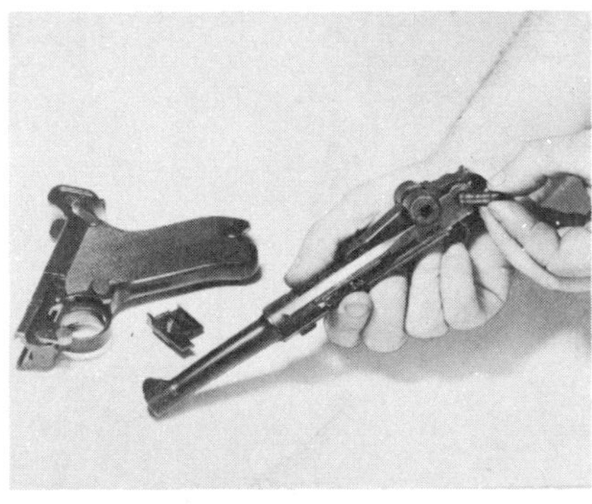

Buckle the toggle slightly to relieve tension and extract retaining pin on the left hand side.

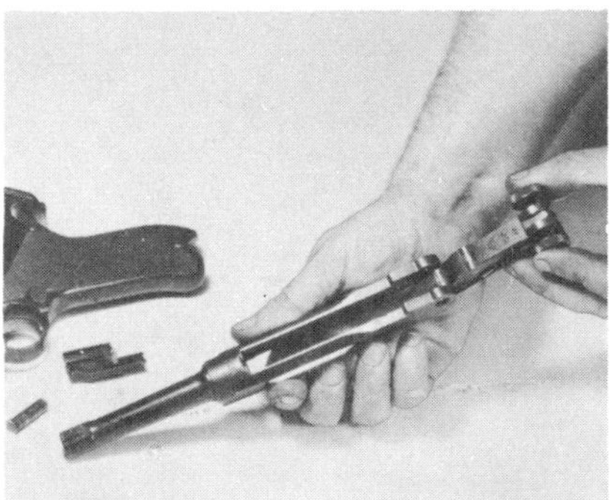

Now pull toggle assembly, breechblock containing firing pin, and extractor directly back in their guide and out of the frame. No further dismounting is necessary or recommended.

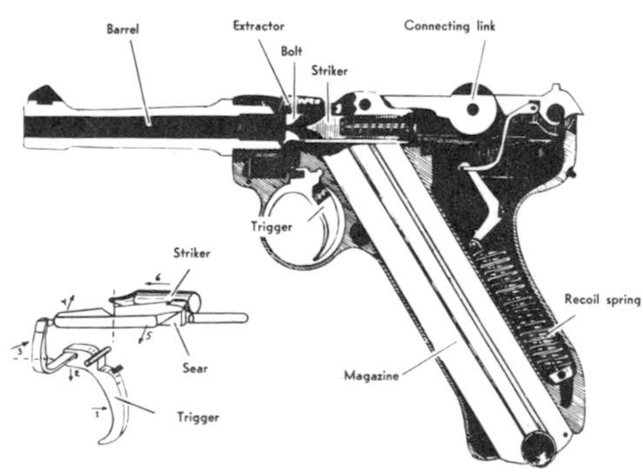

Note on Reassembling

Merely reverse stripping procedure. Take care hook suspended from rear of the Toggle Assembly drops into proper place, which is in front of the inclined ramps. Also note that when replacing the side plate, the tongue on the rear end must be inserted in the recess in the receiver and the projecting section of the trigger bar must fall into the proper slot at the top of the trigger.

Instructions for Loading and Firing Luger Pistols

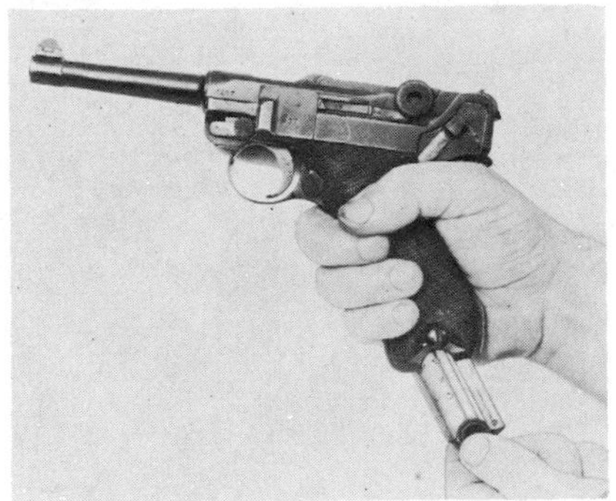

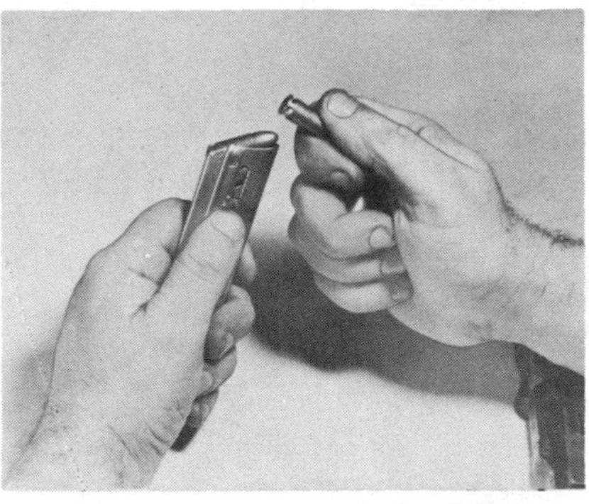

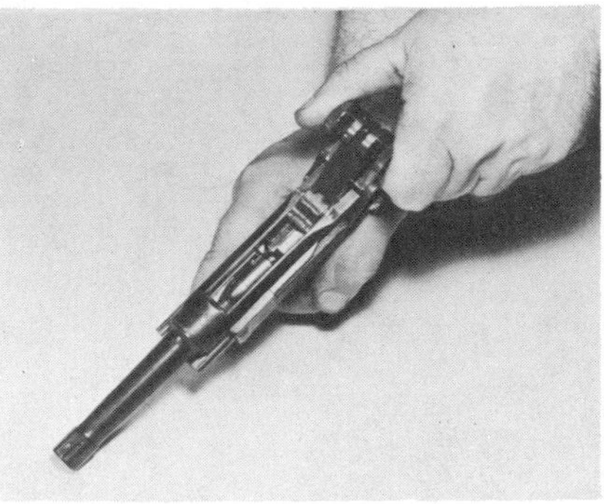

To extract magazine: Press magazine release stud near trigger on left hand side and withdraw magazine from butt of pistol.

To load magazine: Hold magazine firmly in left hand. Pull down stud attached to magazine platform. This will compress spring and permit cartridges to be dropped into the magazine.

To load firing chamber: (a) Holding pistol pointed down toward ground with right hand, grip the milled knobs on the toggle and pull up and back as far as the breechblock will go. This compresses the recoil spring in the grip and permits the first cartridge in the magazine to rise in line with the breechblock. (b) Release grip and spring will force breechblock back into locked position driving a cartridge into the firing chamber.

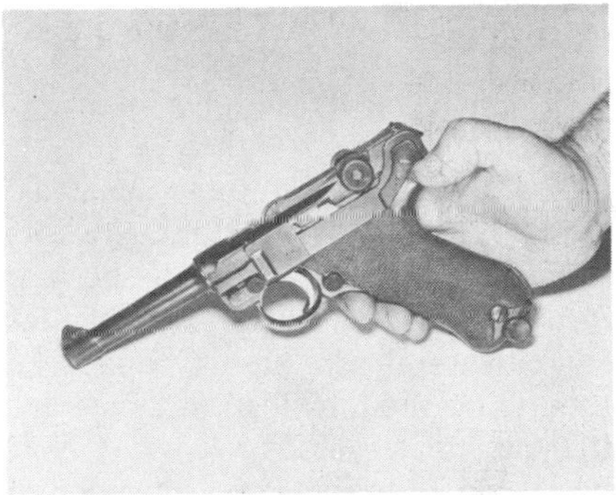

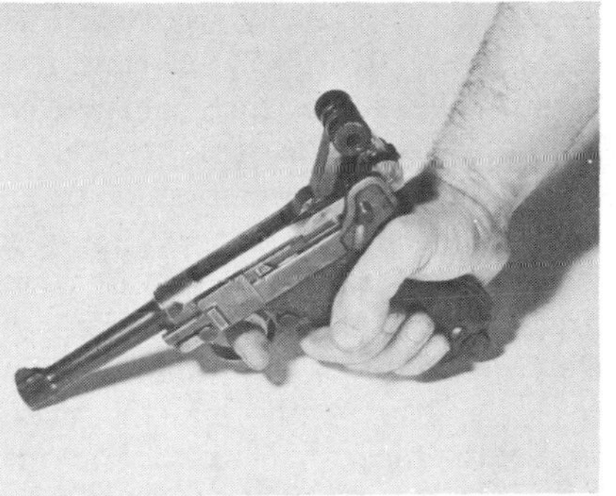

To set thumb safety: Pull thumb piece back and down. This will expose the German word "Gesichert," "Made safe." At the same time a flat solid steel piece will be seen to rise directly in front of the milled knob on the toggle. This locks the sear so the weapon cannot be fired.

Breech Block Stop: When the last cartridge has been fired, the stud of the magazine follower will force the catch up and hold the breech open with toggle joint buckled.

Reloading from open breech: (a) Remove empty magazine. (b) Replace with loaded magazine. (c) Pull back on milled surfaces and permit breech block to drive forward loading firing chamber.

How the Pistol (Luger) 08 Works

Starting with the pistol loaded and cocked, the action is as follows: The trigger being pressed, a connecting piece forces back a pin which presses out a spring-retaining lock permitting the striker to go forward and fire the cartridge in the chamber. (The involved trigger system of this pistol is one of its greatest weaknesses.) As the bullet goes forward down the barrel, the barrel and the recoiling mechanism locked together move backwards about half an inch. There is a toggle joint behind the breechblock which functions exactly as a human knee. A strong pin at the rear fastens this toggle securely to the barrel extension. At the point where the breech pressure has dropped to safe limits, the center part of this toggle joint strikes against a sloping part of the frame, buckling the toggle exactly as a human knee; but continuing to draw the breech block in a direct line in its guide in the barrel extension. During this opening movement a short coil spring, which drives the firing pin and is situated inside the breech block, is compressed and caught and held by the sear. The extractor, fitted in the top front of the breech block pulls the empty cartridge case back until it strikes an ejector piece and is hurled out of the pistol. A small coil spring snaps the extractor back into place. As the toggle joint buckles upward, a hook lever hanging from its pin and hooked under claws attached to the recoil spring in the grip, compresses the recoil spring, storing up energy for the return movement of the action. The magazine spring forces a cartridge up into line with the breech block. A shoulder below the rear end of the barrel contacts a shoulder in the receiver in front of the magazine space stopping further travel. The rearward motion is now complete.

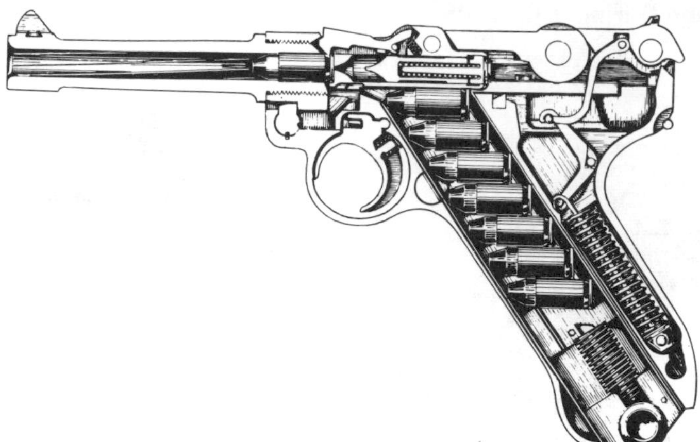

Action closed showing details of mechanism.

Action open, showing recoil spring hook-up.

Return Movement of the Action. The compressed recoil spring pulls down against the hook lever drawing down the bent toggle exactly as a bent knee straightens out when one stands up. This forward action drives the attached breech block straight ahead in its guide and strips the top cartridge out of the magazine and into the firing chamber. The extractor springs over the head of the cartridge and locks in the cannelure of the cartridge case. This raises the height of the extractor so that it is above the face of the breech block. Looking at the extractor—or touching it if in the dark—tells if the chamber is loaded. The breech block and the two levers of the toggle are now in a straight line and the axis of the toggle is slightly below the other axes. The pistol is thus securely locked. The sear now connects with the trigger mechanism; trigger spring pushes trigger into place; and pistol is ready for the next shot.

How the Thumb Safety Works. While the normal method of applying the thumb safety on this pistol is to push it back and down, there are models in which the procedure is the exact reverse. When the pistol is on safe, a flat steel piece attached to thumb-piece is forced up out of the receiver on the left hand side just above the stock. This prevents the outward expansion of springs which lock the striker back in firing position.

Special Models of the Luger

The customary Naval Model has a 6″ barrel. Special carbine models are issued with 8″, 10″, 12″, and sometimes 16″ barrels. Some of these have a wood fore-end and some do not. All are customarily issued with wood holsters which can be attached to the grip of the pistol to transform it into a carbine. These models are normally fitted with elevating rear sights capable of adjusting to 800 meters. (The model illustrated has an 8″ barrel and a carbine-type holster stock.)

A special 32-shot magazine is sometimes issued for these pistols. These are not in general use, having been largely supplanted by Machine Pistols. However, very large quantities of them were manufactured and doubtless are still to be found.

To Load Special 32-Shot Magazines

Each magazine comes with a filler. The lever must be wound against the tension of the magazine spring and locks into position by means of a spring loaded catch. The loading tool is slid over the mouth end of the

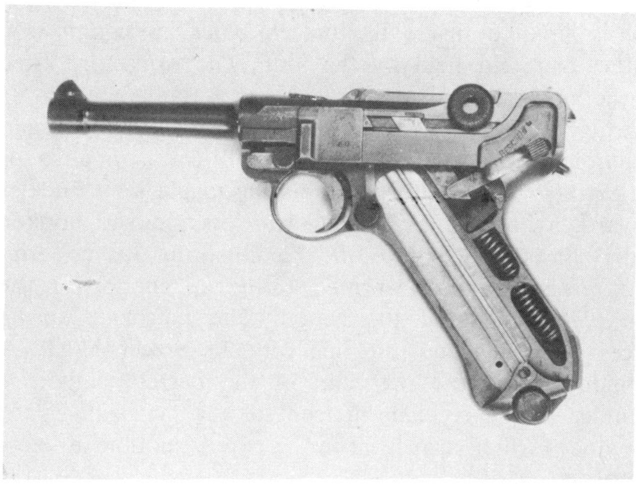

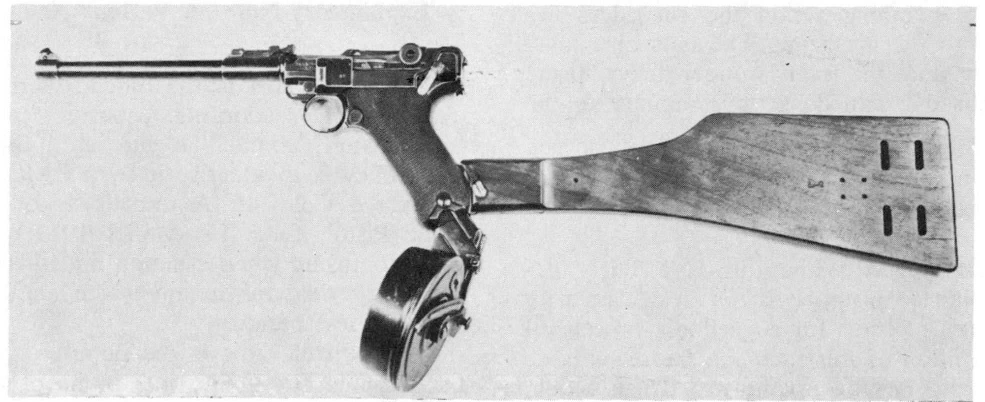

Luger with shoulder stock attachment.

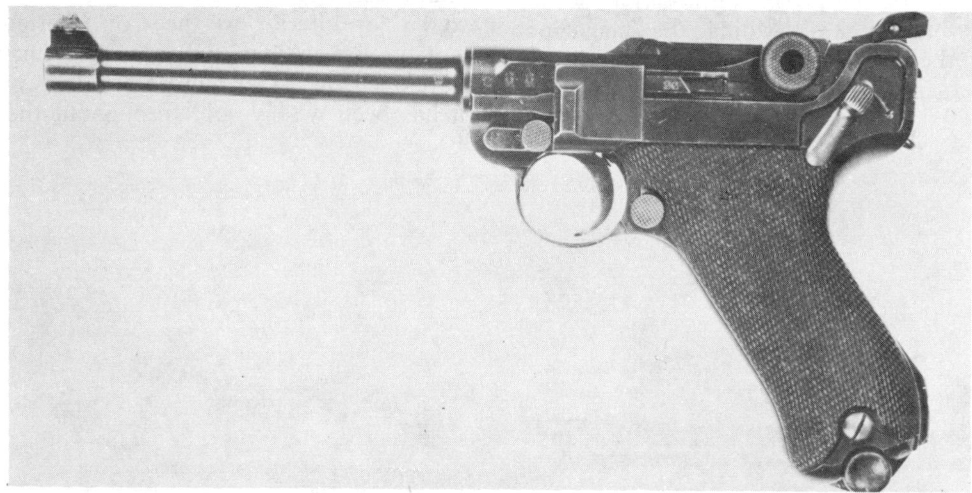

Luger Navy pistol.

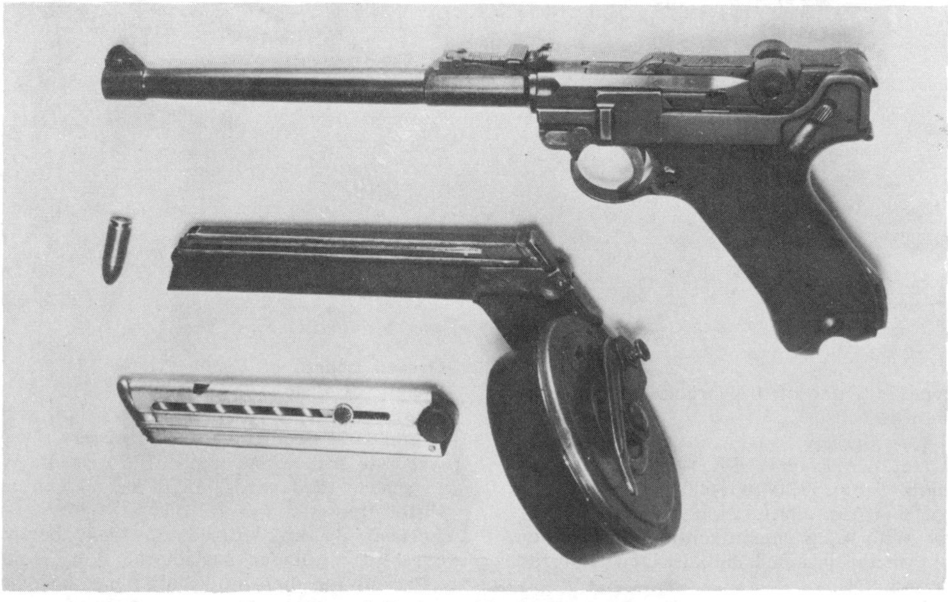

Long Barrel Luger with 32-Shot Magazine.

magazine and by a pumping action the cartridges are forced downward into the magazine. The magazine must be loaded cautiously since the lever is under heavy spring tension and if released it can do serious damage to the fingers.

(Note: this magazine may also be used in the earlier models of the Bergmann Machine Pistols.)

Note on German Luger: While this is a finely designed, superbly balanced pistol, it is not in a class with the U. S. Army service pistols for ruggedness or general reliability. In recognition of this fact, the Germans issue the pistol in a special heavy duty holster which covers the entire length of the weapon enclosing it completely. A pocket for an extra magazine will be found inside this holster. Inside the flap is a small dismounting tool. By placing the hole of this tool over the stud of the magazine, and pressing down on the projecting hook, a special lever is provided which makes loading the magazine much easier than if the spring is compressed entirely by the thumb and fingers.

Explanatory Note on Various Names For German Pistol 08

Pistole 08. This is the official German name for the weapon. When adopting a basic weapon in any class (rifle, pistol, submachine gun, etc.) the customary military policy is to identify it by YEAR OF ADOPTION. (Thus the Colt .45 Automatic is officially The Automatic Pistol, Cal. .45, Model 1911.) This system prevents confusion when a nation finds it necessary to utilize subsidiary weapons in any given class during an emergency or test period.

Luger Pistol. This is the popular American name for the weapon. From the time of its original manufacture, this pistol has been a very popular one in the United States, particularly in caliber .30 (7.65mm). Its excellent balance and hang, its high velocity, and fine general performance made it the accepted favorite of many pistol enthusiasts. (As a military pistol it is generally conceded to be far inferior to the Colt.) Originally designed by a naturalized American named Borchardt, it was further developed by a German named Luger. Under that name it has been widely sold throughout the world.

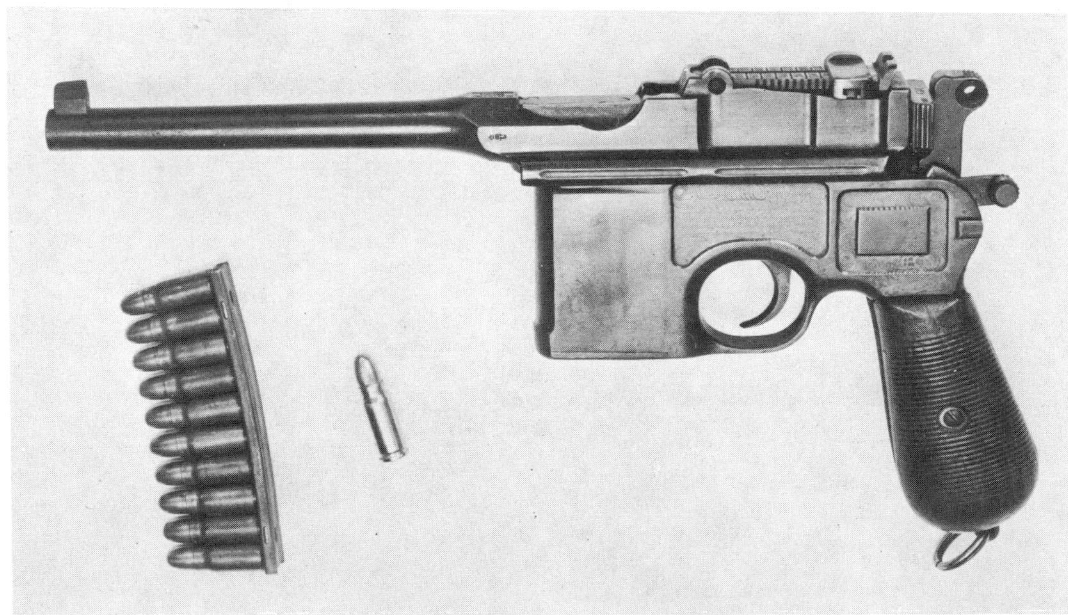

German Mauser 7.63mm Automatic.

Caliber: 7.63mm.
Magazine: Fixed-box type in front of triggerguard. Loaded by clips stripped in from top.
Magazine Capacity: 10 cartridges.
Muzzle Velocity: 1420 feet per second with standard manufactured U. S. ammunition. From 1320 to 1600 feet per second with varying types of German ammunition.
Muzzle Striking Energy: With U. S. manufactured ammunition, 380 foot pounds with metal jacketed bullets; and 400 foot pounds with soft point bullet.
Barrel Length: 5¼″.
Overall Length of Pistol: About 12″.
Weight of Pistol: 45 ozs.
Sights: Fixed front sight. Rear sight adjustable for elevation, graduated from 50 to 1000 meters.
Accurate Range: As a pistol, 75 yards. With shoulder stock attached, 1000 yards (1800 meters extreme range).
Pistol Operated by: Recoil.
Locked: By link forced up from below engaging in locking recess on under surface of bolt. Bolt and barrel are thus locked together until bullet has left barrel and sliding members have recoiled about 3/16″.

Type of Fire: Single shot only. Trigger does not engage with hammer release mechanism until bolt is locked firmly in forward position.

Safeties: (a) There is a heavy thumb catch on the left side of the pistol near the hammer. When this is horizontal the pistol may be cocked and fired. When it is pushed up as far as it will go the pistol is on "Safe." (b) As in automatic pistols generally, this weapon is fitted with an automatic disconnector which prevents more than one shot being fired at each pull of the trigger.

Loading and Firing

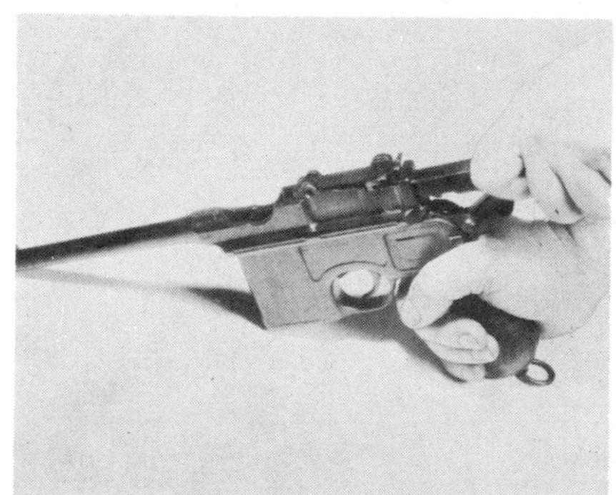

Grasp bolt wings firmly and draw bolt straight to the rear as far as it will go. The magazine follower will rise and hold the bolt open.

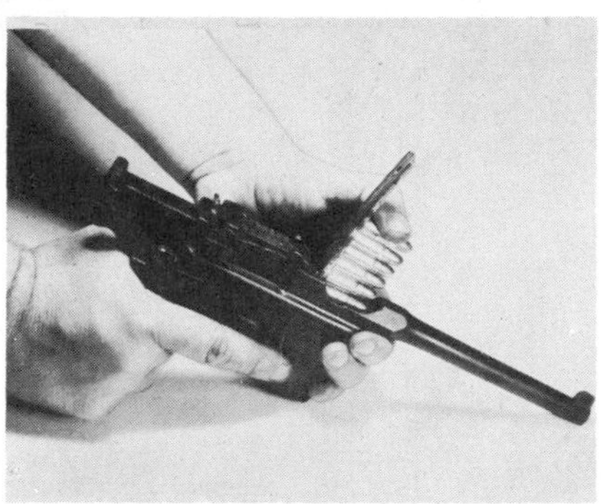

Now insert a loaded clip in the clip guide directly in front of the rear sight. Exert firm even pressure with thumb and strip cartridges down into the magazine.

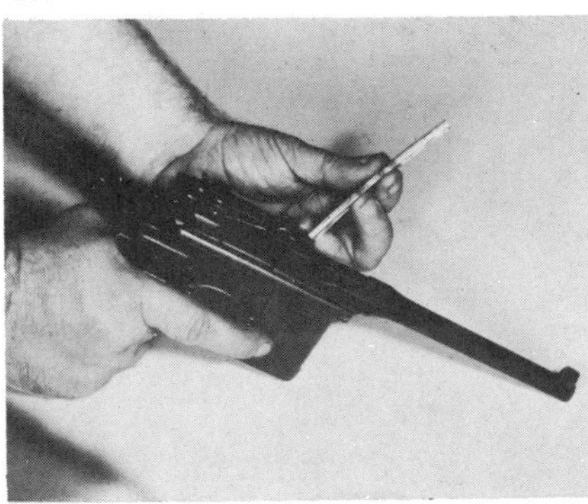

Now pull clip straight up out of pistol. The bolt will run forward and load the firing chamber the instant the clip is withdrawn.

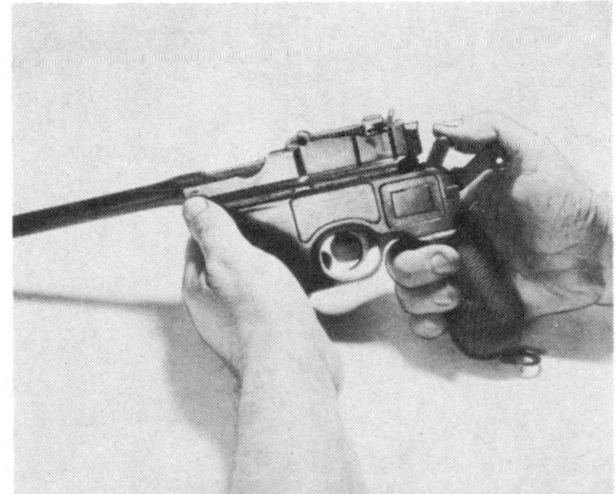

Unless pistol is to be fired immediately, set the thumb safety by rocking it forward as far as it will go. Thumb safety may be easily released by pulling back slightly on hammer and tilting pistol up and back.

Field Stripping

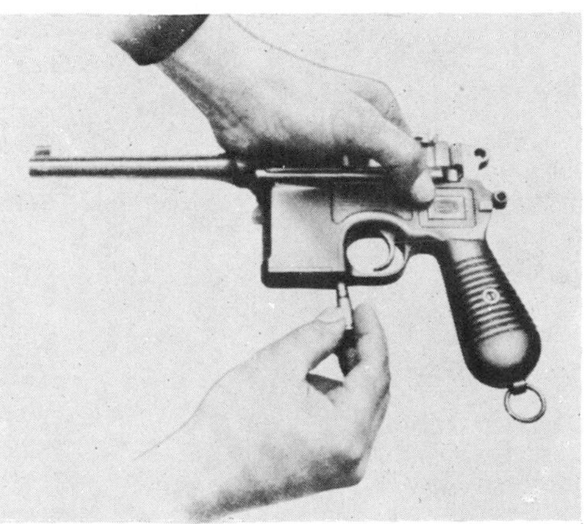

To dismount magazine: Insert nose of a bullet in hole in magazine base plate and push up lock stud. With tension thus removed, slide plate forward slightly. It may now be eased out together with magazine spring and magazine follower.

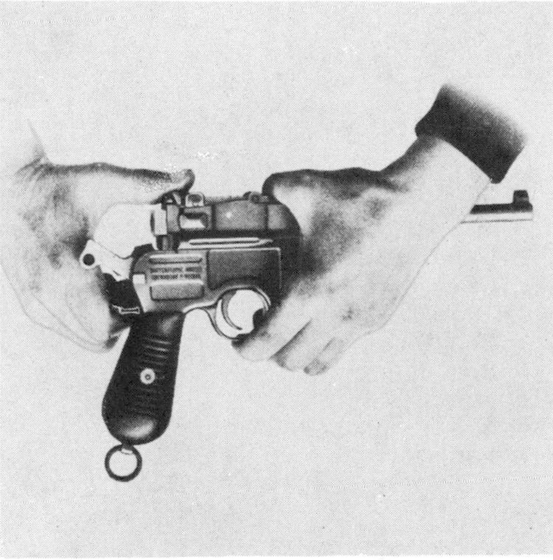

Cock the hammer. Using a cartridge clip, or screwdriver, press up the catch just below the base of the hammer and pull back barrel.

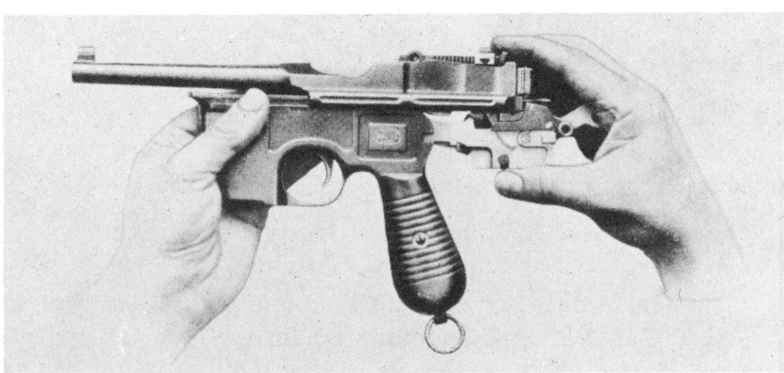

Now withdraw barrel, barrel extension, and hammer mechanism clear of the receiver.

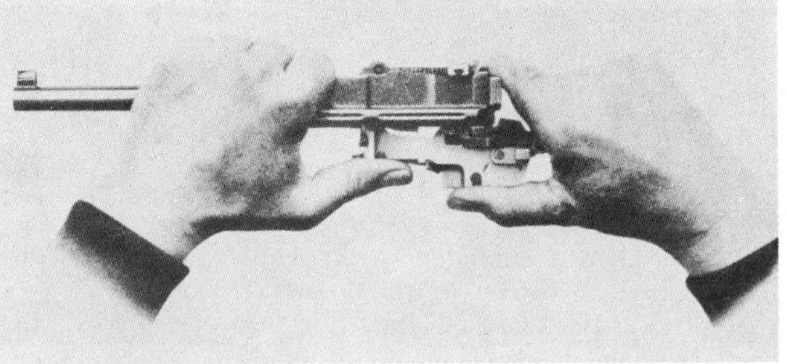

Lift hammer mechanism out of barrel extension.

Action Closed.

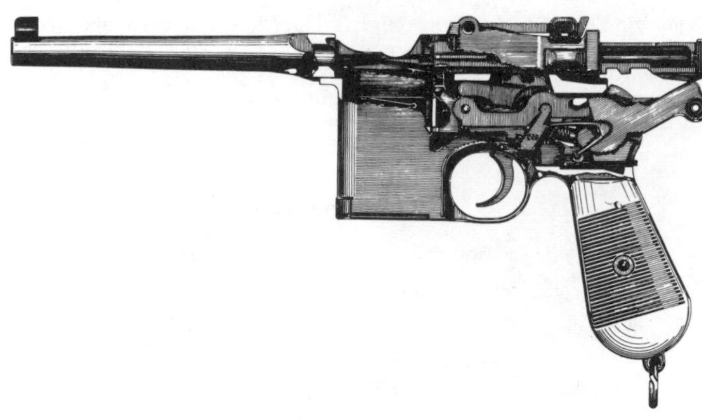

Action open and side cut away to show details of cocking mechanism.

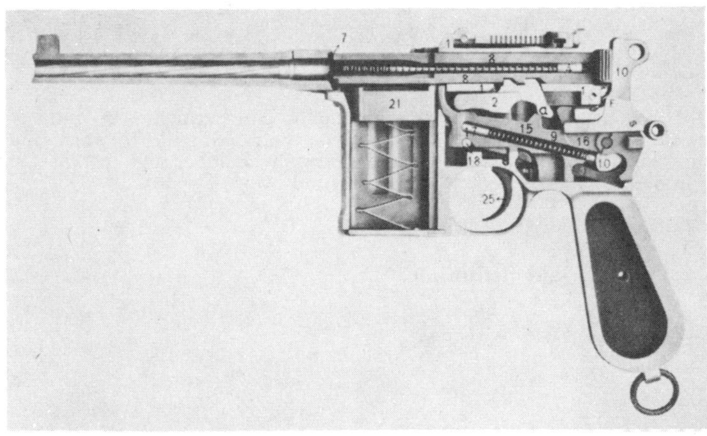

Pistol with Action in Full Forward Position.

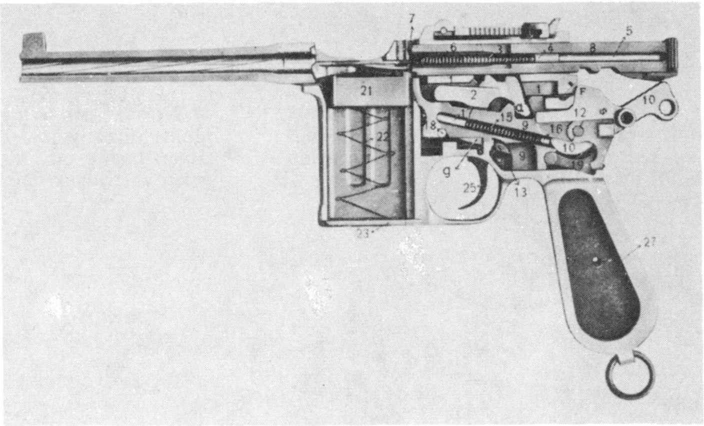

Pistol Open, Bolt Drawn Back, Ready for Loading.

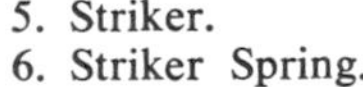

1. (front) Barrel.
1. (rear) Barrel extension.
2a. Bolt Lock.
3. Bolt Spring.
4. Bolt Spring Stop.
5. Striker.
6. Striker Spring.
7. Extractor.
8. Bolt.
9. Lock Frame.
10. Hammer.
12. (F-S) Safety.
13. Sear.
15. Mainspring.
16. Spring Bolt.
17. Rocker Plunger.
18. Coupling.
19. Lock Stop.
21. Magazine Follower.
22. Magazine Spring.
23. Magazine Bottom Plate.
25. Trigger.
27. Handle.

Use of the Mauser 7.63mm Automatic Pistol as a Carbine.

This pistol is usually issued in a wooden holster shaped so as to form a shoulder stock. The front end of this holster fastens rigidly to the lower end of the grip of the pistol. Because of the rifle-type design of the cartridge and its special ballistics, this weapon makes a very efficient carbine. Its penetration is very great indeed.

Mauser Military Pistol Designed for 9mm Parabellum Cartridge

Special models of this pistol manufactured during the first World War are encountered throughout Europe and Asia bored to take the 9mm Parabellum (Luger) cartridge. Such pistols will customarily have a large figure 9 carved into the stock which is usually painted red.

Caliber 9mm Mauser

Although this caliber is no longer manufactured, cartridges are available and there are thousands of the pistols in use. Many were exported to South America, Turkey, and the Balkans after World War I. This 9mm Mauser cartridge is a straight-cased cartridge whose overall length is .21″ longer than the standard Luger cartridge. It will not chamber in weapons designed to handle the Luger-type cartridge. However, in certain 9mm Mauser models, the shorter Luger ammunition may function fairly well, although it is always susceptible to serious jams.

German Mauser 7.65mm (.32 ACP) Automatic M1910.

This pistol requires a fuller description than most of the small pocket type pistols found in military use, because of its widespread popularity throughout Europe, and because it has several features which make it dangerous to handle unless the pistol is understood.

Magazine catch is in the bottom of the butt and must be pushed back to release the magazine. Magazine will hold 8 cartridges.

When loaded magazine has been inserted in handle, slide is drawn fully to the rear exactly as in the case of the Colt automatic pistol and then permitted to run

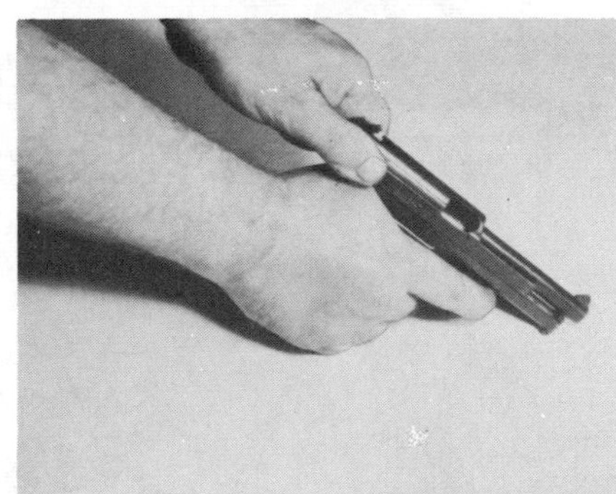

forward under the influence of the compressed recoil spring. The indicator pin protrudes from the rear of the breech block when the pistol is cocked, giving warning that weapon is dangerous.

Pressing down on the milled thumb catch on the left side of the pistol, just back of the trigger, sets the pistol at "safe." To release this safety, press in the small button directly below the thumb piece.

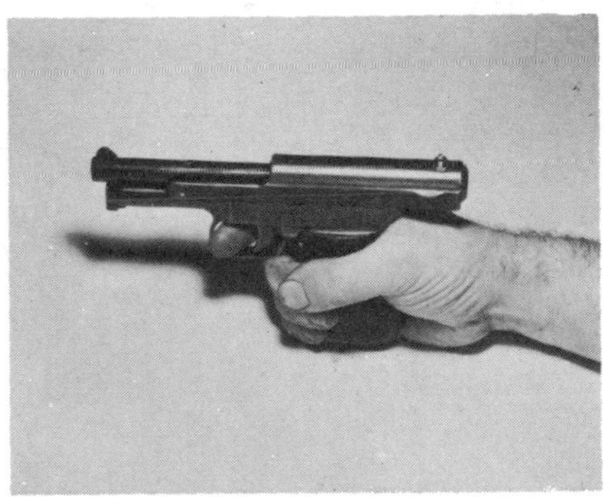

Warning. When the action is open and a magazine whether loaded or unloaded is inserted into the handle, the slide runs home immediately upon the magazine being seated. Should your finger be on the trigger when the slide goes forward unexpectedly, a cartridge may be fired. On the other hand, if the chamber is loaded, but there is no magazine in the handle, the trigger cannot be pulled. This feature acts as a safety.

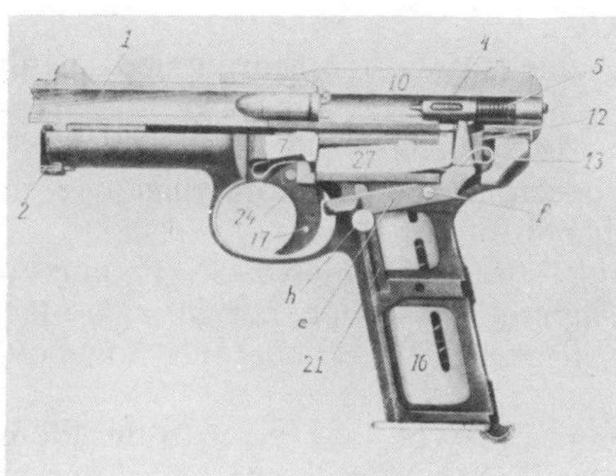

Safety in Position and Chamber Loaded.

1. Barrel.
2. Barrel Retainer.
4. Striker.
5. Striker Spring.
7. Interceptor.
10. Breech Cover (or Slide).
11. Recoil Spring.
12. Ejector.
13. Double Action Spring.
16. Magazine.
17. Trigger.
21. Safety lock spring.
24. Trigger Catch.
27. Sear.

e. Thumb Safety Bar.
f. Safety Pivot Pin.
h. Safety Release Button.

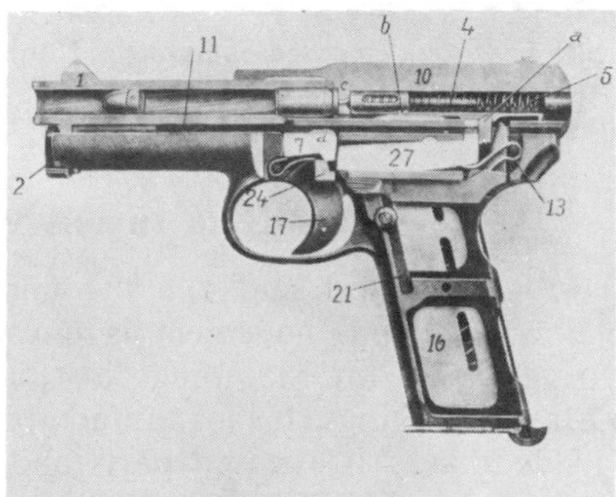

Pistol Fired, Parts Still Locked.

German Mauser Caliber 7.65mm Model H SC.

Caliber: 7.65mm Browning (.32 Colt Automatic Pistol).
Magazine: Box type, single line.
Capacity: 8 cartridges.
Muzzle Velocity: Standard for this cartridge.
Striking Energy: Standard for this cartridge.
Barrel Length: 3⅜ inches.
Overall Length: 6½ inches.
Weight: 20.63 ounces.
Locked: Unlocked, a straight blowback design.
Safety: Thumb safety on left side of slide.
Magazine Release Catch: On bottom of grip.
Slide: Stays open when pistol is empty. Goes forward when magazine is withdrawn and reinserted whether loaded or empty.
Special Feature: Exposed hammer. Double action movement, permitting the hammer to be rolled back and tripped by direct trigger pressure in the event of a misfire.

Special Note on this Pistol

This is the latest and one the finest Mauser designs. The double action movement is unusually good, though the trigger bars are stampings instead of the customary fine Mauser forgings. It is manufactured this way to speed up production. All exposed parts and surfaces are up to the customary Mauser high standard. The weapon has been streamlined to make it an excellent instinctive pointing pistol.

Loading and Firing

The slide is pulled back its full length to cock the hammer and permit the magazine spring to force a cartridge up to the feed way. This movement also cocks the hammer. Releasing the slide permits the recoil spring, which is wrapped around the barrel, to pull the slide forward and load the firing chamber.

When the last shot has been fired, the magazine follower holds the slide open as a notice. When the magazine is removed, and then reinserted, the slide goes forward automatically.

A positive magazine safety is incorporated in this weapon. When the magazine is withdrawn the trigger cannot be pulled.

A positive disconnector prevents more than one shot being fired for each pull of the trigger.

The action, being a straight blowback, permits the weapon to be of comparatively simple design, as no locking mechanism is necessary to shoot this low-power cartridge.

The exposed hammer may be lowered with the thumb. When it is necessary to fire, a pull on the trigger will function the hammer in the same general way that it does in a double action revolver.

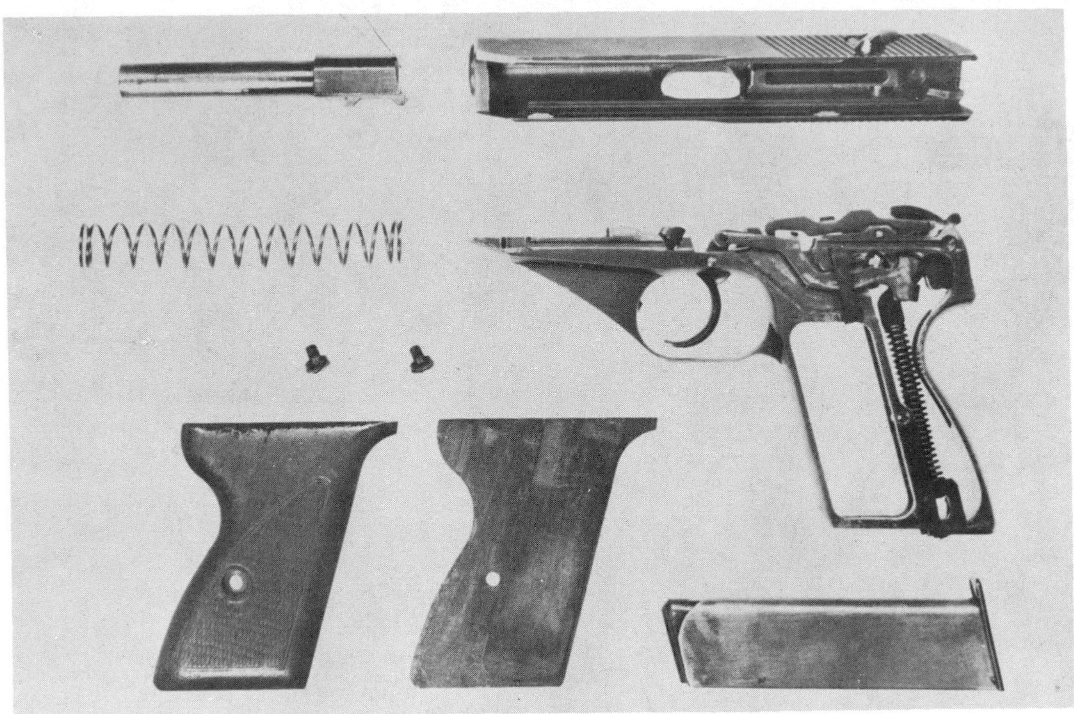

Field Stripping

Push the small spring supported piece inside the triggerguard directly in front of the trigger. While maintaining this pressure, push the slide forward a short distance.

Move the slide slightly backward. It may then be lifted up and off the receiver.

The barrel may be pushed forward against tension of the recoil spring and lifted up and out of the slide.

Removing the stock screws and lifting off the stocks exposes the firing mechanism for complete attention.

German Sauer Caliber 7.65mm Automatic Pistol.

Caliber: 7.65mm Browning (.32 Colt Automatic Pistol).
Magazine: Box type, single line.
Capacity: 8 cartridges.
Muzzle Velocity: Standard for this cartridge.
Striking Energy: Standard for this cartridge.
Barrel Length: 3⅜ inches.
Overall Length: 6½ inches.
Weight: About 22 ounces.
Locked: Unlocked, straight blowback.
Safety: Thumb piece on left side of slide.
Magazine Release Catch: Button on left side of receiver behind triggerguard.
Slide: Stays open when pistol is empty. Goes forward when magazine is withdrawn.
Special Feature: Cocking and uncocking lever on left side of receiver above magazine catch. This is a double action automatic pistol.

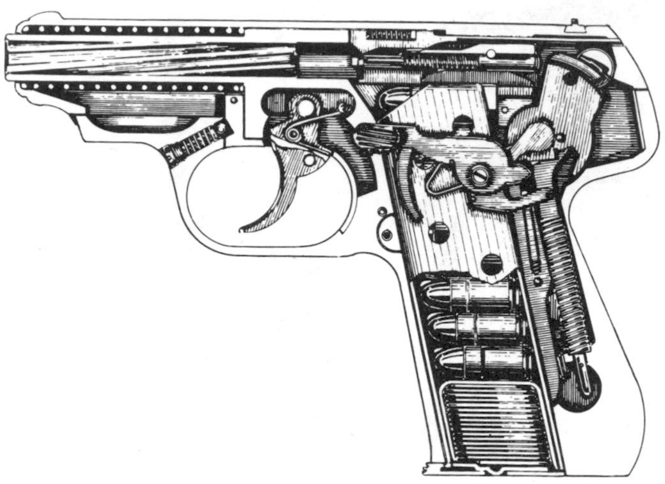

Action Closed.

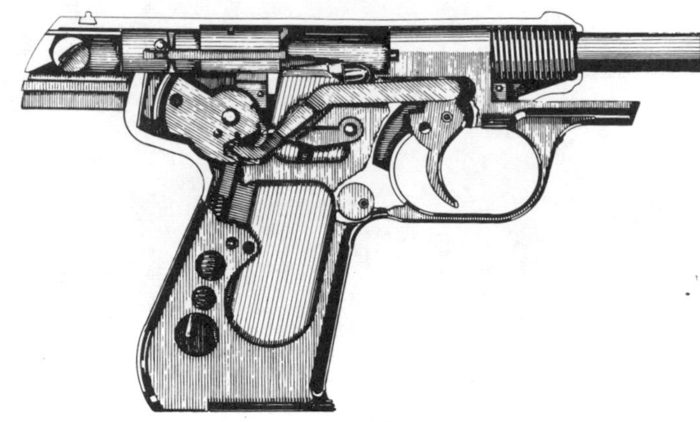

Action Open.

Field Stripping

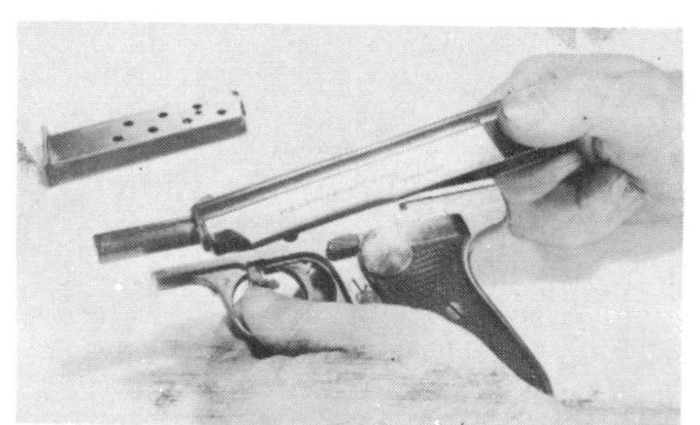

Pull down the locking latch in front and above the trigger. Draw the slide back to its full extent lifting upward as you draw.

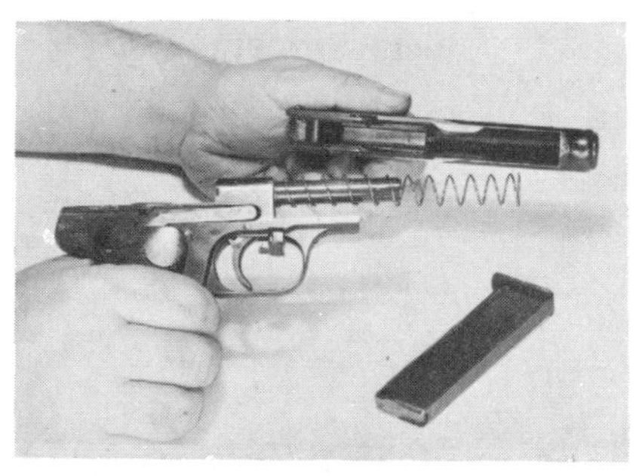

Let the disengaged slide move forward and push it off the barrel.

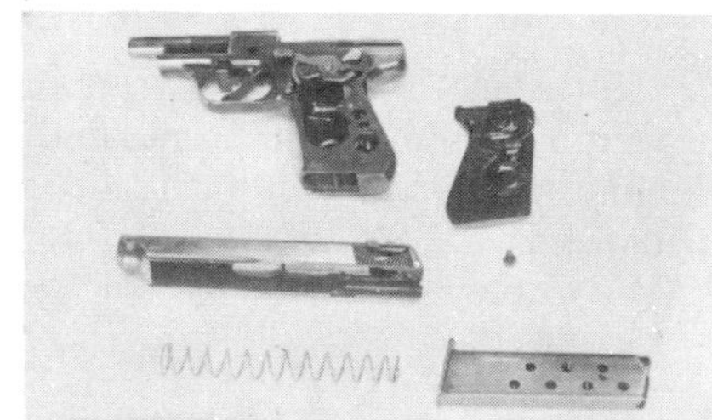

Recoil spring may be drawn off the barrel. Removing the grips exposes all working parts for attention. No further stripping need be done.

Special Note on this Pistol

This is the most advanced form of pocket pistol in the world today. It combines all the good features of other pocket pistols with a set of new designs which point the way to development in this field.

It is included here as a military pistol because of its very wide use by staff officers and air corps personnel in the former German Wehrmacht.

It is noteworthy that this weapon was being manufactured during the course of a war.

The balance and pointing factors have been given particular attention. The top of the slide is ribbed and checked as an aid in quick sighting. Detachable radium sights are sometimes provided to be snapped on over the front sight for use in dusk or night conditions.

When the magazine is removed, the weapon cannot be fired. This is a safety feature designed to prevent accidental discharge when the weapon is being cleaned.

The thumb safety not only blocks the hammer when it is applied, but pushes it back out of engagement with the sear.

The double action firing system is by far the best developed up to this time. It utilizes a minimum of springs and is entirely enclosed.

One of the very unique features is an exposed cocking lever which does not move with the action. When the weapon has been loaded and cocked by a movement of the slide, pressing down on this lever will safely lower the hammer so that a cartridge may be carried in the firing chamber in complete safety. Pulling straight through on the trigger will cock and trip the hammer to fire the cartridge. However, pressure on the cocking lever will also recock the hammer should it be desirable to take more deliberate aim.

All movement starting with a firing of the cartridge is accomplished in the standard automatic pistol fashion by the recoil. The barrel being rigidly sweated into the receiver gives a maximum of accuracy.

Walther PPK. The PP is the same but larger.

WALTHER PISTOLS. Models 1 and 2 (1908 and 1909) are elementary blowback Vest Pocket Pistols using the .25 Colt Auto cartridges. Internal striker firing units. Detachable box magazines. Thumb safeties but no grip or other automatic safeties.

Model 3 (1909) is a blowback for the .32 Colt Auto cartridge. Ejection is through a left side port.

Model 4 (1910) is a longer version of Model 3. It was the first Walther police type pistol.

Model 5 (1913) is a streamlined quality Vest Pocket pistol for the .25 Colt Auto cartridge. Ejects to right. No grip safety.

Model 6 (1915) is an obsolete heavy pistol for the 9mm Luger cartridge. This is a blowback pistol with heavy spring. It was not used in quantity. Unless it is in good condition, continued use of the powerful 9mm Luger ammunition may injure the pistol, usually jamming the slide back. Internal hammer construction; recoil spring around barrel.

Model 7 (1917) is a pocket pistol version of the Model 6 designed for the .32 Colt Auto cartridges.

Model 8 (1920) is a streamlined pocket pistol for the .25 Colt Auto cartridge. Internal hammer construction. Recoil spring around barrel. A precision built arm.

Model 9 (1921) is a modern version of the Model 1. It somewhat resembles the Browning outlines, has recoil spring below barrel, and is striker fired. Caliber .25 Colt Auto.

Evaluation. Walther pistols before War I were good commercial arms of their types. After War I they were precision built and among the world's finest of their types. World War II manufacture deteriorated after 1944.

Ammunition. As indicated above.

WALTHER MODELS PP (1929) AND PPK (1931): These pistols were widely used during World War II. They differ in exterior details and in weights and lengths only. The common forms are in 7.65mm (.32 Colt Auto) caliber, though they were also made for the .22 Long Rifle and the .380 Colt Auto cartridges on a production basis; and for the .25 Colt Auto and the Pistole 08 (9mm Luger) cartridge on an experimental basis.

Characteristics of PP Model. Length 6.9″. Barrel 3.8″. Weight about 23 oz. Capacity 8 in .32 caliber; 7 in .380 caliber.

Designation PP means Police Pistol. This was a standard police arm.

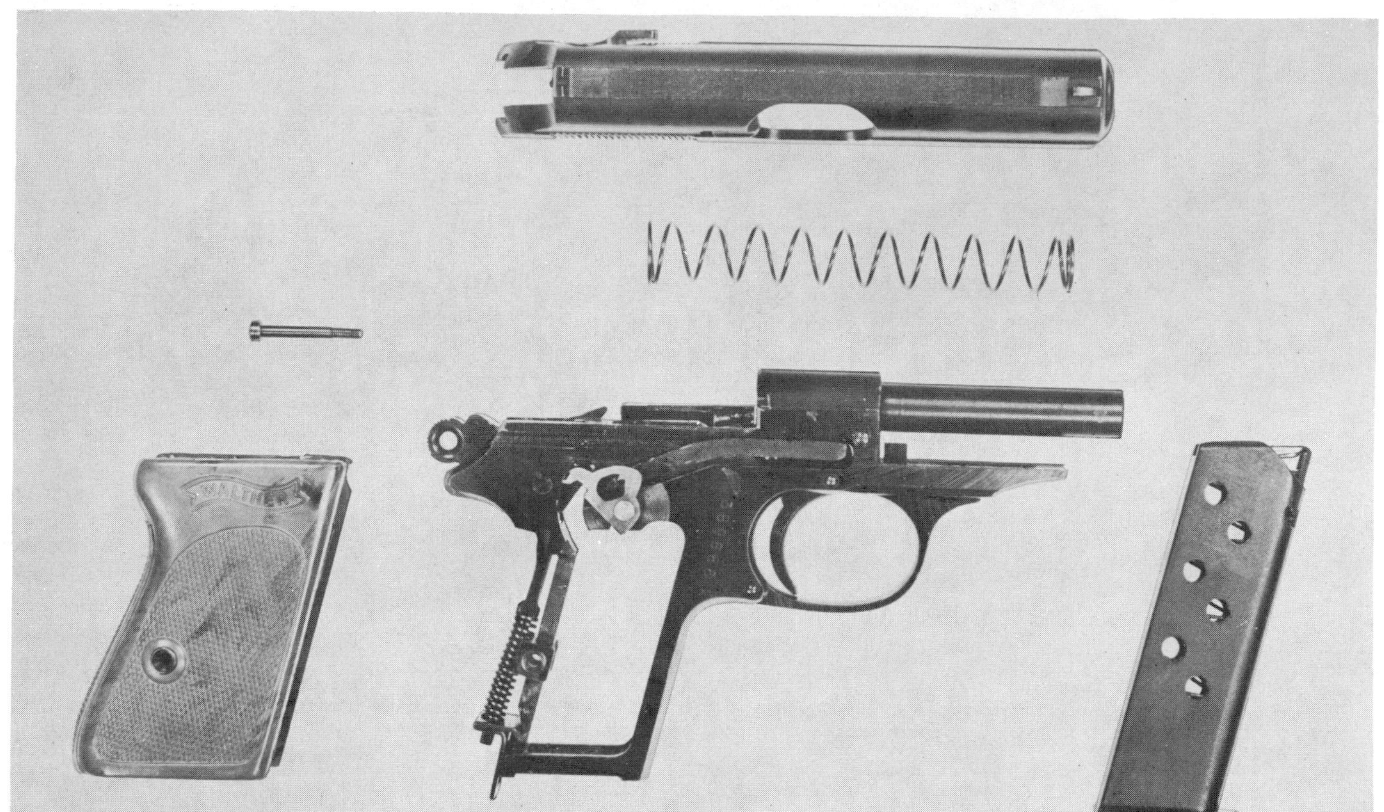

PPK Field Stripped. Hammer is cocked. Pull on trigger will draw trigger bar ahead to disengage sear from hammer. Pulling triggerguard down lowers slide locking lug seen under barrel.

Characteristics of PPK Model. Length 5.8″. Barrel 3.25″. Weight 19 oz. Capacity 7.

Designation PPK means Polizei Pistole Kriminall, indicating a short concealable model for detectives, as opposed to the longer PP which was intended as a belt pistol.

Description. These are blowback pistols of most advanced design. External hammers, double action triggers, positive manual safeties.

The recoil spring is positioned around the barrel. When the slide is drawn back over the top of a loaded magazine in standard automatic pistol fashion, the rear of the slide runs over and cocks the hammer. The recoil spring is compressed between a shoulder in the front end of the shaped slide (which surrounds the barrel muzzle) and the receiver abutment into which the barrel is secured. Releasing the slide permits the spring to pull it forward. The breechblock face of the slide chambers a cartridge from the top of the magazine. The extractor claw in the right side of the breechblock is snapped into cartridge engagement by its spring.

Pulling the trigger will cause an attached trigger bar to draw the sear out of engagement with the hammer to fire the cartridge.

When the chamber is loaded, the front end of a floating pin in the slide is raised. The rear end of the pin projects from the rear of the slide. If this pin can be seen or felt, the chamber is loaded.

Safety Systems. A special hammer block of steel prevents any forward hammer movement until the trigger is deliberately pulled. When the trigger bar pulls the upper section of the rotating sear, a nose on the sear raises the hammer block until it is opposite a cut in the hammer face. Only at this point can the hammer fall far enough to hit the firing pin.

The firing pin is the spring-controlled flying type which is shorter than the length of its stroke. Its spring pulls it back into the breechblock as soon as its forward drive is halted.

The rearward thrust of the gas within the cartridge case drives the slide to the rear to extract and eject and reload in standard blowback fashion.

Disconnector. The opening movement of the slide runs over and forces down a section of the trigger bar. This disconnects the trigger bar from effective sear contact. Until the trigger is released permitting the spring to force it ahead into firing position, the trigger bar attached to the trigger cannot rise into a slide undercut. Only when it can rise in this undercut can the trigger bar tip draw the sear out of engagement to let the hammer fall.

Thus one pull is necessary for each shot fired.

Manual Safety. A thumb piece projects from the left side of the slide. When the hammer is down, if this safety is turned it will bring a steel face between the hammer and the head of the striker and will lock the sear so that the trigger cannot be pulled far enough to raise and drop the hammer.

If the thumbpiece is turned while the hammer is

cocked, the safety face will come between the hammer and the firing pin, and the safety arm will then trip the sear to let the hammer fall on the steel safety. Note that this differs entirely from the P-38 design, in which the pin is locked, but the hammer hits the pin head.

WALTHER MODEL MP. This is an oversized PP Model using the 9mm Luger cartridge. Very few were manufactured, as the makers concluded that the Luger cartridge power warranted a locked breech design.

Variations. All the foregoing models have minor variants. Styles of grips, types of stocks, lengths and weights, and types of magazine release may vary. Dozens of experimental changes were made in these pistols. None are of particular importance except to the most rabid collector.

Identification. The unusual safety system identifies these pistols.

Takedown. Takedown system is also unusual. Pulling down the triggerguard, which is hinged at the rear to the receiver, unlocks the slide. Pulling the slide back and lifting its rear end frees it from the slide runners. It and the recoil spring may then be eased forward over the barrel.

Evaluation. Excellent to fair depending upon period of manufacture. Safety system is perhaps too embracing. In its commercial forms this is one of the world's best accepted pistols.

The .22 caliber version in particular is one of the most desirable pocket designs ever created, and will undoubtedly be imitated in eventual American design.

Ammunition. As indicated above.

EXPERIMENTAL WALTHER PISTOLS. These cover a vast range. The most interesting is the hammerless (enclosed hammer) Armee Pistole. This is an enclosed hammer version of the HP, caliber 9mm Luger. The production did not pass 200. Some types were made with duralumin receivers and slides for lighter weight.

Individual models of freak turning-barrel and blowback types have turned up. These are too numerous and unimportant to deal with here.

EXPERIMENTAL MAUSER PISTOLS. Mauser offered a complicated locked-breech pistol for tests at the time of the adoption of the P-38 pistol by Germany. Known as the HSv model, this arm was never produced. From available records there seem to have been only a few specimens hand made. Much publicity has been given to the sole known HSv to reach here, and it should be noted that while this is a valuable collector's piece, it has no practical place as a successful arm. It is entirely in the freak category.

Like every other manufacturer, Mauser maintained an experimental department which was constantly at work on new developments. Like European manufacturers generally, they also maintained an extensive collection of arms of competing manufacturers. Such competitors' products were often stamped with the familiar Mauser trademark as an indication of factory ownership.

Weapons in these classifications are very rare collector's items. Any attempt to describe or picture them here would be prohibitive, since the author's own collection of data and photographs could easily fill 400 pages; and the data would have no practical value from a design or use standpoint.

OTHER GERMAN POCKET PISTOLS. (1) Dreyse, Heim, Helfricht, Kaba, Kobra, Kommer, Langenhan, Lignose, Lilliput, Mann, Melior, Menta, Menz, Ortgies, Simson, Stock, Stosel, Zehna.

.25 caliber Auto pistols made by the above firms or under those trade names. They were fair to excellent quality.

(2) Beholla, Dreyse, DWM, Nordheim, Jager, Kebler, Langenhan, Leonhardt, Mann, Melior, Menz, Ortgies, Rheinmetall, and Stock.

.32 caliber Auto pistols made or trademarked by the above were fair to excellent quality.

(3) Mann and Ortgies.

Fair to good .380 caliber auto pistols.

S&S Vest Pocket, 6.35 mm. Type 1.

SAUER & SOHN 6.35MM PISTOLS. There are many slight variations in these designs. The common ones are pictured herewith.

The common WT or Vest Pocket Models (Type 1) somewhat resemble the conventional Browning design in external appearance. However they are rather more complicated in construction, though basically simpler to machine. Detachable box magazine holds six cartridges. These are elementary blowback pistols with internal striker firing mechanisms. Breechblocks are separate units carried in the slides. May be removed when slide is to the rear. Thumb safety on left side of receiver.

The two pictured are the common production forms for the 6.35mm cartridge (.25 A.C.P.)

M1914, which is larger and differently shaped, may be encountered with light weight duralumin slide and receiver.

Identification. Top of slide cut away at rear section of barrel. Separate breechblock in slide. Slide comes off to front when breechblock is removed. General Browning outline.

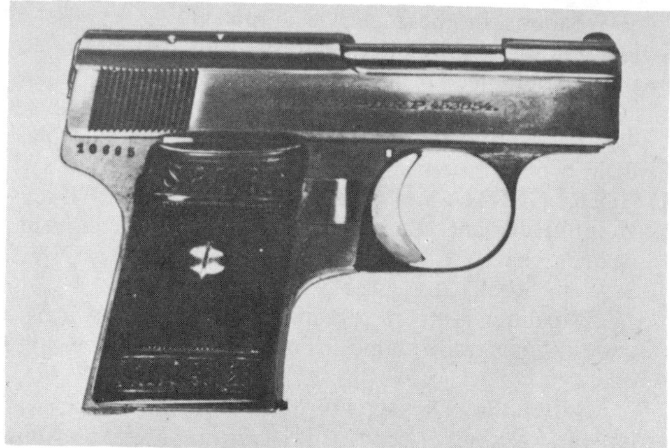

S&S Vest Pocket, 6.35mm. Type 1A.

Evaluation. Good quality, well made, Complicated design. No grip safety, an item which is desirable in a Vest Pocket pistol.

Ammunition. All Sauer & Sohn pistols for 6.35mm ammunition will take U. S. .25 Colt Auto cartridges.

S&S Pocket, 7.65mm. M1914.

SAUER & SOHN 7.65MM PISTOLS. There are three basic types in this caliber. Experimental types and variations with slightly different grips will be encountered.

MODEL 1914. Straight grip. Blowback design. Separate breechblock inserted in slide from rear. Cylindrical pattern slide. Recoil spring around barrel. Concealed striker firing mechanism. Detachable box magazine 7-shot capacity. Manual safety on left side of receiver. When slide is held back, safety may be turned to hold slide open. Pressing down on rear sight will permit breechblock to be unscrewed and withdrawn. Slide may then be released and moved forward off receiver.

BEHORDENMODELL. This is the same as the M1914 except for minor details. Grip, receiver and slide are streamlined. This pistol takes its name (Authority Model) from the fact that it was widely carried by police and military officials.

This design was also manufactured with light weight duralumin slide and receiver.

S&S Behordenmodell, 7.65mm.

Evaluation. Precision built arms. Construction comparatively complicated. Lightweight models should not be blued, as slide and receiver metal will corrode. No grip safety.

Double Action Model. This differs radically from all other S&S models. Instead of a separate breechblock, the rear of the slide forms the breechblock as in conventional Browning design.

Identification. Thumb safety on rear of slide. Thumb piece for cocking and uncocking on left side of receiver. Enclosed hammer. Special double action system.

Evaluation. Quality excellent to fair depending upon time of manufacture. Complicated by comparison with ordinary blowback pistol design, but embodies factors of safety and convenience which has forced a change in American pocket pistol design.

Thumb safety is a positive hammer block. Streamlined shape, light weight, and enclosed hammer are desirable pocket pistol features. This is the only production made enclosed hammer pistol on which the hammer may be safely lowered and carried with a cartridge in the chamber ready for instant firing by pulling the trigger. The factor of instant readiness coupled with relaxed springs is an important item.

Also made in a duralumin model. These pistols were realistically manufactured for average use where light weight is more important than long firing life, since the normal pocket pistol is seldom used.

Ammunition. .32 Colt Auto cartridges.

MAUSER VEST POCKET PISTOLS. There are two major forms, the WTP I and II. The Type II is a streamlined version of the original, and was introduced in 1919. These are elementary blowback pistols resembling the Browning types in general outline. Detachable box magazine holds seven cartridges. These are hammerless pistols with internal striker firing mechanisms. Caliber 6.35mm.

Evaluation. Well made of excellent materials. Compact and light. Have the disadvantage of not having an automatic grip safety.

Ammunition. .25 Colt Auto cartridges.

Note: A Pocket Pistol in 6.35mm caliber, Model 1910, holds eight cartridges in magazine. Mechanically this is the same as the 7.65mm pistol.

MAUSER POCKET PISTOLS. Several slight variants of these will be encountered. The basic form is the M. 1910 pictured and described earlier in this section.

The Neues Modell is a streamlined version of the 1910, differing in shape and pitch of grip.

Identification. Peculiar slide is cutaway just forward of ejection port on top, and has extending side arms. Front sight is on barrel. Striker firing mechanism. Recoil spring guide rod forms part of takedown system. Slide stays back when last shot is fired, but runs forward when magazine is released. Marked curve in grip near thumb position indicates new model. Two-part safety, consisting of a lever pushed down to apply, and a button pushed to release safety.

GERMAN SERVICE RIFLES AND CARBINES

The basic German infantry arm in World War II was the Kar. 98 k. The Kar. designation indicates "carbine," though the arm is really a short rifle. The designation "98" indicates year of adoption of the mechanical action. The "k" (for "kurz" short) indicates a shortened form of the original Kar. 98. Year of manufacture, such as "42" is often used in connection with the service designation. Code letters or numbers indicate point of manufacture.

All the general mechanical data given in chapter 19 for Belgian F.N. rifles and in chapter 22 for the Czech Model 1924 rifle applies to the German Mauser rifles and carbines in the Kar. 98k classification. Austria, Belgium, Czechoslovakia, Poland, Portugal, Spain, and Yugoslavia all manufactured rifles on this system.

Germany utilized wherever possible the weapons of every country she overran. Weapons were modified to take the standard German 7.9mm cartridge. This procedure resulted in a tremendous number of minor modifications.

Moreover, as the war developed and Germany's position and manufacture deteriorated, all early forms of obsolete and obsolescent weapons were brought into service.

In the closing days of the war the Germans produced a long line of experimental arms, made from castings or stampings, in order to speed up production.

This section is presented as a detailed coverage of all major forms and modifications of rifles and carbines used by the Germans. Hundreds of experimental weapons appeared in such small quantity that cataloging them would serve no good purpose. Any arm used in quantity is in the following list.

The photographs of training rifles show at a glance the story of one of the most ambitious rifle training systems ever devised to make a nation war conscious and to train military riflemen.

It will be noted that the length, sights, overall appearance, slings, stacking rods, and bolts on all these rifles are essentially similar. The weights too are practically identical. Yet these arms—though all military in intent—are not all of military caliber.

The first rifle is an air rifle specially designed by the Germans to give basic training to youths and recruits. This arm uses a special 4.5mm lead slug and is fitted with a 5-shot magazine—the same capacity as their standard military rifle. When the magazine is inserted the bolt is lifted and manipulated exactly as in the mili-

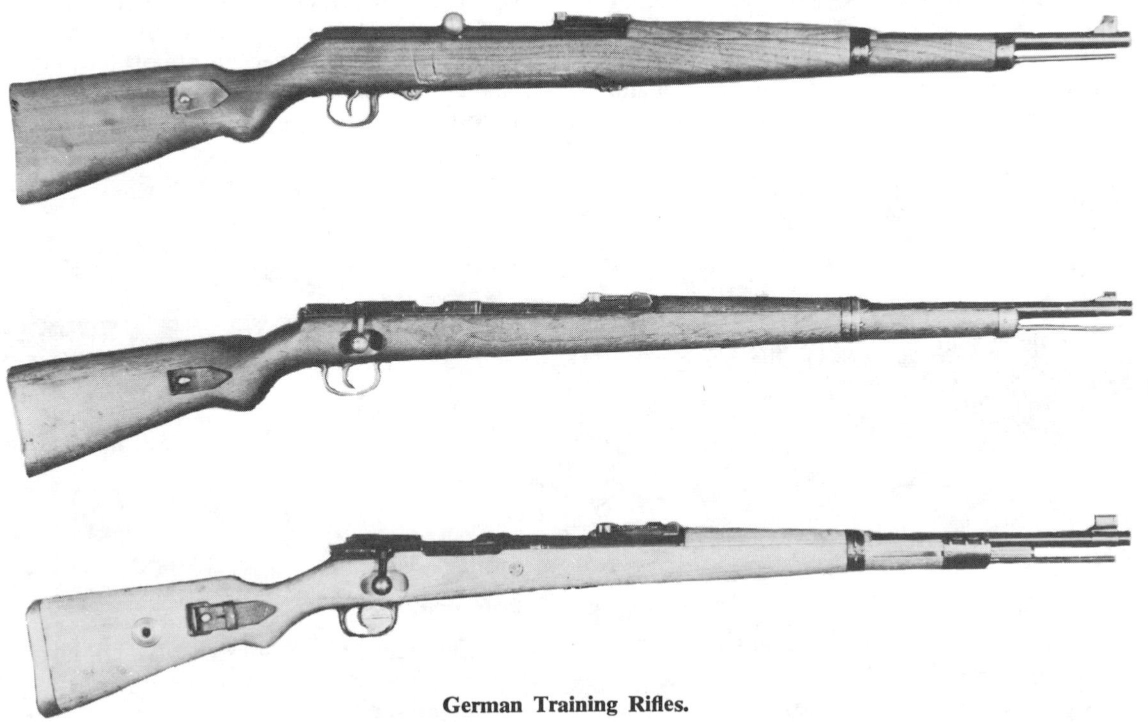

German Training Rifles.

tary arm. The safety is applied in the same manner. The sights, although adapted only to short distances, of course, function exactly as in the big brother. In short this rifle can be used to teach the entire theory of drilling, sighting, loading, and firing which will later be used in handling the Military Mauser, the Kar. 98k.

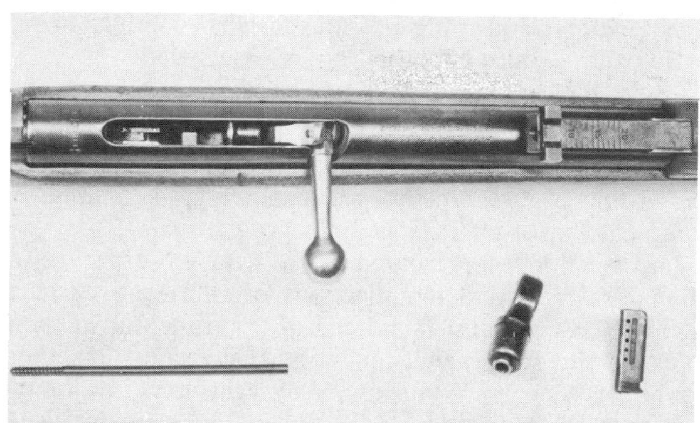

Military Air Rifle Trainer.

Top view of breech section. Note that bolt is manipulated exactly as in the Mauser. Stacking rod (for military drill use), muzzle cap, and 5-shot magazine are shown below. Note that rear sight is Mauser type, as is the safety.

The second rifle marks the next step in the training of a military rifleman as distinguished from a sporting rifleman. This arm shoots the .22 Long Rifle cartridge. Here the neophyte is introduced to the use of ball ammunition. The bolt is practically the same as that in the Mauser and the takedown system is identical. The sights again are purely the military type and are not designed for sporting or target shooting; they have just one purpose—to teach the user how to handle the Mauser!

All the great rifle manufacturers of Germany—notably Mauser, Walther, Haenel and Henschow—were mass producing .22 caliber rifles both single shot and magazine types of this same trainer design. These firms also manufactured standard types of .22 rifles for legitimate target and sporting use; but their emphasis once the Nazis came into power was entirely on military trainers.

These rifles indicate graphically the training system employed by the Germans and adopted to some degree by both the Italians and the Japanese.

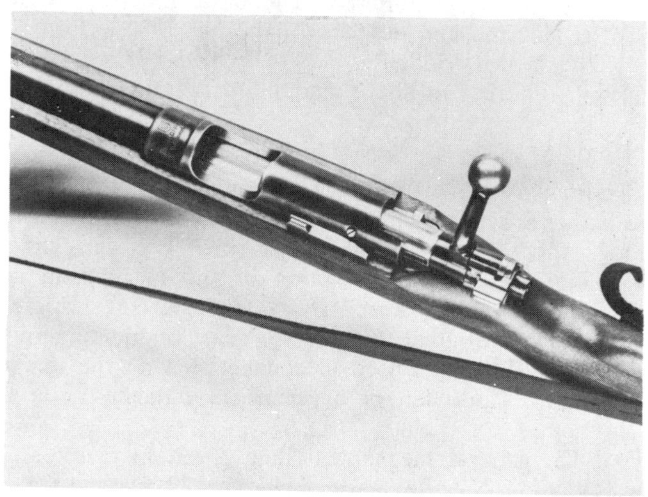

Military .22 Cal. Trainer.

Top view with bolt open. Note that Mauser-type bolt and bolt release stop are features of this design.

The third rifle is the famous German Army rifle—the Kar. 98k. This particular specimen was manufactured in 1944. Its weight, length, balance, and general principles are entirely familiar to anyone who has used the two trainers. It should be emphasized that these are not unusual or hand-picked specimens. Air rifles of the design shown are entirely unlike air rifles made for sport or target use. They were manufactured by at least six firms in Germany during the period between World Wars I and II. At first they were employed as a subterfuge to give military training in violation of the Treaty of Versailles. Later they played an important part in the general teaching of the theory of military rifles for military purposes.

German Gew. 71, Short Rifle.

This is a single shot turn bolt action, cal. 11mm (.433). This was the first production model Mauser rifle. The bolt is of 2-piece design and has a removable head, unlike all later German Mauser designs which have solid heads. (Made as both rifle and carbine.)

Ammunition. Not made in U. S.

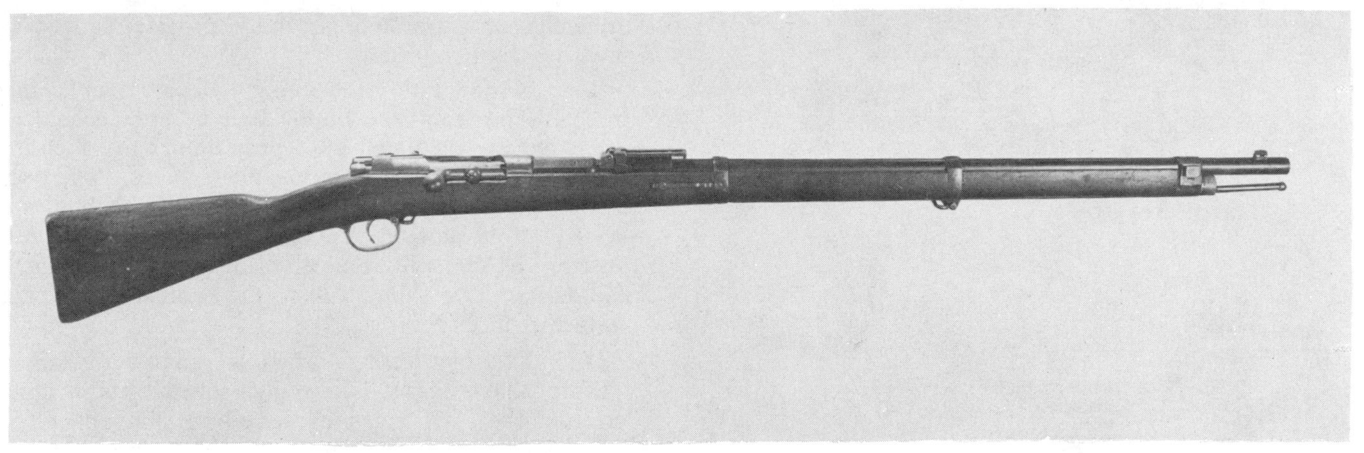

German Gew. 71/84.

This is the 71 modified and fitted with a magazine tube below the barrel in the forestock. It is loaded through an open action. Capacity eight cartridges. Many of these receivers were used to make shotguns.

Ammunition. Same as Model 71 above.

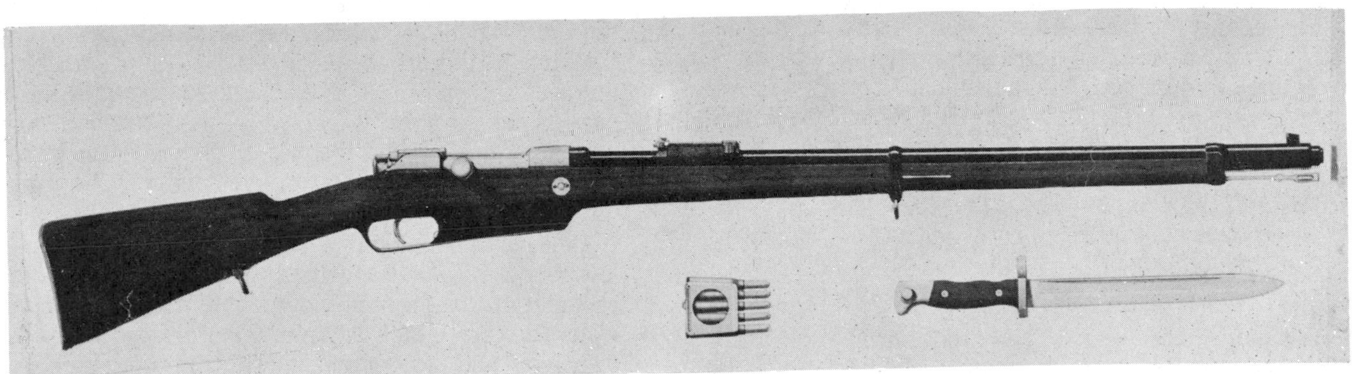

German Gew. 88.

This is neither a Mauser nor a Mannlicher. It was officially adopted in 1888 after being developed by a German Military Commission. It was listed as M. 88 or Mauser and Commission.

Our best authority on this rifle, which has long been the subject of misconceptions, is L. Loewe & Co. of Berlin. This firm made the first 500,000 Model 1888's though the design was later made at all the German arsenals and by several private firms, notably Haenel and Schilling. Loewe was a partner in the Mauser firm and was one of the founders of the Belgian F.N. works before the beginning of the present century.

Loewe catalogs of the early 90's, at which time the firm was the largest manufacturer of official German rifles, state that the bolt mechanism of the Model 1888 was evolved by the Army Commission from the Mauser 71 bolt; and that the magazine system was improved by the same Commission from Mannlicher's patents. Mannlicher clips up to that time could be inserted only one end up. The M. 1888 was the first to permit insertion from either end.

The 1888 introduced also the first of the series of German official 7.9mm rifle cartridges. Bullets, primers, and propellants have been improved with the years, but the basic case dimensions remain the same. Pressures as given at time of introduction of the first cartridge are unreliable. Pressure testing techniques then in use have been superseded.

Forms of the Model 1888

Original Gewehr. This type has a barrel jacket. Length about 49″. Barrel 30″. Weight 8.4 lbs. Magazine system uses 5-shot Mannlicher type clip, modified. Bolt handle projects at right angle.

Original Kar. No jacket. No bayonet mounting. 18″ barrel. Forestock almost to muzzle. Stacking hook. Turn down flat bolt handle.

Modified Gew. and Kar. After the official adoption of the Gew. 98, the 1888's were sold for commercial distribution. Many were modified to use Mauser magazines. Many were altered to sporters by altering stocks and changing calibers. It is not possible to catalog the varieties. After World War I in particular huge numbers of rebuilt or remodelled 1888's were imported to the U. S. Some of these are loosely known as Haenel-Mausers, Haenel-Mannlichers, Schilling-Mausers and Schilling-Mannlichers because the receivers bore the stamp of the original manufacturer and magazines were in the one case modified and in the other original.

M1888 Sectioned to Show Locking, Firing, and Magazine Systems. Magazine Loaded. Bolt Head is Detachable. Note Relation of Locking Lug Seats in Relation to Face of Breech. Note Magazine Follower Driving Cartridges up between Clip Walls. This is the Mannlicher Clip System.

The quality of these rifles varies greatly. Scores of accidents were reported from use of 1918 type German ammunition. On the other hand many experimenters reported them as thoroughly safe and dependable rifles, although the pointed bullet ammunition in German service use in 1918 was ballistically better than the type for which the 1888 was originally designed; and bullet diameter was larger.

Safety Factors of the Models 1888

The Weapons. The U. S. made the mistake of using brittle steel in the early Springfield manufacture, and in recent years these rifles have given much trouble when used with high velocity loads. The Germans from the first used low carbon steels. While use will result in bolt "set-back" more quickly with steels which "give," the danger of sudden blowout without warning is not nearly as great as with steels which will shatter. The condition of the fired cases and the difficulty of extraction generally provide danger signals in German rifles.

The M1888 bolt head being a separate unit, theoretically the front end of the bolt is not mechanically as strong as the later 98 types, though it is entirely satisfactory for any recommended loads. There are strong dual lugs at the forward end of the bolt body to give firm support. The handle, which locks down in front of the split receiver bridge, is a safety factor.

Ammunition. Two things add to the confusion of dealing with cartridges for the 1888.

(1) Pressure testing varied so greatly in the last century that it is possible to give several sets of figures for the same cartridge as tested in different places. The figure generally given by the best authorities with methods in use about 1900 is about 47,000 foot pounds. On the other hand, the pressures listed by British ICI for the current cartridge with 227-grain round-nosed bullet and essentially the original ballistics average 15.5 British Tons (34,875 foot pounds). U. S. manufacturers do not release pressure figures.

(2) Powder technology has advanced greatly since the introduction of the Model 1888. It is possible to produce the ballistics of the old loads with smaller charges of progressive burning powders and lower pressures. Conversely, loading to the pressures as originally given from early testing methods may be dangerous.

German manufacturers advocated the use of much lower powered loads in the 88 than in the 98. American and British ammunition manufacturers developed loads for the so-called "8mm Mauser" based on their own tests and on complaints from users. These average about 35-40,000 foot pounds. Unless an 88 rifle has been checked and proofed to higher loads, it is recommended that the advice of the ammunition makers be followed.

Commercially made in U. S. as 8mm Mauser (7.9mm). Modern German Service ammunition will chamber but is not recommended.

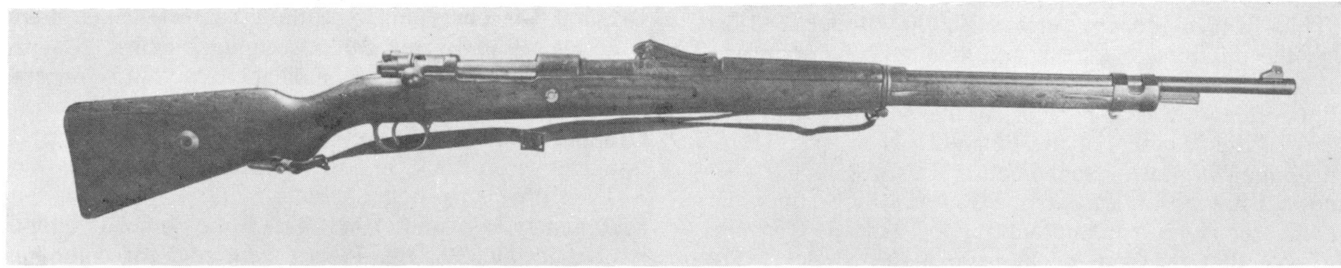

Gewehr 98.

GEW. 98. This is the early form of the later German Service rifle. Length 49.25″. Barrel 29.15″. Weight 9.5 lbs. Caliber 7.9mm (nominal designation). The round nosed bullet used in the 1888 was retained for use in the first forms of the Gew. 98. Most Gew. 98's were rebored in 1905 for a larger diameter bullet. Bolt handle is straight.

This design used the clip loading system developed by Mauser for the Belgian 1889, the flush staggered magazine he developed for the Spanish 1893, and an improved bolt. The Belgian and Spanish rifles had solid one-piece bolts with dual front locking lugs. The 98 bolt added the third rear (safety) lug.

The bushed hole in stock was added in 1916.

GEW. 98 Modified. Same as 98 except for a tangent leaf rear sight.

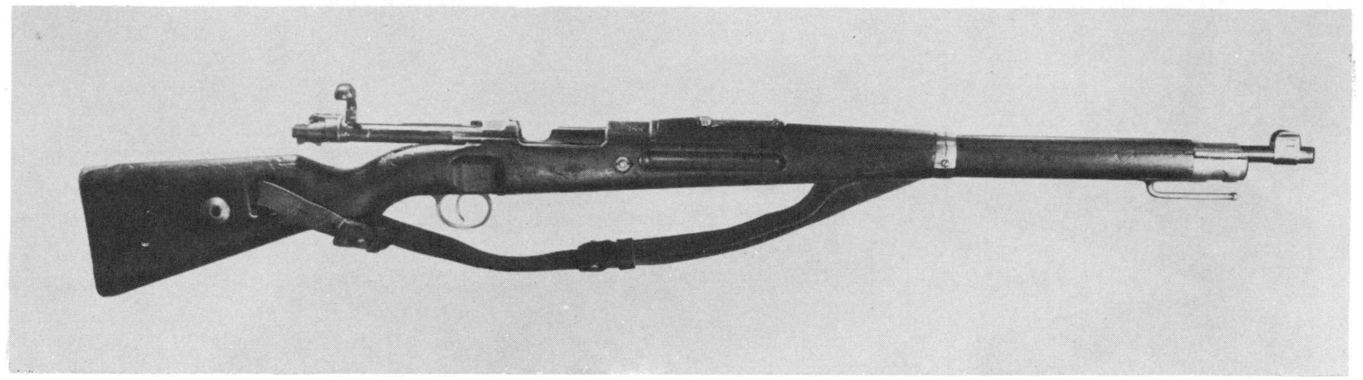

Kar. 98a.

KAR. 98 (Original). This was the Cavalry version of the Gew. 98. Barrel 18″. Equipped for bayonet. Turn down bolt handle, unnotched stock. Forestocked to muzzle. Front sight guard on nose cap.

KAR. 98a. Though officially called a carbine, this is really a short rifle. This is the Gew. 98 modified to bring it in line with the U. S. (Springfield) Model 1903.

The Kar. 98a was introduced in 1904 and adopted in 1908. Barrel 24″. Bolt handle turned down. Stock notched to give handle clearance. Stacking hook similar to that on Kar. 88. This was essentially a pioneer (engineer) and artilleryman's arm in War I.

War I Modifications. About 1916 the hole (eye piece) was provided in the stock. Earlier models used a stud whose purpose was to form a resting point for the striker when dismounting the bolt. (Czech types still use studs.) This hole permitted similar usage, but also served to permit passage of locking rods when rifles were cased for shipment or racked in barracks.

War developments included the sliding bolt cover to keep out snow and dirt (a development discarded by everyone but the Japanese in recent years) and a 20-shot box magazine.

The "Scharfschutzen" model was fitted with telescope for sniping. The telescopes themselves are very rare, as during World War I snipers were under orders to destroy optical equipment when it was in danger of capture.

Identification of German Gew. and Kar. Prior to 1918 manufacture. Arms made before and during World War I, many of which were captured during World War II, customarily bear the makers name on the receiver. They were made at the Arsenals at Amberg, Danzig, Erfurt, and Spandau, and by Loewe, Mauser, Haenel, and Schilling in Germany and by Steyr in Austria.

German Service Rifles and Carbines After World War I

At the close of World War I the German Army was limited to 100,000 men by the Treaty of Versailles. Not only was their equipment limited, but ball ammunition use was restricted to 60 practice rounds per man per year. The restriction prevented the German Army from changing over to an experimental rifle which they had developed in 1918.

An earlier experimental rifle (the 98/17) had been developed to use some parts which could be mass manufactured, yet could be assembled to major parts of standard 98 pattern. The 98/18 advanced this experimental design. It used a built-in bolt cover, a new firing pin design, detachable 10- and 25-shot magazines which could replace the standard 5-shot built-in magazine, and a rising magazine follower to hold the action open when empty.

Improved Gewehr 98. Since the Treaty prevented a changeover, the Germans applied themselves to reworking the Gewehr 98 itself to make it more efficient and to permit speedier and easier manufacture. This work progressed from 1920 to 1924.

The magazine follower was altered to hold the action open when empty. During the war the Germans had discovered that this was an important military rifle design feature, as shown by their Intelligence reports. The bolt plug (or sleeve) was fitted with a wider collar as a further protection from gas blowback in the event of a pierced primer or blown cartridge head. A 100-meter sight was added for close quarter firing. Interchangeable sight ramps were developed which permitted the soldier to alter his sights to meet ballistics of improved cartridges (specifically in this case the change from "S" (flat base) bullet to "sS" (boat tail) bullet). The magazine floor plate was altered to serve as a dismounting tool in bolt disassembly. The bolt still projected at a right angle.

The Kar. 98 b.

Kar. 98b. For cavalry and armored force use the bolt handle on the new short rifle was turned down and slings were side mounted. This variation, named the Kar. 98 b, was widely used in World War II, as was the old War I Kar, which was renamed Kar 98a.

Sniping Rifles. Standard rifles as above were sometimes fitted with Zeiss telescope sights. Twelve such were issued to each company during this period.

Training Rifles. To circumvent the Treaty regulations, the Germans now turned to designing air rifles and .22 trainers whose general weights, lengths and operation would permit wide-scale training within the restrictions imposed upon them.

Note on Foreign Mauser Type Rifles

It is worthy of note that in 1924 both F. N. in Belgium and Z.B. in Czechoslovakia introduced Mauser type rifles and carbines in all but the most superficial aspects identical with the German.

These firms undertook commercial military rifle sale on a world scale, supplying these latest Mauser types to nations which had formerly purchased from Germany.

Mauser-type rifle development from that period on followed the German in Poland, Portugal, Spain, and Yugoslavia as well as in Belgium and Czechoslovakia. Whether the caliber is 7mm, 7.65mm or 7.9mm, the arms themselves are all the same, though due to varying points of manufacture their parts are not strictly interchangeable. Occasionally minor parts such as ejectors and bolt stops were slightly modified.

Some Yugoslav rifles, while mechanically the same as the German, are built on shorter receivers.

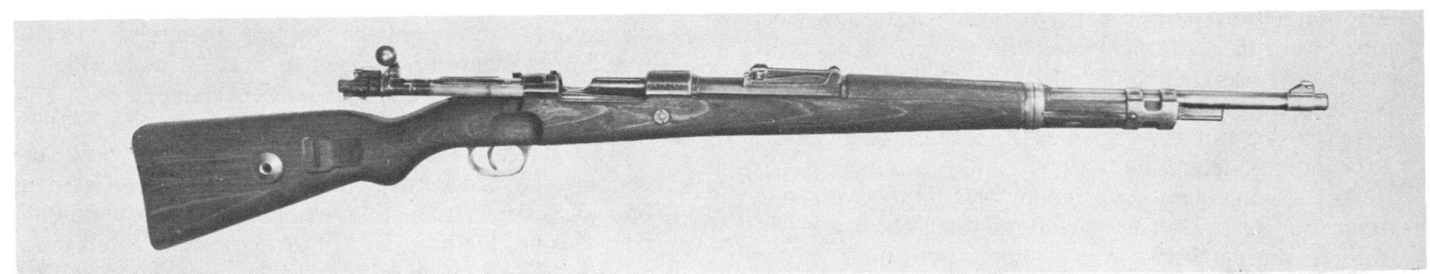

Kar. 98k. Action open. Sling and cleaning rod removed.

The Germans now applied themselves intensively to ballistic experiments and war maneuvers. They found that for practical purposes a shorter and lighter rifle was advisable.

Tests showed that a reduction in barrel lengths from 740mm (28.86″) to 600mm (23.40″) gave about the same accuracy at usable military ranges. Velocity loss was only 25 meters (82.02 feet) per second, which was negligible for military purposes. While muzzle flash and recoil were somewhat greater, the factors of weight and ease of handling far outweighed these disadvantages.

In 1935 this new pattern, whose characteristics had appeared in commercial Mausers in 1924, was formally issued to German troops as the Kar. 98k. The "k" is an abbreviation for "kurz," signifying short. This was the primary German rifle arm of World War II, all later changes being superficial to speed manufacture.

Kar. 98k Stocks. Considerable work was done on developing stocks for the Kar. 98k. During World War I the Germans ran short of the walnut which had originally been used. Substitute woods shrank and warped and proved generally unsatisfactory.

Light metal butts were tested early in the 1930's but were not considered satisfactory. Beech plywood was tried, and eventually a laminated beech stock was evolved.

According to official German reports, beech proved more desirable in every way than the original walnut. The laminated beech withstood all field and laboratory tests, it was available in quantity, and factory waste averaged 1.5% to 2% as against 10% for walnut.

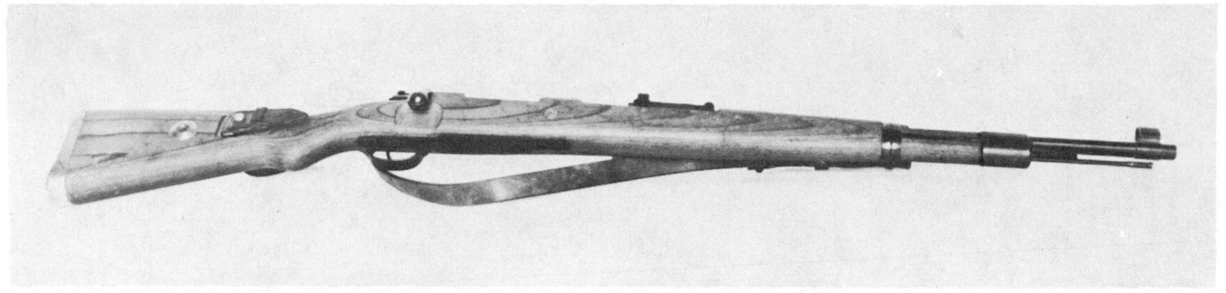

German Mauser Carbine 7.92mm Kar. 98k.

Caliber: 7.9mm (.312 inch).
Magazine: Staggered box. 5 round capacity.

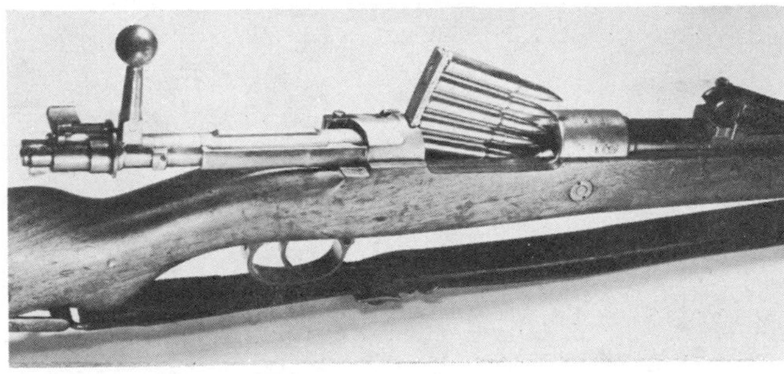

Muzzle Velocity: Approximately 2564 feet per second with standard German rifle ammunition. Note: High velocity German machine gun ammunition should not be used in these weapons.
Barrel Length: 23.4 inches.
Overall Length Without Bayonet: 43.5 inches.
Weight: Approximately 9 pounds.
Sights: Front, inverted V blade. This may be fitted with a hood. Rear, leaf type. Has open V notch which slides on ramp. No windage. Graduated from 100 to 2000 meters.
Magazine Cut Off: None provided.
Locked: Turning bolt action. This is the original Mauser design from which our Springfield was developed.
Safety: Thumb lever on bolt plug similar to our Springfield. The action is locked when the safety is moved to the right; it can be pushed only when the rifle is cocked.
Stock: Semi pistol grip. Sling on left side. Metal lined hole through stock serves as an aid in dismounting the striker; and also serves to permit locking rods to pass through and secure rifles when they are packed in cases.
Range: Approximately 3000 yards maximum. Effective range is about 800 yards.

Special Note: The Mauser system is the most widely used military rifle system ever developed. Several types and barrel lengths of earlier design were in use by the Germans, but they differ only in details.

After 1941 the Germans were striving desperately to develop automatic rifles of the type of our successful Garand.

Field Stripping

To remove bolt. Proceed as for U. S. Rifle Model 1917. With rifle cocked and safety lever vertical, half way between safe and locked position, pull out near end of bolt stop on left side of receiver and draw bolt straight out to the rear.

To dismount bolt. Proceed as for Springfield.

To remove magazine mechanism. Same as for Springfield.

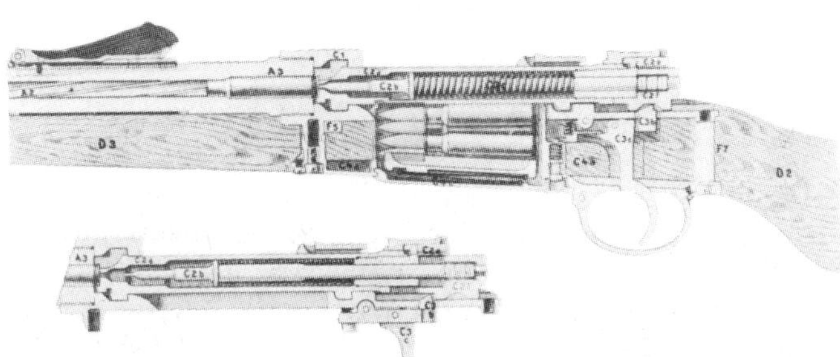

Kar. 98k sectioned to show details of locking, firing and magazine systems.

Note position of dual forward locking lugs which assure maximum support to case head at instant of firing.

A 2. Rifling. A 3. Reinforced chamber section of barrel screwed into receiver. C 1. Receiver. C 2a. Bolt body (cylinder). C 2b. Striker. C 2c. Mainspring. C 2e. Manual safety wing. C 2f. Cocking piece. C 3c. Trigger. C 3b. Trigger bar (carries sear nose at its rear). F 7. Triggerguard screw. D 2. Stock. C 4c. Magazine spring.

Other Bolt Actions Used by Germany

All Belgian, Czech, and Polish rifles described under those countries were used by the Germans to some extent. Important arms were the following:

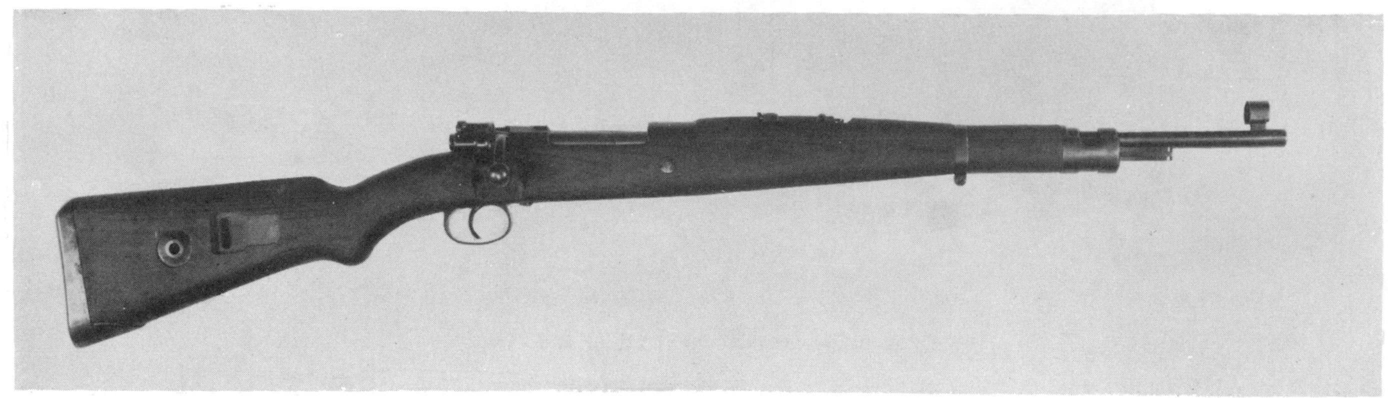

The Gew. 33/40.

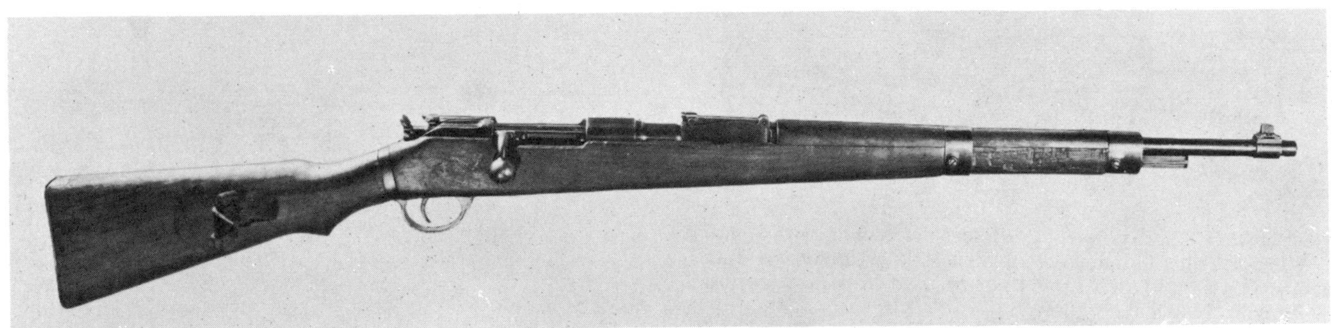

The Gew. 98/40.

THE 33/40. In the case of the Czech Model 33, a short form of the original Model 24, the Germans put the rifle into service on a wide scale as the 33/40. This rifle is occasionally encountered with a special steel attachment on left side of stock to permit the arm to be used to assist mountain and ski troops when climbing steep places. Barrel is 18″.

GEW. 98/40. This is NOT a Mauser type action. It is a modification made in Hungary of the 1935 Hungarian Service rifle (See chapter 28.)

Characteristics. Length 43.5″. Barrel 24″. Weight 9 lbs. Caliber 7.9-mm German. This rifle is essentially the same as the Mannlicher-Schoenauer turn bolt, but is equipped with a Mauser type magazine. It can be immediately identified by the two-piece stock joined at the grip as in the British Enfield. The bolt handle turns down ahead of the split receiver bridge. When the bolt handle is turned up, primary extraction is produced in standard Mannlicher fashion by cams on the locking lugs working against receiver cams as the lugs clear their locking seats. The top of the bolt is shallowed out to make it lighter. A thumb piece at the end of the cocking piece is shaped like that on the Mannlicher Model 95 straight pull. This arm can be cocked by pulling back on the cocking piece in case of a misfire, thus making it unnecessary to risk opening the action. However, the striker should never be lowered on a loaded chamber by use of this cocking piece, as the pin will rest on the primer.

The 5-shot magazine is loaded with a standard Mauser clip or with a single cartridge through the top of the open action.

This rifle is customarily stamped with the actual bore measurement at time of inspection. Thus it will commonly be encountered stamped 7.87mm or 7.88mm. Stampings may indicate either higher or slightly lower millimeter measurements. In all cases the rifle will handle the standard German 7.9mm rifle cartridge when the magazine is Mauser-type.

Identification. Mannlicher turn bolt with dual front lugs and removable bolt head. Mauser type magazine. Two-piece stock joined at grip.

Evaluation. Generally strong well-built action. While the use of a removable bolt head requires setting the lugs farther back than in Mauser practice, this type of Mannlicher action has the added safety factor of the bolt handle being forward of the receiver bridge. Except for magazine system, the action is essentially the same as the famous Mannlicher-Schoenauer which has been adapted to magnum cartridges.

Ammunition. German 7.9mm. Because of difficulty of assaying strength of individual rifles without testing, it is recommended that American commercial 8mm Mauser (7.9mm) ammunition be used. This is loaded below military requirements, but is ample for any American hunting purposes.

The VG 1.

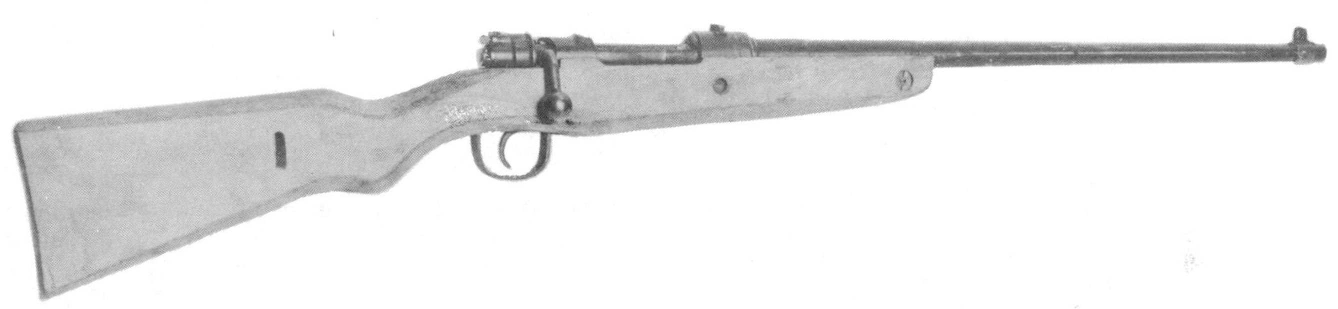

The VG Kar. 98.

German "People's Rifles" (Volks Gewehr).

In the last stages of desperation the Germans turned to all kinds of expedients to defend themselves. To arm the populace for a hoped-for last ditch defense which never came, a number of makeshift weapons were devised. The principal rifles in this category are the two described below.

VG 1. This extremely crude arm is definitely not recommended except as a souvenir. The receiver is the split bridge type. The magazine is the detachable 10-shot box designed for the semi-automatic Kar. 43. The caliber is the standard 7.9mm rifle. Receivers and parts are extremely crude. As cheap, quickly made emergency arms with a short life expectancy they evidently met German desperation requirements. Many had cast receivers of questionable strength, however, and in any case the tolerances were not adequate for any extensive use of the rifle. The firing lock design is also an adaptation of a cheap low power rifle form, and in case of a blown cartridge case or pierced primer the shooter is in real danger.

Modified VG Kar. 98. Mauser receivers and barrels were sometimes assembled to cheap wood stocks without magazines to form single shot VG rifles. A fixed V sight for 100 meters was provided. When properly fitted and headspaced, these are strong rifles. However, many represent cannabalized parts or unchecked assembly, and should be adequately checked before being used.

Some of these rifles have been found with the Kar. 43 (semi-auto) 10-shot magazine.

Note on VG Rifles: These weapons were developed by different firms and were manufactured in small shops.

GERMAN SEMI-AUTOMATIC RIFLES

Germany experimented with semi-automatic military rifles before the beginning of the twentieth century. Mauser's original long-recoil patterns did not prove successful in the field, and experiments were not maintained. The Germans kept fully abreast of the development of the semi-auto rifle in the U. S.; but they pinned their reliance in the light machine gun and in motorized and air equipment to the point of underrating the infantry semi-auto rifle.

It was not until they encountered the Russian Tokarev rifle in quantity in field use that they awoke to their error in the matter of rifle design.

Once the lesson was brought home they gave intense attention to development. The result was the series of semi-auto weapons listed and illustrated below.

Gew. 41 W Rifle, left side.

Gew. 41 W Rifle, right side.

Caliber: 7.92mm German Service cartridge.
Magazine: Fixed rectangular box extending below the stock at front of the triggerguard.
Magazine Capacity: 10 cartridges from 2 Mauser 5-round clips.
Overall Length: 45 inches.
Weight: 10 lbs. 14 ozs.
Sights: Leaf rear sight, graduated from 100 to 1200 meters.
Gun Operated By: Gas. Barrel is not tapped as in most gas operated weapons. As bullet leaves barrel, expanding gas is trapped in a cone attached to the muzzle. Gas drives back a floating piston, operating the gun.
Locked: Securely locked at moment of discharge.
Cooled: Air.
Position of Cocking Handle: Right side of rifle.
Type of Fire: One shot for each pull of the trigger.
Safety: Thumb safety catch extends from rear of receiver. Turned to the right it is "Safe." Turned to the left it is ready to "Fire."
Bolt Release Stud: On left side of rifle in stock above the rear end of the magazine. When weapon is open, pressing this stud will release the bolt and permit it to go forward.

THE 41 W SEMI-AUTO RIFLES. These rifles employ the muzzle blast cone along the general lines of the 41M, but with the operating rod mounted on top of the barrel. The breechlock is a modification of an early European type. Mauser, Kjellman, and others experimented with it. The basic principle involved, that of having detachable locking bolts so mounted in the sides of the bolt (or breechblock) that movement of the firing pin carrier forces them into and out of locking engagement, was first successfully worked out by the Russians in their Degtyarev LMG.

This gas trap system, while superficially it has something in common with the early Danish Bang System as used in U. S. tests in 1914, is a fundamentally different action. The Bang cone blows forward and pulls an operating rod below the barrel ahead to function the action. A modified Bang tested in 1934 in Denmark proved unsatisfactory, though its improved cone operation approximated that of the later German 41 M type. The Walther system traps the gas in a fixed cone and reverses gas flow to drive back a circular floating piston which operates the rod.

Identification. Gas blast cone at muzzle. Projecting 10-shot box magazine. Operating rod on top of barrel. Exterior bolt slide. Cylindrical bolt with dual locks cammed by firing pin carrier. 41 W model has button slide release on left side of receiver.

Evaluation. Heavy and clumsy. Experimental designs not made in very large quantity. Subject to excessive muzzle fouling. Corrosion will injure gas system if rifle is not given unusual attention. Locking design is commendable.

Ammunition: 7.9mm German Service.

Loading and Firing

Pull back cocking handle as far as it will go and push bolt lock up to the right. Place a clip in the magazine clip guide and force the five cartridges down into the magazine. Insert a second clip in the clip guide and strip the next five cartridges down to fill the magazine.

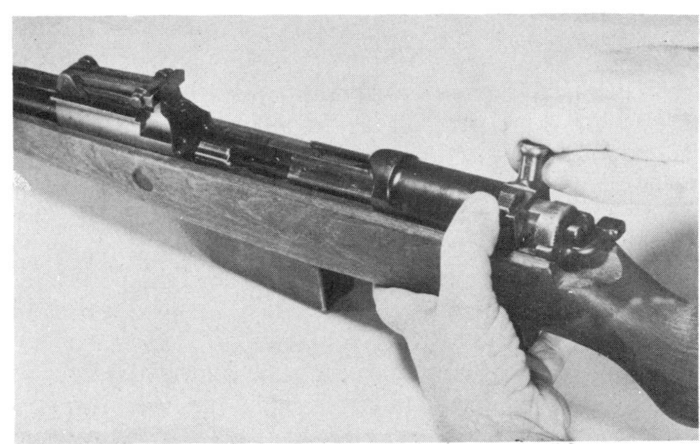

Locking Bolt Back for Loading.

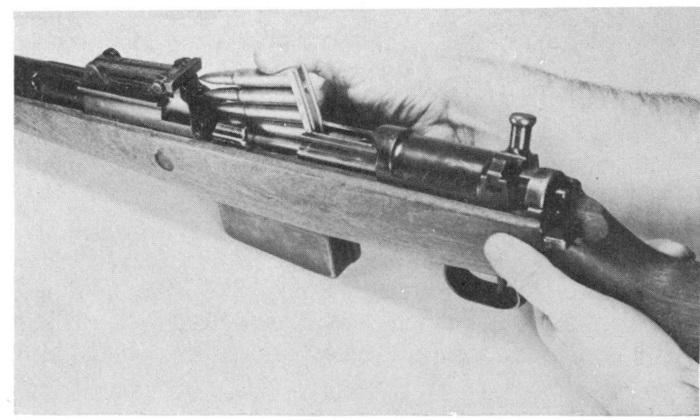

Stripping Cartridges into Magazine.

Push in the stud on the left side above the rear of the magazine. This will release the bolt which will be driven forward by the recoil spring, permitting the bolt to strip a cartridge from the magazine and feed it into the firing chamber.

Pressing the trigger will now fire the cartridge in the chamber; the gas caught in the trap at the muzzle will operate the action to unlock the bolt and eject the empty shell, compress the recoil spring and permit the magazine spring to force the next cartridge up into line to be driven forward by the bolt in forward motion. This operation will be repeated at each pull of the trigger.

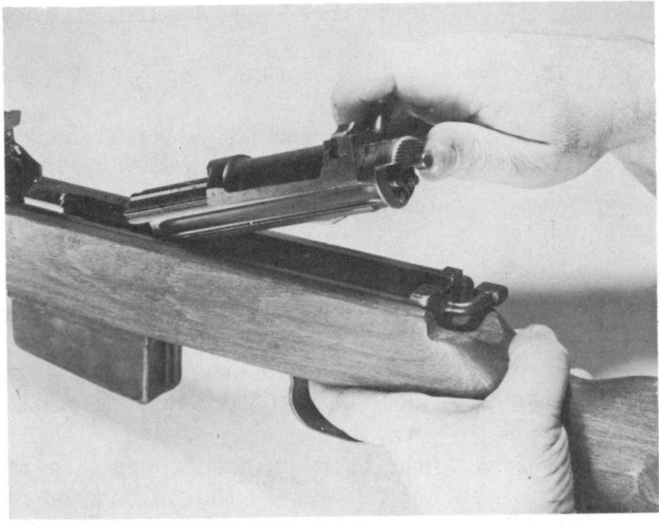

Bolt Removal.

Safety is set, bolt is locked back by catch and recoil spring guide rod is being pushed in to free the assembly.

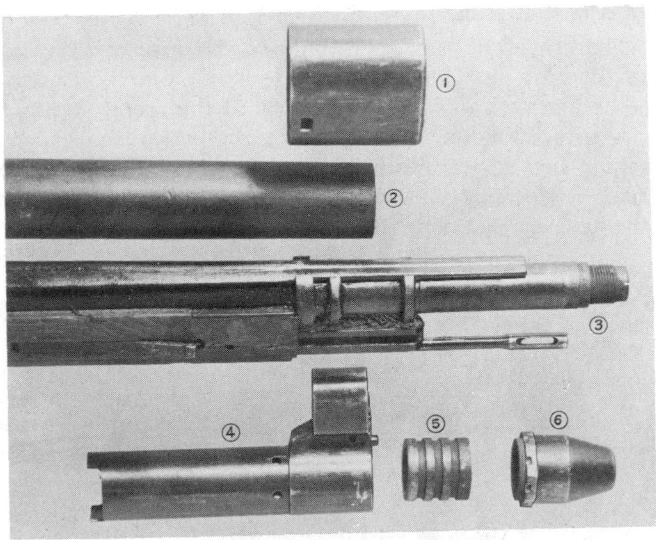

Gas Operating Assembly.

1. Front band lock. 2. Plastic handguard. 3. Barrel threaded for blast cone. Flat operating rod on top of barrel. 4. Operating rod cover which fits over barrel. 5. Piston which mounts around barrel and floats inside operating rod cover. 6. Blast cone which screws on barrel and traps gas to force floating piston back against operating rod.

Field Stripping

Pull the cocking handle back as far as it will go to open the breech.

Press the locking bolt over to the right. This bolt operates through the cover just ahead of the cocking handle in the forward position, to hold the mainspring compressed.

Set the safety catch at the safe position; this is done by rotating it to the right.

At the rear end of the breechblock is a locking plunger. Push this plunger in and raise the rear end of the block; this permits the breechblock to be withdrawn from the receiver.

Turn the safety catch to the fire position and press the trigger to release the catch on the hammer.

A small plunger in the sight base locks the muzzle cap; pressing this in permits the cap to be unscrewed and the gas cylinder and piston to slide out the front.

Removing the upper and lower bands permits release of the handguard. Next the operating rod is lifted from its seat. Then the recoil spring assembly is lifted out of the stock.

The magazine is removed as for the U. S. Springfield Rifle.

Note: The bolt, slide, and the slide and receiver groups may be lifted out by locking the slide in its full forward position.

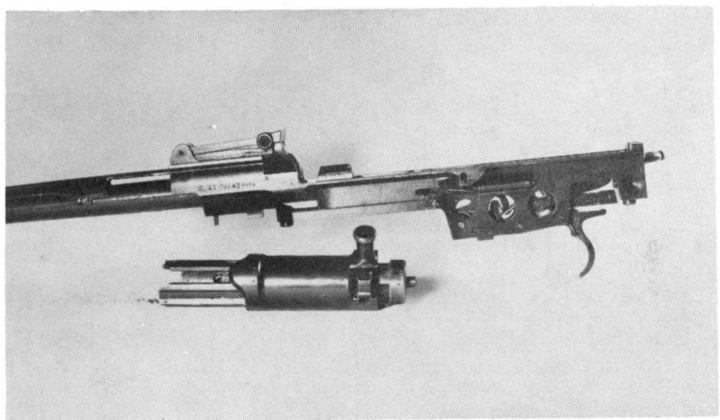

Bolt assembly and wood work removed to show receiver details.

Note that operating rod is shaped to lie on top of barrel and pass through cut in the receiver.

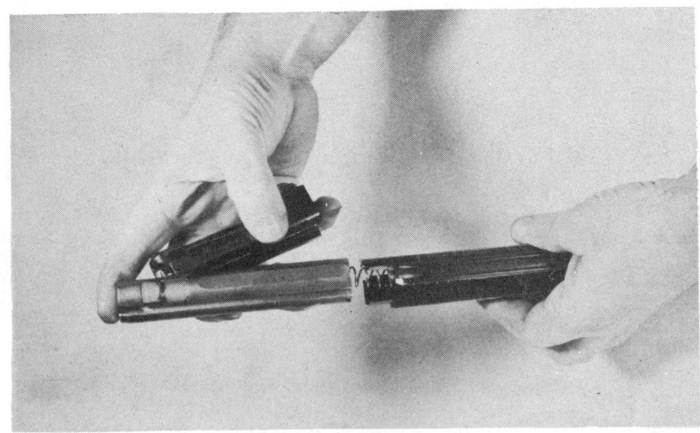

Dismounting Bolt.

When bolt catch is released, recoil spring will force stamped carrier back from its position between the bolt and the bolt slide. Bolt slide may be lifted off, firing pin assembly removed and bolt locks withdrawn.

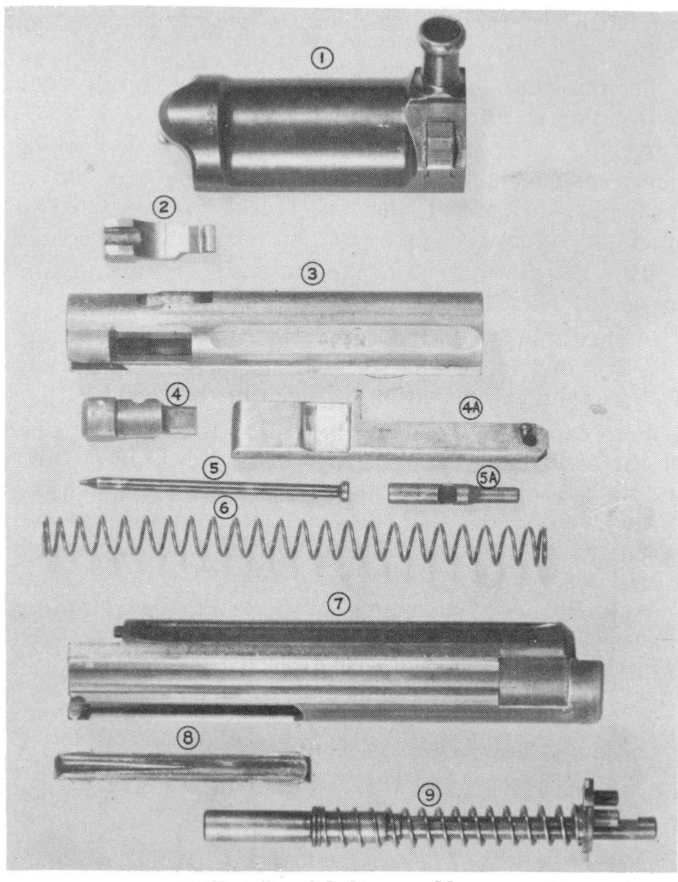

Details of bolt assembly.

1—Bolt slide. Note projection on front end at left for pulling back firing-pin housing. Note bolt handle at upper right and slide lock in line with it.
2—Bolt lock right side.
3—Detail of bolt. Note slot in left side to receive bolt lock. Also cut in top to receive bolt slide projection. Also note cam-face at lower right of bolt body which serves to cock the hammer by riding over and depressing it.
4—Left side bolt lock and 4A—hollow firing-pin housing.
5—Firing-pin and 5A—firing-pin extension which are inserted in the housing. Extension is retained by pin at rear of housing.
6—Recoil or operating spring.
7—Bolt carrier.
8—Sliding cover for carrier.
9—Recoil spring guide with secondary or buffer spring affixed. Right end of this rod projects through bolt carrier. The two lugs lock in slots in the receiver to hold the bolt assembly securely in place.

Field Assembly

Turn the safety catch to the "Fire" position.

Push the hammer down until it engages with the bent of the sear.

Turn the safety catch to the safe position (right). Insert the breechblock in the receiver, holding the front end down and move it slightly to the front. Push in the plunger at the rear end which will permit the rear of the breechblock cover to position properly in the receiver.

Release the pressure on the plunger and turn the safety catch to the left.

Press the release stud to close the weapon.

How the Gew. 41 and 41 W Work

This rifle does not have a gas port tapped in the barrel. Instead a gas trap, cone-shaped, is screwed onto the muzzle.

As the bullet leaves the barrel, it jumps a gap which for just an instant permits the gas to stop up the muzzle end of this cone.

The pressure thus trapped rebounds against the gas piston which fits around the barrel end, and against the rear of the blast cone.

This pressure thrusts back the floating operating rod which rests against the cylindrical piston working on top of the barrel and under the handguard below the rear sight base.

The end of the operating rod touches the front end of the slide and hence drives it to the rear under the force of the back pressure.

The travel of the operating rod is only about 1½" but the blow imparted to the slide is stiff enough to drive the action back against the tension of the recoil spring.

A projection on the bottom of the slide engages with locking lugs inside the bolt. For the first half inch of its travel it does not affect the lock which gives sufficient time to permit the high breech pressure to drop. Then it cams the lugs inward out of their recesses in the

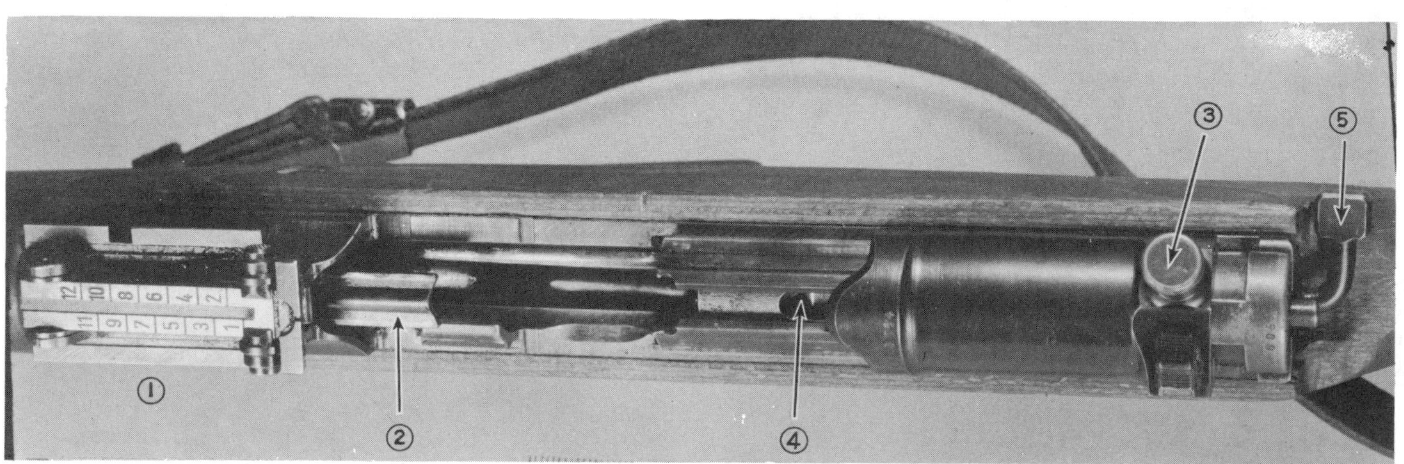

Top Receiver Details. 1. Beginning at extreme left, note standard Mauser Tangent sight. 2. Operating rod is being forced through slot to indicate its position. 3. Bolt slide is fully retracted and has been manually locked by pushing bolt slide lock to the right. Magazine cannot be loaded until this has been manually locked. 4. Note opening in top of bolt and firing-pin housing. Bolt assembly rests inside the carrier. 5. The arm projecting from the rear of the receiver and turned up to the right is the safety which positively blocks sear action. Swinging it over to the extreme left sets it in the firing position.

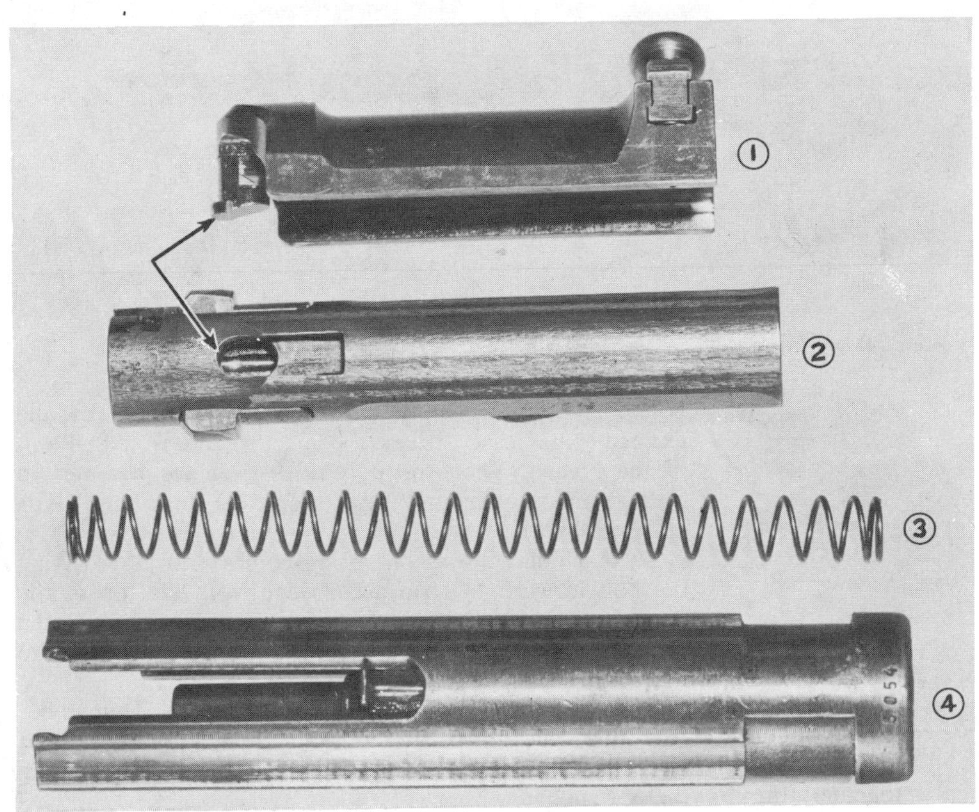

Details of bolt assembly. 1. Bolt slide. Note projection at front end which seats in top of bolt and when driven back functions the firing pin carrier to unlock the bolt. 2. Bolt complete with two lugs in locked position. Note firing pin housed inside carrier within the bolt. 3. Operating and recoil spring, which seats inside the hollow bolt. 4. Stamped bolt carrier which guides the travel of the bolt.

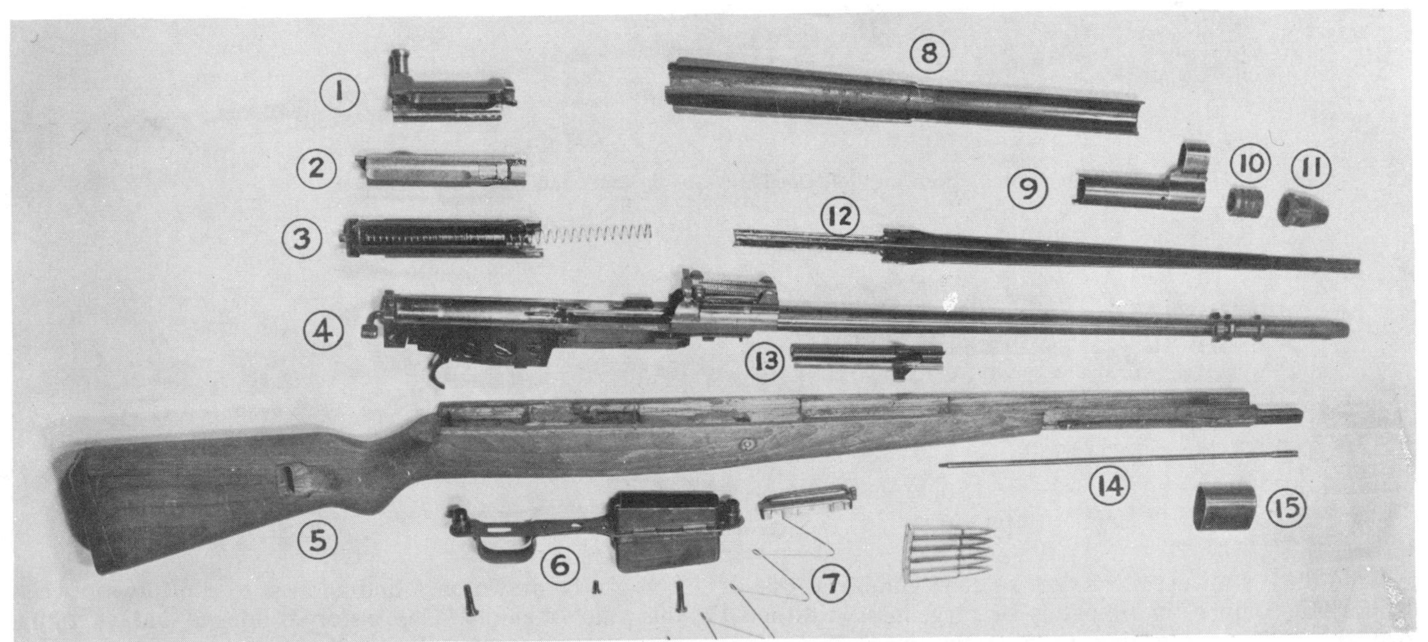

Detailed Stripping to Show Gas and Locking Systems. 1. Bolt slide. 2 Bolt. 3. Bolt carrier with buffer and recoil springs. 4. Receiver and barrel assembly. 5. Stock. 6. Triggerguard and magazine. 7. Magazine follower and spring. 8. Forearm. 9. Gas cylinder. 10. Gas piston. 11. Gas cone. 12. Operating rod. 13. Operating rod trough and spring. 14. Cleaning rod. 15. Front band.

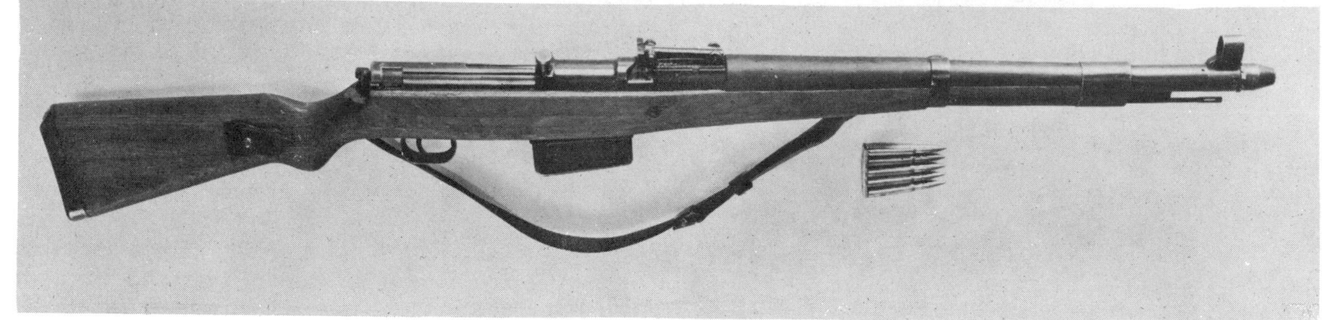

Gew. 41 W Right Side View, Bolt Closed.

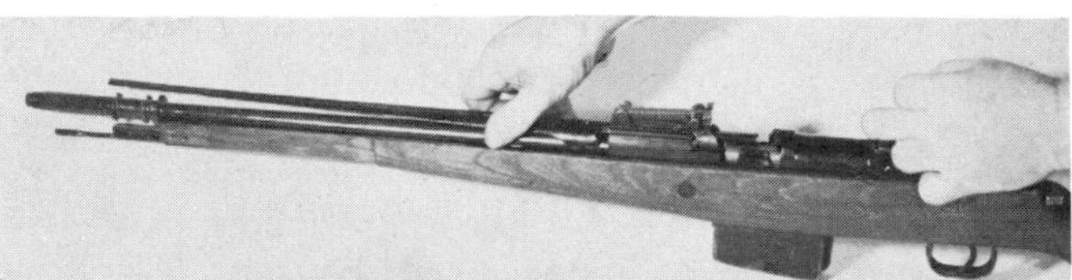

Front end assembly removed to show how piston is driven back to unlock bolt.

receiver, thus unlocking the rifle and permitting the assembly to travel straight back to the rear to eject, compress recoil spring, and prepare for forward motion of loading.

As the bolt assembly and bolt go back together, the bolt carrying the empty cartridge case gripped by the extractor, the case strikes the ejector and is tossed out of the breech. Then the bolt rides over the hammer to cock it and a cam on the bolt forces it down until it is engaged by the sear.

At that point the recoil spring comes into play driving the bolt forward to strip a cartridge from the top of the magazine and feed it into the firing chamber, while the projection on the slide cams the bolt locking lug into the recesses in the receiver.

The weapon is now ready to fire again. Remember that this rifle, like our Garand, fires from a closed bolt. There are various minor details which differ among these weapons.

Gewehr 41M. Showing Bolt Open and Gas Cylinder and Gas Trap Removed.

Gewehr 41M.

While this is an excellent type of semi-automatic rifle, it does not compare in simplicity or ruggedness with our own rifle. It is interesting to note, however, that the Germans in experimenting with such a weapon have also hit upon the gas-operating principle.

The 41 and 41W are standard rifles; the 41M is so infrequently met with that it is considered merely experimental and does not warrant attention here.

Gew. 41W differs in having no bolt release button. Magazine follower must be depressed with fingers before bolt can be drawn back and allowed to run forward when this rifle is empty. Gas piston is longer and operating rod correspondingly shorter than on the Gew. 41.

GEW. 41 M. This arm was developed by Mauser. It uses the principle of trapping gas in a cone at the muzzle of the rifle, deflecting some gas to the rear to operate a below-barrel operating rod as the bullet leaves the muzzle.

The breechlock is a modification of an early Mauser experimental form. The operating rod forces back the

Bolt Cover Open. Showing Detail of Bolt and Recoil Spring. This is the Gew. 41 M. It employs a turning bolt-head for locking. Weight is about 11½ lbs. This rifle is muzzle-heavy and clumsy.

rear section of a two-piece bolt. As the rear bolt section travels back it rotates the front bolt (locking) section out of receiver engagement. When the dual front lugs have turned enough to unlock, both parts of the assembly travel back in a straight line in the receiver to eject and to compress the recoil spring and cock the striker. This turning lock functions on the general idea of the common "automatic" screwdriver in which a push on the handle (rear) revolves the blade (front) end as forward movement telescopes the two parts.

Identification. Projecting 10-shot fixed box magazine. Blast cone at muzzle. Operating rod below barrel. Top of receiver hinges up for dismounting. Two-piece elongating principle bolt resembling modified Austrian 95 system.

Evaluation. Very few issued. An experimental weapon. Heavy and clumsy and subject to excessive muzzle fouling. A collector's item.

Ammunition. German Service 7.9mm.

German 7.92mm Kar. 43 (Gewehr 43).

Caliber: 7.92mm German Service.
Magazine: Detachable box extending below stock ahead of trigger-guard.
Magazine Catch: Housing at rear of box.
Magazine Capacity: 10 cartridges from 2 Mauser 5-round clips.
Loading: By insertion of box or through top.
Overall Length: 44¼ inches.
Barrel Length: 22 inches.
Weight: 8.9 pounds.
Sights: Hooded front. Tangent rear 100 to 1200 meters. Receiver equipped to receive telescope sight.
Gun Operated by: Gas. Barrel tapped on top as in Russian Tokarev Rifle.
Locked: By retractable lugs on each side of the bolt.
Cooled: Air.
Position of Cocking Handle: Left hand side of rifle.
Type of Fire: Single shot only. One pull of the trigger for each shot.
Safety: Thumb piece projecting from rear of receiver. Turned to the right it is on safe.
Hold-Open Device: On bridge at right rear of receiver. Is pushed in to hold bolt open for loading.

GEW. 43 AND KAR. 43. These are essentially the same arm. Several variations were made as happens in all experimental forms. These are all modified forms of the 41 W lock combined with a variant of the Russian gas system. (This gas system differs from the very early Italian designs only in mounting the gas units on top of the barrel instead of below.)

Identification. Detachable 10-shot box magazine. Two-thirds stock. Gas port in top of barrel. Operating rod on top of barrel. Crude receiver. Many stampings, including triggerguard assembly and bolt slide guide. (**Note:** Some have slide locks, some do not. Barrel lengths differ, as do stock designs and form of some stampings.)

Evaluation. Manufacture crude. Design good. These arms were made with an idea to rapid manufacture and ready expendability. While they are constantly being reported as satisfactory in actual hunting use, we do not as yet know enough about the metallurgy of the receiver to warrant recommendation. One specimen has been reported with a cracked locking bolt.

This design may yet lend itself to further military development. The Germans issued these weapons with low-power scopes for extensive sniper use, and heavy barrel sniping models were under development when the war ended.

Ammunition. 7.9 German Service.

Loading and Firing

Insert a fully loaded magazine from the bottom. Pull back handle as far as it will go to compress recoil spring and permit magazine spring to raise a cartridge in line with the bolt when the handle is released and the compressed recoil spring drives forward the bolt for loading.

To load from top without removing magazine: pull bolt handle back and push in holding catch. Insert a clip of cartridges in the clip guide and press them down into the magazine. Withdraw empty clip and repeat with a second clip. Push in holding open device to permit bolt to ride forward and load the weapon.

Field Stripping

Pull bolt handle back as far as it will go and while holding it push in the holding-open device to secure the bolt in rearward position.

Turn the safety as far over to the right as it will go.

The end of the recoil spring guide projects from the rear of the weapon. Push it in against spring tension and the rear end of the bolt may be lifted up.

The bolt assembly may now be drawn to the rear and upwards out of the receiver.

Holding fast to the bolt cover, press down the holding-open catch and the cover, recoil spring, and recoil spring guide will come out.

The bolt cover (or housing) may be separated and the operating slide and loose bolt locks removed from the bolt. Firing pin, its extension, and the extractor may be easily removed.

Gas Mechanism Removal: Unscrew cleaning rod under barrel and remove. Press in spring holding band on right side of fore-end and slide off the forearm cap. The wooden upper handguard may now be lifted off. The short tappet piece of steel may be withdrawn from the gas chamber and the long connecting piece and its return spring may be removed from the receiver. No further dismounting is normally necessary.

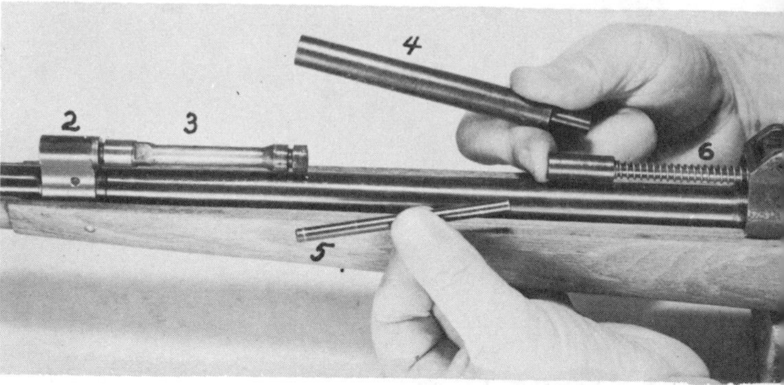

2—Gas chamber above port in barrel into which gas escapes as bullet travels down barrel. 3—Gas cylinder screwed on. 4—Outside gas piston just pulled off the gas cylinder. 5—Connecting tappet piece. When piston is in place over cylinder, the front end of this tappet piece seats in the recess in the front end of the moving piston while its rear end seats in the base of the operating rod. 6—Operating rod and spring being held back to permit removal of gas piston and tappet.

How the Gewehr 43 Works

This latest German semi-automatic rifle is a take-off on the Russian system as far as gas is concerned. Instead of the gas cone of the Gewehr 41, this new rifle has a gas vent drilled in the barrel about 12½ inches back from the muzzle. It is on top of the barrel and leads into a gas chamber rising above the barrel which is fitted with a cylinder to receive a very short piston.

As the bullet passes the gas vent in the barrel, a portion of the gas enters the port and expands in the cylinder driving back the short piston violently.

This piston, acting on the tappet principle, strikes the operating rod which extends backward into the receiver. As the end of this rod passes through a hole drilled in the receiver above the line of the bolt, the thrust imparted to it is transmitted to the operating slide on top of the bolt. Meanwhile a spring around the operating rod is compressed to provide energy to return the rod to its forward position.

At the start of its rearward travel the operating slide moves independently, leaving the weapon securely locked until the pressure has dropped. The slide carries the firing pin housing back independently of the bolt at this point also.

After a short travel, the slide and firing pin housing attached to the bolt pick up the bolt. The firing pin housing is so constructed that it cams in two locking lugs, drawing them out of their seats in the receiver walls and into the surface of the bolt.

From this point on the parts travel to the rear together extracting and ejecting the empty shell and compressing the recoil spring around its guide.

Forward Movement of the Action. The recoil spring compressed around its guide now exerts a forward thrust against the bolt assembly. The bolt strips a cartridge from the magazine and chambers it, the extractor set in the face of the bolt snapping into the extracting groove of the cartridge as it is chambered.

As the bolt reaches its fully forward position, it stops against the face of the chamber. The spring still exerts forward pressure and drives the firing pin housing straight

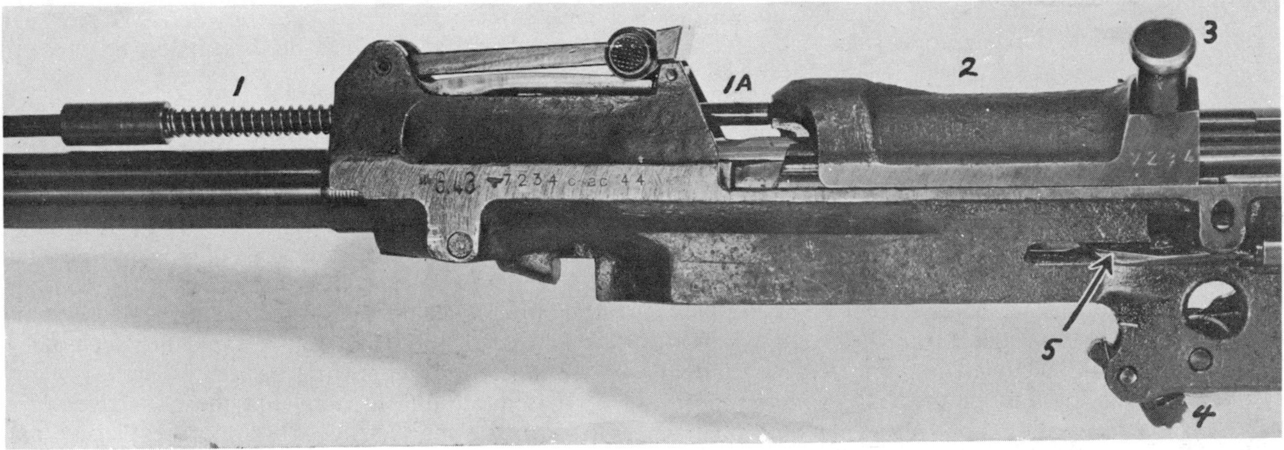

Details of operating rod system.

1—Operating rod being driven to the rear. As it passes through the hole in the receiver above the line of the bore, the spring around it is compressed to store up energy for the forward movement. 1-A—Rear end of operating rod moving back to drive the bolt slide to the rear. 2—Bolt slide moving back in its tracks. Finger on its underside will carry the firing pin carrier to cam the bolt locks in so that the bolt may be unlocked and travel back to the rear. 3—Bolt handle used for cocking weapon. 4—Magazine release catch. 5—Ejector. (Note that the receiver and the bolt slide are steel castings.)

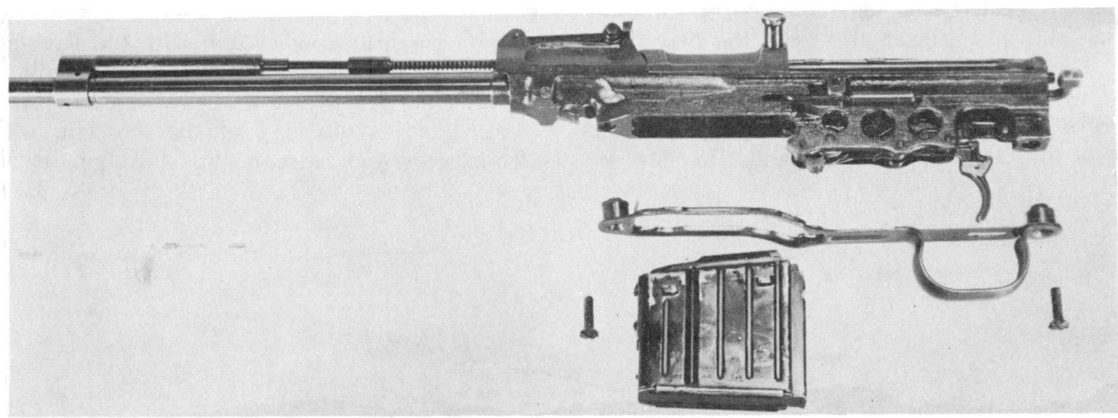

Details of operating system, with all metal work.

Action is fully forward with gas piston in place over the stationary gas cylinder. Note that the operation is entirely in a straight line to the rear.

ahead independently of the bolt. This is so constructed that it forces the locking lugs which are loosely set into each side of the bolt out into the receiver walls in a fashion not unlike that of the Russian Degtyarev Light Machine Gun.

When the bolt is fully home in forward position, the slide mounted on top of it is forced still farther forward into its niche in the receiver, where it rests against the operating rod hole.

When the trigger is pressed, the sear is rotated away from the hammer (which has been ridden over and cocked by the rearward motion of the bolt). The hammer spring drives the hammer forward to strike the firing pin extension. This in turn strikes the firing pin and drives it against the primer to fire the cartridge in the chamber.

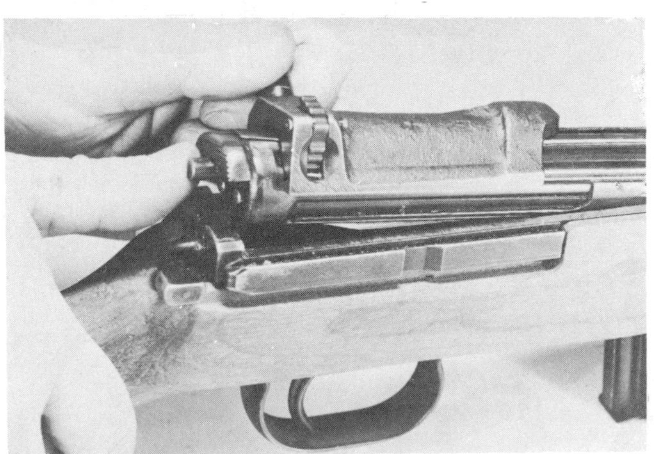

Details of bolt removal. Bolt and bolt slide have been pulled fully to the rear by pressure on the bolt handle; and the bolt slide lock on the right side has been pushed in to hold the bolt slide locked firmly to the bolt assembly. The safety has been turned over to the right to the safe position to permit take down. The recoil and buffer spring rod projecting from the rear of the bolt assembly has been pushed in to receive spring tension and permit the upper end of the assembly to be lifted out of the guide tracks in the receiver. Drawing the locked bolt assembly to the rear will permit it to be lifted out of the weapon.

(Note the guides in the receiver directly above the triggerguard to receive the telescope sight.)

Differences Between the Kar. 43 and the Gewehr 41

While the handguard of the Gewehr 41 is usually plastic, that of the Kar. 43 is usually made of wood. The G41 has a rigid ten-round box attached to the triggerguard. The Kar. 43 is provided with a stamped ten-round detachable magazine. The receiver of the G41 is machined while that of the Kar. 43 is cast. A telescope mounting lug is machined into the receiver of the Kar. 43. This is not present in the G41. The gas port, piston, and cylinder on the Kar. 43 are mounted on the top of the barrel, which is tapped. The bolt housing of the G41 is machined, as is the bolt slide. The operating handle is on the right side and the safety on the left. In the Kar. 43, the bolt housing is die stamped and has a sliding cover which moves with the bolt slide. The operating handle is on the left side. The bolt is the same as the bolt in the G41. The trigger groups in the two differ considerably. The trigger assembly in the Kar. 43 resembles our own Garand in many respects. However, the trigger works on the sear instead of on the hammer as in the case of the Garand. The front and rear hammer hook principle is employed, however. Trigger parts are stamped and springs are of the torsion type.

Special Note

While this weapon in many respects is a development of the Gewehr 41 and 41W, it has been simplified from a manufacturing standpoint and improved from an engineering standpoint to a very marked degree.

From the fact that it is not equipped to be fitted with a bayonet, and that it is fitted with a mounting for a telescope, it would seem that the tactical use is intended to be that of the Russians—a rapid fire accurate weapon for sniper and supporting use.

It is interesting to note that the bolt cover or slide is a sturdy casting instead of the more expensive machined piece of the earlier model and that a sliding cover moves with the operating slide. The bolt itself is the same as in the 41 but the position of the operating handle has been changed.

Few of the unexposed parts have been machined on their outside surfaces. In operation the combination of this German locking system with the Russian gas system makes a most interesting and efficient rifle.

It is particularly noteworthy that the weapon can be loaded, as in the case of the Russian, with magazines from below or standard clips through the action.

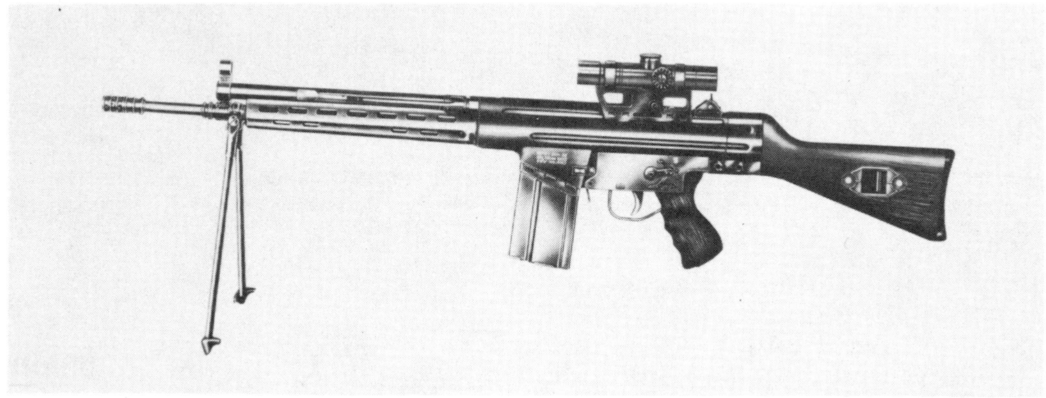

CETME 7.62mm Assault Rifle, Model 58, with Telescope Sight and Bipod.

(This is a prototype form of New West German G3.)

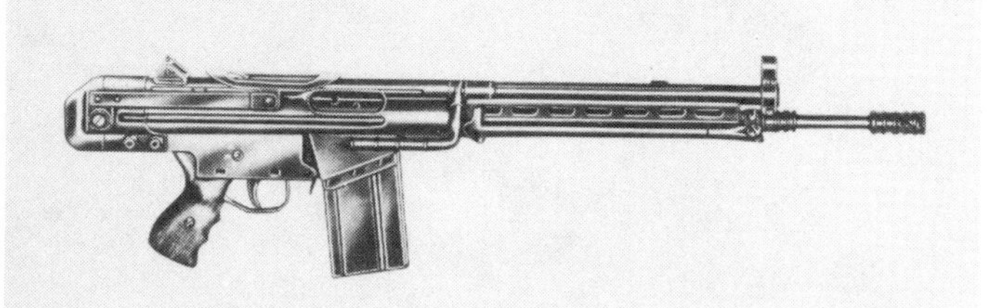

CETME 7.62mm Assault Rifle, Model 58, with Folding Stock.

(A prototype form of the West German G3.)

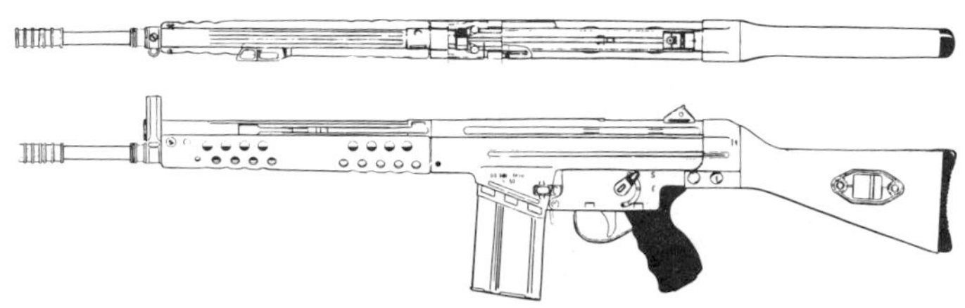

Production Version of West German CETME.

These are versions of the Spanish CETME which have been adopted by the West Germans. See chapter 39 for details of this weapon.

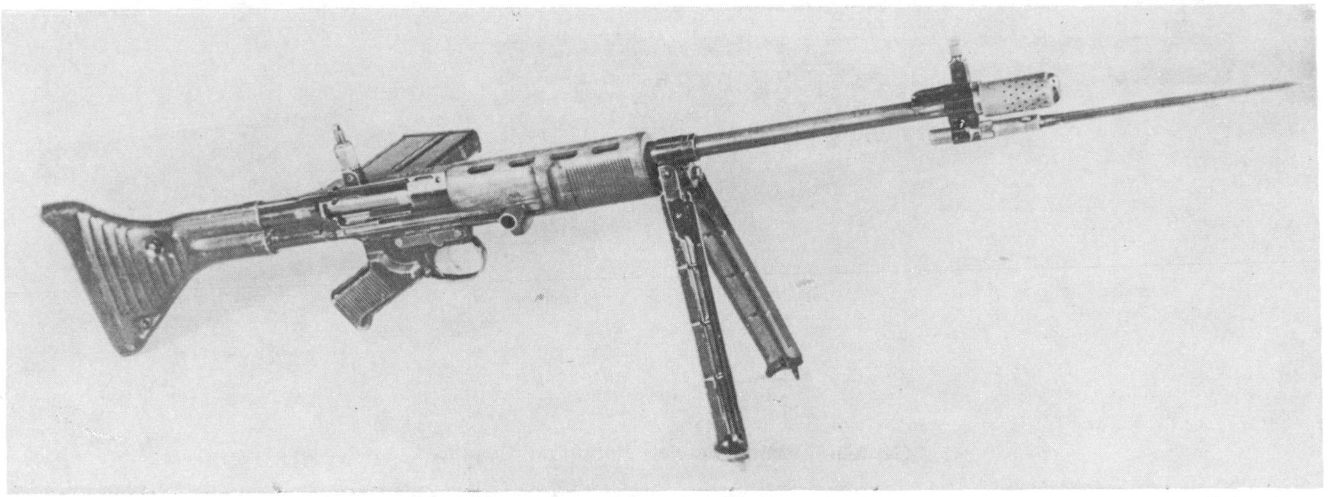

German 7.92mm Fallschirmjaeger Gewehr 42 Automatic Rifle.

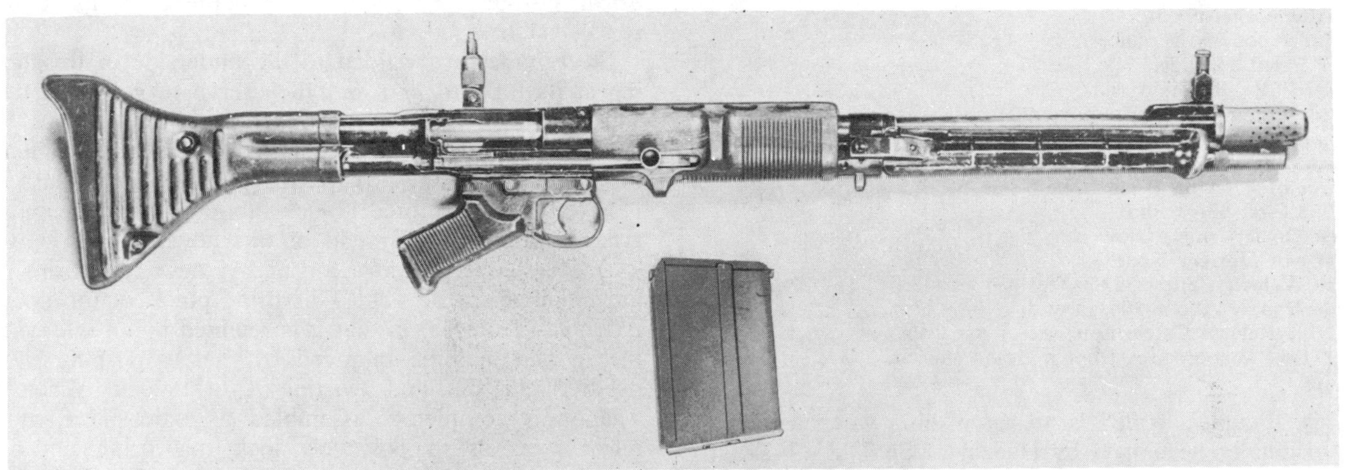

The FG 42 with the bipod folded and the magazine detached.

This is a revolutionary military development. It is a paratroop weapon, fitted with a folding bipod mount. When fired semi-automatically, the bolt is in full forward position, which permits maximum accuracy as a rifle. When the change lever is moved to permit full automatic fire, the bolt remains open when the trigger is released to permit cooling, thus giving the full value of a light machine gun. It will be noted that this weapon uses the short gas stroke of a type originally developed for our Winchester carbine. Firing from both open and closed bolt was pioneered by the American Johnson Light Machine Gun.

Caliber: 7.92mm.
Magazine: Straight box, inserted on left side.
Barrel Length: About 19 inches.
Overall Length: 43.5″ (without bayonet).
Weight: 10.5 lbs. without magazine.
Sights: Special folding post sights for both sniping and automatic firing.
Cocking Handle and Change Lever: Left side of trigger group.
Locked: By turning bolt, similar to American Lewis Gun.
Operation: Gas on short stroke principle.

FG 42 with wood stock and handguard.

German 7.92mm (Special) Volksturm Gewehr.

Caliber: 7.92mm Short.
Overall Length: 34⅞ inches.
Barrel Length: 14⅞ inches.
Magazine Capacity: 30.
Weight: 9 pounds, 7 ounces.
Sights: Fixed on Slide.
Operated By: Recoil.
Locked: Original system utilizing escaping gases in special gas chamber. No formal breech lock.
Cooled: Air.
Position of Cocking Handle: Left side of slide.
Type of Fire: Single shot.
Safety: On left side of Receiver.
Hold-Open Device: None.
Muzzle Velocity: About 2250 feet per second.
Usable Range: About 300 yards.
Magazine Release Catch: Left side of Receiver.
Note: This weapon fires from a closed breech.

This "People's Rifle" is an astonishing weapon which was originally developed by Haenel of Suhl in 1942 but was not introduced in general field use until 1945.

Originally intended as a cheap expendable arm to be issued to the people for home defense, it represents an entirely new departure in the field of low-cost machine weapons which can be manufactured with a minimum of machinery.

Where heretofore the use of a powerful cartridge has required the employment of locked breech weapons of costly design or of very powerful springs and unwieldy weight, this arm uses gas from the discharge to hold the forward action locked in such a way as to keep the breech firmly closed long enough to permit the use of the powerful 7.92mm German Short cartridge.

This weapon is noteworthy not only for the simplicity of this locking system and for cheapness of manufacture, but also because it permits manufacture with very little machinery, and that of the commonest design. Preventing underground manufacture of powerful arms on this system calls for the most rigid policing imaginable.

This design may be applicable to arms of great power, while the engineering principles involved lend themselves to further experimentation in many industrial fields.

This weapon consists of a stamped receiver to which the barrel is mounted securely by rivets. A plain wood stock is fastened by rivets to an extension of the receiver.

Over the barrel from the front end is mounted a tubular sliding member or housing 15½ inches long. Its forward end is machined to receive a removable cylindrical muzzle piece which is retained by an outside spring catch.

Steel guides are welded to the underside of this housing at its forward end and they serve to guide the rearward travel of the housing in the receiver.

The underside of the housing is cut away for a length of about 5¾ inches to permit it to fit down into the receiver. A steel breechblock about 3 inches long is riveted inside the rear end of this housing.

A Russian type extractor and a new type firing pin are mounted in the bolt. This firing pin is of the floating type and is unusual in that it is retained by an interrupted thread and may be removed by merely pushing in the head of the pin and twisting it to unlock. When the weapon is completely assembled a guide piece on the receiver serves to positively lock this firing pin as a notch in the pin rides over the guide piece during forward and backward movement. The recoil stroke of the housing is about 4 inches.

Sights are mounted on the housing and are fixed. The sight radius is about 8 inches.

The barrel has 4 holes drilled above and below and on either side about 2½ inches from the muzzle.

A heavy recoil spring with 23 turns in a length of 6¾ inches is mounted around the barrel to be compressed by the housing in its backward movement.

The gas ports themselves are about 2½ inches from the muzzle and are exposed after the housing travels back about one inch.

Field Stripping

The magazine may be removed by pushing in the catch in the receiver above and ahead of the magazine.

Pressing down on the spring catch on top of the housing ahead of the front sight will permit the muzzle sleeve to be rotated and withdrawn when the housing is pushed back a short distance (this muzzle sleeve is 4¾ inches long and requires a ¼ turn to ıelease it).

The safety is mounted on the left side of the receiver above the magazine. When it is pushed up it may be pulled out bringing its pin with it. The weapon must be cocked to permit removal.

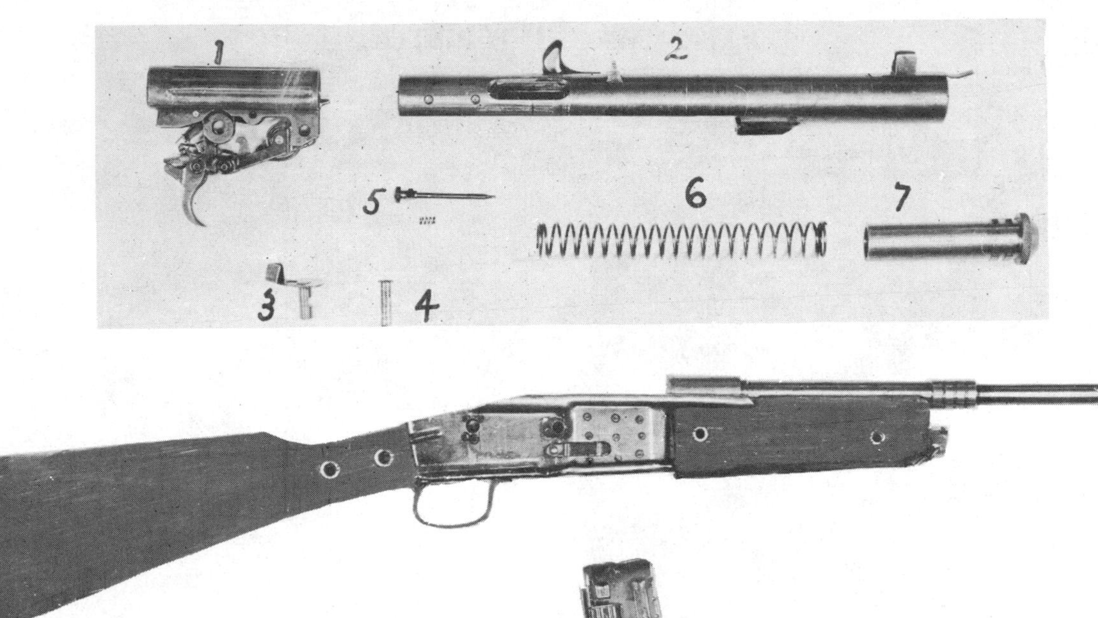

1. Bolt Housing and Firing Assembly. The Bolt and Slide assembly can move back in this housing when it is in place in the receiver.
2. Bolt and Slide Assembly. The bolt is riveted into the rear of this hollow sliding member.
3. Safety. 4. Retainer Pin. 5. Firing pin and Spring. 6. Recoil spring.

7. Gas chamber which locks inside front end of slide when the latter is in place around the barrel.
Barrel, Stock and Receiver assemblies. Note slide stop abutment on barrel at forward end of the forearm. Standard M.P. 44 Magazine for 7.92mm Short bottle neck cartridge.

Push the housing back about ½ inch and lift its rear end clear of the receiver. It may now be pushed forward and removed, together with the recoil spring, forward off the barrel.

The firing pin may be removed by pressing in its head and twisting it to unlock.

No further dismounting is normally necessary.

How the Weapon Operates

A standard MP 43-44 magazine loaded with 30 cartridges is inserted in the magazine housing from below and pushed in until it locks.

The bolt handle which is a heavy steel piece riveted to the left side of the housing is pulled back. This draws all the moving members to the rear, and the bolt rides over and compresses and cocks the hammer which is held by a simple sear arrangement.

When the bolt handle is released the compressed recoil spring pushes the members forward and strips a cartridge from the magazine into the firing chamber, where the extractor grips it as it seats.

Pressure on the trigger is communicated through the sear to release the hammer, which flies forward to strike the firing pin and discharge the cartridge.

As the bullet travels down the barrel it passes over the 4 gas ports about 2½ inches before reaching the muzzle. Thus it will be seen that gas escapes from the barrel into the space between the removable sleeve and the housing to exert a forward thrust as the bullet continues out of the muzzle. The sleeve is shaped to insure that most of the gas thrust will be exerted toward the concave forward end.

As this is a straight blowback weapon without a lock, the recoil force of the rearward action of gas against the head of the cartridge case drives the action to the rear. However, the thrust has to overcome not only the inertia and weight of moving parts as in the standard blowbacks, but also the forward action of the gases which have expanded in the moving housing. This check system delays the opening of the action long enough to permit the use of a cartridge so powerful that normally a locking device would be required to permit its use.

Rearward action ejects, recocks, and reloads in standard automatic fashion.

Note on this Weapon

On the underside of the housing, just ahead of the housing guides, a large hole is provided to permit escape of exhaust gas. A similar hole is provided ahead of the bolt on the upper left of the housing as a safety valve in the event of a blown cartridge head.

GERMAN MACHINE PISTOLS

German Mauser 7.63mm 1932 Machine Pistol.

Note: This is a full machine pistol. It is a freak weapon intermediate between the pistol and the submachine gun.

Caliber: 7.63mm Mauser.
Magazine: Sheet metal detachable box.
Capacity: 10-shot or 20-shot depending on length of magazine. It is inserted into magazine housing from below until is locks. It may be loaded with clips from the top through the open action exactly as in the case of the standard Mauser Military Pistol.
Type of Fire: Single shot or full automatic. Turning ring button on left side of pistol above and behind the trigger prevents the disconnector from functioning and allows the pistol to fire as long as the trigger is held back and there are any cartridges left in magazine.

How Automatic Firing Mechanism Works

The ring button lever on the left side of the pistol is turned to letter "N." There are two teeth on the axis of this lever, one engaging the catch hook bar and the other one working on the pawl. Turning the ring button pushes the catch hook bar forward (allowing it to operate) and pushes pawl forward. When this pawl is in forward

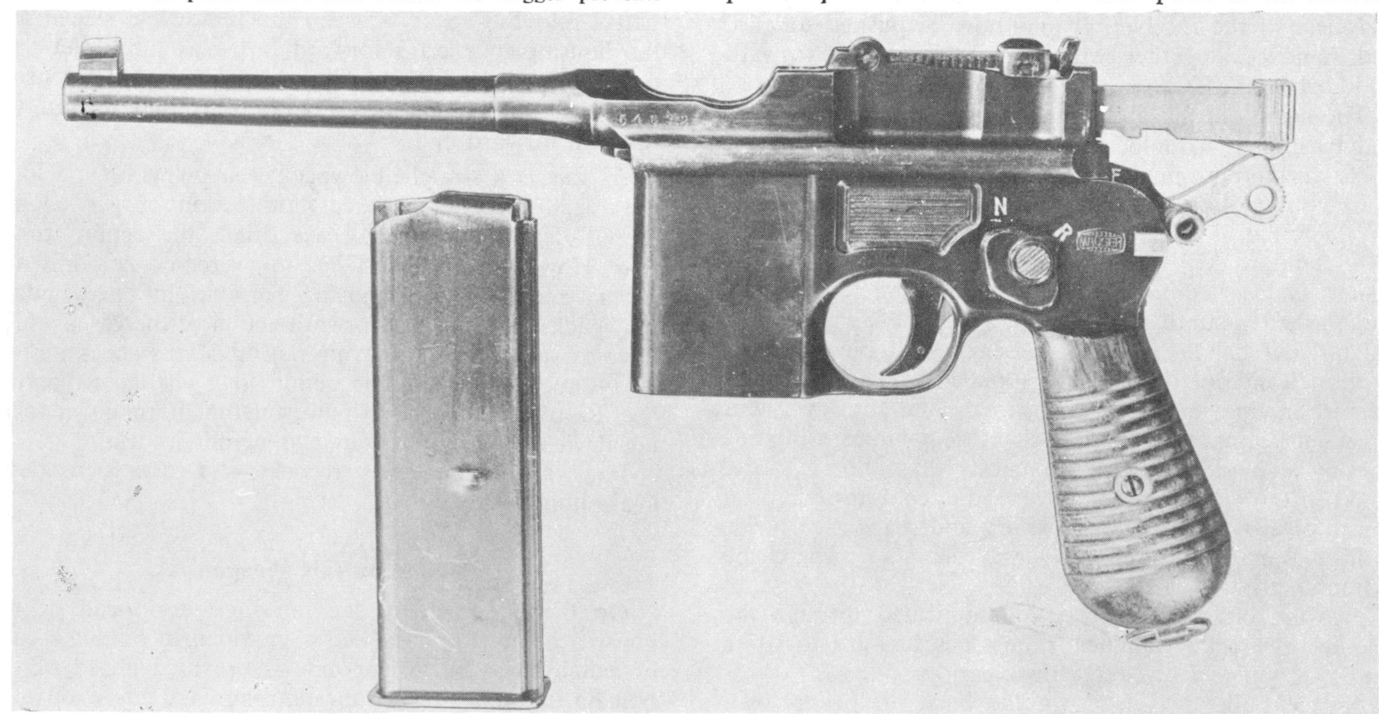

1932 M.P. Bolt in full rear position. Magazine removed. Note selector.

position the sear is held out of engagement with the hammer as long as trigger is held back. When catch hook is in operating position, its middle arm engages notch in the hammer and holds the hammer cocked. The tip of the upper arm of the catch hook works in a slot in the bottom part of the barrel extension sleeve. When the barrel extension strikes the catch hook it revolves it, releasing the hammer. Hence the hammer falls automatically as soon as the action is locked; and the pistol continues to fire so long as the trigger is held back. When the trigger is released the sear engages the hammer and stops the firing.

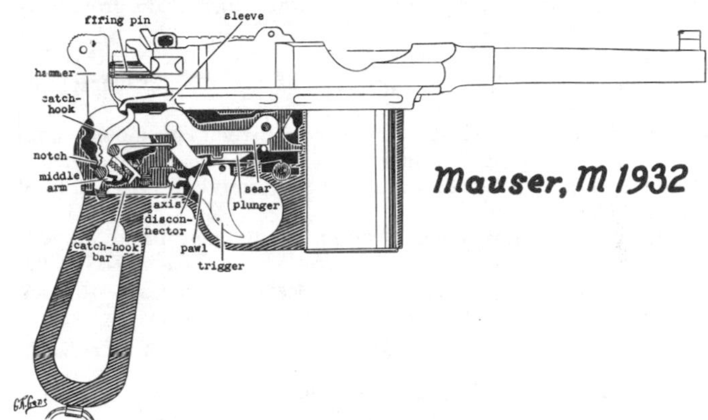

Mauser, M 1932

Note On Use of This Weapon As a Machine Pistol

This weapon should be used as a machine pistol only when the shoulder stock is attached, so that stock may be pressed rigidly against shoulder or against side, with right hand firmly gripping handle and left hand holding rigidly to magazine housing.

Because of the high power of the cartridge and the low weight of the pistol and its recoiling members, the cyclic rate of this weapon is entirely too high to make it of any value for ordinary military use. It was in wide use among the S. S. Troops for the value its automatic firing device might have against mobs. Used as a pistol, this weapon functions so rapidly that it is almost impossible to distinguish between the report of the different cartridges as they are exploded. Regardless of the strength of the firer, the recoil throws the weapon upward and backward so that it is utterly impossible to hold it down even if both hands are used. While the first shot may hit the point of aim, the succeeding shots, except at ranges of a few feet, are bound to go high and miss. This merely wastes ammunition.

Using this weapon as a carbine, it is possible to fire in bursts of three or four shots. In this case, it has a practical military value.

Note: The Model 1932 Mauser is also manufactured in Spain where it is produced under the name of ASTRA Machine Pistol.

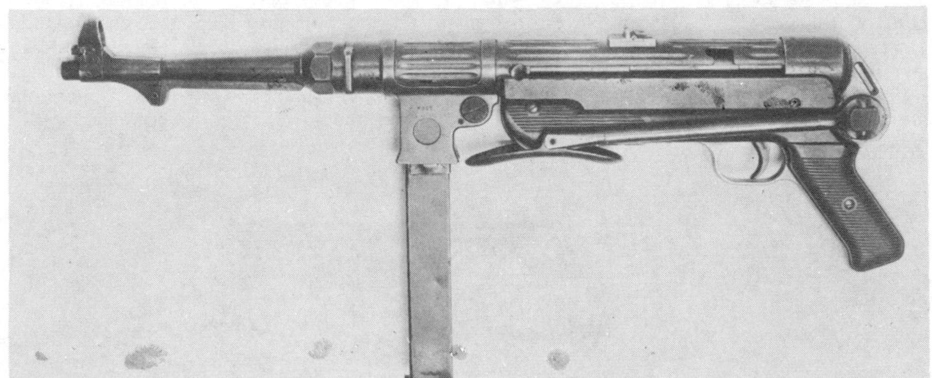

German 9mm Model 38 Machine Pistol (Sometimes Called Parachute Model, Schmeisser).

Note: This weapon was originally designed for use by Parachute Troops. It was so much superior to all other types of German submachine guns (or machine pistols, as the Germans call them) that this and its modification, the MP40, have rapidly supplanted all other types of machine pistols in use in the first line German

Army. It was issued to Platoon and Section commanders, to the Armored Force Units for racking up in tanks, armored vehicles, and lorries, and to parachute troops. The design is excellent.

Caliber: 9mm Parabellum, ball.

Magazine: Single line box type, capacity 32 cartridges. (As in most machine pistols, best results are obtained by loading the magazine to less than full capacity; 26 or 28 cartridges are recommended for this weapon.)

Weight: 9 lbs. without magazine.

Weight of Magazine: Loaded, 23 ozs.

Overall Length with Stock Folded: About 25 inches.

Overall Length with Stock Extended: About 35 inches.

Sights: Fixed front with sight cover.

Sights Rear: Open. A standing leaf is sighted at 100 meters. Behind this is a folding leaf which when turned up provides a sight for 200 meters.

Accurate Range: About 200 meters.

Gun Operated By: Blowback pressure of gas forcing empty cartridge case back against bolt.

Locked: Straight blowback, unlocked. Breech is closed until bullet leaves barrel by inertia of moving parts and heavy recoil spring moving forward and pressing bolt against head of cartridge.

Cooled: Bolt remains open between shots, permitting air circulation through breech and barrel. Below barrel is a flat aluminum stamped or plastic bar, designed primarily to lock the barrel in the pistol ports of armored vehicles.

Cyclic Rate of Fire: 450 to 540 rounds per minute, depending largely on type of ammunition used and strength of springs.

Position of Cocking Handle: On left sight of receiver. It is hook shaped.

Magazine Locking Catch: On left side at rear end of magazine housing. It is a large, milled thumb piece It is pressed in to release magazine.

Stock Release Catch: On receiver just above grip. Pressing the milled stud in the left side of the weapon releases the spring and permits the stock to be unfolded; the butt piece for the shoulder can then be opened.

Type of Firing: Full automatic only. Burst of two or three shots are possible by tapping trigger.

Safety: The only safety provided in this weapon is a safety recess with the letter "S" stamped near it at the rear of the cocking handle slot. Pulling the cocking handle past the full cocked position and then up into this slot locks the weapon. This type of safety is subject to jarring or turning out of engagement without being noticed; it is a practical military device, but not a foolproof one.

A modified form of safety was also issued. The cocking piece and receiver were altered to take a spring-loaded sliding cover on the cocking piece. This could engage in a cut in the receiver to lock the bolt in forward position.

Loading and Firing

Six spare magazines and a special magazine loader are issued in a web haversack with each one of these guns. The loader is a simple lever device with an attached housing into which the magazine is inserted. Snapping a cartridge into the top of the housing and pushing down firmly on the lever loads the individual cartridge into the magazine. This motion is repeated until the magazine is filled. If no loader is available, cartridges may be inserted by the normal procedure for loading automatic pistol magazines; leverage for inserting the last few cartridges may be exerted by pressure of both thumbs, once the cartridge has been seated.

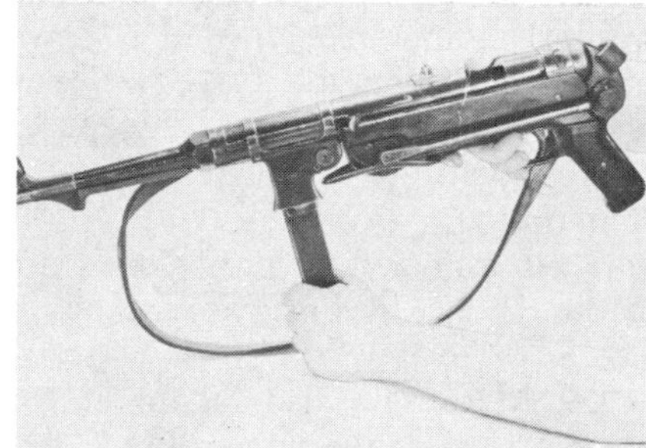

Insert loaded magazine from below into the magazine housing and push up until it locks. Note: A stud on the outside of the magazine will prevent it from going in beyond the proper length.

Pull back cocking handle and lock it up in its recess in the safety slot.

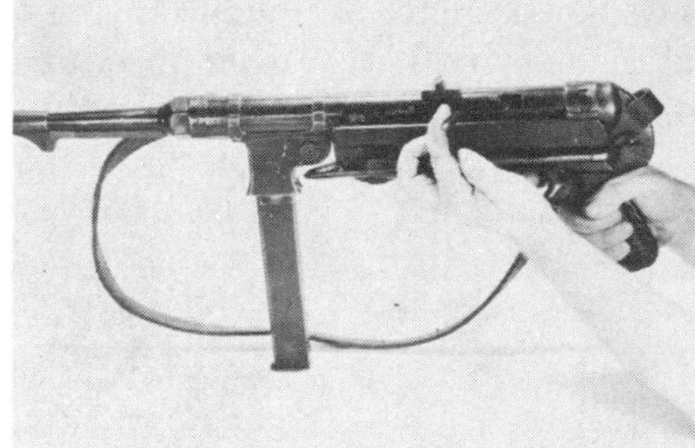

Warning: Always remember that this weapon fires when the bolt goes forward! Never, therefore, let the bolt go home while the loaded magazine is in position. Unless you wish to fire the weapon, always extract the magazine before easing the bolt home.

Whenever possible, always use this weapon as a carbine. To do this, press the catch stud as indicated. This will release catch and permit you to unfold the stock and turn the butt piece down into proper place for firing from the shoulder.

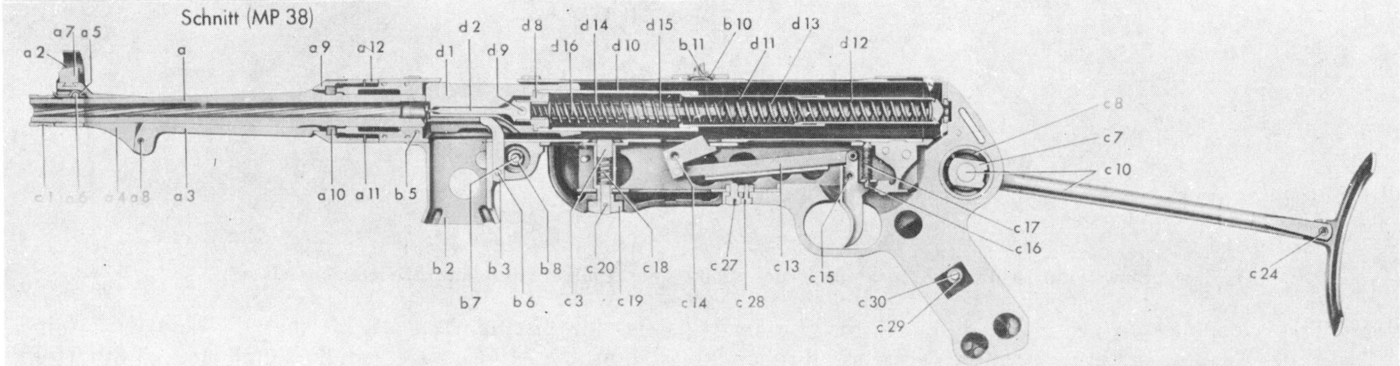

Sectional View of M.P. 38 Showing Mechanism in Rest Position. The M.P. 40 is identical except for minor manufacturing differences.

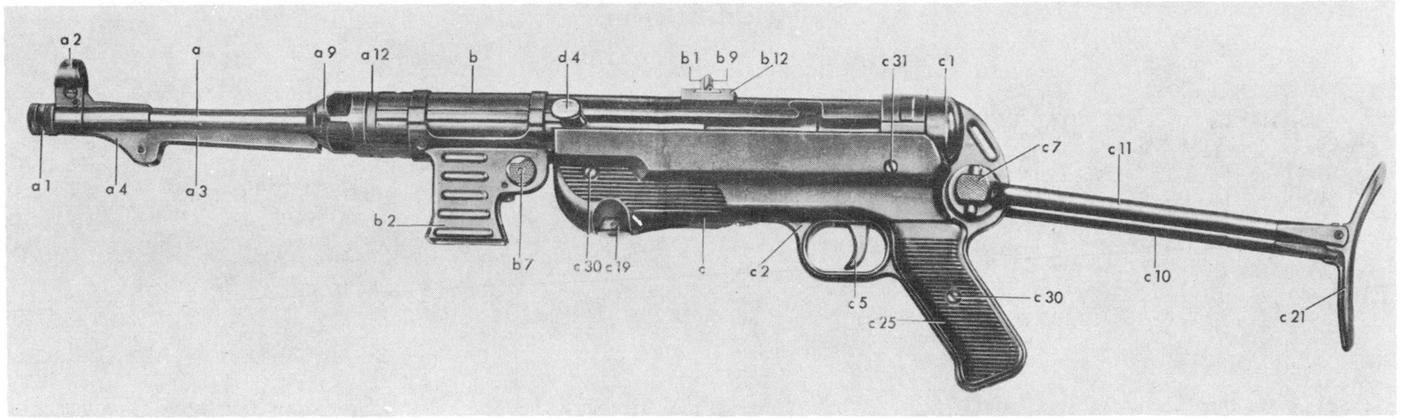

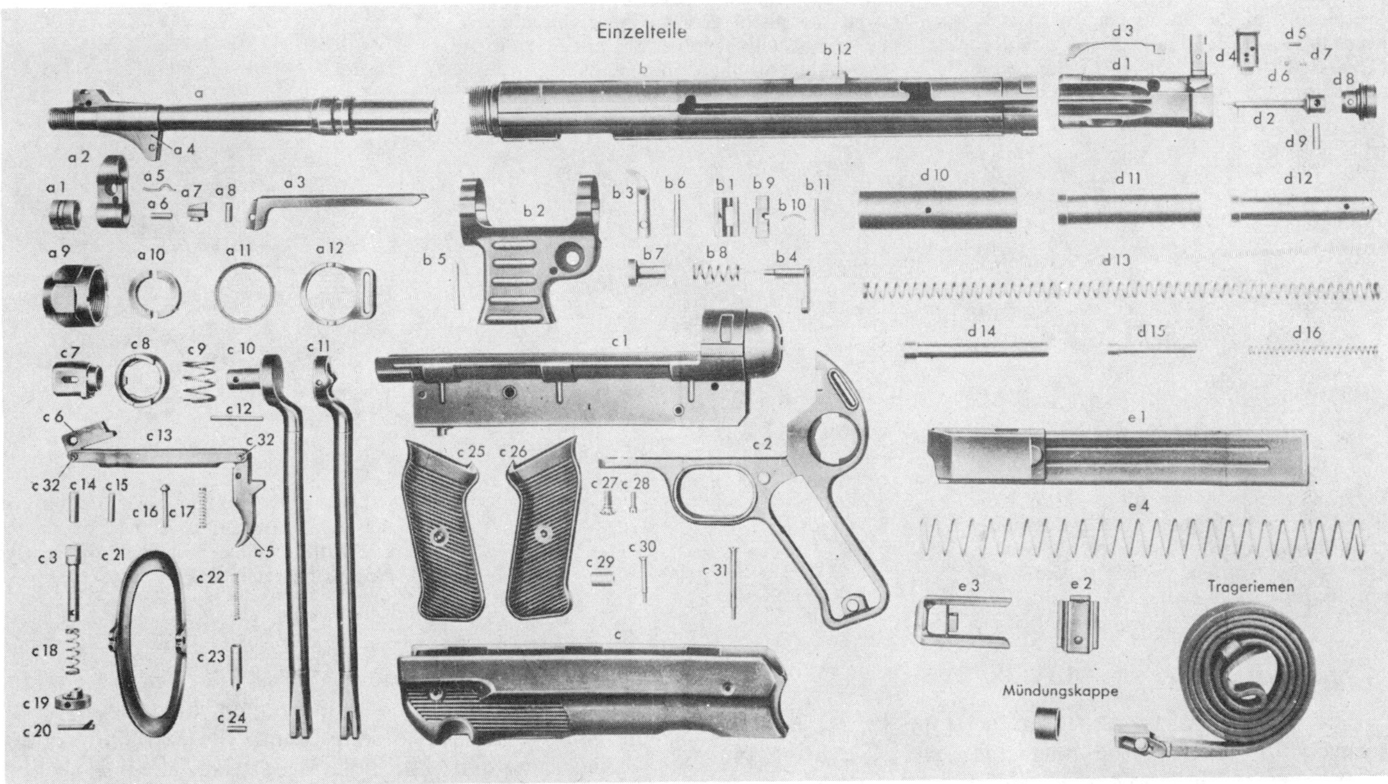

a2 Front cap cover
d10 Recoil spring tube large
a7 Front sight
a5 Front sight retainer
a Barrel
a9 Barrel nut
a12 Collar
d1 Bolt
d2 Firing pin
d9 Firing pin retaining pin
d8 Recoil spring tube end
d14 Recoil spring
d10 Recoil spring tube large
d15 Recoil guide
b10 and b11 Rear sight leaf spring
d11 Recoil spring second tube
d13 Buffer spring
d12 Buffer spring tube
c10 Stock arm
c7 Stock Pivot
c8 Stock release
c24 Shoulder piece pivot

a1 Barrel cap
a6 Cover retainer
a4 Barrel Jacket
a8 Resting bar pin
a3 Resting and retracting bar
a10 Barrel nut washer
a11 Barrel threads
b2 Magazine guide
b7 Magazine release cap
b3 Magazine release screw
b6 Washer
c3 Receiver lock
c20 Receiver lock screw retainer
c19 Receiver lock screw
c18 Receiver lock spring
c14 Sear
c27 and c28 Frame screws
c13 Sear lever
c15 Trigger axis screw
c17 and c16 Trigger spring
c29 and c30 Grip screws
a Barrel
a1 Barrel Cap

a2 Front sight cover
a3 Resting bar
a9 Barrel nut
a12 Collar
b Chamber cover
b2 Magazine guide
b7 Magazine release cap
d4 Bolt handle
b1 and b9 Rear sight leaves
b12 Rear sight base
c31 Lock Frame screw
c1 Buffer housing
c7 Stock release button
c10 and c11 Stock arms
c21 Shoulder piece
c30 Forend screw
c19 Dismounting screw
c Forend
c2 Trigger guard
c5 Trigger
c25 Pistol grip
c30 Grip screw

Field Stripping

After extracting the magazine, and seeing that the bolt is in its forward position, pull out the receiver lock against the tension of the spring and twist it to keep it locked in the outward position. (This stud is on the bottom of the frame at its forward end.)

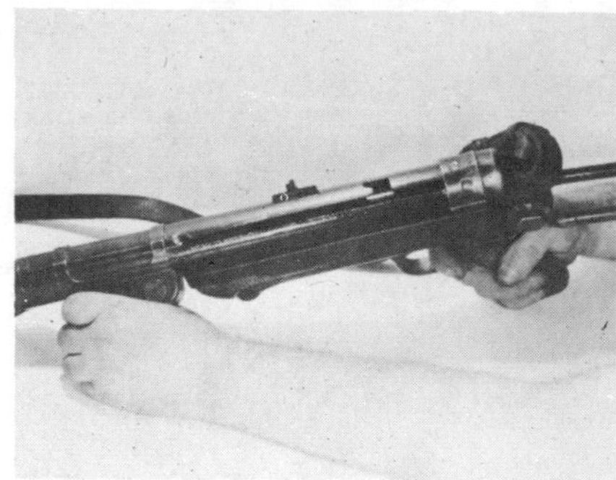

While pressing the trigger with the right forefinger, hold firmly to the magazine housing with the left hand, then twist the pistol grip to the right, about 80°; this will revolve the entire frame assembly and the components.

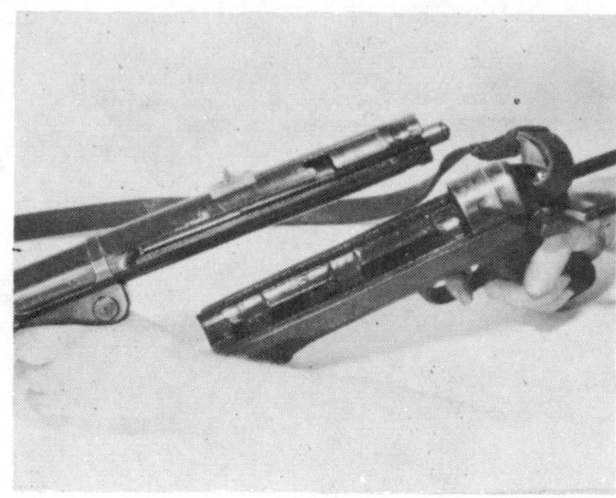

Now draw the frame group back and out of the receiver.

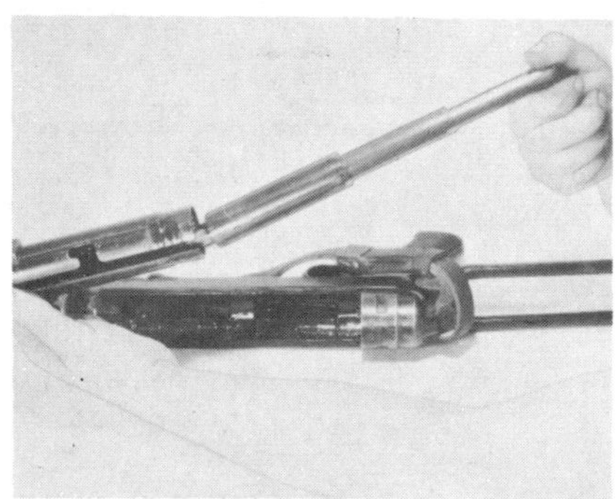

Draw back slightly on cocking handle. This will bring out a telescoping tube inside which is the recoil spring, and at the front of which is the firing pin. Remove this unit.

Now draw straight back on the cocking handle which is a part of the bolt and withdraw the bolt from the receiver. No further stripping is required.

How the M.P. 38 Works

The loaded magazine inserted from below is held securely in place by the magazine lock. The firing pin is attached to the forward end of the telescope housing. It passes through the hole in the center of the bolt, while the abutment behind it lodges into the head of the bolt recess. As the bolt is drawn back by its handle, or forced back by the explosion, it telescopes the three-piece recoil spring housing (which carries the firing pin) and compresses the recoil spring which is inside the telescope. The rear of the recoil spring housing rests against the inside of the rounded buffer end of the frame, which is securely locked to the receiver.

When the bolt is in the fully cocked position, the sear locks into the bottom of the bolt and connects with the trigger. Pressing the trigger depresses the sear and permits the bolt to run forward under the influence of the recoil spring acting through the telescopic section to force the bolt forward.

As the feed ribs on the bottom of the bolt strip the top round from the magazine and push it into the firing chamber, the face of the extractor set in the bolt blocks the base of the cartridge. When the cartridge is fully seated, the further forward movement of the bolt pushes the heavy extractor to snap it into the extracting groove. At the same time the bolt face strikes against the base of the cartridge. The firing pin, a separate unit from the bolt, is under the pressure of the recoil spring and functions in the same manner as a fixed firing pin—it protrudes at all times. This pin now strikes the cartridge and discharges it.

During the backward action the extractor hook withdraws the empty cartridge case, carrying it back until it strikes against the ejector and is ejected. This cycle of operation continues as long as the trigger is held back and there are any cartridges left in the magazine.

Note on this Weapon

This machine pistol was developed by the Haenel factory at Suhl, Germany. It uses steel and plastics throughout—no wood is used in its construction. It is possible to use the weapon as a machine pistol, using one or both hands, or as a machine carbine shooting from the shoulder.

German Schmeisser machine pistol MP41. Cal. 9 mm. Special modification of the MP 40, by using wooden stock.

This is essentially the same weapon as the Model 38. Most of the changes made in it are to facilitate ease of manufacture. The receiver casing has been made smooth instead of corrugated as in the case of the M. P. .38.

On certain models a special locking device is incorporated on the cocking handle. Instead of the hook-shaped cocking handle, these models are fitted with a knob type. The knob must be pulled out slightly against the spring tension before the cocking handle can be drawn back to the rear, or released from the safety slot. This design is intended to overcome the danger of a cartridge being fired when the cocking handle is accidentally freed from its locking recess, as by catching against clothing.

The correct position of the left hand when firing this

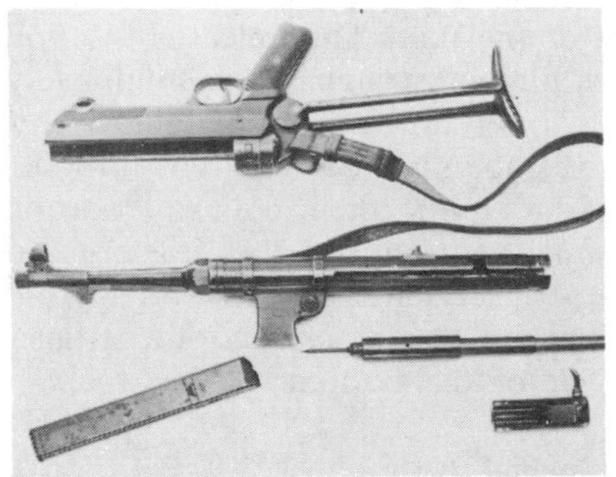

Weapon dismounted, complete field strip.

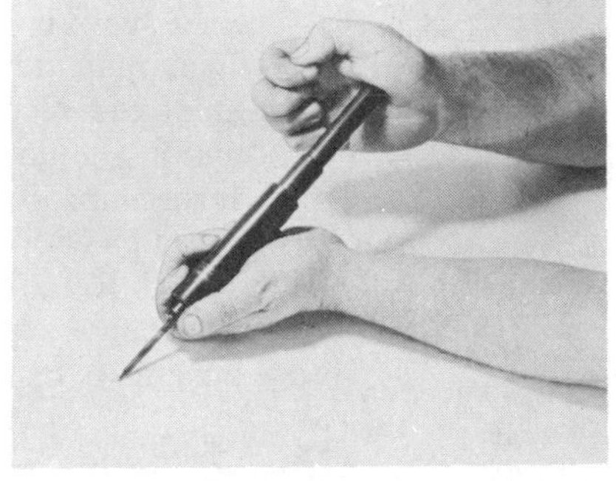

Recoil spring housing, showing firing pin and telescoping of tube.

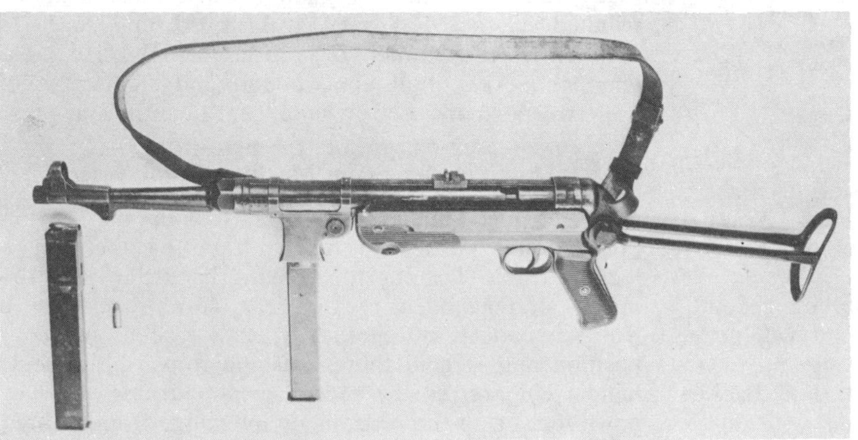

German 9-mm Model 40 Machine Pistol.

Increasing magazine capacity in submachine guns has been quite successfully worked out by the Germans.

The German device is built into the late model Schmeisser machine pistol. It consists of a spring locked movable magazine housing. Instead of the standard magazine holding a maximum of 32

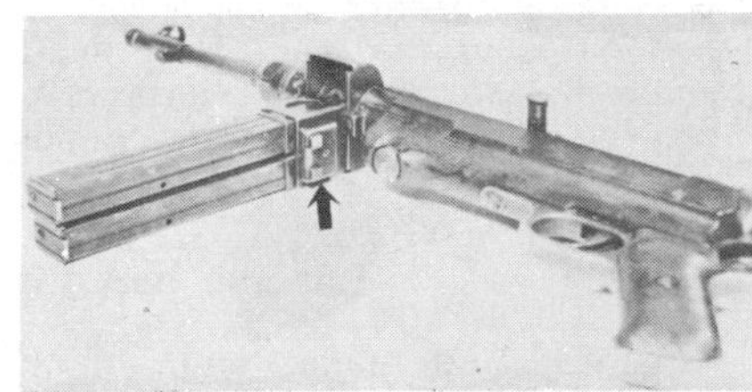

cartridges, this magazine housing will take two magazines in parallel position. The magazines are inserted in the housing from below in standard fashion and one is in direct line with the chamber and the bolt. When that magazine has been emptied, pressing in the spring catch in the housing permits the housing to be pushed across in its track so that the second magazine is brought into direct line for continued firing.

weapon is gripping the corrugated section of the frame directly to the rear of the magazine housing. Holding the magazine itself, may cause serious jams. There is inevitably a certain amount of play in any magazine when it is locked into place; and if it is being used as a rest for the left hand during the course of recoil, it may rock the magazine mouth sufficiently to cause poor feeding.

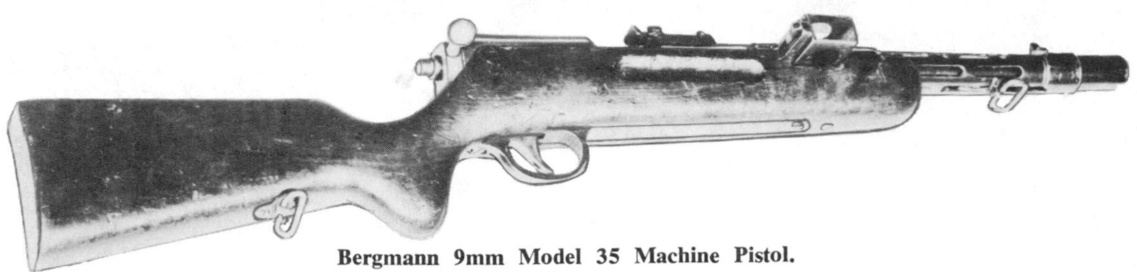

Bergmann 9mm Model 35 Machine Pistol.

This is a development of the original German Machine Pistol 18-1 (Bergmann blowback), a design which is the forerunner of practically all the straight blowback designs. The 1935 model was officially adopted by Sweden in 1939.

Caliber: 9mm Parabellum (08 Pistol).
Magazine: Removable box type, capacity 32 cartridges.
Position of Magazine: Right side of weapon pointing slightly toward the front. Earlier models may feed from the left side.
Ballistic Data: Approximately 10% better than for the 9mm cartridge used in the standard pistol. This is because of the extra length of barrel in the Bergmann—7¾" as against 4".
Barrel Length: 7¾".
Overall Length: 33".
Weight: About 9 lbs. without sling.
Sights: Fixed front. Open rear with elevation from 50 to 1,000 meters.
Operation and Locking Data: Same as for other blowbacks. This weapon is the original of all the blowback type submachine guns.
Cooled: Has a perforated casing around the barrel which helps radiation and dissipates heat. Bolt stays open between shots, permitting additional air circulation through barrel.
Cyclic Rate of Fire: 540 shots per minute.
Type of Fire: Either single shot or full automatic. A very light pull on the trigger fires single shot. Pressing the trigger still farther back brings the main trigger into action and the weapon fires full automatic.
Position of Cocking Handle: A rotating lever with a knob on the end of it is placed at the end of the receiver on the right hand side.
Safeties: A thumb operated safety is placed on the left side of the receiver just to the rear and left of the rear sight. Safe position is forward when letter "S" can be seen; the fire position is to the rear, when the letter "F" is visible. An automatic safety device is incorporated in this weapon which prevents the trigger from being pulled unless the operating handle is locked down.

Loading and Firing

Insert loaded magazine in magazine housing on right side of receiver and push it home until it locks. Note: Magazine release catch is on the near side of this housing.

Turn the bolt handle up exactly as for the bolt action type rifle and pull it straight back as far as it will go. This cocks the bolt.

Now push the bolt handle forward and turn it back down into its locked position. The bolt itself will stay back, leaving the ejector port on the left side of the weapon open.

There are two triggers, a main trigger and an auxiliary trigger which is located at the rear of the main trigger. If the main trigger is pressed above the auxiliary trigger, semi-automatic fire will be produced. If the main trigger is pressed at its mid-point so that the auxiliary trigger is also pressed, the main trigger will go all the way to the rear and full automatic fire will be produced.

Field Stripping

Turn the cocking handle up as far as it will go and pull it to the rear to its full extent. Now push down the vertical bolt stop which rises on the left side of the receiver just at the front of the bolt. This releases the bolt which may now be withdrawn straight back completely out of the receiver. Normally no further stripping is required. Should further dismounting be required, turn the triggerguard locking screws until their cutaway portion lines up with the similar portion of the triggerguard screws. Removing the triggerguard screws will permit the receiver to be lifted off the stock and the trigger housing to be pulled out of the bottom of the stock.

Special Note

The weapon illustrated is the M. P. 35. There are many variants of the Bergmann. Those most widely distributed are the Models 1934, 34/I, 35, and 35/I. They vary from each other in various details, i.,e., barrel lengths, jackets, bolt construction and sights. None of these weapons are used in significant quantities at present.

How the Bergmann Machine Pistol Works

The loaded magazine is inserted in the magazine housing and pushed in, it is locked by the magazine locking catch. Turning the cocking handle up and drawing it straight back to the rear draws back the bolt which is caught by the sear when it reaches full cocked position and is held there. Pushing forward the cocking handle compresses the recoil spring; turning the handle down locks it to the receiver by interrupted screw threads. Pressure on the trigger drives a plunger forward pushing a trigger barrel which forces the sear down out of engagement with the barrel bolt. This trigger plunger now slides off the shoulder trigger bar and releases the sear so it can snap back in position to engage the bolt when it travels rearward from the force of the recoil. Hence the trigger must be released before it can be again squeezed to fire the weapon for the second semi-automatic shot.

If on the other hand the trigger is pulled back as far as it will go, it draws back the secondary trigger; as the trigger plunger slides off its bar, a projection in the automatic trigger rotates back and away from the trigger, allowing it to be drawn all the way to the rear. This increased amount of rotation permits the upper part of the trigger bar to push all the way forward, holding the sear down for full automatic fire as long as the trigger pull is maintained.

While the cocking handle on this weapon functions in the same manner as the rotating bolt handle on a rifle, it does not duplicate the unlocking action of the bolt action rifle.

The trigger being squeezed, the bolt goes forward under the compulsion of the compressed recoil spring. The top cartridge in the magazine is stripped into the firing chamber and the extractor in the bolt snaps over the cannelure of the cartridge before it is chambered.

However, just before the bolt reaches its full forward position, the hammer comes in contact with a projection on the bottom of the receiver which compels the hammer to rotate and drive the firing pin forward to fire the cartridge.

As the bolt travels rearward under the force of the recoil, the extractor draws out the empty cartridge case and it is hurled out of the left side of the weapon. The empty case strikes a rigid ejector, which in this weapon is in the rear of the magazine slide on the right side of the receiver.

The recoil spring is compressed, and at the end of the motion the recoil spring guide over which the spring compresses, strikes the buffer spring, and stops the recoil of the bolt.

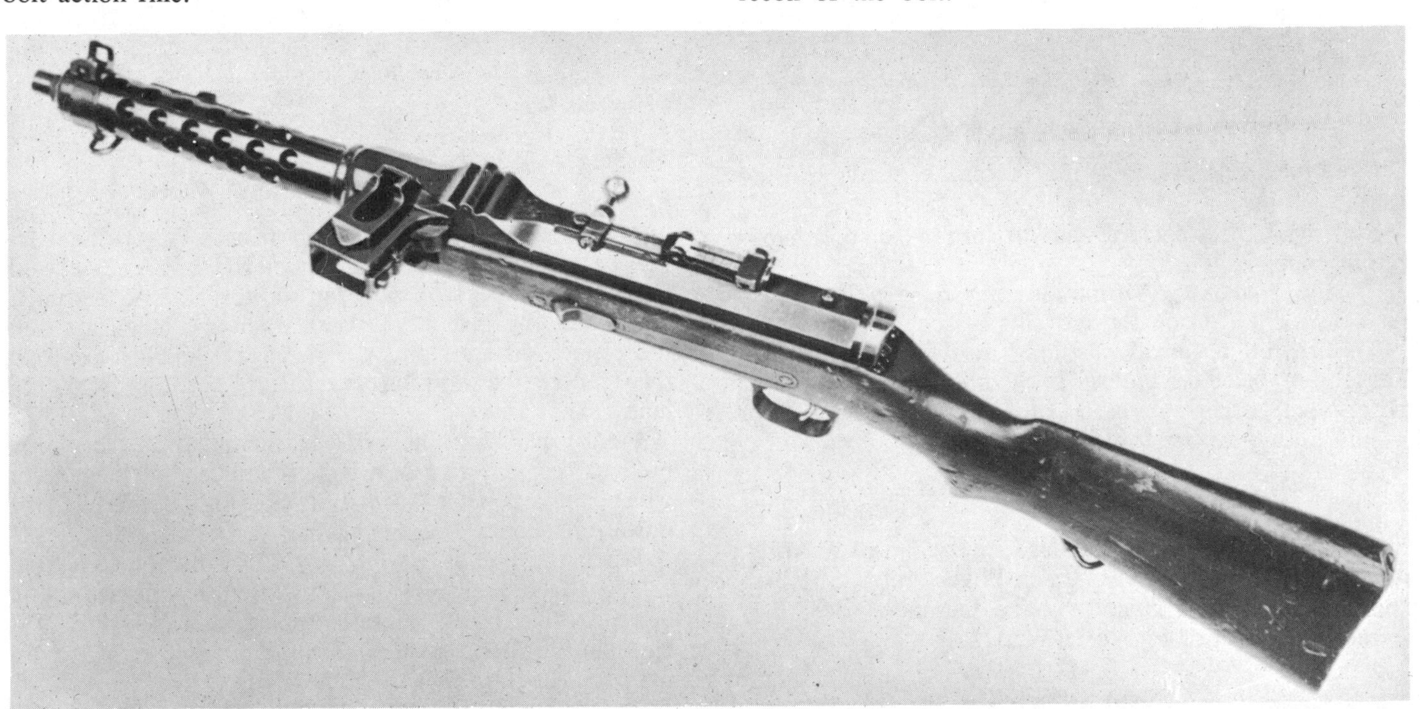

Steyr-Solothurn 9mm Machine Pistol.

Note: In the United States, this weapon would be called a submachine gun.

Caliber: 9mm Steyr (some made for 9mm Parabellum, 9mm Mauser, and 7.63mm Mauser.

Magazine: Detachable box type, capacity 30 rounds.

Muzzle Velocity of Cartridge: 1100 to 1600 feet per second in this barrel length.

Muzzle Energy: 400 to 480 foot pounds.

Magazine Positioned: On left side of receiver slanting somewhat from the front.

Length Overall: 32¼".

Weight: 9⅞ pounds.

Sights: Rear sight adjustable to 500 meters.

Accurate Range: About 300 yards.

Gun Operated By: Recoil on the blowback principle.

Locked: Strictly unlocked. Weight of recoiling parts and strength of recoil spring combine to keep breech closed until period of dangerous pressure has passed and bullet has left barrel.

Cooled: By perforated jacket surrounding barrel permitting air circulation.

Cyclic Rate of Fire: 400-450 per minute.

Position of Cocking Handle: A knob on the right side of the receiver.

Bolt Position When Ready to Fire: Open.

Type of Fire: Either single shot or full automatic. Selector device is positioned in slot on left side of stock. Push it forward to uncover the letter "E" for single shot fire. Pull it back to uncover the letter "D" for full automatic fire.

Safety: Catch is on top of receiver directly ahead of the rear sight. Pushed forward against the stud it is "Safe." Pulled back against the sight, it is ready to "Fire." Safety may be applied both in the fired and the cocked position.

Special Note on Loading Magazine

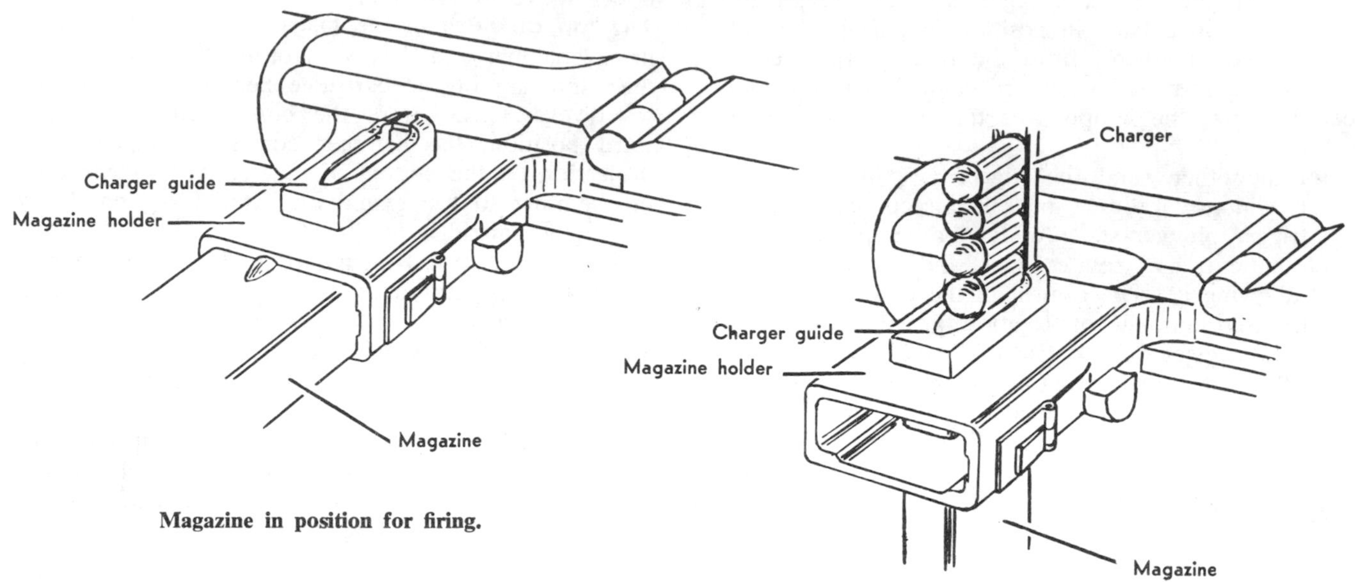

Magazine in position for firing.

Magazine in position for loading.

Instructions for Loading and Firing

Load magazine exactly as for automatic pistols if using loose cartridges.

Pull back the cocking handle until the bolt stops at full cock.

To fire a shot each time the trigger is pulled, push the selector button on the left side of the stock forward.

To fire full automatic as long as the trigger is held back, pull selector button back uncovering the letter "D." Note: except in cases of emergency the selector should always be set for single shot fire.

Special Note

This weapon was not standard in the German Army; it was widely used by the German Police and S. S. It was among the materiel gained by the Germans when they seized Austria prior to World War II.

Field Stripping

On the cover directly behind the rear sight is a spring stud. While pressing this stud down, push in the catch at the end of the cover where it joins the stock. Now raise the cover. This cover is hinged directly above the firing chamber and to the side of the magazine housing. The entire bolt and breech mechanism are now open.

Draw the cocking handle back slowly, and when narrow portion of the bolt emerges grasp that section firmly with the left hand. Hold the bolt securely while completing the back movement and pull out the cocking handle.

Now lift the front end of the bolt out of the guides, holding it firmly to prevent the mechanism from flying out under the pressure of the recoil spring and rod.

The recoil spring is removable through a small slot in the butt plate.

How the Steyr-Solothurn Works

Magazine is loaded with 30 cartridges (it will hold 32, but best feeding results are achieved by loading with the lesser number). A ridge on the top side of the magazine strikes against the housing when the magazine is in the proper distance and the magazine locking catch on the rear of the housing snaps into place securing the magazine.

Pulling back on the cocking handle draws back the bolt, to the rear end of which is attached a hinged rod which pushes back against a housing, compressing a powerful recoil spring in the butt.

When the bolt is all the way back, the sear engages.

The trigger being pressed, the bolt is released to be driven forward by the compressed recoil spring. The feed slots on its underside strip the top cartridge from the magazine into the firing chamber.

The firing pin in the bolt explodes the cartridge as it is being seated and the extractor snaps into the cannelure of the cartridge case.

The heavy bolt and powerful recoil spring during the forward motion hold the bolt safely closed until the bullet has left the barrel.

This weapon has a unique magazine loading device machined into it. To load with this device:

Insert magazine into bottom of magazine housing. A special slot is cut on the underside of the housing to permit this.

The special lock catch on underside of housing will lock it into place.

Now insert a standard 8-shot clip in the clip guide on top of the magazine housing.

Press the cartridges straight down into the magazine exactly as in rifle loading. When magazine is fully loaded, press release catch and pull it out from the bottom of the housing. It is now ready for insertion in the side of the housing for loading the weapon to fire.

Added Note: The right side of the barrel casing is equipped to permit fixing a standard Austrian Army bayonet.

The Steyr-Solothurn used by the Japanese takes the 7.63mm Mauser cartridge.

If this weapon is stamped "MP 34 (ö)" it indicates it was issued for Austrian use and takes the long 9mm Steyr cartridge—not the 9mm Parabellum.

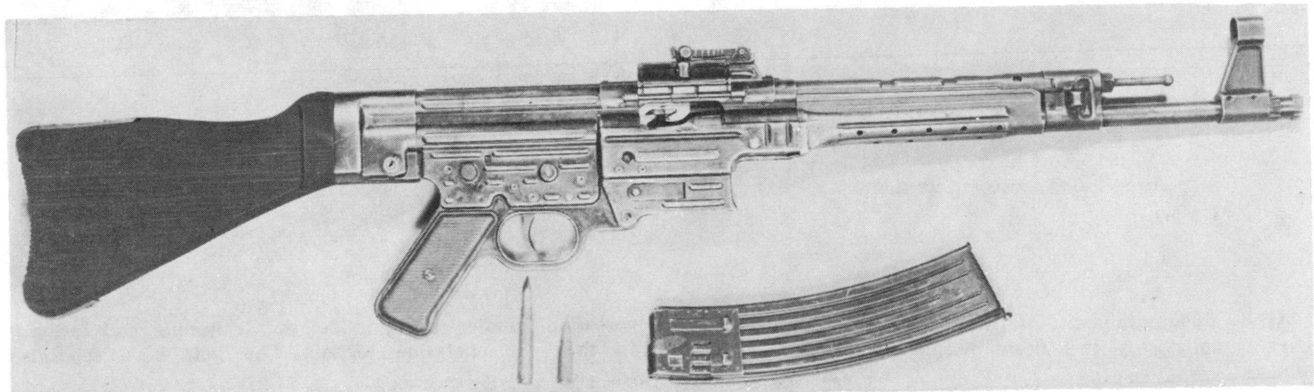

Machine Pistol 43, 43/1, 44, and STG44.

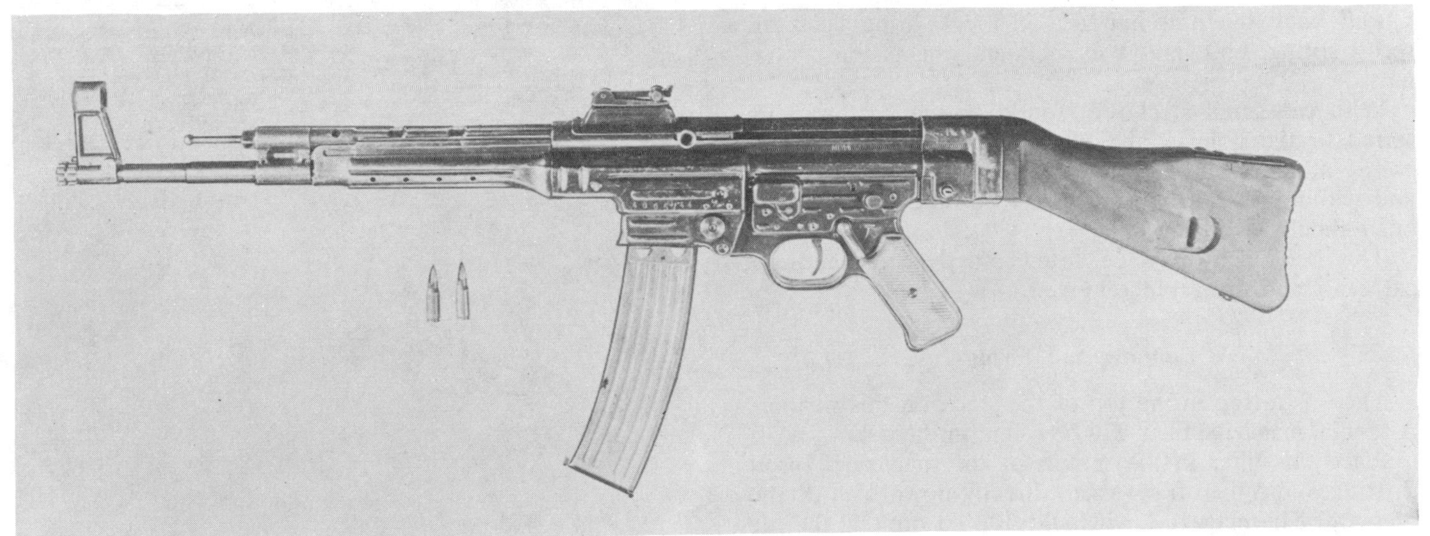

MP 44. Left Side View.

Caliber: 7.92mm Short. (Not the rifle cartridge.)

Cartridge: The standard rifle cartridge case, bottle necked, shortened to take a boattail bullet of 120 grains. The case is made of steel. The bullet is a gilding metal coating over a soft steel jacket. Inside this jacket is a lead sleeve surrounding a steel core. A newer type of powder was used, charge is 32 grains.

Magazine: A double row staggered box positioned from below ahead of the triggerguard.

Magazine Capacity: 30 rounds.

Overall Length: 36¾ inches.

Barrel Length: About 16 inches.

Sights: Tangent and peep 100 to 800 meters.

Gun Operated by: Gas; on an improved system operating on top of the barrel.

Locked: Securely locked by separate locking block forcing against the bolt. Fires from a closed breech.

Cooled: Air. Has casing around most of barrel.

Position of Cocking Handle: Left side of receiver.

Type of Fire: Selective. Push-through button above trigger functions as in Sten gun to give single shot or full automatic fire at will.

Safety: Mounted on left side at rear of triggerguard, where it can be readily pushed into firing position by the thumb of the right hand as the weapon is raised for firing.

Hold-Open Device: None.

Dust Cover: A spring loaded dust cover can be pushed down over the ejection port on the right side of the receiver. When the bolt travels to the rear in recoil, or when the bolt handle is pulled back, this special cover opens automatically. This is a simple and efficient protective device.

Muzzle Velocity: About 2250 feet per second.

Penetration in Mild Steel: About .25 inch.

Rate of Fire: About 800 per minute, cyclic.

Magazine Release Catch: Left side.

Field Stripping

A spring-held pin passes through the receiver and stock from the right. Pull this out from the right side.

The stock may now be withdrawn exposing the recoil spring.

Press the trigger and swing the triggerguard and

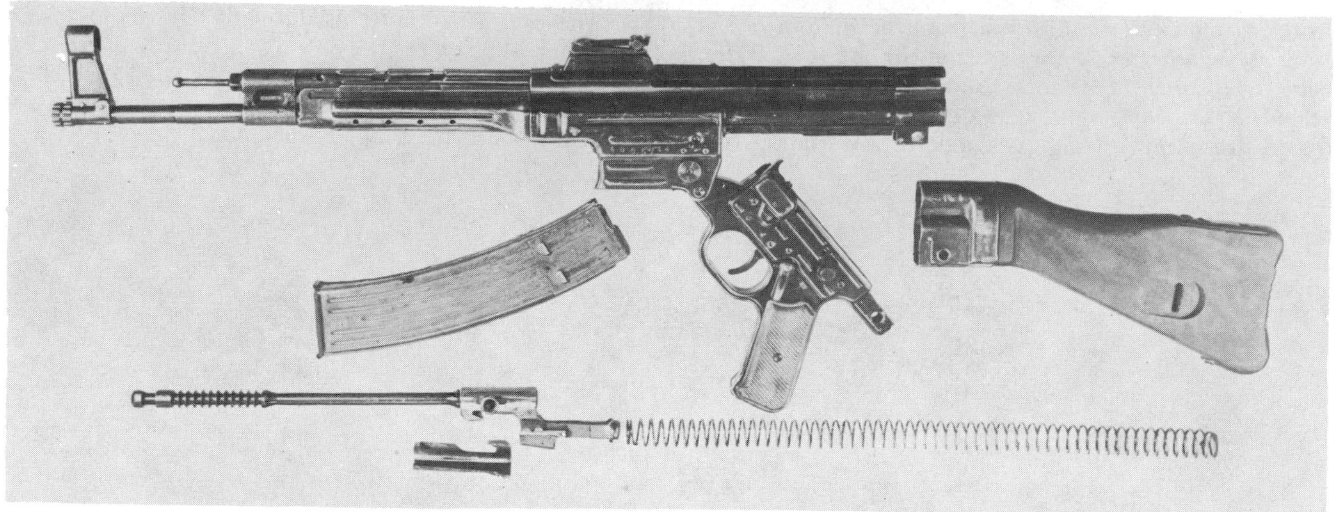

MP 44 Field Stripped. Note that the gas piston, operating rod, operating handle, spring guide, bolt camming and locking units are actually only two units. A pin secures the rod section to the rear operating section. The bolt is a separate unit.

all its contained units (these are not dismountable) down on its hinge.

Pull back the bolt handle. This will bring back the recoil spring, bolt, and bolt lock and the piston for removal.

With the small steel tool found in the butt trap inserted in the hole of the gas cup protruding from the casing at the front end, the gas cup may be unscrewed and withdrawn. The cylinder may now be cleaned without difficulty.

The bolt lock may be lifted off the bolt and the extractor and firing pin removed.

Loading and Firing

There is a trap in the top of the stock on this weapon. A special magazine filler will be found in the hollow.

Place this filler in the mouth of the magazine. Insert cartridges and then force them directly down with thumb pressure. The magazine will hold 30. To prolong the life of the magazine spring, 28 is the correct number to be used, however.

Pull bolt handle to compress recoil spring and cock the hammer and let it fly forward. It will pick up the top cartridge from the magazine and load it into the chamber. The dust cover will open automatically.

Push safety up unless weapon is to be fired at once. If it is left down, pressing the trigger will fire a single shot or full automatic fire depending on which way the control button has been pushed through the receiver.

How This Weapon Works

When the trigger is pressed the hammer is released to strike the inertia firing pin. This is a wedge-shaped pin which does not have a conventional spring. It is primer retracted.

As the bullet passes the gas port in the barrel it expands into the gas chamber or cup which is screwed into the housing around the barrel and on top of it.

The gas impinges on a piston somewhat resembling the old Lewis piston and drives it to the rear. In the start of its rearward travel the piston (which has attached to it by a fixed pin the bolt locking mechanism) can move without interfering with the secure locking of the weapon. A gas vent in the top of the casing permits the gas to escape as the gas end of the piston clears it.

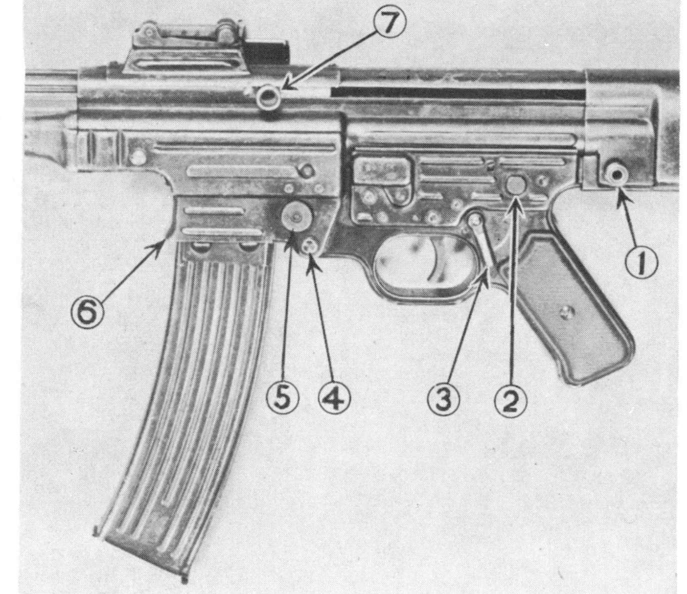

1. Receiver lock pin.
2. Push-through firing control switch.
3. Thumb safety, in off position.
4. Trigger housing pivot pin.
5. Magazine release catch.
6. Magazine housing. Note magazine housing to prevent overinsertion.
7. Bolt handle.

After a short rearward travel the bolt lock hook picks up the separate bolt member, mounted below it, and pulls it down and back to perform the unlocking action.

The recoil spring is mounted behind the bolt extending back to the stock. This spring is compressed as the moving members travel to the rear to extract and eject the empty case in normal fashion and to cock the hammer.

This weapon is fitted with a special disconnector.

The first weapons for this short cartridge were the MKb 42 (W) and the MKb 42 (H). The MKb 42 (W) was a Walther design and utilized a somewhat unusual gas take-off system similar to that now used on the Czech Model 52 Rifle. The MKb 42 (H) was the direct prototype of the MP 43 series of weapons. Both of these weapons were issued in quantity for field trial and the MKb 42 (H), a Haenel design won the competition.

A later development the StG 45 (M), a Mauser development, has been used as the basis for the design of the Spanish CETME Assault Rifle. The 45 (M) was a delayed blowback weapon using a two-piece bolt with roller bearings for locks. (See also Swiss Model 57 Assault Rifle.)

Special Note on this Weapon

The MP43, 44 series of weapons are a direct outgrowth of a German Army requirement for a weapon to replace the rifle, submachine gun, and pistol. The 7.92mm short cartridge used in these weapons was designed by Polte and adopted in 1941 as the 7.9mm Kurz Infantrie Patrone (7.9mm short Infantry cartridge). A later version, using a mild steel core ball bullet, was adopted as Maschinen Karbiner Patrone S. This nomenclature was later changed to Pistolen Patrone 43me (Pistol Cartridge 43 with steel core).

Schmeisser Machine Pistol 28 II.

Caliber: 9mm Parabellum (Luger, Pistole 08).
Magazine: Box type, capacity 32 cartridges. Staggered box.
Position of Magazine: Left side of receiver.
Ballistic Data: Standard for cartridge used in submachine gun.
Barrel Length: 200mm (7.8 inches).
Overall Length: 810mm (31.59 inches).
Weight: 4.1 kg., 9.02 pounds.
Sights: Tangent leaf sight graduated 100 to 1000 meters.
Operation and Locking Data: Standard for Bergmann type blowback.
Cooled: Air. Has ventilated jacket around barrel. Bolt stays open when trigger is released. This weapon fires from an open bolt.
Cyclic Rate of Fire: 600 per minute.
Type of Fire: Single shot or continuous.
Change Lever: A button just above the trigger. Pushing it through gives selective fire.
Note: This weapon is also manufactured in caliber 7.63mm Mauser and 9mm Mauser.

How the Schmeisser MP 28 II Works

This weapon is fitted with a stationary barrel mounted in a barrel casing which is hinged just ahead of the wooden forearm. Behind it is a moving bolt which is pressed forward by the operating spring positioned between the rear of the bolt and the receiver.

Pulling back on the bolt handle draws the bolt back and compresses the spring. The bolt is caught and held by the sear in rearward position.

When the trigger is pulled, the operating spring pushes forward. A feed lug machined into the bolt strips the first cartridge from the magazine and into the chamber.

During the last moment of the closing action, the extractor fitted into the bolt slips into the cartridge extracting groove.

The firing pin, which is not retractable, fires the cartridge at this instant.

As the bullet is driven out of the barrel, the backward pressure against the empty cartridge case is transmitted to the bolt driving it back and compressing the operating spring. At the same time the empty cartridge case is ejected.

This continues as long as there are any cartridges in the magazine and the trigger is held back in full automatic fire.

The diameter of the operating spring in this model is much greater than in the original MP 18I, thus eliminating the need for a guide rod. Otherwise the two are much the same.

Field Stripping

Press the release catch behind the receiver and hinge up the barrel and barrel casing group.

Press in on the receiver cap, twist and remove.

Lift out recoil spring. Pull out the bolt.

Special Note

This weapon has a most interesting history in the light of present day events. It was developed by the German engineer, Hugo Schmeisser, from his original simple MP 18I, the original submachine gun.

Schmeisser transferred the manufacturing rights of this new design to the Haenel firm at Suhl. Under the Treaty of Versailles, Germany was prohibited from manufacturing these weapons. German documents establish that Haenel then transferred the manufacturing rights to the firm of Pieper at Herstal, Belgium.

This weapon was adopted by the Belgian army under the name "Mitraillette Model 34."

What is of more interest to us is that it was also sold in large quantities to the Japanese. Until they developed a somewhat similar weapon in 1940, the Japanese submachine guns were all MP 28 II's or Steyr Solothurns. It might be noted here that the Germans also evaded the treaty regulations by manufacturing the Steyr in Swiss factories. In fact the Solothurn works were owned by the German Rheinmetall firm.

Hugo Schmeisser later developed the German MP 38 and MP 40, the first submachine guns capable of mass production at very low cost.

It should be noted that all these German weapons were manufactured and sold at a fraction of the cost of American-made submachine guns.

Germany's ability to rearm in the face of the Treaty of Versailles was due very largely to the development of simple and efficient weapons and to their manufacture in the small countries of Europe.

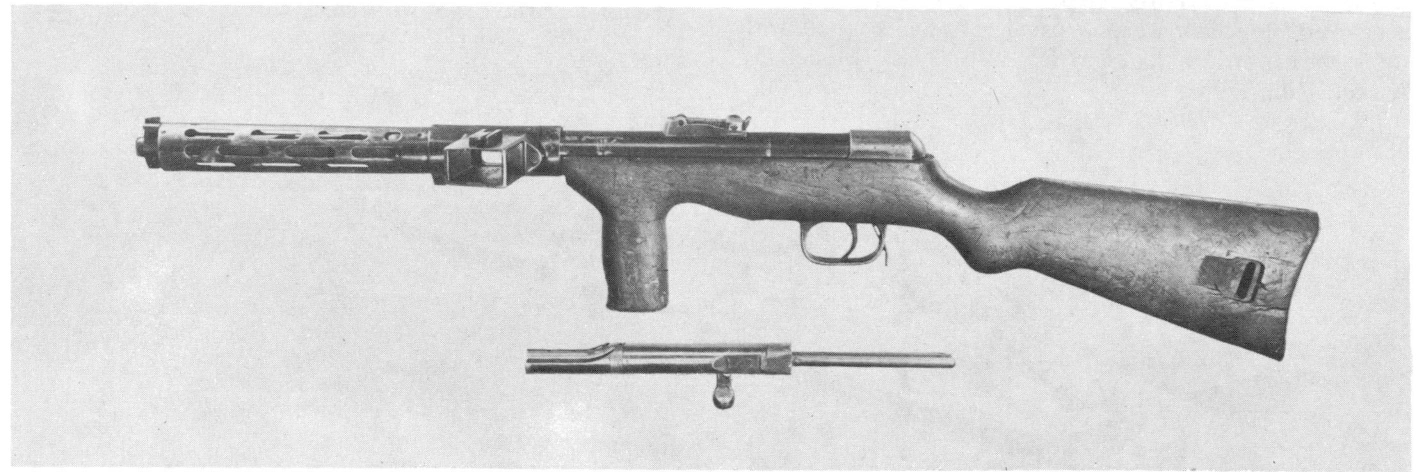

Erma 9mm Machine Pistol (EMP).

Caliber: 9mm Parabellum (Pistol 08).
Magazine: Removable box type, single line. Positioned in housing on left side of weapon at an angle forward.
Ballistic Data: Same as for Steyr-Solothurn.
Overall Length: 35.5".
Weight: 9 lbs. 12 oz.
Cyclic Rate of Fire: 520 rounds per minute.
Operation in Locking: Blow back.
Cooling: Similar to Solothurn. (Barrel casing and radiation slots of different shape.)
Type of Firing: Single shot or full automatic. Selector device will be found on right side of weapon directly above front end of triggerguard.
Safety: The only one on this weapon is a recess to the rear of the cocking handle slot. When the cocking handle is at full cock, it may be drawn still farther back, then turned up and pushed into locking slot.
Note: A specially-designed, pistol-type grip for the left hand extends downward from the front end of the stock.
Modifications: There are several variations of this arm. Sights may consist of two notched leaves. Saftey may be on top of receiver to rear of ejection port, sliding from right to left; and when in engagement safety locks in a groove across top of bolt. This weapon was reportedly manufactured in Switzerland as well as by the Erfurter Werkzeug u Maschinenfabrik prior to WW II. It has been made in a number of different calibers.

Loading and Firing

Insert magazine in magazine housing on the side of the weapon and push home until the catch locks.

(The locking catch is placed on the top near side of the magazine housing.)

Pull cocking handle back as far as it will go. Bolt itself will stay open.

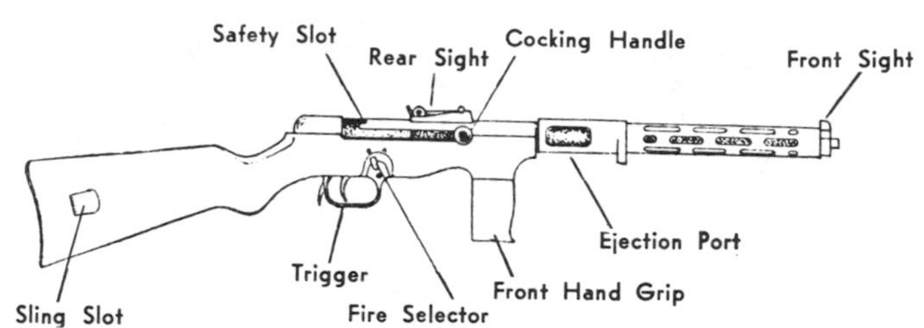

Pull cocking handle back and up into locking recess for safety. Now set thumb selector for "single" or "full automatic" fire as desired.

Special Note

This weapon was not an official German Army submachine gun in W.W. II. It was used by the German Police and SS, and to a limited extent by the French.

Special Note on German Machine Weapons

The following German infantry and Volkssturm arms fall into this classification for purposes of Federal Registration:

(1) Mauser 7.63mm and 9mm Luger or Mauser semi-auto military pistol when equipped with detachable shoulder stock.
(2) Mauser M32 machine pistol (with full auto switch).
(3) All arms listed as machine carbines (MKb), machine pistols (MP), light machine guns (LMG), and heavy machine guns (SMG).

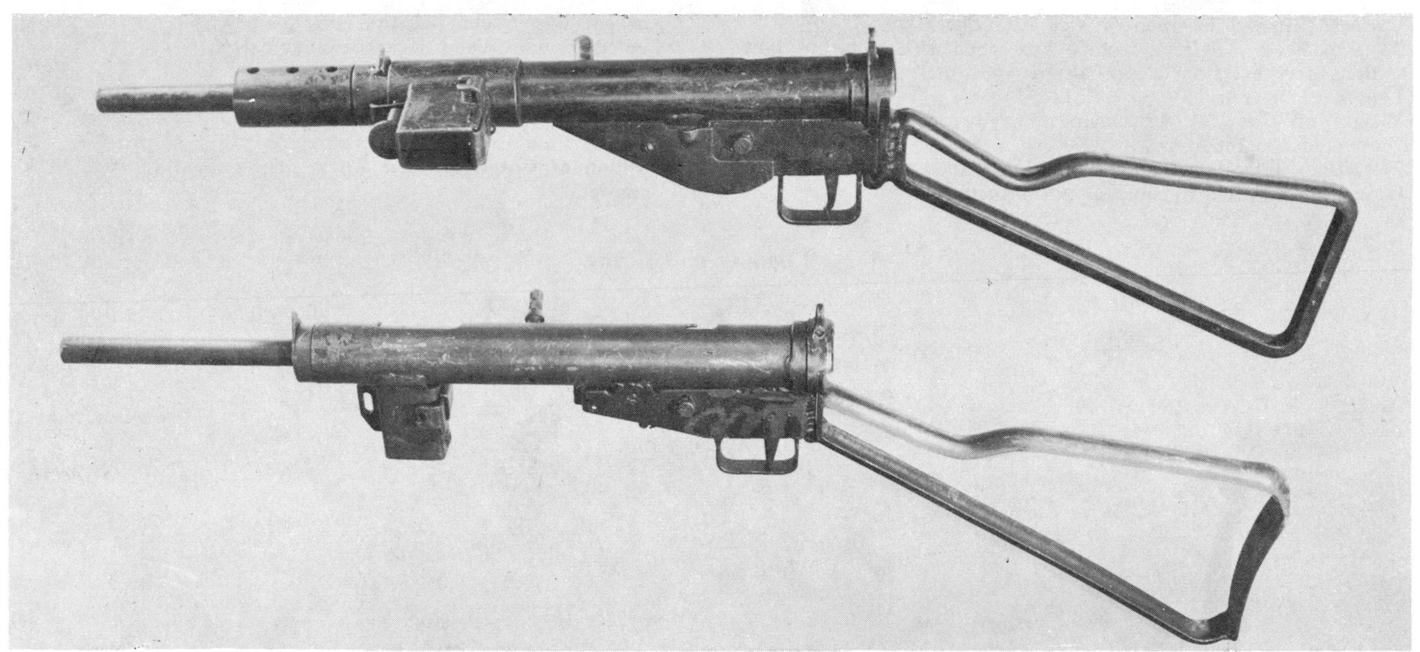

Comparison of British Sten Gun (Upper View) and German Imitation (MP 3008) (Lower View).

(4) FG 42 Gewehr (paratrooper's rifles). These arms have full auto switch.

Many of the foregoing are adequately pictured and described in this section.

Note on Machine Pistols. The Germans made use wherever possible of the arms of all conquered countries. Equipment of their allies or their victims, therefore, may be traced to German units in many cases.

The Germans further simplified the Elementary Sten Gun for mass production toward the close of the war. In the German version, the magazine is mounted from below instead of from the left side.

These guns are extremely cheap and easy to manufacture, and illustrate the difficulty of preventing rearming by any country which has even the simplest machine facilities.

GERMAN MACHINE GUNS

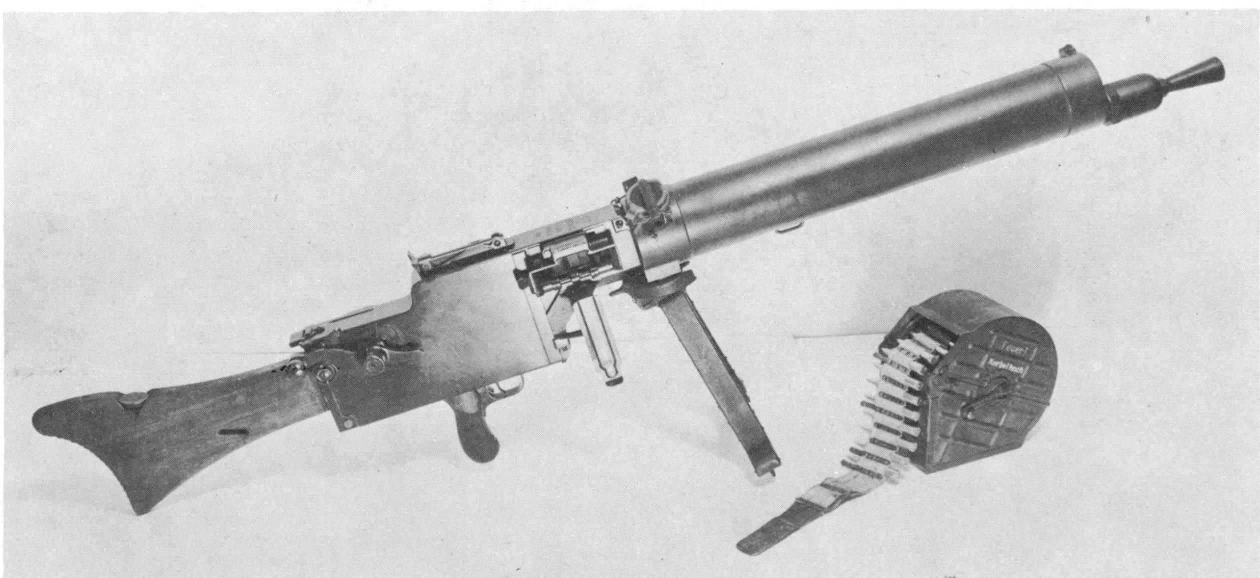

Maxim 7.92mm MG08/15 (Light MG).

The operating principles of this weapon are essentially the same as those of the other Maxim types. It was designed to provide greater mobility and to be handled by one man if necessary.

Caliber: 7.92mm German Service cartridge.
Type of Feed: Belt feed from a box when used by a gun crew. Belts unreeled from a steel drum when used by an individual.
Length of Barrel: 28¼".
Weight of Gun: 31 lbs. when adapted for tripod; 34 lbs. if adapted for bipod rest.
Mounting: Tripod weighing 51 lbs.; or bipod weighing 2½ lbs.
Gun Operated by: Recoil. Maxim principle.
Locked: Toggle joint Maxim principle.
Cooled: Water. Water jacket around barrel.
Cyclic Rate of Fire: 500 a minute.
Sights: Barleycorn front and open V rear, adjustable to 2000 meters.
Type of Fire: Full automatic only.
Position of Crank Handle: Right side, pushed forward to load the gun.

Loading and Firing

Loading. If belt is used from box, load exactly as for heavy Maxim. If drum is used, the cartridge belt is wound around the wheel which revolves within the drum. An indicator on the outside shows the number of cartridges remaining: Slide this drum into its locking slot (directly below the feed block on the right hand side of the gun). A catch at the forward end of the feed block will lock it securely.

Now proceed exactly as for heavy Maxim. First pull the belt through with a slight draw to the front. Then while retaining a firm hold push the crank handle forward as far as it will go and holding it in that position, pull the belt through. Release the crank handle and let it slide back under the influence of the spring. Now roll the crank handle forward a second time, pull the belt through again, and release the crank handle to fly back for the second trip.

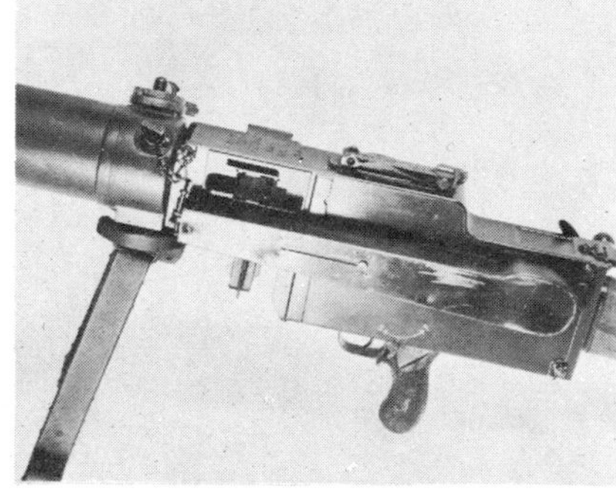

To fire: This weapon is fitted with a rifle type butt. It is intended to be held against the shoulder. It also has a pistol grip and standard type trigger and triggerguard, below the receiver. On the left side of the receiver above this pistol grip will be found the safety lever. Pushed forward to the letter "S" it is safe and the gun cannot be fired. Drawn down to the rear to "F" it is in firing position. When the gun is loaded, and the selector set at "fire," pressing the trigger will fire the gun. Operation will continue as long as there are any cartridges being fed into it.

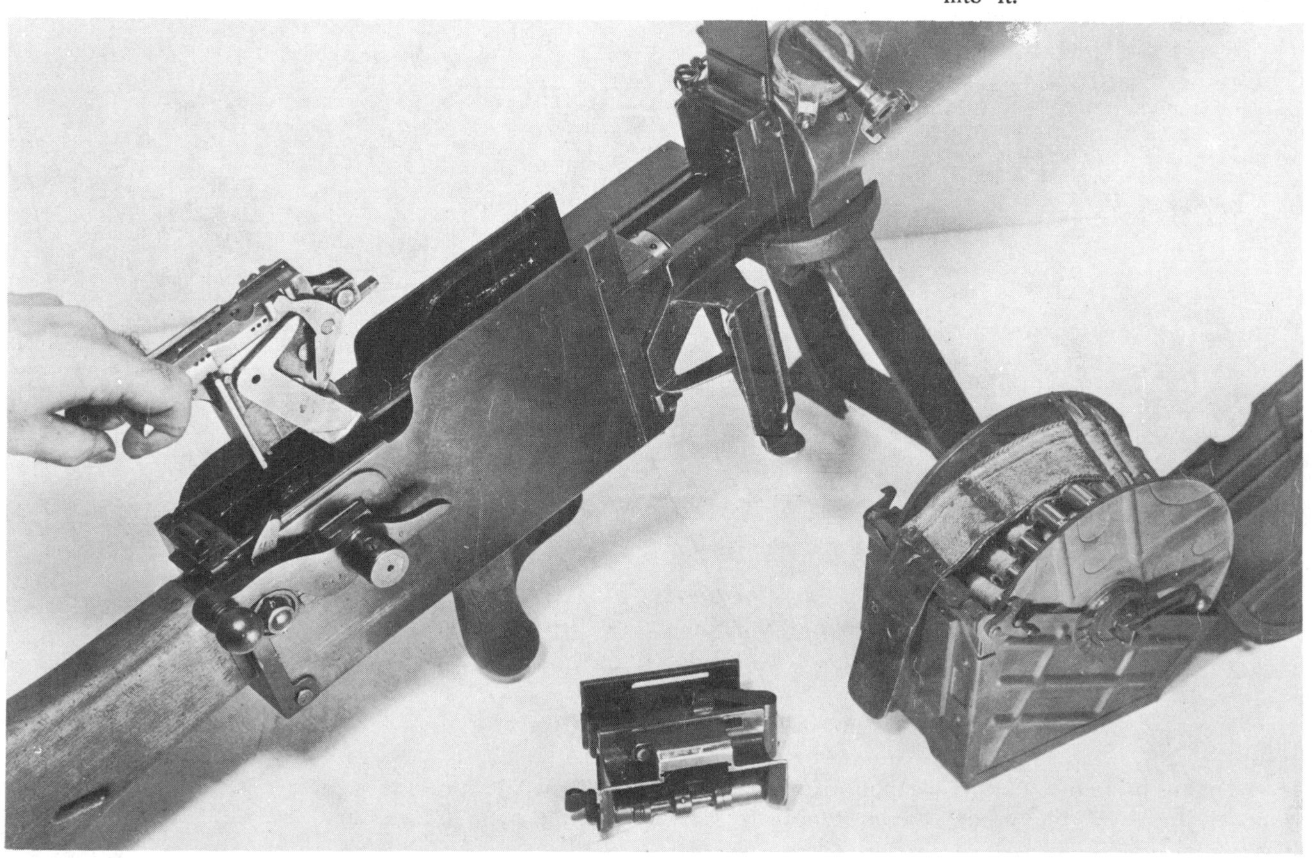

Field Stripping

Dismounting this weapon is essentially the same as dismounting other Maxims. The cover is raised by pushing up on the spring cover latch at the rear of the gun where the butt joins the frame. The cover is lifted, the feed block lifted directly out of its seating, the crank handle pushed forward and held there while the lock is lifted out. The lock is then twisted on the stem connecting it to the connecting rod. The lock is then lifted out. Spring box on the left side of gun is sprung forward, down and off as in the case of other Maxims. Locking pin passing through gun above crank handle is released from the left side and pushed through to the right after which the butt may be dropped down out of line with the barrel extension. Side plates, barrel extension, and barrel may then be withdrawn directly to the rear.

Note: On Maxim Guns, there is an indicator on the fusee spring box indicating the weight of the spring.

The bipod mount is so arranged that it can be fastened near the muzzle or just ahead of the feed box below the gun.

Another model of the Maxim known as the Light Machine Gun 08/18 also was manufactured in Germany. This gun is practically identical with the model 08/15 except that it has no water jacket; instead, it is fitted with a heavy barrel and an outer barrel casing. It is air cooled. A carrying handle for the barrel is provided on the barrel just forward of the feed block.

Maxim 7.92mm MG08 (Heavy MG).

This is no longer used in the German first line armies, having been supplanted by the MG34 and MG42. However, it was an excellent type of heavy machine gun, and tremendous quantities were provided for Home Guard and fortress defense in Germany.

Caliber: 7.92mm German Service cartridge.
Type of Feed: Fabric belt with brass eyelets as in the case of the British Vickers.
Capacity of Belt: 100 and 250 rounds.
Ballistic Data: Standard for this cartridge.
Barrel Length: 28¼".
Weight of Gun: 44 lbs.
Mounting: Tripod type, weighing 65½ lbs. and sleigh type weighing 83 lbs.
Accurate Range: About 600 yards. So called "effective range" with telescopic sight about 3800 yards and maximum range about 5000 yards.
Gun Operated By: Recoil of weapon aided by rebounding gas from muzzle attachment as in Vickers. This is the basic Maxim principle.
Locked: By toggle joint on general principle employed in Vickers. Barrel and locking mechanism recoil together for a short distance, barrel then halts while lock continues to rear.
Cooled: Water. Water jacket surrounds barrel.
Cyclic Rate of Fire: About 500 a minute.
Type of Fire: Full automatic only. Single shot fire can be obtained if trigger can be released quickly enough; otherwise it can be obtained only by method of loading the belt.
Safety: Safety on thumb trigger must be pushed to the right before trigger will go in. Automatic safeties customary to machine guns to prevent cartridge from being fired until action is completely locked are also incorporated in the mechanism.

Loading and Firing

The tag end of the loaded belt is fed through the breechblock from the right side and given a sharp pull through and somewhat ahead. Then holding the pressure on the tag, push the crank handle forward as far as it will go. Note that the crank handle is pushed forward, not pulled back as in the Vickers.

Now with the left hand pull the cartridge belt through again. Release crank handle and let it fly back.

Pull with the left hand, roll the crank handle forward as far as it will go for a second time. Pull belt through again. Release crank handle again.

To Fire: In the center of the split thumb-trigger, is a small lever. While grasping the traversing handles when ready to fire, the left thumb must push this safety over toward the center to permit the thumb trigger to be pushed in with both thumbs. When the thumb is removed from the safety, the weapon stops firing.

Field Stripping

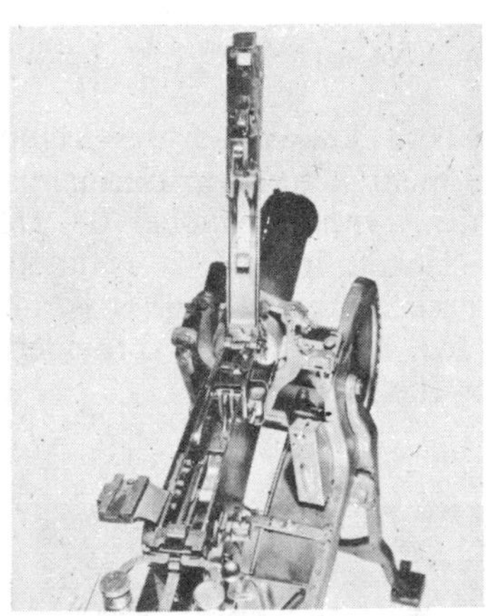

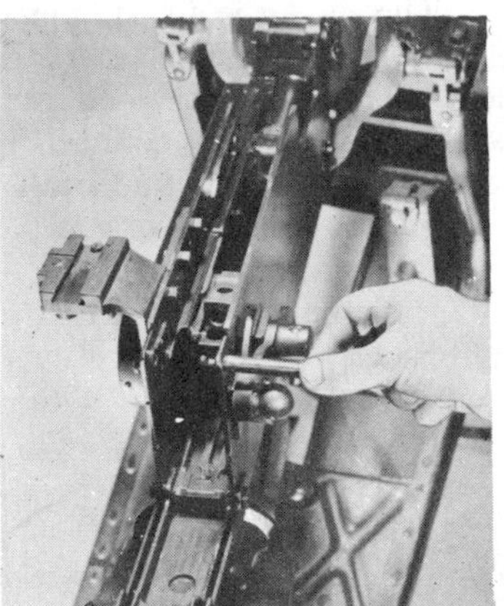

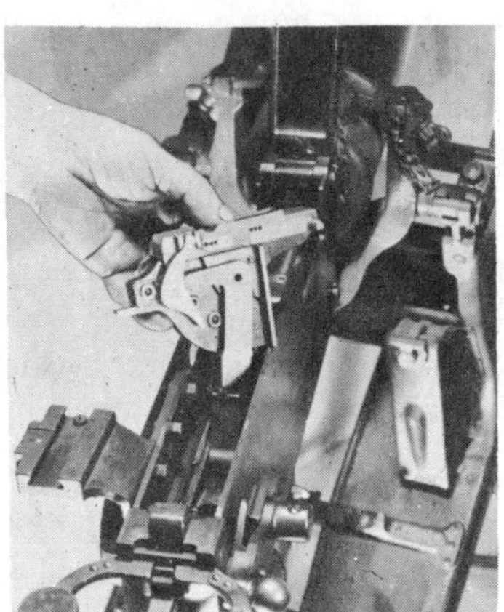

The top cover catch is located at the end of the cover just over the traversing handle. Push this up against this spring and raise the cover as far as it will go.

The feed block, positioned just behind the hinge of the top cover may now be grasped by the hands on either side and lifted straight up and out of its place in the receiver. (Note that the cover on the Maxim extends the full length of the receiver.)

Push forward the crank handle with the right hand and reaching inside with the left hand grasp the lock firmly, pull it straight up out of the receiver. Then twist the lock on its stem on the connecting rod, which will free it and permit it to be lifted off the connecting rod.

Note: This lock resembles the Vickers lock but is much more massive and rather more complicated. However, the stripping sequence is close enough to the Vickers so familiarity with one will enable you to dismount the other.

Press the locking spring on the pin which passes through the gun directly above the crank handle at the rear of the gun. The spring pin is located on the left side of the gun. Push it through and remove the pin from the right. The traversing handles may now be pulled down to the horizontal position.

Spring box and fuse pin are removed as for the Vickers.

Side plate, barrel, and barrel extension may now be pulled directly to the rear as in the Vickers. This completes field dismounting.

NOTE: Unlike the Vickers it is not necessary to remove the muzzle attachment in order to pull the barrel out of this gun. In the Vickers the barrel cap is screwed onto the barrel itself. In the Maxim it is screwed onto the water jacket.

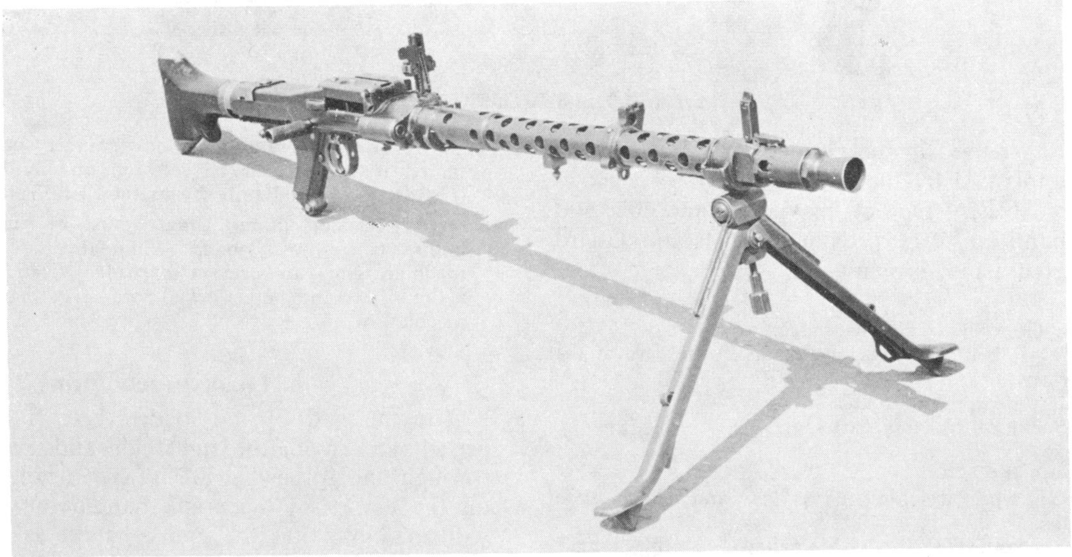

7.92mm MG34 Machine Gun.

The Treaty of Versailles prohibited the Germans from manufacturing heavy machine guns. Their way around this restriction was to develop an all-purpose machine gun which could officially be called a light machine gun, but which had the necessary characteristics built into it to enable it to be used as an antiaircraft gun or in a special mounting as a heavy machine gun. Originally, a light machine gun was a weapon with a magazine capacity of 20 or 30 cartridges, and a light, not easily removable barrel. Thus it could not be used for sustained firing nor was it valuable for long range use as a tactical weapon.

The Germans were able to develop a lightweight machine gun whose barrels could be changed so rapidly that the disadvantage of overheating was completely eliminated. This compensated for the heavy weight and water cooling devices necessary on the typical heavy machine gun. By developing a special metal link belt whose sections can be fastened together speedily to provide a belt of any length, they overcame the factor of feeding. By developing a special form of mount, in which the excessive recoil of the gun in continuous operation is utilized to work the elevating movement when mounted in a heavy tripod, they made the weapon suitable for long range searching fire.

This weapon can be used by an individual or by a gun crew of three or more men. Each gun is issued with three spare barrels. These barrels can be changed in a matter of seconds.

This was the most widely used machine weapon in the German Services in World War II.

However, a new light machine gun, resembling this one in exterior appearance but surpassing it in simplicity, reliability, and ease of manufacture, was introduced to the German Services in 1942.

In passing it should be noted that the MG34 is intended as an all-purpose weapon.

Caliber: 7.92mm German Service cartridge.

Feed: Metal belt feed is normal. Capacity of belt is 50 rounds. Any number of belts may be fastened together.

In tank and antiaircraft uses, this gun may be fitted with a 50-round belt contained in a drum type magazine, attached to the left side of the feed block.

On antiaircraft types of this kind, a saddle-type drum is used. In this type, which holds 75 cartridges, two drums are connected by a center strip which locks down over the feedway so that a drum lies on each side of the receiver.

Barrel Length: 23½″.

Overall Length of Gun: 48″.

Weight: 26½ lbs. with the attached bipod mount.

Sights: V-notch rear is graduated from 200 to 2000 meters. A folding peep on the rear sight may be used with an antiaircraft ring. Also an antiaircraft sight is issued which fits on the barrel jacket. A telescope sight is also provided for mounting on the tripod when gun is used as a heavy machine gun. This is graduated to 3500 meters.

Effective Range of the Gun: German sources claim 2000 yards used with the bipod and about 3800 yards with the tripod mount.

Maximum Range: About 5000 yards.

Ballistics: Standard for type of German cartridges employed. Muzzle velocity may vary from 2500 to 3000 feet per second.

Gun Operated By: Recoil. A special recoil booster screwed onto the muzzle causes some of the expanding gases that follow the bullet after it has left the barrel to rebound against the face of the barrel, thus speeding up the rearward action of the recoiling parts.

Locked: Breech block is firmly locked to the barrel at the moment of firing by interrupted screw threads.

Cooled: Air. Barrel is mounted in a fixed barrel jacket or casing which is perforated. This gun fires from an open bolt. As it stays open between shots, air can circulate through the breech opening and the barrel. Since there is no cartridge in the chamber, except at the instant of firing, there is no danger of a cook-off in this weapon.

Cyclic Rate of Fire: 800 to 900 per minute. This high rate of fire is one of the defects of this gun. While it is desirable for firing against aircraft, the rate is entirely too high for effective use as a ground weapon. It wastes ammunition.

Position of Cocking Handle: On right side of receiver.

Ejection of Empty Cartridge: From bottom.

Type of Fire: Single shot or full automatic. This gun is equipped with a special trigger. The top part of this trigger is marked "E." Pressing in will fire one shot and then the weapon will stop until the trigger is released and pressed again. The bottom part of the trigger is marked "D." Pressing this bottom half lets the gun fire automatically as long as the trigger is held back.

Safety: A safety lever is placed just above the trigger. Pushing it to the "S" position locks the sear so that the bolt cannot go forward.

Loading and Firing

A machine is provided but is not needed to load this form of belt. The belt consists of a series of individual metal links, joined together by small pieces of coiled wire. These links are shaped much like an ordinary pencil clip. Press the cartridge down into the clip so that the spring sides fasten around the cartridge and retain it. A nib at the end of the clip will spring into the cannelure of the cartridge and hold it in the correct

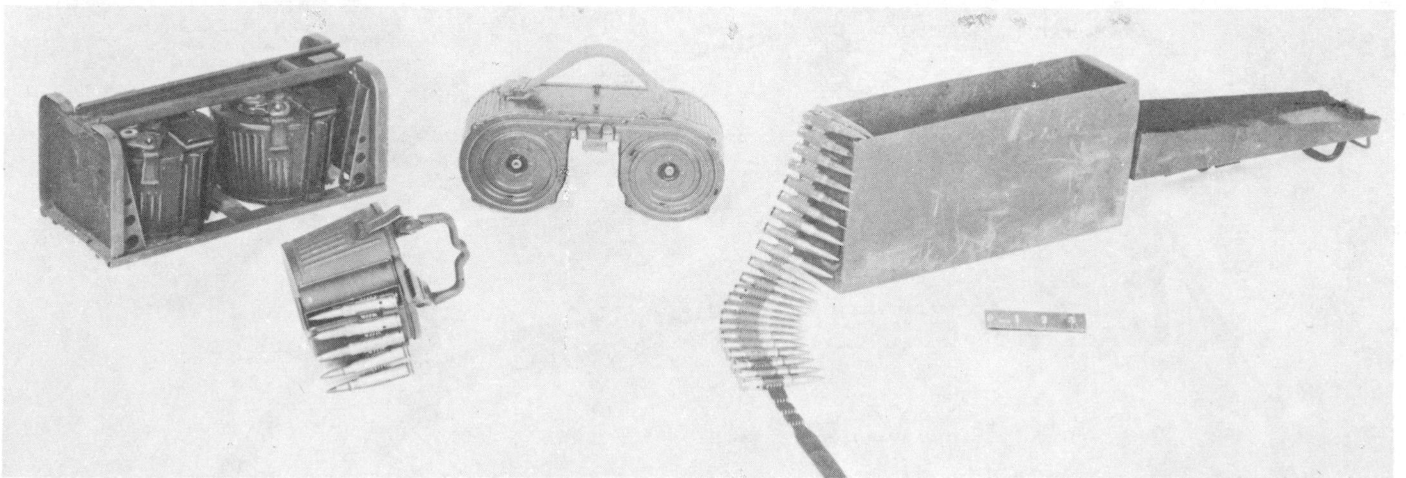

German Machine Gun Belt and Box, Saddle Drum Magazine, Basket Magazine, and Carrier with two Baskets. Used with MG34.

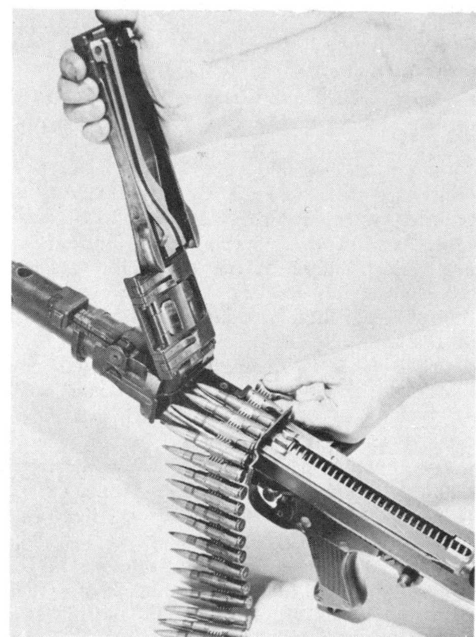

position. It will be evident that in this form of belt there can be no malfunction of the type common to web belts which may expand when wet and to brass-studded belts which must pass through a complicated feed mechanism.

In the 50-round drums, the loaded belt is inserted in the drum, being wound around the center piece.

The 75-round, saddle-type drums, do not use a belt. The drum itself contains the cartridges. The springs force them around into position, one coming alternately from each side.

Tabs are provided on the end of each belt. If several sections are being fastened together, or if no tab is available, then the first two or three cartridges should be removed from the metal belt.

Insert the feeding end of the belt in the feedway on the left side of the receiver, and pull through as far as it will go.

Warning: Unlike the Browning and the Vickers, the belt on this gun lies on top of the cartridges as they pass through the feed block. An alternate way of loading is to push forward the cover catch (which is on top of the receiver at the rear of the gun) and lift the feed cover to vertical position. The belt may then be laid in the feedway; make sure that the first cartridge rests against the stop on the right side of the guide. Close the cover and snap it down in place.

Pull back the cocking handle as far as it will go and the bolt will be caught and held in rearward position by the sear. Now push the cocking handle forward as far as it will go. If this is not done it will be carried forward as the bolt moves to the front, and this additional weight may cause malfunctioning.

Pressing the upper part of the trigger will now fire a single shot. Pressing the lower part of the trigger will fire the weapon automatically.

Note: If the cocking handle will not come back, it indicates that the safety is on. Move the lever to the "Fire" position.

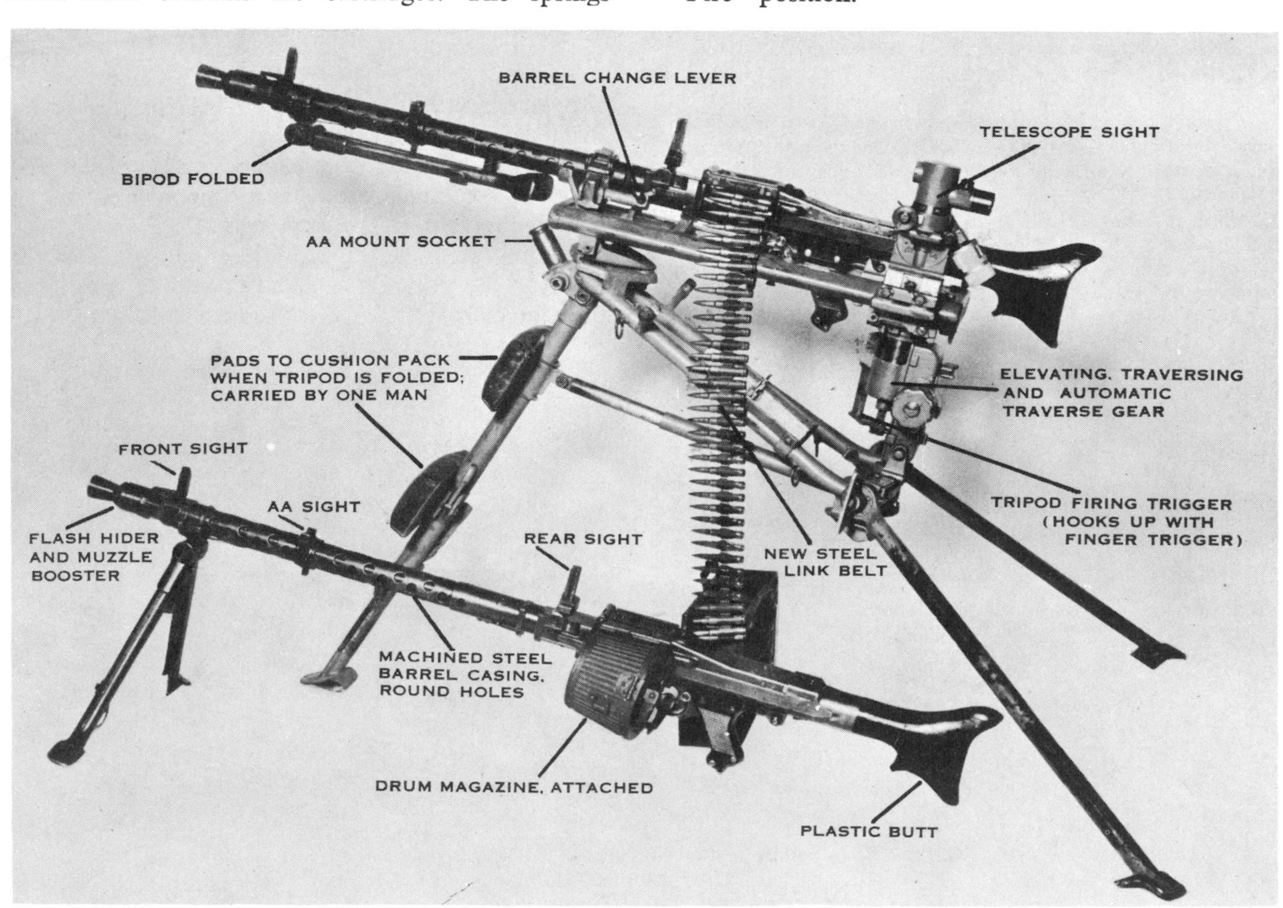

Firing with the 50-Round Drum

Press the catch on the sliding cover of the drum and open the cover so that the tag end of the belt can be pulled out. Insert the tag of the belt in the feedway as for the ordinary belt. The narrow end of the belt is the front end. Engage the hook on the front end with the lug on the rear end of the lower part of the feed plate. Now swing the rear end of the drum around until the spring catch engages with the lug on the rear end of the feedway. Pulling back the cocking handle now leaves the weapon ready for firing.

75-Round Saddle Drum

With this drum the feed cover is removed and a magazine holder is substituted. The feed plate is also removed. Belts are not used in this type of feed. The drum is placed directly over the magazine holder ahead of the triggerguard. Its center piece pushes down the dust cover in the magazine holder. A spring catch at the top center of the connecting piece can be pressed to release the drum and a hand-strap is provided to lift it off the gun.

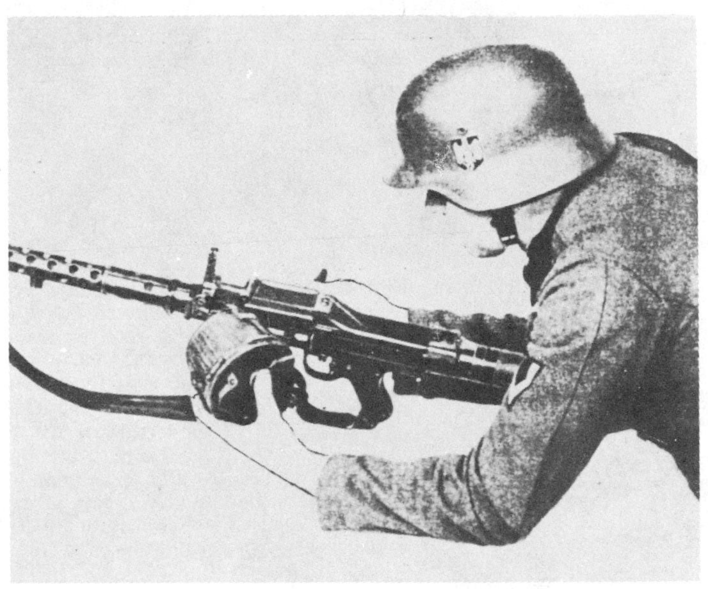

Field Stripping

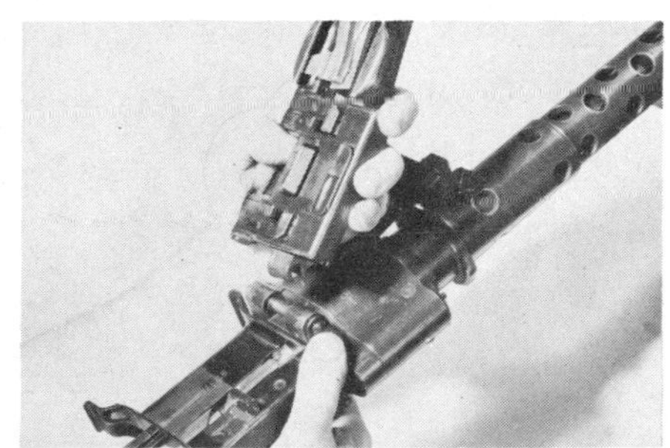

Order of Stripping: Push the spring catch at the extreme rear of the cover on top of the receiver and lift the cover to a vertical position. Push the cover hinge pin from the right and lift out the cover. The feed block may be lifted off.

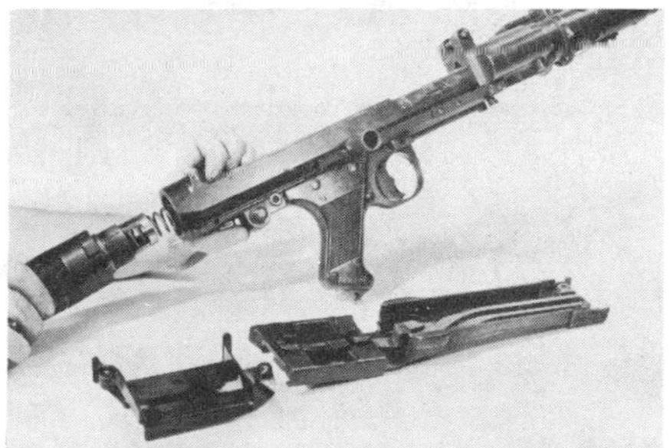

The butt catch is on the underside of the receiver a few inches behind the pistol grip. Press this up with the left thumb. With the right hand, turn the butt a quarter-turn left or right. (Note: The bolt should be in forward position when this stripping motion is being done. Otherwise, the very powerful recoil spring cannot be controlled.) The recoil spring will now force the butt out of the receiver. Now remove the recoil spring.

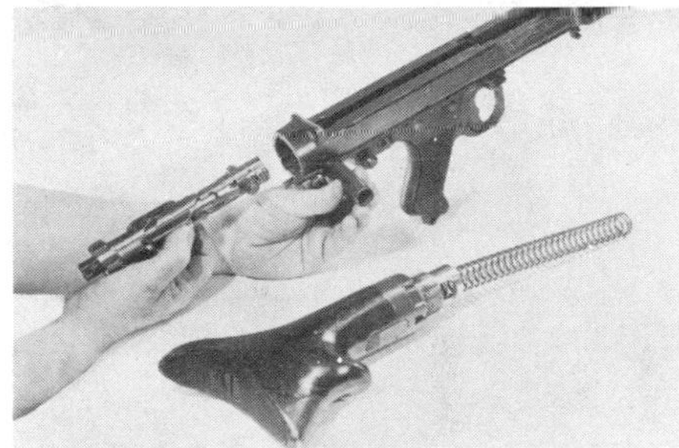

Pull the cocking handle back with a quick motion. (A jerking motion is required here because the action in releasing the bolt, twists the barrel extension and the barrel. Watch that the bolt and its carrier do not fly out the back of the receiver.)

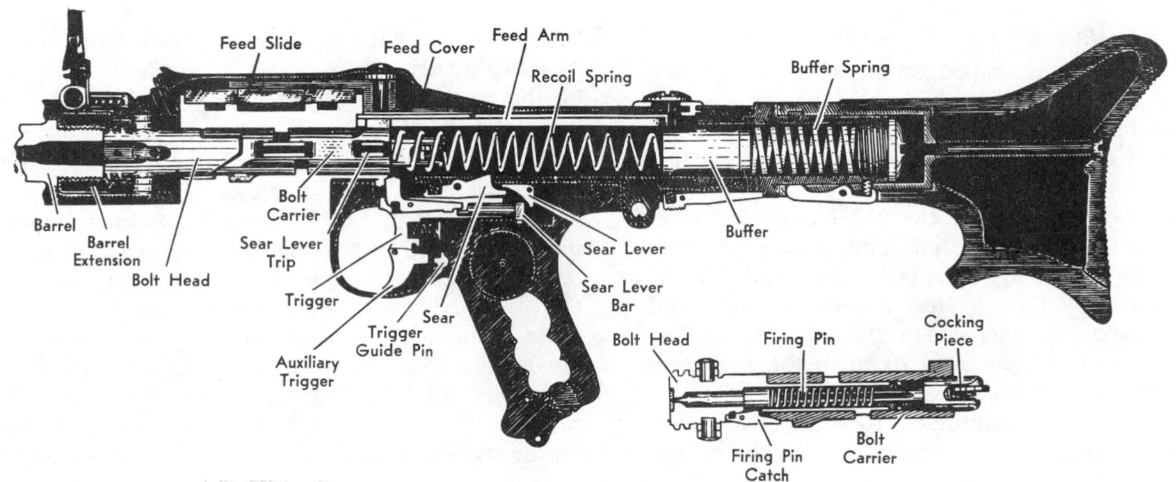

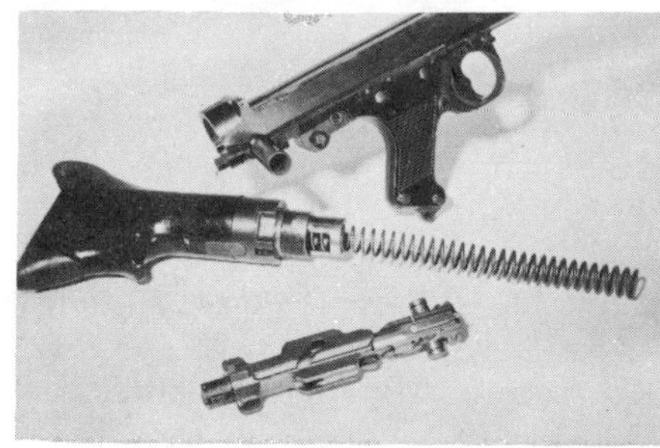

Bolt and carrier may now be removed.

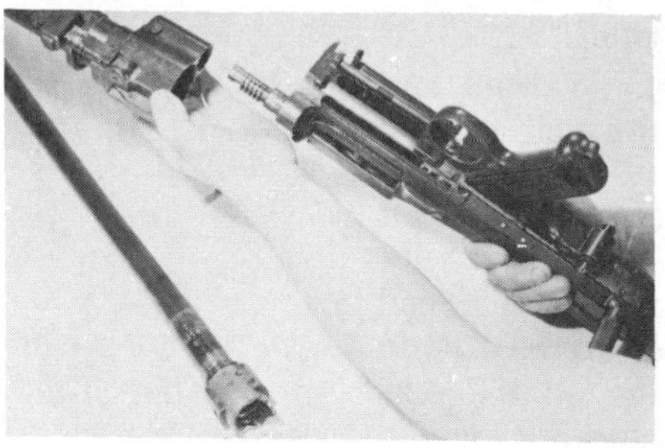

Pressing the locking catch on left of receiver, below and behind rear sight, twist receiver from left to right until it clears the barrel casing. Raise the muzzle and slide the barrel out of the casing. A hinge pin catch will be found on the underside of the barrel casing, near its end and to the right. Press this up and while maintaining pressure twist the receiver, left to right, until it has completed its full half turn. It may now be pulled out to the rear.

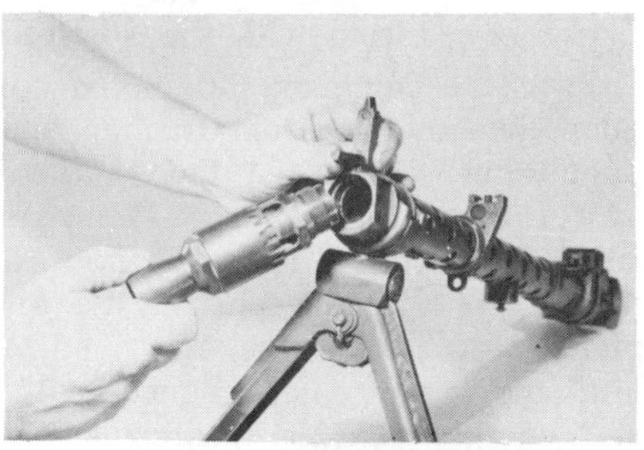

A catch will be found in front of the foresight. Lifting this permits you to unscrew the flash hider over the muzzle. Inside it is a mouthpiece and a recoil cone. Remove them.

The trigger assembly is locked to the receiver by two automatic locking pins. Pinching the split ends together permits them to be pulled out. (Removal of this assembly is not recommended without suitable tools.)

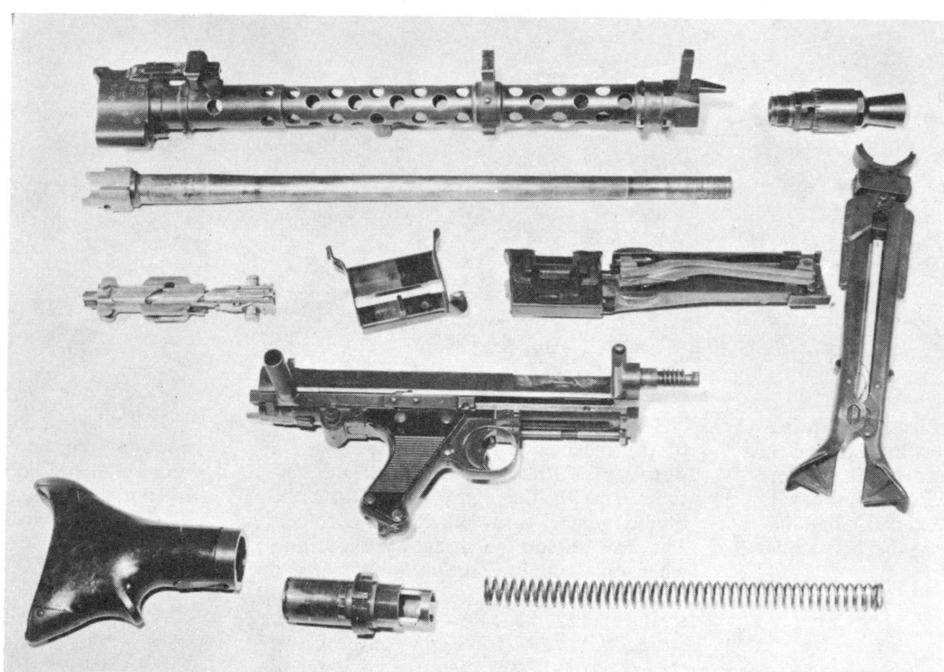

How the Gun Works

Starting with the gun loaded and cocked, the action is as follows: Pressing the trigger pulls the sear out of its bent in the breech block and allows it to go forward under the thrust of the compressed recoil spring located in the butt.

A feed piece on the top of the breech block strikes the base of the cartridge in line and pushes it from the belt toward the firing chamber. The feed arm is hollow and is operated by a stud on the top rear end of the breech block carrier, which rides in this hollow groove and causes the feed pawl to push the next cartridge in the direction of the firing chamber.

As the breech block continues forward, two inner rollers on its head strike two cams on a cam sleeve and rotate the heads of the breech block from left to right so that threads on the breech block lock engages threads on the cam sleeve; this effectively locks the breech block to the barrel.

As the cartridge chambers, the extractor in the bolt face slips over the cannelure of the cartridge. Meanwhile the breech block carrier continues forward, tripping the firing pin lever and allowing the firing pin to go forward through the face of the bolt to strike the primer. The forward movement of the bolt is stopped when a shoulder on its right front side strikes the cocking handle stop which is in its forward position at the end of its slot. Just before the cartridge is fired, a locking catch on the breech block engages behind the outer roller on the right side of the head of the breech block.

Return Movement of the Action. This gun is fitted at the muzzle with a recoil increaser somewhat resembling that operating on the Vickers gun.

As the bullet leaves the barrel, part of the gas pressure behind it expands in the muzzle attachment and rebounds against the cone to give additional backward thrust to the barrel. This action, together with the rearward thrust of the gas in the firing chamber against the head of the empty cartridge case, which transmits it to the bolt, starts the action to the rear.

Barrel and breech block start back, firmly locked together during the period of high pressure. After a backward travel of about 3/16″, the outer rollers on the breech block head again engage with the two cam faces in the forward end of the receiver, thus forcing the breech block head to rotate from right to left, thereby unlocking the breech block from the barrel.

The rearward motion of the barrel is stopped, as soon as the unlocking operation is completed, when its cam sleeve strikes against shoulders in the front end of the receiver.

The stud riding straight to the rear on the breech block carrier, its head caught in the groove in the feed arm above it, twists the feed arm which forces the feed pawl slide to move back and permits the feed pawl to lock behind the next cartridge in the belt.

The empty case, being drawn from the firing chamber by the extractor in the face of the bolt, is struck by the ejector and hurled out of the gun. The ejector is a pin in the top of the breech block; during the backward movement of the breech block the rear end of this pin strikes against a stop which forces the front end through its hole in the breech block to hit the base of the empty cartridge case. The ejection is downward. The end of the breech block carrier strikes against the buffer, the compression of the recoil spring is completed, and, if the semi-automatic portion of the trigger is being pulled, the bolt will stop open, engaged from below by the sear forced up by its spring. If the automatic trigger is being pressed, the firing cycle will be completed and continued as long as there are any cartridges left in the belt.

Six modifications of the MG34 are known. Differences are slight, however. Some models may have only a full automatic trigger and a push through safety.

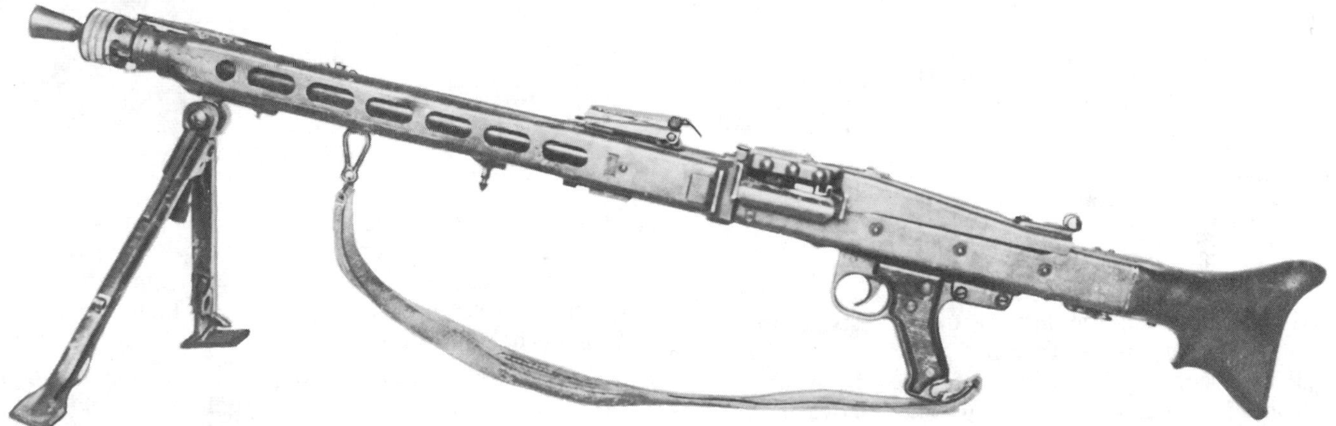

German 7.92mm MG42 Machine Gun. This weapon is being used by the W. German Army with the 7.62mm NATO cartridge.

This is the latest German machine weapon. In many respects it is the most remarkable gun of its type ever developed. The cheapness and simplicity of its manufacture, as well as its superior performance, have led to its supplanting the MG34.

Following in the footsteps of the Russians, the Germans in developing this gun ignored all the shibboleths of machine gun designing. The result is an all-purpose machine gun, which can be produced cheaply and rapidly and which is amazingly simple and reliable. Like MG34, it has the one defect of trying to be too many weapons. With a bipod mount it can be used by one or two men. On an antiaircraft mount it is a truly excellent antiaircraft gun. On a tripod mount it fills many of the uses of the heavy or medium machine gun. However, the rate of fire is so very high (a very valuable characteristic for antiaircraft work) that the weapon suffers as a ground light machine gun. It wastes ammunition and climbs entirely too much to utilize the accuracy inherent in the German service cartridge.

Caliber: 7.92mm German Service Cartridge.

Feed: Non-disintegrating 50-shot steel belts, which can be linked together to give any capacity desired; or 50-shot belts wrapped in individual steel drum as for the MG34. Like the MG34, some models are fitted to receive the saddle type dual drums holding 75 cartridges, one drum on each side of the receiver with a solid connecting piece joining them across the bridge of the receiver.

Ballistics: Standard for this cartridge.

Weight of Gun With Bipod: About 25 lbs.

Sights: As for MG34. Has special attachments for antiaircraft sight. Telescope sight provided for use with tripod. This is mounted on the tripod, not on the gun.

Gun operated by: Short recoil and muzzle recoil booster as for MG34.

Locked: By a unique locking system. The essential principle had previously been utilized in an automatic rifle of Mannlicher design. However, the development of this principle in the MG42 is quite new. There is no rotating lock in this gun nor any rising or falling wedge systems. The bolt is securely locked to the barrel by two locking studs in the bolt head which are free to move under the action of locking cams on the barrel extension.

West German MG42—1958 Model for 7.62mm NATO Cartridge.

Cooled: Air; bolt open between shots. Heavy ventilated barrel casing.
Cyclic Rate of Fire: 1100 to 1200 per minute. With some types of ammunition, this gun is capable of a speed close to 1500 per minute. This speed is too high for any practical use except on or against aircraft.
Type of Fire: Full automatic only.
Flash Hider: On end of barrel casing as in MG34.
Barrel Removal: This is probably the most remarkable feature of the gun. On the right side of the barrel casing where it joins the receiver is a spring catch. When the gun is cocked, a forward and outward push on this catch with the heel of the hand will lever out a hinged side-piece which will bring the rear end of the barrel completely out of the gun. If the gun is so mounted that the muzzle can be elevated and the butt depressed, the barrel will slide out of its own accord. If the gun is level the extension on the barrel may be quickly grasped and the barrel whipped out of its seating. Inserting the muzzle of a new barrel through the hole in this lever and pushing it forward until its muzzle enters the forward end of the barrel casing, then slamming the side piece shut, locks the barrel in position to resume firing. No weapon made compares with this one on barrel change.
Length of Gun: 48 inches.

Loading and Firing

To Load: As for MG34. Feed cover may be open or closed. Be sure that the first cartridge rests against the stop on the right side of the feed guide.

Pull back cocking handle on left side of gun as far as it will go. The bolt will stay open. Then shove the cocking handle fully forward until it clicks.

Unless gun is to be used immediately, set the safety. On this gun the safety is just above the pistol grip. Push the button from the right side and it sets the safety. Push the button from the left as far as it will go and the gun is ready to fire.

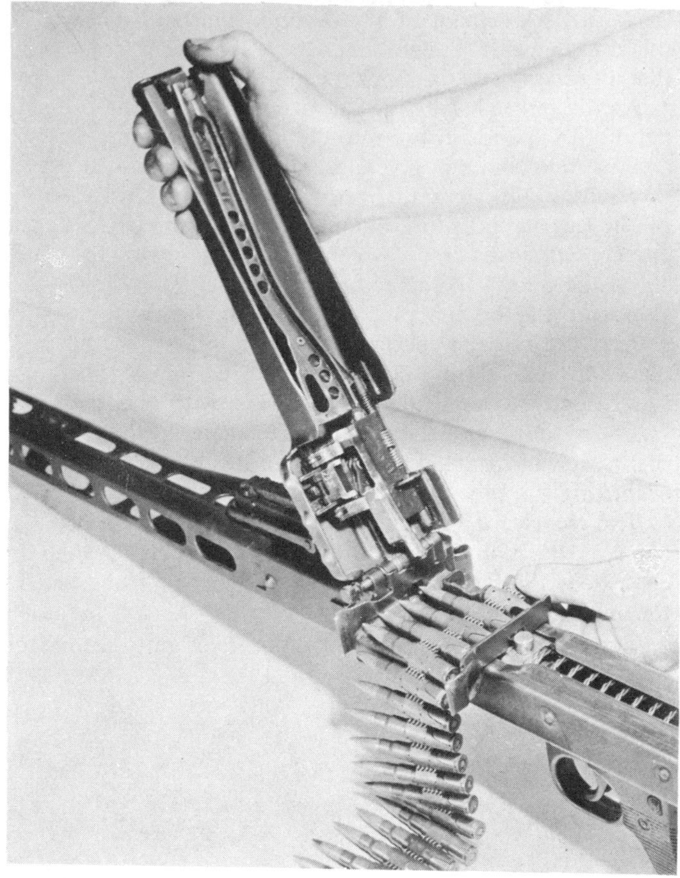

Notes on Unloading. Unloading this gun is a very simple operation. First pull back the cocking handle as far as it will go. Then set the safety. Push forward the cover catch and raise the cover as high as it will go. Lift the belt out of the gun.

It is not good practice to permit the bolt to go home on an empty chamber. Always hold the cocking handle firmly while pressing the trigger and ease the bolt into forward position.

Note that there is a spring cover over the ejection opening in these guns. It flies open when the trigger is pressed. On "Cease Fire" always push it shut. This will keep dirt and dust out of the mechanism.

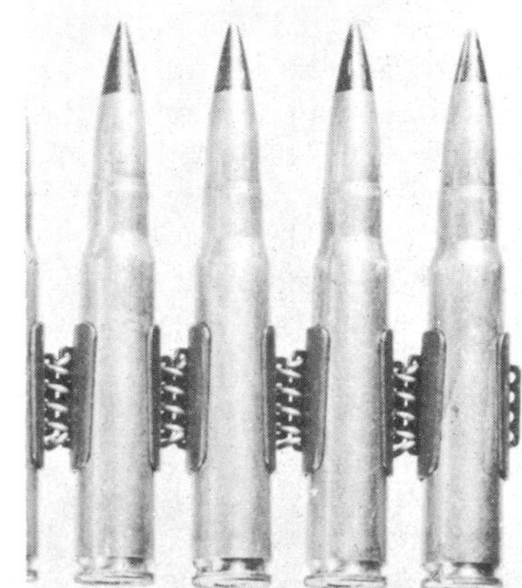

German metal belt showing detail of cartridges, locking system and tab.

Field Stripping

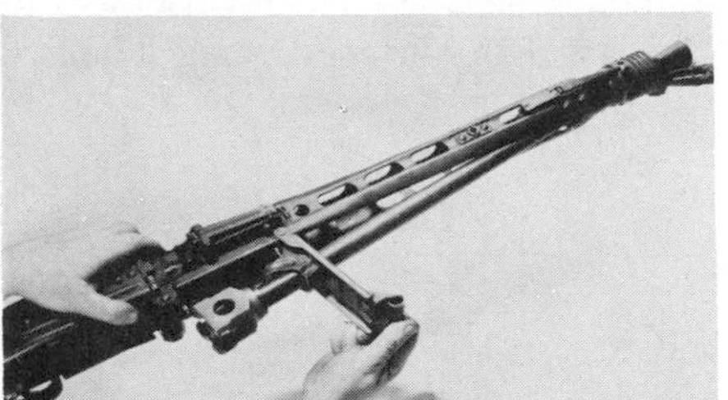

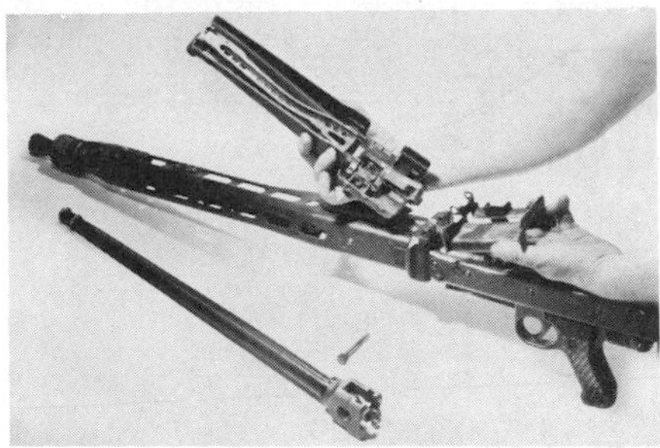

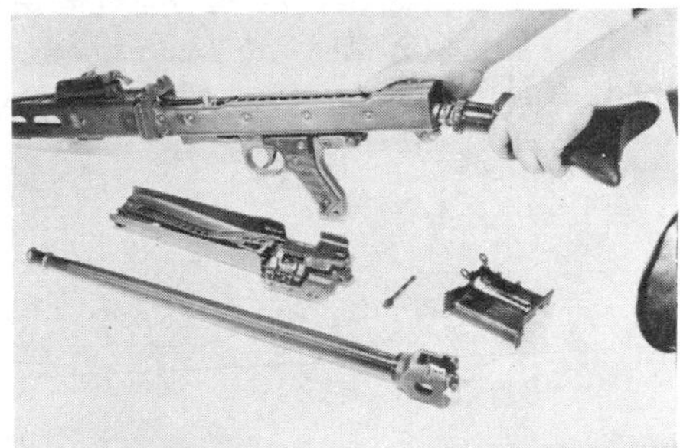

In general field stripping this gun is similar to the MG34. There are, however, some few differences.

Remove Barrel. It is first necessary to cock the weapon. This is done by pulling back the cocking handle. Then thrust forward and outward on the heavy release catch jutting out from the rear of the barrel extension on the right hand side of the gun, below the feed block. This draws the rear of the barrel out of its seat and permits it to be drawn from the rear of the gun.

The feed resembles the MG34. Push forward the feed cover catch on top of the gun near the stock and lift the cover. Pull out the feed cover hinge pin and remove the feed block from the gun. Dismounting this is very simple.

Remove buttstock, same as for MG34, Be sure bolt is in forward position before removing buttstock. Catch is on the under side of the stock. Push it and twist the butt a quarter turn, right or left.

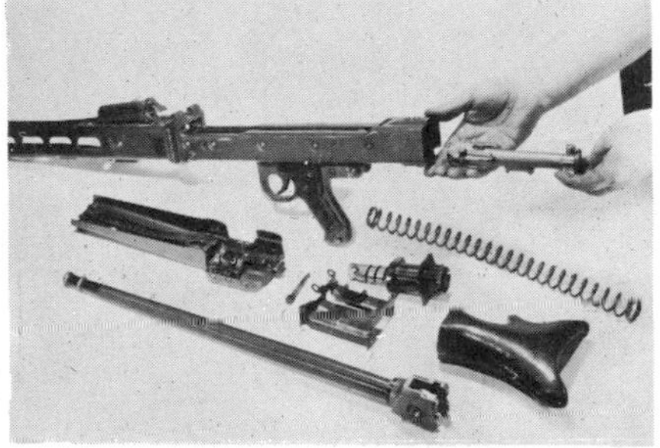

Remove buffer and recoil spring. As in the MG34, the housing catch is on the rear end of the receiver, just back of the pistol grip. Press the catch and control the buffer housing that moves away from the receiver under tension of the powerful spring. Remove the bolt. Press the trigger and strike the cocking handle a sharp rearward blow. This will drive the bolt to the open rear of the receiver where it may be withdrawn.

No further stripping is normally necessary.

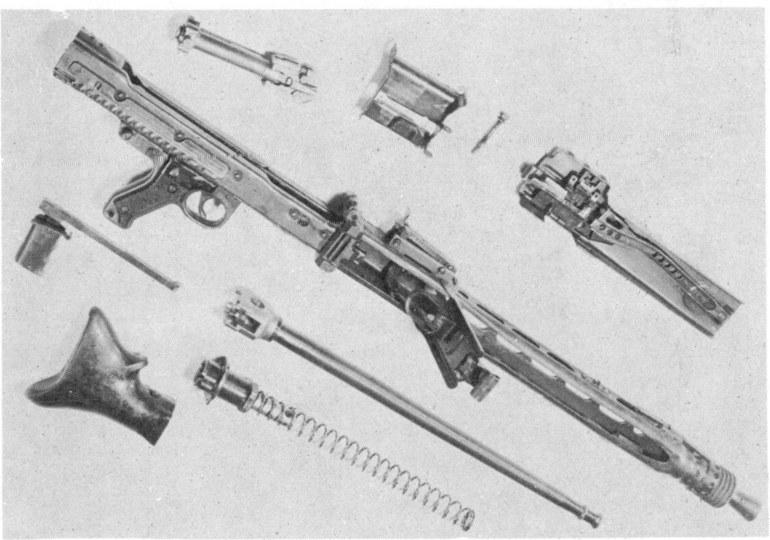

How the Gun Works

In general this gun follows the operating detail of the MG34.

However, an entirely new design of bolt and locking mechanism is employed. The barrel and bolt in this gun travel back in a straight line during the period of recoil. There is no turning action.

A heavy barrel extension is screwed onto the chamber end of the barrel. In its sides are slots into which cams are machined. As the bolt goes forward, a movable locking stud on each side of the front end of the bolt strikes a corresponding cam in the barrel extension. This forces locking lugs out and into slots in the barrel extension as the face of the bolt comes flush with the base of the cartridge in the firing chamber. The extractor slips over the base of the cartridge. The firing pin, mounted in the rear of the bolt assembly, is driven forward to explode the cartridge. Note that a stud, driving from the top of this rear bolt assembly, travels in a groove in the curved feed arm and shuttles the feed across and back to operate the feed mechanism.

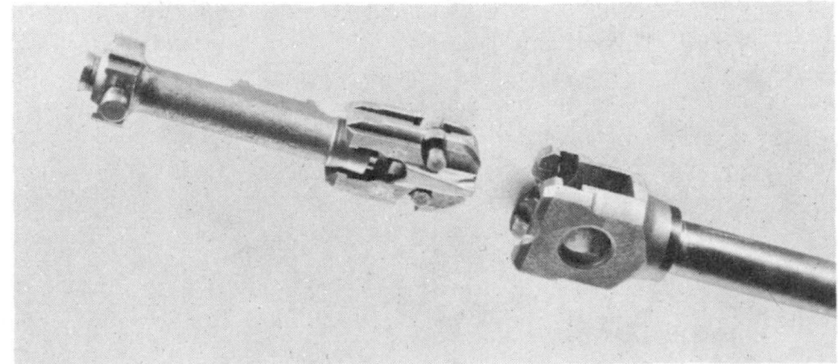

Showing detail of the bolt with feed operating stud, bolt locks, and barrel.

During the recoil movement, barrel extension and bolt are firmly locked together during the moment of high breech pressure. Then as the barrel extension and barrel are stopped in rearward travel, the studs on the bolt head are cammed out by the camming surfaces on the barrel extension and the locking lugs are thus withdrawn from their seats in the barrel extension permitting rearward direct line motion in the action. This action is patterned after a simple pile-driver, the bolt resembling the pile-driver hammer being pulled up (or out) to its full extent, then the gripping surfaces being cammed out to release it.

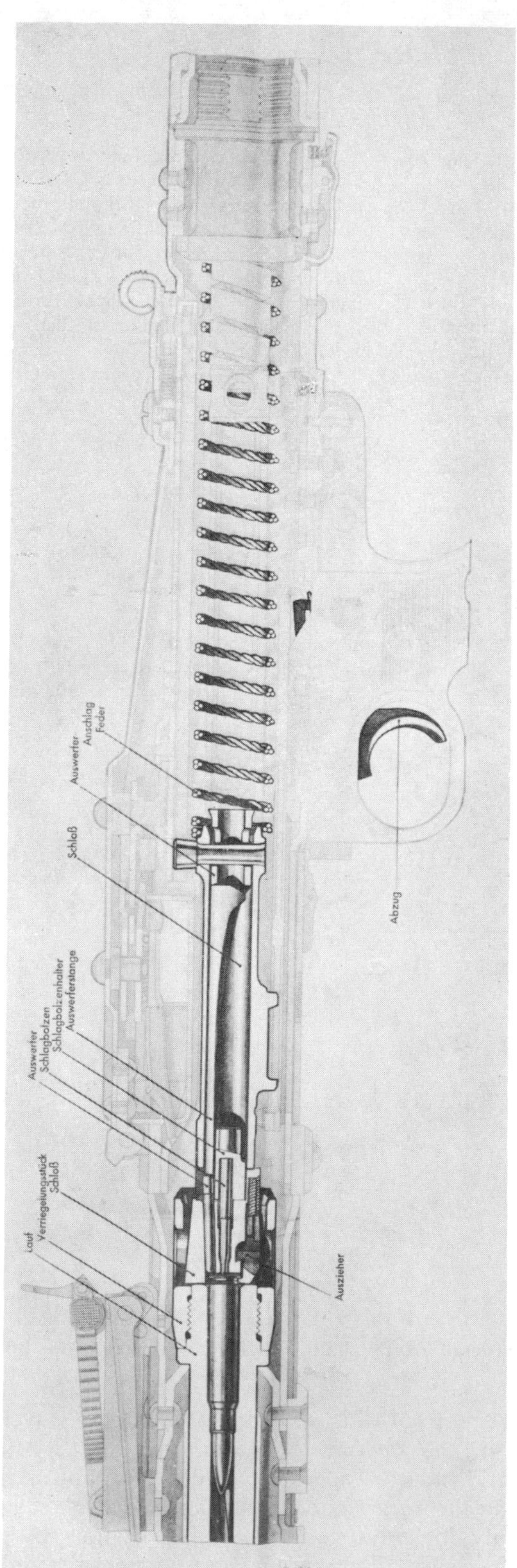

Phantom view, left side, showing full details of operating mechanism, parts fully forward, weapon about to fire. Nomenclature, top of gun, left to right: 1. Barrel. 2. Barrel extension. 3. Lock. 4. Extractor. 5. Firing pin. 6. Firing pin extension. 7. Carrier. 8. Lock. 9. Feed stud. 10. Recoil spring. Bottom of gun, left to right: 1. Ejector. 2. Trigger.

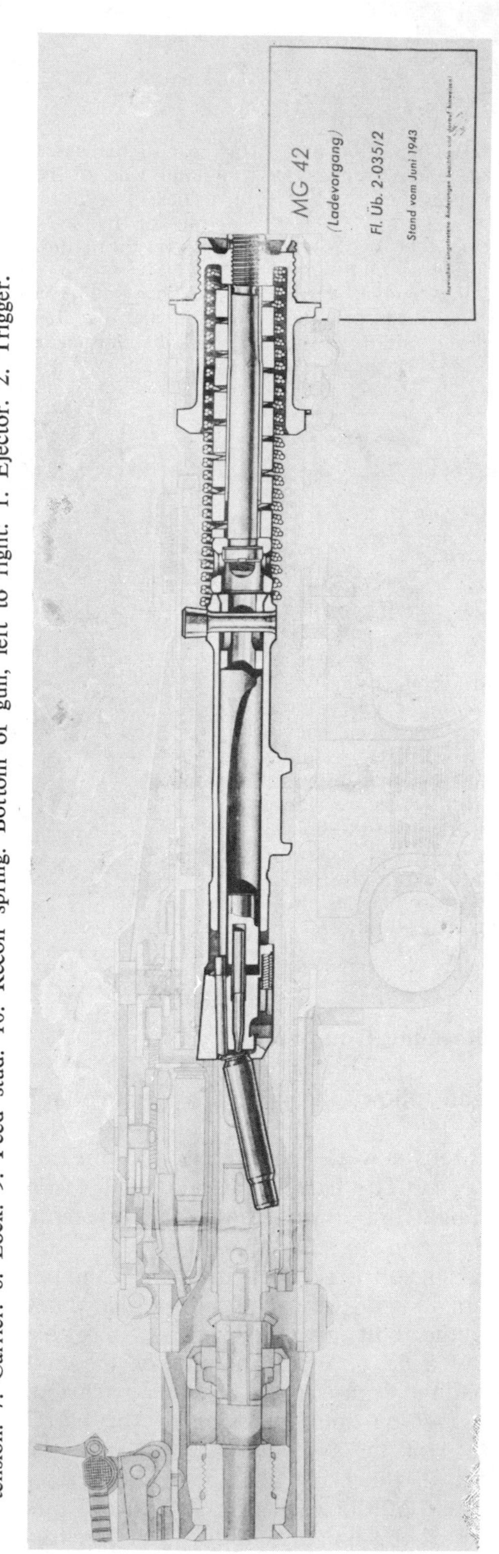

Phantom view, left side.
Shows operating parts in partial recoil, new cartridge ready for feeding on forward stroke. and empty shell about to be ejected.

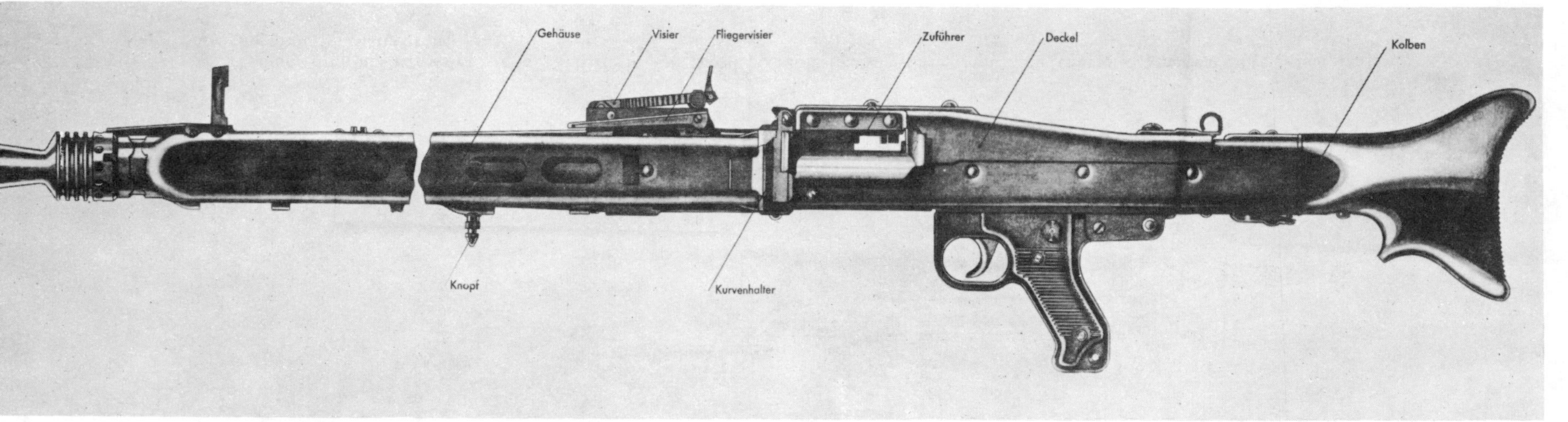

Exterior view, showing all important outside parts. Nomenclature, reading left to right, top: 1. Barrel Jacket. 2. Rear sight. 3. Sight base. 4. Feed box. 5. Cover. 6. Stock. Left to right, bottom: 1. Mounting screw. 2. Receiver.

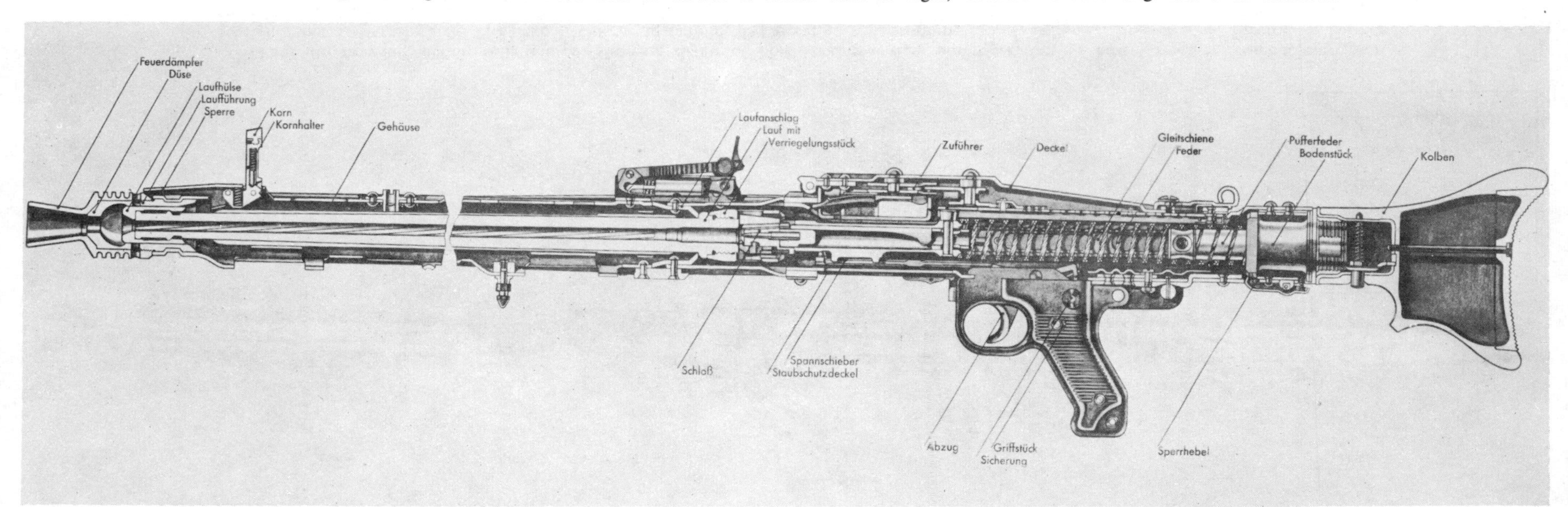

Phantom drawing showing all operating parts in full closed position. Left side view. Nomenclature, left to right, top: 1. Flash-hider, 2. Barrel mouth. 3, 4, and 5. Blast cone assembly. 6 and 7. Front sight and spring. 8. Housing. 9. Barrel retainer. 10 and 11. Barrel and barrel locks. 12. Feed. 13. Cover. 14 and 15. Recoil spring and guide. 16. Buffer spring. 17 and 18. Butt assembly and butt. Left to right, bottom: 1. Lock. 2. Bolt. 3. Bolt extension. 4. Trigger. 5. Safety. 6. Grip. 7. Buffer release.

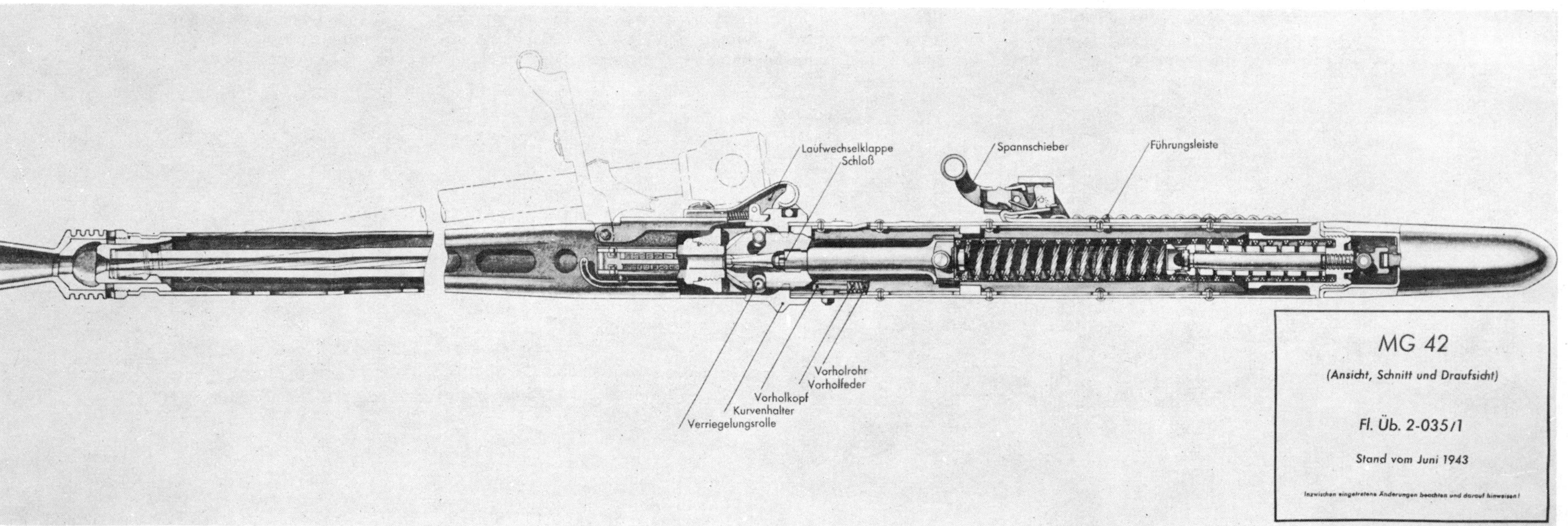

Phantom drawing, action fully closed, showing detail of bolt locking system and operation of barrel release. Nomenclature, left to right, top: 1. Barrel catch. 2. Lock. 3. Operating handle. 4. Operating rod. Bottom: 1. Bolt roller. 2. Bolt stop. 3. Ejector. 4. Ejector spring. 5. Spring cover.

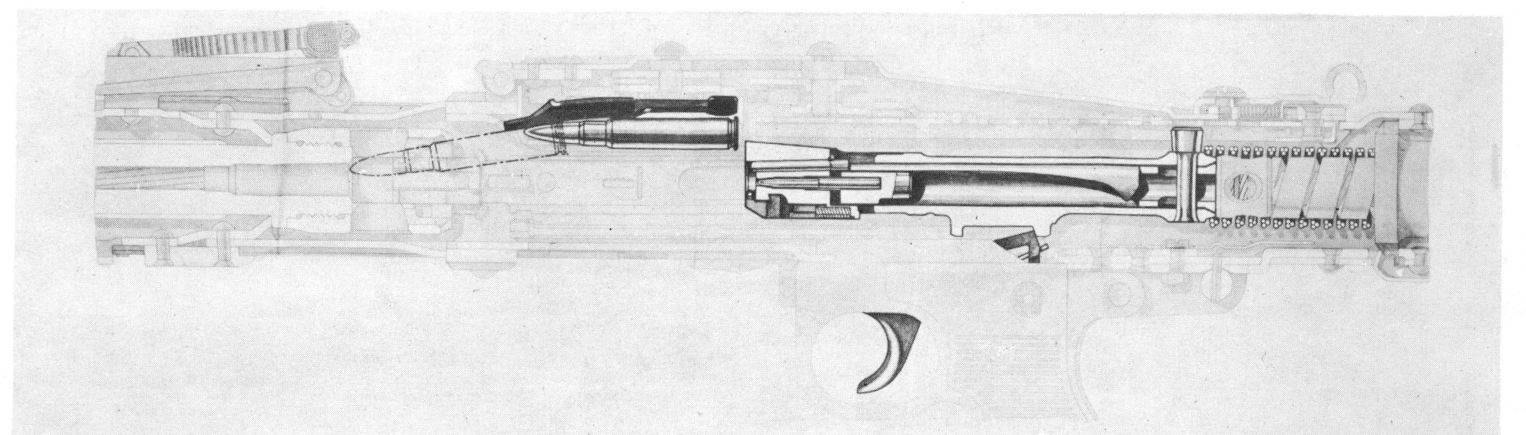

Phantom drawing, left side. Shows all parts in full recoil position ready to fire, indicating course of the cartridge when parts move forward to chamber it.

1. MG 34. Single Shot and Full Auto.
2. Modified MG 34. Single Shot and Full Auto.
3. MG 34S. Full Auto.
4. MG 34-41.
5. MG 42. Differs Mechanically from 34's.

Chapter 27. Greece

THE modern Greek Army is equipped with U. S. and British small arms. The greater number of small arms used by the Greeks in their postwar fight against the Communists were British. Since that time, the Greeks have been supplied with some U.S. weapons.

GREEK RIFLES AND CARBINES

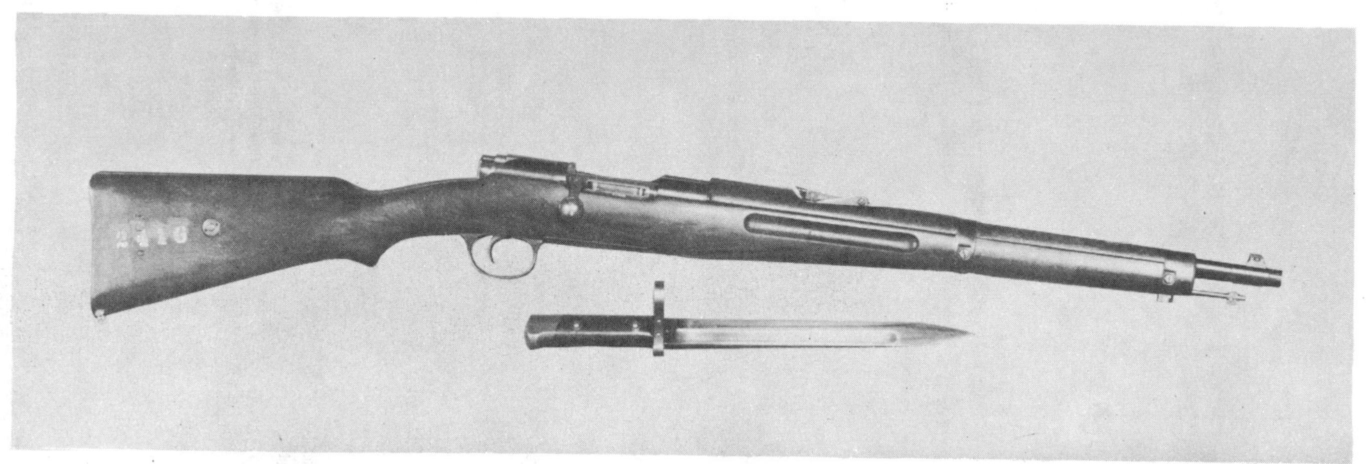

Model 1903/14 Carbine.

The former Greek service rifle is the same as the carbine illustrated except for barrel length, sights, and weight. The carbine barrel is 20.5″ long. This is a turning bolt action of Mannlicher design with a revolving box (also called spool or drum) magazine.

Caliber: 6.5mm Greek.
Barrel Length: 28.27″.
Overall Length: 48.3″.
Weight: 8.3 lbs.
Sights: 200-2000 meters on Model 1903/14. (400-2000 on M1903.) Barleycorn front and V-type rear.
Operation: Standard for turn bolt rifle.
Magazine: Revolving; follower inside fixed vertical box. Loads by insertion of single cartridges or from charger clip of Mauser type.
Special Feature: No cutoff, but magazine may be held in reserve each time action is opened by forcing a cartridge down into position before bolt.

Unusual design feature is a magazine release stud on right side receiver lip. Pressing this stud when action is open will free magazine follower, permitting magazine spring to expel cartridges through top of rifle.

Safety: Manual safety on bolt.

Operation

The bolt handle is turned up and drawn back. A stud on the cocking piece rests in the customary tang groove. When the handle is lifted a cam cut at the rear of the bolt cylinder pushes the stud and the cocking piece assembly straight back as the bolt itself turns.

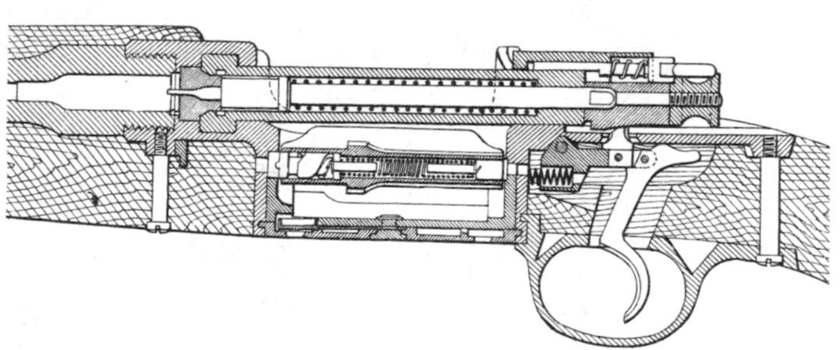

Section of rifle with action closed. Note position of locking lugs in rear of bolt head.

This cocking piece stud pushes down and rides over the sear nose. The firing pin is drawn back inside the bolt body, since it is attached to the cocking piece.

Dual front bolt lugs are turned out of their locking seats in the receiver as the bolt body turns. The lugs then move along cam grooves, thereby forcing the entire bolt assembly back to start the cartridge case out of the chamber. This is primary extraction actuated by great leverage.

The bolt is pulled back until it ejects the empty case carried back by the extractor. It hits the bolt stop and its rearward travel is halted.

The magazine spring forces the follower around the distance of one cartridge until it is halted by the stop.

On forward thrust of the bolt, the cartridge in the boltway is chambered. The cocking piece stud is stopped by the holding face of the sear nose just as the lugs reach their cam grooves in the receiver. As the bolt handle is turned down, the bolt lugs are driven along their grooves into their receiver locking seats as the bolt handle works against the front face of the split receiver bridge. Since the bolt body is forced ahead, while the sear nose holds the cocking piece back, this closing action completes the cocking.

Loading and Firing

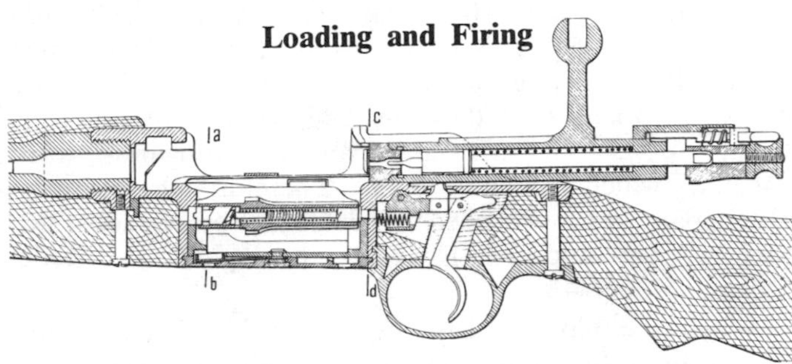

Rifle section, with action open, ready for firing.

With the action open a loaded clip is inserted in the receiver guides and the cartridges stripped down into the magazine. Alternatively, single cartridges may be dropped in the action and successfully forced into the magazine.

The magazine follower is forced to turn on its front and rear retaining studs, thus coiling an attached spring and progressively increasing its tension. As each cartridge goes in, the cartridge stop lip is sprung out to let it enter the magazine, then back to prevent the cartridge from escaping.

Pressing the projecting thumbpiece on this stop pulls a lip out of the path of the cartridges and the wound-up magazine spring revolves the follower to expel the cartridges.

The trigger pull is the double pull type as used in all Mannlicher rifles.

Each time the action is opened, the magazine spring drives the follower around until the stop halts it, leaving a cartridge in the path of the bolt.

Field Stripping

Open action. While pressing in bolt stop catch on left side of receiver, pull bolt back out of action.

Let cocking piece down to fired position. Push safety forward and turn to right. Turn striker nut one-quarter turn to left and remove. Turn safety one-quarter turn to left and remove. Spring cocking piece and withdraw it.

The bolt head in Mannlicher turn bolt designs is removable. Give bolt head a half turn to the right and remove it. Extractor and ejector will come off with bolt head. Remove striker and mainspring from front of bolt body. Lift extractor and pull it forward.

Use bullet point to push down magazine bottom plate catch. Turn bottom plate a quarter turn and remove. Lift front end of follower and remove follower.

Identification. Mannlicher turn bolt with dual front lugs and removable bolt head. Revolving box magazine. Military type stock.

Evaluation. Best quality materials and workmanship in weapons made between war periods. Magazine design highly regarded by many qualified gunsmiths. Converts to excellent sporter when in good condition. Mannlicher type bolts having removable bolt heads carry lugs farther back than in Mauser solid head type, but if head space is properly adjusted the Mannlicher will take pressures almost comparable to Mausers.

Ammunition. Designed for Greek 6.5mm cartridge; 6.5mm Mannlicher-Schoenauer caliber as commercially available in U. S. is satisfactory if sight adjustments are made.

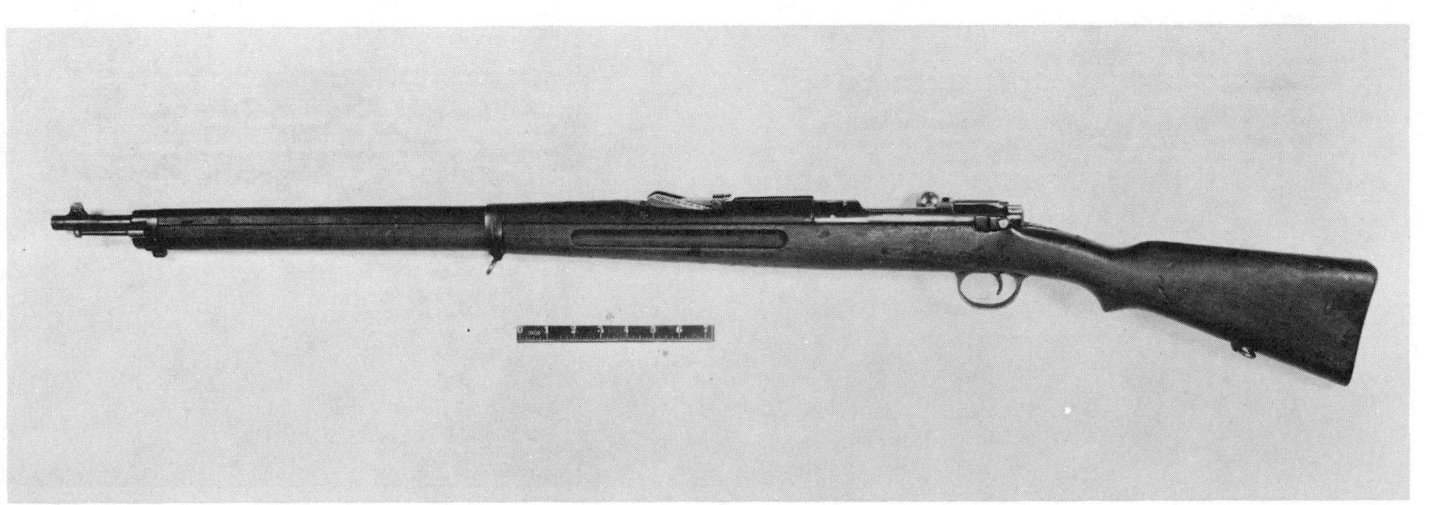

Greek 6.5mm Mannlicher Schoenauer M1903/14 Rifle.

Chapter 28. Hungary

AT the conclusion of World War II, the Hungarian Army, which had fought on the Axis side in the war, was equipped with a combination of Hungarian and German weapons. The Hungarians changed their service rifle and pistol cartridges during the war, in order to standardize on the German calibers. The prewar Hungarian pistol cartridge for use in submachine guns was the 9mm Mauser cartridge. The prewar rifle and machine gun cartridge was the 8mm Model 31, a rimmed cartridge which was used by Austria (prior to Hitler's seizure of that country) as the Model 30. The Hungarian M35 rifle and M31 machine gun were chambered for this cartridge. During the war, the M35 rifle was altered to use the 7.92mm cartridge, and the magazine was changed from a Mannlicher type requiring the use of a Mannlicher-type clip to a Mauser type fed from a five-round charger (stripper clip). The resultant weapon was called the Model 43. The M31 machine gun design also was modified to use the 7.92mm cartridge, and the weapons manufactured for the use of that cartridge were called M43 machine guns. As a matter of interest it should be pointed out that Hungarian weapons are frequently called Model—M. This is the result of misunderstanding the M designation as used by the Hungarians. They do not say "Model 43"; they say "43 Model" or, in short form, "43M." The M stands for the Hungarian word "Minta," which means "Model." Therefore, there are no Hungarian weapons called Model 35M or Model 43M; their correct model designations in English are Model 35 and Model 43.

When the Communists took over in Hungary they standardized on Soviet equipment, and the Hungarians have produced some of the older Soviet small arms. The Soviet M1891/30 rifle, the Soviet PPSh M1941 submachine gun, and the Soviet TT M1933 (Tokarev) pistol have all been produced in Hungary where they all are called Model 48, after the year of their adoption by the Hungarians. The Hungarians also use the Soviet DP light machine gun, the Soviet Goryunov (SG-43) heavy machine gun, and the Soviet DShk M1938 12.7mm heavy machine gun.

HUNGARIAN PISTOLS

Older Hungarian pistols are the same as for Austria except for the Frommer series; and the M1937 and M1939 Browning type hammer blowback models.

FROMMER 1912. This was an official service pistol in caliber 7.65mm Browning (.32 Colt Auto) and 9mm Browning Short (.380 Colt Auto).

Variants. This design was also commercially made in smaller size as the Frommer "Baby" in calibers .32 and .380 Colt Auto; while the official 1912 was also marketed commercially as the Frommer "Stop" pistol also in calibers .32 and .380 Colt Auto.

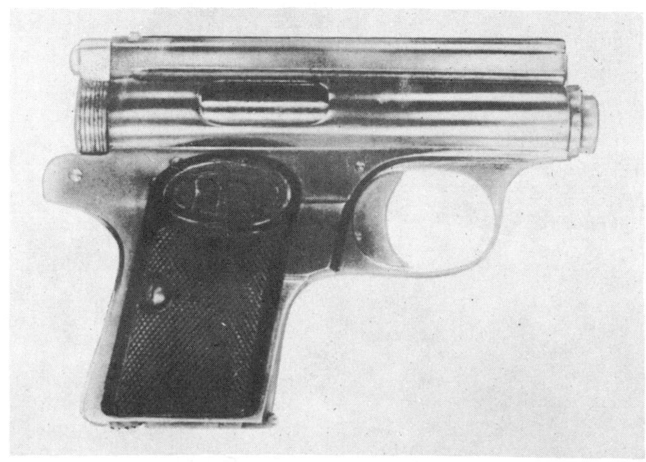

Frommer Baby. Locked Breech. .32 and .380.

Frommer Stop. .32 and .380.

Frommer Lilliput. Blowback .25 Auto.

FROMMER LILLIPUT. While it resembles other Frommers in external appearance to a degree, and has an exposed hammer, this pistol is a common blowback, as opposed to the locked breech designs of the other Frommers.

Identification Frommer Locked Breech Types. Detachable magazine in handle. Long recoil operation. (Only muzzle of barrel ever emerges from barrel cover during operation. Breechblock projects from rear of barrel and receiver housing.) Exposed hammer. Grip safety.

Evaluation. All Frommers are well made of the best materials. The design is complicated. Locking system is too involved and is not necessary with low power cartridges used. If barrel cover (exterior casing) is dented, malfunctions may result.

The Lilliput is a common blowback .25 Auto, whose sole value is its sturdy build. Exposed hammer is not desirable in vest pocket pistols.

Ammunition. U. S. .25 Colt Auto. .32 Colt Auto or .380 Colt Auto according to caliber.

M1939. This design may be encountered in either 7.65mm (.32 A. C. P.) or 9mm Browning (.380 A. C. P. caliber).

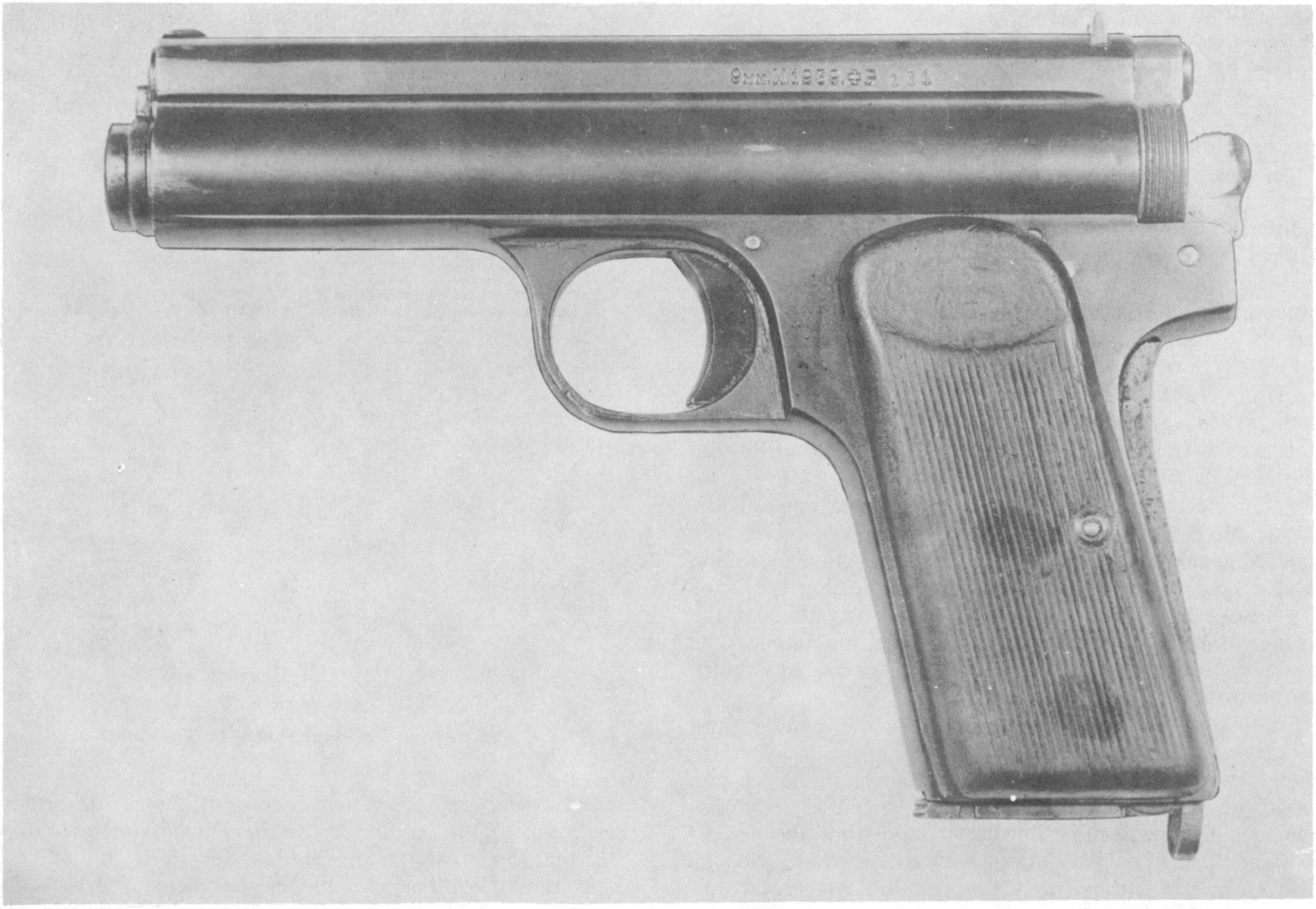

Frommer M1939. Caliber .380. Obsolete in Hungary.

Frommer 7.65mm Automatic.

Caliber: 7.65mm Browning (.32 Colt Auto).
Barrel Length: About 3¼".
Overall Length: 6½".
Weight: About 20 oz.
Accurate Range: 50 yds.
Operated By: Recoil.
Locked: Special long-recoil system.
Type of Fire: Semi-auto only.
Magazine Capacity: 7.
Magazine Release Catch: Bottom rear of grip.
Muzzle Striking Energy: 152 foot pounds.
Safety: Colt grip type.
Muzzle Velocity: About 980 feet per second.

This is a Hungarian weapon formerly very widely used in the Balkans. The design is simple and very efficient, but the cartridge is of the type considered a pocket pistol cartridge in the United States. It uses the Standard United States .32 caliber Automatic Colt Pistol cartridge.

While this is a well-designed and beautifully-made weapon, it does not qualify as a military pistol in the accepted sense of the term. However, it was esteemed by Austrian officers.

This is a locked breech pistol of unusual design. It belongs to the long recoil class of firearms in which the barrel travels to the rear the full distance of the cartridge length.

The receiver is so designed that it carries all the parts of the pistol. The handle section receives the magazine and accommodates the trigger, hammer, safety, and mainspring mechanisms. The upper section is shaped to receive and cover the barrel in a lower tube at the front, and the bolt at the rear; while the upper tube receives the recoil spring, bolt return spring, and return spring follower.

A loaded magazine is inserted in the handle until it locks. The bolt is drawn fully back and released to run forward and load the firing chamber. If the weapon is held securely, the grip safety is forced in; this disengages the projection on the safety from the trigger bar hook normally engaged with it. Pressure on the trigger is now transmitted through the trigger bar directly to the broad sear, pushing the sear nose out of its retaining notch in the hammer.

The coil mainspring drives the hammer to rotate it on its axis, strike the firing pin, and discharge the cartridge.

As the pistol fires, the barrel and bolt start back locked together while the bullet goes down the barrel. When the full length of the possible recoil stroke is reached, a bolt catch mounted on the receiver is forced up by a spring to engage with a cut in the bolt cylinder. During rearward movement of the recoiling parts, the springs mounted in the tube above the barrel are compressed.

The barrel return spring now pushes the barrel forward, while the bolt is held back by the catch. The bolt consists of two pieces; as the barrel starts forward it pulls the front head of the bolt and this causes the bolt head to rotate and unlock from the rear bolt cylinder.

The barrel continues to be driven forward by its spring, the extractor grips the empty case, and a spring ejector emerges to hit the case and hurl it out of the pistol.

When the forward barrel travel is completed, the barrel extension is in position where it forces the bolt catch down out of engagement. This permits the compressed bolt return spring to drive the bolt forward to strip a cartridge into the chamber for the next shot.

During rearward movement of the action, the bolt has ridden over and cocked the hammer which is held by the sear. The tail of the sear cannot be disengaged until the barrel is fully home and the action locked; until this position is reached the bolt catch interferes with action of the sear, and this catch is held down when the rear of the barrel extension rides over it.

Hungarian 7.65mm Model 48 Pistol.

Only one weapon which is not of Soviet design is known to be in common use in Hungary today—the 7.65mm Model 48 pistol. The Model 48 is a modified copy of the Walther PP, and is chambered for the cal. .32 ACP cartridge which is called the 7.65mm Browning short in Europe.

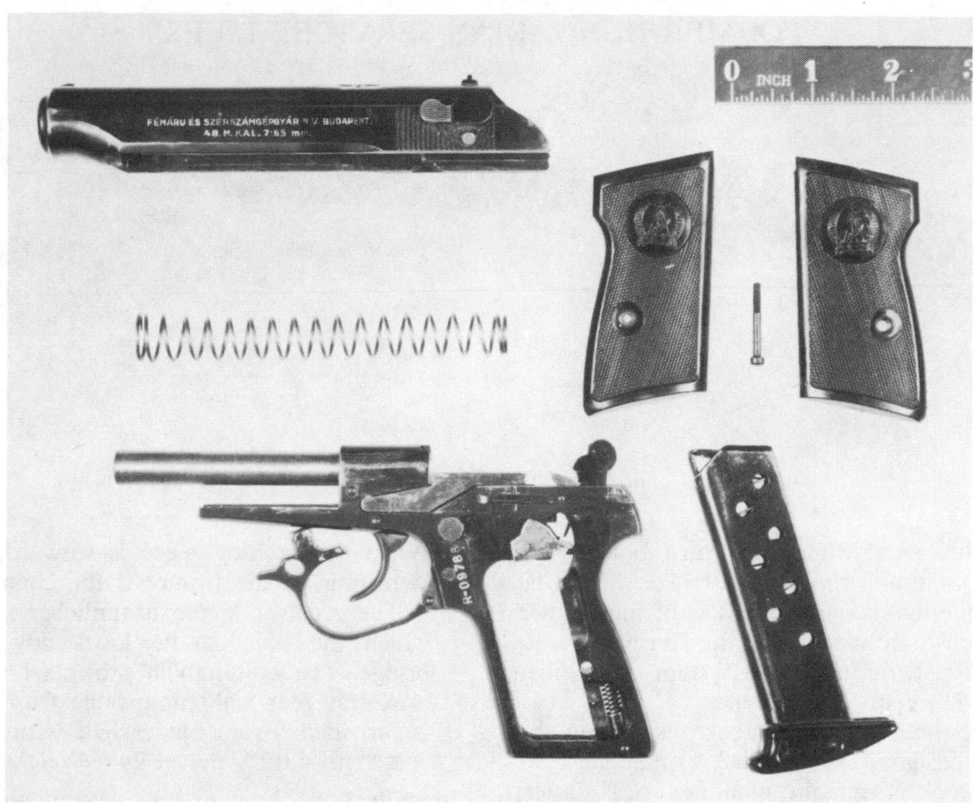

Model 48 Field Stripped.

System of operation: Blowback, semi-automatic fire only.
Weight, loaded: 1.92 lb.
Length, overall: 7 in.
Barrel length: 3.94 in.
Feed device: 8-round, single-row, removable box magazine.
Muzzel velocity: 920 f.p.s.
Sights: Front: Blade.
Rear: U-notch.

Special Note on the Model 48 Pistol

The loading, firing, functioning, and field stripping of the Model 48 pistol are the same as for the Walther PP, which is covered in this book in chapter 26. There are some slight differences in construction between the Model 48 and the Walther, and the Model 48 is approximately three-quarters of an inch longer than the Walther.

Hungarian 7.62mm Tokarev, a copy of Soviet TT M33.

FORMER HUNGARIAN SERVICE RIFLES

The M35 Rifle made at Budapest.

MODEL 1935. This is a Mannlicher turn bolt design using an 8mm x 56mm rimmed cartridge. The rifle itself is not commonly encountered. It is of importance in that it lent itself to conversion to the German 98/40 during World War II, the magazine system and caliber being altered to German Service types.

The Model 35 has a 2-piece stock resembling the British Enfield design. The official explanation for the use of this stock is that the manufacture is easier, and that replacement in case of damage is cheaper. The small of the stock is also said to be strengthened by the stock bolt which attaches the two pieces. (Note: This is the statement of British and Hungarian ordnance men, not of the author.)

The receiver and bolt are practically the same as the other turn bolt Mannlichers. (See chapter 27 for description of typical Mannlicher turn bolt operation.) The magazine is a 5-shot straight line vertical box which projects below the line of the stock.

A cocking piece of the Austrian M95 type is incorporated in this design to permit recocking the rifle without opening the action in case of a misfire. The striker should never be lowered on a loaded chamber. When the cocking piece is forward, the striker point is resting on the primer if the chamber is charged.

The receiver is the Mannlicher split-bridge type in which the bolt handle locks down forward of the bridge. The bolt handle projects horizontally.

A leaf rear sight adjustable from 100-2000 meters is provided. Front blade sight is protected by a hood.

Length 43.5″. Barrel 24″. Weight about 9 lbs.

Identification. 2-piece stock. Mannlicher turn bolt. Austrian M95 type cocking piece head. Projecting vertical box magazine.

Evaluation. Good design, materials, and workmanship. Magazine type is good for rimmed cartridges, but any conversion to a rimless caliber should include magazine alteration to Mauser type.

Ammunition. 8mm x 56mm Hungarian. Not available in U. S.

MODEL 43. This is the Hungarian M35 above with the following changes: Caliber changed to 7.9mm rimless. Magazine changed to standard Mauser double column vertical box, fully inside stock. Bolt handle turned down. No hood on front sight.

Hungarian 7.92mm M43 Rifle.

(This rifle, except for sling swivels and bands, is similar to the 98/40 made in Hungary for the Germans.)

HUNGARIAN MACHINE WEAPONS

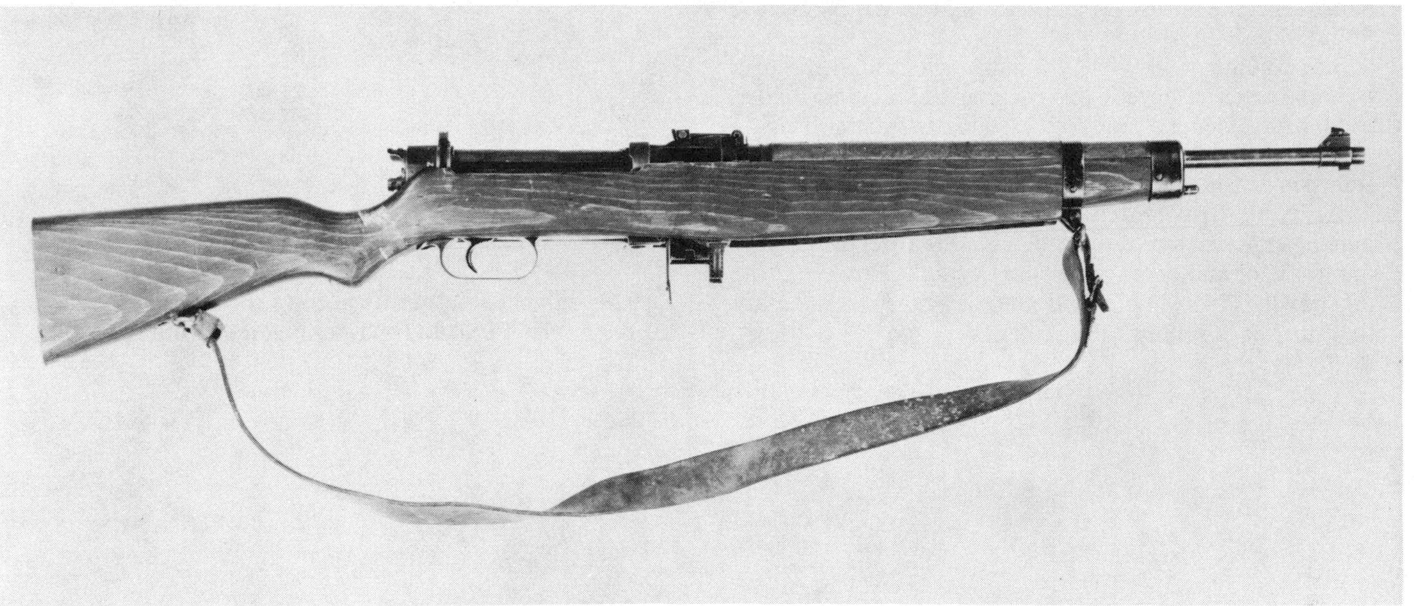

Hungarian 9mm Model 39 Submachine Gun. No longer in Service.

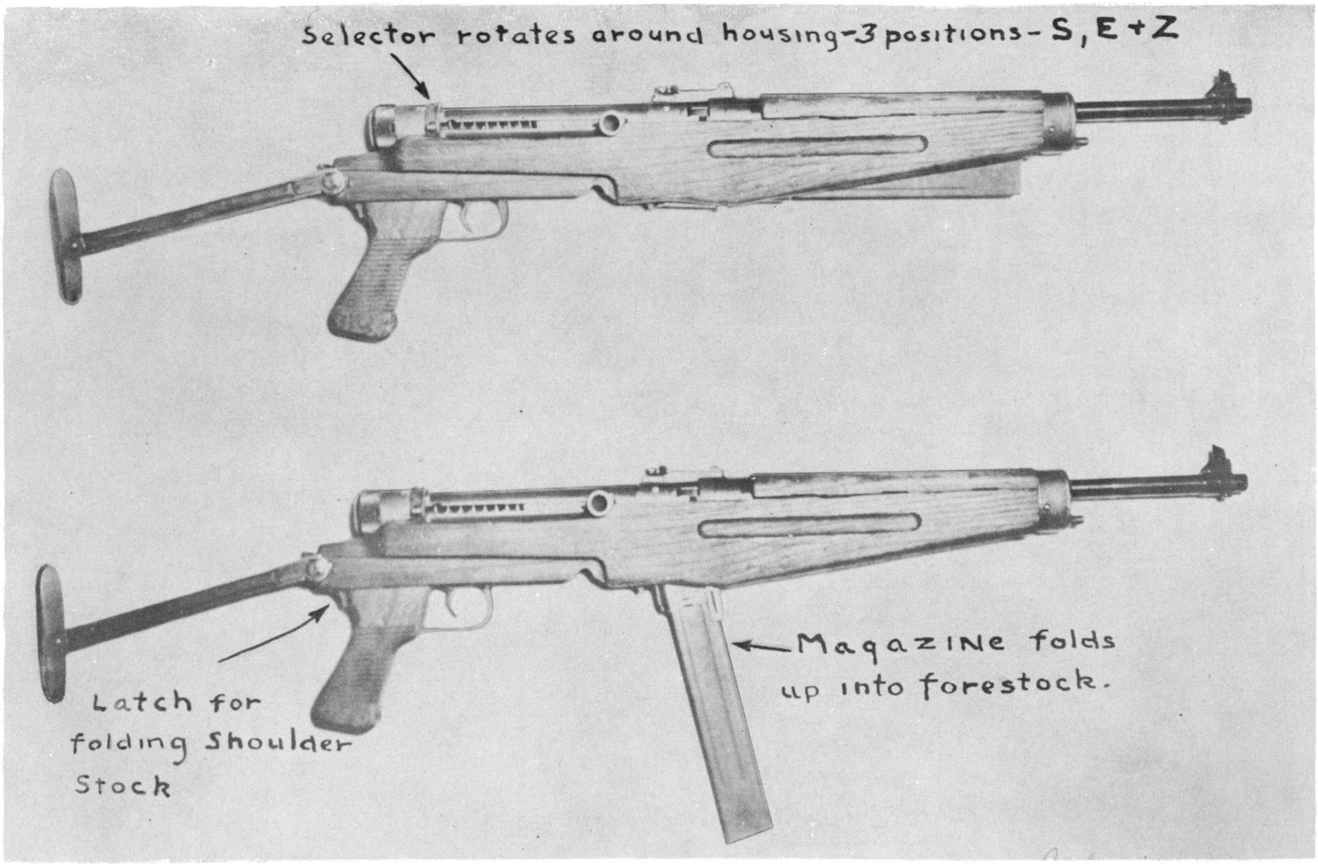

Hungarian Model 43 Submachine Gun.

This arm appeared in caliber 9mm Mauser. This is a Hungarian development in the submachine gun field which was designed originally by SIG of Switzerland.

There are no really new features—all have appeared in earlier European weapons, but the combination is interesting and unusual.

The magazine, which can be folded up under the

stock when not in use, affords unusual compactness with large magazine capacity (30). The caliber is the 9mm Mauser.

The folding stock is crude but efficient, and the arm is capable of a reasonable degree of accuracy when used with extended stock as a semi-automatic arm.

A rotating selector can be speedily changed to safe, single shot (semi-auto), or full auto fire.

As in the British Sten, the travel slot for the cocking handle exposes the action to a marked degree, allowing foreign matter to enter the action. However, the takedown is so simple and the design so elementary that this is a minor disadvantage.

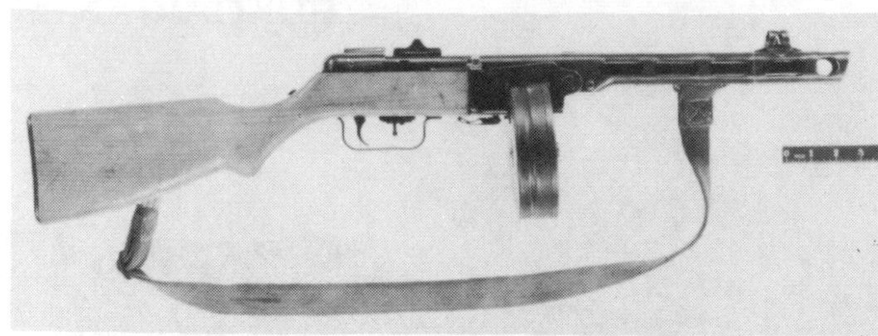

Model 48 7.62mm Submachine Gun.

This submachine gun is a copy (produced in Hungary) of the Soviet PPSh M1941 submachine gun.

Chapter 29. Iran (Persia)

The Iranian government, as a result of various defense agreements with the United States, has adopted most U. S. small arms. The Iranian Army uses the U. S. cal. .30 M1 rifle and some cal. .30 Browning machine guns, the M3A1 submachine gun, and other U. S. weapons. Iranian Mauser rifles have been sold to United States dealers and are therefore in common circulation among United States arms enthusiasts for the first time.

IRANIAN RIFLES

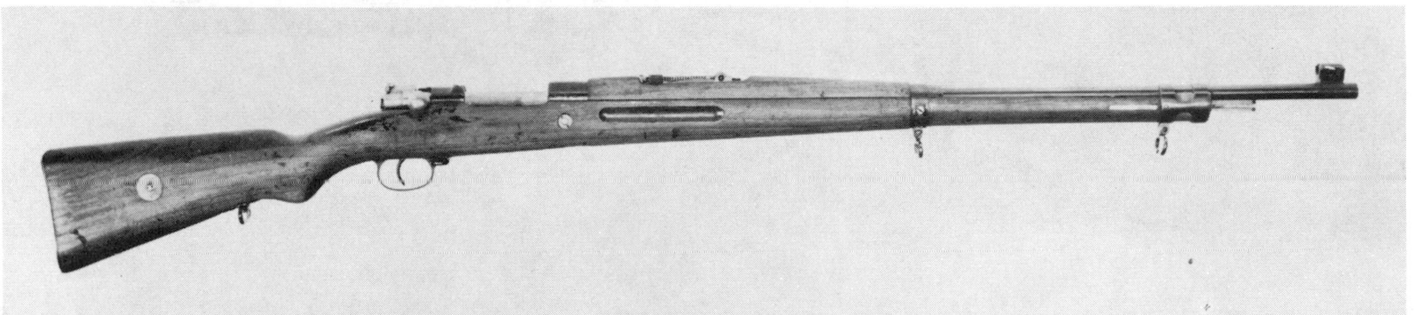

Iranian 7.92mm Model 98/29 Rifle.

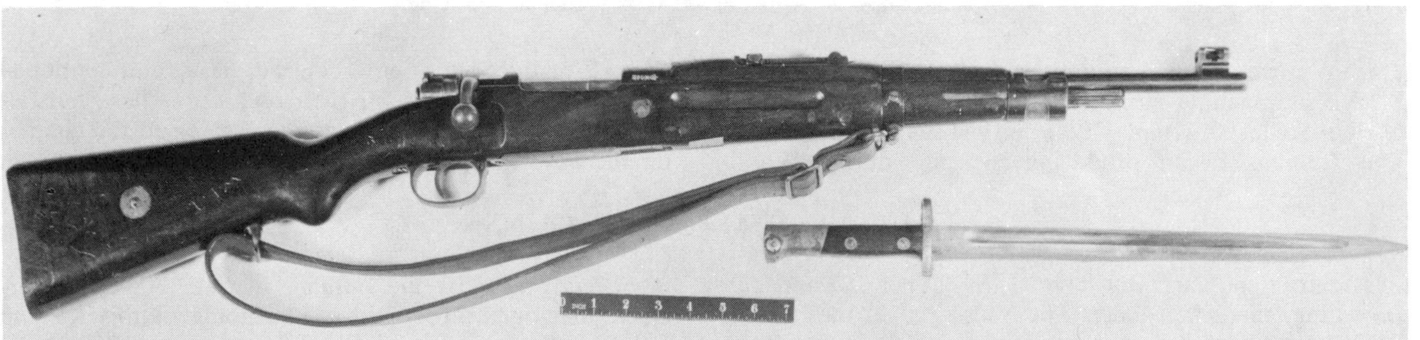

Iranian 7.92mm Model 98/29 Short Rifle.

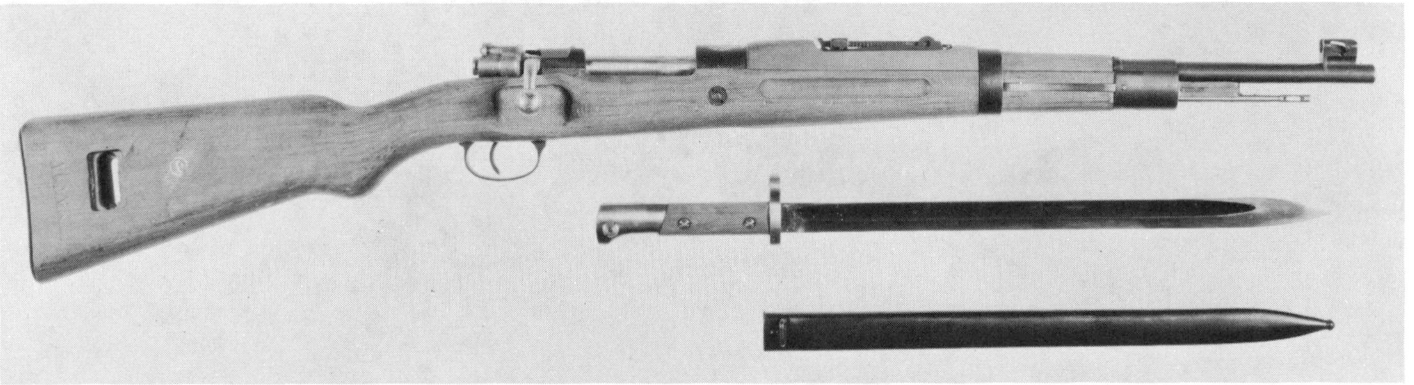

Iranian 7.92mm Model 49 Short Rifle.

	98/29 Rifle	98/29 Short Rifle
Caliber:	7.92mm.	7.92mm.
System of Operation:	Manually operated turning bolt action.	Manually operated turning bolt action.
Weight:	9.1 lbs.	8.4 lbs.
Length Overall:	49.2 in.	38 in.
Barrel Length:	29.13 in.	17.91 in.
Feed Device:	5-rd, staggered row, non-detachable box magazine.	5-rd, staggered row, non-detachable box magazine.
Sights, Front:	Protected barley corn.	Protected barley corn.
Rear:	Tangent with V-notch, grad. from 100-2000m.	Tangent with V-notch, grad. from 100-2000m.
Muzzle velocity:	Approx. 2800 f.p.s.	Approx. 2600 f.p.s.

These Mauser type rifles were made both at ZB in Czechoslovakia and in Iran. A later model, called by the Iranians Model 49, is a modified version of the 98/29 short rifle. Differences between the Model 28/29 and the Model 49 are confined to sling swivels and minor fittings. All of these weapons are loaded, fired, and field stripped in the same manner as the Czech Model 24 rifle which is covered in detail in the chapter on Czechoslovakia. These rifles are being replaced by the U. S. cal. .30 M1 rifle.

IRANIAN SUBMACHINE GUNS

Iranian Copy of Soviet PPSh M1941 Submachine Gun.

Iran currently has quantities of U. S. caliber .45 M3A1 submachine guns. Iran has also produced copies of the Soviet 7.62mm PPSh M1941 submachine gun. The Iranians began producing the gun during World War II for the Soviets on a contract basis, and continued to produce the weapon for their own use. Characteristics of the weapon are the same as those given in the chapter on the Soviet Union.

IRANIAN MACHINE GUNS

The Iranians currently have U. S. caliber .30 and .50 Browning machine guns. They also have the Czech ZB30 machine gun which they make in Iran. This weapon was originally manufactured in 7.92mm, but is currently used by the Iranians in Cal. .30. Characteristics, loading, firing, and field stripping of this weapon are basically the same as those given for the ZB30 in the chapter on Czechoslovakia.

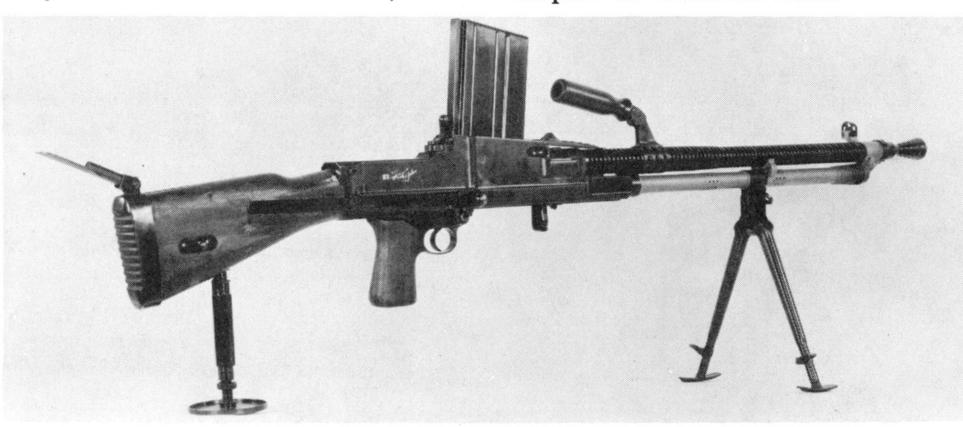

Iranian 7.92mm Model 30 Light Machine Gun.

Chapter 30. Israel

THIS new state has a very active arms industry and is, in some categories, an exporter of weapons. The Israeli Defense Forces were equipped mainly with British equipment when the state was founded. Purchases were made, the bulk apparently from Czechoslovakia, in the 1948 period; and Israel then standardized, as much as she could, on the 7.92mm cartridge for rifles and machine guns and on the 9mm Parabellum cartridge for pistols and submachine guns. Czech and German Mausers were—and still are—in wide use, as is the ZB 37 and (on armored vehicles) the 7.92mm Besa. Browning's were also procured, for armored vehicles. At a later date, the Type D FN Browning automatic rifle was also bought, and the Uzi submachine gun, a native weapon, was put into production. Since that time, Israel has now standardized on the 7.62mm NATO cartridge (which she produces locally), and has adopted the FN NATO "light rifle" (FAL). The heavy-barreled version of this weapon is used as the squad automatic weapon. Some of the weapons procured earlier are being rebarreled for the 7.62mm NATO cartridge. From a hodgepodge of 9mm, cal. .38, cal. .45, and cal. .455 pistols, Israel has adopted the 9mm Beretta M1951 pistol as standard.

Israel is a young state and has a considerable amount of vim and vigor in small arms development as well as in other things. The Israelis are willing to, and can (because of the size of their state), take chances that larger nations cannot consider. As a result they have had their failures in small arms development, but, because of their "youthful" approach, they are worth watching for new developments. The frequent fighting which goes on around their borders gives them ample opportunity to try out their weapons in active service.

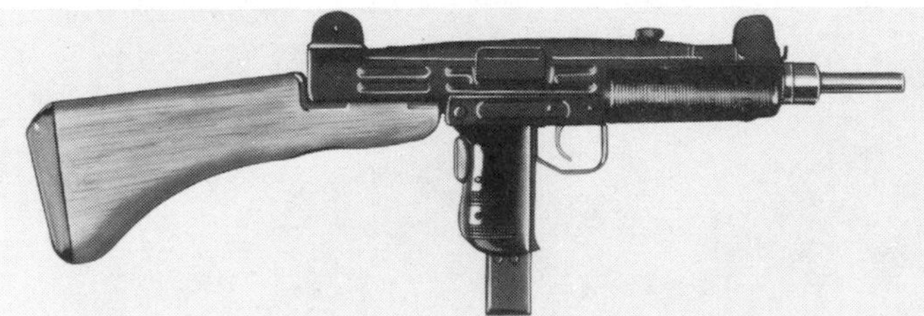

Israeli 9mm Uzi Submachine Gun with Wooden Stock.

The Uzi is named for Major Uziel Gal, its developer. It is the standard submachine gun of the Israeli Army, and also has been sold to other countries. In basic operating principles, the Uzi is quite similar to the Czech ZK 476 and its descendants, the Czech Models 23 and 25 submachine guns. As far back as 1945, the UK had an experimental gun which also had a bolt that telescoped the barrel—the telescoping bolt is a feature common to all of these weapons and to the Beretta Model 12 as well.

The Uzi is a very well-made gun, and its performance leaves little to be desired. FN of Belgium is now marketing this weapon in Europe.

Caliber: 9mm Parabellum.
System of operation: Blowback, selective fire.
Weight: 8.9 lb. w/loaded 25-round magazine and metal butt.
8.8 lb. w/loaded 25-round magazine and wooden butt.
Length, overall: 25.2 in. (wooden-butt model, and metal-butt weapon with stock extended). The length of the metal-butt model with the stock folded is 17.9 in., and the length of the wooden-butt model with the butt removed in 17.3 in.
Barrel length: 10.2 in.
Feed device: 25-round or 32-round, detachable, staggered box magazine.
Sights: Front: Truncated cone w/protecting ears.
Rear: L-type w/setting for 100 and 200 yards.
Muzzle Velocity: 1310 f.p.s. w/8-gram 9mm Parabellum bullet.
Cyclic Rate: 650 r.p.m.

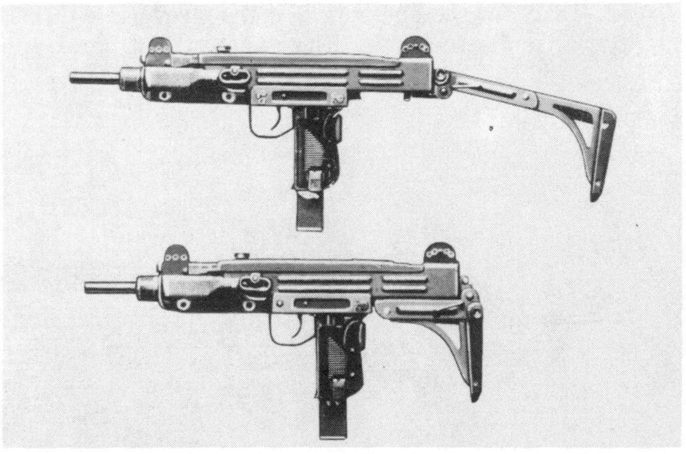

Uzi with Folding Metal Stock.

How to Load and Fire the Uzi

Insert a loaded magazine in the magazine well located in the pistol grip. Pull the cocking handle, located on the top of the receiver, to the rear. The Uzi fires from an open bolt, and the bolt will remain to the rear. To fire single shots, set the change lever, located on the top left side of the pistol grip, to the letter R (this is the mid-position). To fire automatic fire, set the change lever at the letter A (this is the forward position). To put the weapon on safe, set the change lever at S (this is the rear position). Pressure on the trigger will fire the weapon, if the change lever is set on the semi-automatic or automatic fire positions. The grip safety must be squeezed when firing the weapon.

Field Stripping the Uzi

To release the cover, press the catch in front of the rear sight housing to the rear. Raise the cover and remove it from the receiver. Raise the bolt from the front; when its forward part is completely disengaged, withdraw it from the receiver together with the recoil spring, giving

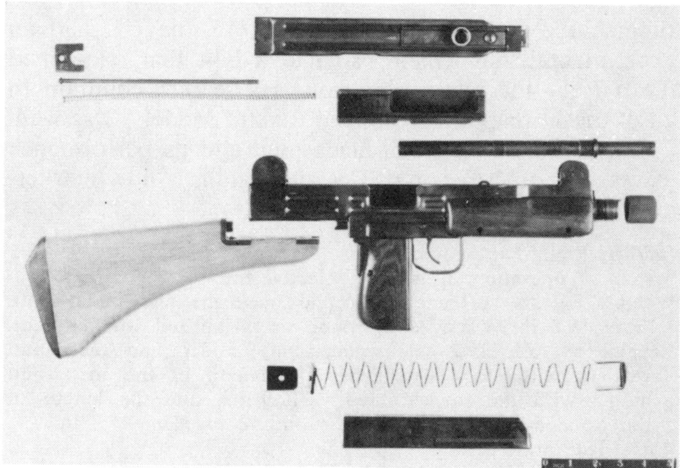

Uzi Field Stripped.

the whole assembly a short pull forward. To remove the extractor, take out its retaining pin. Press in the lock of the barrel retaining nut; unscrew the nut and withdraw the barrel. Take out the split pin and the sleeve in which it is housed, and remove the trigger group and pistol grip from the assembly. To strip the folding metal butt, unscrew the hexagonal head of the nut retaining the butt (the nut is located in the rear of the receiver). To remove the wooden butt, press in the butt retaining catch, and pull the butt to the rear. No further disassembly is recommended.

To reassemble the weapon, follow the above procedure in reverse order.

How the Uzi Works

With the exception of the trigger mechanism, the functioning of the Uzi is quite similar to that of the Czech Model 23 submachine gun.

Special Note on the Uzi

The current model designation of the Uzi in Israeli service is No. 2 Mark A. The Uzi has a grip safety (as have the Belgian Vigneron and several other submachine guns available today), which makes the weapon much safer to handle than were various World War II submachine guns. As an example, the Uzi cannot be fired accidentally when dropped, since its grip safety locks the sear to the extent that it prevents the rear of the bolt from overriding, which is necessary if the bolt is to go far enough to the rear with enough kinetic energy to pick up a cartridge and fire it. The Uzi is composed mostly of stampings. It is one of the best examples of a modern post-World War II submachine gun. The West German government has adopted the Uzi, and it is not too unlikely that this weapon will, in the future, secure a much wider distribution than it has at present.

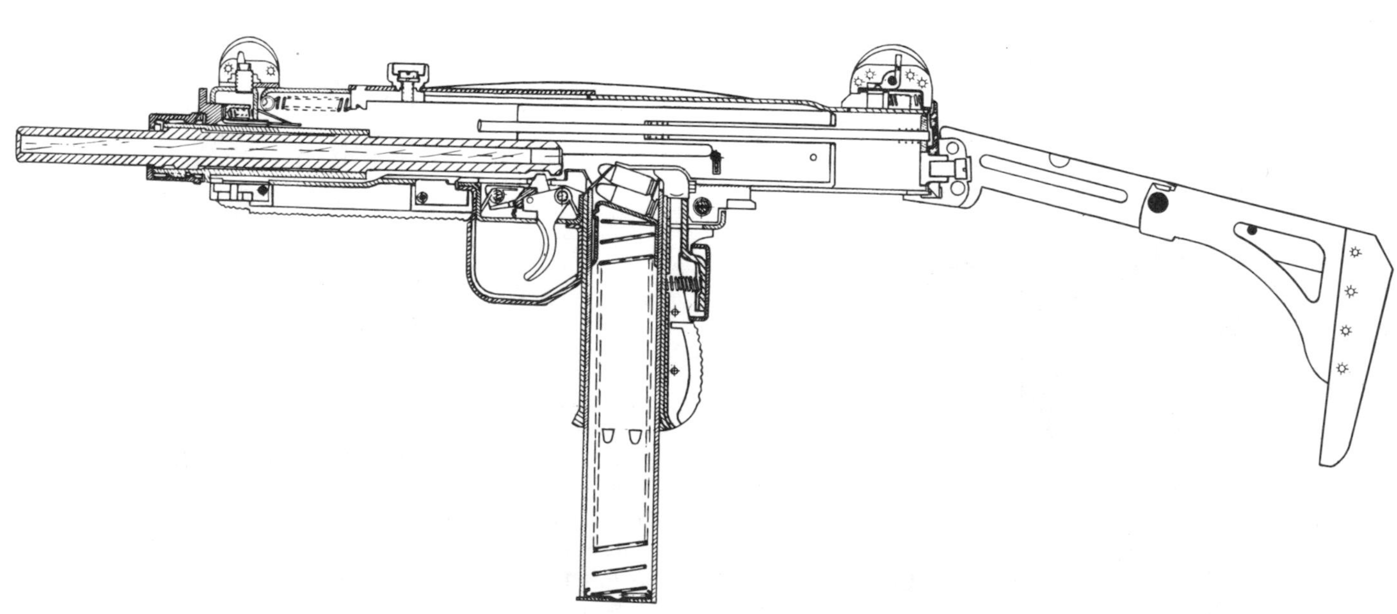

Israeli 9mm Uzi Submachine Gun, section view.

Chapter 31. Italy

SINCE World War II, the Italian Army has been armed mainly with weapons of United States or British design and/or manufacture, but some of the best weapons of Italian design and manufacture have been retained. Outstanding among these are the Beretta 9mm Corto (cal. .380 ACP) Model 1934 pistol, various models of the Beretta 9mm submachine gun, and the Breda 8mm Model 1937 heavy machine gun. Italy has adopted the Beretta 7.62mm BM59 rifle as standard.

ITALIAN PISTOLS AND REVOLVERS

Beretta 1915 Enclosed Hammer Pistol Caliber .32.

The standard Service types are described and pictured in this section. The following supplemental data is essential because of the appearance in this country of pocket and substitute standard types brought to the U. S. as souvenirs.

BERETTA PISTOLS. Beretta was the prime Italian manufacturer. A very wide variety of minor modifications may be encountered in these arms, but basically they fall in two classes—enclosed and exposed hammer designs. All are blowback types, though some have extra buffer springs to slow down opening.

Enclosed Types. The common Vest Pocket forms have grip safeties. Such pistols were often carried by staff officers.

The common early pocket forms in caliber 7.65mm and 9mm Corto (short) take the standard .32 or .380 Colt Auto cartridges. They are normally fired by internal hammer.

The model 1915 resembles the pocket model except that it is larger and is equipped with a special buffer spring to absorb shock. A version of this model uses the 9mm Italian Service (Glisenti) cartridge as used in War I. Modern Luger ammunition will chamber and function, but will shortly batter the slide and may injure the pistol.

Exposed Hammer Types. These are all in the class of the basic design pictured and described in this section. They vary little except in caliber and size.

The Models 1923, 1931, and 1938 are common. They may be caliber .32 Colt Auto or .380 Colt Auto.

Model 1915/25 is a heavy model of the Service type. It is chambered for the 9mm Model 1915 (Glisenti) cartridge. This model works well with 9mm Luger cartridges; though care should be taken that such ammunition be of pistol type.

Evaluation. All Beretta models are well made of good materials. The models from 1923 on have several interesting design features, such as system of barrel mounting, ease of disassembly, minimum use of pins and screws.

Most models stay open when empty. The magazine follower catches and holds the slide. A poor feature is that the slide runs forward when the magazine is withdrawn. A stiff pull is necessary to withdraw the magazine when the slide is being held open.

A serious design defect is that the manual safety locks only the trigger. This does not preclude accidental slipping of the hammer to fire the pistol.

Ammunition. .25, .32 or .380 Colt Auto according to caliber.

In pistols for the 1915 Service and the 1915/25 9mm, Luger 9mm ammunition as made in the U. S. may be used, but slide and buffer units should be watched for evidence of battering. High pressure Luger loads are not recommended.

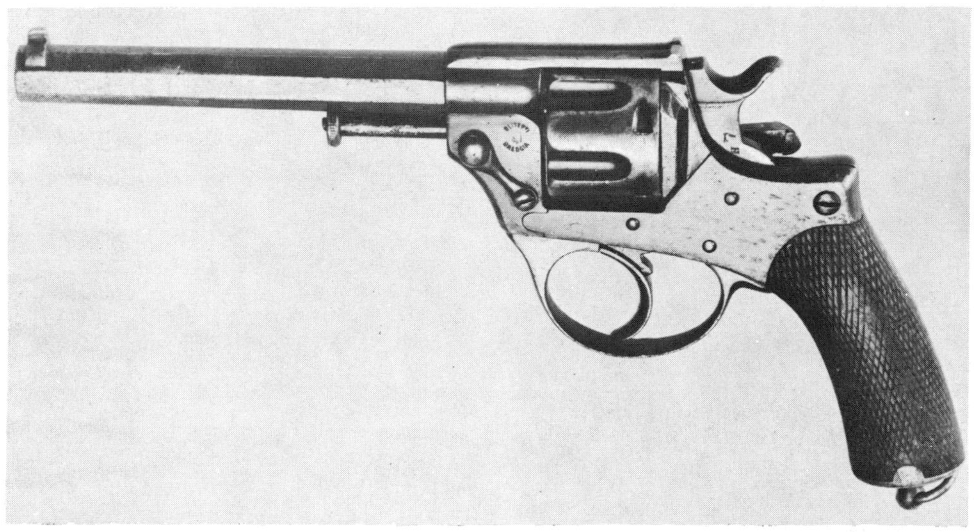

Italian Glisenti Service Revolver 10.35mm.

Caliber: 10.35mm (about .41).
Cylinder: 6 chambers.
Barrel Length: 6¼ inches.
Overall Length: 11 inches.
Weight: 40 ounces.
Frame: Solid.
Ejection: Rod ejector.
Action: Double action, rebound hammer.

Revolvers. Italian Revolvers are all based on black powder specifications. No ammunition of the standard Italian 10.35mm caliber is made in the U. S. These are specimens suitable only for hanging on the wall.

Special Note on this Revolver

This was probably the best known of the Italian Service Revolvers. It is often referred to as the "Bodeo" or "Bodego" revolver. Actually it bears the manufacturing stamp of Glisenti of Brescia.

It is a type of revolver considered obsolete in this country for over 40 years.

To load, it is handled exactly like our Colt Frontier Model. A loading gate is tipped back (instead of out as in the Colt). The weapon is half cocked which permits the cylinder to be revolved by hand so cartridges can be fed individually into each chamber.

Unloading the weapon requires opening the loading gate, half cocking the hammer, and pushing the ejector pin on the right side of the weapon up into the chamber to eject. This operation is repeated, revolving the cylinder by hand, until all chambers are empty. This weapon and the other revolvers illustrated are obsolete.

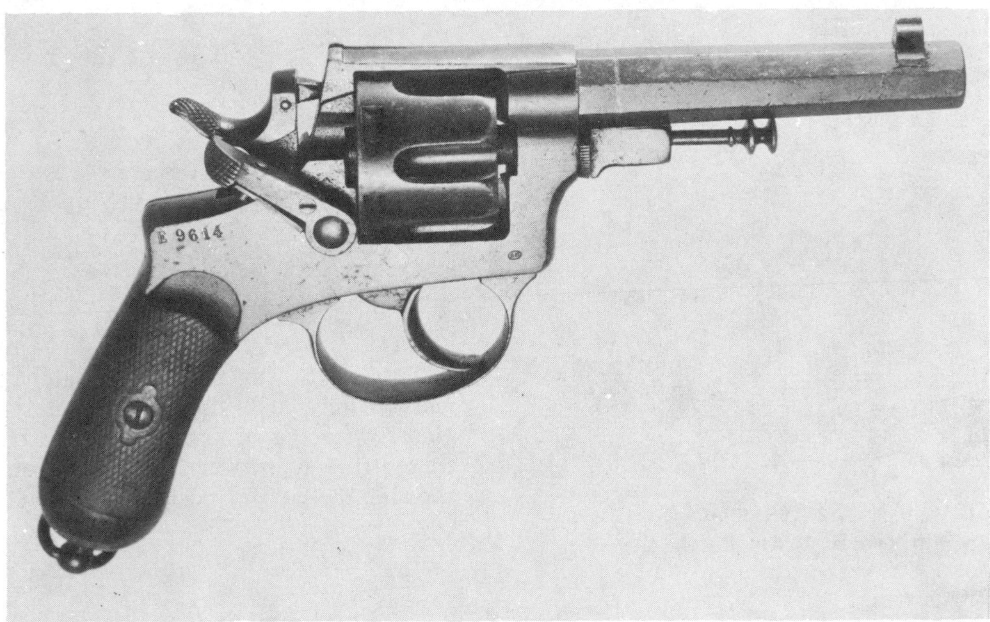

Former Italian Service Revolver.

Caliber: 10.35mm (about .41).
Cylinder: 6 chambers.
Barrel Length: 4⅜ inches.
Overall Length: 9 inches.
Weight: 30 ounces.
Frame: Solid.
Ejection: Rod ejector.
Action: Double action, rebound hammer.

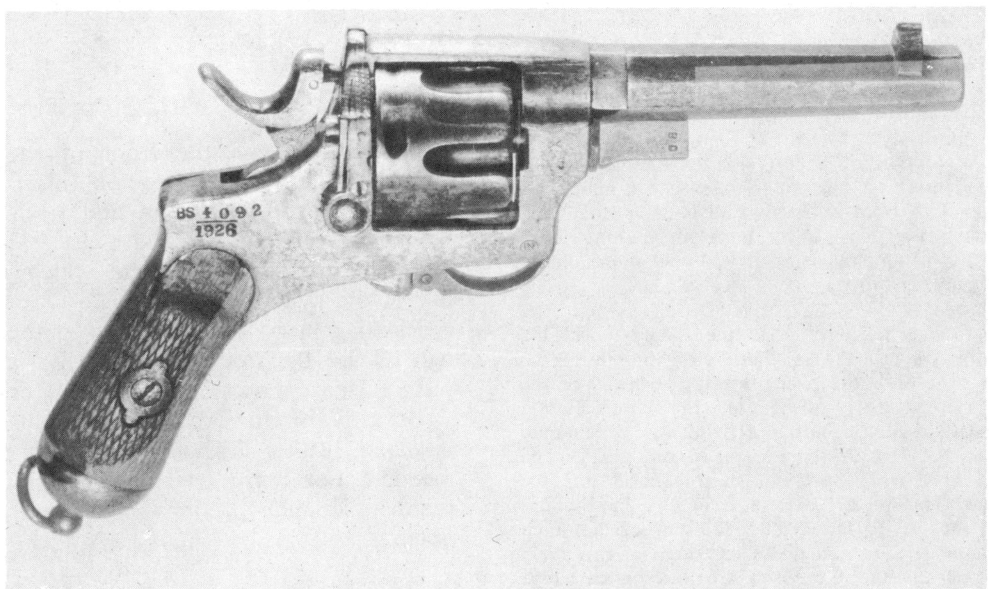

Former Italian Service Revolver.

Caliber: 10.35mm (about .41).
Cylinder: 6 chambers.
Barrel Length: 4⅜ inches.
Overall Length: 9¼ inches.
Weight: 31 ounces.
Frame: Solid.
Ejection: Rod ejector.
Action: Double action, rebound hammer.
Note: This weapon is fitted with a folding trigger and no trigger-guard.

Note

These revolvers are fitted with swinging rod ejectors. To unload them:

Open loading gate and half cock hammer so cylinder can be turned.

Pull ejector pin (under barrel) straight forward until it clears the frame. Then turn it on its collar until it lines up with the chamber to be emptied.

Push rod up into chamber to eject empty cases; pull it back free of the cylinder; turn cylinder to next chamber and repeat.

The ejector pin passes through the center of the cylinder axis pin in this type. To remove cylinder, swing ejector pin out. Then pry the axis pin out of frame. Open loading gate. Remove cylinder.

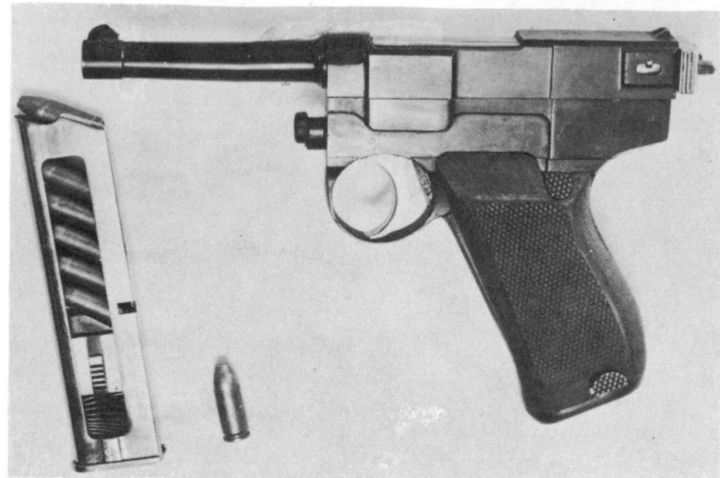

Italian Glisenti 9mm 1910 Automatic.
This was an Official Italian Pistol.

Caliber: 9mm Parabellum type.
Magazine: Box type, single line, capacity 7 cartridges.
Muzzle Velocity: About 960 feet per second.
Weight of Bullet: 125 grains, lead with full metal jacket, truncated cone type.
Muzzle Striking Energy: About 320 foot pounds.
Barrel Length: About 4".
Overall Length of Pistol: 8¼".
Sights: Luger type, fixed.
Accurate Range: 75 yards.
Maximum Range: About 1000 yards.
Pistol Operated By: Recoil.
Locked: By locking arm moving up through sleeve of barrel extension, into notch in bottom of bolt.
Type of Fire: Single shot only.
Magazine Release Catch: On lower left side of handle, it is a milled button which must be pressed to release the magazine.
Position of Bolt When Last Shot is Fired: Full back; pistol open.
When a Loaded Magazine Has Been Inserted: Pulling back slightly on the open bolt and releasing it will reload the chamber and lock it ready for firing.
Weight of Pistol: 32 oz.
Safety: (a) An automatic grip safety is in the front end of the grip underneath the trigger. As in the Colt Automatic, the weapon cannot be fired until the pistol is gripped firmly in the hand so that this grip safety is pushed in. (b) Thumb Safety: At the extreme rear end of the bolt is a flying nut which may be turned down to the left to set the pistol on "safe." The weapon cannot be fired when safety is in this position.
Note on Ammunition: This pistol takes a Luger or Parabellum type cartridge. However, it is about 2/100ths of an inch shorter than the standard German pistol cartridge of this type. The Glisenti will not handle the 9mm Corto type cartridge used in the Beretta and similar automatic pistols. The standard German ammunition is unpleasant to shoot in this pistol, while the high velocity ammunition developed for use in such weapons as the Machine Pistol 38 may be actually dangerous because of the excessive breech pressure developed.

Instructions for Loading and Firing

Insert magazine in handle and push up until it locks securely.

Grasp the bolt wings at the rear of the weapon firmly and pull straight back. This will cock the striker and permit the first cartridge to rise in line with the bolt. Now release the bolt to drive forward, loading the firing chamber.

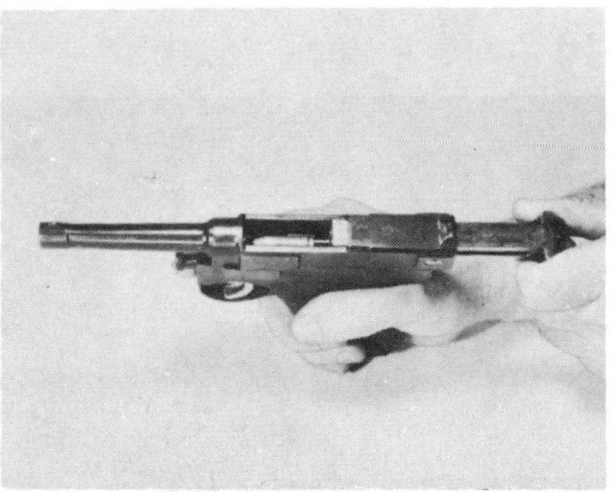

Turn up the fly nut thumb safety as illustrated. This will securely lock the pistol against accidental charge. Note: when the striker is cocked, a circular plunger protrudes slightly between the wings of the thumb safety, showing the cocked position.

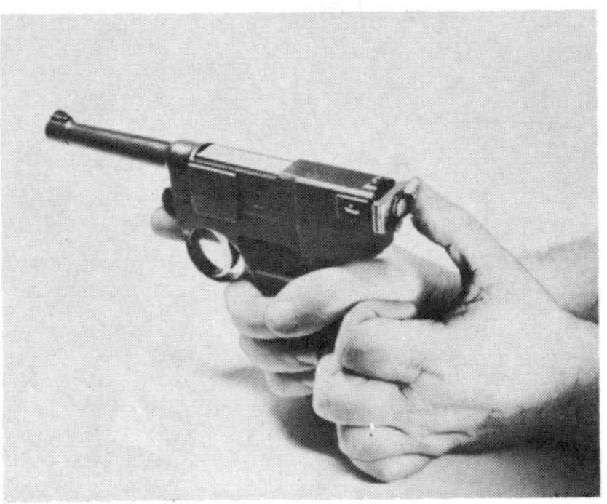

Field Stripping

Protruding from the front of the triggerguard is a circular milled screw. Beneath this is a pin retained by a spring. Push this pin in and while holding it in pull the screw out slightly and twist it in locking position. This will free the side plate which may then be lifted out of the pistol.

Pressing in on milled button at top of left hand stock will release the stock so it may be pried loose from the pistol. This exposes most of the working mechanism.

Because of the variety of small springs and pins involved, further dismounting of this pistol is not recommended. For barrel cleaning, insert empty magazine in the handle and withdraw bolt. The bolt will now stay open.

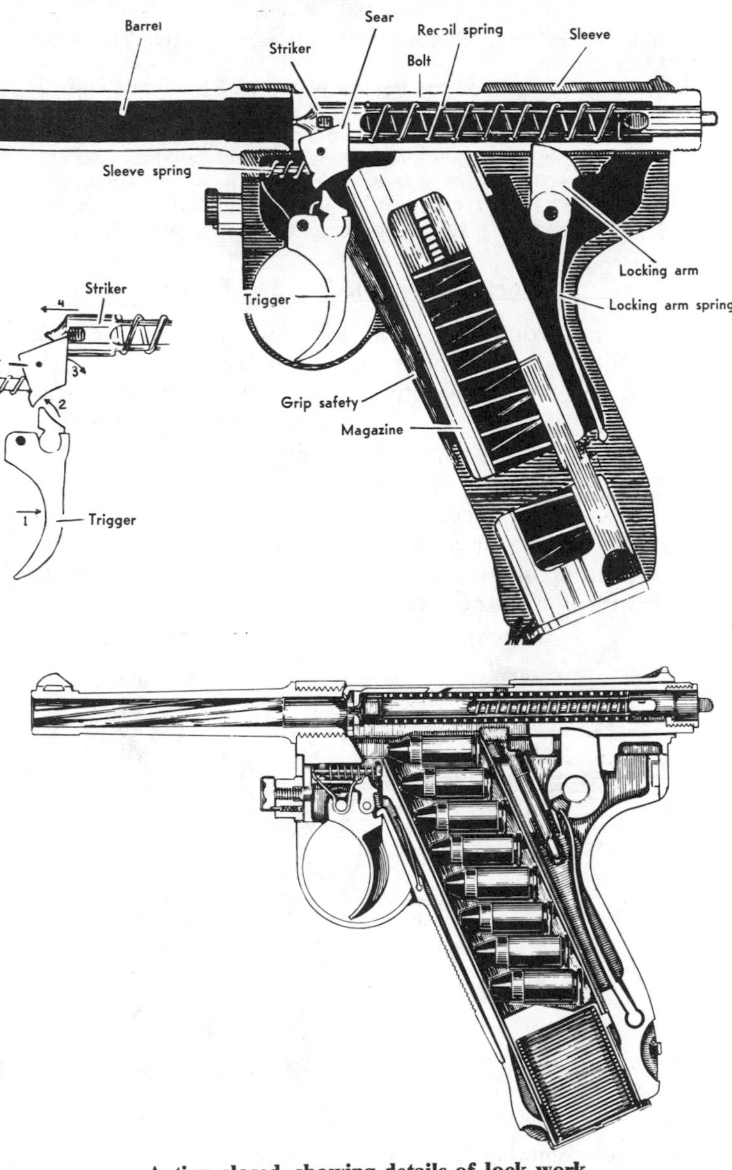

Action closed, showing details of lock work.

Action open, showing operation of recoil mechanism and magazine.

How the Glisenti Pistol Works

Starting with the pistol loaded and cocked, the action is as follows: The grip safety being pressed and the trigger squeezed, the sear is permitted to revolve and the striker is released and driven forward by its spring. As the cartridge is fired, the bullet moves forward out of the barrel and the rearward pressure of the gas forces the cartridge case and the locked bolt, barrel, and barrel extension directly to the rear. They travel back locked together for about 5⁄8″. Here the barrel halts against the barrel stop; the locking arm moves down out of its notch in the bottom of the bolt and out of line with the barrel extension. During this action the locking arm spring is compressed, as is the combination striker and recoil spring. The extractor fitted in the head of the bolt draws with it the empty cartridge case, which strikes against the ejector and is hurled up and out of the pistol.

The magazine follower spring drives the top cartridge up in line with the bolt.

Return Movement of the Action. The bolt is now pulled forward by the force of the recoil spring. Nearing its forward position it picks up the top cartridge from the magazine and drives it ahead into the firing chamber. The striker lug makes contact with the sear and is held in position by it, the spring partially compressed. This action cocks the striker for the next shot. The locking arm, driven by the locking arm spring, now moves up through the sleeve into the notch in the bottom of the bolt, securely locking the bolt to the sleeve (or barrel extension). The combined pressures of the locking arm spring and the recoil spring carry the barrel and barrel extension forward for the additional distance necessary to complete the locking motion. The sear is mounted on the sleeve (barrel extension), and cannot be operated unless the action is fully forward and locked.

Italian Beretta 9mm 1934 Automatic.

Caliber: 9mm Corto (identical with .380 Colt Automatic Pistol cartridge).
Magazine: Box type, single line, capacity 7 cartridges.
Muzzle Velocity: 970 feet per second.
Weight of Bullet: 95 grains, lead with full metal jackets.
Muzzle Striking Energy: About 195 foot pounds.
Barrel Length: 3½″.
Overall Length of Pistol: 6″.
Weight of Pistol: 23½ ozs.
Sights: Fixed, front sight machined into slide.
Accurate Range: 25 yards.
Maximum Range: About 800 yards.

Locked: Blowback type, unlocked. This is a low power cartridge, and heavy recoil spring and slide keep the breech closed until bullet has left barrel.

Type of Fire: Single shots only.

Magazine Release Catch: Thumb piece on lower rear of handle. Must be pushed back to release magazine.

Position of Slide When Last Shot is Fired: Open. This is a tricky arrangement. When magazine is extracted, slide moves forward immediately. Thus this feature is intended merely to advise you that the pistol is empty; and is not to be used as a reloading help as in the Colt and Luger hold-open devices.

Safety: Directly above the trigger on the left side of the pistol. When catch is pushed down and to the rear, it covers a small red ball and the letter "F." It is now safe. The letter "S" is exposed.

Note: Earlier models of the Beretta pistol used the 9mm Glisenti cartridge which is more powerful than the 9mm Corto. These models have an additional heavy recoil spring in the handle to act as a buffer. They are not particularly reliable weapons, and can be dangerous if used with high-power German ammunition. The M1934 is still in wide use in Italy. It was one of their best made Italian weapons in World War II.

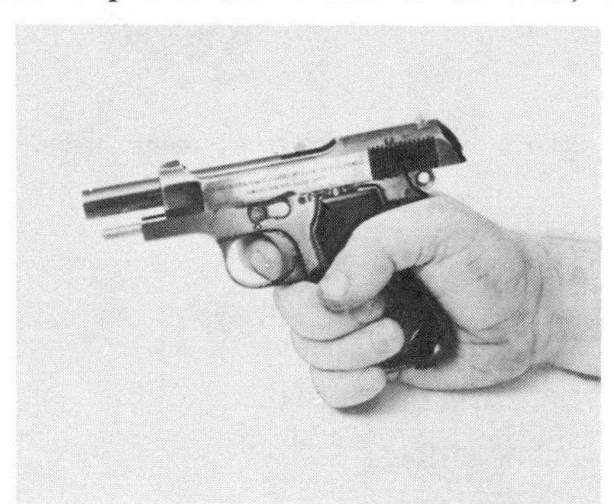

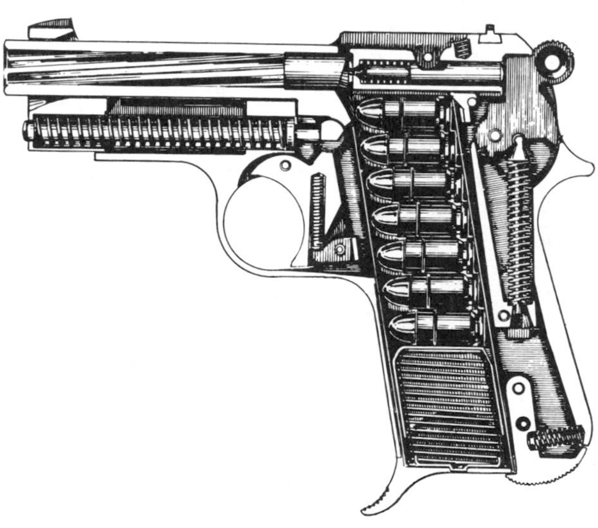

Action closed, showing detail of firing mechanism.

Instructions for Loading and Firing

Load magazine exactly as for Colt Automatic Pistol. Insert in handle and push in until it locks.

Draw back slide exactly as for Colt Automatic. Release slide and let it drive forward pushing cartridge into firing chamber and closing pistol.

Push safety catch around into locking position unless weapon is to be fired.

(**Note:** The exposed hammer may be let down gently on the firing pin if care is taken and the operation is done with both hands. It may also be set at half-cock.)

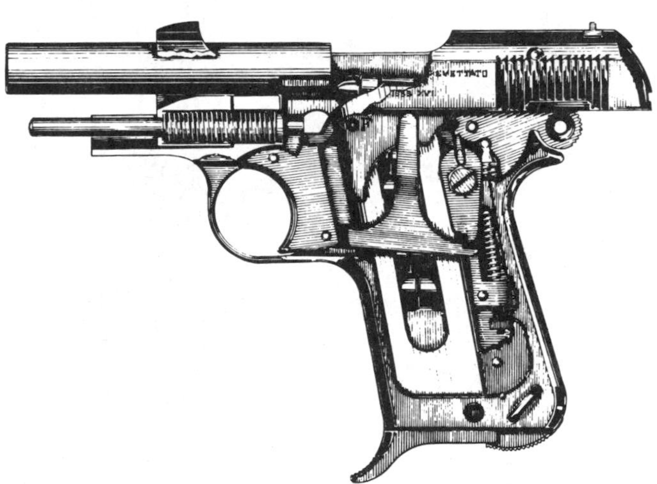

Action open, showing operation of recoil and feeding mechanism.

Field Stripping

With magazine out of weapon, pull back slide as far as it will go; hold it with right hand and with left thumb push safety catch up into locking notch in under side of slide.

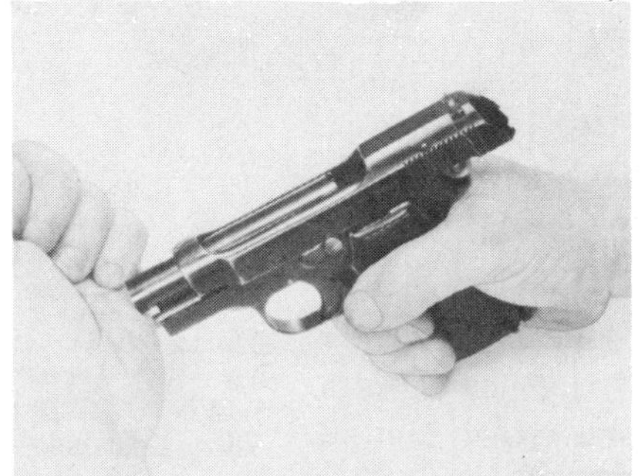

Now push straight back on barrel with palm of hand. This will free barrel from its locking recess.

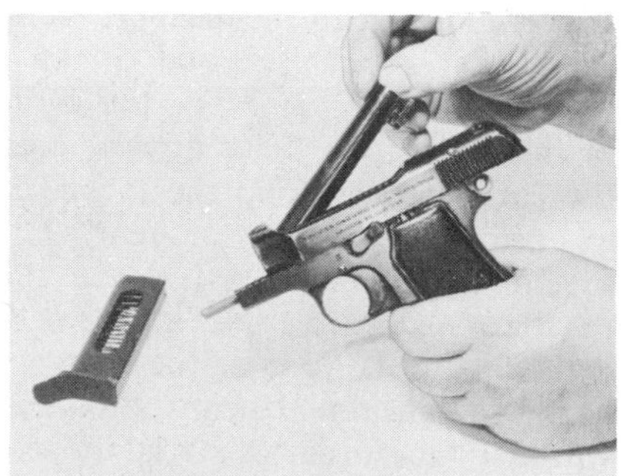

Pull barrel straight back and up, drawing it out of the slide as shown.

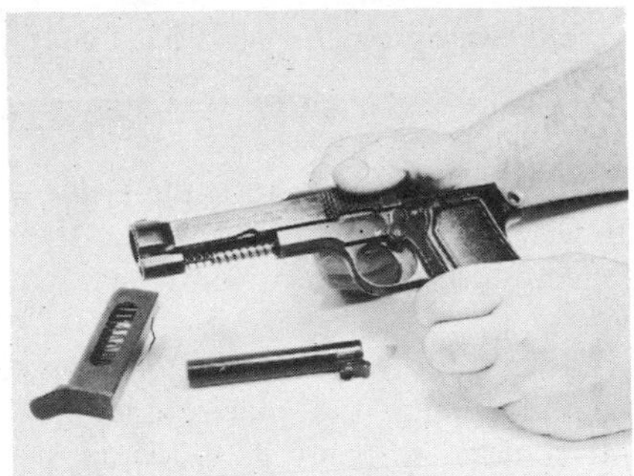

Push slide, recoil spring and recoil spring guide straight forward off the receiver. Spring and guide may now be removed from their seats. Safety locking stud may also be lifted out now. No further dismounting is necessary with this pistol.

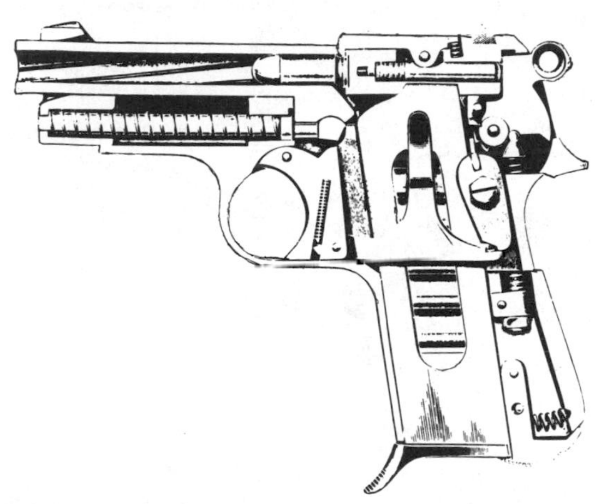

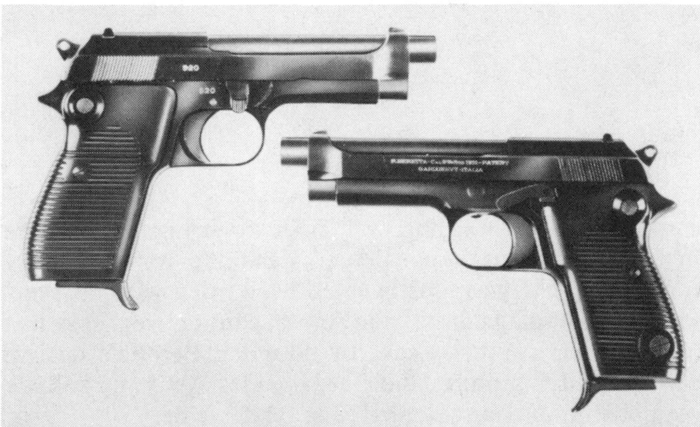

The 9mm M1951 Beretta Pistol.

System of Operation: Recoil, semi-automatic fire only.
Weight, Unloaded: 1.57 lb.
Length, Overall: 8 in.
Barrel Length: 4.51 in.
Feed Device: 8-round, detachable, single-column box magazine.
Sights, Front: Blade, integral with slide.
Rear: Notched bar, dovetailed to slide.
Muzzle Velocity: 1182 f.p.s. (approx.).

The interesting 9mm M1951 Beretta pistol has been adopted by the Italian Army and Navy, and is also used by the Israeli Defense Forces. It is a very well-made weapon, and has many interesting features, among them an aluminum alloy receiver. The weapon, which fires the 9mm Parabellum cartridge, also is known as the Model 951.

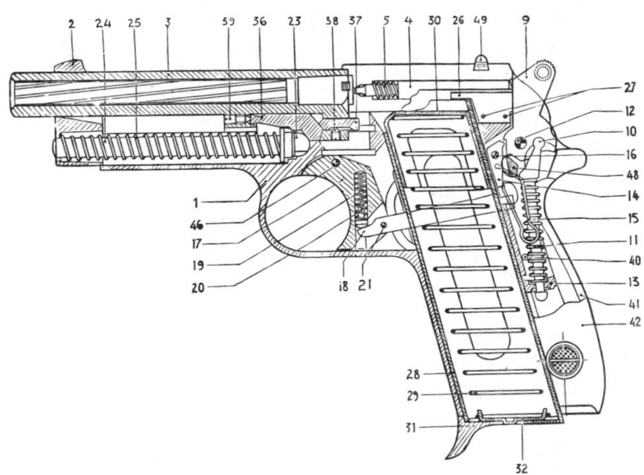

Section View of 9mm M1951 Beretta.

1. Receiver
2. Slide
3. Barrel
4. Firing pin
5. Firing pin spring
9. Hammer
10. Hammer spring rod
11. Hammer spring
12. Hammer pin
13. Hammer spring rod support
14. Sear lever
15. Sear lever and safety catch spring
16. Sear lever pin
17. Trigger
18. Trigger bar
19. Trigger bar spring
20. Trigger bar spring rod
21. Trigger bar pin
23. Dismounting latch
24. Recoil spring rod
25. Recoil spring
26. Ejector
27. Ejector pin
28. Magazine body
29. Magazine spring
30. Magazine follower
31. Magazine base
32. Base plate
36. Locking wedge
37. Unlocking plunger
38. Unlocking plunger screw
40. Grip screws
41. Right grip
42. Left grip
46. Trigger pin
48. Safety catch
49. Rear sight

How to Load and Fire the M1951 Pistol

The magazine is loaded the same as any single-column pistol magazine. Insert loaded magazine in magazine well which is located in pistol grip. Pull the slide sharply to the rear, and release; the slide will run home and chamber a cartridge. The weapon may now be fired by squeezing the trigger. The safety is a button type, and is mounted at the top rear of the grip; to put the weapon on "safe," push the button from right to left. The M1951 is not a double action weapon. With a cartridge in the chamber and the hammer down, the weapon must be manually cocked before it will fire.

How the M1951 Pistol Works

Loading, cocking, and chambering. A magazine containing eight rounds is inserted into the bottom of the grip section of the receiver. The slide is drawn to the rear by hand; it forces the hammer downward and to the rear. The full-cock notch of the hammer engages the nose of the sear and the hammer remains in its rearward position. When the slide is released, it goes forward under the pressure of the recoil spring. The slide feed rib forces a round from the magazine into the chamber of the barrel.

Locking. As the slide goes forward, the locking wedge is cammed into its locked position in the locking grooves of the slide by the cam surfaces on the receiver. The locking mechanism of this pistol is similar to that of the Walther Pistole 38.

Firing. When the trigger is pulled, the trigger bar is forced to the rear. The trigger bar pushes the disconnector up into the disconnector notch in the slide. If the weapon is not completely locked, the disconnector will be held down by the slide, and will force the trigger bar down and out of contact with the trigger (this arrangement is similar to that of the M1934 Beretta). When the weapon is locked, the trigger bar forces the sear backward against the pressure of the sear spring; the hammer then disengages itself from the sear and moves forward under the pressure of the hammer spring. The hammer strikes the firing pin, forcing it forward against the pressure of the firing pin spring. The firing pin strikes the primer of the cartridge, and immediately rebounds under the pressure of the firing pin spring. The M1951 is not a double action pistol; if a misfire occurs, the hammer must be recocked manually.

Unlocking. The barrel and slide recoil together for a distance of one-half inch; then the unlocking plunger on the rear barrel lug abuts against the receiver and, moving forward, forces the locking wedge out of the locking grooves in the slide, and down into the cammed surface on the receiver. Having been disconnected from the barrel, the slide (with the empty cartridge case gripped by the extractor) moves to the rear for an additional two inches, cocking the hammer in the process. The cartridge case is knocked out of the grip of the extractor claw, and out of the pistol, by the nose of the ejector. When the last round is fired, the slide stop is forced up by the magazine follower and holds the slide to the rear.

Field Stripping the M1951 Pistol

Remove magazine by pushing the magazine catch inward.

Draw the slide to the rear and align the dismounting latch with the dismounting notch of the slide.

Push the dismounting latch upward, toward the muzzle end of the pistol.

Pull the slide group forward and off the receiver.

Pull the recoil spring and guide assembly slightly to the rear, and remove it from its position in the slide.

Push the barrel backward and withdraw it from the rear of the slide.

No further disassembly is recommended.

M1951 Field Stripped.

ITALIAN RIFLES AND CARBINES

Among rifle-caliber weapons, the United States cal. .30 weapons predominate in the Italian Army at present, although Brens, Lee-Enfields, and Vickers guns also are available. The firm Pietro Beretta made significant quantities of United States M1 rifles for the Italian government. Beretta has also made M1 rifles for Indonesia and Denmark, and in addition has developed a series of prototype rifles which are based on the M1 action and chambered for the 7.62mm NATO cartridge. These weapons are very interesting, in that they show what can be done to existing M1 rifles to bring them more in line with what is considered desirable for a military rifle today. The weapons have all been fitted with charger-loaded box magazines, and most can deliver selective fire. Various countries can, by adopting Beretta's design, economically modify their M1 rifles into up-to-date weapons. Italy has adopted the BM59 rifle.

Below is a chart comparing some of these Berettas with the basic M1:

	M1	BM59	BM59 D	BM59 GL
Overall length (in)	43.6	37.2	37.2	43
Barrel length (in)	24	17.7	17.7	21
Weight (lb)	9.5	8.15	9	9
Feed Capacity	8 rds	20 rds	20 rds	20 rds
Cyclic rate (r.p.m.)		750	750	750
Muzzle velocity (f.p.s.)	2800	2620	2620	2730
Ammunition	cal. .30 M2	7.62mm NATO	7.62mm NATO	7.62mm NATO

Beretta 7.62mm NATO BM59 Rifle.

Beretta 7.62mm NATO BM59D Rifle. Stock changed and Bipod Attached.

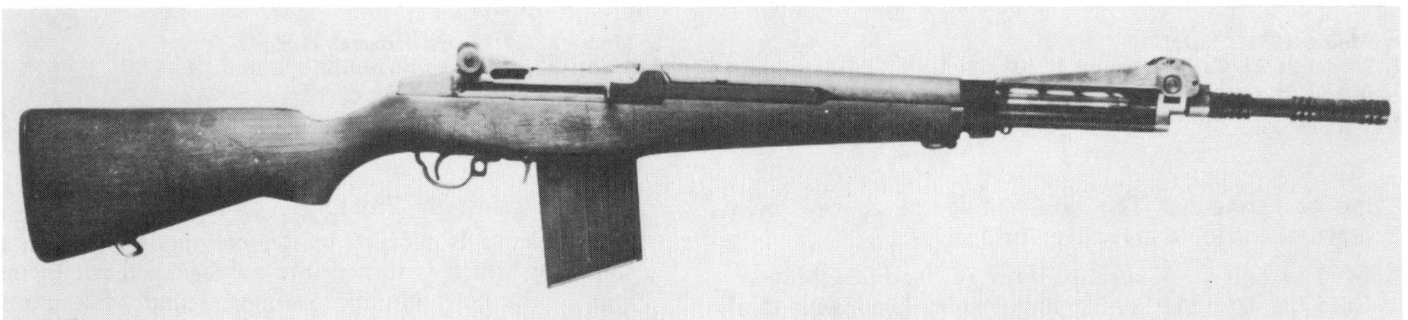

Beretta 7.62mm NATO BM59GL Rifle. Permanently attached Grenade Launcher and Grenade Sights.

OTHER ITALIAN RIFLES

All major Italian bolt action rifles and carbines are minor variants of the original Model 1891. These are often called Carcano after one of the designers, Mannlicher-Carcano after the magazine system and the Italian designer, or Parraviccini-Carcano after the two Italians credited with producing the original bolt design.

Early type rifles have horizontal projecting bolt handles. Carbines and late model rifles usually have turned-down bolt handles. Stocks and sights differ. Mechanically all are practically identical.

MODEL 1891 TYPE DESIGN. The magazine is the original Mannlicher pattern which requires a special clip to load it. While a single cartridge may be loaded directly into the firing chamber, the magazine is useless unless the cartridges are available on their special clips.

All Model 91 patterns take a clip with 6 rimless cartridges of 6.5mm (.256) caliber. The Model 1941 caliber 6.5mm takes the same clip.

MODEL 38 RIFLES AND CARBINES. Mechanically these are essentially the same as the M1891. Caliber may be either 7.35mm or the standard 6.5mm. Both calibers are loaded with 6-short Mannlicher clips.

Receiver. The receiver is the split bridge type as found in the turn bolt Mannlichers. When the bolt handle is raised, it can be drawn back through the center cut in the receiver bridge to open the action for load-

1. Model 1891: Barrel 30.7".
2. Model 91 TS Carbine: Barrel 17.58".
3. Model 91 Carbine: Barrel 17.5".
4. Model 91/24 Rifle: Barrel 27".
5. Model 91/24 Carbine: Barrel 17.5".
6. Model 38 (7.35mm) Short Rifle: Barrel 21.49".

ing or extraction. The bolt handle, of course, locks down ahead of the receiver bridge.

Bolt. The bolt is a curious form of modified Mauser. Like the late Mausers it has a solid head with dual opposed locking lugs at the front end. It is one-piece construction, being bored out from the rear. A single gas escape hole is provided on top of the bolt near the front end where it enters the striker travel path.

Extractor. The extractor is designed to turn with the bolt. This requires chambering off part of the barrel surface at the breech so the extractor can pass between barrel and cartridge case head as the bolt handle is raised to start unlocking and primary extraction. This factor weakens the barrel.

Bolt Sleeve. The bolt sleeve (or plug) in general practice is the unit which permits assembling the cocking piece and firing mechanism to the bolt, and permits the bolt to be turned to unlock without turning the firing mechanism. In this design it is also the manual safety.

This sleeve is pierced to permit passage of the firing pin. The rear end of the mainspring is compressed against the front face of this sleeve.

The sleeve is secured to the bolt body by a small single lug which is turned into an S-shaped cut in the rear of the bolt. (In the Springfield and Mauser designs this plug is screwed into the bolt.) The sleeve is secured to the receiver by a lug which engages the receiver when the bolt is locked.

Recommendation. Use only recommended ammunition. If arm is converted to American caliber, keep pressures well within official Italian pressures (about 38,000 foot pounds). It must be kept in mind that many are very old weapons which have not had the best of care.

In 1938 caliber change was started from 6.5mm to 7.35mm. However, supply problems and war conditions made conversion impossible. Model 38 arms were then changed from 7.35mm back to 6.5mm where possible.

In 1941 a rifle similar to No. 9 was issued with 26.9" barrel.

The cartridge for the Youth Rifle (No. 10) was a special short 6.5mm blank cartridge.

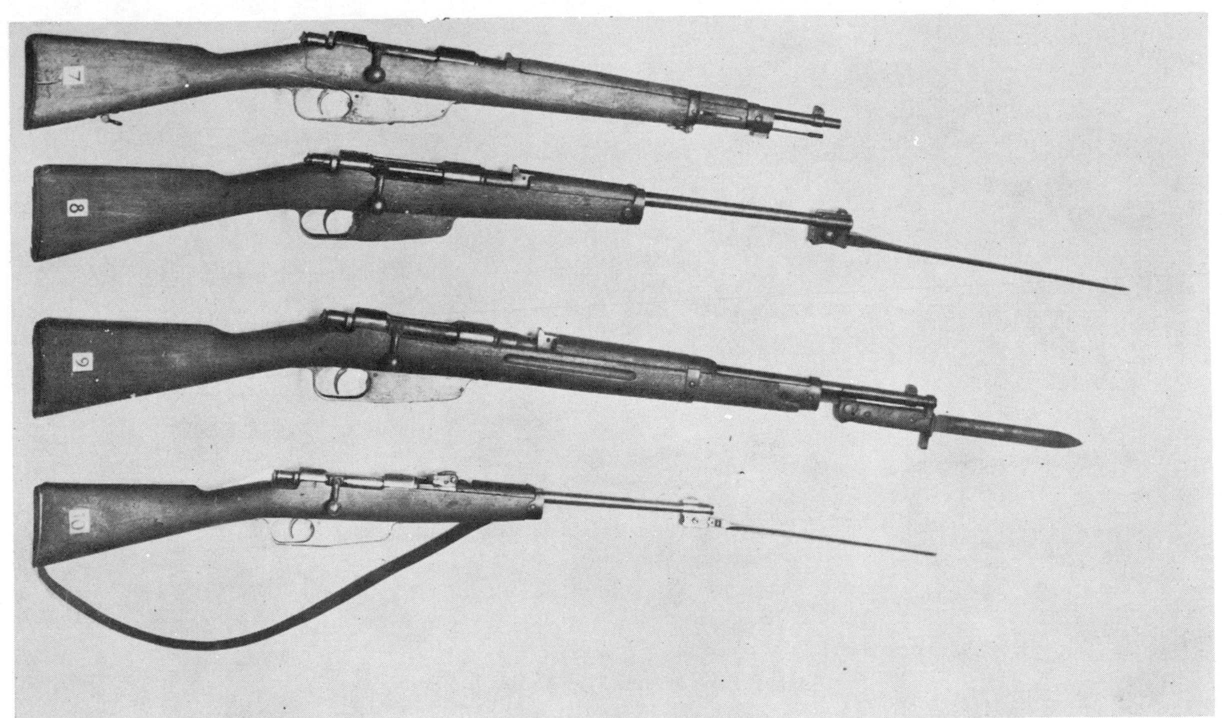

7. Model 37 (7.35mm) Carbine. Barrel 17.58″.

8. Model 91 Carbine. Barrel 17.5″.

9. Model 91/38 (Caliber 6.5mm): Barrel 21.49″.

10. Model Youth Rifle (Moschetto Ballila). Caliber special 6.5mm. Barrel 14.43″. (Weapon does not fire ball cartridges.)

SEMI-AUTO RIFLES. Italy conducted advance experimentation with both gas and recoil operated rifles and conversions very early in the century. Terni, Scotti, Cei-Rigotti conversions, and similar designs may occasionally be encountered.

In all cases they represent development or experimental arms. They are essentially collector's items.

Evaluation. As a class Italian rifles are reasonably well made of good materials. However, in the face of the design failings pointed out, it is evident that care must be exercised in converting them.

Ammunition. 6.5mm Italian Service rimless.

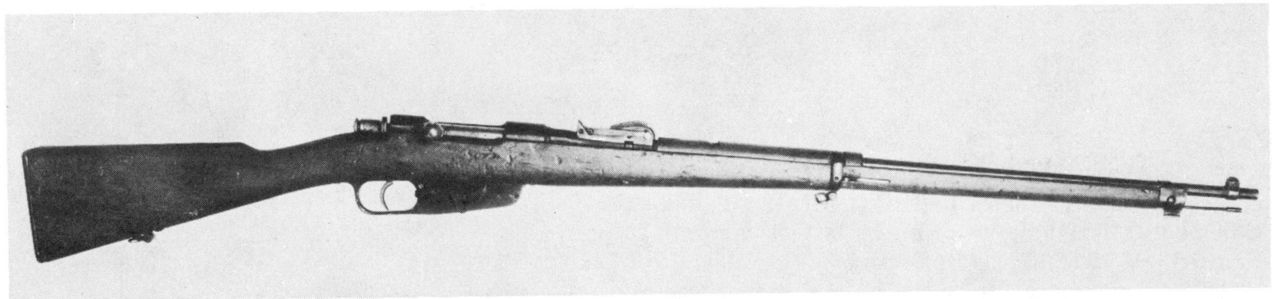

Italian Mannlicher-Carcano Rifle, 6.5mm.

Caliber: 6.5mm Italian service.
Magazine: Mannlicher type. In this weapon, the cartridge clip is inserted together with the cartridges into the top of the rifle.
Barrel Length: 30¾″.
Overall Length of Rifle: 4′ 2¾″. With bayonet about 1′ longer.
Weight of Rifle: 9 lbs. Bayonet weighs about 13 ozs. more.
Sights: Barleycorn front and V rear, adjustable 600 to 2000 meters.
Magazine Capacity: 6 cartridges.

Loading and Firing

The bolt being raised and pulled back to the rear by the bolt handle, a loaded clip is inserted in the breech and forced down into the receiver. Pushing home the bolt handle drives the cartridge into the firing chamber, and turning the handle down revolves the locking lugs into their recesses, locking the weapon. The manual safety resembles that on our own Springfield rifle. When the weapon is cocked, the thumbpiece can be swung over to the right putting the rifle at "Safe." Over to the left the safety is inoperative and the weapon can be fired by pressing the trigger.

As in the case of the Springfield, if the bolt is not properly closed it will be closed by the cocking piece as it moves forward. This will usually result in a misfire.

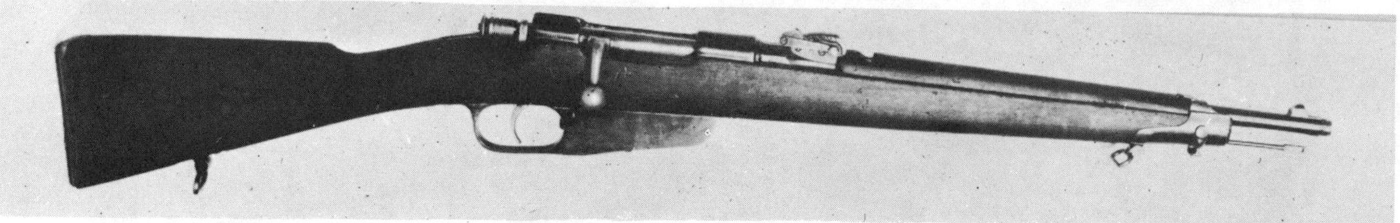

Mannlicher-Carcano M91 T. S. Carbine, 6.5mm (original design).

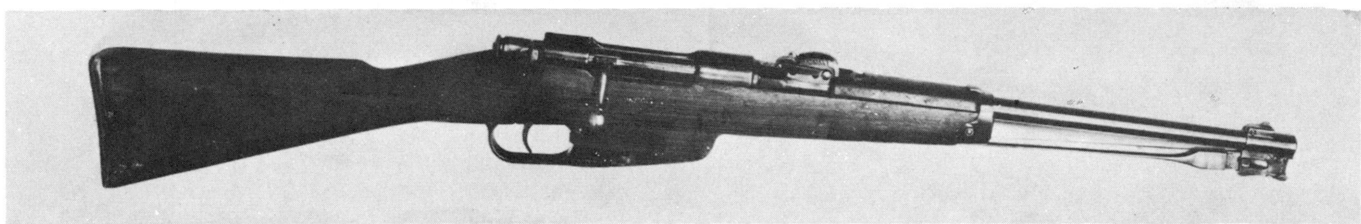

Mannlicher-Carcano M91 Carbine, 6.5mm.

Mannlicher-Carcano M38 Rifle, 7.35mm.

The Mannlicher System

While this system resembles that of a Mauser, it has some differences. The bolt lever is set farther forward than is customary with the Mauser system.

The principal difference, however, is in the magazine construction. There is no bottom plate covering the magazine opening as in the Mauser type. In place of the standard magazine, there is a spring-supported arm on the underside of the receiver. When the clip is loaded in from the top with its six cartridges, it compresses this spring arm so that the arm can force cartridges up into line as the bolt is worked. This arm presses against the cartridge case and not against the clip. As a result when the last cartridge has been chambered, the empty clip falls clear through the bottom opening.

Stripping. Turn down the retaining catch on the right side of the receiver, pull the trigger, and the bolt may be drawn back out of the weapon.

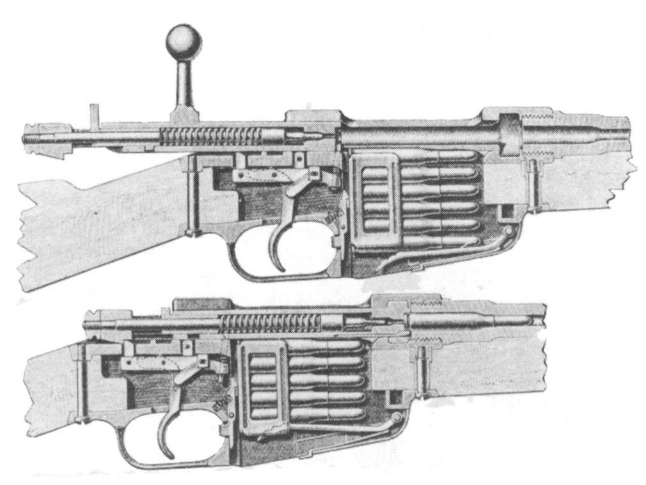

Sub-Caliber Juvenile Rifle.

Among the weird weapons of all history, perhaps the outstanding one is the sub-caliber rifle developed under Mussolini to arm and train the youth of his nation. This weapon is almost a line-for-line reproduction of the Mannlicher-Carcano Italian Carbine. It is even designed with the Mannlicher-Magazine, to be fed from the top with a clip of special caliber cartridges.

To add to the viciousness, a folding bayonet is attached to the muzzle.

These weapons were issued to children as young as six years of age for training as "warriors."

Note that this is in no sense a sporting rifle of the popular .22 caliber type used for hunting, target work, or sporting work. It is strictly a military-type weapon in every sense of the word, built specifically to warp children at their most impressionable age. It is chambered for a special blank cartridge.

ITALIAN AUTOMATIC CARBINES

The Italians developed a wide range of semi- and full automatic carbines for police and coast guard work. The principal forms are shown. Arms of these types normally use the 9mm Glisenti cartridge, which is the German 9mm Luger with a light powder load.

Warning. These arms are all subject to Federal registration. Barrel lengths are all below the required 16″ limit, and some of these arms are fitted with full auto switches.

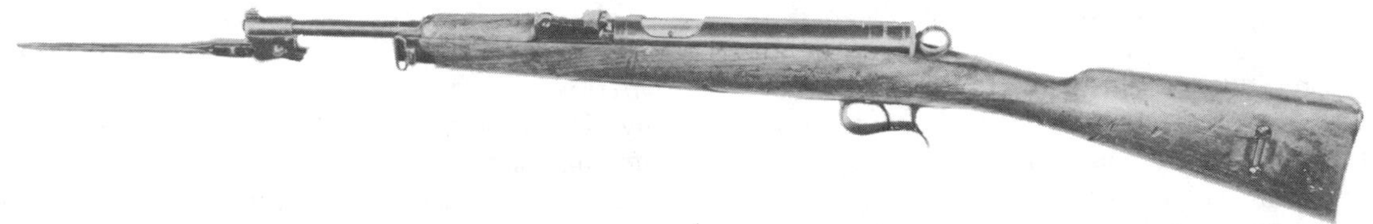

Beretta 9mm Semi-automatic Carbine.

This semi-automatic carbine is based on Beretta 1918-30 patents. It is a blowback weapon chambered for the 9mm 1910 (Glisenti) Parabellum cartridge. The box magazine is inserted from the bottom and ejection is through a port in the top of the receiver. Barrel length is 12.75 inches, making the weapon registerable under the Federal Firearms acts.

Villar Perosa Carbine.

VILLAR PEROSA CARBINE. While this arms does not normally have a full auto switch, its barrel length brings it within the scope of the Federal Firearms registration act.

It was designed as a sporting and police arm for the 9mm cartridge. Top mounted magazine. The cylindrical slide around the receiver is depressed slightly and then slid to the rear to cock the action, somewhat in the fashion of the American pump rifle. Bottom ejection. Some of these have two triggers and are capable of full automatic fire.

Beretta Modified Villar-Perosa Submachine Gun.

This is a delayed blowback weapon. The magazine is mounted on top of the gun. The magazine release catch is in front of the mounting. This gun fires from an open bolt. The cocking handle is on the right side of the receiver just to the rear of the magazine. As the bolt goes forward, it strips a cartridge from the magazine into the firing chamber and fires it. Under the influence of the blowback, the empty cartridge case is expelled through the bottom of the gun. The magazine follower spring drives the next cartridge down in line. The bolt goes to the rear and stays open waiting for the next pull on the trigger.

Magazine may hold 20, 25, or 32 cartridges. Its rear face is somewhat cut away so that the primers of the cartridge in the magazine are visible to the man shooting. He thus has an idea of how many cartridges are in the magazine at all times.

It will be noted that this weapon is fitted with the same type of folding bayonet provided on the sub-caliber rifles issued to children. Pressing in a catch permits this bayonet to be swung out on a hinge and locked in position. When folded it fits into a slot on the underside of the forearm.

ITALIAN SUBMACHINE GUNS

Italian 9mm Submachine Gun Model 15, Villar Perosa, Dual

Caliber: 9mm Glisenti (the Luger cartridge with a light load).
Magazine: Box type, capacity 25 cartridges (some for 32 cartridges are known).
Position of Magazines: On top of receivers.
Muzzle Velocity: About 970 feet per second.
Lengths of Barrels: 315mm (12.285 inches).
Overall Length: 600mm (23.4 inches.)
Weight: 8.23 kg (without magazines)—18.10 pounds.
Sights: Graduated 100 to 500 meters.
Operation and Locking Data: Delayed blowback with loose firing pin.
Cooled: Air. Cyclic rate of fire 1200 per barrel per minute.
Type of Fire: Full automatic only.
Safety: Has a trigger safety.

Special Note on This Weapon

While the German MP18 was the first really successful infantry machine pistol or submachine gun, this freak Italian weapon actually preceded it into use as a quick firing sub-caliber firearm.

It was introduced by the Italians shortly after 1914 and by the end of 1918 infantry squads were in many cases equipped with two of these guns. It was used by Italians on airplanes in some instances.

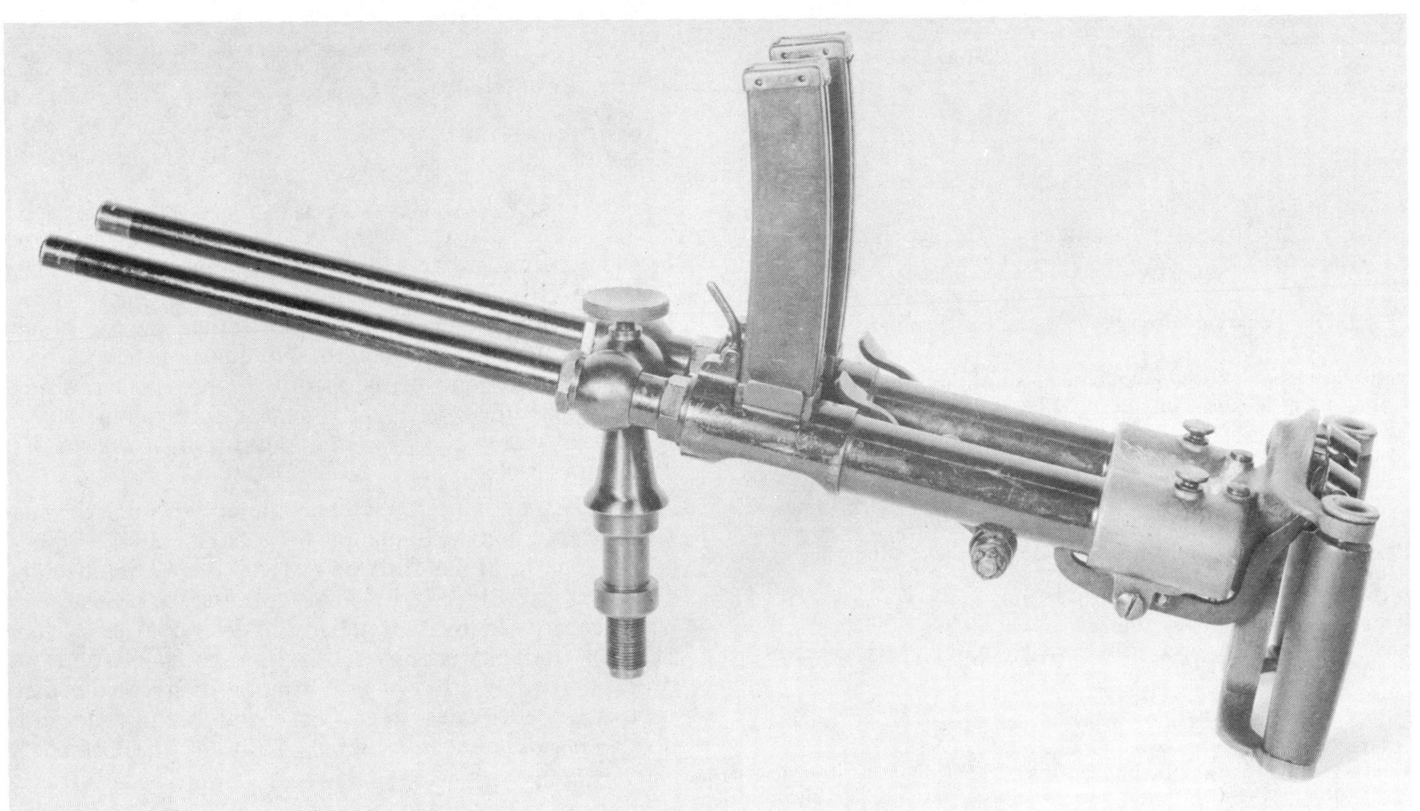

Italian Beretta 9mm Submachine Gun Model 38.

How this Weapon Works

It is actually made up of two machine pistols fastened together by a cross bar in front and a Vickers type handle in back. Like the Vickers it has thumb triggers—one for each barrel.

The barrels are stationary and have a retarded blowback action, which does not constitute a complete lock but does cause a safety hesitation.

Each bolt turns slightly to the left under recoil and back to the right when moving forward. The bolt is delayed from closing by a camming action when firing. There is a separate box magazine mounted on top of each barrel and the trigger mechanism, which is in the handle of each one, permits separate firing if desired.

This weapon comes equipped with a bipod; it was also used with a shield through which it fired, from a bicycle, and from a strap hung around the neck of the gunner. When fired from this strap the bipod was rested in a special holder on the gunner's belt buckle.

The rate of fire of this weapon is so terrific that it is impossible to direct it, and, because of the short range cartridge involved, it is a practically useless weapon.

While some of these guns were captured from the Italians in War II, their basic submachine gun was the blowback Beretta 38.

Italian Beretta 9mm Submachine Gun Model 38.

This was the finest and most important Italian submachine gun.

Caliber: 9mm Parabellum type cartridge.

Note on Ammunition: This weapon uses a Parabellum type cartridge with round nose bullet and a special high velocity load. Cartridges are normally packed on clips for loading and are popularly known as the M38 in Italy.

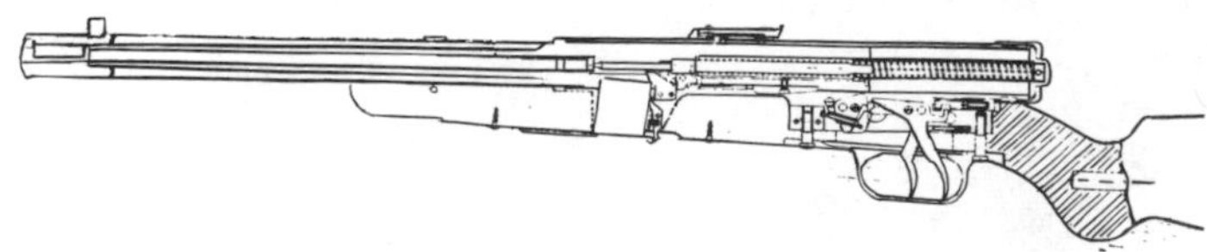

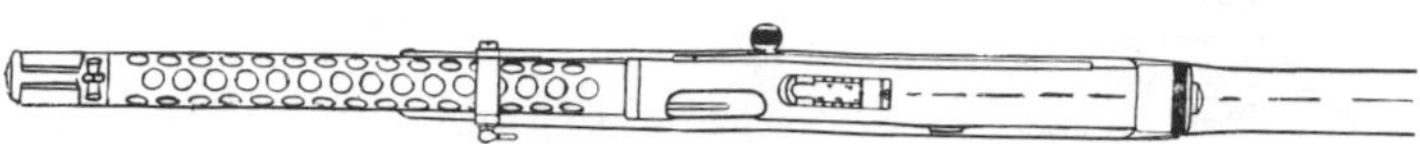

Diagram from Official Italian Manual.

Ballistic Data: This ammunition is much more powerful than that used in the Glisenti or Beretta 1915 type pistol. The submachine gun itself is very heavily constructed and well made to stand a cartridge developing several hundred feet per second more velocity than the standard Italian pistol loading.
Magazine: Straight box type: 10-20-40 round capacity.
Position of Magazine: Directly under receiver. Magazine catch on under side of weapon.
Weight: 10.3 pounds with loaded 40-round magazine.
Accurate Range: About 300 yards.
Sights: Fixed front, open rear elevating in 100 meter stages from 100 to 500 meters.
Operation: Blowback.
Cyclic Rate of Fire: 400 to 500 rounds per minute, depending largely on type of ammunition used.
Compensator: Like the Solothurn, this weapon has a built-in compensator which permits escaped gases to rise freely and straight ahead and force down the shelf on the bottom of the compensator, thus tending to hold the weapon down and forward against the thrust and rise of the recoil.
Note: This weapon is issued with a folding bayonet. The blade folds and locks back on the under side of the barrel casing.
Position of Cocking Handle: A knob on the right side of the receiver.
Type of fire: Single shot or full automatic. Weapon has two separate triggers. Pressing the forward trigger fires a single shot. Pressing the rear trigger fires full automatic as long as pressure is maintained.

Loading

Insert a loaded magazine from the underside, push in as far as it will go.

Pull back cocking handle to cock bolt; then push the handle forward as far as it will go, or the bolt will have to carry it forward in its motion, giving a weak striking action which will cause a misfire or jam.

Beretta Model 38A Submachine Gun.

This weapon is a modification of the famous Beretta Model 38 submachine gun. The general bolt design of the Beretta has been retained as well as the general lock work.

However the barrel jacket has been dispensed with and a lighter barrel has been fluted its entire length to

Beretta Model 38/42 Submachine Gun.

provide cooling surfaces. Near the muzzle end, the barrel has been cut away on top to provide the general function of a compensator and prevent undue muzzle climb. The sights have been changed. Folding sights have been provided on the rear of the top of the receiver. The dual triggers, one for single and one for full automatic fire have been retained, as has the safety switch on the left side of the receiver.

This weapon is normally encountered with the German proof marks and with stamp "MP Beretta 38-42 9mm."

The Beretta Model 38A and Model 38/42 submachine guns were considered by many people to be the best small arms used by the Italians in World War II. The Germans thought enough of the Beretta to continue its production for their own use. Among many gun addicts in the United States, there has long been a question about the differences between many of these models.

Beretta 9mm Model 38/49 Submachine Gun.

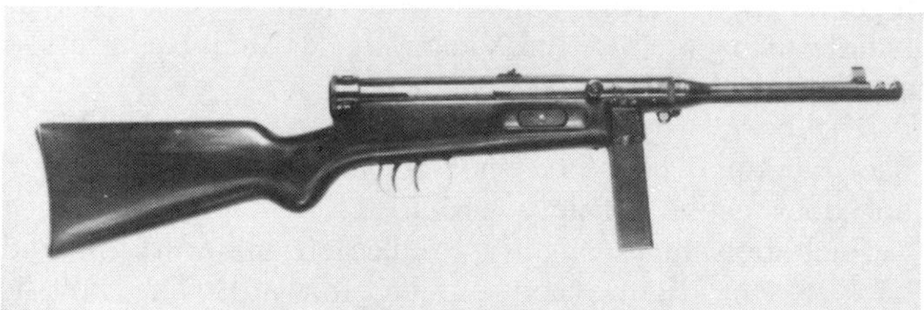

Beretta 9mm Model 5 Submachine Gun.

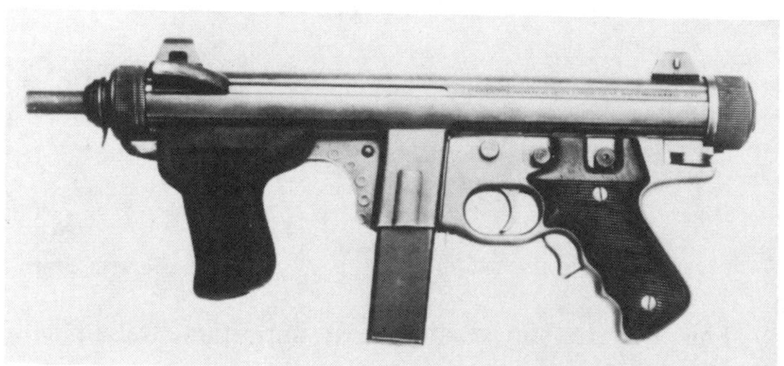

Beretta 9mm Model 12 Submachine Gun.

Listed below are the principal differences between these guns:

Model 38A: full-length ventilated barrel jacket, 12.8-inch barrel, 7.1-inch bolt, and a detachable firing pin.

Model 38/42: no barrel jacket, 8.2-inch barrel, 7.1-inch bolt, and a fixed firing pin.

Model 38/44: no barrel jacket, 8.2-inch barrel, 5.9-inch bolt, and a fixed firing pin.

Model 38/49: like Model 38/44, but with cross bolt safety.

Model 5: like Model 38/49, but with grip safety on stock.

The 38/42, 38/44, and 38/49 have been made with the 12.8-inch barrel.

A new submachine gun, the 9mm Model 12 has been introduced by Beretta. This weapon—like the Israeli "Uzi" and the Czech Model 23 and Model 25 submachine guns—has a bolt which telescopes the barrel.

Beretta Model 12 Field Stripped.

ITALIAN MACHINE GUNS

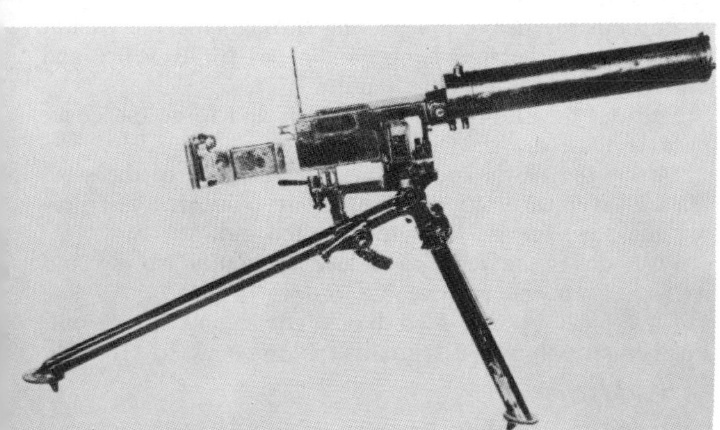

Revelli (Fiat 1914) 6.5mm Machine Gun.

This is sometimes called the Fiat 1914 Model after the arsenal of manufacture.

Caliber: 6.5mm Italian service cartridge (Caliber .256).
Magazine: Mouse trap type, holding 50 cartridges in 10 lines of 5 each.
Muzzle Velocity: About 2000 feet per second.
Weight of Bullet: 162 grains, lead with full metal jacket.
Barrel Length: 25¾".
Overall Length of Gun: About 46".
Weight: 37¼ lbs.
Mounting: Tripod mount is provided with this weapon. It weighs 49½ lbs.
Sights: Barleycorn front and V type rear sight, adjustable from 200 to 2000 meters.
Accurate Range: About 500 yards.
Gun Operated By: Recoil and blowback. This is a freak design. Rearward thrust of gases in the firing chamber against the case push it back against the breech block, compelling the locking and recoiling mechanism to move backwards compressing a recoil spring and working the weapon.
Locked: This is not locked in the true sense of the word, but employs a so-called hesitation system. During the period of high breech pressure, opening of the breech is delayed by a rotating wedge which connects breech lock and barrel during the first stages of the movement to the rear.
Cooled: By water. A water jacket surrounds the barrel.
Cyclic Rate of Fire: About 500 a minute.
Position of Cocking Handle: Protrudes from rear of gun below rear sight. It is shaped like a cross, permitting fingers to be locked around both arms so it may be drawn back against the tension of the recoil spring.
Type of Fire: Single shot or full automatic. Like the Vickers, this gun is fitted with traversing handles and fired by a thumb actuated trigger in between the two handles. Directly above this thumb trigger is a lever which when swung over to the left permits one shot to be fired each time the thumb trigger is pressed. Pushed up into the vertical center position it is safe. Pushed over to the extreme right, it fires automatically as long as the trigger is pushed in by the thumb.
Note: A special cooling device is provided with this gun which permits the water jacket to be connected with a can holding about 2½ gallons of water; and a pump which circulates the water through the jacket.

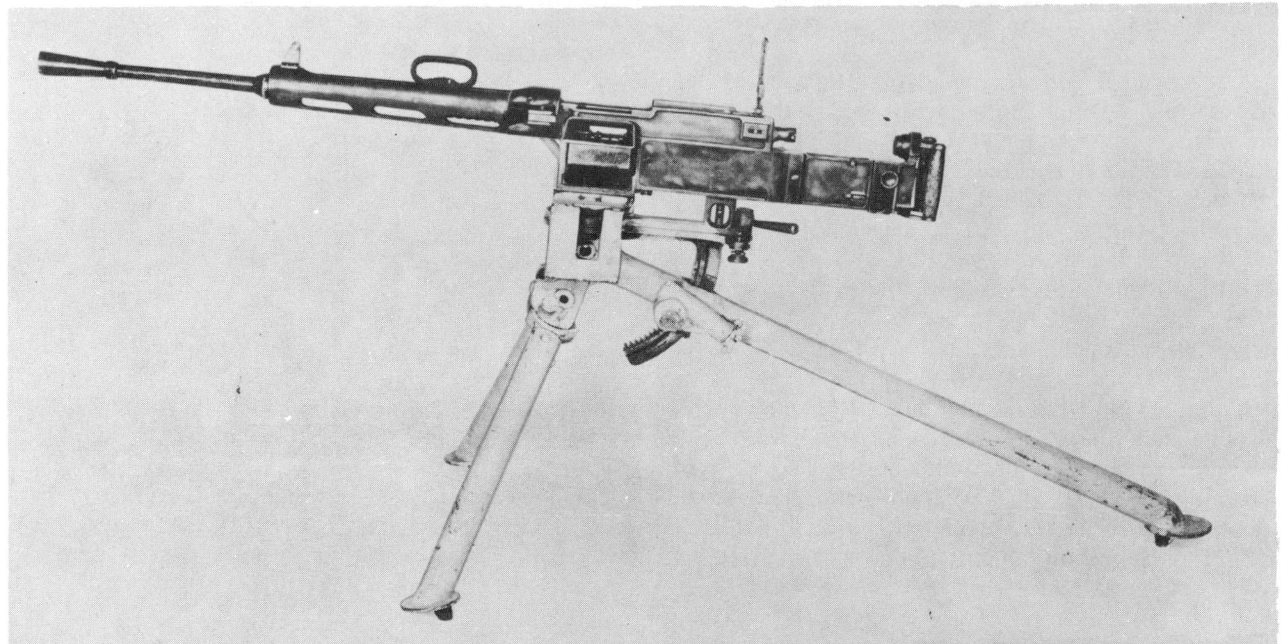

Fiat 8mm Model 35 Machine Gun.

Caliber: 8mm.
Feed: 50-round belt; additional units may be added to this.
Overall Length of Gun: About 50″.
Weight: About 40 pounds. Weight of tripod: about 50 pounds.
Locked: Semi-locked. This is a modification of the Revelli machine gun.
Position of Cocking Handle: Directly below and behind rear sight. Same as Revelli.
Cooled: Air cooled. Has barrel jacket and heavy barrel.
Cyclic Rate of Fire: About 120 a minute.
Type of Fire: Single shot or full automatic as for Revelli.
Sights: Adjustable 200 to 2400 meters.

Loading and Firing

Open ejection cover on top of gun. Insert belt (make sure cartridges are on top) into feed block from left side of gun.

Pull the cocking handle as far back as possible. Pull the belt through the feed block as far as it will go. Release cocking handle and let it fly forward under compression of the recoil spring. Set the selector lever as on Revelli for safe, single, or full autofire. A fire control lever is mounted on the left side of the receiver ahead of the traverse handle. Set this in vertical position and the gun will be slowed down; set it at horizontal and it will speed the gun up.

Stripping

Barrel Removal: In the left front end of the receiver is the barrel catch. Push this in. Turn the barrel handle to top of its slot and push the barrel forward until its end comes clear of the barrel casing. Now lift the rear of the barrel out of the slot and turning the barrel to the right withdraw from rear.

Pull out the heavy pin passing through the receiver at the rear near the traversing handle (as for Revelli) and pull down the traversing handles.

Pull out the side plate cover catch and force the cover back to the rear.

Lifting the pawls and turning the rear end of the pawl release lever up until the featherway coincides will permit the pawl release lever to be lifted out.

Push down the feed pawl lever actuating spring and its rod. Turn and remove it.

Now push up the feed block cover and lift it out. Further stripping is essentially the same as for Revelli.

How the Gun Works

Except for the feed mechanism, this weapon is essentially the same as the Revelli. Smooth functioning depends to a large extent on easy extraction of empty cartridge cases. Therefore an oiling device is necessary to lubricate the cartridges as they are fed into the firing chamber. Proper oiling of all parts is very necessary in this gun.

This necessity for special lubrication, together with the complicated semi-locking system, and the fact that firing from a closed bolt means that the barrel heats so rapidly that it must be changed after three or four belt lengths have been fed through the gun all combine to make this a very poor type of weapon.

This weapon is obsolete.

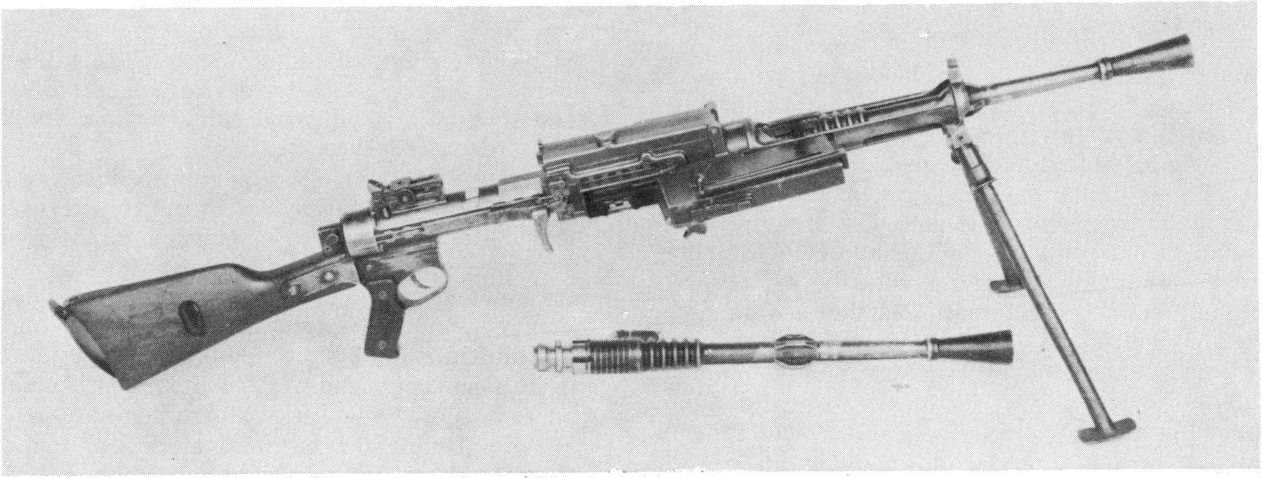

Breda 6.5mm Model 30 Machine Gun.

Caliber: 6.5mm or 7.35mm. While this gun was originally designed to take the 6.5mm Italian Service cartridge, some will be found chambered to take the 7.35mm cartridge used by the Italians in the last few years. Note: The larger caliber gun is referred to as Model 38.

Feed: A magazine is attached to the right side of the gun where it swings forward when unlocked. It is fed by a clip. Capacity is 20 cartridges.

Overall Length of Gun: 48.5".

Weight of Gun: 23½ lbs. with bipod mount.

Sights: Barleycorn front and V-rear.

Battle Sights: Set for 300 Meters: Sights adjustable to 1500 meters but actually not intended for use over 450 yards.

Gun Operated By: Recoil and inertia.

Cooled: Air. Barrel has jacket. Cooling very poor. As this gun fires from a closed bolt, no air can circulate down the barrel through the ejection port between shots.

Locked: By rotating fermature nut.

Cyclic Rate of Fire: 450 to 500 per minute. (Actual rate delivered is about 120 per minute.)

Position of Cocking Handle: On right side of gun. Gun ejects from lower left.

Type of Fire: Full automatic only. Note: Gun has bipod mount at end of barrel casing below front sight. A pistol grip is provided; also a butt strap extending from the upper end of the butt, and a special ground extension to the rear of the pistol grip.

Caution: When firing this weapon, cocking handle should always be drawn back when the firing is stopped. It can be locked in the rear position by pushing in the catch just behind the handle. If this is not done, the heat in the barrel may explode the cartridge. To release the cocking handle pull it back to the rear. This will pull the catch out of engagement and let the breech block go forward.

Loading and Firing

The magazine projects from the right side of the gun. Push in the magazine catch located on the near side of the magazine and turn the magazine forward on its pivot.

Draw back the cover over the ejection opening on the left side of the gun.

Insert the clip in the magazine, pushing it in until all the cartridges have been caught by the cartridge catch. Now withdraw the clip. Swing the magazine back into position until it locks. Pull the cocking handle to the rear as far as it will go and let it run forward. If weapon is not to be fired immediately, push the safety catch at the rear of the receiver. Otherwise press the trigger and the gun will fire automatically as long as there are any cartridges in the magazine.

Field Stripping

A barrel catch is located on the left side of the gun at the forward end of the receiver. Pull this out and lower it. The barrel will now turn about 90° to the left. Grasp the barrel handle to turn it and slide the barrel forward to clear the receiver, then withdraw it to the rear.

A butt catch is located below the rear sight. Push it forward to release the butt. Now twist the butt from right to left and draw it out to the rear together with the recoil spring and its guide and the buffer spring. Be careful of the tension of these springs as the butt is removed.

Pulling back the cocking handle will now permit you to withdraw the breech block, the firing pin, and its spring. Pulling the cocking handle farther to the rear now permits it to be pulled out of the right side of the receiver.

At the rear of the cover on the top of the gun, above the ejection port, is a turning catch. Turn it to the right, lift the cover, pull out the hinge pin in the cover, and remove the cover itself.

Slide the magazine off its hinge.

Remove the magazine mouthpiece plate (this is just to the rear of the magazine mouthpiece). Slide the mouthpiece to the rear and lift it off.

Now lift out the ejector.

Turn the gun upside down. With a small screwdriver or the point of a bullet, press in the locking catch cover retaining stud. The catch cover may now be slid off to the rear.

Push out the locking catch hinge pin and remove the catch and its spring.

Turn the gun right side up. An H-piece retaining catch will be seen on the left of the receiver. Lift it and withdraw it to the left.

Move the H-piece locking nut as far as it will go to the rear and lift it out. The locking nut may now be removed.

No further dismounting is ordinarily necessary.

How the Gun Works

Like the Revelli, Fiat, and Schwarzlose, this gun is operated partly by recoil of the moving parts and partly by what is called "projection of the spent case," which means simply blowback as the empty case is forced back against the face of the bolt. This system, as in the case of the early Japanese machine guns, requires the incorporation in the gun of a special device which will spray oil on the cartridges as they are inserted in the firing chamber. This device also lubricates the moving parts.

As in the case of the Thompson submachine gun, unless this oiling action functions properly, trouble will be encountered.

Another grave defect in this weapon, as already pointed out, is that it fires from a closed bolt. While this is an excellent system in a heavy machine gun, in a light one it can be very dangerous. As the barrel heats up, the cartridge in the chamber may be "cooked off" by the barrel heat.

Starting with the gun loaded and cocked, the action is as follows: As the trigger is pressed it rotates on its pin, causing the rear end to force the sear release forward and cam the sear out of contact with the rear of the firing pin; this compresses the sear spring and also releases the firing pin which is driven forward by its spring and strikes the primer of the cartridge in the firing chamber.

Return Movement of the Action. As the bullet travels down the barrel, the gas pressing rearward against the empty cartridge case drives back against the face of the bolt. This pushes the bolt, bolt lock, and the barrel (which at this point are securely locked) a short distance to the rear. During this travel, the lug on the top of the bolt lock cams to the left. At the proper moment, this unlocks the bolt lock and permits the bolt to travel independently to the rear carrying the empty cartridge case gripped by the extractor. An ejector traveling in the right side of the bolt swings out on spring tension and the right side of the head of the cartridge strikes against it, pivoting it on the extractor and hurling it out the left side.

The firing pin is also carried to the rear by the bolt and its spring is compressed between the forward shoulder of the pin and the buffer housing. The rear end of the pin passes through the buffer and into the sear housing where it cams the sear down compressing its spring until the sear notch is directly above the sear. Then the spring forces the sear up to grasp the firing pin and hold it to the rear. A safety device is incorporated which prevents the firing pin from going forward except when the bolt is fully locked.

Special Note. Although it is unlikely that any machine weapons will ever again be manufactured using such an oiling device, a short explanation of the functioning of this pump may be of interest. As the bolt goes forward, a piston is cammed up into a cylinder in the oiling device. This exerts a driving force on the oil which forces it out a small spout on the right side of the cover. This spout leads to the mouth of the magazine, and thus sprays oil over the cartridge case of the first cartridge. During the rearward motion of the bolt, the oil piston rides in a groove on top of the bolt until the bolt nears its rear position. Then the piston is cammed down a beveled surface, releasing pressure and letting in air for the next forward stroke.

This weapon is obsolete in the Italian Army.

Breda 8mm Medium Machine Gun, Model 37.

The 8mm Breda medium machine gun Model 37 is a reasonably good, though heavy, gas-operated, air-cooled gun. Cocking handle is on the right side, and traversing handle and thumb triggers are provided as in the Revelli gun.

The M38 Breda 8mm is a standard Italian Tank Gun employing a staggered box magazine fed from the top. Like the M37 it employs the Breda rising-block lock and rapid barrel change.

Chapter 32. Japan

The Japanese Army is currently equipped with U.S. small arms. Production of pistols and submachine guns has begun again in Japan. The submachine gun is a copy of the U.S. M3A1; the pistols are covered in detail below. Excepting these pistols, the remainder of the weapons covered are those used by the Japanese in World War II and are not currently in Japanese service. The Japanese press indicates that development of rifles and machine guns is now active in Japan.

Japanese 9mm Model 57 New Nambu Automatic Pistol

Caliber: 9mm Parabellum (also made in .45 cal.).
System of Operation: Recoil operated, semi-automatic only.
Weight: 2.12 lbs.
Length, Overall: 7.8 in.
Barrel Length: 4.6 in.
Feed Device: 8 round, single line, detachable box magazine.
Muzzle Velocity: 1148 f.p.s.

This weapon which is called the "New Nambu" is a modified copy of the U.S. M1911 automatic pistol. It does not have a grip safety and has its magazine catch mounted on the bottom of the grip, but is otherwise much the same as the U.S. pistol. It is manufactured by Shin Chuo Kogyo K.K. (New Central Industrial Company, Ltd., of Tokyo). Loading, firing, field stripping, and functioning are the same as the U.S. M1911 pistol with the exception of the features noted above. The pistol is well made and of very good finish.

Cal. .32 Model 57B New Nambu Automatic Pistol

Caliber: .32 ACP (7.65mm Browning).
System of Operation: Blowback, semi-automatic only.
Weight: 1.3 lbs.
Length, Overall: 6.3 in.
Feed Device: 8 round, detachable in-line box magazine.

Cal. .32 Model 57B New Nambu Automatic Pistol.

This weapon is also called a New Nambu. It is basically a Browning type blowback pistol and loading, firing, field stripping and functioning are the same as the Browning M1910 pistol. This pistol is also made by Shin Chuo Kogyo K.K. in Tokyo. This firm is also making a copy of the .38 Special Smith and Wesson which they call the New Nambu Model 58 revolver.

Nambu 8mm 1914 Automatic. The Original Japanese Service Pistol.

Caliber: 8mm. This is a specially designed cartridge, its general appearance being bottle-necked and patterned after the Luger .30 cartridge. Its diameter however is larger than the Luger .30 which is 7.65mm.

Magazine: Box type single line, capacity 8 cartridges.
Muzzle Velocity: About 950 feet per second.
Weight of Bullet: 102 grains (steel jacketed).
Muzzle Striking Energy: About 230 foot pounds.
Barrel Length: About 4½″.
Overall Length of Pistol: About 9″.
Weight: About 30 ozs.
Sights: Front sight fixed. Rear sight has sliding leaf and is adjustable for elevation.
Accurate Range: 50 yards.
Maximum Range: About 1400 yards.
Pistol Operated By: Recoil.
Locked: By locking bolt swinging up through barrel extension into underside of breech lock as in the Glisenti and Mauser type pistols.
Type of Fire: Single shot only.
Magazine Release Catch: Button as on Colt .45 and Luger.
Position of Bolt When Last Shot is Fired: Open. When magazine is extracted or loaded magazine inserted pulling back on bolt head slightly will free the bolt and permit it to run forward.
Safeties: (a) Automatic grip safety directly under triggerguard. As in Colt and Glisenti pistols, when pistol is gripped firmly, safety grip moves in, permitting pistol to be fired. (b) Automatic disconnector prevents pistol from being fired until bolt moves forward and breech is completely locked.

This pistol comes in a very heavy leather or wooden holster stock, which can be attached to the slot in the handle of the pistol to form a carbine. Unlike the Mauser pistol, this holster is not long enough to make a satisfactory shoulder stock. Instead it is provided with a telescopic extension which may be pulled out to lengthen the shoulder stock. This device is of questionable value in actual combat use. The sighting arrangements for firing with extended hand, as in pistol operation, or from a shoulder stock, in carbine fashion, are entirely different.

To Load

Insert loaded magazine in handle, push it in until it locks securely. (Just as for Colt and Luger Automatic.)

Grasp bolt wings securely, pull bolt back as far as it will go, release. The recoil spring, compressed by pulling the bolt back, strips the top cartridge from the magazine, loads it into the firing chamber, and snaps the head of the extractor into the cannelure of the cartridge case.

When pistol is empty, bolt stays open. Insert loaded magazine and pull back slightly on bolt. This will release the holding catch and permit the bolt to run forward. (This is adapted from the Glisenti.)

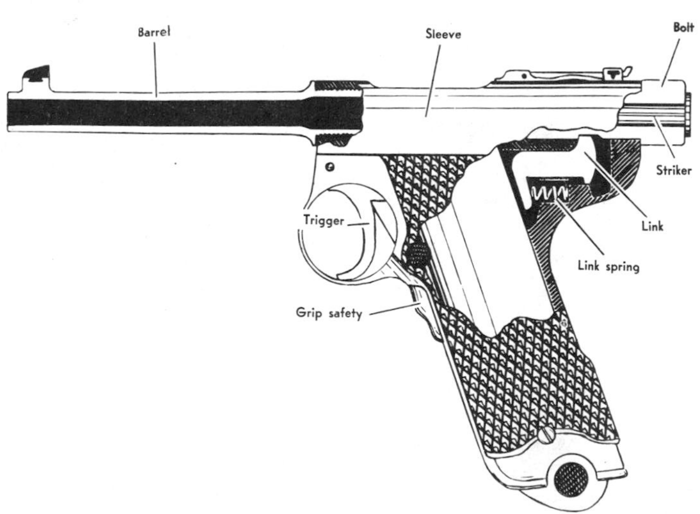

Section View, Nambu 8mm 1914 Automatic Pistol.

Field Stripping

Remove magazine catch from receiver.

With bolt held back, pull triggerguard down.

With muzzle pressing against a solid surface to remove tension of spring, give breech plug a one quarter turn and withdraw.

Bolt may now be pulled out of sleeve. Firing pin may be removed from bolt.

Revolve the rear stop to the left and unscrew it.

Remove the mainspring and the plug from the front end.

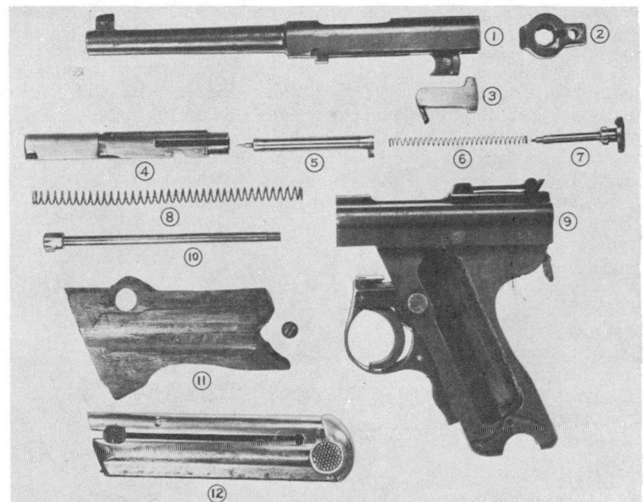

1. Barrel forging, which consists of barrel proper, and barrel extension which houses bolt.
2. Bolt retainer. 3. Bolt lock.
4. Bolt. 5. Firing pin. 6. Firing pin spring.
7. Firing pin extension.
8. Recoil spring. 9. Receiver.
10. Recoil spring guide. 11. Stock.
12. Magazine.

Nambu Pistol Field Stripped.

How the Nambu Pistol Works

While in appearance and balance this weapon on the outside resembles the Luger Pistol, the mechanism actually is related more directly to the Glisenti. As the cartridge is fired, the breech block, locked firmly to the barrel extension by the locking bolt, which is pivoted so it can swing up from below to lock the parts, travels straight to the rear for a short distance with the barrel. The barrel strikes against the barrel stop and is held up in its rearward motion. At this point, the locking bolt reaches a cut in the receiver down which it can swing to unlock the breech block from the barrel. The breech block now continues rearward drawing with it the empty cartridge case which strikes the ejector and is hurled out of the pistol. During this motion the recoil springs are compressed. When the rearmost position has been reached by the bolt, the magazine spring lifts a cartridge in line with the bolt, the compressed mainspring reasserts itself, drives the bolt forward stripping a cartridge into the chamber. Meanwhile the locking bolt swings up on its pivot through the slot in the receiver and locks into the under side of the breech block; and the locked barrel and breech block are thrust home to their forward position. At this point the disconnecting mechanism removes interference from the striker.

Type 14 (1925) 8mm Automatic Pistol.

Caliber: 8mm Japanese Pistol (.31 caliber).
Magazine: Single line box, capacity 8 cartridges. Fitted with follower pressure button on right side.
Muzzle Velocity: About 950 feet per second.
Weight of Bullet: 102 grains, jacketed.
Muzzle Striking Energy: About 230 foot pounds.
Barrel Length: About 4½ inches.
Overall Length: About 9 inches.
Weight: About 30 ounces empty.
Sights: Fixed.
Accurate Range: About 50 yards.
Maximum Range: About 1400 yards.
Pistol Operated By: Recoil.
Locked: Locking bolt swings up through barrel extension to lock into the under side of the breech block.
Type of Fire: Single shot only, has positive disconnector.
Magazine Release Catch: Left side on receiver behind trigger. Is difficult to operate. Button must be pushed in and magazine pulled out.
Bolt: Stays open when last shot is fired.
Rifling: Six grooves, right hand twist.
Safety: A swinging piece on barrel extension above left hand stock.

Special Note on This Weapon

This is a production model replacing the original so-called Nambu Pistol as the principal Japanese side arm

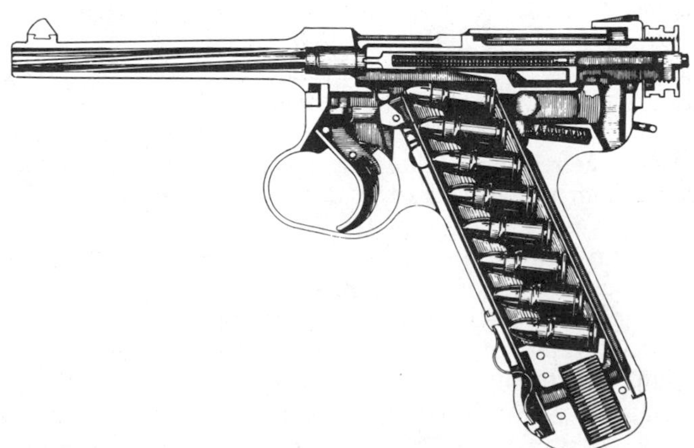

Japanese Type 14 (1925) with magazine loaded and action in full forward position. Note that this arm does not have the grip safety of the earlier model.

Field Stripping

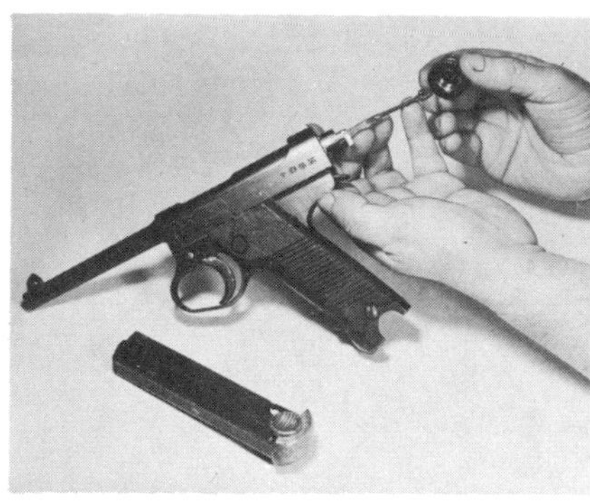

The head of the firing pin extension protrudes through the center of the bolt nut. Press this in and turn the bolt nut to unscrew it. As it is removed, the firing pin spring will force the firing pin extension out of its seat in the bolt. This permits removal of the firing pin, firing pin spring, and firing pin extension.

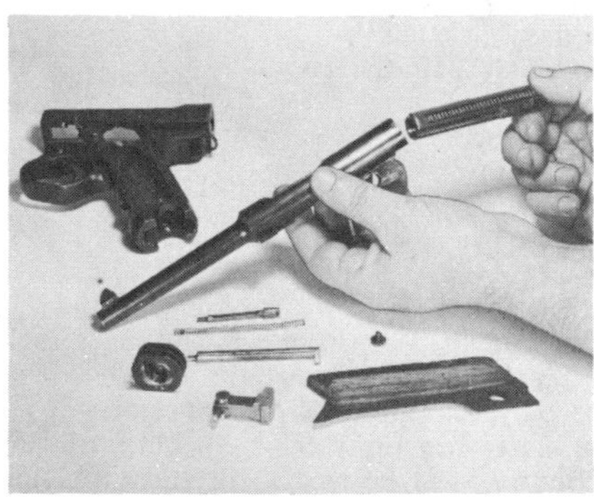

The locking link may be removed from its pivot. The bolt with the recoil springs fitted on each side of it may be withdrawn from the rear of the barrel extension, and if necessary the firing pin may be driven out of the bolt together with its spring.

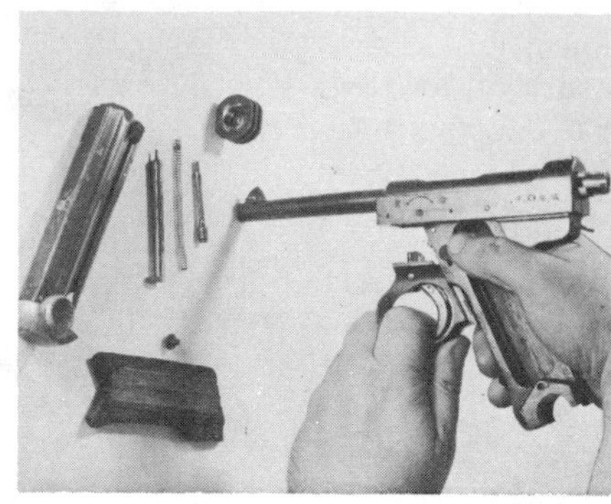

Remove magazine. Press muzzle down on a solid surface to force the barrel back to the limit of its recoil, and while holding it in that position, push in the magazine catch as far as it will go (it is usually well to remove the left hand stock before doing this). While barrel is depressed and magazine release catch is being forced in, pull straight down on the triggerguard. This operation usually is a very difficult one. It may be necessary to hitch the triggerguard over a heavy spike driven into a board or some similar object, and while pressing in the catch and forcing back the barrel to pull so that the triggerguard comes down out of the groove in the frame of the receiver.

While the magazine release catch locks in a slot in the upper front section of the magazine, the magazine is also retained near the bottom of the grip by the flat spring which is buckled to catch in a lower notch in the magazine. Thus to remove the magazine it will be necessary not only to push the catch but also to pull the magazine with considerable force to free it from the lower spring.

The barrel may now be slid forward on its grooves out of the receiver, bringing the bolt with it. Note that the barrel extension is an integral part of the barrel itself, and that the extension acts as a housing for the bolt.

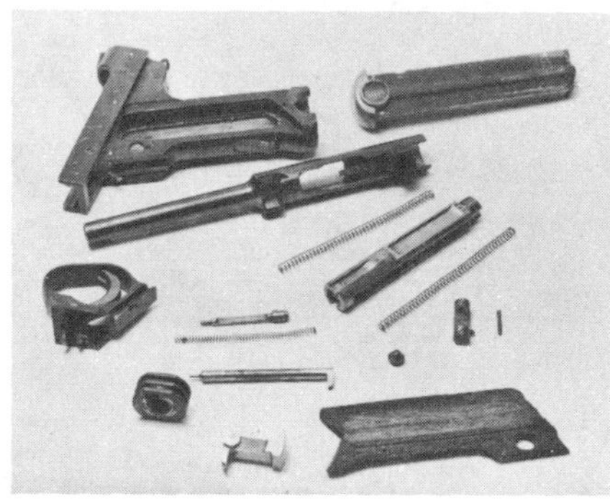

Pulling the triggerguard straight down permits the trigger assembly to be withdrawn from the receiver. The magazine catch may be now lifted out together with its small spring. No further stripping is necessary. The remaining parts must be removed by driving out fixed pins.

of its type. The grip safety has been eliminated. The cocking piece on the bolt differs from that of the earlier model in that it is circular. Two general types of it are known, differing only in slight details. One has the normal triggerguard; the other has an elongated trigger guard to permit use of the weapon with a glove on.

It will be noted that while the exterior appearance somewhat resembles the German Luger, the actual locking design is more like the Italian Glisenti and the German Mauser.

In this model two recoil springs are used. They lie along each side of the receiver and are compressed by the barrel extension (which is an integral part of the barrel forging) during recoil of the pistol. The original Nambu had only one recoil spring on the left side.

In this pistol, the bolt stays back when the last cartridge has been fired. However, when the magazine is withdrawn, the bolt flies forward. When a new magazine is inserted, the bolt must be drawn back and released manually in order to load the chamber.

Japanese Type 14 (1925) action open at end of recoil stroke ready to go forward and load the chamber.

A magazine safety is provided which prevents the weapon from being fired when the magazine is withdrawn.

While the design of this pistol is reasonably efficient, its manufacture does not measure up to our standards.

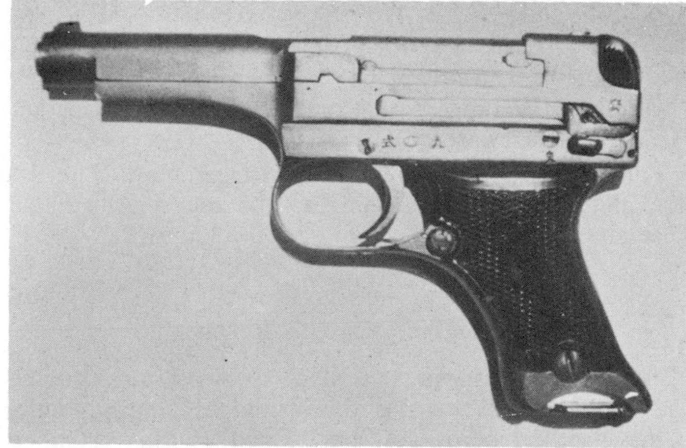

Japanese Type 94 (1934) 8mm Automatic Pistol.

Caliber: 8mm Japanese Pistol.
Magazine: Box, capacity 6 rounds.
Muzzle Velocity: About 900 feet per second.
Barrel Length: 3⅛ inches.
Overall Length: 7⅛ inches.
Weight: 27 ounces empty.
Sights: Fixed.
Pistol Operated by: Recoil.
Locked: By block cammed up as action closes.
Type of Fire: Single shot only.
Magazine Release Catch: Button on receiver on bottom of triggerguard, left side.
Safety: Thumb safety at rear of receiver above left hand grip.

Special Note on This Weapon

This freakish weapon was originally developed for export sales. Japanese catalogues listed it for sale in South American countries before the war. It is of definitely inferior construction, some of the parts being castings.

The recoil spring is around the barrel. The weapon is cocked by pulling back the knurled surfaces at the rear of the bolt. The sear projects from the left side, and is an extremely dangerous feature in that pressure on it will fire the weapon without the trigger being touched.

Field Stripping

Insert empty magazine into pistol and pull back slide until it catches.

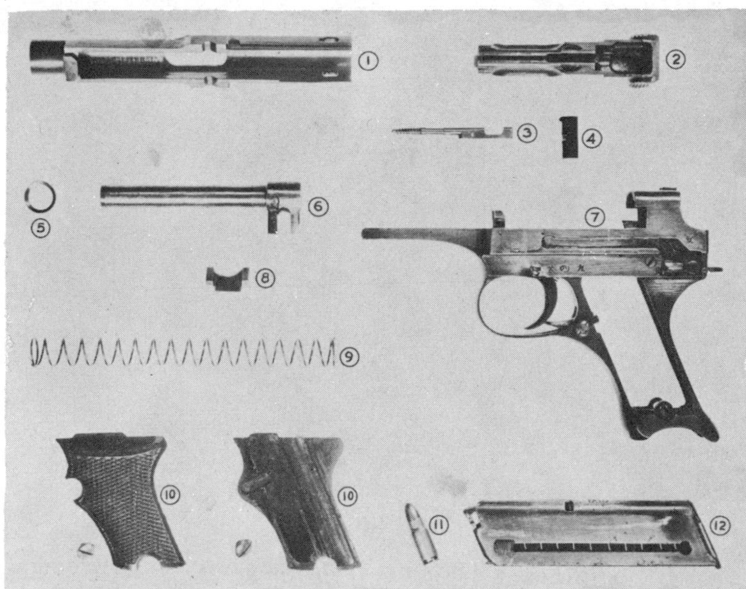

1. Slide. 2. Bolt. 3. Firing pin.
4. Firing pin retainer. 5. Barrel bushing.
6. Barrel. 7. Receiver.
8. Locking block. 9. Recoil spring.
10. Stocks. 11. 8mm cartridge.
12. Magazine.

Hold pistol slide down and rear end to the front, and push firing pin as far forward as it will go.

Using a punch push slide cap lock out to the left. Handle carefully so slide and its cap do not come apart.

The slide, barrel, and recoil spring will now come forward off the receiver. Withdraw slide cap from rear end of receiver.

Japanese Revolver 9mm Type 26 (1893).

Caliber: 9mm Japanese.
Cylinder: 6 chambers.
Muzzle Velocity: About 750 feet per second.
Overall Length: 9.4 inches.
Weight: 32 ounces.
Barrel Length: 4.69 inches.
Sights: Fixed.
Type of Action: Hinge frame, S & W pattern with lock on the barrel extension.
Action: Double action only. This weapon cannot be thumb cocked.
Safety: Rebounding hammer.
Note: All cartridges found for this revolver, which was originally a cavalry weapon in Japan but is now found in all branches of the service, have lead bullets.

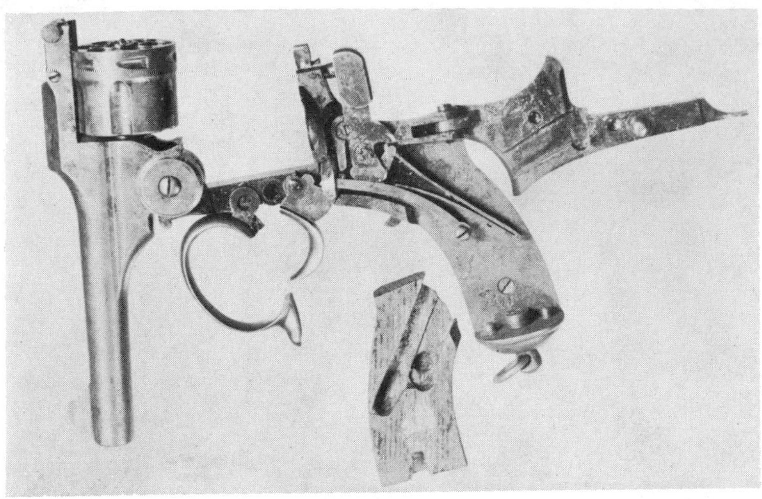

Field Stripping

Pull up the latch and open the revolver. Holding the latch up, unscrew the cylinder and withdraw it and the extractor.

Unscrew the hinge screw and remove the barrel and extractor lifting washer.

Pull down the rear end of the triggerguard. The left side plate can now be swung to the rear on its hinge. This gives access to the working mechanism.

Special Note on This Revolver

This weapon is operated like its American counterparts. The barrel catch is raised and the barrel hinged open. The six cartridges are loaded in the chambers and the revolver closed. One pull through on the trigger revolves the cylinder, cocks and drops the hammer. The firing pin is an integral part of the hammer. Workmanship is poor. The cartridge somewhat resembles the .38 S & W but is fitted with a very thin rim. It is also longer.

Scale Photos of 8mm and 7mm Nambu Pistols.

Discussion

Evaluation. By American standards the caliber is not an efficient military type. The pistol itself is reasonably well made (in prewar types, very well made) of good materials. Thumb safety is clumsy. Grip safety is a trigger lock only. Striker spring is comparatively weak, with resulting slow action time. Breech lock and firing designs are good.

Ammunition. 8mm Japanese Service. Bottle necked. Not made in U. S. (Note 7mm Nambu ammunition also is not made here.)

TYPE 14 (1925). This is a considerably modified version of the Nambu. It was designed for mass manufacture and was the major Japanese pistol of War II.

Identification. Dual recoil springs housed in sides of bolt. No grip safety. Manual safety lever on receiver directly above trigger.

Two types of triggerguards were issued, a standard type and one with a large forward sweep for use with glove in cold climate.

Note. This pistol may also be found with grip permitting attachment of a shoulder stock. When stock accompanies such a pistol, arm must be registered.

Evaluation. Fair to poor manufacture. While the design and manufacturing factors are an improvement over the Nambu, the product is not.

Ammunition. Same as for Nambu 8mm.

TYPE 94 (1934). This pistol was sold commercially, particularly in South American areas of large Japanese population, before the war. It is the poorest of all the Japanese designs.

Identification. Peculiar breech lock whose tip may be seen rising out of receiver above line of triggerguard when pistol is closed. Recoil spring around barrel. Sear projects from left side of receiver.

Evaluation. Dangerous. The sear on the outside of the receiver will fire the weapon if accidentally pressed in. The pistol can fire before the breech is locked. Workmanship and materials as well as design were poor in several dozen specimens examined.

Ammunition. 8mm Japanese. Not available.

TYPE 26 REVOLVER, 1893. This is a hinged frame revolver. The barrel strap is locked to the breech by an American-type catch, but the firing mechanism is adapted from European design.

This was the only revolver manufactured in quantity in Japan. Ideographs on right frame translate "26th Year Model."

Identification. No cocking spur on hammer, which cannot be thumb cocked. Left hand side plate hinges out from front to expose firing mechanism. Hinge frame construction.

Evaluation. Poor. Cylinder indexing is bad. Firing mechanism does not lend itself to accurate firing.

Ammunition. 9mm Japanese with rim. Not available in U. S. This cartridge has some points of resemblance to the familiar .38 S & W, but is not interchangeable.

7MM NAMBU. The 7mm Nambu pistol shown here is in every respect except sights and similar detail relating to caliber, the same as the official 8mm. This 7mm pistol is quite rare. It handles a bottleneck cartridge which is much like a reduced 8mm. This pistol was made before the outbreak of the war, and its workmanship is far superior to most of the later models. It was designed as a staff officer's model and some were exported.

Following are the official Service Models.

NAMBU MODEL. The Japanese ideographs on the right side of the receiver translate "Nambu Model." The design is named after General Nambu of Japanese Ordnance. It is popularly but incorrectly called a "Japanese Luger." Except for superficial outside appearance, it has nothing in common with the Luger. The breechlock actually indicates that Nambu was influenced by Italian design, though the lock is simpler and more efficient than the Italian Glisenti, with which it has some points in common.

Identification. Grip safety in handle below triggerguard. Single recoil spring housed in a separate tunnel in left side of receiver parallel to bolt. Pistol was made with standard pistol type grip and with grip design to permit attachment of holster to convert to a shoulder weapon.

Note: When this pistol has an attachable shoulder holster accompanying it, the weapon is subject to Federal registration.

JAPANESE RIFLES

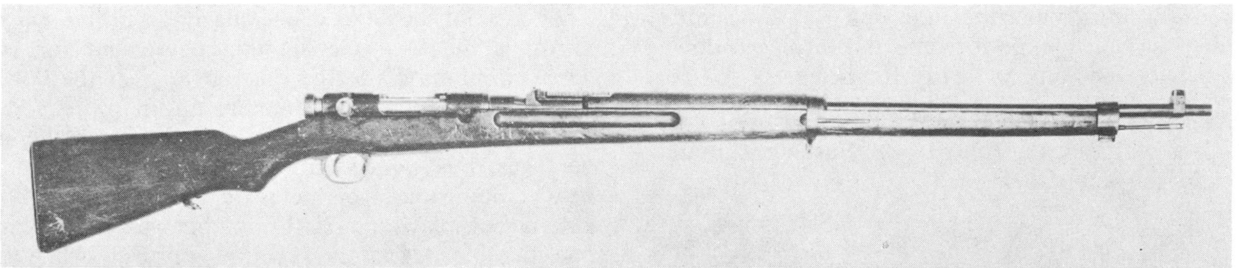

Type 38 (Arisaka) 6.5mm Rifle.

Caliber: 6.5mm Japanese Service cartridge.
Magazine: Mauser type 5-shot capacity.
Barrel Length: 31.4".
Overall Length of Rifle: 50.2" (with bayonet 1' 2½" longer).
Weight: 9 lbs. 4 oz. (with bayonet 1 lb. heavier).
Sights: Inverted V-post front and V-rear.
Elevation: From 400 to 2400 meters.
Type: This is a Mauser-type with action much like our Springfield.
Sling: This rifle has a sling used for carrying. It cannot be adapted as a support for the rifle.
Cocking: Like the British Enfield, this weapon cocks on the forward thrust of the bolt.
Muzzle Velocity: About 2400 feet per second.
Weight of Bullet: 138 grains, pointed lead bullet with nickel-steel jacket.
Accurate Military Range: About 500 yards.
Extreme Range: About 4000 yards.
Bolt Cover: See illustration.

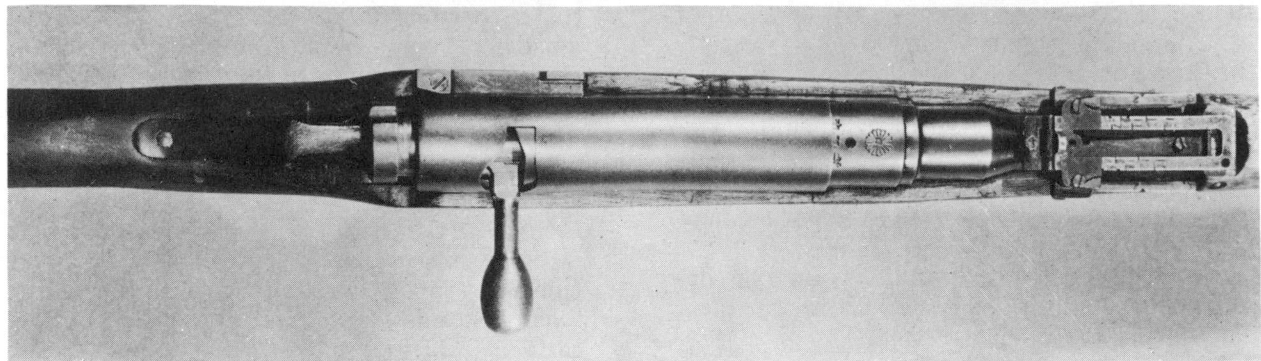

A sliding metal piece is fitted over the bolt. This is intended to keep dirt and mud out of the action. As the bolt is drawn to the rear, the cover slides back with it.

Field Stripping

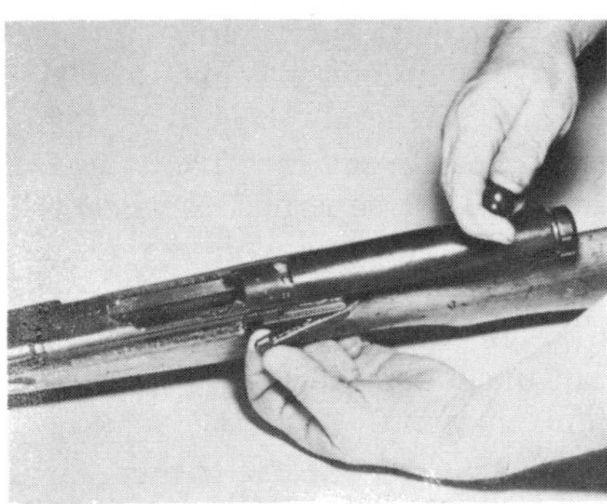

Pull out on forward end of bolt lock which is located on extreme left end of receiver. While holding this out against the spring tension, turn up the bolt handle and draw it straight back to the rear.

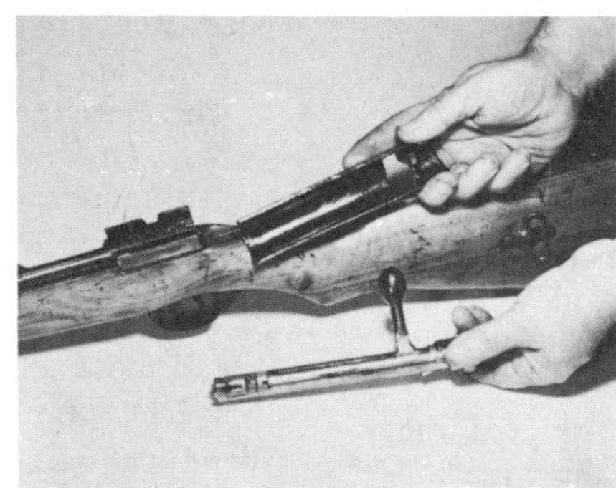

Remove the bolt cover from the bolt.

Magazine has a spring catch on the inside of the forward end of the triggerguard. Press this and the magazine spring will force the bottom plate out of the magazine. The magazine follower, spring and bottom plate may be lifted out completely. No further stripping is normally necessary.

Loading

Turn bolt handle up and draw straight back to the rear. Insert loaded clip in clip guides in receiver. Press cartridges down into magazine and pull out the empty clip; pushing the bolt handle forward and turning it down into place leaves the weapon ready for firing.

Safety. Push in on the head of the bolt and twist it to the right. This will lock the rifle at safe. Pushing it in and twisting it to the left will unlock it.

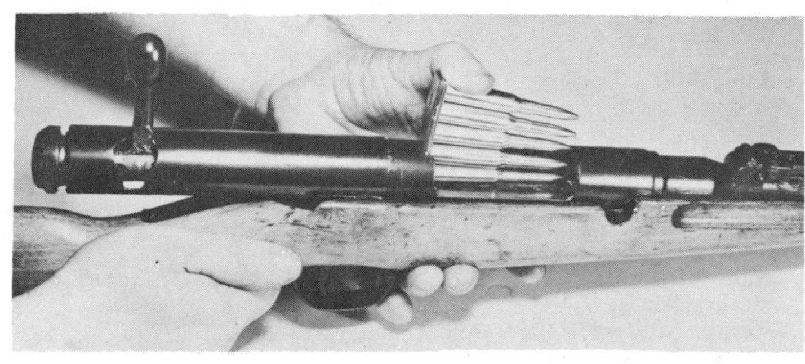

Special Note on Japanese Rifles

Former Japanese Army rifles follow the general Mauser design which is the finest of the bolt action types. They are not, however, particularly accurate, and no provision is made in the sighting equipment for windage. They continue to use the dust cover over the bolt. While this device does unquestionably afford protection to the bolt in its closed position, it is doubtful whether the advantages thus gained are worth the disadvantages of the heavy sliding piece of metal on the top of the bolt. The amount of play and rattle as the weapon is carried is considerable. Certainly stealthy approach while carrying such a weapon is quite a good trick. Headspace adjustment on Jap rifles is notoriously poor. The bolt cover protects the face from flash-backs from the firing chamber.

Note on Italian-Made Japanese Rifles

Japanese rifles are occasionally found in the standard 6.5mm Japanese caliber stamped "Beretta." These rifles have Italian 1891 type receivers and bolts, the receivers being modified for Mauser type magazine. The stocks are the standard Japanese design of two-piece construction.

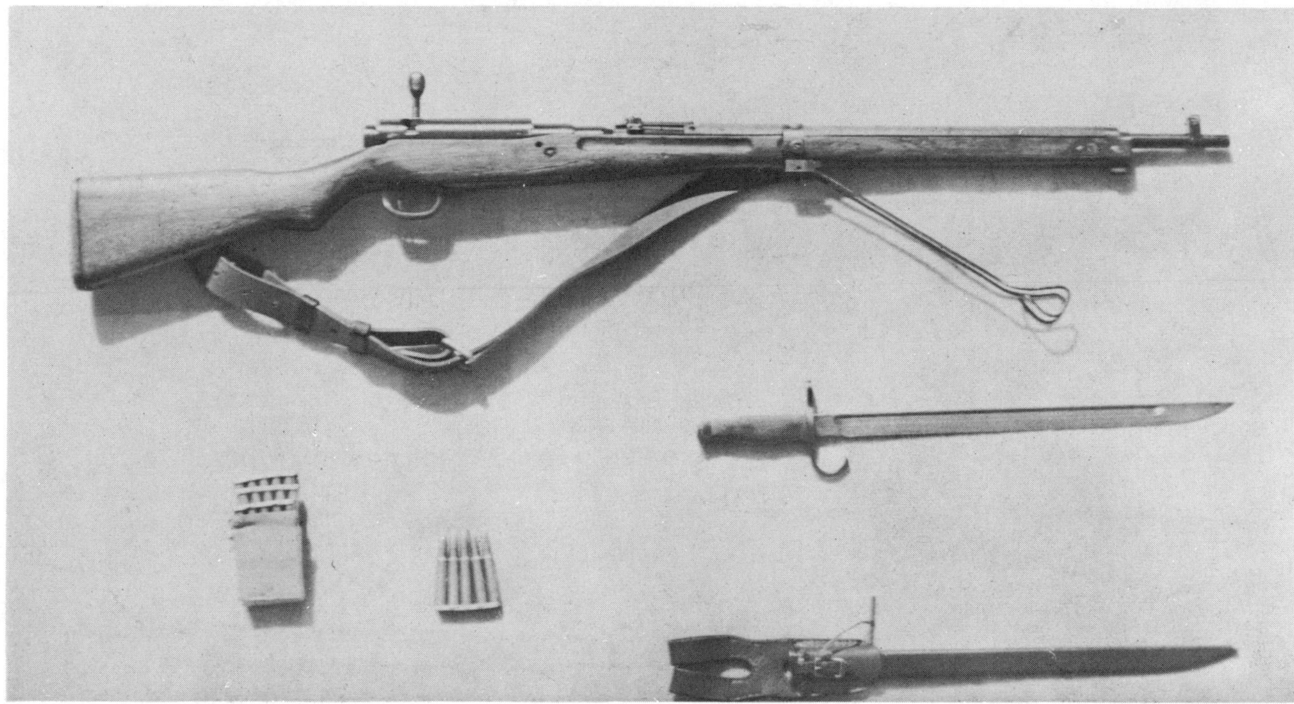

Type 99 (1939) 7.7mm Rifle.

Caliber: 7.7mm Rimless Japanese ammunition.
Magazine: Mauser type, capacity 5 rounds.
Barrel Length: 31.37 inches.
Overall Length of Rifle: 50 inches without bayonet.
Weight: 8.8 pounds (with bayonet, one pound more).
Sights: Tapered blade front and leaf rear. No windage provided for. Leaf is graduated from 300 to 1500 meters and has a peep. Two arms attached to the slide on rear sight unfold outward to a horizontal position. These are used for giving lead on airplanes.
Cocking: Cocks on forward thrust of bolt.
Muzzle Velocity: About 2400 feet per second.
Weight of Bullet: 192 grains, metal jacketed.
Cartridge: Resembles U. S. .30 ammunition, base diameters of cases are the same, taper of cases is almost identical, but Jap cartridge is more sharply necked and is ¼ inch shorter in overall length.
Bolt Cover: Similar to Jap Model 38.
Safety: A flat knurled knob replaces the cocking piece on the bolt. Pushing this in and twisting 45 degrees to the right sets the safety. Pushing it in and twisting it back releases it.

Special Note on This Rifle

This weapon was designed to meet the need for a more powerful arm than the 6.5mm with which the Japanese started the war. In an attempt to make it a mass production item, such parts as bolt cover, butt plate, floor plate, follower, swivels, etc., are stampings.

The bayonet used on this rifle also fits the Type 38 Rifle and the Types 96 and 99 L.M.G.

The action of this rifle is Mauser bolt type, but cocks on the closing stroke. A steel cover fits over the bolt handle and slides back and forth in grooves at the left side and right side of the receiver as the bolt is operated. It is very much worth while in jungle fighting because it keeps dust and leaves and similar matter from entering the action. However, it rattles and is too noisy for use when scouting.

The magazine floor plate together with the spring and follower are removed by pushing on the small button inside the triggerguard ahead of the trigger. The magazine holds five cartridges.

A steel cleaning rod is fitted under the barrel.

The so-called airplane sight consisting of two arms, which can be unfolded one on each side of the rear sight slide, is an innovation on this weapon. Two V notches are located on each side of the center of the peep. They are intended to provide a lead on flying aircraft.

The wire monopod fastened to the front band is intended to provide a support when firing from slit trenches. It can be folded back when not in use. In actual practice it tends to buckle when the weapon is fired.

The butt on this rifle, as in other Japanese types shaped somewhat like our Springfield, is made of two pieces of wood dovetailed together.

This weapon is generally well made and must be considered an effective fighting instrument, though by no means in a class with either our Springfield or our Garand.

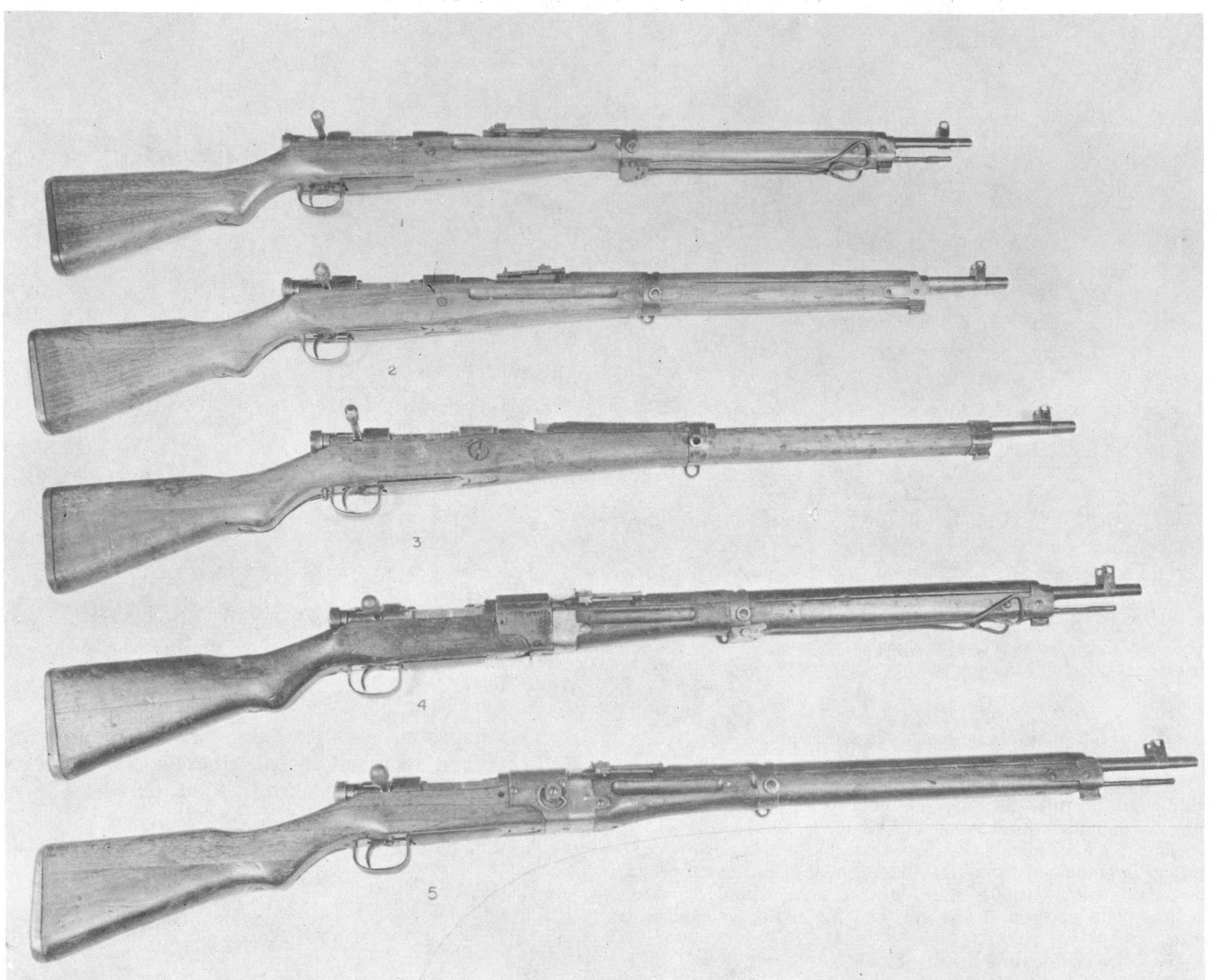

1. Length 44″. Barrel 27.25. Weight 8.3 lbs. Sights 300-1500 meters. Original issue with folding monopod.
2. Same without monopod.
3. Same but with longer stock and fixed rear sight.
4. Takedown rifle. Not manufactured in quantity. Designed for paratroopers. Quick detachable barrel is locked to receiver by interrupted threads. Assemblies are retained and released by means of a spring-loaded plunger. Bolt handle is detachable. Workmanship crude.
5. Takedown paratrooper rifle introduced in 1942. This is a superior design, well constructed and well made. No monopod. Solid bolt handle. A heavy barrel locking lug and a simple efficient cross bolt with a screw locking key swivelled to it fasten the assemblies rigidly.
Note: In 1939 a Sniper's rifle, identical with the Type 97 (6.5mm) except for caliber, was introduced.

In 1939 the Japanese began change-over to caliber 7.7mm (.303) as a result of battle experience. In accordance with mass production procedure in all countries (even the U. S.) at that time, all possible non-critical parts were made of stampings. These included butt plate, swivels, magazine bottom plates, and followers.

Mechanically, however, these arms are the same as the Type 38 in all essential details.

The caption under the picture covers all production variations.

Near the end of the War the Japanese manufactured a small number of semi-automatic rifles based on captured Garands. These were built to use the 7.7mm rifle cartridge.

The author has seen only two of these rifles. One was of fair manufacture. One was poor. The gas action had not been developed to the point of smooth operation, and the recoil was particularly violent.

These arms when encountered are collector's items. They are discussed here because of modifications made.

Description. General locking and gas design adapted directly from U. S. Rifle M1 (Garand). Length 43.2″. Barrel 24″. Weight 9.12 lbs.

The magazine system was changed to the conventional Mauser type but holding 10 cartridges. The rifle was loaded through the top of the open action by stripping in cartridges from two 5-shot clips. This system is superior to the Garand in that it permits recharging the magazine at any time, while the Garand magazine must normally be expended before being reloaded.

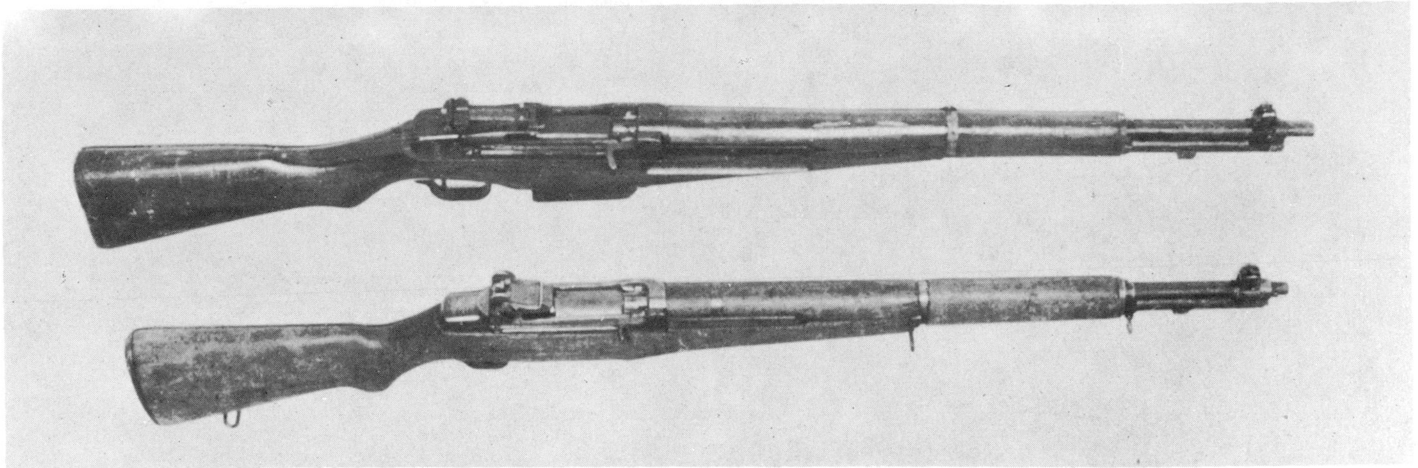

Jap and U. S. Garand. Note Magazine Difference.

Jap M99 with an LMG Type Box Magazine.

The use of this magazine did away with the necessity for the involved feeding system of the Garand, which works off the operating rod.

The operating rod was fitted with a straight piston.

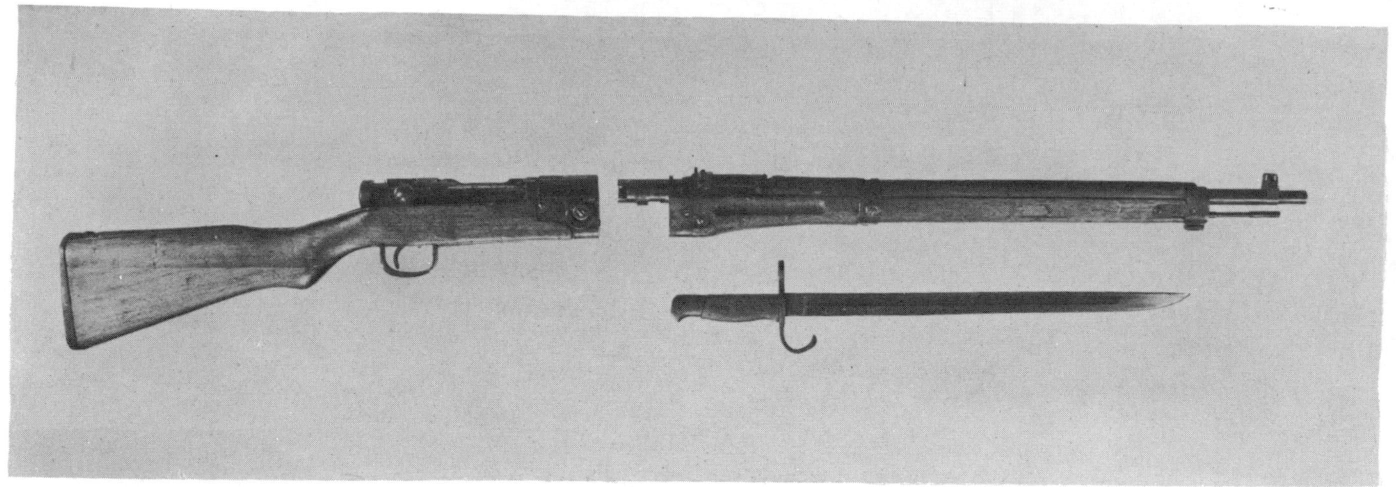

Jap Paratroopers Takedown Rifle, 7.7mm (.303), Type 2 (1942). Described Under Type 99 Rifles.

This required removal of front handguard before piston could be withdrawn; not a desirable factor.

The rear bolt lug was moved ahead about .25″ as required by the difference in feeding systems.

Japanese Experimental Developments

Scores of variations could be listed, but few have any practical potential value.

The adapting of LMG magazines to standard rifles is an old story in warfare. Shown is the last Japanese version.

The Japanese takedown rifle shown is, however, an interesting and worthwhile design. All such designs are essentially unsatisfactory for high power, light weight rifles. Mechanically this is one of the soundest yet evolved.

JAPANESE SUBMACHINE GUNS

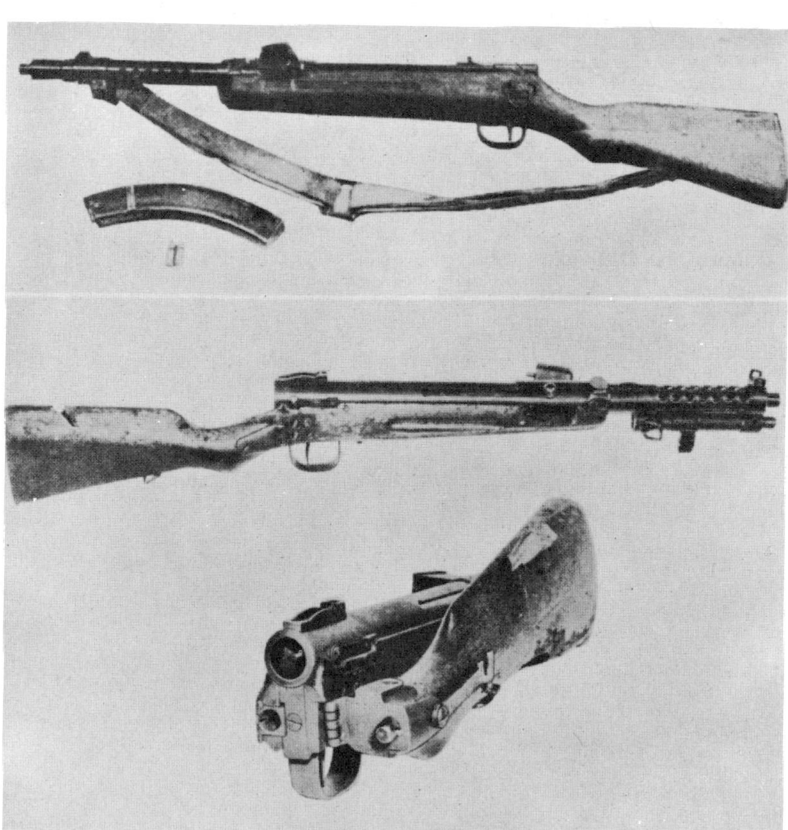

Upper. 8mm Type 100 Submachine Gun with Standard Stock.
Lower. 8mm Type 100 with Folding Stock.

The Japanese failed to grasp the value of the submachine gun until War II was well advanced. Their original supply was a sprinkling of German and Swiss types.

Few Japanese submachine guns were manufactured. However, the war designs showed an adaptability not expected from the Japanese, hence the major types are listed below as interesting experimental arms.

Submachine Gun Type 100. This was named after the Japanese calendar year of its adoption, 2600 (Our year 1940). It was used to some extent by the Jap Navy, and was part of the armament of Jap paratroop units at Leyte in 1944.

This is an elementary blowback design firing from an open bolt. It uses the standard 8mm pistol cartridge. While many stampings are used and welding is generously resorted to, it is fundamentally a well-built weapon.

Characteristics. There are two types, one with standard rifle stock and the other with a folding stock which can be hinged around to the left.

Length 36″. Barrel 9″. Weight about 8.75 lbs. Caliber 8mm pistol cartridge.

Folding stock type measures 34″ with stock extended.

The magazine is a detachable box carrying 30 rounds in staggered formation. Rate of fire is about 800-1000 per minute. A perforated barrel jacket is employed to aid in cooling and to protect the user against barrel heat. Magazine is inserted in left side of action. Ejection is to the right.

The design is quite simple. The bolt has the firing pin screwed into its face. The recoil spring and a buffer with spring are positioned directly behind the bolt. A feeding bar precedes the bolt to assure that the action is very nearly closed and the cartridge satisfactorily chambered before the firing pin hits the primer. Full auto fire only. Trigger safety only.

The folding stock design has a leaf sight of sliding ramp type. The rigid stock design has a non-adjustable sight.

Cases ejected from guns tested have generally been too badly expanded and dented to permit reloading. The use of bottlenecked cartridges in an arm of this type does not give as satisfactory performance as the usual straight-sided cases. Residual pressure is evidently quite high, judging by both cartridge case condition and spitting of smoke at ejection port.

Evaluation. Cheaply and simply made, but inferior in most respects to European and American standards.

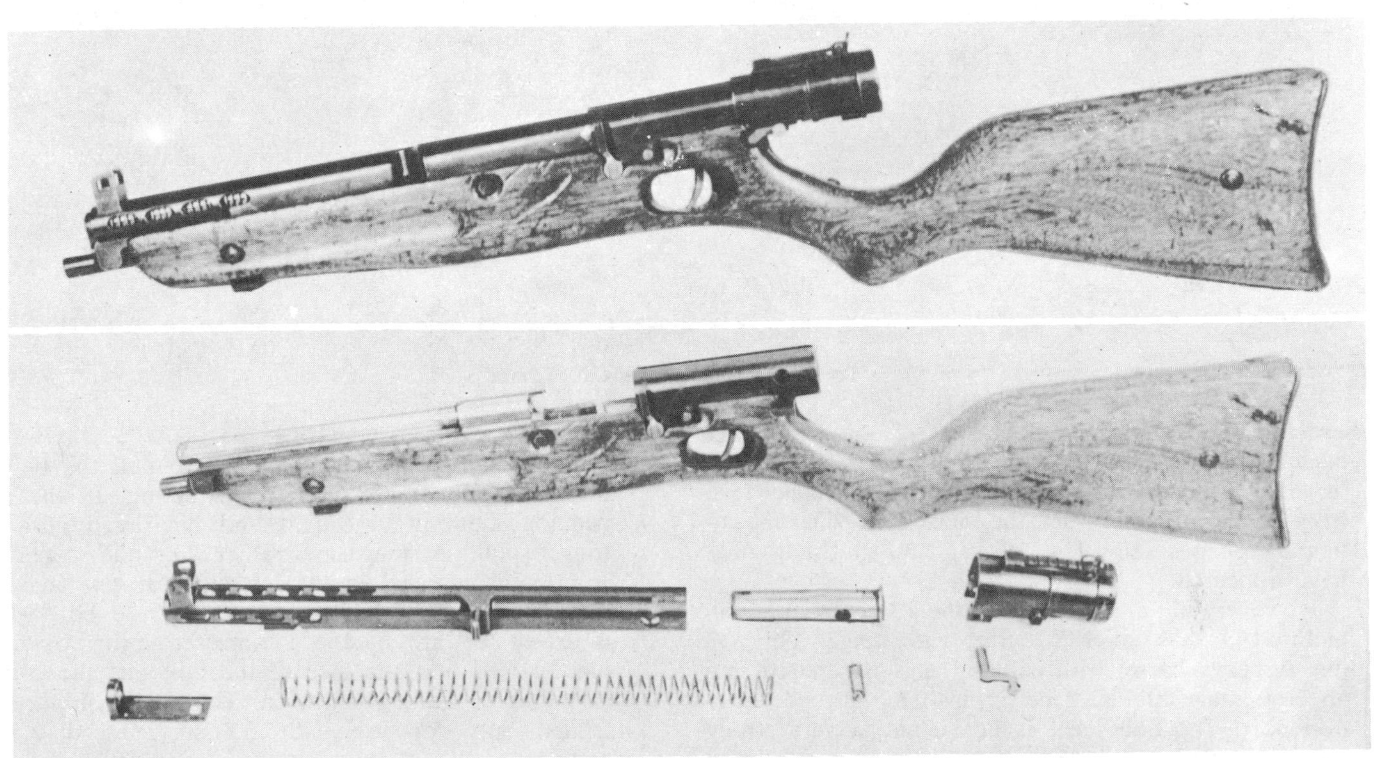

A Prototype "Bull Pup" Jap Submachine Gun.

This arm was not put into production. It was a late development with several unusual features which have some design significance.

Characteristics. Length 29.75″. Barrel 9.12″. Weight 7.16 lbs. Sights are barleycorn and sliding leaf types.

This is an ordinary blowback action for the 8mm Jap pistol cartridge. It is equipped with a selector to give either semi- or full auto fire. A combined selector and safety is mounted on the left side of the receiver above and ahead of the triggerguard. When the selector is horizontal the sear is positively locked; in the center it permits semi-auto fire; and when vertical, it gives full auto fire as long as the trigger is held.

The bolt is mounted in a housing which extends forward around the barrel and the recoil spring. The recoil spring is positioned around the barrel. The unusual compactness and "bull pup" stock design are clearly shown in the accompanying picture.

Special Rate Changer. A very unusual development is the special system incorporated in this design to alter the rate of fire.

A special air lock is provided to accomplish this. The lock is at the rear of the receiver. As the bolt is blown back it is secured to an extension arm on the piston of the air lock. An escape valve can be set to allow the air compressed within the lock to escape at different rates. By thus speeding or slowing down the travel rate of the bolt, the cyclic rate of fire can be increased or decreased.

JAPANESE MACHINE GUNS

Training Machine Gun Cal. 6.5mm.

Characteristics. Several modifications of this type have been encountered. All are full auto blowback weapons for the standard 6.5mm rifle cartridge. Some load from the top, some from the side. Magazine capacities and shapes vary; 15-, 20-, and 30-shot magazines have appeared.

However, all are essentially the same as the arm pictured. It has an 18″ barrel and weighs only 12 lbs. A heavy barrel with cooling rings is screwed into an elementary tubular receiver with a right side ejection port. The bolt itself is heavy and a very strong recoil spring is mounted behind it. A weak bipod mounting is affixed to the underside of the receiver ring. Sights are elementary.

The bolt handle is drawn back to pull the bolt to the rear and compress the recoil spring. In the rear position the bolt is caught and held ready for the trigger pull. A magazine rather like the American Johnson is inserted in the left side (or top on some models). Pressing the trigger releases the bolt which is driven forward by the compressed spring. A firing pin screwed into the face of the bolt hits the primer as the cartridge is chambered. These weapons are intended only for use with 6.5mm reduced charge cartridge.

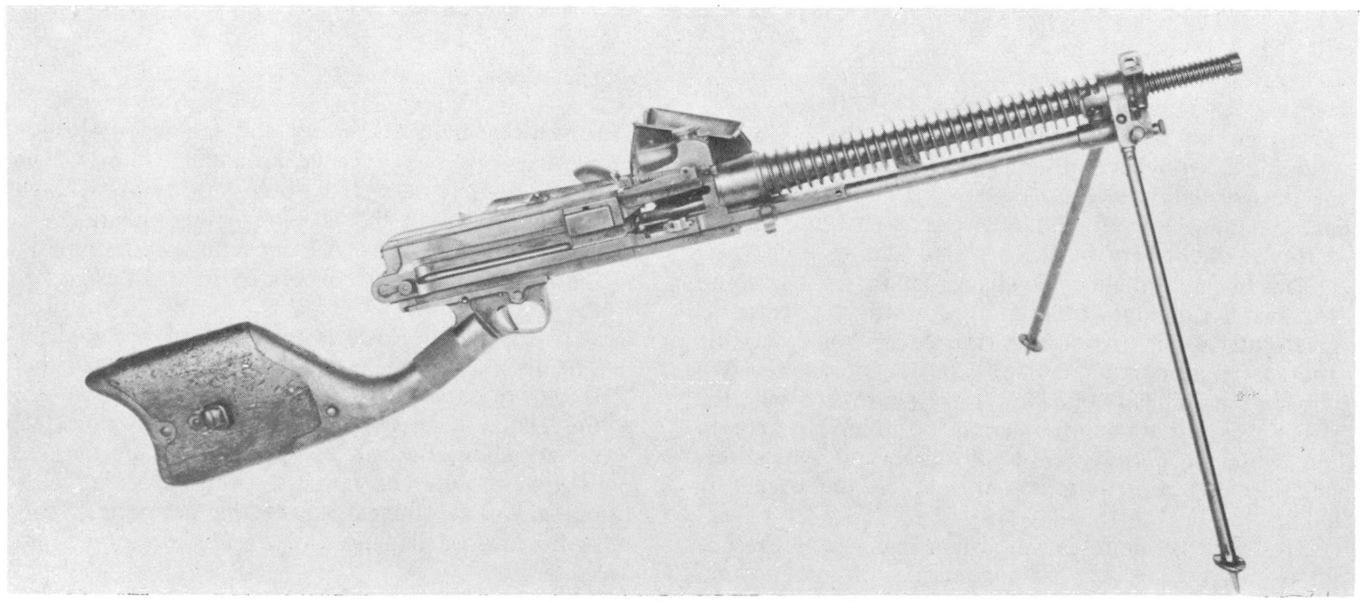

Nambu 6.5mm Type 11 (1922) Light Machine Gun.

This gun is designed on the French Hotchkiss principle. It is equipped with a special feeding system, which while theoretically good evidently did not work very well in practice; newer Japanese light machine guns utilize the standard magazine or strip type of loading.

Caliber: 6.5mm Japanese service cartridge with reduced charge.
Magazine: A hopper. Six clips of five cartridges each are placed on top of each other in the magazine and a heavy spring follower is lowered down on top of them. Clips feed down and successively through the action from the left side.
Ballistics: Standard for Japanese service cartridge.
Barrel Length: Amout 19".
Overall Length of Gun: About 43".
Weight of Gun: About 23 lbs.
Gun Operated By: Gas on the general Hotchkiss principle.
Locked: By bolt locks thrust down behind locking lugs on sides of receiver.
Cooled: By air. Heavy barrel with radial fins. Weapon fires from an open bolt permitting circulation of air through barrel and breech between shots.
Cyclic Rate of Fire: About 500 a minute.
Sights: Radial rear sight adjusted to 1500 meters. Adjustable front sight.
Position of Cocking Handle: On left side behind magazine hopper.
Type of Fire: Full automatic only.
Type of Mount: Bipod securely attached to the gun.

Field Stripping

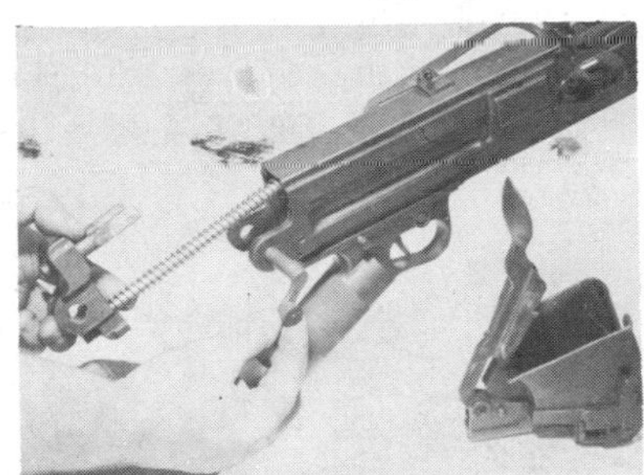

At the rear of the receiver is a pin which, when turned down to vertical position and pulled out, permits removal of the back plate group and the recoil spring.

Draw the cocking handle to the rear and it will bring back the slide together with the bolt and the bolt locks. When the lugs on the bolt slide are properly lined up with the openings on the side of the receiver, the bolt slide may be removed from the left.

A lock is provided on the front side of the receiver which when pulled back permits the bolt slide to be removed from the left.

Directly in front of the rear sight is a stud which when pressed down permits removing an oil pump device on the receiver, by sliding it out to the left.

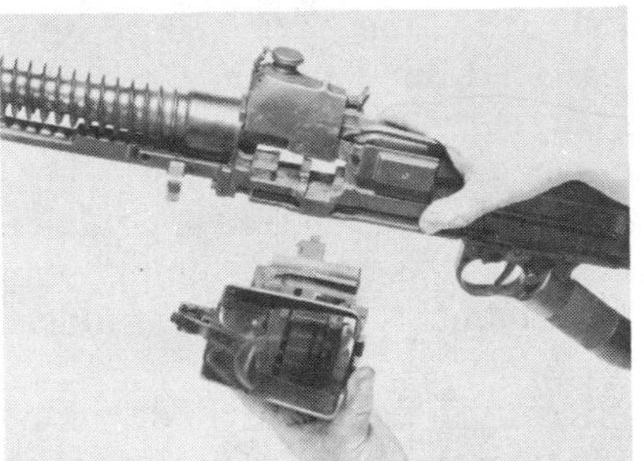

The housing pin mounted between the triggerguard and the receiver, just behind the trigger, may now be punched out from right to left. This permits the triggerguard group to be slid out the rear of the receiver on guides.

On the left to the rear of the gas piston screw is a lock plate, which when removed permits the barrel housing lock to be pushed out to the front. The barrel housing may now be unscrewed from the receiver.

How the Gun Works

Starting with the gun loaded and cocked, the action is as follows: The trigger moves the sear down against the tension of its spring, disengaging it from the slide. Driven forward by the recoil spring, the slide together with the bolt and bolt lock travel forward and the bolt drives the cartridge in the feedway into the chamber. The operating slide continues forward after the bolt is seated and cams a bolt lock down behind lugs on the sides of the receiver. Continuing forward it strikes the firing pin and drives it ahead to explode the cartridge.

Return Movement of the Action. The bullet travels down the barrel and gas passes into the gas port, thence to the cylinder below the barrel. This forces back the piston which is attached to the slide; and as they go back the slide cams the bolt lock up and the firing pin back in the face of the bolt, then draws the bolt and empty cartridge straight to the rear until the case strikes the ejector and is hurled out of the gun. The recoil spring is com-

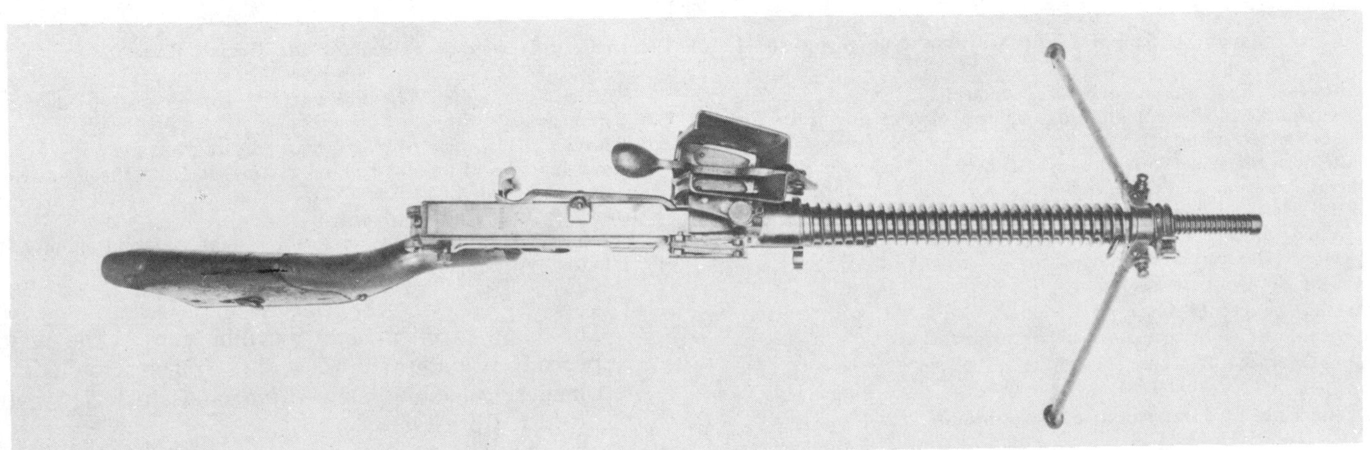

pressed and the bolt lock strikes against the buffer halting the rearward action.

During the rearward motion, an involved feeding mechanism cams the slide over to the right and permits racks to pull a round from a clip, position it in front of the bolt, and set it for the next feeding operation.

As cartridges feed into line, they operate an oil pump which oils each cartridge just before it is chambered; unlike better types of light machine guns, there is no period of slow extraction of the cartridge case. Hence oiling is necessary to keep the empty cartridges from sticking in the chamber under the sudden jerk of the extractor.

At the front end of the gas cylinder is a device fitted with five regulator holes which can be set to increase or decrease the amount of gas striking the piston.

Note: This gun has long been standard in the Japanese Army but is now rapidly being replaced by models resembling the British Bren gun, caliber 7.7mm (.303). The feed mechanism makes the gun entirely unreliable. Incidentally, this gun may occasionally be found with a tripod or an antiaircraft mount.

Loading and Firing

Caution. This gun fires from an open bolt and can be unloaded safely only by removing the hopper.

Lift the handle protruding through the slot in the rear end of the hopper and raise the cover attached to it as

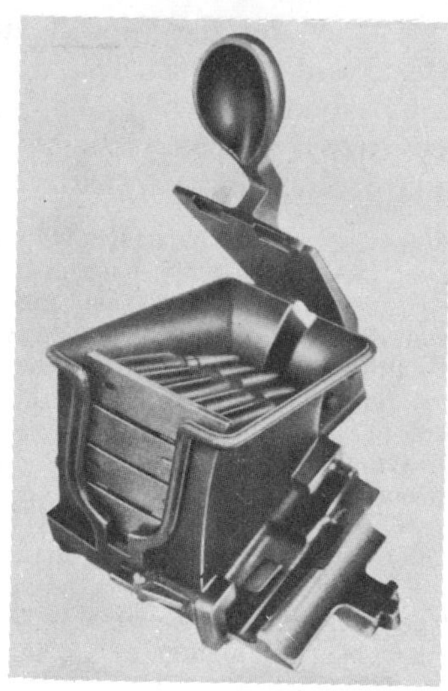

high as it will go. Place six loaded clips one on top of the other in the hopper and pull the lever down until the spring cover rests on top of the cartridges.

Pull the bolt handle back to the rear until it is cocked and held in open position. This not only cocks the gun but moves the feed slide over to the right.

Pressing the trigger will now permit the bolt to go forward, loading and firing the cartridge. This action will continue as long as the trigger is held back.

Japanese 6.5mm Light Machine Gun Type 96 (1936). Externally this weapon resembles the British Bren Gun.

Caliber: 6.5mm Japanese Service cartridge.
Magazine: Arc-shaped, mounted on top of gun as for Bren gun.
Capacity: 30 rounds.
Ballistics: Standard for these cartridges.
Barrel Length: About 22 inches.
Barrel Removal: Barrel catch on receiver in front of magazine. When turned, it frees the barrel which may then be pulled out of the receiver.
Weight of Gun: 20 pounds.
Overall Length of Gun: 41.5 inches.
Sights: Rear sight drum as for Bren gun.
Gun Operated By: Gas, Hotchkiss principle.
Cooled: Air. Very heavy barrel with outside cooling fins.
Cyclic Rate of Fire: About 600 per minute.
Position of Cocking Handle: Left side of receiver below line of magazine.
Safety: On left side of pistol grip ahead of trigger.
Mounting: Bipod attached about six inches from the muzzle. This may be folded.
Type of Fire: Full auto only.
Telescope: Has 2½-power telescope sight of good quality, prismatic type angled to right side.

Special Note

This is an excellent light machine gun. While in some respects it is patterned after the French Hotchkiss, its top magazine feeding, sight drum, and stock derive from the British Bren Gun.

This weapon has a lug to permit the use of a bayonet.

As in the case of the Bren gun, the top feeding requires that the sights be offset to clear the magazine and carrying handle. The receiver is machined to receive a telescopic sight of 2½ -power with range scale graduations from 100 to 1500 meters.

Field Stripping

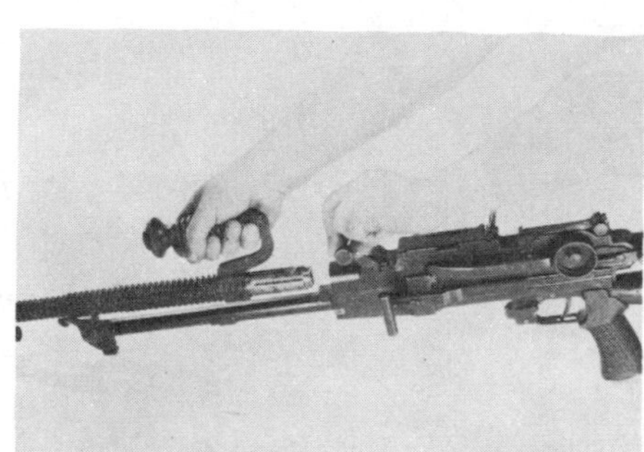

Turn barrel lever lock up to twist the attached locking bolt out of its slot in the barrel top. Push barrel forward out of engagement with the receiver and lift off.

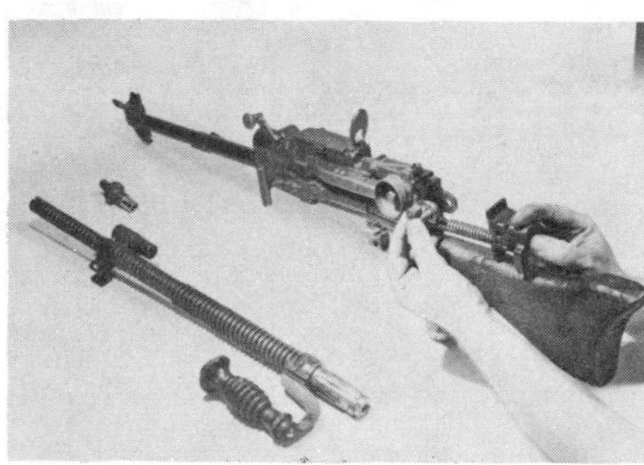

Revolve and pull out the buffer locking pin directly behind the sight drum from the left side of the receiver. This permits the buffer housing, guide and operating spring to be withdrawn from the rear.

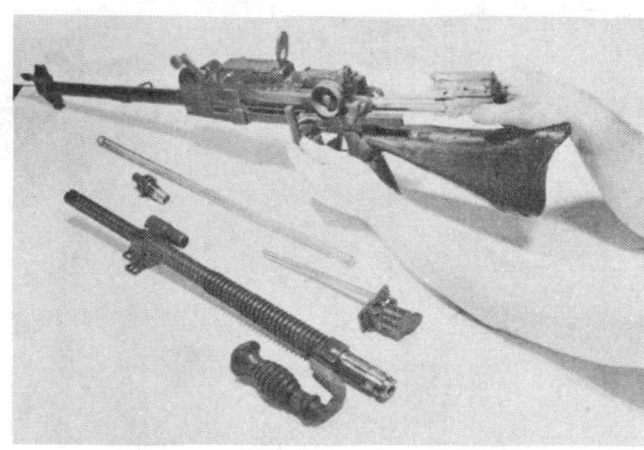

Pull back the bolt handle to bring the piston and bolt assembly back. Withdraw the bolt and piston.

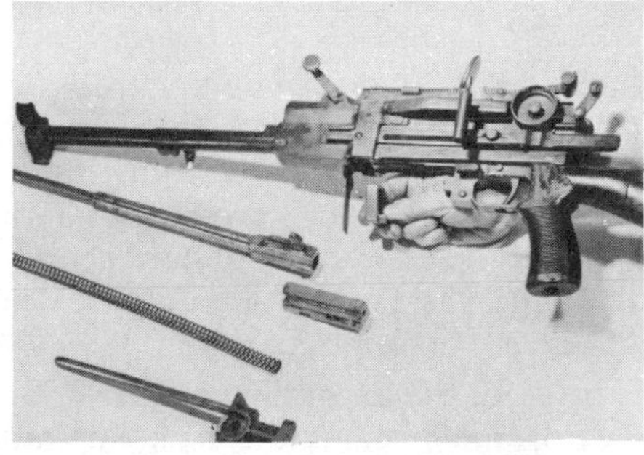

The bolt lock may now be removed through the bottom of the receiver.

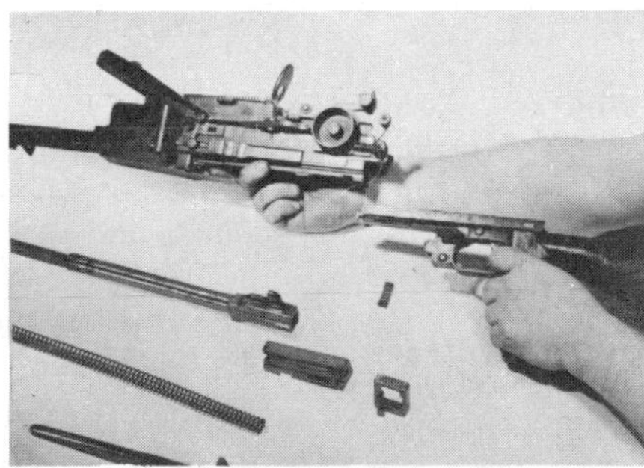

Remove the receiver locking pin and pull the butt assembly back out of the guides in the receiver.

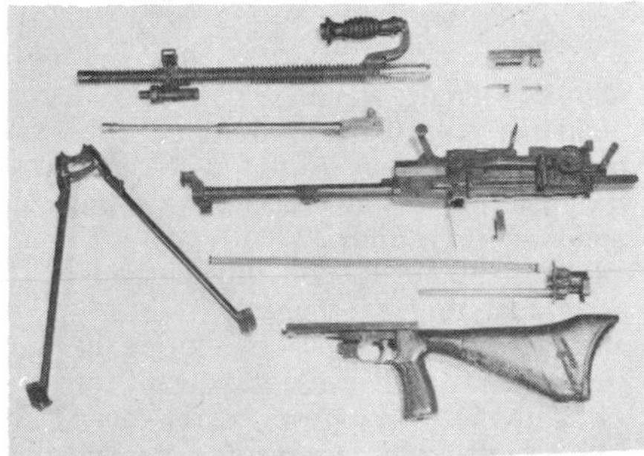

Bipod may be removed by turning the assembly 180 degrees to the right. Bolt may be lifted off its mounting on the piston and firing pin and extractor withdrawn.

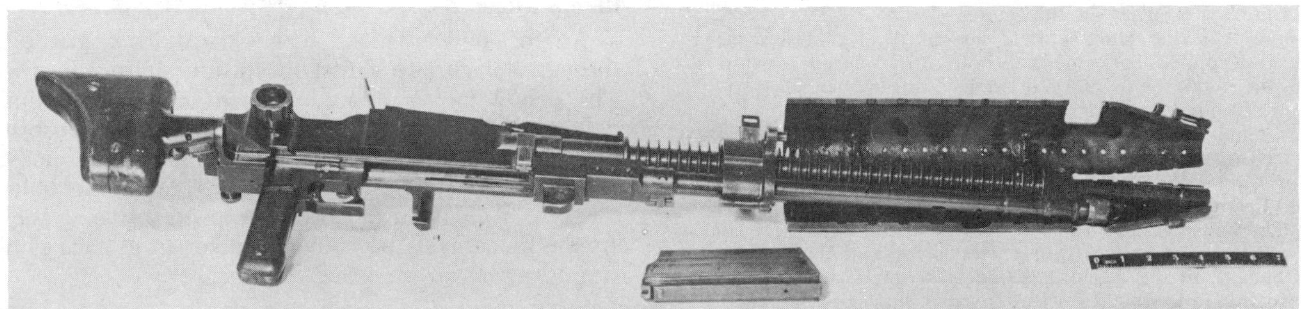

Japanese 7.7mm Tank Type 97 Machine Gun. Right side view with magazine withdrawn and protective shield open to show cooling rings. This weapon is a copy of the Czech ZB26.

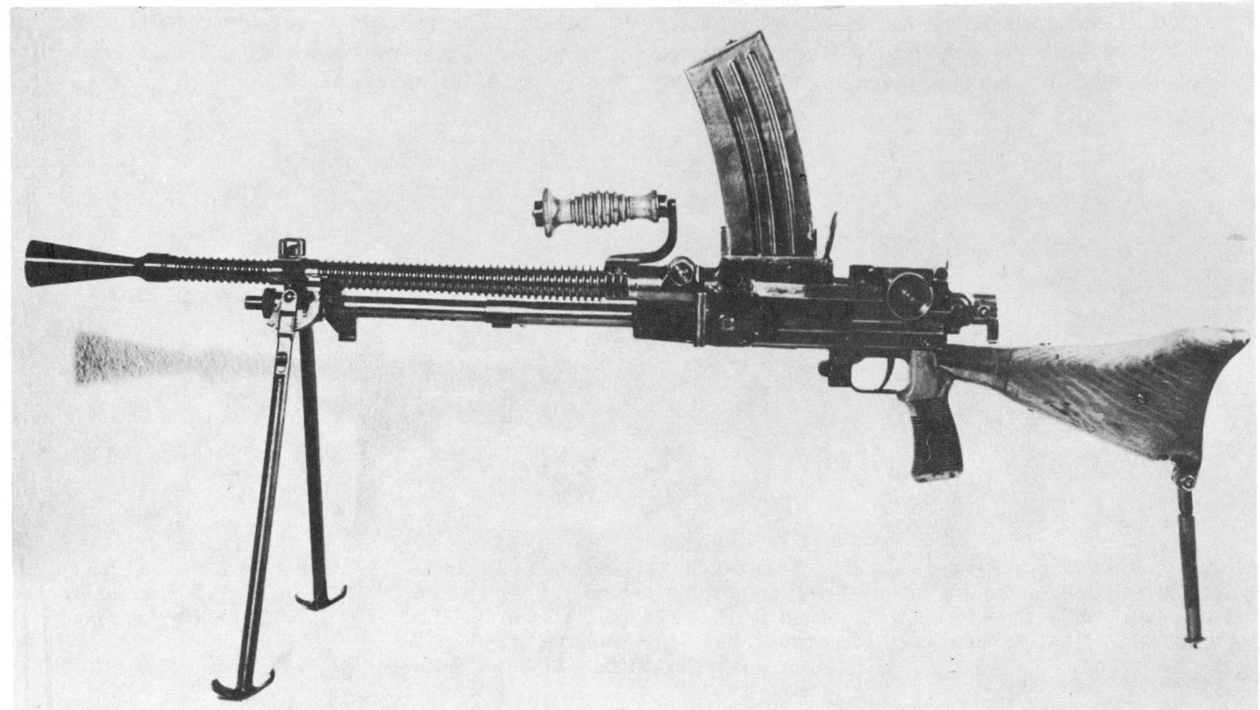

Japanese 7.7mm Light Machine Gun Type 99 (1939).

Caliber: 7.7mm Japanese Rimless Service Cartridge.
Magazine: Arc shaped, mounted Bren fashion on top of gun.
Magazine Opening: Fitted with a spring cover which must be opened to permit insertion of magazine.
Capacity: 30 rounds.
Ballistics: Standard for this cartridge.
Barrel Length: 2¾ inches.
Barrel Removal: Unscrew large hexagonal nut on left side just ahead of magazine and pull out to the left. This withdraws locking bolt from top barrel slot. Pushing forward on carrying handle will remove the barrel.
Weight of Gun: 20 pounds.
Overall Length: Approximately 42 inches.
Sights: Bren drum type, graduated 200 to 1500 meters. 10 points windage right or left.
Cooled: Air. Fins along entire barrel length. Weapon fires from an open bolt to permit air circulation between rounds.
Cyclic Rate of Fire: About 850 per minute with new type rimless 7.7mm ammunition. Note that HMG 7.7mm semirim will not function properly in this gun.
Position of Cocking Handle: Left side of receiver below magazine. It is pulled back to cock bolt, then pushed forward so bolt will not have to carry it on its firing thrust.
Safety: Left side of pistol grip ahead of trigger.
Bipod: Removable. Can be folded. Bayonet attachment also provided.
Type of Fire: Full automatic only.
Special Feature: Equipped to use 2½-power telescope sight. Graduations from 100 to 1500 meters are etched on the telescope reticule. A mil scale and circles for antiaircraft fire are also etched on the reticule. Scope is prismatic as required by necessity of allowing for offset to clear magazine mounted on top of receiver.
Carrying Handle: Attached to barrel on top. Also helps in barrel removal.

How This Gun Works

The locking system in these weapons is unique. The bolt rides on a lug on the rear of the gas piston and moves straight back and forth. It does not tip up as in the case of the Bren. The lock itself is a hollow square with cams cut on the upper rear and lower front inside edges; and it is raised and lowered in grooves cut into the front sidewalls of the receiver by action of corresponding cams on the rear of the gas piston. A safety device blocks the sear if the lock is not in place.

When the trigger is pressed, the expanding recoil spring drives the piston forward, and it cams the lock up into its locking slot which is cut into the bottom surface of the bolt. At this point the bolt is in its fully forward position, having stripped a cartridge from the magazine and chambered it. The slide is still free to move forward, however, until a tang on the firing pin hits the bolt lug and the pin is thrust through the firing pin hole to fire the cartridge.

As the bullet passes down the barrel, gas escapes through the port to thrust the piston sharply backwards. The piston moves about ¼ inch before unlocking the bolt, allowing time for the breech pressure to drop. The front surface of the firing pin tang strikes the lock and withdraws the firing pin from the face of the bolt; and the lock is cammed down by the piston, freeing the bolt. As the bolt travels back the extractor in its face pulls the empty case from the firing chamber.

When the piston is removed, the lock may be removed by opening the cover in the bottom of the receiver.

Note on Ammunition. All Japanese 6.5mm cartridges are self-rimmed. This type of 7.7mm machine gun uses rimless ammunition only! Both weapons require lubricated cartridges as there is no initial slow extraction and the cartridge cases are soft annealed.

Additional Notes

While these weapons have features closely resembling the British Bren and the Czech Brno guns, they are different.

The barrel change and locking systems merit special attention. On both the 1936 and the 1939 models there is a beveled, transverse cut across the rear top of the barrel.

In front of the receiver of the Type 96 (the 6.5mm caliber) there is a cross bolt with a clearance cut along its top surface. By revolving this cross bolt so the handle comes into top position, the barrel is immediately unlocked and can be removed to the front.

The barrel change on the Type 99 (the 7.7mm caliber) is similar, but a headspacing device is also incorporated —though its value is questionable. To remove this barrel it is necessary to unscrew the large hexagonal nut on the left side of the receiver and pull the bolt to the left. The barrel can then be drawn straight to the front.

Note that these barrels do not rotate, nor are they threaded!

The Type 99 is essentially the same as the Type 96 except that it is of 7.7mm (.303) caliber instead of 6.5mm (.256).

A monopod has been provided at the rear of the butt to support this weapon.

A flash hider screws on to the barrel.

The barrel retaining bolt screws forward to permit the bolt to be withdrawn for barrel removal; and can be screwed backward to adjust headspace. The magazine is necessarily of somewhat different shape than that of the Type 96.

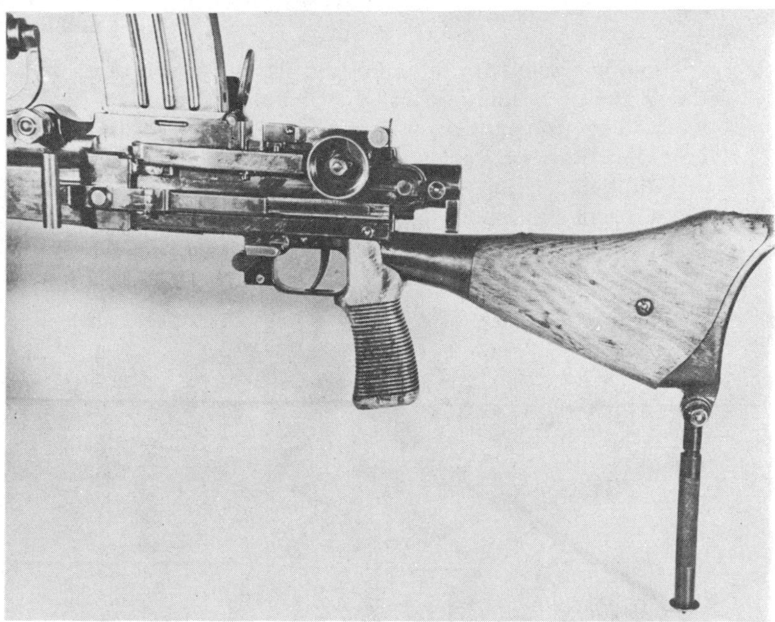

Special Features of Type 99. Note Monopod and Hexagonal Nut Barrel Release.

Workmanship in all samples of this gun studied was uniformly good. It must be rated as a good type of LMG.

Operation and Field Stripping. Same as for Type 96 LMG; except barrel removal as noted above.

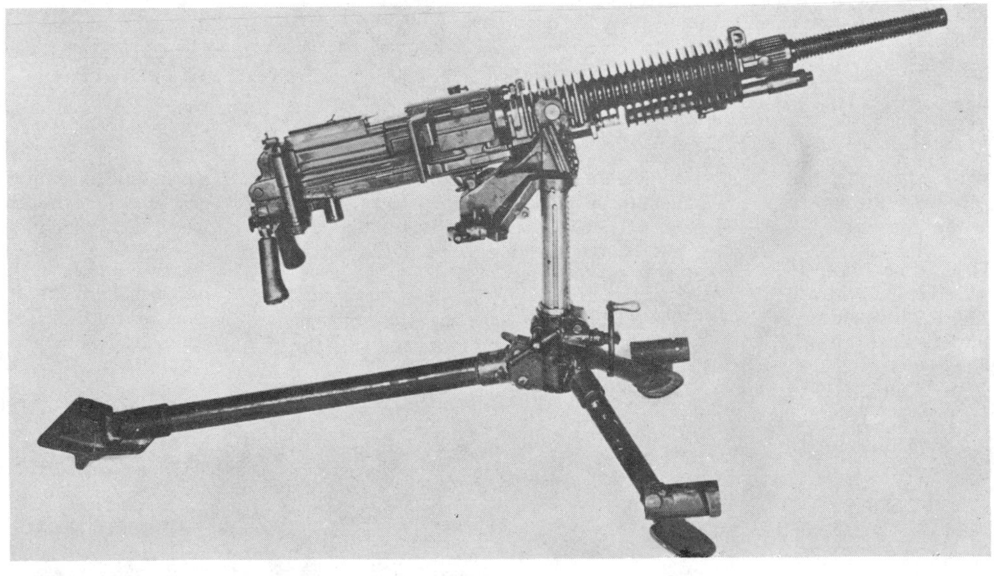

Japanese Heavy Machine Gun Type 92.

Caliber: 7.7mm semi-rimmed or rimless Jap.
Feed: Hotchkiss type strip, 30-round capacity. Fed from the left hand side.
Barrel Length: About 30″.
Overall Length of Gun: About 45″.
Weight of Gun: 61 pounds.
Gun Operated By: Gas, Hotchkiss principle.
Locked: Hotchkiss principle, slide camming down the bolt lock behind locking lugs on sides of receiver.
Cooled: Air. Barrel partly enclosed with a sheath of heavy radial cooling rings.
Cyclic Rate of Fire: About 450 rounds per minute.
Position of Cocking Handle: Right side of receiver. This gun fires from an open bolt.
Type of Fire: Has selector device, permitting single shot or full automatic fire.
Mounting: Tripod. Weight about 60 pounds. Has elevating and traversing gear.

Loading and Firing

Caution. Semi-rim ammunition is normally used in the 7.7mm version of this gun. Rimless cartridges will work. The rim cartridges definitely will not! Strips may be either brass or steel.

Pull the cocking handle as far as it will go to the rear. It will stay open.

Insert the end of the strip into the feedway until it pushes down the holding pawl which permits the bolt and slide to jump forward a short distance; the slide is caught and held by the sear.

Pressing in on the thumb piece of the trigger will now fire the gun.

Field Stripping

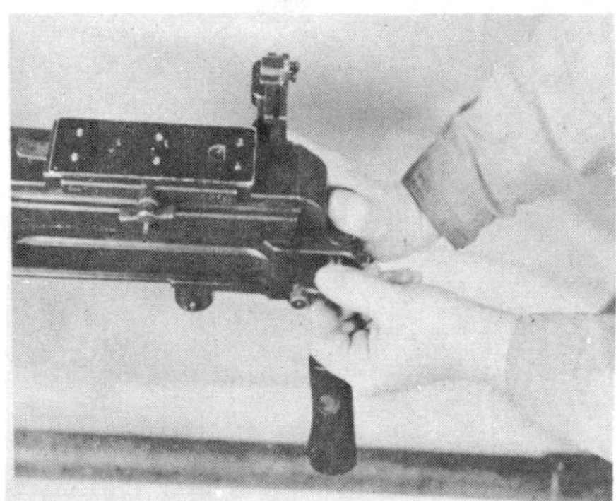

Turn the pin in the back plate down to a vertical position and pull it out.

The back plate group and heavy recoil spring may now be removed.

Pull the cocking handle back and it will bring with it the slide bolt, and bolt lock.

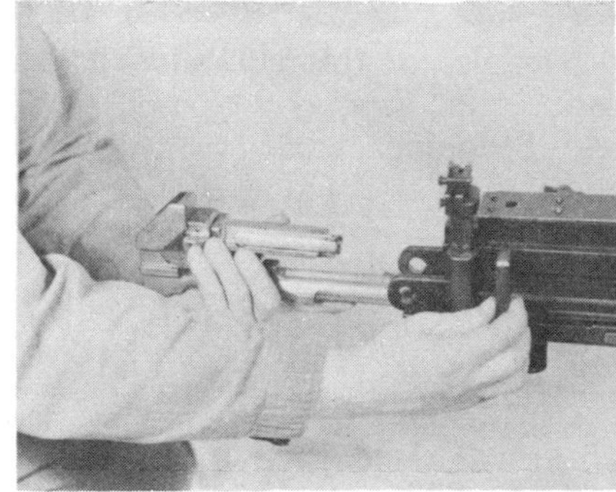

They may be removed when the bolt slide lugs are lined up with the openings for the slide on the receiver.

Cocking handle may now be removed from right side of receiver as shown. Like the light Nambu, this weapon is fitted with an oil pump device. This is mounted on the left side of the receiver and may be pushed forward to raise the rear of the oil device. Removing the screw below it will now permit removal of the oil device.

There is a cover over the gas jet near the forward bottom end of the gas cylinder; removing this permits the gas jet to be unscrewed and withdrawn from the barrel.

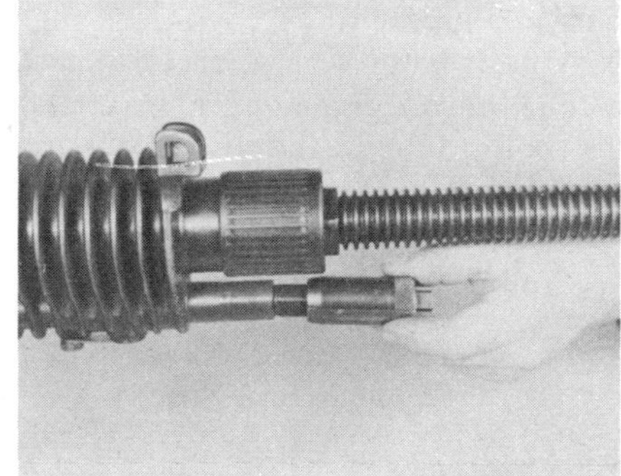

Now unscrew the barrel nut, which lies between the barrel and the jacket just above the forward end of the gas cylinder.

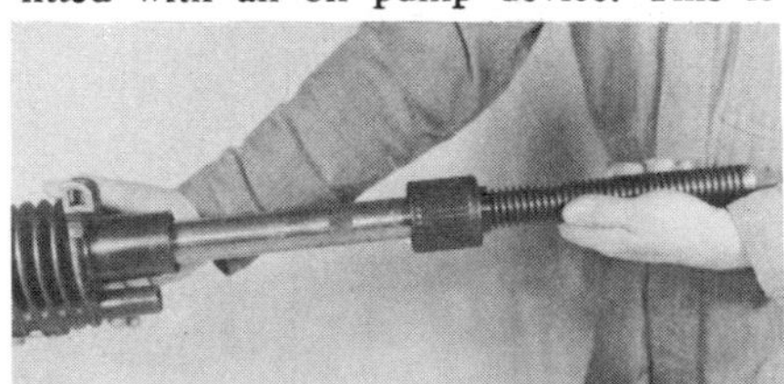

Give the barrel a half turn to the right. Barrel may now be pulled out and barrel sleeve withdrawn. At the bottom of the front of the feed box is a holding pin, which when rotated one-half turn may be pulled out to permit removing the holding pawl and its spring. Line up the marks on the slide with the marks on the feed box, and drive the slide pin out to the front. The feed slide may now be moved out to the left. This completes field stripping.

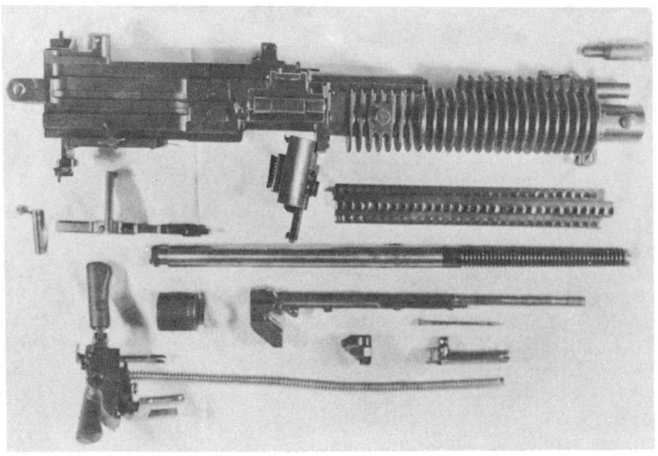

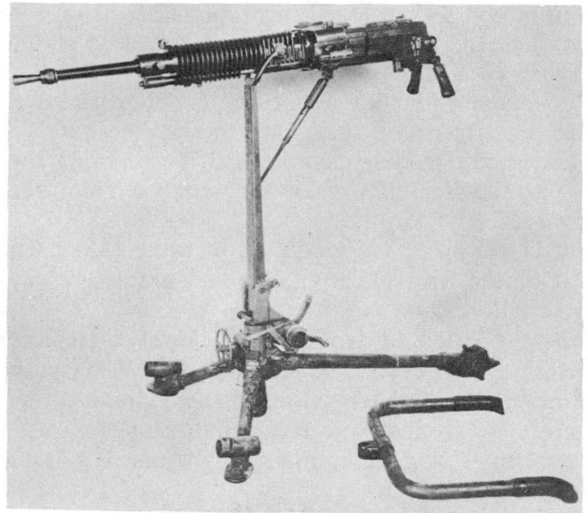

The Antiaircraft Adapter Used on This Weapon.

How the Gun Works

This gun follows the essential pattern of the French and British Hotchkiss gun. Starting with the gun loaded and cocked, the action is as follows: As the trigger is pressed, the slide is freed to be driven forward by the recoil spring. The slide carries with it the bolt and the bolt lock, and the bolt strips a cartridge from the cartridge strip and forces it ahead into the firing chamber. The slide continues to travel forward after the bolt is seated, and one of its surfaces cams the bolt lock down behind locking lugs on the inside of the receiver, thus firmly supporting the bolt. The slide continues its forward movement, and part of it strikes the firing pin driving it forward to explode the cartridge.

Return Movement of the Action. As the bullet passes over the gas port, a small portion of gas passing down through the port into the cylinder drives the piston attached to the slide back to the rear. The slide cams the bolt lock up, thereby unlocking the bolt to permit it to be carried back with the rest of the recoiling action. The bolt lock cams the firing pin back from the face of the bolt. The empty cartridge case, withdrawn by the extractor in the face of the bolt, strikes the ejector and is hurled from the gun through the ejection opening on the right side of the receiver. The recoil spring is compressed. A cam-groove on the front of the slide cams the feed slide out permitting the feed pawl to grasp the next cartridge. The cartridges as they are fed operate the oil device in the cover allowing a small amount of oil to come down on a brush which oils the cartridges as they are fed into the firing chamber. Finally the slide in its rearward motion strikes the buffer spring while the bolt lock strikes a buffer fork, and the remainder of the recoil is thus absorbed. The sear catches in its notch in the slide and holds it if the trigger has been released. If the trigger is held, the action repeats itself so long as cartridges are fed into the action.

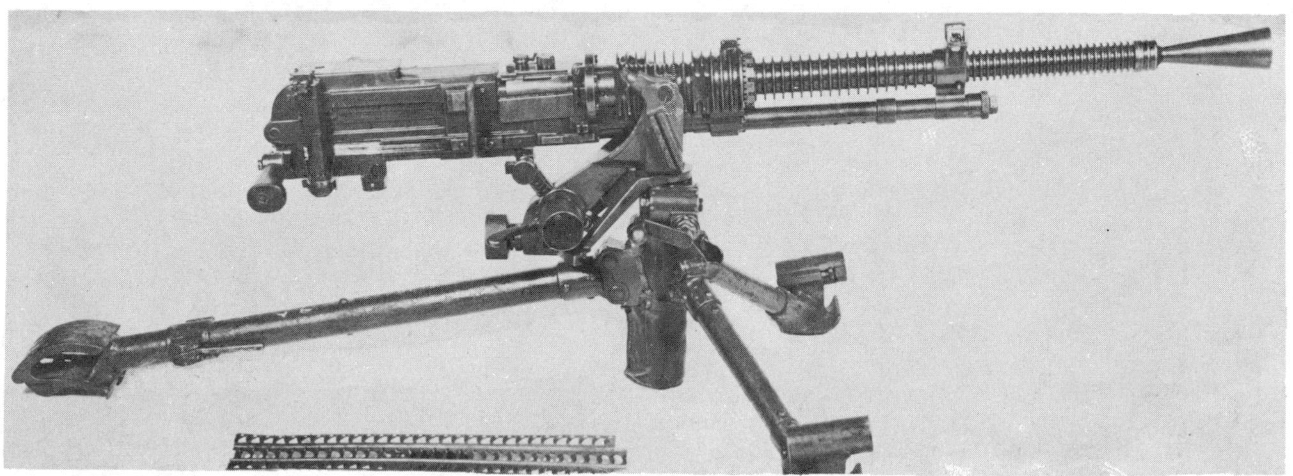

Japanese 7.7mm Heavy Machine Gun Type 01.
Standard cartridge clip which is fed into gun from left side is shown in the foreground.

This combines all the good features of its heavier Hotchkiss-type counterpart with the added features of lighter weight, simplified barrel removal, easy headspacing, and greater mobility.

This weapon resembles the standard Type 92 in general appearance but differs in being very much lighter. It uses only the Type 99 rimless cartridges.

The gun weighs 34 lbs. 2 oz.

The barrel weighs 11 lbs. 6 oz. and is 23¾ inches long; grooved 4 to the right. The gun may be quickly removed from the tripod by a simple clamp. The tripod has a very low silhouette and weighs 47 lbs.

The weight of the gun with tripod is about 82 lbs.

An improved gas adjustment system similar to that in the Jap 99 LMG is employed.

The gun may be loaded with the standard Type 92 rimless strips.

Field Stripping

Turn the locking pin at the extreme left rear of the receiver as far as it will go. Before removing it, be sure the bolt is fully forward as this gun fires from an open bolt and the mechanism is under heavy spring pressure when cocked.

Pull the retainer pin out and ease the backplate out of the receiver. The recoil spring will now come out.

Pull back on the cocking handle and it will bring the bolt and piston assemblies back for removal from the rear of the receiver.

Lift bolt assembly off its mounting on the slide which is attached to the piston. Firing pin and extractor may be removed if necessary.

Press locking catch at rear end of barrel to release adjusting collar. This collar (which is also the headspace adjuster) may be completely unscrewed and pulled forward slightly until it clears the receiver threads.

The barrel may now be drawn straight ahead out of the receiver.

Chapter 33. Mexico

MEXICAN PISTOLS

Mexican "Obregon System" Pistol cal. .45 A.C.P. (11.43mm). External Colt lines. Rotating barrel lock.

Right side view, Mexican Obregon Pistol. Has fewer parts than comparable Colt.

Caliber: .45 U.S. M1911 cartridges, ball ammunition.
Magazine: Standard box design, capacity 7 in magazine and 1 in chamber.
Ballistics: Standard for cartridge used.
Barrel Length: About 5 inches.
Overall Length: About 8½ inches.
Sights: Fixed front. Adjustable windage rear.
Pistol Operated By: Short recoil.
Locked: Rotating barrel, ribs on barrel engage in corresponding seats on top of receiver.
Type of Fire: Single shot only. Pistol has a disconnector to prevent full automatic fire.
Magazine Release Catch: Button on left side as in U.S. Service Automatic.
Safeties: (A) Grip safety automatically locks pistol except when gripped firmly for firing. Safety is purely mechanical. (B) Thumb safety positioned as in U.S. Service Automatic. Pushing it up locks slide and hammer positively. This is an applied safety. (C) Disconnector. Positively prevents pistol being fired until slide and barrel are completely locked. This is an automatic safety.
General Design: Externally this pistol very closely resembles the U.S. .45 Model 1911A1 automatic pistol. It has fewer parts and is of generally simpler construction in many respects.

The locking design is on the Obregon system, which differs radically from the Browning. As the slide moves to the rear, an unlocking cam on the underside of the barrel moves in the locking sleeve camcut causing the barrel to rotate after initial locked short travel with the slide, until its top lugs pass out of engagement with their locking slots in the underside of slide. There is, of course, no downward hinging movement of the barrel as in the Colt-Browning practice.

The functioning of the mechanism, except for the breech locking, is quite similar to that of the conventional Browning pattern. The locking system is a Steyr-Hahn variant.

This pistol was made for the Mexican Army in caliber 11.43mm (.45 Colt ACP). Its general manufacture and design are a credit to its national origin. The pistol has a slide stop to hold it open on the last shot.

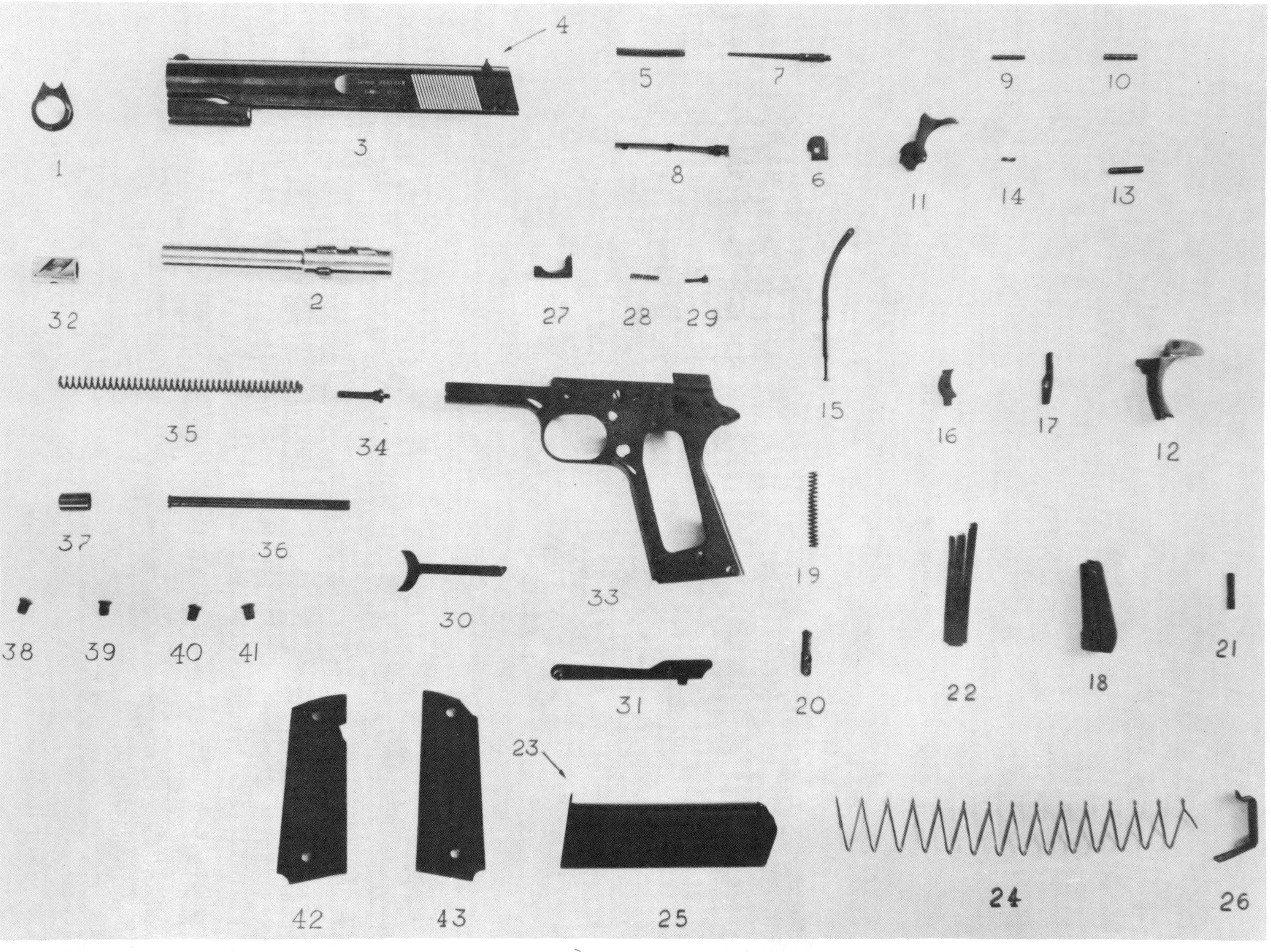

Component parts of Mexican Obregon Pistol. Note that barrel (2) rotates in sleeve (32) to unlock from and lock into slide.

MEXICAN RIFLES

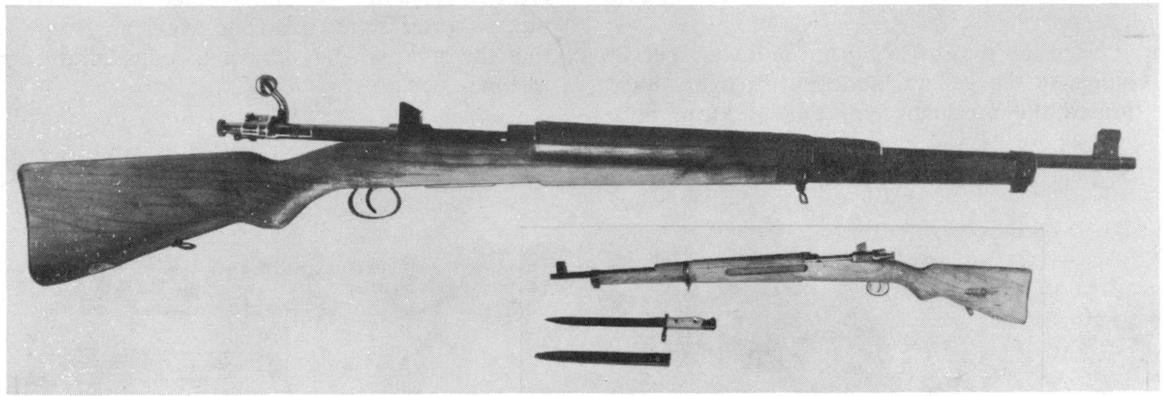

Mexican designed and manufactured service rifle, cal. .30-06 M1954. Composite Mauser and Springfield design. Insert shows left side and bayonet.

Caliber: .30-06, (U.S. M1 and M2).
Magazine: Staggered box type in receiver. Capacity five cartridges. Similar to Springfield.
Cartridge Clip: Holds five cartridges.
Ballistics: Standard for cartridge.
Barrel Length: 609mm.
Number of Lands and Grooves: Four.
Twist: One in 2.54cm.
Length of Rifle: 1405mm.
Weight of Rifle: 4 Kg's.

This rifle is quite similar in design and general appearance to the U.S. rifle Model 1903 (Springfield). It is a conventional turnbolt rifle with dual locking lugs in Mauser fashion at the forward end of the bolt as well as a rear locking lug.

The stock is of 3-ply wood construction to replace the conventional one-piece walnut design. It has a hand guard of Springfield design made of this plywood.

The magazine cutoff as found in the United States rifle has been eliminated. In effect this means that the rifle is not intended to be utilized with magazine held in reserve.

The bolt handle is shorter than the Springfield and curved somewhat to the rear.

The rear sight is a receiver pattern protected by heavy ears.

The mechanism is basically a minor variation of the standard Mauser design. The triggerguard assembly is a stamping to permit rapid production.

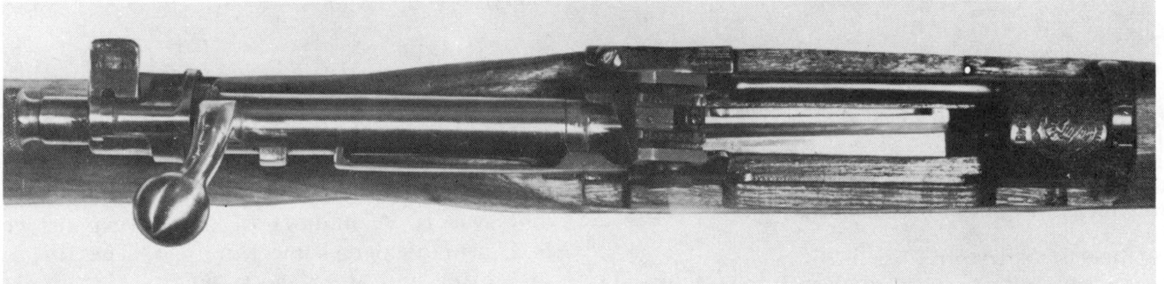

Upper—Top view, Mexican Service .30-06 rifle, bolt closed. Lower—Top view, action open.

Some 7,000 of these weapons have recently been issued to replace the 7mm Mauser patterns in use in the Mexican army.

While the design is praiseworthy in many respects, the current change to the general adoption of light automatic rifles limited the production of this Mexican bolt action design. The fact that the short .30 caliber cartridge is being generally adopted, and that it requires a very much shorter action than the Mexican rifle, also indicates that the rifle will be subject to considerable modification as time goes on.

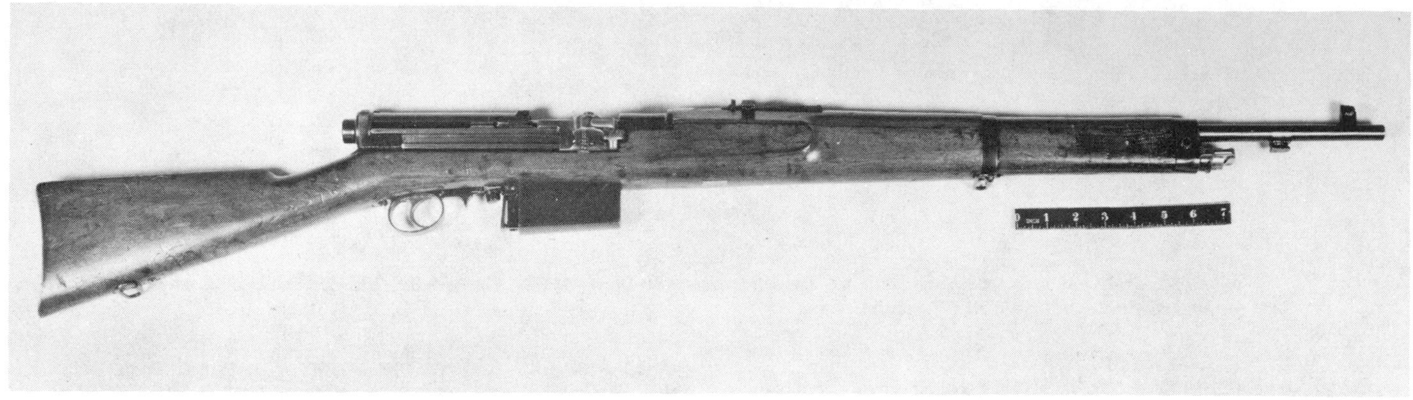

Mexican-designed 7mm M1908 Mondragon Semi-automatic Rifle. This rifle was produced by SIG in Switzerland and, as Model 1915, was used to a limited extent by the Germans in World War II.

One of the earliest reasonably successful semi-automatic rifles of military pattern was that invented by Mexican General Mondragon in 1908. Manufacture of the weapon, which was a gas-operated locked breech rifle, was undertaken in Switzerland at Neuhausen by Societe Industrielle Suisse. When World War I broke out, these rifles were shipped to Germany. They did not stand up well in trench service, but were among the earliest rifles issued to observers in aircraft before the introduction of the machine gun.

The Mondragon was gas operated from a port near the muzzle. The mechanism was actuated by the gas piston driven back by the expanding gas in the cylinder. While complicated and heavy by modern standards, the Mondragon was a very serious attempt at early semi-automatic rifle production.

Mexican 7mm M1936 Rifle

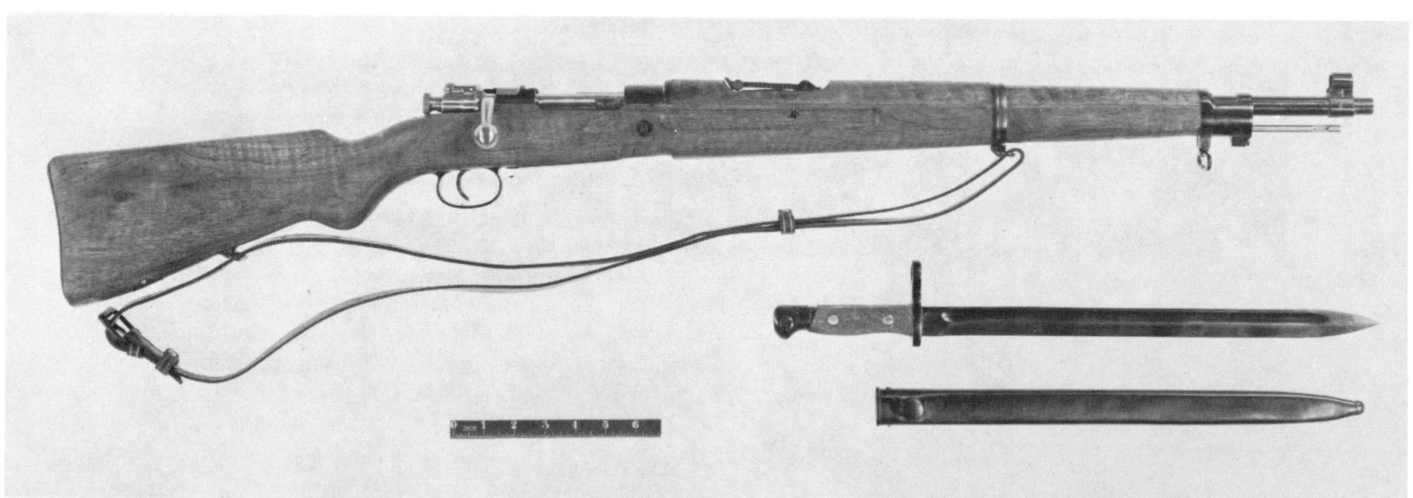

Caliber: 7mm.
System of Operation: Manually operated bolt action.
Weight: 8.3 lbs.
Length, Overall: 42.9 in.
Barrel Length: 19.29 in.
Feed Device: 5 round, staggered-row, non-detachable box magazine.
Sights: **Front**—Hooded barleycorn.
Rear—Tangent with V notch, graduated from 200-1500 meters.
Muzzle Velocity: Approx 2650 f.p.s.

This weapon is basically patterned on the Mauser 98 action; however it uses the knob type cocking piece of the U.S. Springfield M1903 and Springfield type bands and swivels. A number of these weapons were sold to U.S. arms dealers some time ago. The rifles were made in Mexico and are of good quality.

MEXICAN MACHINE GUNS

Mexican Mendoza Model RM-2. L.M.G. Cal. .30-06. Quick dismounting pattern but fixed barrel. One of the simplest of all gas designs.

This is a truly remarkable all-purpose light machine weapon which should receive the fullest attention from a design standpoint.

It has been made lighter than the original 7mm model and is an improvement over it in many ways.

Caliber: .30-06 U.S.
Method of Feed: Top mounted steel box magazine holding 20 cartridges.
Direction of Feed: Top of gun downward.
Muzzle Velocity: Standard for ammunition.
Overall Length of Gun: 1.10 meters.

RM-2. Left side view.

Barrel Length: 24 inches.
Weight of Gun: 6.4 kilos.
Cooling: By air. No special provisions.
Sights: Elevating rear, post front. Special receiver rear. Front sight positioned on gas regulator several inches back from muzzle.
Gun Operated By: Gas. Improved exhaust and piston system. Gas cylinder below barrel.
Locked: Rotary bolt, cam actuated by piston extension.
Cocking Handle: Right side of gun.
Type of Fire: Semi and full automatic through change lever.
Sight: Graduated to 1200 meters.
Cyclic Rate of Fire: About 600 per minute.
Stock: Wood. Forestock likewise.
Special Features: Bipod mount. Muzzle brake to offset climb. Fixed barrel, improved takedown.

A study of the detailed photographs accompanying this descriptive matter will show the clean lines and several of the important features of this Mendoza design.

This weapon is far simpler than the original Mendoza.

Mendoza L.M.G. model RM-2. Hinged open for quick withdrawal of all operating parts. Magazine shown detached. Except for the fact that it does not have the quick-change barrel of the earlier Mendoza 7mm, this new design is superior.

It has been especially designed for easy and low cost manufacture.

While it does not have the quick removal barrel feature of the earlier model, it stresses a very simple, rapid and effective takedown. Pressing the release catch at the rear of the receiver allows the gun to be broken on its hinge much in the manner of the Belgian F. N.

Automatic Rifle. The gas piston and slide with recoil spring and the few operating components may be withdrawn from the rear of the gun. The unusual Mendoza feature of reversible firing pin again appears in this new design but in improved form. In the event of firing pin breakage in the field (a relatively weak point in any full firing machine weapon) merely dropping the rear of the gun will allow the mechanism to be drawn back far enough to lift the bolt off the piston slide. The firing pin has a firing point at each end. If one should be broken, merely withdrawing and reversing the pin and reinstalling it in the bolt prepares the gun for firing again.

Mexican RM-2. Field stripped to show simplicity of design.

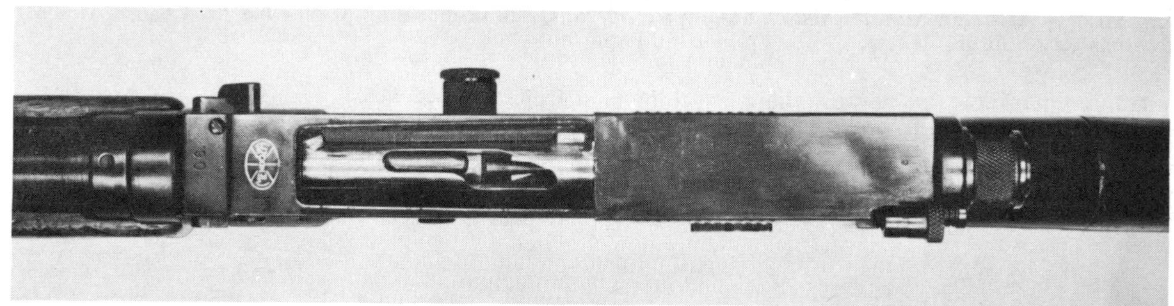

Top view of Mexican RM-2 with magazine removed and action closed.

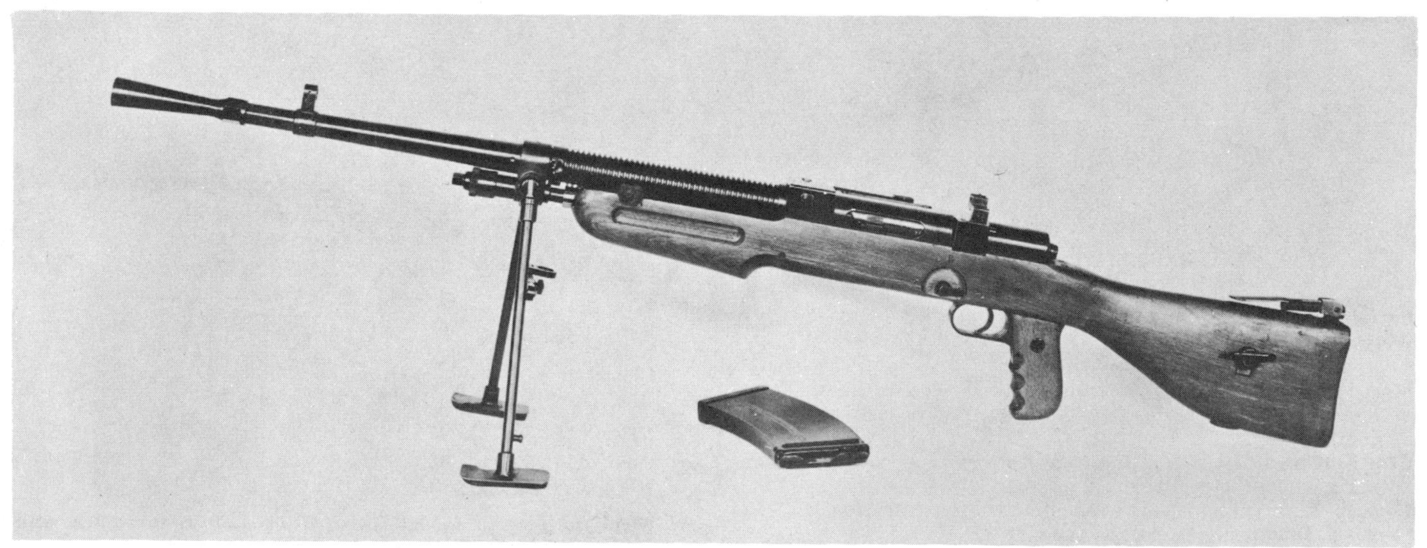

Mendoza 7mm Light Machine Gun.

Caliber: 7mm Mexican Army.
Magazine: Box type, on top of receiver as in the Bren gun.
Capacity: 20 rounds.
Overall Length: 46″.
Weight: 18½ lbs.
Gun Operated By: Gas. Gas escaping through hole in under side of barrel through gas vent into cylinder drives piston back as in the case of the Hotchkiss guns.
Locked: By turning bolt as in Lewis. As piston is driven to the rear by escaping gas, bolt is turned out of locking position by cam arm operating in a curve in the body of the bolt.
Cooled: Air cooled. Has radial fins on rear of barrel. Bolt stays open between shots.
Cyclic Rate of Fire: 500 rounds per minute.
Position of Cocking Handle: On left side of gun near the front of the fore-end. It is a small bar which when pulled directly to the rear cocks the gun.
Type of Fire: Full or semi-automatic. Change lever on left side

of gun, above and in front of the triggerguard.

Flash Hider: Gun is fitted with a conventional bellmouth type flash hider extending from the barrel.

Mounted: Simple bipod mount is normally used. Special anti-aircraft and tank mounts are also provided.

While this gun was not in wide production, it is worthy of attention because of the remarkably fine design and the excellence of manufacture. It was the official light machine gun of the Mexican army and was invented by the famous Mexican arms authority, after whom it is named. Like the Bren gun, the barrel in the Mendoza may be removed easily. The barrel lock is on the right side of the receiver. When it is pulled out it disengages locking lugs from slots in the barrel, permitting the barrel to be pulled forward from the front as in the case of the Bren.

This weapon does not have a conventional gas cylinder. Gas passing through a gas tube is trapped in a cup shaped piston head as in the Russian Degtyarev. The piston head surrounds the rear end of the gas tube. As the piston is thrust back by the escaping gas on the barrel, it revolves the bolt much as in the Lewis gun, unlocking the weapon and permitting the bolt to travel straight to the rear with the piston. This action also compresses the recoil spring.

The gun has a pistol grip notched for the fingers and has a butt-strap similar to that of the Bren gun.

Chapter 34. The Netherlands

The Dutch used U. S. and British weapons for the most part. The 9mm Browning Hi Power is the current service pistol. The Netherlands has recently adopted the F. N. light automatic rifle in 7.62mm NATO caliber. The Israeli-designed 9mm Uzi submachine gun has also been adopted.

The U.S.-designed Armalite AR-10 rifle was formerly made at Artillerie Inrichtingen but is no longer in production.

Model 95 Service Rifle.

Caliber: 6.5mm (.256) rimmed.
Barrel Length: 31.12″.
Overall Length: 51″.
Weight: 9.25 lbs.
Sights: Barleycorn front and V ramp rear. Rear adjustable 400-2000 m.
Operation: Bolt is turned up and pulled back to open action. Loaded 5 shot clip is inserted and action closed.
Magazine: Mannlicher vertical fixed box. Loaded clip forms part of magazine action. Pressing clip catch when action is open will permit magazine follower to expel clip and cartridges at any time.

When last cartridge has been chambered, magazine follower rides up between clip sides. Clip is held only from above by clip catch, hence empty clip falls out bottom recess in magazine.
Carbines: Mechanically the same.
Safety: Positive thumb piece at rear of bolt.
Bolt Release: Pivoted arm at left rear of receiver. Holding it in at rear permits bolt to be withdrawn.
Note: Sights vary. Some models have adjustments 300-2000 meters.
Special Note on Carbines: There are four major variants of these carbines, differing in types of stocks and positions of slings.

F.N. 7.62mm NATO Light Automatic Rifle, as made for the Netherlands. Note the bipod and metal handguards.

Chapter 35. Norway

The Norwegian Army is currently supplied mainly with U. S. small arms.

NORWEGIAN PISTOLS

Norwegian Caliber .45 Model 1914 Automatic Pistol.

This weapon differs only in minor details from the U. S. M1911 Colt automatic pistol.

NORWEGIAN RIFLES AND CARBINES

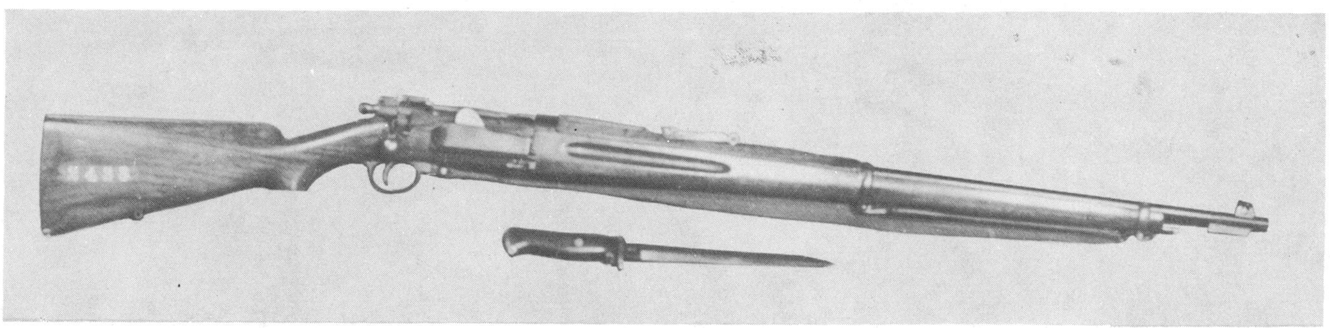

Krag-Jorgensen Rifle.

The original 1894 Model Krag-Jorgensen has gone through numerous minor modifications, all of which are superficial. Mechanically there is very little variation.

The magazine loading gate is turned out to the right to load. The cocking piece has a knob to permit cocking without opening the action in case of a misfire. The Norwegian bolt safety is an adaptation of the common Mauser design.

The caliber is 6.5mm rimless. The cartridge was originally round nosed, but when Germany changed to the Spitzer bullet Norway developed a similar type for her rifles.

Characteristics. Turning bolt action with single front locking lug. No magazine cutoff. Fixed box magazine loaded through right side of action when loading gate is hinged down. No formal bolt stop; locking lug hits a receiver surface at end of travel. (See chapter 21 for method of removing bolt.) Mauser type bolt safety. Magazine capacity five cartridges, normally loaded by insertion of single cartridge. A special type of loading clip was discarded because of clumsiness.

Following is a list of modifications:

Model 1894. Length 49.7″. Barrel 30″. Weight 8.82 lbs. Sights 100-2200 meters. U-rear, barleycorn front. (Model for round nose early bullet ammunition.)

There were also Models 1906, 1923, and 1925.

Model 1930. This is stocked in sporting style about half the length of the barrel. One band and adjustable sling. Special receiver peep and hooded front sights are standard. Sight adjustment in 100-1000 meters.

Length 48.8″. Barrel 29.25″. Weight 11.46 lbs.

This is a sharpshooter's rifle issued for special mountain service. (It was also sold commercially as a hunting rifle.)

Carbine Model 12 Caliber 6.5mm.

MODEL 95 KAR. Length 39.58″. Barrel 20.3″. Weight 7.5 lbs. Half stock.

MODEL 04 KAR. Length 40″. Barrel 20.3″. Weight 8.4 lbs. Stocked almost to muzzle. Carrying sling under forestock to triggerguard.

MODEL 07 KAR. Length 40″. Barrel 20.3″. Weight 8.38 lbs. Same as above except sling from left side of rear band to underside of butt.

MODEL 12 KAR. Length 43.17″. Barrel 23.82″. Weight 8.82 lbs. Same as Model 07 except for full stock and handguard with reinforcing band. This weapon is currently being sold in the U.S.A.

Evaluation of Rifles and Carbines. Excellent materials and good workmanship. While the protruding magazine gate and the single locking lug are points of criticism, the design is still highly regarded by many practical hunters. The single locking lug has proven in scientific tests to be entirely capable of taking any pressure its cartridge normally develops. Pressures should probably be held around 40,000 lbs.

Identification. Horizontal box magazine with gate swinging to right. Mauser type safety. Single forward locking lug. 6.5mm caliber.

Ammunition. 6.5mm by 55mm Norwegian.

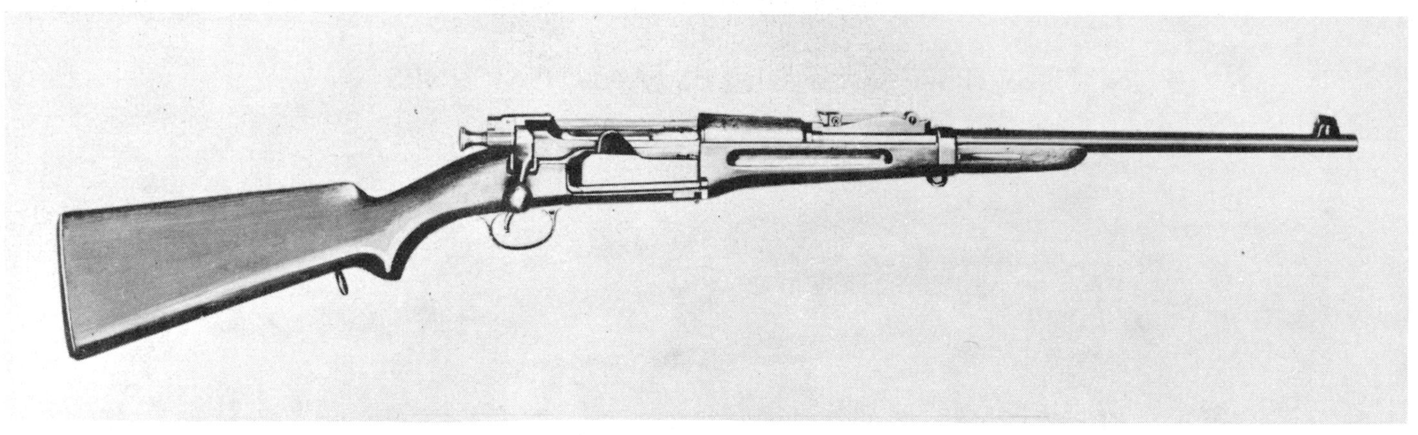

Norwegian 6.5mm Model 1895 Carbine.

Chapter 36. Poland

At the conclusion of World War II, the Poles found themselves stripped of weapons except for some left behind by, or seized from, the defeated German armies. More important, they found themselves behind the Iron Curtain. This geographical and political fact has determined the nature of Polish small arms activities since World War II. The postwar Polish Army was originally equipped with Soviet World War II weapons; many of these weapons, such as the Tokarev M1933 pistol, were put into production in Poland. No native Polish designs have appeared, except for a Polish-produced modification of the Soviet PPS M1943 submachine gun.

Within the past several years, however, Polish troops are being equipped with the postwar family of Soviet weapons. Photographs in magazines show Polish troops with the Soviet 7.62mm AK, SKS, RPD, and RP-46, and 14.5mm ZPU-series weapons. The Polish Army is standardized on Soviet weapons.

POLISH PISTOLS

Polish Pistol Model 35.

This pistol is popularly known as the Radom, after the arsenal where it was built.

Caliber: 9mm Luger cartridge.
Magazine: Colt type detachable box. Single line. Side button release.
Magazine Capacity: 8 cartridges.
Barrel Length: 4.75″.
Overall Length: 7.75″.
Weight: 29 oz.
Sights: Fixed. Mounted on slide.
Pistol Operated By: Recoil.
Locked: Browning HP type. Barrel has upper ribs which engage in corresponding cuts in roof of slide. Instead of Colt-type

swinging barrel link, a nose is forged on the underside of the barrel. Barrel and slide recoil locked together until bullet is out of barrel. Barrel hits stop in receiver and its rear end is forced down as a cam surface on the barrel nose is forced down into a receiver cut. Slide then continues to rear to eject. On forward motion barrel is forced up into locking engagement with slide.

Type of Fire: Single shot only. Positive disconnector prevents more than one shot for each pull of trigger.

Safeties: Colt type grip safety on early models. This type can be fired only when pistol is held firmly in shooting hand.

Note: On many late modifications the safety was dispensed with in order to speed up manufacture.

Hammer Release: On early models a thumb piece on the slide can be used to lower the hammer on a loaded chamber in complete safety. Pushing the release down first brings a steel block between the hammer and the firing pin and then trips the sear to drop the hammer.

The falling hammer hits the steel safety surface harmlessly. The release has a spring which returns it to ready position when pressure is released on it.

Note: Some late modifications do not have this hammer drop device.

Special Feature: Thumb piece on left of receiver looks like Colt manual safety but is actually used only to lock slide back for dismounting.

Note: This slide lock is not used on many late modifications.

Slide Stop: As in Colt Govt. Auto, its pin locks barrel nose to receiver. When magazine is empty, rising magazine follower forces stop up into engagement to hold slide back.

Loading and Firing: Same as for Colt Govt. Auto.

Identification of Polish Model 35 Types: Recoil spring guide rod protrudes through front of slide when slide is pulled back. Nose on underside of barrel below chamber and locking ribs on upper barrel surface.

Evaluation: Early models well made of excellent materials. Late models vary with time of manufacture, some good and some fair. Pistol is heavy for caliber. Recoil comparatively light. The design being Browning is essentially very good, but late modifications may jam from sloppy fitting. This is one of the best Browning types ever made.

Ammunition: 9mm Luger ammunition as made in U. S. This pistol when in good order is husky enough for any 9mm load ordinarily found.

Field Stripping

When pistol has slide lock, force slide back until lock can be pushed up to engage in slide cut. Remove magazine.

If the pistol does not have slide lock, first remove magazine; then pull slide back slowly with thumb pressing on hammer release which is mounted on the slide. Notch on top of hammer will engage slide and hold it to the rear. The dismounting notch in the slide will be lined up with the slide stop and the slide stop can be removed by pushing in the pin end (right side of pistol). Pull slide to rear and slowly let it forward; slide, barrel, and recoil spring can then be removed.

If pistol has slide lock, remove slide stop, then release lock and ease barrel and slide assemblies forward out of receiver guides.

Remove recoil spring and the guide to which it is assembled from rear of slide.

Lift barrel by barrel nose to free lugs from slide and withdraw from rear of slide.

FORMER POLISH RIFLES AND CARBINES

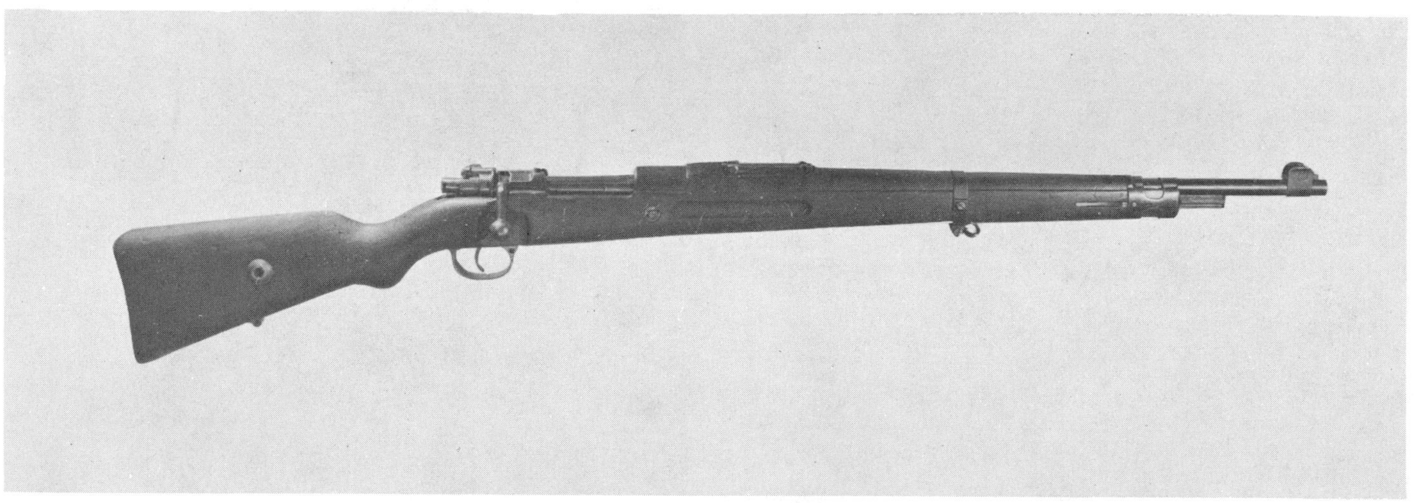

Polish M. 1929 Rifle. This was the most advanced Polish manufactured Mauser. Except for minor stock, sling, and front sight variations, it is the same as the German Kar. 98 Caliber 7.9mm.

Former Polish rifles are based on the German Mauser systems, the caliber being the standard German 7.9mm.

Rifles usually bear the name of the arsenal, either Warszawa or Radom. In general the Warszawa manufacture is based on the German Gew. 98 and the Kar. 98a. In general the Radom manufacture is based on the later German Kar. 98k system. (See chapter 27.) The date of manufacture is customarily found on the top of the receiver ring also.

In 1925 Poland converted a large number of Russian M91 short rifles to caliber 7.9mm.

The following is the official Polish list of rifles and carbines in order of appearance:

POLISH GEW. 98a. This is the same as the German Gew. 98, except for sight graduations.

Length 49.5″. Barrel 29.05″. Weight 9 lbs.

POLISH KAR. 98a. Same as German Kar. 98b of War II. Bolt handle turned down, and stock inlet for the handle.
Length 43″. Barrel 23.4″. Weight 8.6 lbs.

POLISH 91/98/25. The figures indicate the (Russian) M91 system converted to the M98 (German) cartridge in the year 1925. Note that this is a Russian Mosin turn bolt action, not a Mauser type.
Length 42.9″. Barrel 23.4″. Weight 8.16 lbs.

POLISH KAR. 29. This model has the improvements as found in the German Kar. 98k, except that the fore-stock has finger grooves, bolt handle is straight, and slings are on underside.
Length 42.9″. Barrel 23.4″. Weight 8.82 lbs.

Evaluation of Polish Mauser Type Rifles. Early types are all to German Mauser specifications. Late types are generally made to German Kar. 98k mechanical specifications as developed by German Ordnance and made by F. N. in Belgium and CZ in Czechoslovakia.

Not as well finished as average F. N., CZ, or German Mauser.

Ammunition. 7.9mm German Service (8mm Mauser ammunition made in U. S.).

POLISH SUBMACHINE GUN

Polish 7.62mm M1943/52 Submachine Gun.

Although the M1943/52 will probably be replaced by the Soviet AK, it is included here as a matter of interest. The M1943/52 submachine gun is a modification of the Soviet PPS M1943. Its characteristics are basically the same as those of the Soviet weapon, except that it has a wooden stock and is reportedly capable of semi-automatic as well as automatic fire.

System of Operation: Blowback, selective fire.
Length, Overall: 32.72 in.
Barrel Length: 9.45 in.
Feed Device: 35-round, detachable staggered box magazine.
Sights, Front: Flat-topped post, adjustable for elevation and windage.
Rear: L-type, open V-notch with setting for 100 and 200 meters.
Muzzle Velocity: 1640 f.p.s. w/Soviet 7.62mm Type P pistol cartridge.
Cyclic Rate: 600 r.p.m.
Weight: 8 lb.

Special Note on the Polish M1943/52

Loading, firing, functioning, and disassembly of this weapon are the same as for the Soviet 7.62mm submachine gun PPS M1943.

Chapter 37. Portugal

During the period preceding World War II, and during the war itself, Portugal procured a large number of different types of small arms from Germany and Great Britain. There were still some quantities of the older Portuguese weapons in service as well. As a result Portugal holds a somewhat varied collection of small arms in various calibers.

Among the weapons used by Portugal are the following:

Pistols: 7.65mm Savage M908 and M915 9mm M/43 Parabellum (Luger) 9mm M/908 Parabellum (Luger).

Rifles: 7.92mm Mauser M937 (same as Kar. 98k).

Cal. 303 Lee Enfield M917 (same as SMLE MkIII and III*).

Portugal has adopted the German G3 (CETME) assault rifle in 7.62mm NATO caliber as standard. The Portuguese call this weapon, Rifle 7.62mm M/961.

Submachine Guns: 9mm M1934 Bergmann, 9mm M43 (Sten), 9mm Model 48 F.B.P., 9mm M42 (Schmeisser).

Machine Guns: Cal. .303 Lewis M917 (same as British M1915 Lewis)

Cal. .303 Vickers M917 (same as British MK 1 Vickers)

7.92mm Breda M938 (Breda M1937 in 7.92mm)

7.92 Madsen M940

Cal. .303 M/931 (Vickers Berthier)

7.92mm Dreyse M938 (same as German MG 13)

Cal. .303 M/43 (Bren)

Cal. .303 M/930 (Madsen).

PORTUGUESE PISTOLS

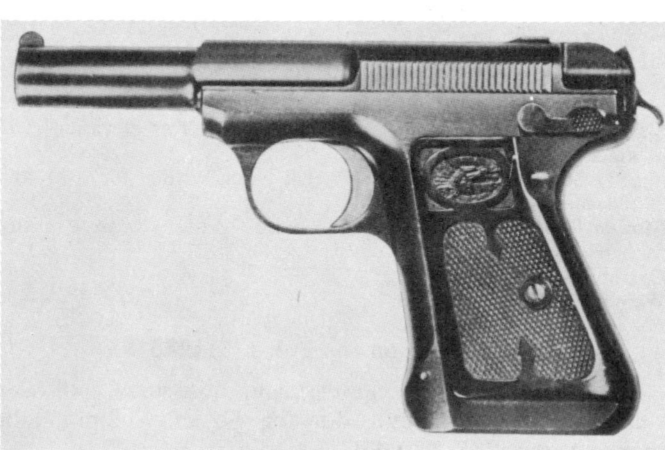

Model 915 Pistol.

Caliber: .32 Colt Auto (7.65mm).

Magazine: Double line staggered box. Detachable. Magazine release in front of grip at lower edge. Capacity 9 cartridges.

Barrel Length: 4.49″.

Overall Length: 7″.

Weight: 24.1 oz.

Sights: Part of slide.

Pistol Operated By: Delayed blowback.

Breech: Opening delayed slightly by barrel which turns slightly. A lug on barrel is engaged in a cam groove in the top of the slide when pistol is closed.

When barrel has been turned out of slide engagement, slide and breechblock assemblies travel back to eject.

Slide: Cylindrical type to enclose barrel. Recoil spring is mounted around barrel under slide.

Breechblock: A separate unit joined to slide by interrupted rings.

Firing Mechanism: Striker type of unusual design. Striker is drawn back and cocked during rearward slide movement when an attached under-lever is forced up as it is pushed back over the inner grip surface.

Manual Safety: Thumb lever on left side of receiver. If slide is held back, turning the safety up will lock the slide open.

Warning: This pistol has an exposed cocking indicator resembling a hammer. Actually it is not a hammer. It must never be lowered on a loaded chamber. When this cocking piece is down, the firing pin is resting on the primer if there is a cartridge in the chamber.

Type of Fire: Single shot.

Note: The striker and sear release mechanism is extremely delicate and lends itself to dangerous full automatic fire.

Loading and Firing: Standard for pocket type auto pistols.

Identification: Double line magazine. Separate breechblock. Turning barrel with cam lug working in roof of slide.

Evaluation: Well made of best materials. Good grip. Excellent pointing. Light weight. Large magazine capacity for caliber. Weak sear device. Pistol subject to uncontrolled fire if not properly cared for or in case of wear of small parts. No longer manufactured.

Ammunition: .32 Colt Auto.

Field Stripping

Press bottom catch and remove magazine.

Push slide back and while holding it to the rear turn up thumb safety. This will hold slide locked to the rear.

Press in striker cocking lever and twist breechblock to right. Withdraw breechblock.

Hold slide under control and press down safety catch. Ease slide and recoil spring forward off receiver.

Lift out barrel.

If trigger and sear mechanism is lifted out, be careful not to lose parts or spring.

PORTUGUESE RIFLES AND CARBINES

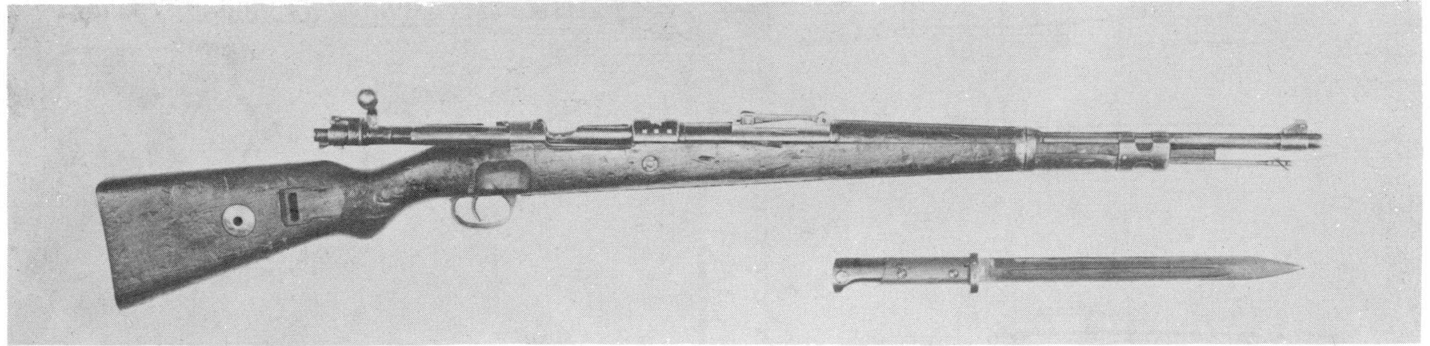

Portuguese Mauser 7.9mm Model 937. This is the same as the German Kar. 98k in all details including caliber 7.9mm.

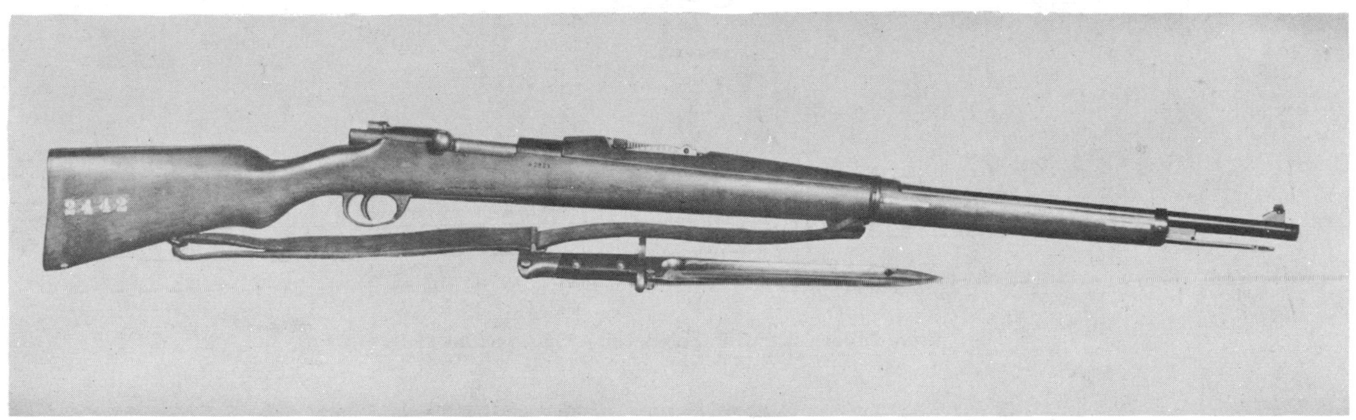

Model 1904 Mauser-Verguiero. Cal. 6.5mm. Note that bolt handle locks down in front of split receiver bridge as in Mannlicher turn bolt practice.

Caliber: 6.5mm Portuguese (.256).
Magazine: Mauser type double line staggered box. Capacity 5 rounds.
Barrel Length: 29.08″.
Overall Length: 48″.
Weight: 8.8 lbs.
Magazine Cut-Off: None.
Locked: Modified Mauser system with some Mannlicher features. Has bolt with dual opposed lugs which lock into seats in receiver ring; but receiver bridge is split and bolt handle turns down in front of the receiver bridge.
Turn bolt action.
Safety: Modified Mauser wing safety.
Stock: Standard military one-piece design.
Sights: Barleycorn front and V ramp rear. Adjustable 200-2000 meters.
Note: Because the bolt handle locks down in front of the receiver bridge, the handle is much farther forward on the bolt than in Mauser practice.
Identification of Mauser Verguiero: Split bridge receiver, Mauser type magazine.
Evaluation: Well made of good materials. Placement of bolt handle does not permit ease of operation found in conventional designs.
Ammunition: 6.5mm Portuguese.

PORTUGUESE SUBMACHINE GUN

This is a conventional blowback weapon. It is made in Portugal. A bayonet is provided. The stock is retractable.

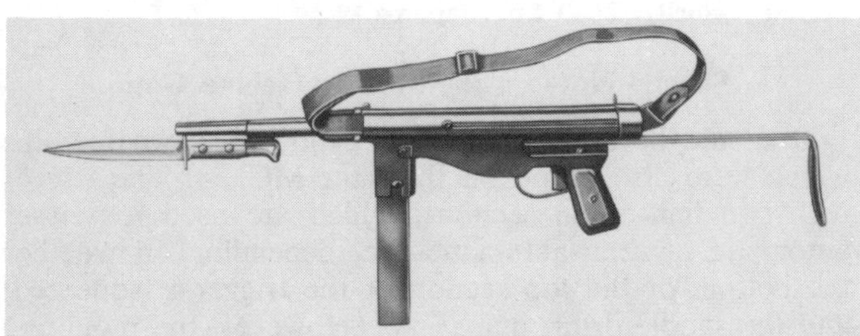

9mm Model 48 Submachine Gun, F.B.P.

Caliber: 9mm Parabellum.
System of Operation: Blowback.
Weight, Empty: 8.2 lbs.
Length Overall; stock extended: 32 inches. stock folded: 25 in.
Barrel Length: 9.8 ins.
Sights, Front: Blade.
Rear: Fixed aperture graduated for 100 meters.
Feed Device: 32-round, detachable staggered row, box magazine.
Muzzle Velocity: 1280 f.p.s
Cyclic Rate: 500 r.p.m.

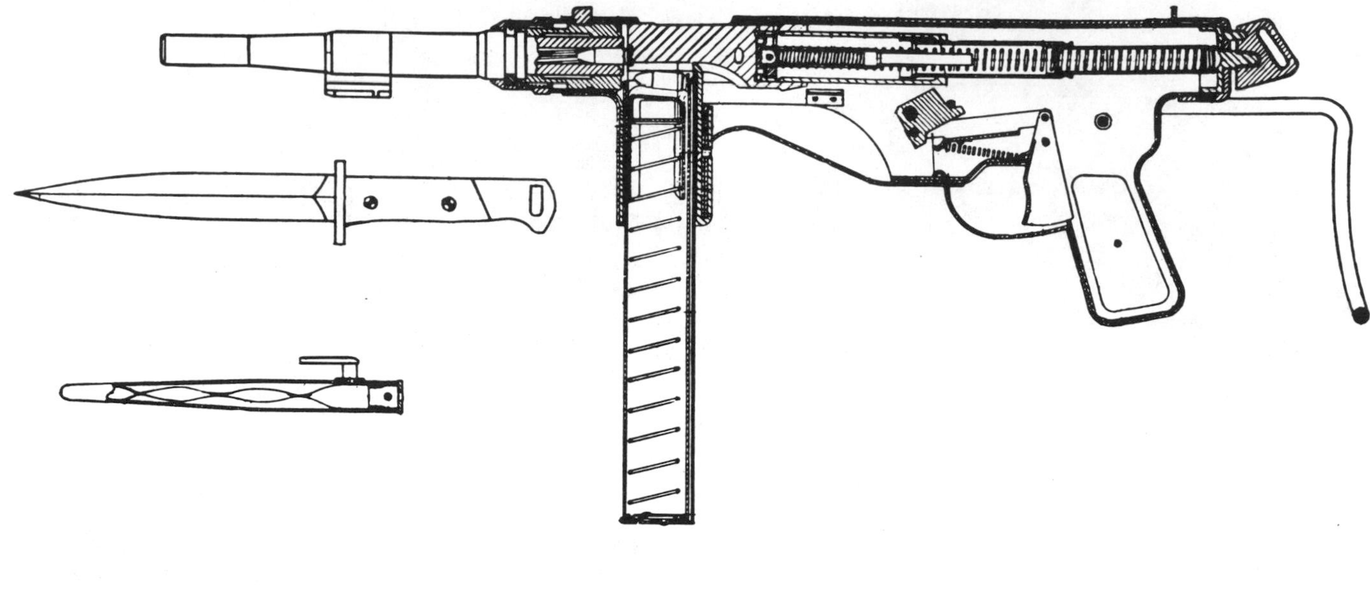

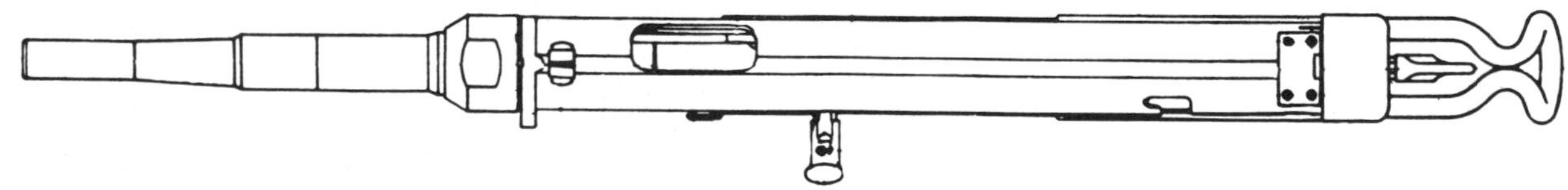

9mm Model 48 F.B.P. Submachine Gun, section view.

PORTUGUESE MACHINE GUN

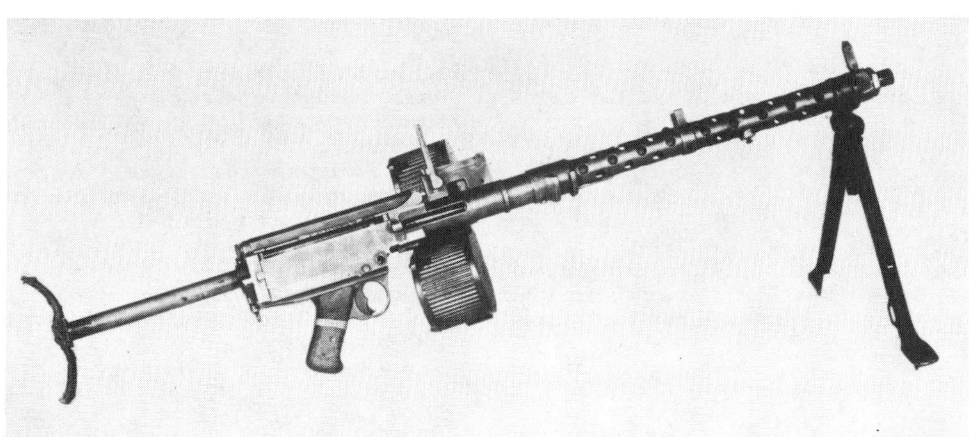

Portuguese 7.92mm M938 Machine Gun.

This weapon is the German MG 13, which was sold by Germany to Portugal in 1938. It was used as the standard German light machine gun until the adoption of the MG 34. The weapon is a modified Dreyse M1918.

Caliber: 7.92mm.
System of Operation: Recoil, selective fire.
Weight: 26.4 lb.
Length, Overall: 57 in. (approx.).
Barrel Length: 28.25 in.
Sights, Front: Folding blade.
Rear: Tangent leaf.
Cyclic Rate: 750 r.p.m.
Feed Device: 25-round box magazine or 75-round saddle drum.
Muzzle Velocity: 2600 f.p.s. (approx.).

Special Note on the M938 Machine Gun

It should be noted that this weapon uses two features which were also found on the later MG 34. The trigger with two half-moon sections, which are used for either automatic or semi-automatic fire, depending on whether the bottom or the top section of the trigger is squeezed; and the saddle drum magazine. (However, the mounting of the saddle drum on the MG 34 is different.)

Chapter 38. ROMANIA

The Romanians ended World War II with a hodgepodge of small arms of many different designs and in many different calibers. Most of these weapons were not of Romanian design, and few were of Romanian manufacture. Czech-designed M1924 Mausers were held in quantity, as were Czech-designed Model 30 light machine guns (ZB 30). The Romanians also held a fair quantity of French equipment, including the 13.2mm Hotchkiss heavy machine gun.

Since Romania slipped behind the iron curtain, she has been receiving Soviet weapons, although some of the older weapons also remained in service. Most of the pre-World War II and World War II Soviet small arms are in service in Romania at present. Recently, photographs of Romanian troops equipped with some of the newer Soviet weapons, such as the SKS and the 14.5mm ZPU series of heavy machine gun, have appeared.

ROMANIAN RIFLES AND CARBINES

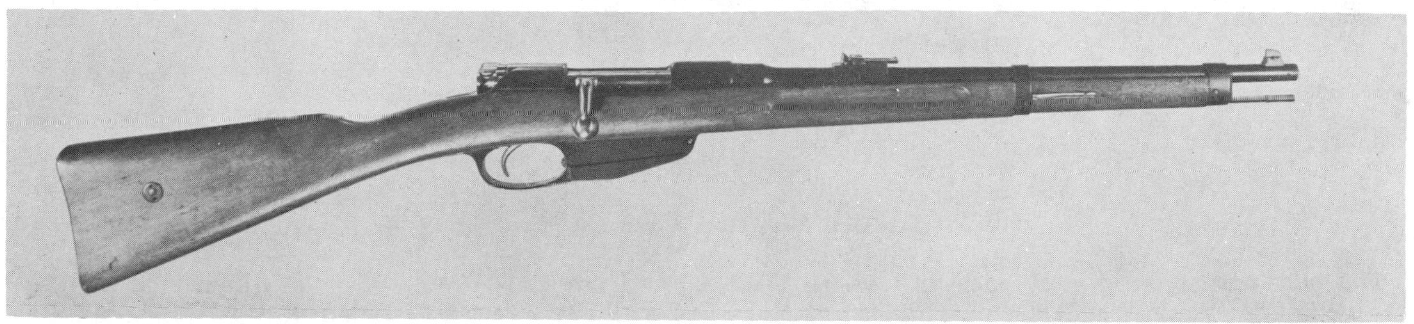

Model 1893 Romanian Mannlicher (Obsolete).

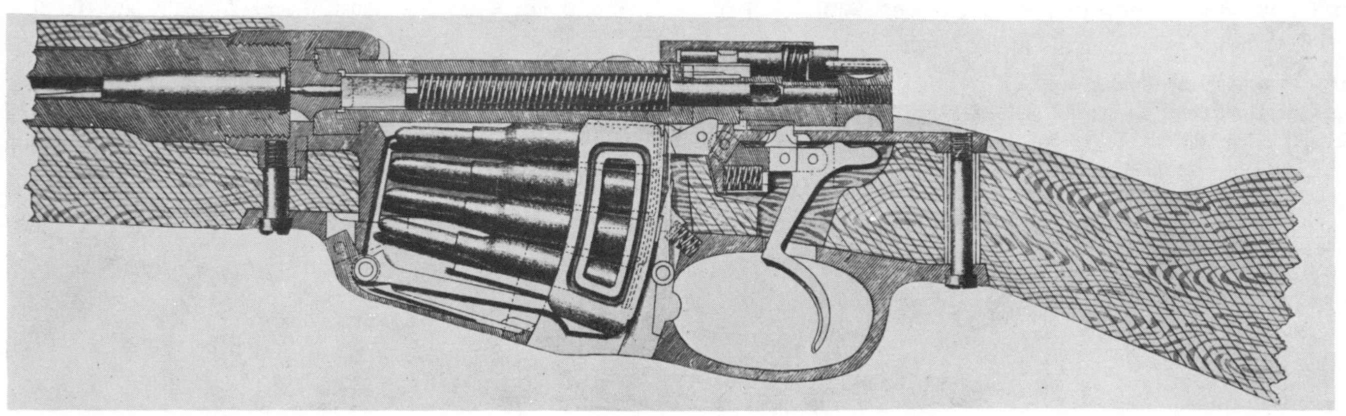

Romanian Mannlicher sectioned to show details of magazine, bolt, and firing mechanism. The Netherlands types differ only slightly from this.

Caliber: 6.5mm Romanian with rim.
Magazine: Mannlicher type vertical box requiring use of inserted clip.
Barrel Length: 25.5".
Overall Length: 48.5".
Weight: 8.76 lbs.
Sights: Barleycorn front and V ramp rear. Adjustable 200-2000 meters.
Note: Sights vary with several minor modifications.
Magazine Cut-Off: None possible with Mannlicher type vertical magazine.
Locked: Turn bolt with dual front lugs. Handle locks down in front of receiver bridge which is split for bolt handle passage.
Bolt: Mannlicher type with removable bolt head.
Safety: Mannlicher wing pattern at rear of bolt.
Note: Except for minor details of extractor and ejector types, the bolt design is the same as for the Netherlands and the Greek Mannlichers. (See description in chapter 27.) (For magazine description, see chapter 34.)
Carbines: Differ only in stocks, slings, lengths, and weights.

Other Former Romanian Service Rifles

Austrian 1895 Straight Pull, Cal. 8mm Austrian.
French 1907, Cal. 8mm French.
Russian Mosin/Nagant M1891 Cal. 7.62mm Russian.
German (also Czech and Belgian F. N.) Model 1924, Cal. 7.92mm German.

ROMANIAN SUBMACHINE GUN

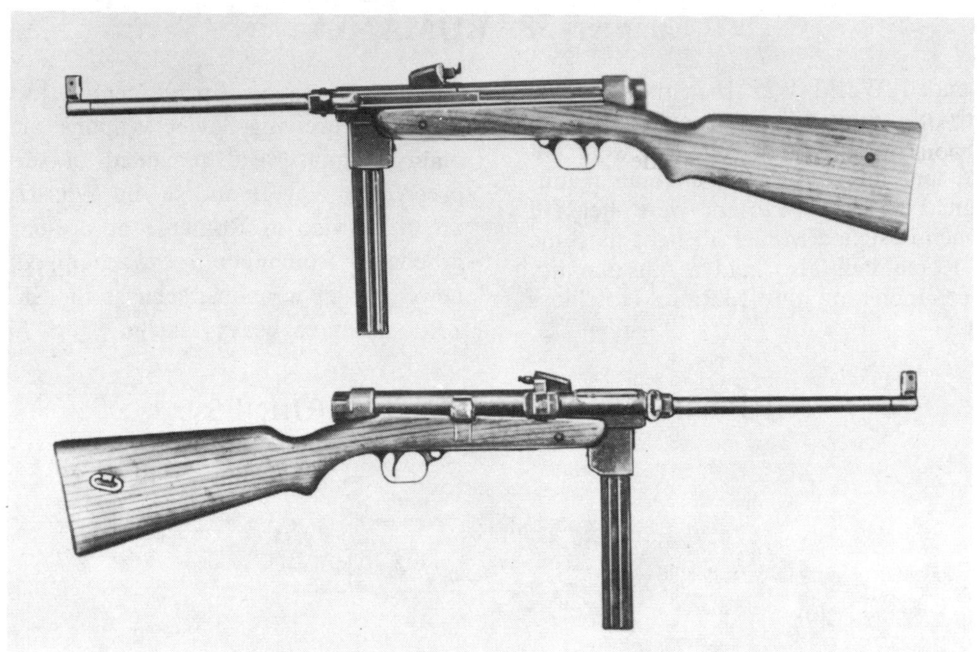

Romanian 9mm Orita Submachine Gun.

The only notable weapon of Romanian design that was used during World War II was the Orita submachine gun. This weapon has been replaced by Soviet weapons in Romania at the present time, but is covered as a matter of interest.

Caliber: 9mm Parabellum.
System of Operation: Blowback, selective fire.
Weight, loaded: 8.8 lb.
Length, Overall: 35.2 in.
Barrel Length: 11.3 in.
Feed Device: 32-round, staggered row, detachable box magazine.
Sights, Front: Hooded blade.
Rear: Open V, adjustable, graduated from 100 to 500 meters:
Muzzle Velocity: 1280 f.p.s.
Cyclic Rate of Fire: 400 r.p.m.

There is also a version of the Orita submachine gun with a folding metal stock.

Chapter 39. Spain

Spain now has a locally developed pistol, submachine gun, rifle, and heavy machine gun in service, and is gaining a reputation as the exporter of some very interesting designs of small arms. Unfortunately for the Spanish, their low-quality pistols, which were made and apparently exported by the millions between World Wars I and II, gave Spanish-made weapons a bad name. These weapons were often home produced. However, the products of such firms as Star and Llama were quality products even then. World War II brought large arms contracts for the Spanish makers, and since that time only arms of first quality have been exported.

At the conclusion of World War II, a group of German arms technicians from some of the outstanding German plants, including Mauser, emigrated to Spain. The Spanish government employed these men at the Centro de Estudios Tecnicos de Materials Especiales, or CETME, as it is commonly known. This organization has produced many interesting designs but the most interesting, and by far the most successful, has been the CETME assault rifle which is described later in this chapter. Spain is gradually converting her rifle caliber arms to 7.62mm NATO.

SPANISH PISTOLS

Since the close of World War II the production of semi-automatic pistols (and some automatic pistols with stock attachments) has become a major business with Spanish Arms Industries. The largest pistol manufacturer is "Star," Bonifacio Echeverria S.A. Their locked breech pistols of general Colt .45 automatic lines, but with different firing mechanisms as discussed herein, are produced in calibers 9mm Luger, .38 ACP, and .45 ACP.

In addition this firm manufactures scaled down versions of this same type of very well made pistol in calibers .32 (7.65mm) and .380 (9mm Corto). These pistols have the exposed hammers, push button magazine release, and slide stop systems found in the Colt Government Model. Much of their success in export sale stems from their external resemblance to the Colt .45. This styling was intentional and intelligent.

All the foregoing pistols qualify as military arms or police arms to some extent. They are exported throughout the world. The smaller calibers are generally sold in the United States as pocket pistols, since currently there is no equivalent American production. The larger calibers, however, having competition from American makers do not have wide sale here. Pistols of these patterns are widely sold in Mexico and in some South American countries.

This company also manufactures a wide variety of .22 caliber blowback pistols, some patterns being modeled again on the external appearance of the Colt .45 in miniature; while others follow quite closely the general pattern of the original .22 Walther automatic pistol. These do not, of course, qualify as military arms.

The second largest producer is Gabilondo y Cia. The brand name here is "LLAMA." The larger models are exact copies of the Model 1911 Colt Government Model automatic. Other locked breech calibers are 9mm Luger, .38 ACP, 9mm Bergmann, and .45 ACP. In addition the firm produces .32 ACP (7.65mm) and .380 ACP (9mm Corto) models based on the external lines of the .45 automatic. As in the case of Star, in the pocket types these arms are sold extensively on a commercial basis in the United States. The military and police versions, however, are confined largely to Spanish or Portuguese speaking countries.

Gabilondo also produces a copy of the Smith & Wesson M&P revolver in .38 caliber special with 4-, 5-, and 6-inch barrels. Imitations of the Smith & Wesson Regulation Police are also produced in calibers .22 and .32 and are marketed under the trade name "Ruby." Among other Smith & Wesson models currently being imitated exactly (the work being done from templates taken from recent Smith & Wesson models) are the K-38 Masterpiece and the .22 Kit gun. In view of the excellent manufacture and material of these pistols, they constitute a serious threat to export markets for the American product but are not competitive in the United States as are the automatic pistols made by the same firm.

All these revolvers except the .22 caliber are used extensively in South America as military and also as police arms.

The third largest firm is Unceta Y Cia, S.A. at Guernica. Their brand name is "Astra."

The Astra Model 400 auto pistol in caliber 9mm Bergmann was the official Spanish military pistol prior to 1946. This is a straight blowback design with heavy recoil spring positioned around the barrel. It resembles externally the old United States Savage automatic pistol. However, it evolved from the Spanish Campo-Giro. (Note: Currently, the "Super Star," imitation of the Colt-Browning as already discussed as made by Echeverria, is the standard Spanish military sidearm.

Astra Model 200 in caliber .25 ACP (6.35mm) is a very close external approximation of the prewar Colt .25 vest pocket automatic. The Model 300 in calibers .380 ACP and 9mm or 7.65mm Luger (Parabellum) all follow the general external lines of the early American Savage pistol. These are firearms of excellent manufacture and design. They are equipped with both manual and automatic grip safeties and are fired by internal hammer mechanisms. The quality of these pistols, and particularly their finish, is uniformly extremely high. However, for some obscure psychological reason, the compact streamlined form of the Savage external appearance has never caught the fancy of American purchasers. Pistols of this design simply do not compete for general sale with those patterned after the Colt-Browning lines.

Since all these pistols, including the .25 caliber, are used by staff or other officers in various South American countries, as well as by occasional European police organizations, they rate some attention as quasi-military weapons.

Spanish "Star" Automatic Pistol, Cal. .45 Model M.

Caliber: .45 Automatic Colt Pistol.
Magazine: Box, single line. Capacity 7 cartridges.
Muzzle Velocity: Standard for cartridges used.
Barrel Length: About 5 inches.
Overall Length: About 8¼ inches.
Sights: Partridge. Adjustable rear.

Operation: Recoil.

Locked: Colt-Browning system, ribs on barrel lock in slots in roof of slide. Swing link.

Type of Fire: Single shot or full automatic at will.

Magazine Release Catch: Colt type on left side of receiver.

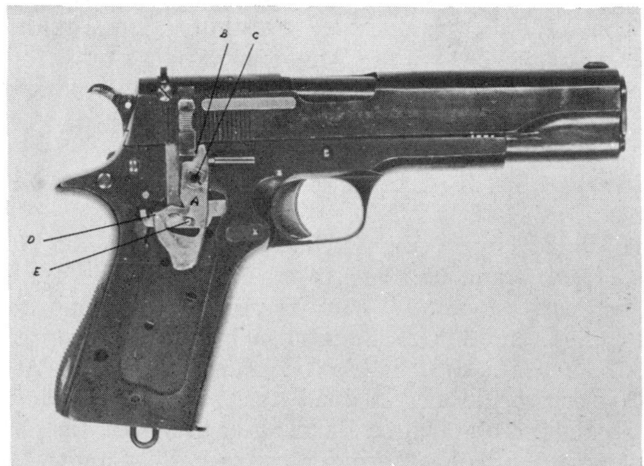

Right Side View of Star with Stock Removed to Show Full Auto Mechanism.

A. Automatic sear release. B. Switch. C. Sear pivot. D. Contact. E. Trigger bar catch.

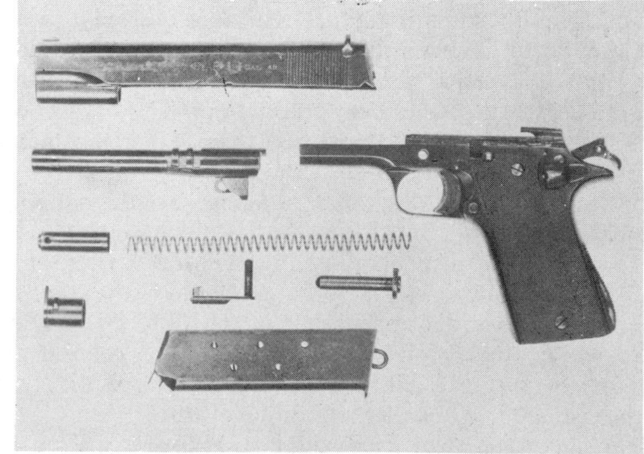

Spanish Star Field Stripped.

Slide, barrel and receiver, recoil spring plug and recoil spring, barrel bushing, slide stop pin, recoil spring guide and magazine. Note that all these units resemble the Colt .45 Auto parts very closely.

Hold-Open Device: Same as Colt .45 Auto; slide is held open when last shot has been fired by magazine follower pushing up slide release catch.

Safety: Thumb safety on left side. No grip safety.

Full Auto Switch: On right side of slide ahead of rear sight. When pushed into position it moves a lever which automatically trips the sear each time the breech closes, thereby giving full automatic fire.

While this pistol was extensively distributed throughout South America and Europe, it is not a desirable weapon. While the design follows that of the Colt .45 Auto very closely, neither the materials nor the workmanship approach that of the American pistol. Furthermore, the full automatic feature empties the pistol so rapidly (about 800 per minute rate) that it is not possible to use it for anything but a pure assassination weapon. No accuracy is possible, even when the arm is fitted with a shoulder stock. This weapon is not a Spanish service weapon.

Spanish Astra 9mm Long Automatic Pistol Model 400.

Caliber: 9mm Bergmann Bayard.
Magazine: Single line box. Capacity 8 cartridges.
Muzzle Velocity: About 1200 feet per second.
Striking Energy: About 400 foot pounds.
Weight of Bullet: 126 grains.
Barrel Length: 5½ inches.
Overall Length of Pistol: 8¾ inches.
Weight: About 32 ounces.
Sights: Fixed.
Locked: Strictly unlocked, straight blowback. Weapon is held closed at moment of firing only by weight of the moving parts and by the powerful spring positioned around the barrel.
Type of Fire: Single shot only.
Magazine Release Catch: At bottom of handle.
Safety: Thumb piece on left of receiver.

This was an official Spanish pistol. It has an enclosed hammer. The cartridge it uses is not very well known in the United States where no weapon is chambered to take it. The 9mm Bergmann Bayard cartridge which it fires normally is a longer cartridge than our .38 Colt Automatic. It is interesting to observe that a cartridge of this type can be safety handled in a blowback action.

The magazine and feeding construction of the Astra permit it to handle varying lengths of cartridges of 9mm (.38) caliber without adjustment. This is the only commercial automatic pistol which will handle successfully more than one length of cartridge. This weapon will fire the following cartridges: 9mm Parabellum, 9mm Steyr, 9mm Browning Long, 9mm Bergmann Bayard, (9mm Largo).

Spanish 9mm Super Star Pistol

Caliber: 9mm Largo.
System of Operation: Recoil operated, semi-automatic only.
Weight: 2.21 lbs.
Length, Overall: 8.03 in.
Barrel Length: 4 in.
Feed Device: 9-round, in-line detachable box magazine.
Sights, Front: Blade.
Rear: Fixed V notch.
Muzzle Velocity: Approx. 1200 f.p.s.

The Super Star is the standard Spanish service pistol. It is similar in design and operation to the U.S. caliber .45 M1911A1 with the following principal exceptions:

1. The trigger is pinned in place and pivots rather than slides.
2. Slide stop is of two-piece construction.
3. There is no grip safety.

This pistol is of good design and construction and is sold commercially in the United States in .38 Super automatic, 9mm Parabellum and .45 ACP.

SPANISH SERVICE RIFLES AND CARBINES

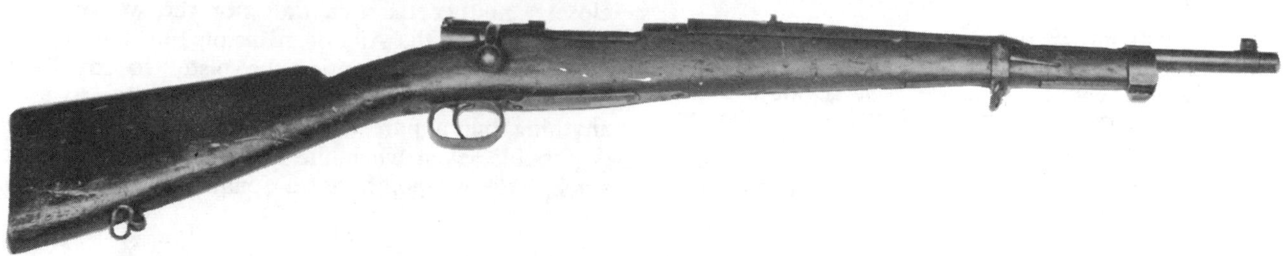

7mm M1893 Short Rifle.

The 1892 and 1893 Mausers made for Spain introduced the now common Mauser staggered box magazine. Mausers made in Germany for Spain, and also made in Spanish arsenals, bear varying dates for model modifications.

Models 1892 through 1895 have only two front locking lugs. They do not have the third safety lug found on the German Gew. 98 and later patterns, except when they are arms which have been specially modified.

Magazine followers act to hold the action open when magazine is empty. Handguards on rifles commonly extend from receiver to lower band.

Bolt sleeve does not have locking pin found on German 98. No gas protection flange on bolt sleeve.

Sear has a forward projection which serves as a safety on the system found in the U. S. Model 17 (Enfield). Sear nose cannot be lowered out of contact with cocking piece nose to fire until bolt handle is fully down in locked position; only at that point can front sear projection rise into niche in bolt. That action permits the rear section of the sear to operate. However, cocking is completed on forward bolt stroke. Some of the 7mm Mausers have recently been converted to caliber 7.62mm NATO. Spain also uses a copy of the German 7.92mm Kar 98k which they call the Model 43.

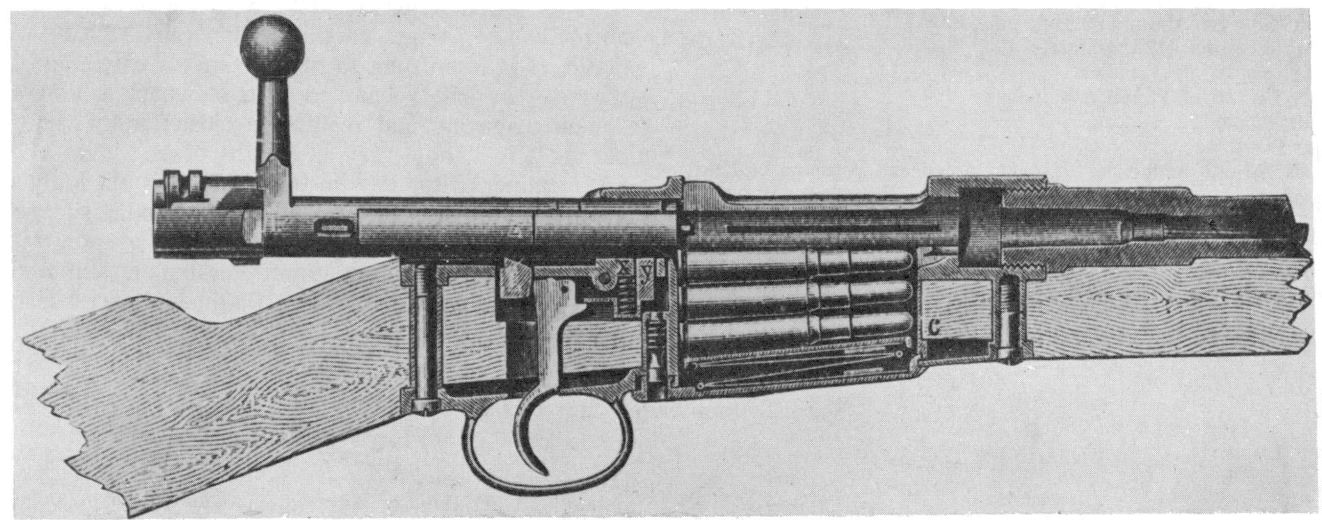

M1893 Spanish Mauser, 7mm. Note that there is no rear safety lug. Inferior to later designs.

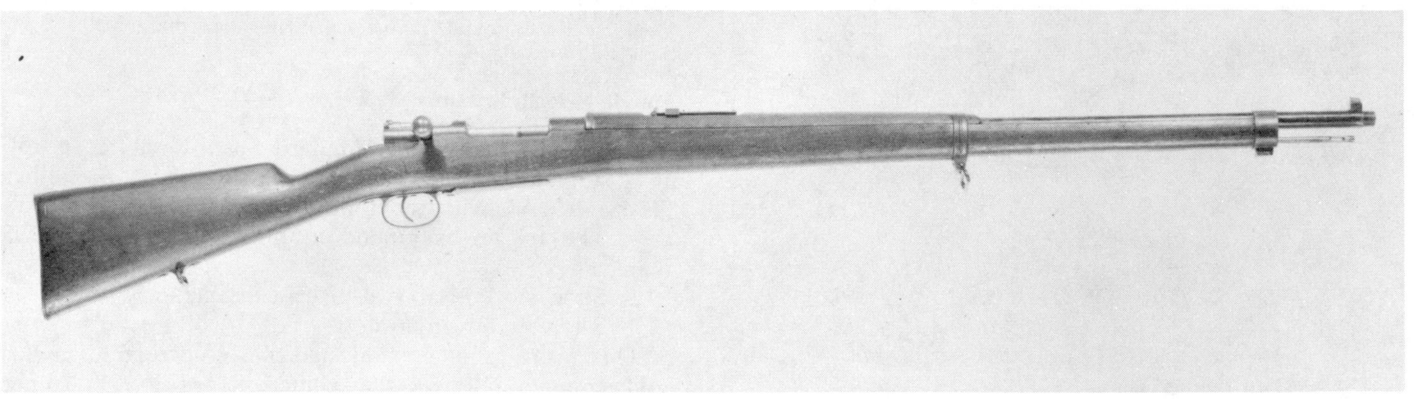

Spanish 7mm Model 1893 Mauser Rifle.

Model 1893.
Caliber: 7mm Spanish.
Magazine: Mauser standard staggered box. Five shot capacity.
Barrel Length: 29.1″.
Length: 48.7″.
Weight: 9.4 lbs.
Sights: Barleycorn front. V ramp rear, adjustable 400-2000 meters.
Locked: Turn bolt. Dual front lugs only.
Magazine Cut Off: None.
Safety: Mauser wing type.
Cocking: Cocking piece nose forced back over sear on opening motion. Sear catches and holds cocking piece about one inch from closing. Continuing forward thrust cocks mainspring.
Mechanical Safety: Front sear projection as in U. S. Model 1917.
All Carbines: Mechanically same as rifle. May be full stocked to muzzle or half stocked. Many variants. Barrels normally 17.56″ to 19.12″.
Note: The foregoing are the rifles usually referred to when speaking of "Spanish" Mausers.

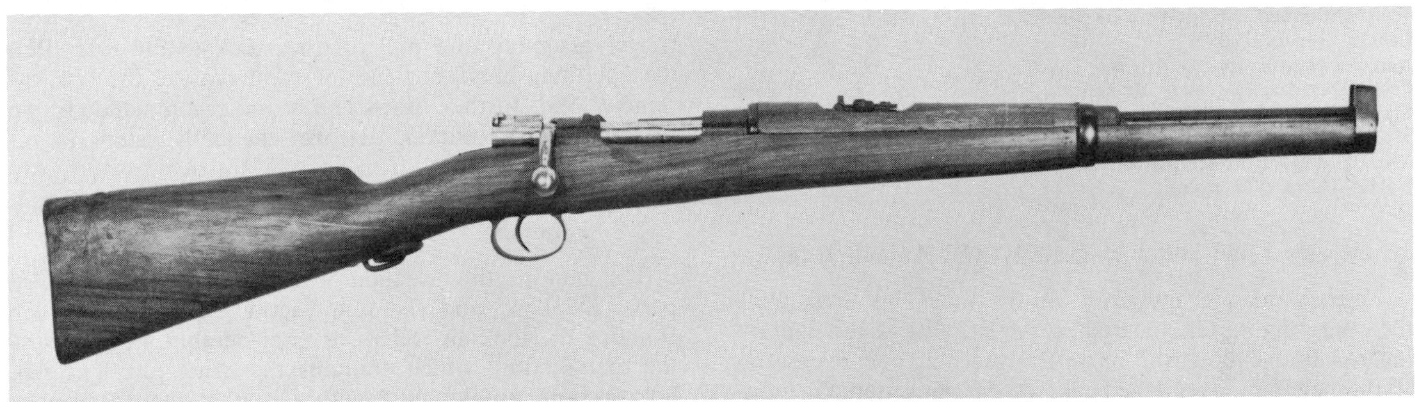

Spanish 7mm Model 1895 Carbine.

Spanish CETME 7.92mm Assault Rifle, the prototype CETME.

This weapon apparently is mostly the work of E. Vorgrimmler, a former Mauser Werke engineer. The design is based for the most part on the German prototype StG. 45M. As originally introduced by CETME, the weapon was chambered for an original 7.92mm short cartridge which had a long spire-pointed bullet made of aluminum with a small section of gliding metal jacketing attached to engage the rifling. It has since been made to chamber the 7.62mm NATO cartridge.

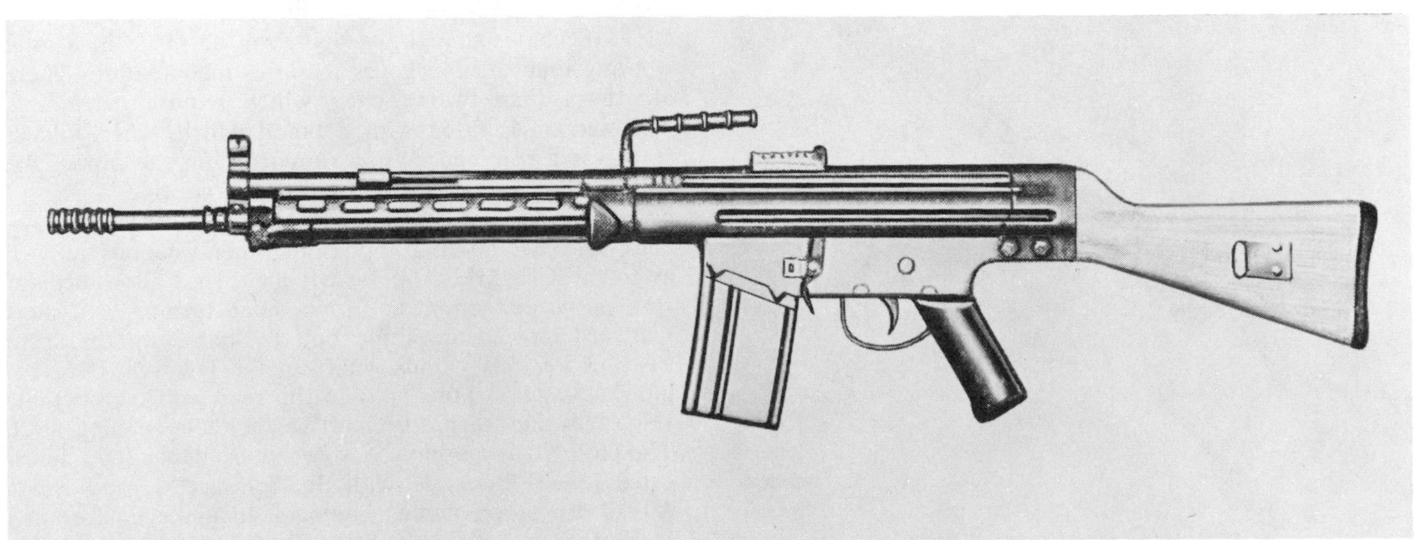

Spanish 7.62mm CETME Model 58 Assault Rifle.

The Spanish CETME uses a special 7.62mm NATO load which gives lower pressures than those encountered with the NATO cartridge as loaded in other countries. The CETME can be used with the NATO cartridges of other countries by changing the bolt head. The official nomenclature for the CETME rifle in the Spanish Army is: Assault Rifle CETME, Model 58.

Caliber: 7.62mm NATO—special Spanish load.
System of Operation: Delayed blowback, selective fire.
Weight (loaded w/bipod): 11.3 lbs.
Length, Overall: 39.37 in.
Barrel Length: Approx. 17 in.
Feed Device: 20-round detachable, staggered-row box magazine.
Sights, Front: Hooded blade.
Rear: Tangent with V notch.
Muzzle Velocity: Approx. 2500 f.p.s.
Cyclic Rate: 600 r.p.m.

How to Load and Fire the CETME Assault Rifle

Insert a loaded magazine in the magazine well. Pull the operating handle located on the left side of the operating rod tube (above the barrel) to the rear and release it. If the selector lever has been set on the letter "T," the bolt will run home, chambering a cartridge, and the weapon will fire single rounds when the trigger is pulled. If the selector has been set on the letter "R," the bolt will remain to the rear when cocked. When the trigger is pulled, the weapon will deliver automatic fire. The CETME commences semi-automatic fire from a closed bolt and automatic fire from an open bolt. The operating handle does not reciprocate with the bolt. To put the weapon on SAFE, set the selector lever on the letter "S."

How to Field Strip the CETME Assault Rifle

Remove the magazine by pushing on the magazine catch. Remove the two pins at the rear of the pistol grip-

CETME Field Stripped.

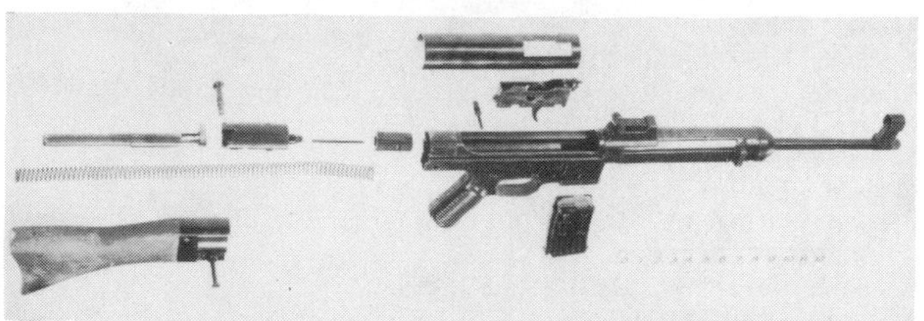

German WWII Prototype of 7.92mm CETME.

trigger assembly and pull off the stock to the rear. Pull the operating handle to the rear and remove the bolt assembly. No further disassembly is recommended. To reassemble the weapon, perform the above steps in reverse order.

How the CETME Assault Rifle Works

The bolt in this weapon is composed of two major parts: the head and the rear section. The head, which contains the locking rollers, is considerably smaller than the rear section, which contains the firing pin. The two bolt sections are joined together so that they can move horizontally with respect to each other. The large rear section of the bolt has a nose end which is pointed to fit in the head of the bolt. When the bolt runs home, this nose end enters the head of the bolt and cams the locking rollers into their locking recesses in the receiver. When the cartridge is fired, the pressure on the base of the cartridge, after a period of time, forces the locking rollers back against the nose of the rear bolt section. The rear bolt section, which is held in position only by the energy of the recoil spring, starts to the rear. The bolt is unlocked and the firing pin drawn to the rear, away from the primer, by the rearward movement of the rear bolt section.

Special Note on the CETME Assault Rifle

The CETME assault rifle is worthy of note in several respects. It is composed mainly of stampings, and CETME claims that the weapon can be made in a total working time of nine hours in series manufacture. There are fewer than twenty parts which require machining. The weapon is fitted with a bipod which, when folded, serves as a fore-end. When supported on the bipod, the gun can be used as a squad automatic weapon. There is, however, one unfortunate aspect to the delayed-blowback system, and this applies to other weapons as well as to the CETME. The system makes no allowance for slow initial extraction, i.e., for a small turning or a short rearward movement of the bolt to loosen up the spent case before it is withdrawn from the receiver. Delayed-blowback action bolts start to the rear with considerable velocity when the pressure arrives at their opening level. Therefore, delayed-blowback weapons depend on lubricated (oiled) cases, as with the Schwarzlose and Breda Model 30, or on fluted chambers, to make up for their lack of slow initial extraction. Lubricating prevents the case from expanding fully against the walls of the

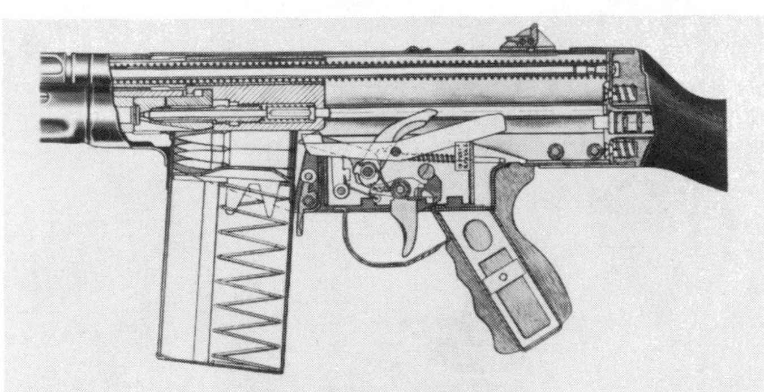

Section View of CETME.

chamber and a fluted chamber allows the forward part of the case to float on gas and therefore not expand completely to the walls of the chamber. Without lubricated cases or fluted chambers (the degree of fluting varies from three-quarters the length of the chamber to only the length of the neck and shoulder), a delayed-blowback may pull the base off the case in extraction. These weapons must therefore be designed around brass cartridges of a certain hardness. If a weapon with a fluted chamber is used with brass considerably softer than that for which it was designed, the brass may be engraved by the flutes and the bolt may lose enough kinetic energy in extracting the case to prevent it from going into full recoil, with resultant feed jams. It is probable, however, that a delayed blowback designed around the softest brass likely to be encountered in service will do very well with all sorts of brass, hard or soft. Delayed-blowback weapons do not usually give any trouble with steel cases.

Specimens of the CETME assault rifle have also been made for the Soviet 7.62mm M1943 "intermediate-sized" cartridge. The operating system of the CETME is similar to that of the Swiss SIG Model 57 assault rifle.

SPANISH SUBMACHINE GUNS

Star 9mm Model Z-45 Submachine Gun.

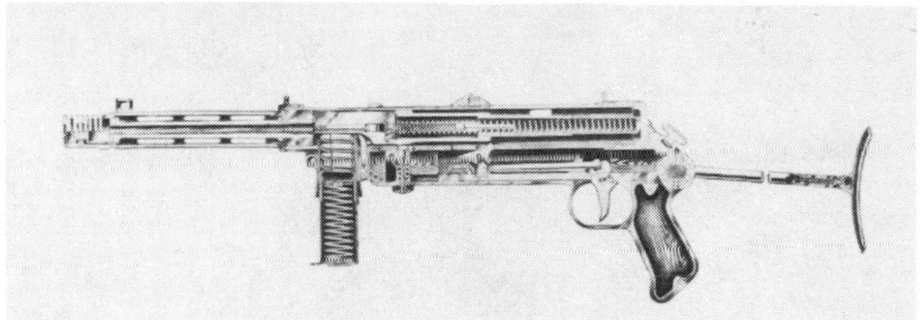

Section View of the Star Z-45.

A great many of the German Erma submachine guns are apparently still in service in Spain. Two native weapons have been introduced into the Spanish Army, however. One is the Star Model Z-45 sub-machine gun. This weapon is quite similar in construction (excepting the barrel jacket) to the German MP38 and MP40 submachine guns.

The cyclic rate of the Z-45 is 450 rounds per minute.

This weapon is chambered for the Spanish service pistol cartridge, the 9mm Largo. This cartridge is similar to the 9mm Bergmann Bayard cartridge.

Caliber: 9mm Largo.
System of Operation: Blowback, selective fire.
Weight, Loaded: 10 lbs.
Length, Overall:
Stock Extended: 33.1 in.
Stock Folded: 23 in.
Barrel Length: 7.9 in.
Feed Device: 30-round, detachable, staggered-row, box magazine.
Sights, Front: Blade w/protecting ears.
Rear: L-type w/notch.
Cyclic Rate: 450 r.p.m.
Muzzle Velocity: 1220 f.p.s.

The Z-45 has been made in a fixed-wooden-stock model in addition to the folding-metal-stock model.

Spanish 9mm Parinco Model 3R Submachine Gun

Caliber: 9mm Largo.
System of Operation: Blowback, selective fire.
Weight (w/empty magazine): 6.8 lbs.
Length, Overall:
W/stock Extended: 31.5 in.
W/stock Folded: 24.4 in.
Feed Device: 32-round, staggered-row, detachable box magazine.
Sights, Front: Blade.
Rear: V notch.
Cyclic Rate: 600 r.p.m.
Muzzle Velocity: Approx. 1230 f.p.s.

The Parinco is a conventional blowback type submachine gun with telescoping type wire stock. It has a compensator and a grip safety and is constructed mainly of stampings, as are most modern weapons in the submachine gun category.

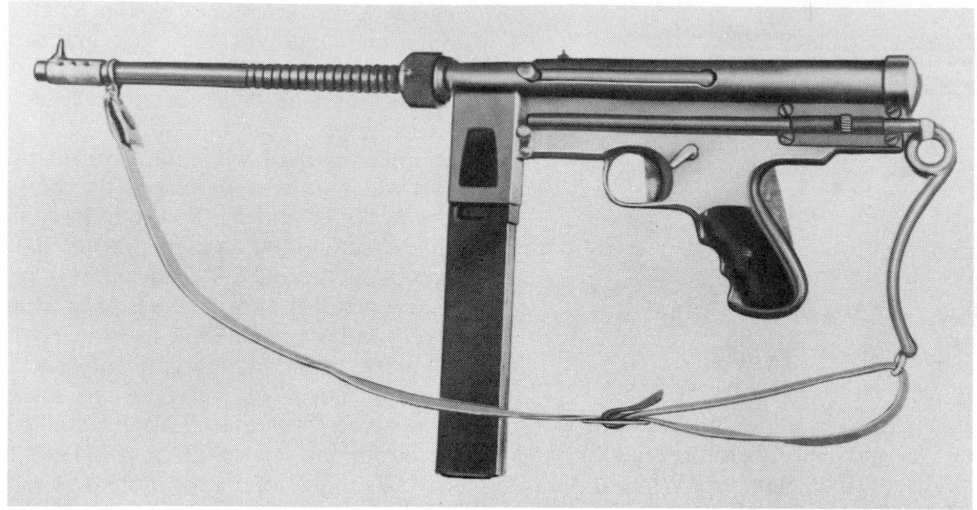

Spanish 9mm Parinco Model 3R Submachine Gun.

SPANISH MACHINE GUNS

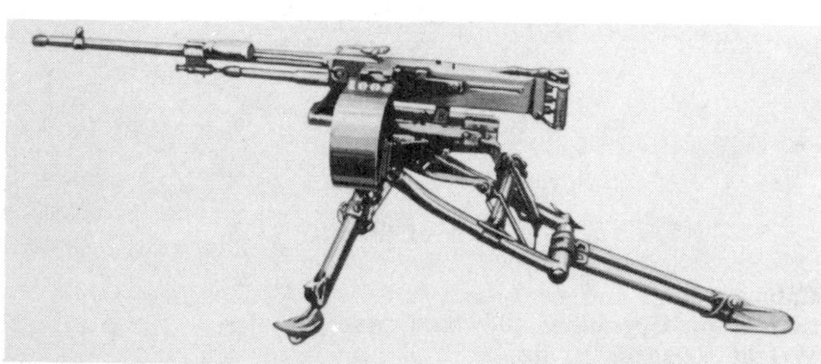

Spanish 7.92mm Alfa Machine Gun M1944.

The Alfa, besides being used by the Spanish Army, also was (prior to 1952) exported to Egypt. The Alfa is a heavy gun, suitable for use only on a tripod.

Caliber: 7.92mm (rimless).
System of Operation: Gas, selective fire.
Weight of Gun: 28.66 lbs.
Weight of Tripod: 59.52 lbs.
Barrel Length: 29.53 in.
Feed Device: 100-round metallic link belt, loaded in drum.
Sights, Front: Adjustable blade.
Rear: Leaf.
Muzzle Velocity: 2493 f.p.s.
Cyclic Rate: 780 r.p.m.

How to Load and Fire the Alfa Machine Gun

Pull the charging handle to the rear, and release; it will return to its forward position. Insert the end tab of the belt in the feed port on the left side of the receiver, and pull it through the ejection port on the right side of the receiver. Lift the safety lever from the trigger and press the trigger. The weapon will fire; when the trigger is released, the safety lever will again snap into place.

How to Field Strip the Alfa

Cock the gun, to permit the operating rod to clear the gas port collar. Remove the knurled handle of the barrel latch from the locking recess in the receiver and rotate the latch to lock the handle in the upper locking recess. This operation will permit the barrel to pass through the groove cut in the barrel latch, and will also retract the operating rod housing tube out of the gas chamber.

Grasp the barrel handle and rotate the barrel to the right until it is arrested by the stop in the receiver. At this point the interrupted thread will disengage, and the barrel can be pulled forward and out of the receiver.

To remove the feeder mechanism support, grasp the support retainer key (linchpin) by its handle, and slide it back out of the keyway in the support. Remove the support by pulling it out the left side of the receiver.

To remove the operating spring and guide, release the operating rod by firing the trigger. Press the head of the guide rod and rotate it a quarter turn to the left, so that the keys on the rod will be in line with the keyways on the backplate. The operating rod spring will force both the rod and spring through the hole, facilitating its removal.

To remove the backplate, remove the backplate retainer pin. If the backplate does not drop out, hit it with a wooden or fiber hammer. The backplate will slide out of the grooves in the receiver.

To remove the sear housing, pull the housing back out of the receiver.

To remove the charging handle, pull the handle back to the end of the slot and then to the right, away from the receiver.

To remove the operating rod and bolt assembly (removal of the charging handle leaves the operating rod partly out of the receiver), a slight pull is necessary. To disassemble the bolt from the operating rod, retract the bolt until the locking block engages the cam on the operating rod, and raise the bolt out of its seat.

To remove the ejector, index the ejector 90 degrees and pull out of the receiver.

To reassemble the weapon, reverse the above procedures.

How the Alfa Works

When the cartridge is fired, the pressure of the propellent gases drives the bullet down the bore. As soon as the projectile passes the gas port in the barrel, a portion of the propellent gases will flow through the opening in the regulator and into the gas cylinder. The gases impinge on the piston, driving the operating rod to the rear and compressing the operating rod spring.

As the operating rod moves to the rear, it withdraws the firing pin from the primer and continues until the ramp raises the locking block. The locking block unlocks, and the operating rod and bolt continue to the rear together. Since the spent case is held by the extractor, it is withdrawn from the chamber and carried backward until the base of the case strikes the ejector blade. The blade deflects the case against the rubber deflection pad on the right side of the receiver, and ejects it through the ejection port.

As the operating rod retracts, the lug on the operating rod frees the lower arm of the belt feed lever which, being spring loaded, drags the belt feed slide from left to right, placing a new cartridge in feeding position before the chamber. The bolt is locked in position by the action of a lug (at the forward end of the central part of the operating rod) resting against the lower arm of the belt feed lever.

The backward motion of the operating rod is limited by the striking of its rear end against the buffer spring.

Spanish 7.62mm ALFA Model 55 Heavy Machine Gun

Caliber: 7.62mm NATO (Spanish or normal).
System of Operation: Gas, selective fire.
Weight of Gun: 28.66 lbs.
Weight of Tripod: 43 lbs.
Length, Overall (gun): 43.4 in.
Feed Device: 100-round metallic link belt, loaded in drum.
Sights: **Front**—Adjustable blade.
Rear—Leaf.
Muzzle Velocity: 2825 f.p.s.
Cyclic Rate: 780 r.p.m.

This is the 7.62mm version of the ALFA Model 44 described above. Loading, firing, stripping, and functioning are essentially the same for this weapon as for the 7.92mm Model 44. The Model 55 has a ribbed barrel, is shorter than the Model 44 and has a lighter tripod, but is otherwise much the same.

Spanish FAO and FAO Model 59 Light Machine Guns

The 7.92mm FAO (Fabrica de Armas de Oviedo) is a Spanish manufactured copy of the Czech ZB26 and ZB30 machine guns. These weapons are covered in detail in the chapter on Czechoslovakia. This weapon has been used by the Spanish as a squad automatic weapon. The FAO Model 59 is a modified 7.62mm NATO version of the FAO and feeds from a fifty round metallic link belt held in a drum attached to the left side of the receiver. The FAO Model 59 is normally used with a tripod.

Chapter 40. Sweden

SWEDISH PISTOLS

Swedish M1940 (Lahti) Pistol.

Caliber: 9mm Luger (round nose bullet ammunition works best).
Magazine: Detachable single line box in handle. Release catch in bottom of handle.
Barrel Length: About 5.5".
Length Overall: 10.5".
Weight: About 36 oz.
Sights: Front blade adjustable laterally. Rear open sight machined in barrel extension.
Locked: By rising and falling lock piece engaging in rear of breechblock and locking that unit to the barrel extension.
Operation: Short recoil. Barrel and breechblock assemblies recoil locked together for a short distance before barrel travel is halted.
Safety: Turning lever on left side of receiver. Positively locks sear.
Special Features: Internal hammer. Separate breechblock. Special accelerator like Browning MG. Recoil spring in breechblock.

MODEL 1940. This pistol was designed and used by Finland under the name "Lahti."

Since this pistol incorporates several unusual design characteristics, a somewhat detailed description is in order.

Description. This pistol is a strange composite of features of the Luger and the Bergmann-Bayard, with several individual characteristics.

Like the Luger the barrel is screwed into an extension which serves as a receiver. This extension, however, is enclosed except for an ejection port on the right side and an emergence cut for the breechblock at the rear.

The exterior appearance somewhat resembles the Luger, the pitch of the grip being very much like it.

The takedown also somewhat resembles the Luger. When the breechblock is back, a dismounting lever above the trigger can be turned to release the assemblies. The barrel and breechblock assemblies will then come off the receiver runners to the front.

The recoil spring is positioned in a tunnel in the rear of the separate breechblock. The head of the recoil spring guide rod projects from the rear of the breechblock.

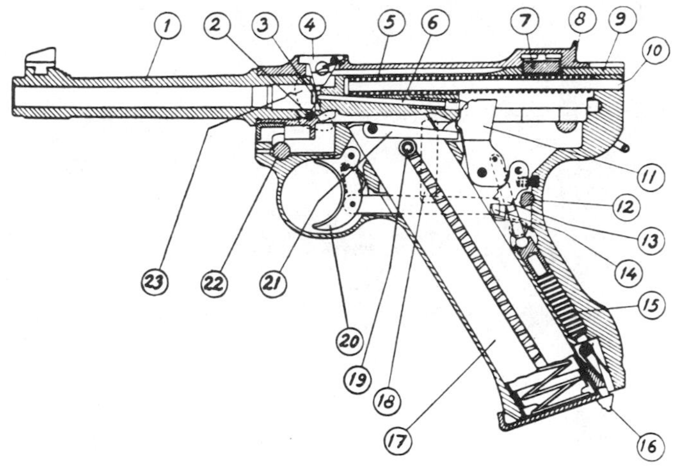

Swedish M1940 (Lahti) Pistol Nomenclature.

1. Barrel.
2. Accelerator pivot.
3. Breechblock face.
4. Extractor.
5. Recoil spring.
6. Firing pin and spring.
7. Locking piece.
8. Rear sight machined in.
9. Breechblock rear.
10. Recoil spring guide.
11. Hammer.
12. Safety.
13. Hammer strut.
14. Sear.
15. Mainspring.
16. Magazine release.
17. Magazine.
18. Disconnector.
19. Magazine platform compressor.
20. Trigger.
21. Breechblock hold-open stop.
22. Barrel and action lock.
23. Accelerator.

Wings with finger grips are machined at the sides of the rear of the breechblock to permit pulling back for loading.

The breechblock travels in the barrel extension. A surface is machined on its under face to force back and ride over an internal hammer. The firing pin is mounted in a sloped tunnel in the forward section of the breechblock below the recoil spring position.

The breech lock is a separate removable unit. It is housed in the bulge in the extreme rear of the barrel extension. When the pistol is locked, the locking piece is in its barrel extension recesses on right and left, and is also in engagement (its inner surfaces) with cuts in the breechblock. During rearward and forward movement, cam faces on the sides of the locking piece are utilized to raise and lower the lock out of and into breechblock engagement.

Magazine is the familiar box type. It has a follower button as in the Luger to make loading easier. The button actuates a pivoted stop when the magazine is empty, to hold the action open.

The trigger is pivoted. It has a bar crossing the grip which transmits the pull on the trigger to release the sear. The internal hammer has the conventional hammer strut which compresses the coil mainspring below it in the handle. The magazine release catch works off the mainspring.

An unusual device is the accelerator in the forward end of the receiver. It is the Browning MG pivoted type. When barrel travel halts, the barrel flips up the point of the accelerator to deliver an accelerating blow to the breechblock to speed up its rearward movement.

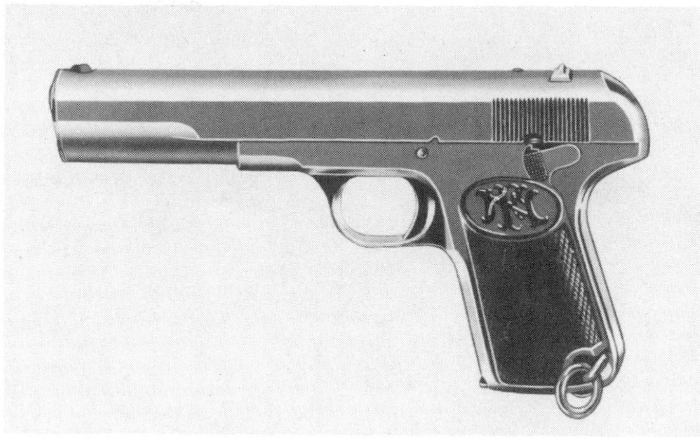

Swedish 9mm Browning Model 07. This obsolete weapon is now on sale in the U. S.

The safety is a positive mechanical block which forces the sear into locked engagement with the hammer notch, making it impossible for the hammer to rotate.

Loading and Firing. Grasp wings of breechblock and pull back over loaded magazine. Release breechblock and let recoil spring drive breechblock ahead to chamber a cartridge.

When magazine is empty, breechblock will be held back. Insert a loaded magazine. Pull back slightly on breechblock wings to release the catch and let the breechblock go forward to load.

Field Stripping. Pull breechblock back over empty magazine. Remove magazine. Turn down dismounting lever above trigger. Pull back breechblock to free it from stop. Ease assemblies forward off receiver. Remove breechblock from barrel extension.

Note: Do not unscrew barrel unless necessary.

Removing stocks will give access to firing mechanism if necessary.

Identification. Exposed barrel with barrel housing enclosing breechblock. Internal hammer firing mechanism. Recoil spring guide mounted in a rise at end of receiver, its button-like projection may be seen jutting out of receiver rear. Ejection port in right side of barrel extension.

Evaluation. Good balance. Exceptionally strong. Very heavy for cartridge used. Well made of excellent materials. Difficult to manufacture. Design uses a minimum of parts and a maximum of machining.

Ammunition. 9mm Luger ammunition will operate. The Swedish service cartridge on limited test appears to be somewhat more powerful, though it is commercially sold in Sweden as "9mm Parabellum," the European designation for Luger.

MODEL 1939. This is the pistol known in Germany as the P-38 (Walther). Caliber is also same as German.

SWEDISH RIFLES AND CARBINES

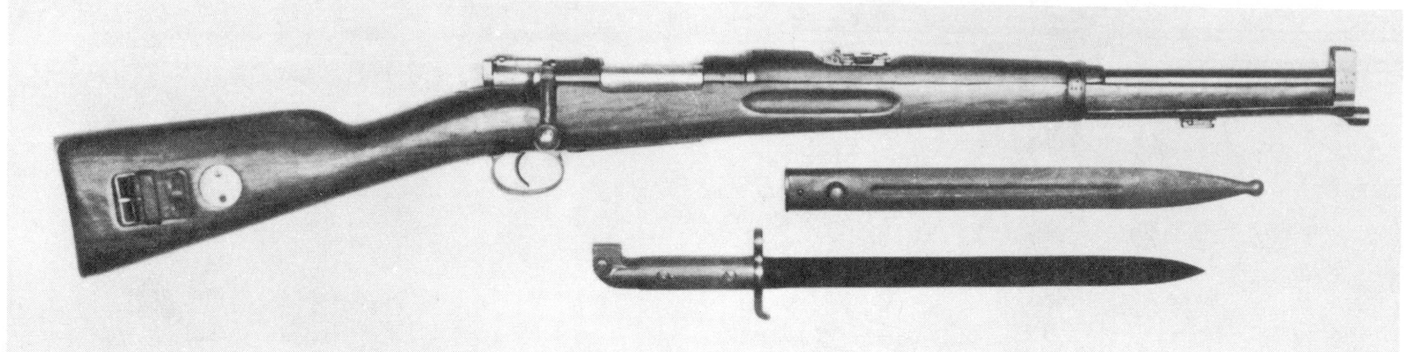

6.5mm Model 94 Carbine.

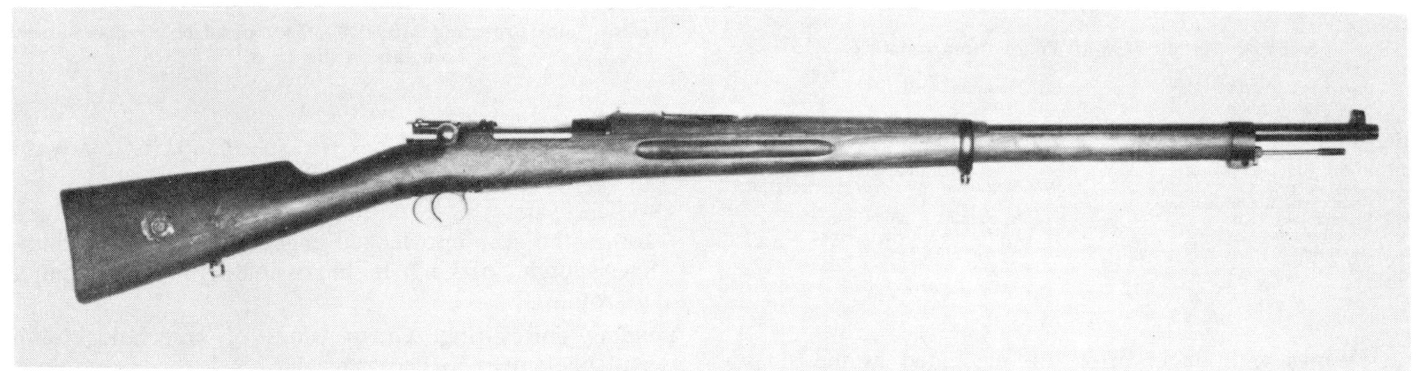

6.5mm Model 96 Rifle.

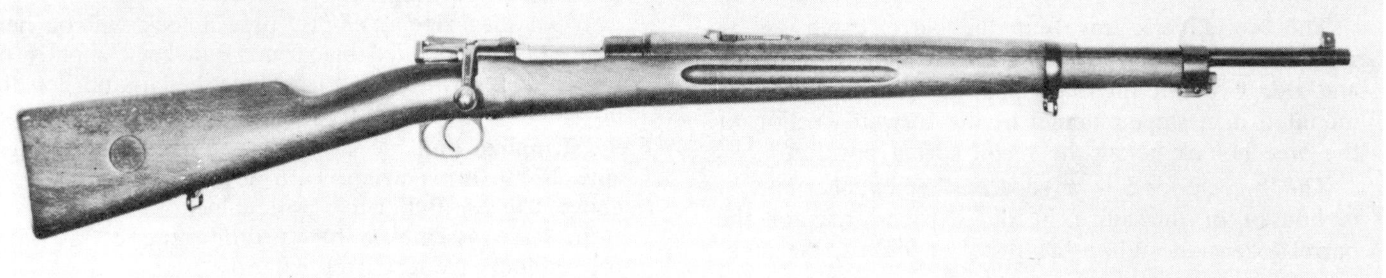

6.5mm Model 38 Rifle. Some had straight bolt handles.

Sweden is disposing of many outdated rifles. Like so many other foreign weapons being sold out these days, a greater number of these excess Swedish weapons are entering the United States. United States gun fans are therefore being exposed for the first time to quantities of Swedish military rifles. Data on old Swedish weapons follows.

The Swedes adopted a 6.5mm Mauser carbine in 1894. This short and light weapon, which is illustrated here, is now obsolete in the Swedish Army. Its action is the same as the M96 rifle, also obsolete, which is now being sold in the United States. The M96 is a very accurate weapon for a military rifle, and very good shooting can be done with it, if it is in good condition and if a micrometer rear sight is fitted to the receiver. The Model 38, a conversion of the M96, is also being sold in the United States at present; a sniper version of this weapon, called the Model 41, is fitted with a telescope that is also called the Model 41.

Swedish Mausers

	M94 Carbine	M96 Rifle	M38 Rifle
Caliber: 6.5mm. x 55mm rimless Mauser cartridge, for all models.			
System of Operation: Manually operated turning bolt action, for all models.			
Weight, Loaded:	7.6 lb.	9.1 lb.	8.5 lb.
Length, Overall	37.6 in.	49.6 in.	44.1 in.
Barrel Length:	17.7 in.	29.1 in.	23.6 in.
Feed Device: 5-round, integral, staggered-row box magazine for all models.			
Sights. Front: Blade, for all models.			
Rear: Leaf with notch, for all models.			
Muzzle Velocity:	2313 f.p.s.	2625 f.p.s.	2460 f.p.s.

The Swedes also used another shoulder weapon, the 8mm M40 rifle. This weapon is a German-produced Kar. 98k which has been rebarreled for the Swedish 8mm x 63mm Bofors M1932 machine gun cartridge. The weapon is fitted with a muzzle brake and has a four-round magazine. It is no longer in Swedish service.

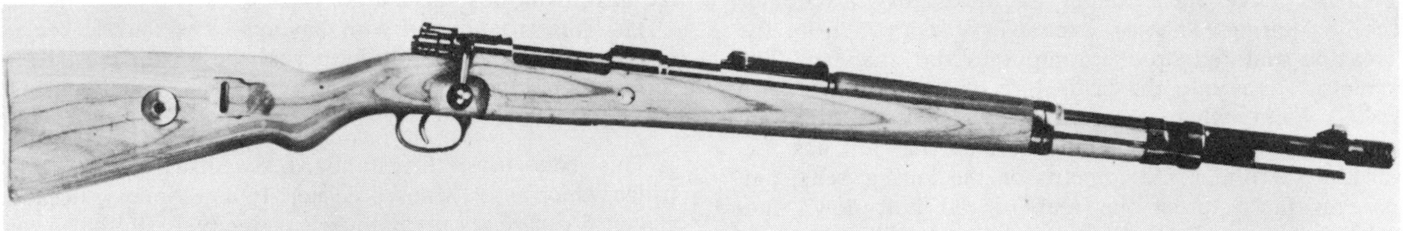

8mm Model 40 Rifle. Note muzzle brake.

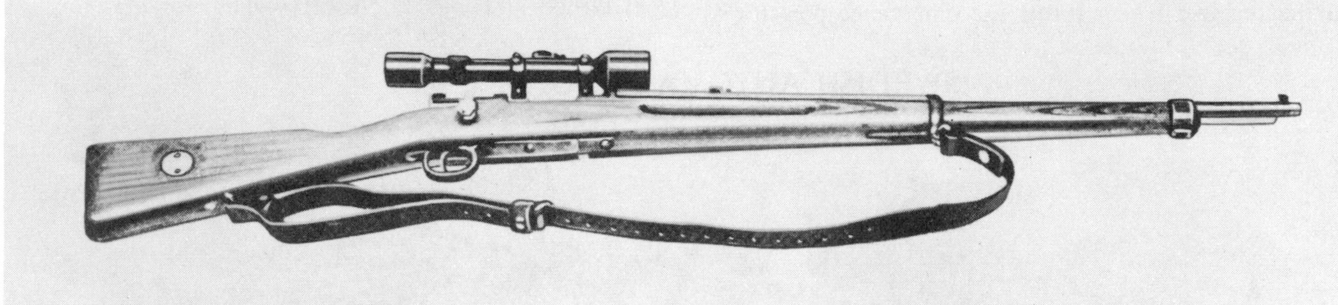

6.5mm Model 41 Rifle. Note scope.

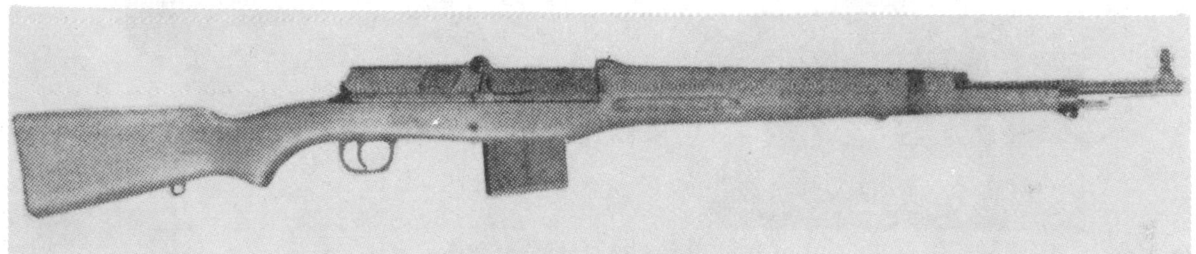

Swedish Gevar AG42B.

The current standard Swedish Army rifle is the 6.5mm semi-automatic rifle Model 42B (called AG 42B by the Swedes).

This rifle was manufactured from the design of the Swedish engineer Ljungman, by the Madsen producers in Denmark and the Swedish arsenal.

Caliber: 6.5mm Swedish service.
Magazine: Protruding double line box below receiver.
Magazine Capacity: 10 rounds. Loadable through top of action with five-shot clips.
Overall Length: 47.9 inches.
Barrel Length: 24.5 inches.
Weight: 10.4 pounds.
Sights: Post front. Receiver rear tangent.
Gun Operated By: Gas through port in top of barrel about one third back from muzzle.
Locked: As in Russian system Tokarev. Rear of bolt cammed down into locking recesses in receiver.
Cocking Handle: Upper right on bolt carrier.
Type of Fire: Single shot semi-automatic only.
Safety: Turn bolt at rear of receiver as in German pattern Kar. 43.
Cooling: Air.
Special Features: Barrel slotted forward of front sight to provide built-in muzzle brake.
Special Note: Gas system is unusual. Direct thrust against bolt carrier.

The gas system is unusual in that it seeks to avoid the use of an intermediary thrusting piston for its actuation.

As the weapon is fired and the bullet passes by the gas port about one third of the distance from the muzzle, gas is tapped off through a hole into the gas cylinder on top of the barrel in standard fashion. The gas is directed back through the gas cylinder where it impinges upon an extension of the bolt carrier whose forward end passes into a mating receiver cut.

The gas thus delivers its thrust directly to the face of the bolt carrier itself.

The bolt carrier has the customary short free travel in its guides in the receiver during which time the bolt itself, lying below the carrier, is locked securely to the receiver by lugs at its rear end being depressed into corresponding receiver cuts.

As the gas pressure drops with the passing of the bullet out of the barrel, cam faces on the bolt carrier engage the bolt and elevate its rear section out of locking engagement. At this point the bolt and carrier with the empty cartridge case gripped in the face of the extractor travel to the rear to compress the recoil springs in the receiver behind the bolt carrier. During the recoil stroke the magazine follower and spring elevate the next cartridge into line for feeding. The bolt and carrier at end of stroke move ahead under the thrust of the counter recoiling spring. The top cartridge is stripped from the magazine and fed up the ramp into the chamber. The extractor snaps into the cannellure of the cartridge case. At this point, where the bolt face is halted against the breech face of the barrel, the bolt carrier still has forward travel under the impetus of the spring behind it. Its cam faces thrust the rear of the bolt down into locking recesses in the receiver. The bolt carrier continues forward as a free member from this point. The front face of the bolt carrier rides into a cup-shaped port in the receiver which forms the emergence port for the gas at the next discharge.

The rifle is equipped with bayonet. The muzzle brake built into the rifle by slotting across the top of the barrel serves to hold the muzzle down to some degree during firing.

This rifle uses the standard Swedish 6.5mm cartridge which is of Mauser design. It is a rimless, necked center fire case. Normal muzzle velocity is of the order of 2400 feet per second. Pressure is low, being of the order of 41,000 pounds per square inch. This rifle has been produced in Egypt in 7.92mm.

SWEDISH AUTOMATIC RIFLES

6.5mm Model 21 Automatic Rifle.

Sweden adopted the Browning automatic rifle in 1921, at which time she bought a quantity of this weapon from Colt. The M1921 is now obsolete in Sweden and some of them, in deactivated condition, have been sold in the United States. The weapon is quite similar to the U. S. M1918 BAR, except that it has a separate pistol grip and dust covers for the ejection port and the magazine well.

Caliber: 6.5mm x 55mm Mauser rimless cartridge.
System of Operation: Gas, selective fire.
Weight: 19.2 lbs.
Length, Overall: 44 in. (approx.).
Barrel Length: 26.4 in.
Feed Device: 20-round, detachable box magazine.
Sights, Front: Blade.
Rear: Leaf w/notch.
Muzzle Velocity: 2460 f.p.s. (approx.).
Cyclic Rate: 500 r.p.m.

Swedish 6.5mm Model 37 Automatic Rifle

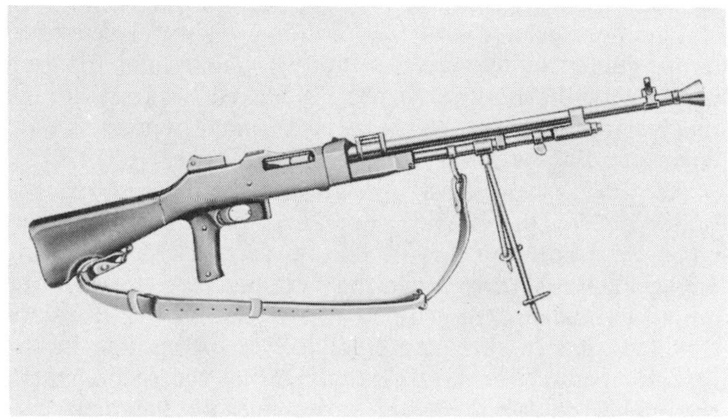

6.5mm Swedish M37 Browning Automatic Rifle, right view.

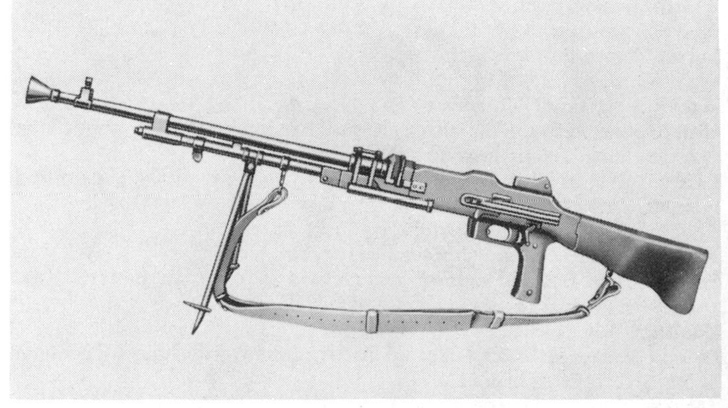

6.5mm Swedish M37 Browning Automatic Rifle, left view.

Caliber: 6.5mm.
System of Operation: Gas, selective fire.
Weight: 21.4 lbs.
Length, Overall: 45.7 in.
Barrel Length: 24 in. (approx.).
Feed Device: 20-round, detachable, staggered-row box magazine.
Sights: Front—Hooded blade.
Rear—Leaf w/aperture graduated to 1200 meters, aperture battle sight.
Muzzle Velocity: 2460 f.p.s. (approx.).
Cyclic Rate: 480 r.p.m.

This modification of the Browning Automatic rifle was developed by the Swedish government arsenal, Carl Gustaf State Arms Factory. It will probably be replaced in the Swedish Army by the 6.5mm Model 58 machine gun.

How to Load and Fire the Model 37. Cock the weapon by pulling the operating handle completely to the rear—push operating handle back to the forward position. The bolt will remain open, since the weapon fires from an open bolt. The safety selector lever is on the left side of the receiver at the top of the pistol grip. Settings are marked "P"-semi-automatic fire; "A"— full automatic fire; and "S"—safety. Insert loaded magazine in magazine well in underside of receiver. If the trigger is pulled and safety selector is set on "P" or "A", the weapon will fire.

Barrel Change. Beginning with an empty weapon, cock gun; push barrel latch (located at top left front of receiver) to the rear. Lift carrying handle and turn 1/4 turn to the right. Pull barrel out.

Field Stripping the Model 37. Remove trigger guard retaining pin, located at left forward end of trigger guard. Pull pistol grip backward and upward and remove. The recoil spring guide bears against the rear of the slide; gently push it back and disengage it from the slide. Line up the hammer pin with the holes in the side of the receiver and with the hole in the operating lever. Push hammer pin out from left to right. Remove operating lever by pulling straight back and remove hammer from the receiver. Push out bolt guide with screwdriver blade and remove bolt link, bolt lock, and bolt. Push barrel latch to rear and remove as described above. Remove gas cylinder retaining pin at forward left side of receiver and slide gas cylinder and bipod straight ahead. Pull slide and gas piston assembly out of receiver. To reassemble the weapon, reverse the above procedure.

How the Model 37 Works. The Model 37 works basically the same as the U. S. Browning Automatic Rifle M1918 covered in chapter 45. The recoil spring in the Model 37 is located in the butt as with the F.N. Type D Browning Automatic Rifle.

SWEDISH SUBMACHINE GUNS

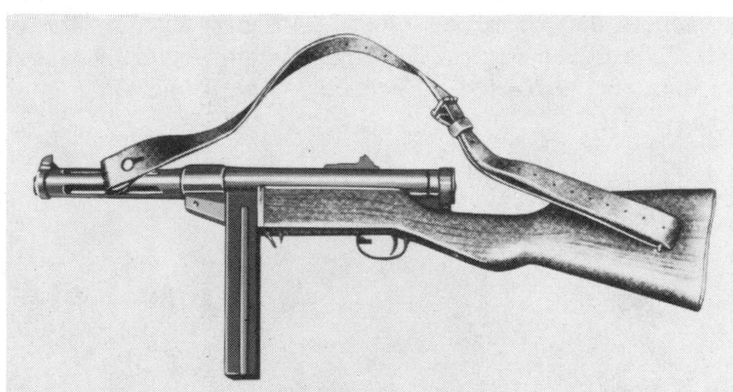

9mm Model 37-39 Submachine Gun.

9mm Model 37-39F Submachine Gun.

The Swedish Army has used a number of submachine guns in the past twenty years. The U. S.-made Thompson was used in limited numbers by the Swedes as the 11mm M40, and the Finnish-designed Suomi was used in two versions, the Model 37-39 and the Model 37-39F. The 9mm Bergmann M34 was used as the Model 39. The 9mm Model 45 (commonly known as the Carl Gustaf) is the current standard submachine gun in the Swedish Army. This weapon has also been produced in Egypt. It was designed and is produced in Sweden at the Carl Gustafs Stads Gevärsfaktori in Eskilstuna. All submachine guns in service fire the 9mm Parabellum cartridge.

Swedish 9mm M45 Submachine Gun with fixed magazine guide, stock fixed.

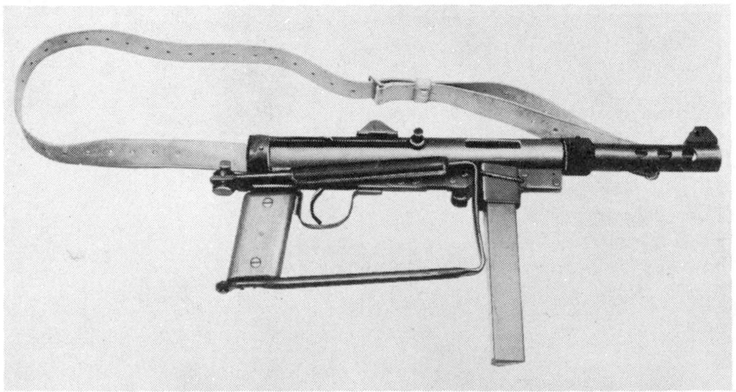

Swedish 9mm M45 Submachine Gun with removable magazine guide, stock folded.

Caliber: 9mm Parabellum.
Magazine: Detachable box, staggered dual line.
Magazine Capacity: 36 cartridges.
Overall Length: 31.8 inches.
Weight: 9.25 pounds (loaded).
Cyclic Rate of Fire: 550 to 600 per minute.
Type of Fire: Automatic.
Operation: Elementary blowback. Actuation of bolt mechanism is by projection of spent case.
Sights: **Front**—Protected post.
Rear—L type.

How to Load and Fire the Model 45. Pull bolt handle to the rear; bolt and bolt handle will remain to the rear since the gun fires from an open bolt. The weapon can be put on safe when the gun is cocked by pulling the bolt handle beyond the sear and engaging it in the cut-out section above the bolt handle track of the receiver. Insert magazine, take weapon off safe, pull trigger, and weapon will fire. To put the weapon on safe with the bolt forward, push down on bolt handle.

How to Field Strip the Model 45. Remove magazine; bolt should be forward. Depress catch in center of the receiver cap (rear of receiver), turn receiver cap slightly counter clockwise, and cap will come off. Remove recoil spring and bolt. Push in on barrel jacket nut catch with a drift and unscrew barrel jacket nut. Remove barrel jacket and barrel. To reassemble, carry out in reverse the steps outlined above.

Special Note on the Model 45. There have been at least three different variations of this weapon since it first appeared in 1945. The variations are in the barrel jacket and magazine guide. Some of the M45s have a removable magazine guide. When the guide is removed the weapon can be used with the thicker Suomi sub-machine gun magazine. The weapon is principally made of stampings and has a folding steel stock.

SWEDISH MACHINE GUNS

The Swedish Army has a collection of various types of machine guns in use at present, but most, if not all, of these weapons will probably be replaced by the Model 58. The Model 58 is the Belgian FN Type M.A.G., and is covered in detail in chapter 16. A Schwarzlose in 6.5mm, the Model 14, was used by Sweden; this weapon is believed to be out of service at present. A series of rifle-caliber Browning guns is used; these weapons are chambered for either the 6.5mm cartridge or the 8mm M1932 cartridge (8mm x 63mm). The Model 36 is a water-cooled gun, and the Model 42 is an air-cooled gun. Both of these guns are similar in loading, firing, functioning, and field stripping to the U. S. cal. .30 Browning guns, although they have a somewhat higher cyclic rate of fire. The Czech-made ZB26 light machine gun in caliber 6.5mm was also used in Sweden as the Model 39.

Swedish 6.5mm M42B Browning Machine Gun

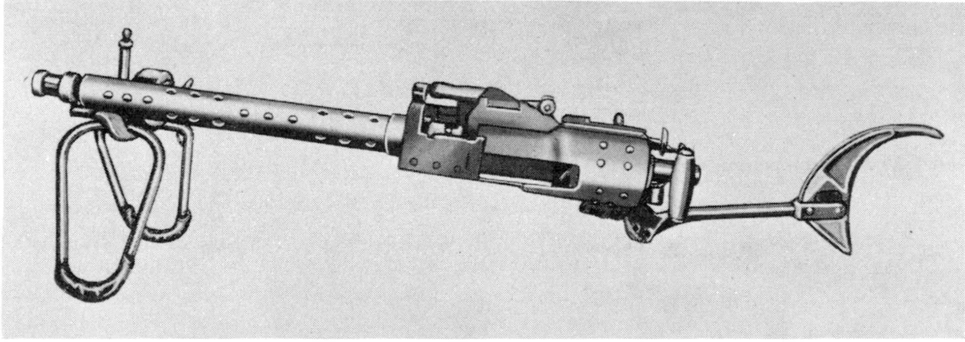

Caliber: 6.5mm or 8mm (8x63mm).
System of Operation: Recoil.
Weight: 35.2 lbs.
Length, Overall: 53.19 in.
Barrel Length: 23.9 in.
Feed Device: 250-round belt.
Muzzle Velocity: 2460 f.p.s. (approx.)
Cyclic Rate: 600-720 r.p.m.

This Browning machine gun is used on a bipod or tripod in the same fashion as the U. S. Browning cal. .30 M1919A6. Its loading, firing, stripping, and functioning are essentially the same as the U. S. Browning. Note that the Swedish Brownings use spade type grips rather than the pistol type grips of the U. S. caliber .30 Brownings. These weapons were also made at the Carl Gustaf plant.

Chapter 41. Switzerland

SWISS PISTOLS

The Swiss service pistol was developed and produced by SIG as the Model 47/8; its official model designation in the Swiss Army is 9mm Pistol Model 49. The older 7.5mm M1882 revolver is no longer being used, and the 7.65mm Model 06/29 Swiss Luger pistols are being disposed of by the Swiss government.

Swiss Automatic Pistol SP47/8 (9mm Model 49).

This is a modified version of the earlier model of the Petter System pistol produced by SIG which replaced the Swiss Luger as the official service arm.

The pistol is a modified Browning locking construction.

Caliber: 9mm Luger (also adaptable to caliber 7.65mm Luger or Parabellum and with special attachments to .22 long rifle).
Magazine: 8 cartridges.
Ballistics: Standard for cartridges used.
Barrel Length: 4.72 inches.
Overall Length: 8.5 inches.
Weight: 2.15 pounds.
Pistol Operated By: Short recoil.
Locked: Ribs on top of barrel engaging in underside cuts in slide as in standard Browning practice. Unlocking through cam on underside of barrel.
Type of Fire: Semi-automatic only.
Magazine Release Catch: Bottom of butt.
Hold-Open Device: Actuated by rising magazine follower in standard fashion.
Safety: Manual. On left side actuated by thumb. Safe in "Up" position.
Unusual Feature: Petter system hammer, sear, and mainspring units combined in single detachable housing.
Sights: Fixed.

Design and Construction

In general this pistol is merely an adaptation of the familiar Browning system. Instead of the hinged locking link as found in the .45 U. S. Government automatic, the unlocking follows more closely that of the later Browning HP 35. A nose on the underside of the barrel is slotted to permit the slide stop pin to pass through, locking it firmly to the receiver. During recoil, the barrel and slide are firmly locked together for approximately ¼ inch of travel. At this point the cam slot in the locking nose below the barrel, working against the transverse slide stop pin, serves to cam the barrel down to draw its locking lugs out of their engaging seats in the underside of the breech of the slide.

This weapon is beautifully made in the finest Swiss tradition. Because of the care taken in fitting the barrel, it demonstrates considerable accuracy.

The takedown is quite simple. In general it follows the standard Colt-Browning procedure to a marked degree except for the firing mechanism.

Dismounting

Hold pistol in right hand. Push magazine catch at bottom of butt with left thumb and withdraw magazine.

Grip right hand around rear of receiver and slide and draw slide back about ½ inch. With finger of left hand push slide stop from right side. Withdraw slide stop from left. This can be done when the thumb piece is lined up with its dismounting notch in the slide.

Ease slide, barrel and recoil spring forward.

Grip hammer with thumb and forefinger and work free and up out of receiver. This unit carries the hammer, disconnector, sear, and mainspring with its guide compression rod. These may be dismounted if desired, but this is not necessary.

Press recoil spring guide forward from rear and lift out. Spring is captive on its guide rod and will not come loose.

Grip barrel lug and work barrel slightly back and up when it can be lifted out of the slide.

Firing pin may be removed if desired by pushing in on its head and drawing stop down out of slide cut as in Colt Govt. .45.

Swiss Model SP47/8 stripped.

Operation

A loaded magazine is inserted in the butt in standard fashion and pushed in until the catch holds it. The slide is then withdrawn to the full length of its recoil stroke to allow magazine spring to force a cartridge up in line for chambering. Releasing the slide permits the compressed recoil spring to drive the slide forward for chambering and locking in standard Browning pistol fashion.

Applying the thumb safety, which is in a particularly advantageous position for easy operation, locks both the trigger and the trigger bar to prevent firing. This design does not have an automatic grip safety as in the case of the Colt Government Model. It does have, however, the automatic disconnector mechanism standard for the Colt-Browning design. If the slide is not fully forward and the barrel not fully locked into position, the slide is automatically depressing the disconnector which in turn is pushing the trigger bar down out of possible contact with the trigger. When the slide is fully forward and locked, the spring can force the disconnector up into its cut in the underside of the slide. This allows the trigger, the trigger bar and the sear to function for firing. As the action opens, the slide automatically cams the disconnector down, forcing the breakage in the trigger contact so that on forward motion of the slide the chambered cartridge will not fire. Thus the trigger must be definitely released before contact can again be made for firing the next shot.

This design has several features which are superior to the Colt Government Model. The forward bushing in the receiver is eliminated, resulting in more machining difficulties but in an inherently simpler design. The recoil spring is under tension in position around its guide rod and during disassembly and reassembly functions as a unit. The unlocking lug on the bottom of the barrel affords much more rigidity during the operation of the pistol. This tends, theoretically at least, to make for more accurate shooting than with the swinging link design. Combining most of the firing mechanism in a single unit (as in the case of the Russian Tokarev pistol) results in a considerable simplification of both design and machining.

As in all weapons of Neuhausen manufacture, the workmanship and materials are impeccable. However, the pistol is costly by American standards, selling for nearly twice that charged for the equivalent Colt pistol.

Because of the extreme care taken in manufacture, the parts of this pistol are truly interchangeable. This applies not only to parts of the same caliber, but to parts for different calibers except, of course, for barrels and springs.

To convert the pistol from 9mm to 7.65mm Parabellum it is only necessary to replace the recoil spring and the barrel. The magazine and all other elements will function with either cartridge, since the 9mm was developed directly from the bottlenecked 7.65mm.

A special .22 caliber conversion training unit is also available for use with this pistol for practice shooting. It consists of a lighter weight slide, a special barrel with recoil spring and a magazine. This conversion, of course, does not require a locked breech, hence the barrel is not equipped with locking lugs and does not have any movement. Once installed it is locked in place. The operation is otherwise identical with that of the heavier caliber.

An additional 4mm barrel is provided for indoor training if desired. This is a single shot conversion, however.

Considerable attention was given to pitch of grip in the design of this pistol. The center of gravity is at about the trigger point. The locking cam system of barrel operation, as opposed to the swinging link system, prevents movement of the barrel out of the firing axis while the bullet is still in the barrel. This together with the lack of a front bushing makes for a much more solid barrel support. This weapon is now called P210 by the manufacturer, SIG.

Neuhausen M1944/16 pistol. Browning-Petter system locked breech, small exposed hammer. Thumb safety and bottom magazine release. Magazine capacity 16 cartridges. Caliber 9mm Parabellum (Luger). Also made with single line 8-shot magazine. Very few specimens of this weapon were made.

SWISS RIFLES AND CARBINES

The Swiss have adopted a new weapon to replace their Schmidt Rubin rifles. This weapon is the SIG-developed Sturmgewehr (assault rifle) Model 57, described later in this section. It is chambered for the same 7.5mm Model 11 cartridge that was used in the M1911 rifle and carbine and in the Model 31, 31/42, and 31/43 carbines. The weapon was originally called the AM 55 by SIG, and is now called the Model 510 by that concern. Considerable quantities of the older Schmidt Rubin rifles and the M1893 Mannlicher carbine have been sold by the Swiss government. Most of these weapons have come to the United States and are quite widely distributed among gun collectors in this country at present. For this reason the coverage on the Schmidt Rubin rifles and carbines follows.

Swiss Schmidt Rubin Rifles and Carbines

The original Schmidt Rubin rifle appeared in 1889. It has a long staggered-row box magazine, and a very long receiver. The bolt of this straight pull rifle had its locking lugs at the rear. Modifications of this basic design are as follows:

M1889/96. The 1889 action was shortened slightly, and the lug system was strengthened.

M97 Cadet Rifle. A single-shot version of the M1889/96 action, made for the training of cadets.

Model 89/00 Short Rifle. A special short rifle designed for the use of Fortress Artillery, Signal, Balloon, and Bicycle troops. This weapon, which weighs approximately seven pounds, has a lower velocity than the M1889 rifle.

Model 1889 Schmidt Rubin Rifle. Should not be used with latest type Swiss cartridges.

M93 Mannlicher Cavalry Carbine. Few made.

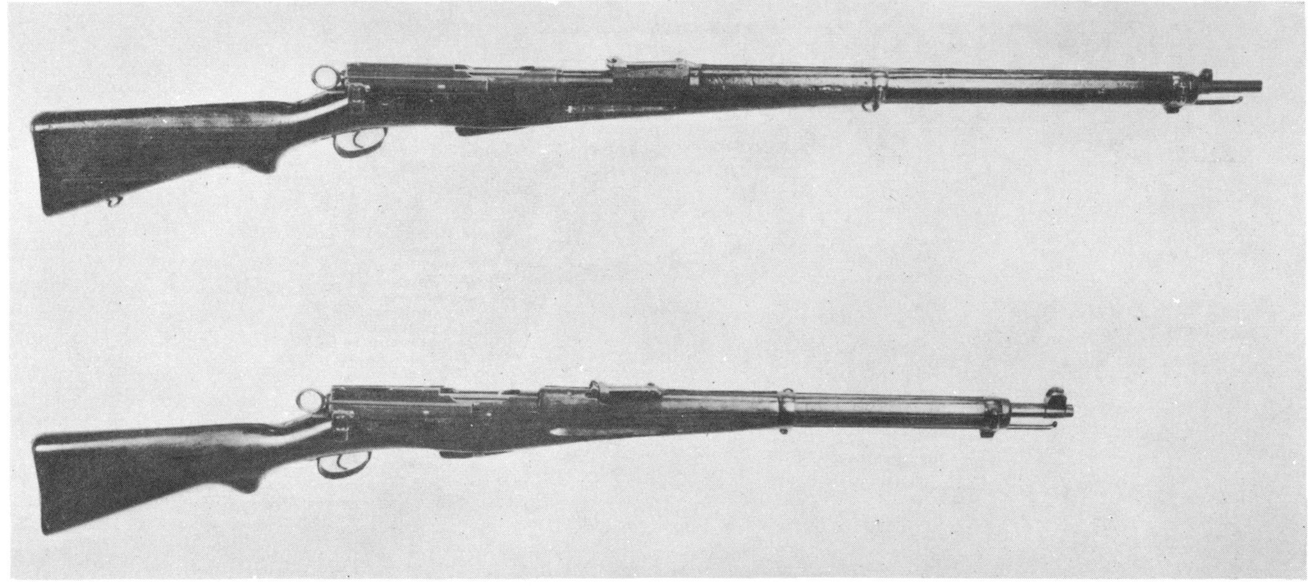

Rifle M1911 and Carbine M1911.

Model 1905 Carbine. Weighs approximately 7.5 pounds; uses the same action as the M1889/96 rifle.

M1896/11 Rifle. An alteration of the M1889/96 rifle, and some of the carbines, to make them suitable for use with the Model 11 ammunition.

M1911 Rifle. The first of the Schmidt Rubin's made specifically for the 7.5mm Model 11 cartridge. The Model 11 cartridge has a much higher pressure than the earlier Swiss cartridges. Therefore the basic 1889 action design had to be modified to handle the new cartridge safely. The locking lugs were relocated from the rear of the locking sleeve to the front of the locking sleeve. The M1896/11 action is similar. The M1911 rifle also had a bolt-holding-open device.

M1911 Carbine. Differs from the M1911 rifle by having a shorter barrel and stock and being lighter. Its rear sight is graduated to 1500 meters, rather than to the rifle's 2000 meters. The M1911 carbine is still in limited use in Switzerland. It can be identified by the red plastic bolt handle knobs.

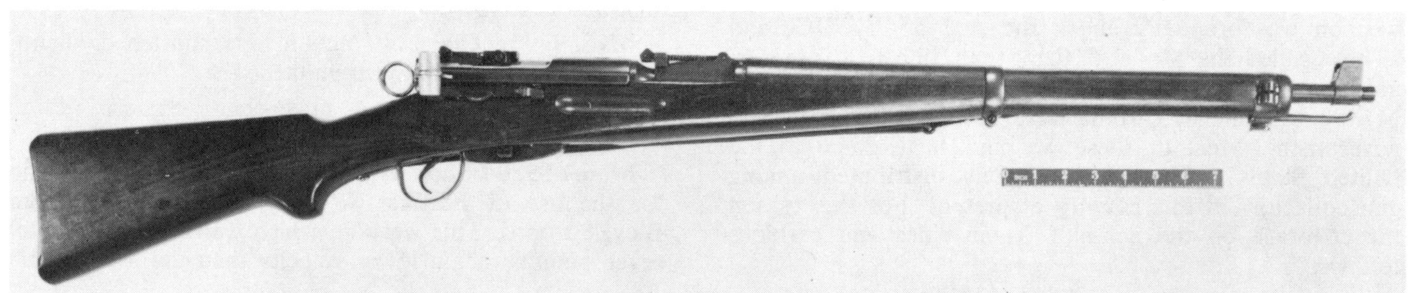

Model 31 (K31) Schmidt Rubin. Best of the designs.

M1931 Carbine. Commonly known as the K31. This weapon represents the last basic change in the design of the Schmidt Rubin. The basic difference between this weapon and the earlier Schmidt Rubins is the elimination of the long bolt extension. All earlier Schmidt Rubin bolts had a long bolt extension which actually rammed the cartridge into the chamber, supported its base, and extracted it from the chamber. It could be considered that this piece was the bolt body. This piece did not rotate in unlocking; the bolt sleeve rotated, instead. The bolt sleeve, a piece which supported the rear of the extension, had the locking lugs. (In the rifles before 1911, the lugs were at the rear; in the rifles after 1911, at the front.) Thus, an abnormally long receiver was needed for these weapons, and the locking lugs were a long way to the rear of the point where they were actually needed. It was not a very satisfactory design from a military point of view, since it meant a great deal of extra length and weight and still did not offer the best type of bolt support. In the K31, the part which was formerly considered the bolt sleeve became the bolt body itself, and the locking lugs were mounted at its head in the position where they were most needed. This shortening of the bolt assembly has resulted in a much better weapon which, although it is about the same overall length as the M1911 carbine, has a barrel 2.5 inches longer (made possible by the shorter receiver). The earlier weapons had their magazines placed a considerable distance in front of the triggerguard, because of the position of the long bolt extension. The magazine of the K31, on the other hand, is immediately ahead of the triggerguard. All in all, the K31 is a vastly superior weapon to the earlier Schmidt Rubins.

Model 31/42 Carbine, K31/42. One of the two sniper versions of the K31. It has a 1.8-power scope permanently built into the left side of the receiver. The head of this scope resembles a periscope, and, when in use, is lifted up; when not in use, it is folded down against the side of the carbine. The weapon has a tangent-type metallic rear sight, graduated from 100 to 1000 meters.

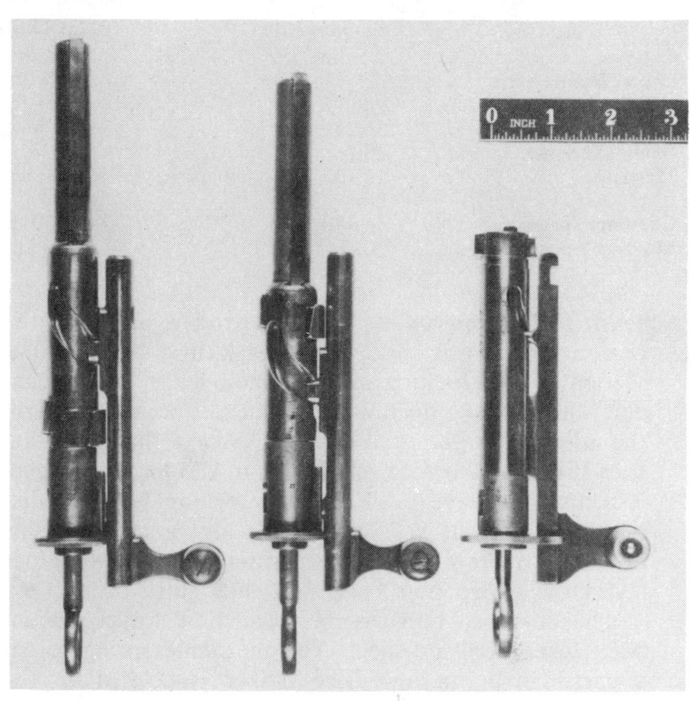

Schmidt Rubin Bolts. Left: M1889 with locking lugs at rear of sleeve. Center: M1911 with locking lugs at front of sleeve. Right: M31 with locking lugs at front of bolt.

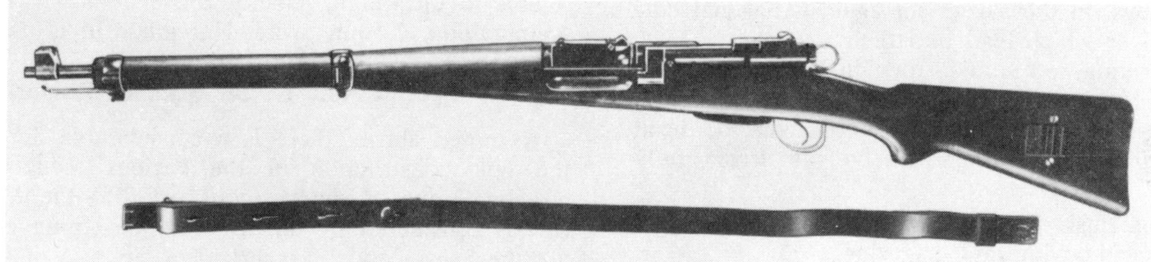

Model 31/43 Carbine. Periscopic type sight folded behind rear sight.

Model 31/43 Carbine, K31/43. Equipped with a 2.8-power scope mounted like that of the K31/42. Its metallic rear sight is graduated from 100 to 700 meters.

Model 31/55 Sniper Rifle. Note bipod position and telescopic sight.

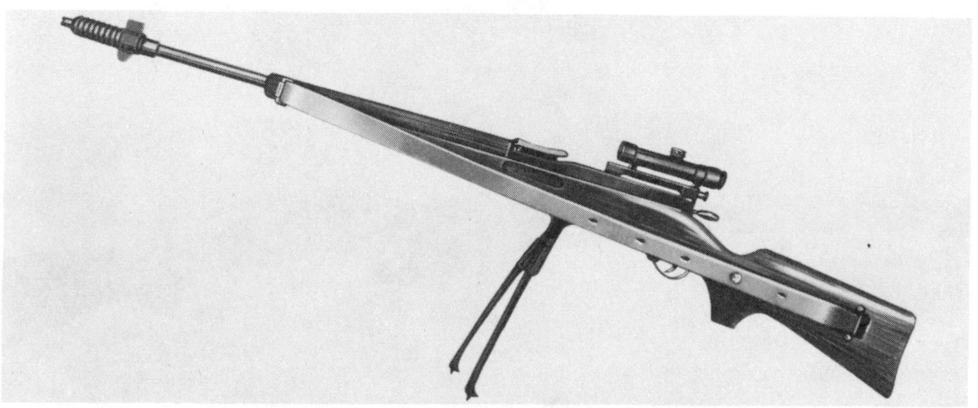

Schmidt Rubin Model 31/55 Sniper Rifle.

Characteristics of the Significant Schmidt Rubins

	M1889 Rifle	M1911 Rifle	M1911 Carbine	M1931 Carbine
Caliber:	7.5mm	7.54mm	7.54mm	7.51mm
Land Diameter:	.295 in.	.2968 in.	.2968 in.	.2956 in.
Weight:	9.8 lb.	10.15 lb.	8.6 lb.	8.83 lb.
Length, Overall:	51.25 in.	51.6 in.	43.4 in.	43.5 in.
Barrel Length:	30.7 in.	30.7 in.	23.3 in.	25.67 in.
Magazine:	12-rd. detachable box	6-rd. detachable box	6-rd. detachable box	6-rd. detachable box
Chamber pressure:	38,400 p.s.i.	45,500 p.s.i.	45,500 p.s.i.	45,500 p.s.i.
Muzzle Velocity:	2033 f.p.s.	2640 f.p.s.	2490 f.p.s.	2560 f.p.s.

Schmidt Rubin Operation. When the rod is pulled to the rear, its operating stud starts back in a straight cut section of the locking sleeve which leads to the cam cut. During this opening movement another stud on the rod draws the striker back. When the operating stud hits the cam face of the cut in the locking sleeve, it turns the sleeve until the two locking lugs are disengaged from the receiver. These lugs and their seats are cut to screw pitch. The turning motion therefore starts the entire bolt back and thus starts extraction.

The unlocked bolt assembly can now travel straight back to extract and eject. The magazine spring forces a cartridge up in line. The striker is cocked on the rearward pull.

Closing. Pushing the operating handle forward drives the bolt assembly forward. The cartridge is chambered and the locking sleeve turned into locking engagement when the lugs on the sleeve act against diagonal cuts in the receiver which lead into their seatings.

The operating rod stud is then in the straight section of the locking sleeve cut ready for the next rearward movement. The extractor snaps over the head of the cartridge case when the bolt is driven fully forward.

Field Stripping. Push down magazine catch lever on right side of rifle and withdraw magazine.

Pull bolt all the way back, then push it forward slightly. Press thumb piece of bolt release on right side of receiver, and while holding it depressed pull bolt out of receiver.

Unscrewing bolt cap and removing it permits removal of locking sleeve and of firing units.

Identification. Operating handle on right side operates on push-and-pull system. Detachable box magazine. Special revolving locking sleeve on bolt locks in receiver bridge.

Evaluation. From the standpoint of materials and workmanship, these are among the finest rifles ever made. Primary extraction is not as powerful as in turn bolt designs. With good ammunition this rifle can be fired at a very rapid rate for a manually operated arm; but this factor is not important in this day of semiautomatic operation.

By American standards this is a complicated design. It has never been submitted to war test, but for accuracy and rapidity of fire as developed in Switzerland for that country's purposes, it has been rated as a most efficient arm. Only the perfection of the semiautomatic type will make it obsolete in Switzerland. The factor of rear locking makes some designs unsuitable to ultra-high velocity conversions.

Ammunition. 7.5mm Swiss. Not made in U. S.

Special Note on the Schmidt Rubins

As noted above, there is a considerable difference in the bolt construction of the various models of this weapon. None of the weapons prior to the M1896/11 rifle is considered by the Swiss to be strong enough to use the Swiss Model 11 cartridge. Because of slight differences in bore diameter and rifling, the early rifles will not shoot the Model 11 cartridge very accurately. The early rifles should be used with the Swiss 7.5mm M1890/23 cartridge; this cartridge has a 190-grain, conical-nosed bullet. They should not be used with the Spitzer-pointed Model 11 cartridge which has a 174 grain bullet.

Swiss SK46 7.5mm Rifle. Left side view with iron sight.

This weapon appeared only as a prototype.

Caliber: 7.5mm Swiss service. (Note: also procurable in caliber 7.92mm German.) Design could be made for any standard rimless military cartridge.
Magazine: Protruding box dual line.
Magazine Capacity: 6 or 12 cartridges in caliber 7.5mm. 5 or 10 cartridges in caliber 7.92mm.
Loading: Clip inserted through bottom of action.
Overall Length: 43.9 inches.
Barrel Length: 23.2 inches.
Weight: About 9.9 pounds.
Sights: Hooded blade front. Tangent rear.
Note: Special detachable telescopic sight provided. Rifle has built-in scope base.
Gun Operated By: Gas. Short stroke system. Gas chamber unusual. On the right side of receiver. Piston in cylinder carries bolt unlocking latch.
Locked: One piece bolt locked by camming up into receiver recess by tilting rear.

Design

The breechblock is a single unit whose rear end is tipped up to engage in recesses in the machined upper section of the tubular receiver. The gas piston, which actuates the bolt, carries a locking arm together with guide and recoil spring and is positioned on the right side of the main breechblock tube. Other details are generally standard for a gas-functioned semi-auto rifle.

Gas operated Swiss SK46 stripped.

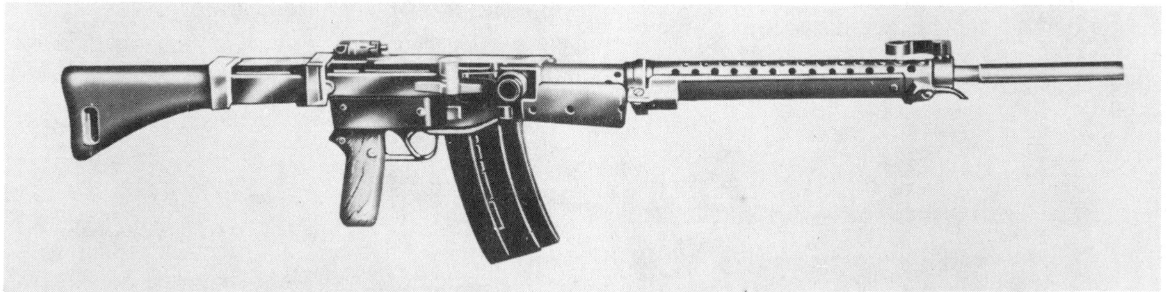

Model 57, Right Side. Current Production.

Caliber: 7.5mm (Swiss Model 11 cartridge).
System of Operation: Delayed blowback, selective fire.
Weight, Empty: 12.32 lb.
Length, overall: 43.4 in.
Barrel Length: 23 in., w/muzzle brake.
Feed Device: 24-round, detachable, staggered-row box magazine.
Sights, Front: Folding blade, w/protecting ears.
Rear: Folding aperture, w/micrometer adjustment graduated from 100 to 650 meters.
Muzzle Velocity: 2493 f.p.s.
Cyclic Rate: 450 to 500 r.p.m.

Swiss 7.5mm Model 57 Assault Rifle.

The selective-fire Model 57 will eventually replace all the Schmidt Rubins in Swiss service. The action of this rifle is similar to that of several weapons which were in prototype stage in Germany at the end of World War II. The developer of this weapon, the Swiss Industrial Company of Neuhausen Am Rheinfalls, Switzerland (commonly known as SIG or Neuhausen) has also developed two machine guns using the rifle's delayed-blowback action—the MG 710-1, and the MG 710-2; these machine guns, formerly known as the MG 55-1 and MG 55-2, are not used by the Swiss Army.

How to Load and Fire the Model 57

Insert a loaded magazine in the magazine well and pull the operating handle to the rear (the operating handle is located on the right side of the receiver). Release the operating handle, and the bolt will go home, chambering a cartridge. Set the safety selector on the letter "E" if semi-automatic fire is desired, or on the letter "M" if full automatic fire is desired. Pressure on the trigger will fire the weapon. To set the weapon on safe, set the safety selector on the letter S.

How to Field Strip the Model 57

Remove the magazine by pushing forward the magazine catch, located at the forward end of the triggerguard. Depress the butt retaining catch, located on the forward underside of the butt; turn the butt approximately one-quarter turn to the right, and remove the butt and recoil spring. Pull the operating handle to the rear, and remove the bolt assembly. No further disassembly is recommended.

To reassemble the weapon, perform the above steps in reverse order.

How the Model 57 Works

When the trigger is pulled, the hammer is released and hits the firing lever mounted on the rear of the bolt. The firing lever strikes the firing pin, which hits the primer of the cartridge. The gas pressure forces the base of the cartridge against the head of the two-piece bolt. When a certain pressure has been reached, the locking rollers begin forcing rearward the nose of the rear section of the bolt. The locking rollers are then free to slip back into their recesses in the bolt head, and the weapon unlocks. The bolt travels to the rear, compressing the recoil spring, extracting and ejecting the spent case, and cocking the hammer. The recoil spring drives the bolt forward again, and the bolt picks up and chambers another round. The nose of the rear section of the bolt cams the locking rollers into their locking recesses in the receiver. If the weapon has been set on semi-automatic fire, the trigger must be pulled again. This weapon fires from a closed bolt on both automatic and semi-automatic fire. If the weapon has been set on automatic fire, it will continue

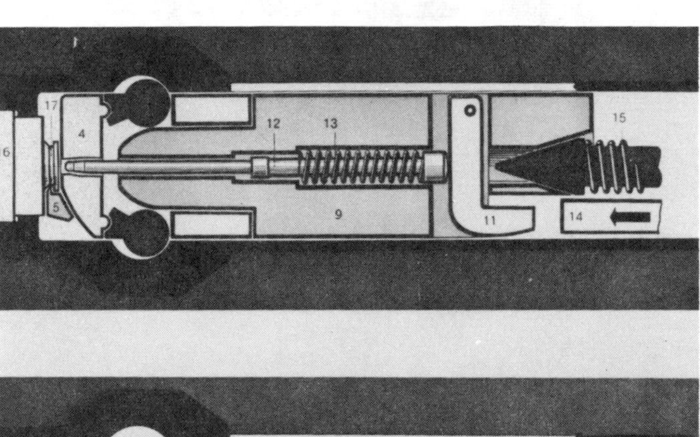

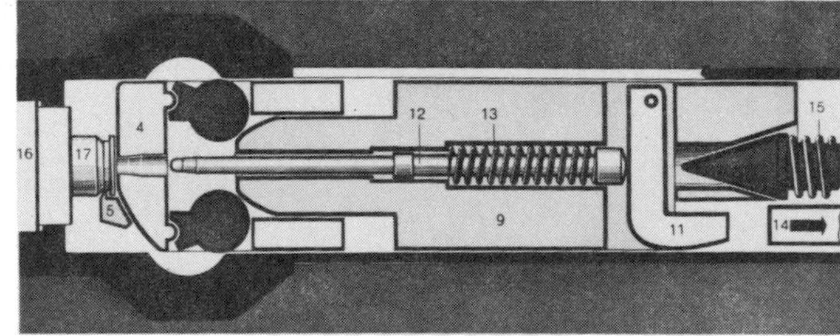

Bolt Action of the Model 57. Upper: bolt locked. Lower: bolt traveling to rear after unlocking.

3. Locking roller
4. Bolt head
5. Extractor
9. Rear bolt section
11. Firing lever
12. Firing pin
13. Firing pin spring
14. Hammer
15. Recoil spring and recoil spring guide
16. Barrel
17. Cartridge case

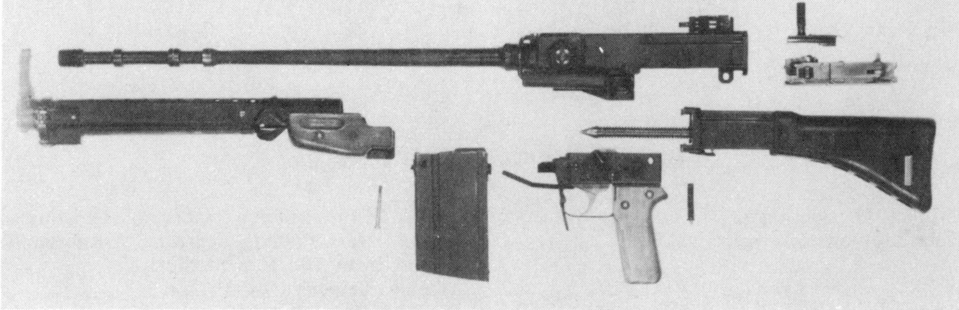

Model 57 Field Stripped.

to fire as long as the trigger is held to the rear and there are cartridges remaining in the magazine.

Special Note on the Model 57

The Model 57 has many interesting features. Its delayed-blowback action is worthy of note. The bolt is composed of two principal parts—the head and the rear section. The head is approximately one-fourth as heavy as the rear section. The head section contains two locking rollers which are cammed into recesses in the receiver by the nose section of the rear part of the bolt. The principal difference between this weapon and the Spanish CETME assault rifle, insofar as the bolt is concerned, is that the CETME fires from an open bolt on automatic fire. Since this system has no provision for slow initial extraction, both weapons have fluted chambers to "float" the neck and forward part of the case on gas.

The Model 57 has a built-in rifle grenade launcher and a rubber butt stock. The rubber butt helps to absorb the shock of firing grenades when a wall, the rear of a trench, etc., is used as a support. A winter trigger is built into the gun. By the use of two spring-loaded catches in the barrel jacket, the bipod can be used to support the weapon either at the rear or at the front of the jacket. Everything considered—method of construction, firepower potential, and ease of maintenance—it is obvious that the Model 57 represents a great advance in the equipment of the Swiss Army.

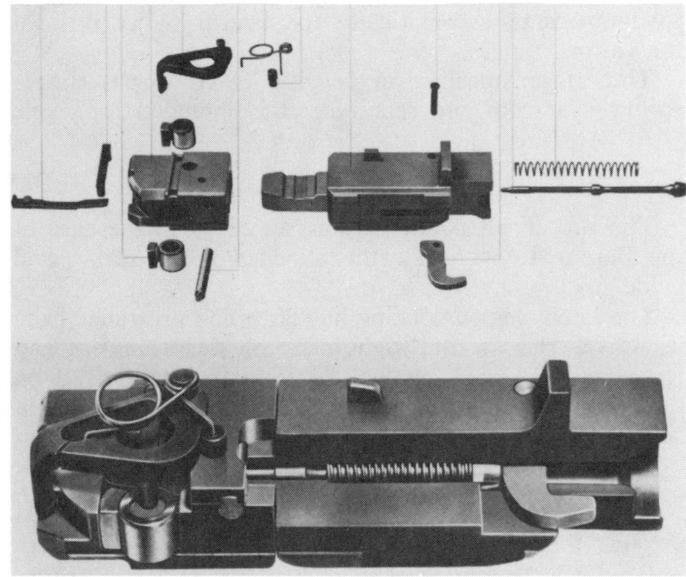

Model 57 Bolt.

SWISS SUBMACHINE GUNS

Since 1934 Switzerland has been a leading submachine gun manufacturer and exporter.

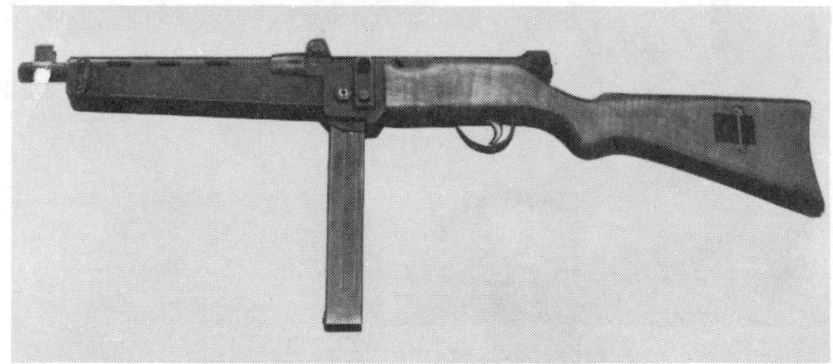

Swiss MP 46 Submachine Gun.

Caliber: 9mm Parabellum.
Magazine: Detachable box through bottom of receiver.
Ballistic Data: Standard for cartridge.
Overall Length: 830mm.
Barrel Length: 300mm.
Weight: With empty magazine 3.95 kg.
Magazine Capacity: 40 cartridges.
Cyclic Firing Rate: 850 per minute.
Type of Fire: Semi-auto or full auto by selector.
Operation: Standard blowback. Projection of spent case.
Stock Type: Standard with shoulder design. (Note: This arm may also be made for other pistol-caliber cartridges.)
Cocking Handle: Protrudes through cut in right side of receiver. Gun fires from open breech in standard fashion as required by rapid heating.
Magazine Release Catch: Stud on left side of receiver.
Cooling: Air. Barrel has perforated jacket.

Construction

This gun is of heavy, exceptionally robust construction. In general, however, it is considered rather too heavy for standard submachine gun use in general world military practice today.

The barrel is pressfit into a tubular receiver and secured with a transverse pin.

The barrel jacket (or casing) is perforated to allow additional radiation. The stock is specially designed to accommodate the folding magazine which is a very interesting part of this arm. The magazine may be retained in the gun but hinged forward to lie parallel to and below the barrel casing when the weapon is being transported and no immediate need is envisioned for rapid use.

This folding magazine design is also utilized as a safety factor. When the magazine is hinged forward there is no danger of accidental firing, since the cartridge column is entirely beyond reach of the breechblock under any considerations.

Pressure on the release catch with the left thumb allows the magazine to drop by virtue of its own weight into the vertical position. It is snapped into locking position. The cocking handle is pulled to the rear and the gun is ready for instant firing. A safety lever is also provided for locking the breech and the trigger.

The cylindrical breechblock is blowback operated. It is of very heavy and rugged construction. It carries the firing pin and extractor.

The sight mounted on the receiver rather far forward has four positions—50, 100, 200, and 300 meter ranges. The sight is unusual in that it has been designed to compensate automatically for lateral bullet drift at the various ranges.

The trigger mechanism consists of a trigger, trigger spring, sear rod, and sear bar. It is intended for single or full automatic fire without the use of a special change lever.

Pulling the trigger forward a short distance allows fire of single shot order. Drawing the trigger back to its full length keeps it entirely out of possible sear engagement to allow automatic fire so long as cartridges remain in the magazine.

Dismounting

The breech plug may be unscrewed as in the case of the Beretta to withdraw the attached recoil spring and guide.

The knob shaped cocking handle which protrudes from its travel slot in the right side of the receiver, and is normally secured in place by the compression rod on the recoil spring, may now be withdrawn from the right side of the receiver. The bolt and firing pin will now come out to the rear.

Unscrewing the front sight nut will permit the front sight to be withdrawn. The barrel casing may now be lifted off. Removal of triggerguard screws permits removal of triggerguard. Remaining elements may be lifted out of the stock and by driving out pins complete disassembly may be continued.

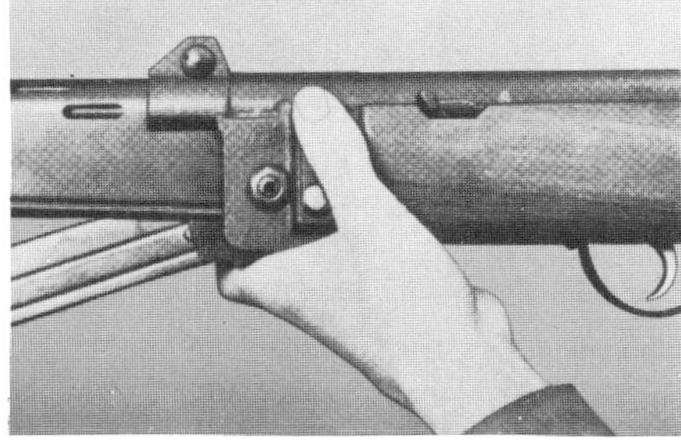

Press catch and lower magazine to firing position.

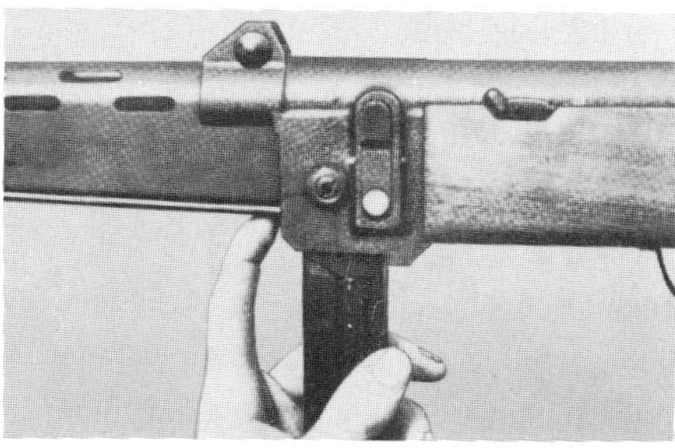

Press magazine lock and withdraw magazine.

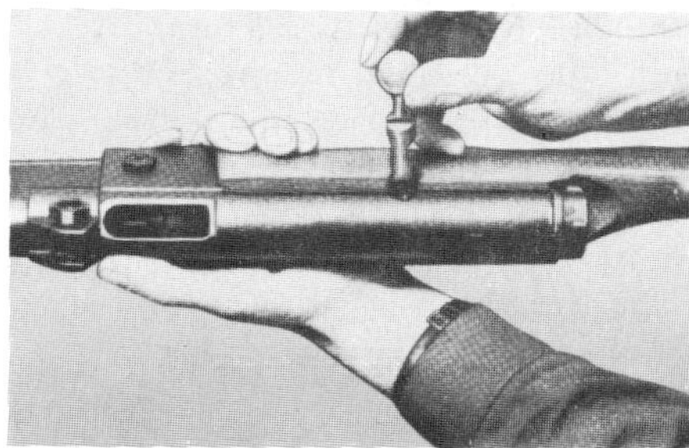

Twist and remove end plug and guide. Then turn gun on side and withdraw cocking handle.

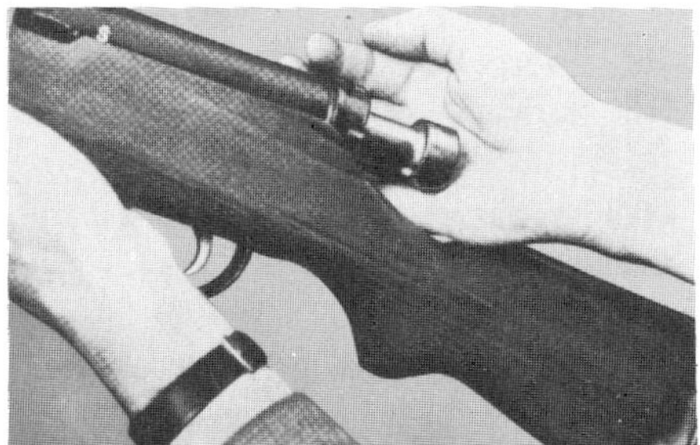

Breechblock may be withdrawn now.

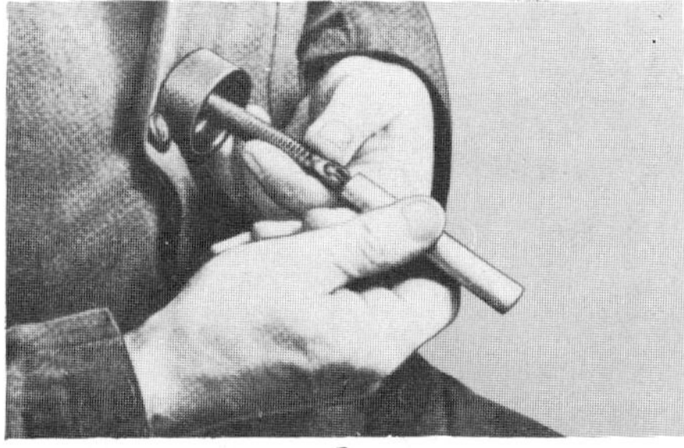

Remove bolt plug and spring from guide.

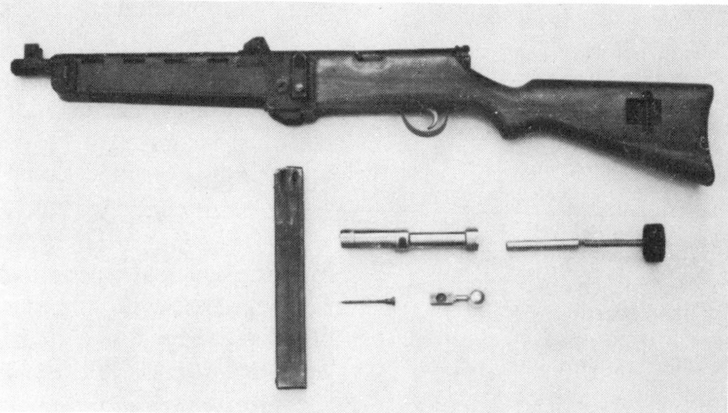

Swiss MP 46 stripped.

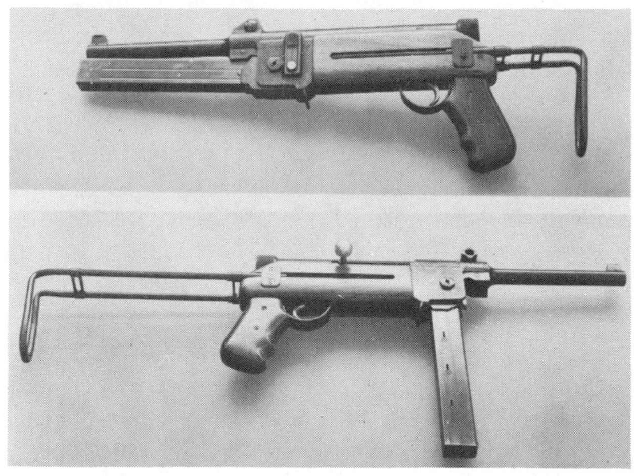

Swiss MP 48 (MP310) Submachine Gun.
Upper: Magazine folded. Stock seated. Gun ready for transport. Lower: Magazine in firing position. Bolt cocked. Stock extended ready for shoulder firing.

This weapon is a modification of the earlier Model 1946. It is a far more practical application of the design from the standpoint of common military usage today.

It is normally supplied in caliber 9mm Parabellum, which is the current caliber of the Swiss forces for pistol and submachine gun use. However, it is also available in other calibers to special order. In particular, it is also used in Switzerland with the 7.65mm Parabellum, which was their standard before adoption of the 9mm.

With stock extended (butt unfolded), the overall length is 42.1 inches. With stock folded it is 28.15 inches.

The weight has been drastically reduced to 6.4 pounds (exclusive of magazine) from the earlier 46 Model. However, the cyclic rate has been stepped up by lightening parts to about 700 rounds per minute, a rate which is high for effective use.

The design utilizes many precision castings instead of stampings in an attempt to provide additional reliability through rigidity. Such castings also allow relatively low cost prototype and limited production runs. In large scale manufacture such castings are normally inadvisable because of cost.

The forward hinging magazine principle of the earlier type is retained. This gives an extremely compact weapon when combined with the pistol grip type wooden stock which is still bulky to permit of balance and ease of handling, but which is grooved on both sides to receive a sliding telescopic steel butt, very much like that of the U.S. M3.

The barrel has been shortened and the barrel casing dispensed with as unnecessary for the type of fire normally visualized for submachine gun use. The sighting radius is deficient in that the rear sight is placed forward of the magazine housing on the receiver. Indicator slots in the side wall of the magazine show the positions of 20, 30, and 40 cartridges in the column.

With its combination of shoulder stock and forward hinging magazine, this is a most compact and one of the most rugged submachine guns ever produced. These factors of compactness and relatively light weight for a weapon of its sort give this Swiss MP 48 a distinction which no other competing weapon possesses. In view of the trigger system which easily permits of either single shot or full automatic fire, this lightness and compactness provide a new approach to the matter of efficiently arming special service groups.

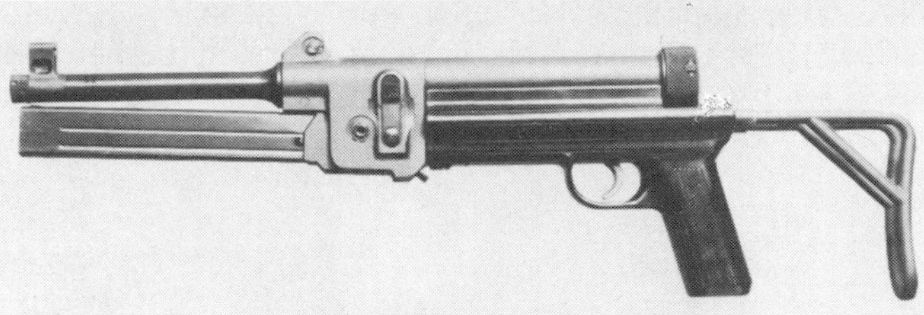

Latest Version of MP 310.

Model 43/44 9mm Submachine Gun.

The Model 43/44 was the main Swiss Army submachine gun during and after World War II, and is still standard. It is a copy of the Finnish Suomi. It was manufactured at the Swiss government arsenal at Bern under Finnish Suomi license, and was also made by Hispano-Suiza in limited numbers for the Swiss government.

Caliber: 9mm Parabellum.
System of Operation: Blowback, selective fire.
Weight, empty: 9.5 lb. (approx.).
Length, overall: 34 in. (approx.).
Barrel, length: 12.5 in. (approx.).
Weight, empty: 9.5 lb. (approx.).
Feed device: 50-rd. box magazine.

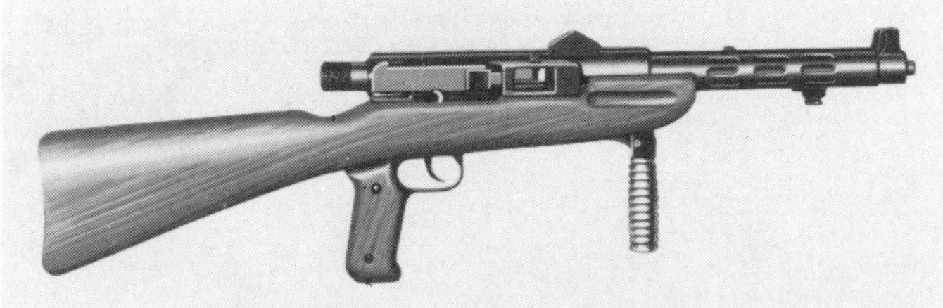

Swiss Model 41/44 Submachine Gun.

This weapon is chambered for the 9mm Parabellum cartridge. It is recoil operated similar to the Model 25 light machine gun. Forward hand grip may be folded forward for carrying. High cyclic rate of 900 r.p.m.

Another popular submachine gun once made in Switzerland is the Erma. This original German design was made in the late thirties and was widely used in the Spanish Civil War of 1937-38. The main information on this weapon will be found in chapter 26.

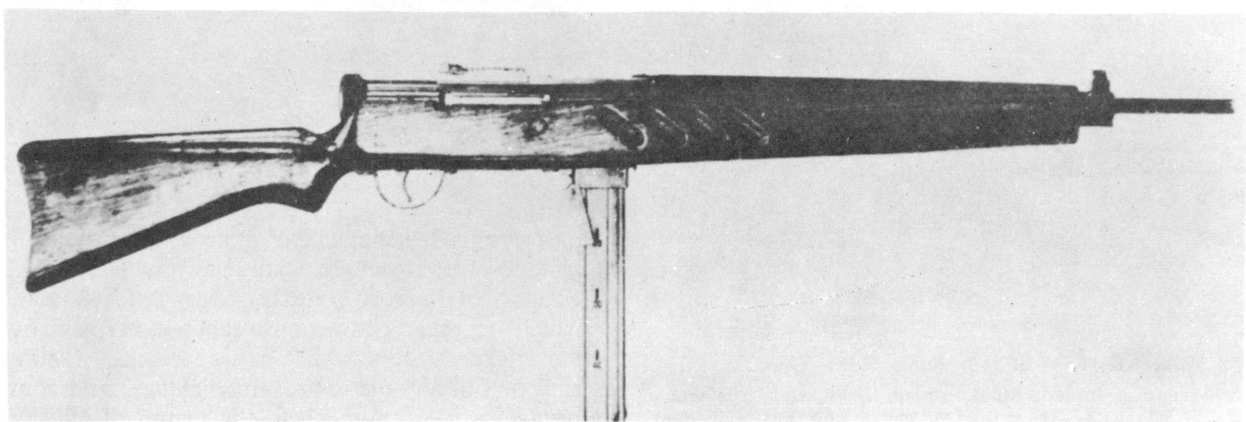

Swiss Model 1934 Submachine Gun.

Caliber: 9mm (in most versions).
Weight: 9 lb. (approx.).
Magazine: 40-rd.
Sights (open): Adjustable from 100 to 1000 meters.
Rate of fire: 800 to 850 r.p.m.

One private firm in Switzerland, the SIG plant at Neuhausen, has made a wide variety of submachine guns. The earliest of these came out about 1934. This model was sold to Germany and several other countries outside Switzerland. The weapon looks like a carbine, but fires from an open bolt and uses pistol ammunition. One interesting feature of this weapon is the magazine which folds into the front handguard under the barrel when not in use. This was the first submachine gun to use this principle. The Model 1934 has a delayed-inertia-blowback type of action that utilizes a two-piece bolt. It has been made in several calibers: 9mm Parabellum; 9mm Mauser; 7.65mm and 7.63mm Mauser.

Because of the long 19-inch barrel on the Model 1934, the velocity and accuracy make the weapon much superior to shorter submachine guns.

In 1941 SIG came out with the 1941 model, which was a short submachine gun using a straight blowback bolt. This weapon had a single rear hand grip similar to that found on the U.S. Thompson submachine gun. The magazine on this weapon also folded forward into the wooden fore-end under the barrel.

Caliber: 9mm.
Weight: 8 lb.
Length of barrel: 9 in.
Magazine: 30-rd. box.
Rate of fire: 850 r.p.m.

Since 1944 SIG has produced the Model MKPS, which is very similar to the Model 46 pictured earlier. The main difference is that the MKPS was the forerunner of the Model 46 and has a full length wood stock running the length of the barrel, while the MP46 has a sheet metal stamping as the fore-end and holder for the magazine when folded forward.

A somewhat new and interesting submachine gun to appear for sale in Switzerland in recent years is the Rexim FV. MK 4, which fires a 9mm round from a closed bolt, semi-locked by inertia. This feature was incorporated to give greater accuracy during semi-automatic firing. The Rexim can be equipped with 8- or 13-inch barrel.

Neuhausen AK 53 Automatic Carbine. Uses standard rifle cartridges. Single shot or full auto. Gas operated by piston. Weight 10.8 pounds. Barrel 23⅝ inches. Overall length 39⅜ inches. Magazine capacity 30 rounds. Unusual mechanism. Barrel is drawn forward after unlocking to eject. Thrust back to reload on version of old Austrian Schwarzlose system. This weapon is a prototype.

SWISS MACHINE GUNS

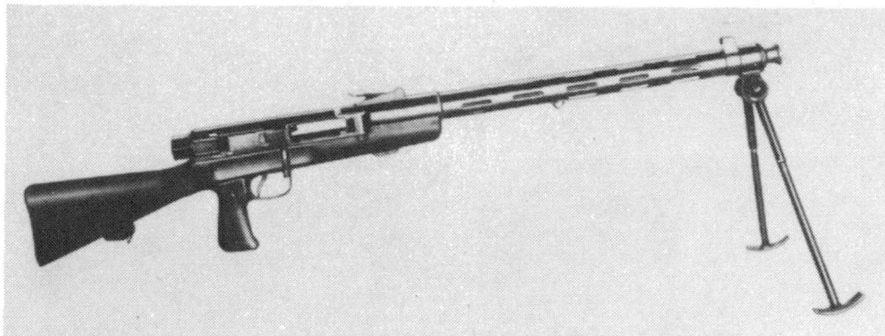

Swiss 7.5mm Model 25 Light Machine Gun.

The Model 25 is commonly known as the Fusil Furrer after its developer, Colonel Furrer, who at one time was the chief of the Swiss government arms plant at Bern. This weapon may be replaced in the Swiss service by the Model 57 assault rifle. The Model 25, a recoil-operated gun, has a toggle-joint action generally similar to that of the Luger pistol. The toggle on the Model 25 breaks to the side, rather than to the top as with the Luger.

Caliber: 7.5mm (Swiss Model 11 cartridge).
System of operation: Recoil, selective fire.
Weight: 23.69 lb. w/bipod.
Length, overall: 45.8 in.
Barrel length: 23 in.
Feed device: 30-round, detachable, staggered-row box magazine.
Sights, Front: Blade, w/protecting ears.
Rear: Tangent leaf w/notch.
Muzzle velocity: 2400 to 2500 f.p.s.
Cylic rate: 450 r.p.m.

A 13mm aircraft version of this gun was also made. This weapon used a metallic link belt.

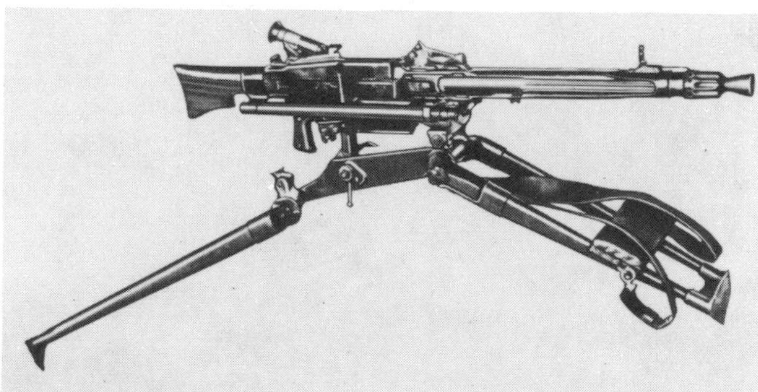

Swiss 7.5mm Model 51 Machine Gun.

The Model 51, which is generally similar to the German MG 42, was developed by the Swiss Government Arms Plant at Bern. It has replaced the 7.5mm Model 11 watercooled Maxim in Swiss service.

Caliber: 7.5mm (Swiss Model 11 cartridge).
System of operation: Recoil, automatic fire only.
Weight: 35.2 lb. w/bipod.
Weight of tripod: 43.5 lb.
Length, overall: 48 in. (approx.).
Barrel length: 20.47 in.
Feed device: 250-round nondisintegrating metallic link belt.
Sights, Front: Folding blade.
Rear: Tangent leaf; an optical sight is used when the gun is mounted on a tripod.
Muzzle velocity: 2510 f.p.s.
Cyclic rate: 1000 r.p.m.

SIG Developed MG 710-1 (55-1). Strikingly similar to German MG 45 (42V). Blowback locking mechanism like the Model 57 assault rifle.

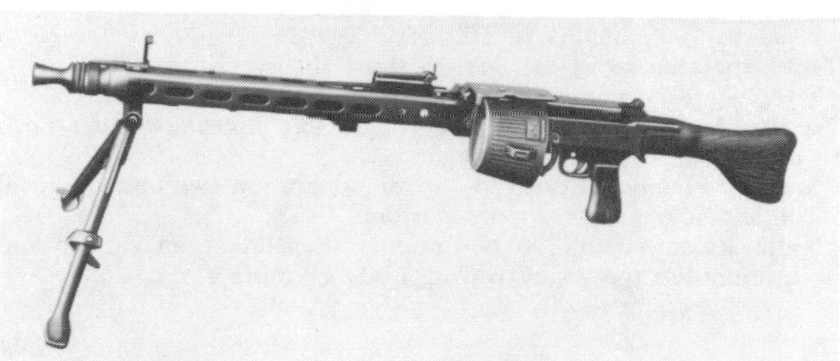

MG 710-1 on Bipod with Drum Magazine.

SIG Developed MG 710-2 (55-2). Locking system like the Model 57 assault rifle.

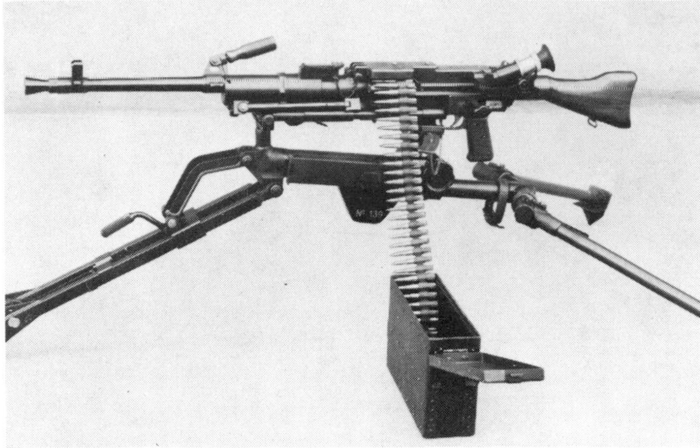

Swiss MG 50 on tripod, belt feed, as a medium machine gun.

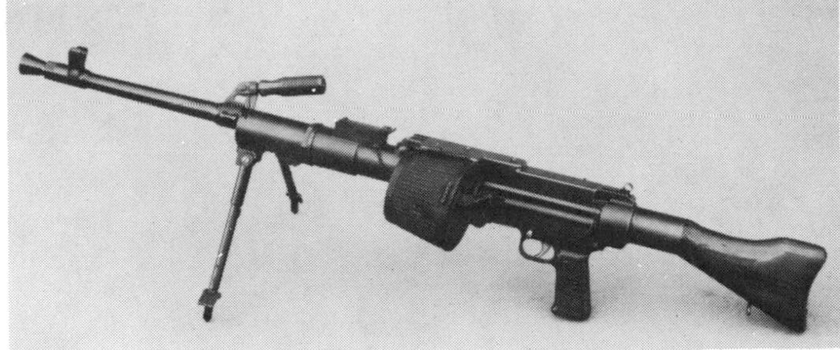

Swiss MG 50 on bipod. Drum feed. Used as a L.M.G.

This weapon is not used by the Swiss Army but is used by the Danish Army in caliber .30.

Caliber: 7.5mm Swiss or 7.92mm German. (Note: May also be made in other rimless military calibers of this general pattern.)
Magazine: Adaptable. Top box magazine or side belt feed.
Barrel Length: 600mm.
Overall Length: 1290mm with flash hider attached.
Mounting: Bipod for light machine gun use. Tripod pattern mount for medium machine gun and antiaircraft use.
Sights: Post front and elevating tangent rear. Graduations from 300 to 2000 meters in 100 meter steps.
Gun Operated by: Gas. Special short thrust piston.
Firing: Full automatic or burst fire only.
Safety: Adjusting lever to lock trigger and breech whether open or closed.
Cocking Handle: Knob to permit operation without removal of shoulder from support position.
Cyclic Rate: About 700 per minute (depending on caliber and ammunition type, may run to 1,000 or more r.p.m.).

This design is air-cooled.

With magazine or belt in place on gun, the cocking handle is pulled to the rear in standard fashion to cock the operating mechanism. Pulling the trigger permits burst fire in elementary gas operation.

As a belt-fed design, the gun is fitted with a hinged breech cover which may be lifted to place the cartridge belt into position on the left, a link belt normally being used. Alternatively, saddle drums are usable. The feed cover for such use is patterned after that of the German MG42.

Drum magazines contain 25 to 50 cartridges. Belt lengths may be increased by coupling together as many belts as desired. The design features a quick-removable barrel. The carrying handle on the gun may be swung down to the right to unlock the barrel, at which time a forward thrust will remove it from its heavy tubular receiver seat.

Dismounting

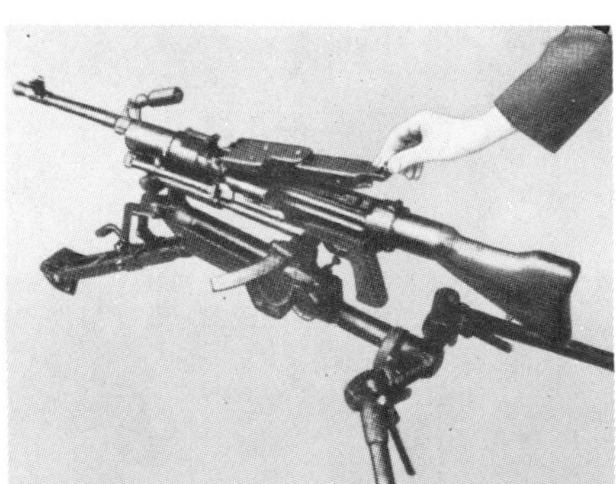

Unlock and lift feed cover.

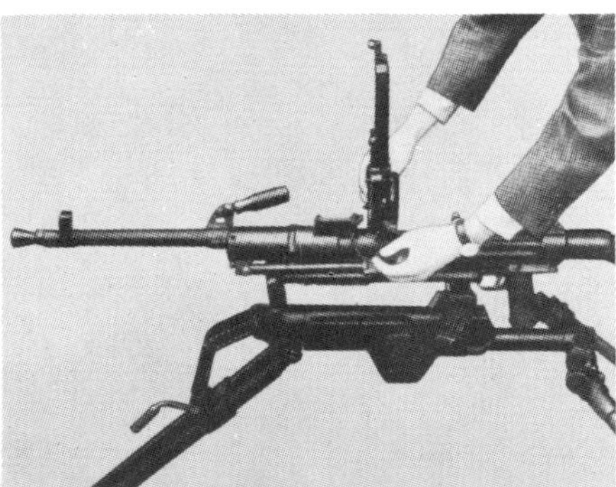

Pull pin and remove feed cover.

Unlock and remove stock.

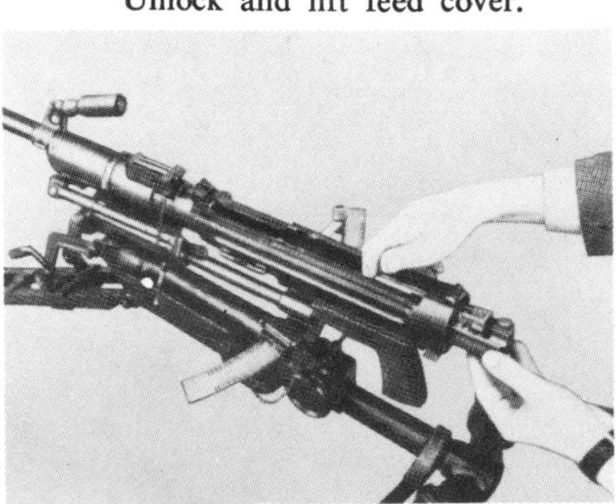

Ease out breechblock.

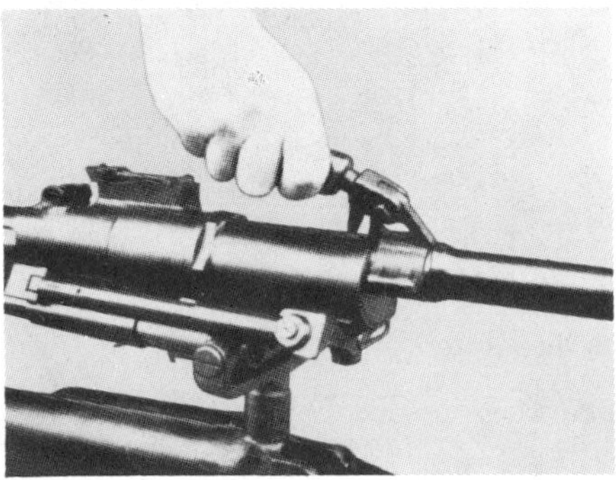

Raise barrel handle to unlock.

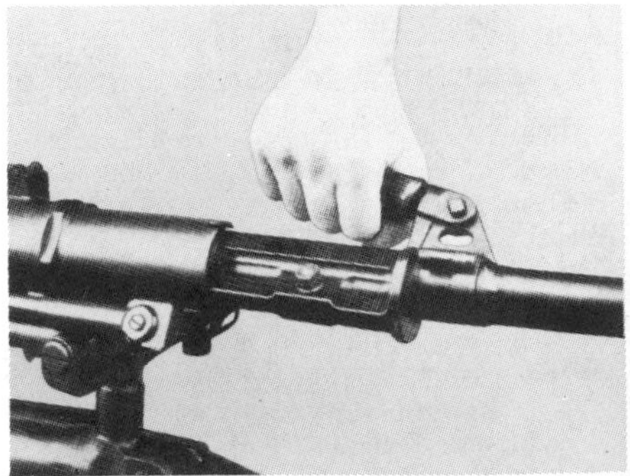

Slide barrel forward out of receiver.

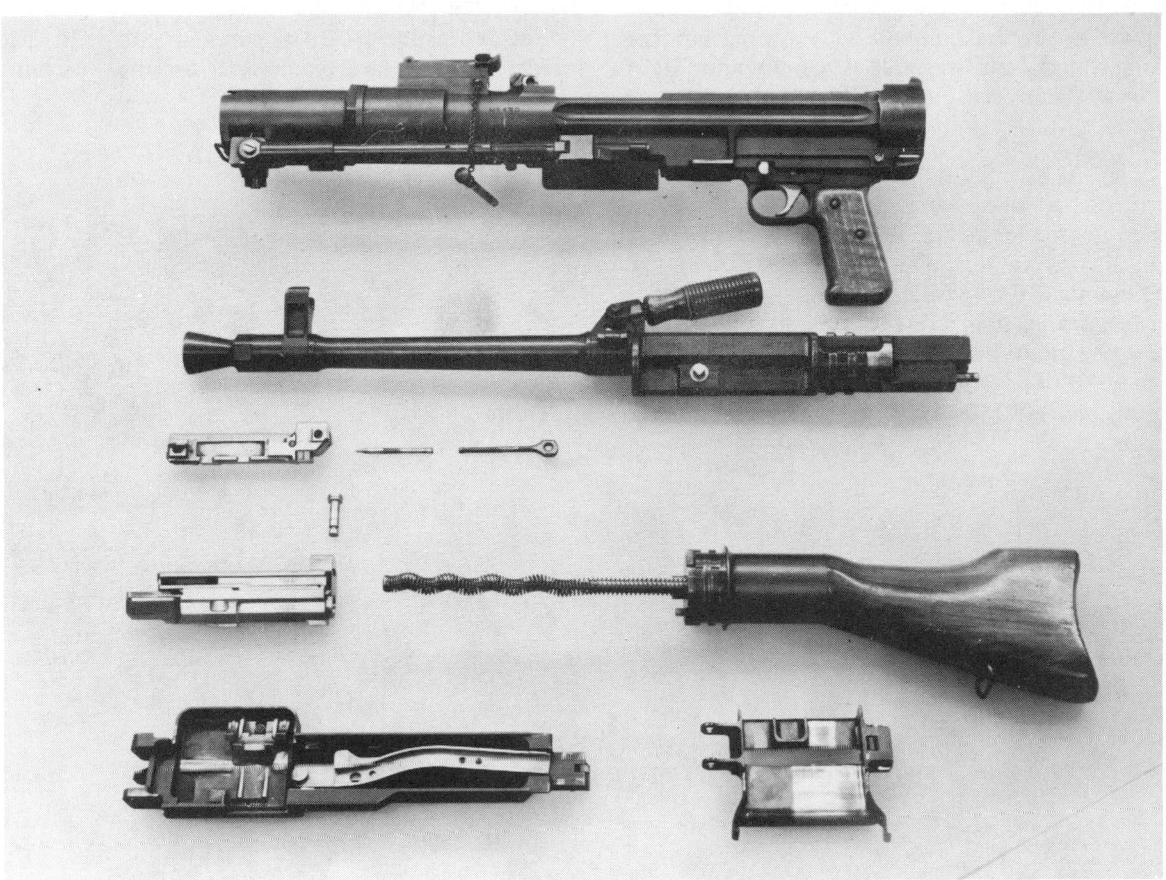

Swiss MG 50 field stripped.

The tripod mount used for adapting the gun to continuous fire is interesting in that springs have been positioned in the cradle to permit a short recoil motion of the weapon without disturbing the laying. The forward legs of the tripod are easily adjustable. Approximate adjustment for elevation or depression of the weapon is done by hand, the locking lever on the right side of the mount being loosened. Final exact adjustment is done by turning the hand wheel provided on the left of the tripod.

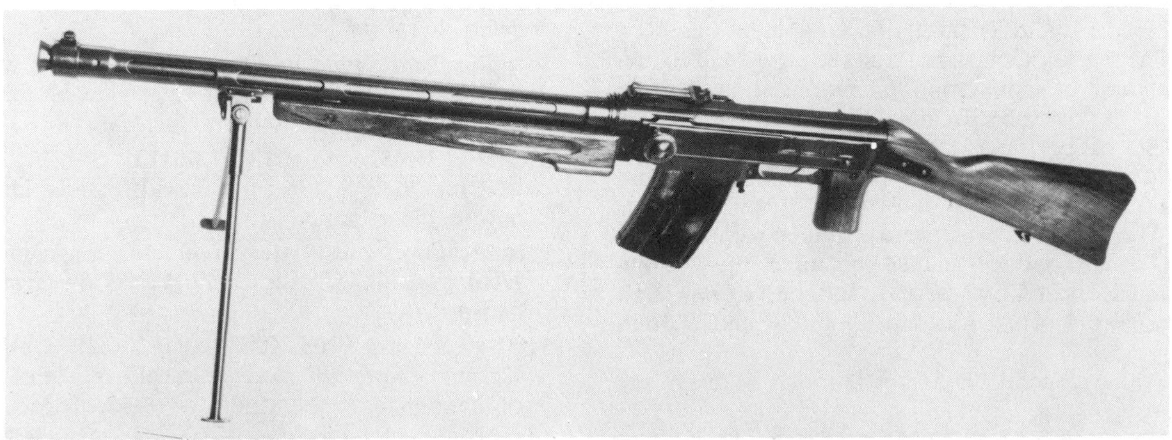

KE 7 L.M.G. This weapon is not used in the Swiss Army.

Chapter 42. Turkey

The Turks are at present equiped with a large number of United States and British small arms. Quantities of earlier weapons—Mausers, Czech ZB 26's, and some French weapons—are apparently still held. Most of the older weapons are chambered for the 7.92mm cartridge.

TURKISH PISTOLS

A native-made pistol is the 9mm Kirikkale. This weapon, which is made at the Kirikkale arms factory in Turkey, is a copy of the Walther PP. It is identical to the late commercial-type Walther, except for variations in machining and the finger-rest extension on the removable magazine floor plate. For data on the Walther PP, see chapter 26. The Kirikkale is chambered for the 9mm Browning short (.380 ACP) or the 7.65mm (.32 ACP) cartridge.

Turkish 9mm Automatic Pistol.

TURKISH SERVICE RIFLES AND CARBINES

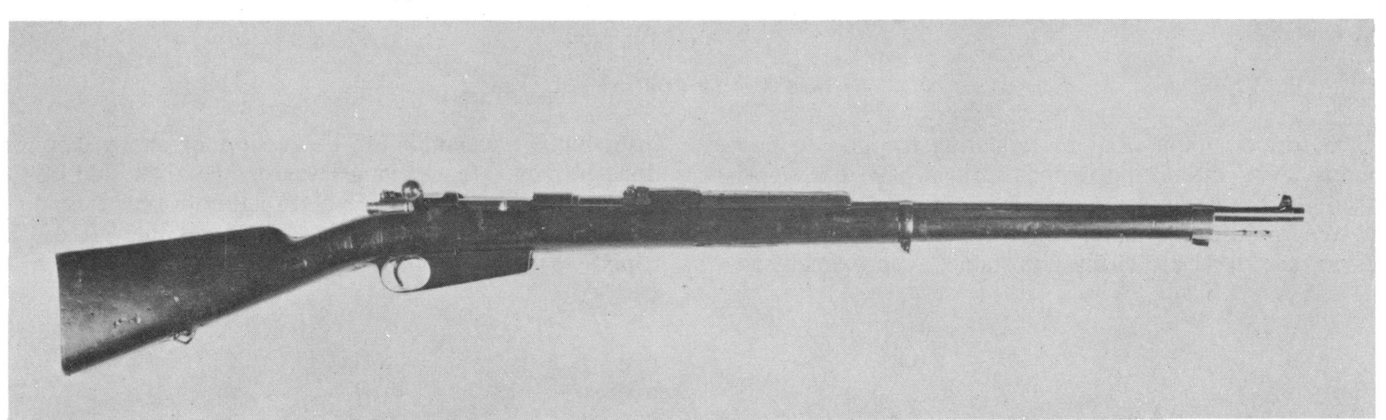

Turkish Mauser M1890 Rifle.

Since 1890 the basic Turkish rifle equipment has been Mausers. The Turks kept abreast of the new Mauser developments, and a wide group of modifications are to be found in Turkish use because of that fact.

The official caliber prior to War I was 7.65mm Turkish. This is a rimless cartridge based on the 7.65mm Mauser design.

During War I the Turks were equipped with many standard German Service items, including the 7.9mm Gewehrs and Kars. of that period. Purchases from Belgium after War I were in both 7.65mm and 7.9mm calibers.

The following general classes of Turkish Mausers are in use:

MODEL 1890, CALIBER 7.65MM ONLY. These have the early Mauser bolt with dual front lugs but no rear safety lug.

Identification. Single line box magazine projecting below line of receiver. Cut-off on right side of rifle (cut-offs are unusual in Mauser design).

MODEL 1893, CALIBER 7.65MM ONLY. This model is a modified Spanish 1893 with caliber changed and cut-off incorporated.

Identification. Flush staggered box magazine. Cut-off. Dual front locking lugs only. Cocks on closing inch of forward thrust.

MODELS 1903-1905, CALIBER 7.65MM ONLY. Like German Gew. 98 except for caliber, sight, and shape of handguard.

Identification. Caliber and markings. Handguard projects slightly forward of band.

Chapter 43. Union of Soviet Socialist Republics (Russia)

The Soviets at the end of World War II were equipped with a plentiful supply of small arms of native design and production. These weapons were all of basically sound design and sturdy manufacture, but many of them lacked the various sophistications to be found in really modern small arms. An outstanding example of this is that the Soviet Army (like all other major armies in the conflict except the United States Army) was almost exclusively equipped with bolt action rifles. The basic design of these Soviet rifles appeared in 1891.

The Soviets began a re-equipment program after World War II and, as a result, have completely outfitted their massive army with a new family of small arms. Only two small arms that were in service in World War II are still used, and even they have been modified. Some idea of the extent of this herculean effort can be gathered from the present distribution of the new weapons. The Soviets not only have supplied their own troops but also, for the past several years, have been furnishing satellite nations ever-increasing numbers of the new small arms. They have even sold some of them to nonsatellite countries, such as the United Arab Republic (Egypt and Syria).

Two new pistols, the semi-automatic Makarov and the selective-fire Stechkin, have appeared. There is a new family of squad-level weapons, consisting of an assault rifle, a semi-automatic carbine, and a light machine gun—all chambered for a new intermediate-sized 7.62mm cartridge. A new company-level machine gun has been adopted and the Goryunov M1943 and DShK M1938 machine guns have been modified. A new 14.5mm heavy antiaircraft machine gun, with a series of mounts, has been adopted.

RUSSIAN PISTOLS AND REVOLVERS

Russian Tokarev 7.62mm Automatic Pistol Model TT 1930.

Caliber: 7.62mm Russian Auto Pistol. This weapon is obsolete in the U.S.S.R.
Magazine: Box type single line. Capacity 8 cartridges.
Muzzle Velocity: 1390 feet per second.
Weight of Bullet: 87 grains.
Muzzle Striking Energy: 365 foot pounds.
Barrel Length: 4½ inches.
Overall Length of Pistol: 7¾ inches.
Weight: About 32 ounces.
Sights: Fixed.
Accurate Range: 50 yards.
Maximum Range: About 1800 yards.
Pistol Operated By: Recoil.
Locked: Browning-Colt System. Ribs on top of barrel locked into corresponding slots on under side of slide near breech at moment of discharge.
Type of Fire: Single shot only. Simple disconnector prevents firing more than one shot for each trigger pull.
Magazine Release Catch: Button on left side of receiver near trigger. Pressing it ejects magazine from handle.
Safety: Half cock notch. No other manual safety.
Special Features: Demountable magazine, simplified hammer mechanism, easy take down, and simplification of manufacturing.
Slide Stop: Operates as in Colt .45.
Loading and Firing: As in Colt .45.

Field Stripping

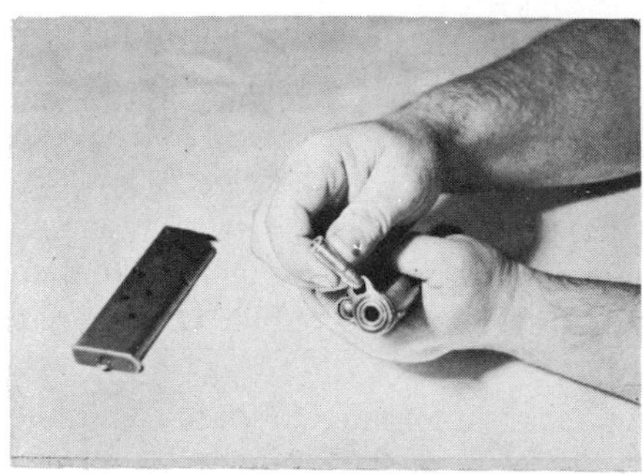

Insert nose of cartridge through hole in bushing below barrel and compress spring until bushing is free to turn.

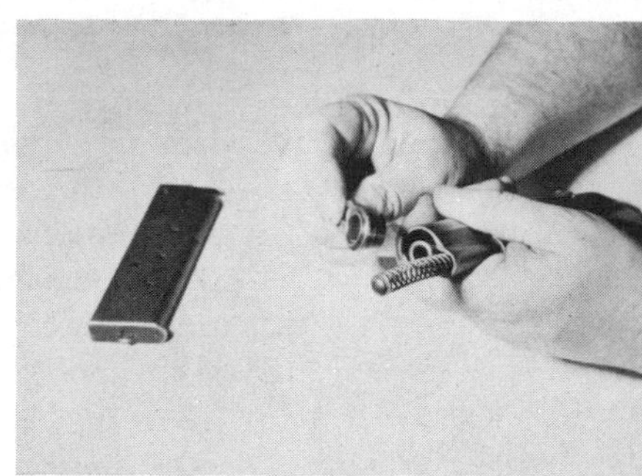

Swing bushing up to the right until its locking lugs disengage. Remove it from the slide. Let the recoil spring protrude.

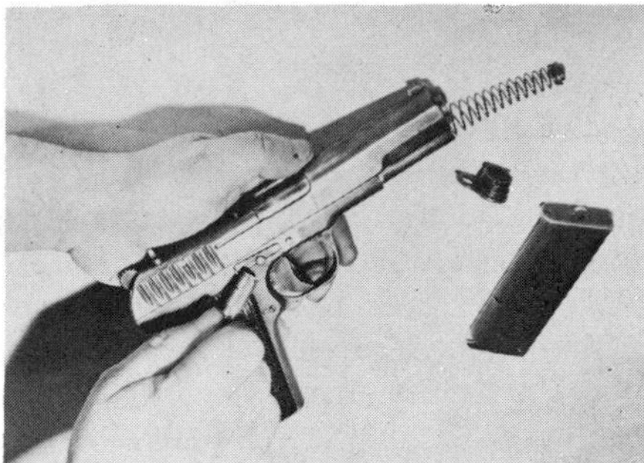

Using a cartridge or the bottom of the magazine, pull back the spring locking clip on the right side of the pistol. This frees the slide stop pin.

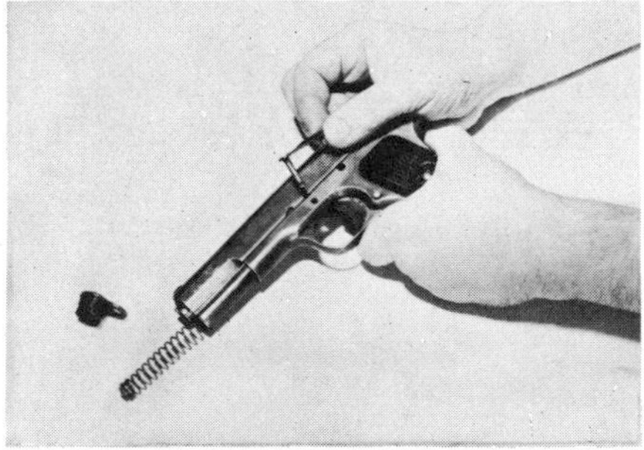

Withdraw the slide stop-barrel locking pin from the left.

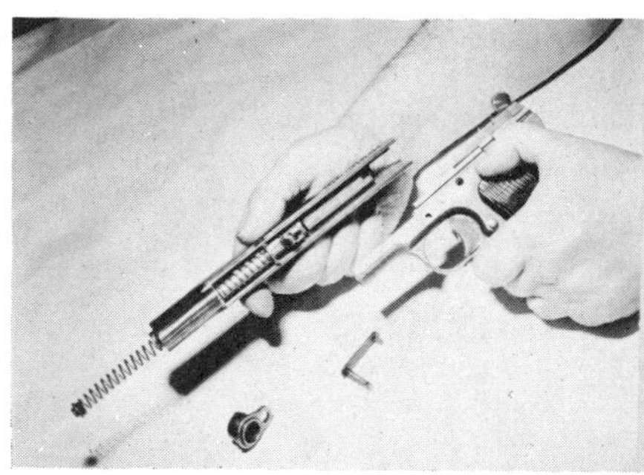

Push the slide and barrel assembly forward out of the guides in the receiver.

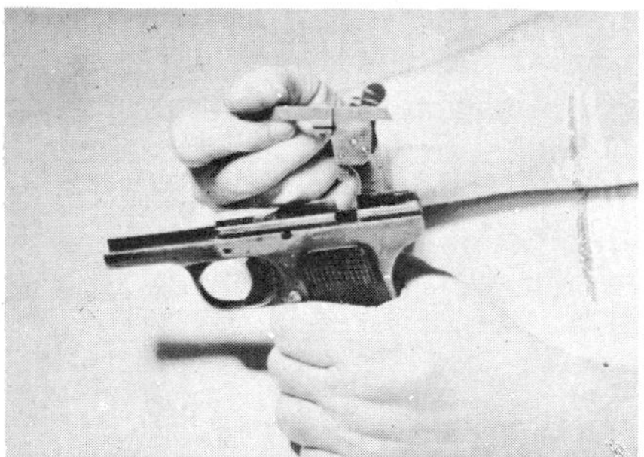

Lift the receiver sub-assembly and hammer mechanism out of the receiver.

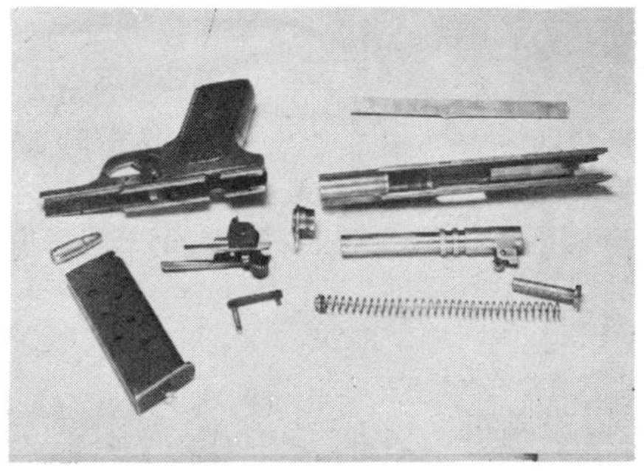

Remove barrel, recoil spring and guide from front of slide.

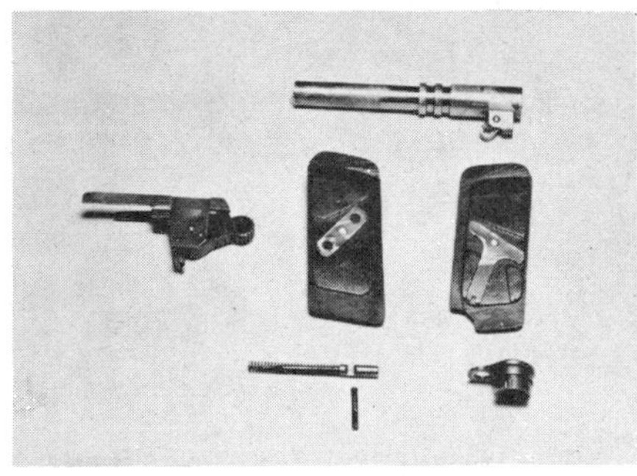

No further dismounting is normally necessary. However stocks may be removed by reaching inside the handle and turning the metal locking buttons. Firing pin may be removed by punching out split pin from right side of slide. Hammer unit may be completely dismounted by pushing out the three retaining pins. The magazine release catch is a split pin which may be driven out from the right side of the receiver. This permits removing trigger and spring to complete entire disassembly.

Special Note on This Pistol

This weapon is one of the most remarkable firearms ever developed. Officially known as the TT30, it is named for F. V. Tokarev, a Russian designer who was a Cossack officer in the army of the Czar at the beginning of World War I.

While the general design and the locking system were copied directly from that of John M. Browning's invention, our service Colt .45 Automatic Pistol, the Russians simplified both manufacture and operation so much that the weapon ranks as a completely modernized version of its famous predecessor.

It costs only a fraction as much to manufacture as does the original Browning design, is much simpler to disassemble and repair, and has removed the various weaknesses of the original type.

It is a most interesting commentary that the Russians found the Browning locking system the most reliable type on which to develop their pistol.

The TT33, a later model, has been manufactured in Poland, Hungary (as Model 48), and Communist China, (as Type 51).

Description of Mechanism

The slide closely resembles the Colt Browning type. However, the barrel bushing which is inserted in the front end of the slide to support the barrel and retain the recoil spring is a heavily forged bushing with one large hole for the barrel and a small hole below it in which the steel disc at the end of the recoil spring seats. This is much stronger than the conventional horseshoe shape bushing and plug.

The firing pin unit is retained in the slide by a simple split pin driven through a hole drilled in the slide, the pin passing through a slotted out section on top of the firing pin. This pin not only retains the floating firing pin but also determines the distance it can fly forward when struck by the hammer.

The magazine is particularly worthy of note in that it can be easily taken apart for cleaning or repairs. The follower, or platform on which the first cartridge rests, is supported from below by the typical magazine spring. The bottom of this spring, however, rests on a flat platform which in turn rests on the magazine bottom. The bottom is tongued into grooves in the magazine case, being slid in from the front. It is retained by a small nib on the platform which protrudes through a hole in the magazine bottom. Pushing this nib in permits the bottom to be pulled forward. The platform, spring, and follower can then be removed.

While the barrel locks in the same manner as the Colt Browning, its manufacture has been greatly simplified. Where the Colt has two locking ribs on the top of the barrel only, the Tokarev locking ribs run entirely around the barrel circumference. The lower sections have no locking function but permit of simpler barrel manufacture. They also provide, together with a thickened breech end, a strong support for the high powered cartridge used.

The stocks are of black plastic and require neither screws nor machined-in supports. A pivoted flat spring is riveted on the inner face of each stock. When turned crosswise each end locks in the frame. Turning the strip disengages it from the frame and permits the stock to be lifted off.

The magazine release catch is a split pin. When punched out it permits easy removal of the stirrup type trigger and the flat spring in the handle which acts as the trigger return spring.

The slide stop and barrel locking pin function as in

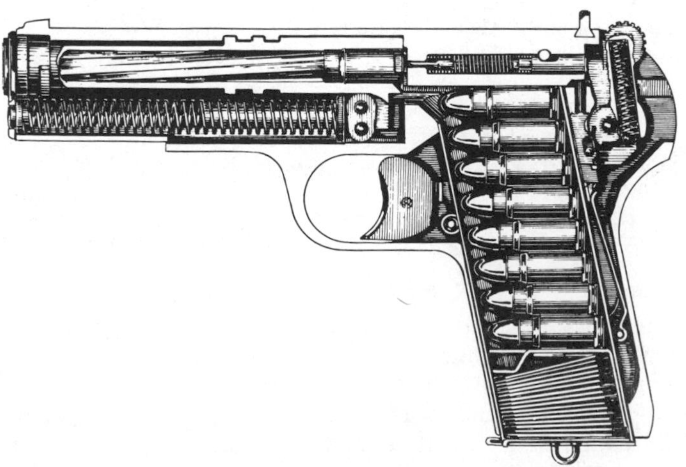

Action closed, showing details of mainspring in hammer and firing mechanism.

Action open, cut away to show details of recoil system and cocking operation.

the Colt Browning, but the retaining system has been simplified. Where the pin emerges on the right side of the receiver, a sliding spring clip is provided. When pushed forward teeth on it engage in notches in the end of the pin. Pulling this back frees the pin to permit removal.

The really startling advance of this pistol over all preceding types, however, is in its hammer mechanism.

This mechanism, consisting of a simple hammer, sear, disconnector, sear spring, and mainspring, is housed in a sub-assembly which forms part of the receiver and carries part of the slide grooves.

This sub-assembly block has two arms of unequal length. While the outside surfaces line up with the regular receiver guides, the inside surfaces are specially grooved to act as cartridge guides to assure proper feeding as each cartridge is stripped from between the very flat lips of the magazine. The effect of this feature is to make the feeding much more positive, as magazine mouths are normally weak points in feeding systems.

The mainspring is a coil which is housed inside the hammer itself. Its lower end rests against a pin driven through the housing in the assemly. As the hammer is rocked back by the slide during recoil, this spring is compressed against the supporting pin to provide the energy source for firing the next shot.

The sear, sear spring, and disconnector are mounted together on a third pin in the housing. When the slide is fully forward the disconnector rises into a slot machined for it in the slide housing below the line of the firing pin.

Operation

When the trigger is pressed, its stirrup forces the flat spring in the handle back to provide energy for returning the trigger to firing position when pressure is released.

The lower end of the disconnector is riding on top of the trigger stirrup while its upper end is in its seat in the breech block. In this position, the sear attached to the disconnector is also in contact with the rear of the trigger stirrups. The trigger forces back against the sear and presses the upper end of the sear out of its engagement in the second hammer notch. The hammer under the pressure of the compressed spring in it rotates on its axis pin to strike the firing pin and drive it forward to fire the cartridge.

As the slide and barrel under force of the recoil start back, they are locked securely together. As the pressure drops, the barrel swings down on its link to unlock from the slide. The slide continues on backwards to extract and eject in normal fashion.

The slide now forces the hammer back to be caught by the sear. When pressure on the trigger is released so that the disconnector can resume its firing position, the weapon is ready for another shot. The slide has moved forward under tension of the recoil spring below the barrel to strip a cartridge from the top of the magazine.

How TT33 Differs From TT30

The 1930 type has a dismountable block assembled into the back edge of the grip frame. This block carries the trigger extension bar operating spring and the disconnector spring. The 1933 type has a solid back edge grip frame with the operating spring and disconnector spring assembled directly into the grip frame.

The firing system frame of the 1930 type differs from the 1933 frame in its cut-outs and general assembly to the grip frame.

The locking lugs of the 1930 type are machined and ground out only on the upper surface of the barrel ahead of the chamber. The lugs on the 1933 type barrel are machined and ground out around the entire circumference of the barrel ahead of the chamber.

The form of the disconnector differs between the two pistols. The 1930 type has a smaller extension bar contacting surface.

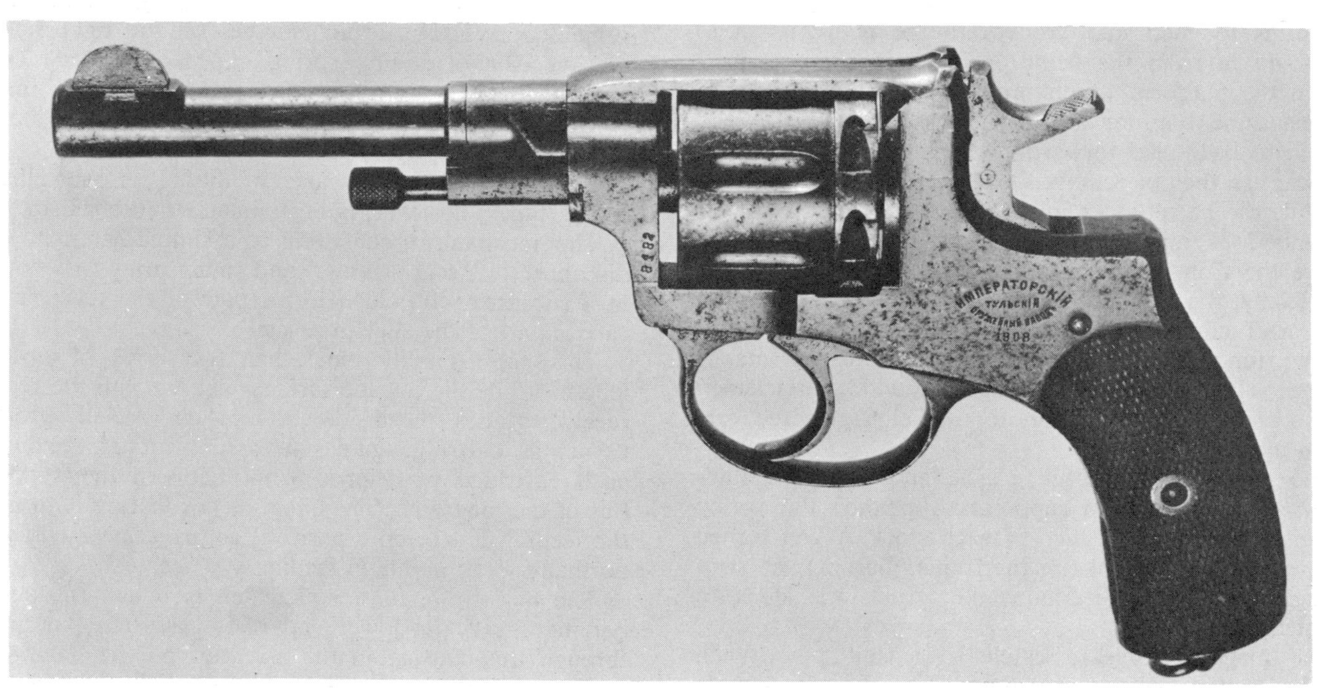

Russian Nagant Revolver Caliber 7.62mm.

Caliber: 7.62mm Russian Nagant Revolver (.30).
Cylinder: 7 chambers.
Muzzle Velocity: 892 feet per second.
Striking Energy: About 125 foot pounds.
Weight of Bullet: 108 grains (both lead and metal jacketed types).

Action closed, showing detail of lock work.

Barrel Length: 4½ inches.
Overall Length: About 9½ inches.
Weight: 28 ounces.
Accurate Range: About 50 yards.
Action: Solid frame. Both single and double action types are used.
Safety: Rebounding hammer. Resistance block prevents rotation of hammer when in rebound position.
Sights: Front sight, barleycorn adjustable. Rear sight fixed V on frame.
Special Feature: A gas block which forces the cylinder forward over the face of the barrel when firing to prevent gas escape.

Special Note on This Revolver

As issued to officers, this revolver is normally double action. Some double action types without gas block are issued.

The revolver differs radically from others in that when the hammer is drawn to full cock the action moves a resistance block out of the frame and against the cartridge in line with the barrel. This forces the cylinder straight ahead on its axis pin. The circumference of the cylinder extends beyond the chambers. The cartridge used resembles the American .32-20 but has the bullet completely hidden inside the cartridge case. As the cylinder is moved forward, the front part of the chamber goes over the back end of the barrel. This forms an effective gas seal. In the ordinary revolver gas escapes when the bullet jumps from the cylinder to the barrel. This is minimized in the Nagant. However, the practical value has never been very well established. This is a rod ejector revolver.

Action cocked, showing operation of pawl and gas check.

The TT 1933 pistol, which is commonly called the Tokarev, has been replaced by two new pistols. The Tokarev automatic was chambered for the 7.62mm pistol cartridge, but the new weapons are chambered for a new 9mm cartridge of Soviet design. The new 9mm round, which is actually of considerably less power than was the 7.62mm pistol cartridge, has a 94-grain bullet and a muzzle velocity of 1115 f.p.s. (for the Stechkin pistol).

The cartridge is intermediate in size between the .380 automatic pistol cartridge (9mm Browning short) and the 9mm Parabellum cartridge. It is quite similar to the German 9mm Ultra cartridge which was in prototype stage at the end of World War II.

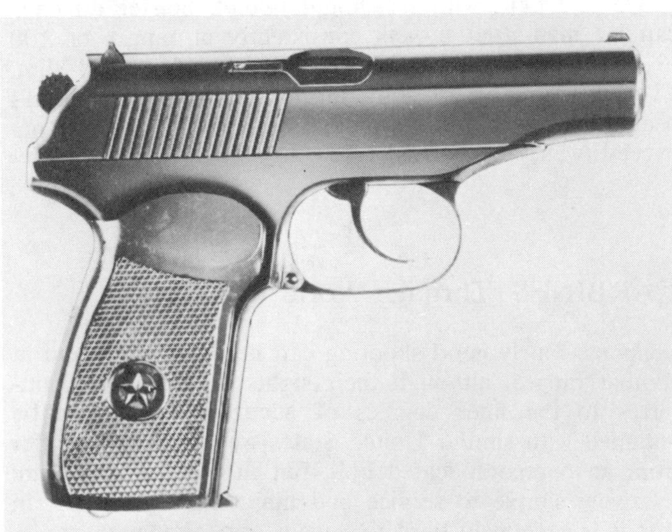

Soviet 9mm Makarov Pistol (PM).

Makarov Field Stripped.

The Makarov, which is called PM (pistol Makarov) by the Soviets, is a scaled-up copy of the German Walther PP pistol of World War II fame. Like the Walther, the Makarov is blowback operated and its operation is the same as the Walther.

Caliber: 9mm (new Soviet design).
System of Operation: Blowback, semi-automatic only.
Weight, Empty: 1.56 lb.
Overall Length: 6.34 in.
Barrel Length: 3.83 in.
Feed Device: 8-rd. single-row box magazine.
Sights, Front: Blade.
Rear: Open, square-notch.
Muzzle Velocity: 1070 f.p.s.

Disassembly

Pull down the triggerguard; pull the slide to the rear and lift its rear end up; then ease forward the slide and

Soviet 9mm Stechkin Machine Pistol (APS).

the recoil spring (which encircles the barrel), and remove them from the weapon. Since the Makarov is a blowback-operated weapon, it has a fixed barrel which should not ordinarily be removed. Further stripping is not recommended.

Soviet 9mm Stechkin Machine Pistol (APS)

Caliber: 9mm (new Soviet design).
System of Operation: Selective automatic or semi-automatic fire.
Weight, Empty: 1.7 lb.; with shoulder stock, 3.92 lb.
Overall Length: 8.85 inches; with shoulder stock, 21.25 in.
Barrel Length: 5 in.
Feed Device: Detachable 20-rd. staggered-box magazine.
Sights, Front: Blade.
Rear: Flip-over L-type with open notches.
Muzzle Velocity: 1100 f.p.s.
Cyclic Rate of Fire: 750 r.p.m.

The Stechkin is a true machine pistol in that it is capable of full automatic and semi-automatic fire. It is equipped with a wooden holster which can be used as a shoulder stock. The Stechkin, like the Makarov, is blowback in operation, but it is a considerably larger weapon than the Makarov and has considerably more potential as a weapon.

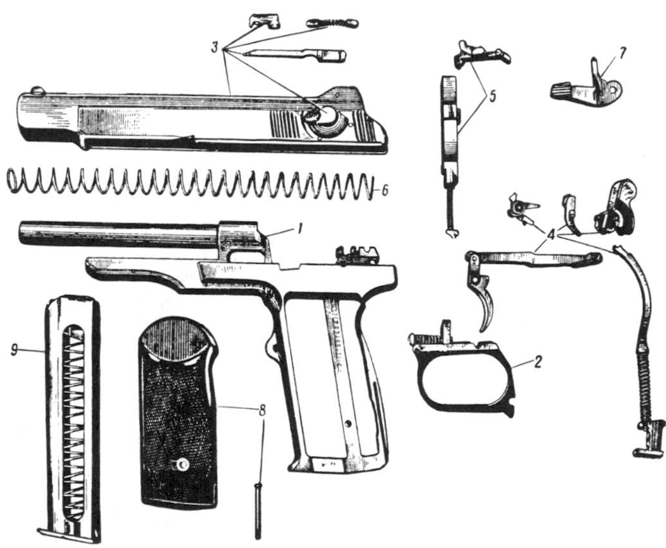

Soviet 9mm Stechkin Machine Pistol (APS), stripped.

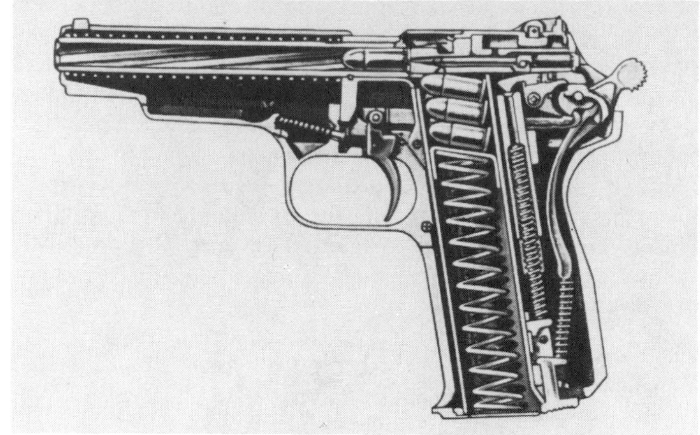

Section View of Stechkin Pistol.

Operation

The Stechkin is loaded by inserting a loaded magazine into the grip (as with the U. S. cal. .45 M1911A1 automatic pistol), then pulling the slide to the rear and releasing it so that it runs home and chambers a cartridge. The safety selector catch is mounted on the left rear side of the slide, as it is on the Makarov and the Walther PP and PPK pistols. The safety selector catch has three positions. The bottom position is safe, the middle position is semi-automatic fire, and the top position is full automatic fire.

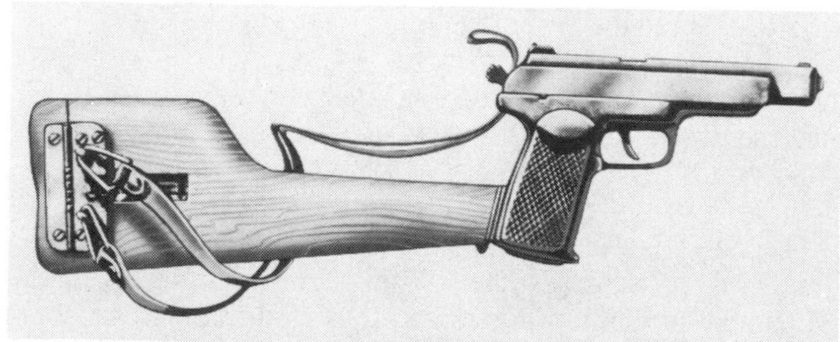

Stechkin with Shoulder Holster Stock.

The Stechkin with its shoulder-stock holster attached can hit man-sized targets consistently at ranges of 100 to 150 yards, when it is in the hands of a good shot. This, of course, is in semi-automatic fire. The Stechkin's usable range in full automatic fire probably does not exceed twenty-five yards.

SOVIET BOLT ACTION RIFLES AND CARBINES (Through World War II)

The Mosin-Nagant rifle was adopted in 1891 by Imperial Russia. The action of the rifle was developed by Colonel S. I. Mosin of the Imperial Russian Army, and the magazine was developed by Nagant, a Belgian. All Soviet bolt action military rifles and carbines are Mosin-Nagant weapons and all are basically similar to the original Mosin-Nagant rifle adopted by Russia in 1891. These weapons can be considered reasonably effective infantry weapons. Fairly good shooting can be done with them at combat ranges, although their sights do not lend themselves to the finer degrees of accuracy which can be obtained with similar United States weapons. They suffer from an overcomplicated bolt, but in other respects are relatively simple to service and maintain. The safety, in that it is extremely hard to engage and disengage, represents a shortcoming of the weapons.

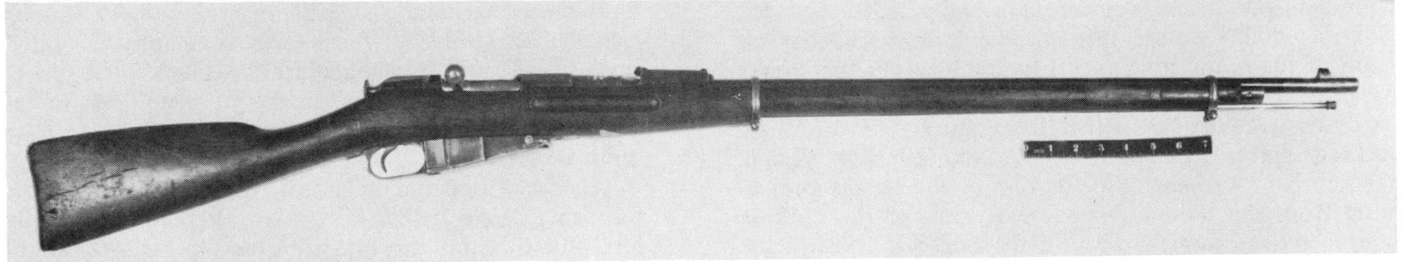

M1891 7.62mm Rifle.

The original rifle M1891 was considerably different than later versions of the same model. The original rifle M1891 had no handguard, was fitted with sling swivels instead of the sling slots used on later versions, and had a leaf rear sight which was designed for the old conical-nosed 7.62mm ball cartridge. In 1908 the Spitzer pointed light ball round (which is still used) was introduced, and the rear sight was changed. About this time handguards were added and the swivels were replaced by sling slots bored in the stock. The original M1891 is now a collector's item. The later versions of the rifle M1891 are obsolete.

The Dragoon rifle M1891 was originally developed as a weapon for heavy cavalry. Manufacture of this rifle was discontinued about 1930, when it was replaced by the rifle M1891/30. The Dragoon rifle M1891 is obsolete. Both the M1891 rifle and the Dragoon rifle have hexagonal receivers.

These rifles are all caliber 7.62mm (.30) for rim cartridges. Mechanically they are all basically the same.

The design differs considerably from the Mauser type on which our own bolt action rifles are all built; and the following descriptive matter is set down to provide an understanding of the Russian design.

Bolt. The bolt is an entirely original design. It has never been imitated. It is a 2-piece design in which a removable bolt head carries the locking lugs. The two locking lugs engage horizontally in the receiver, the opposite of most types. The bolt head turns with the bolt. If this head is accidentally left out when assembling the rifle, the weapon cannot be fired. The extractor is carried by the bolt head.

A special connecting bar joins the bolt head to the bolt itself. This bar does not turn with the bolt; it is positioned in the underside of the bolt assembly and lies in a receiver cut in the boltway. This bar also acts as a guide for the cocking piece, and assists in keeping the bolt securely in the receiver. The bar has a projection rising from its forward end. This projection holds a small hollow cylinder. The rear end of this cylinder nests in the hollow front of the bolt, while the forward end of the cylinder nests in the rear of the bolt head.

The handle is part of the bolt forging. A rib extends forward from the hollowed-out bolt. A cut on the underside of this rib takes the projection on the connecting bar. As the bolt handle is lifted, the connecting bar stays fixed in its groove in the receiver below, but its upper projection in the bolt recess holds the bolt assembly securely together.

A small lug on the front end of the connecting bar fits into a groove inside the bolt head; and a small lug on the rear of the bolt head catches in a recess at the front end of the bolt extension rib. Thus as the bolt turns the bolt head is compelled to turn with it.

The striker and mainspring are inserted from the front end of the hollow bolt. The rear of the striker passes through a small rear hole in the bolt, and a cocking piece is screwed onto it. A collar at the front end of the striker serves as forward mainspring com-

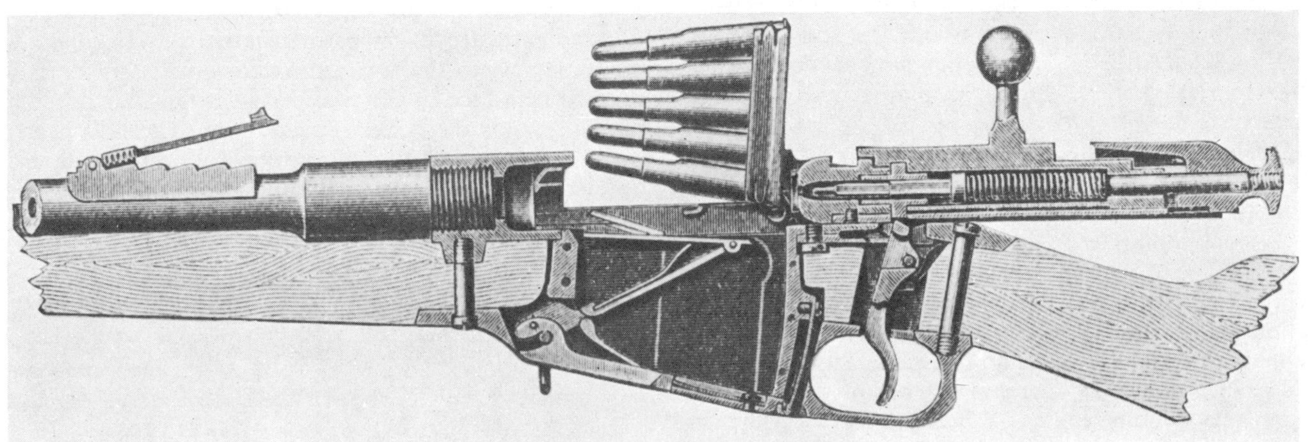

Russian M1891. Details of loading, locking, and firing mechanism. Cartridges are stripped down off clip, but clip must be manually withdrawn.

pression point; and the firing pin end which is forward of this collar passes through the hollow cylinder on top of the connecting bar. Flat surfaces on the striker at this point and corresponding surfaces within the cylinder prevent the striker from turning.

Cocking Piece. This is a simple and effective design. When it is screwed onto the end of the striker projecting from the bolt, an upper extension of the cocking piece passes along the top of the bolt and through the cut in the top of the receiver bridge.

A small cocking nose is machined on the rear lower surface of the cocking piece.

Safety. When the cocking piece is pulled back slightly it draws the attached striker back far enough for the flat surfaces on the striker to pass out of the connecting bar cylinder; and at this point the striker and cocking piece can be turned to the left. A lug on the underside of the cocking piece extension is thus turned into a locking recess at the rear end of the bolt.

Hence by pulling back and turning the cocking piece the following safety results are obtained: (a) The cocking nose on the cocking piece is turned out of contact with the sear—hence a trigger pull cannot affect it. (b) The striker has been turned so that if it were possible for it to slip it could not hit the cartridge primer, because the flat surfaces at its forward end are turned out of line with the corresponding surfaces inside the connecting bar cylinder through which the striker must pass to hit the primer. (c) The lug on the underside of the cocking piece extension is locked into a cut in the rear of the bolt to prevent any forward movement. (d) The long cocking piece extension is turned to the rear of the cut in the receiver bridge, hence cannot move forward since the receiver bridge is in its path.

Magazine. The magazine is a projecting single line box holding five rim cartridges. It forms part of the triggerguard. The magazine floor plate hinges forward and is kept closed by a spring catch. When the catch in the floor plate is drawn back, the magazine follower carrier spring forces the plate down and permits removal of cartridges.

As the accompanying drawing shows, the magazine has not merely a follower on which the first cartridge rests, together with its spring, but also a special "follower carrier" and its spring as part of the cartridge lifting system.

Interrupter-Ejector. This unit is also called "distributor-ejector" and "cartridge valve-ejector." No other rifle needs or uses this device.

The interrupter is a specially shaped plate attached to the left side of the receiver. At its rear is a flat spring held to the receiver by a screw. The thin plate section passes through a cut in the receiver wall above the magazine way. A point on this plate acts as ejector.

The interrupter is operated by action of the bolt. It prevents double feeding. When the top cartridge in the magazine has been chambered, the following cartridge cannot rise because the interrupter is holding it down. Only when the bolt is locked and the extractor engaged around the cartridge case head does a cam-shaped groove in the bolt bear against the interrupter and force it out against the interrupter spring. As the holding projection on the interrupter is forced away from the cartridge, the follower spring can push the top cartridge into line to be ready to feed.

When the bolt handle is raised to open the action, the cam groove in the bolt allows a point on the interrupter to enter the magazine and press against the second cartridge from the top.

An ejecting point on the edge of the interrupter is now in line with a groove in the bolt head. Thus, as the bolt is pulled back, the empty case is struck against this point and ejected from the rifle.

Operation. Lifting bolt handle rotates bolt, bolt head, and extractor as a unit. A cam cut at the rear of the bolt forces against the cocking nose on the underside of the cocking piece. The cocking piece and striker assembly are forced back, thereby pulling the firing pin point back away from the primer. The mainspring is partly compressed.

The rib extending forward from the bolt proper passes along a special cam surface on the top of the overhanging receiver ring. (The bolt head is entirely enclosed by the receiver ring.) This action forces the entire bolt assembly back to give primary extraction, the rearward thrust beginning as soon as the bolt has turned far enough for the locking lugs on the bolt head to clear their seats in the receiver ring.

The turning bolt operates the interrupter as described, permitting the interrupter spring to force the interrupter in to hold the next to the top cartridge in the magazine and to line up the ejector point.

The short extractor in the bolt head carries the empty case back and strikes it against the ejector. At this point a lug on top of the trigger hits against metal at the end of a groove in the connecting bar. (The bar has been traveling back as part of the bolt assembly, once the rearward action started.) This acts as a bolt stop.

The upright bolt handle passes back through the cut in the receiver bridge on rearward bolt pull.

As the bolt is pushed forward the bolt head starts the cartridge in its path towards the chamber. At the point where the forward extension rib on the bolt hits the cam face in the receiver ring, the sear nose catches and holds the cocking piece nose. The bolt head locking lugs are at the cam grooves leading to their locking seats in the receiver ring.

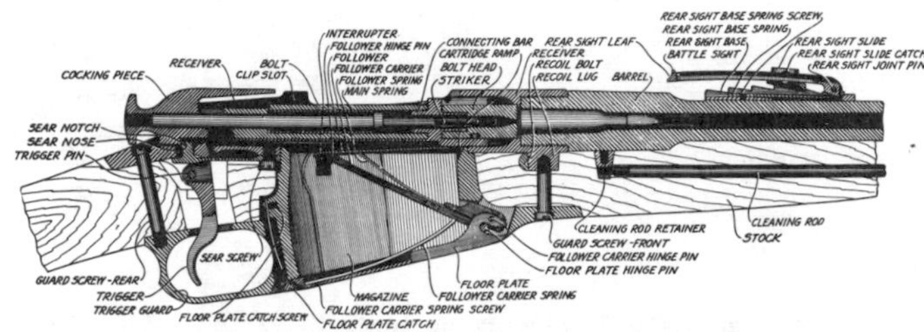

Russian M91 made in U. S. A. during World War I.

As the bolt handle is turned down, the locking lugs are forced along their cam grooves. This draws the bolt forward as the bolt head lugs are locked. Since the sear nose is holding the cocking piece back, this forward pull completes compression of the mainspring. The interrupter works as already described to permit the cartridge to rise below the bolt.

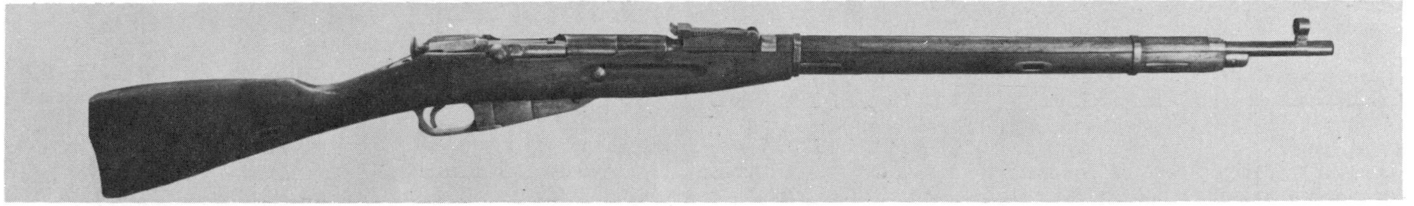

Russian M1891/30. This is a later production version of the original M1891. Sights graduated in meters.

The rifle M1891/30 is about the same length as the M1891 Dragoon, but it represents many improvements over the Dragoon. The sights used on the M1891/30 are superior to those of the Dragoon, and, because the metric system of measurement was adopted in Russia during this period, the sights of the M1891/30 are calibrated in meters rather than in arshins. (One arshin equals 0.71 meters or 0.78 yards.) Manufacture of the M1891/30 was initiated in 1930. This model was used in large numbers in the Soviet Army, but was replaced by the carbine M1944 as the standard Soviet infantry shoulder weapon at the end of World War II. It is still in use in some of the satellite countries.

Scope on M1891/30 Sniper Rifle.

The sniper rifle M1891/30, which is basically the M1891/30 adapted for use with a telescope, is still a standard weapon in Soviet and satellite armies. The telescopes employed are somewhat similar to those used on United States hunting rifles.

M1910 Carbine.

The Carbine M1910. Although Imperial Russia adopted the Mosin-Nagant rifle in 1891, a true carbine did not appear until 1910. The carbine M1910, with its leaf sight and sling slots, has characteristics of both the original and later versions of the rifle M1891. The carbine M1910 has a hexagonal receiver and does not take a bayonet. This model is comparatively rare.

The carbine M1938 replaced the M1910. It is similar in many respects to the rifle M1891/30. It has a tangent-type rear sight, hooded front sight, and rounded receiver. It does not take a bayonet. This model may be encountered in satellite forces, although it is not manufactured at present.

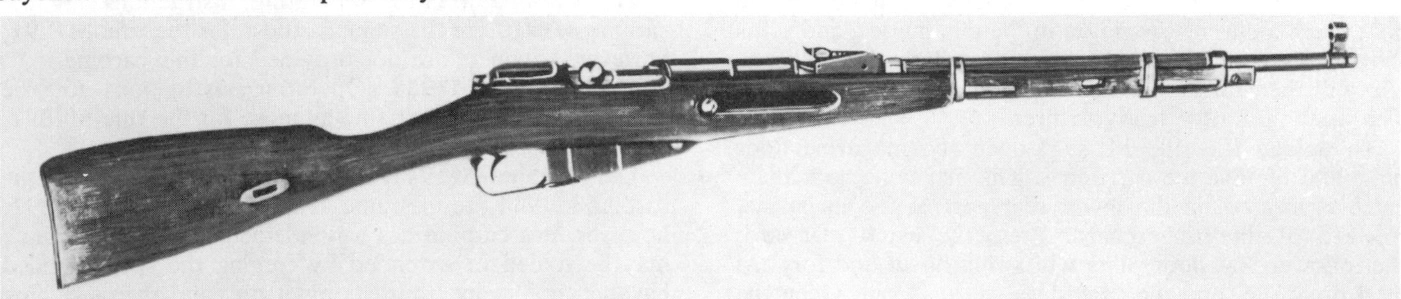

M1938 Carbine.

Characteristics of Soviet 7.62mm Mosin-Nagant Bolt Action Rifles and Carbines

Characteristics	Rifle M1891	Dragoon Rifle M1891	Rifle M1891/30	Sniper Rifle M1891/30	Carbine M1910	Carbine M1938	Carbine M1944
Weight—							
w/o bayonet & sling	9.62 lb.	8.75 lb.	8.7 lb.	11.3 lb.	7.5 lb.	7.62 lb.	
w/bayonet & sling	10.63 lb.	9.7 lb.	9.7 lb.		7.7 lb.		8.9 lb.
Length—							
w/o bayonet	51.37 in.	48.75 in.	48.5 in.	48.5 in.	40 in.	40 in.	40 in. (folded)
w/bayonet	68.2 in.	65.5 in.	65.4 in.	65.4 in.			52.25 in. (extended)
Barrel length	31.6 in.	28.8 in.	28.7 in.	28.7 in.	20 in.	20 in.	20.4 in.
Magazine capacity	5 rounds	5 rounds	5 rounds	5 rounds	5 rounds	5 rounds	5 rounds
Instrumental velocity at 78 ft. w/hvy ball	2660 f.p.s.	2660 f.p.s.	2660 f.p.s.	2660 f.p.s.	2514 f.p.s.	2514 f.p.s.	2514 f.p.s.
Rate of fire	8-10 r.p.m.	8-10 r.p.m.	8-10 r.p.m.	8-10 r.p.m.	8-10 r.p.m.	8-10 r.p.m.	8-10 r.p.m.
Maximum sighting range	3200 arshins (2496 yd.)	3200 arshins (2496 yd.)	2000 meters (2200 yd.)	2000 meters* (2200 yd.)	2000 arshins (1560 yd.)	1000 meters (1100 yd.)	1000 meters (1100 yd.)
Front sight	Unprotected blade	Unprotected blade	Hooded post	Hooded post	Unprotected blade	Hooded post	Hooded post
Rear sight	Leaf	Leaf	Tangent	Tangent	Leaf	Tangent	Tangent
Ammunition**	....	....	....	....	....	....	....

* For iron sights when scope is dismounted. Maximum sighting range for the telescopic sight on this weapon is: PE scope—1400 meters (1540 yd.); PU scope—1300 meters (1420 yd.).

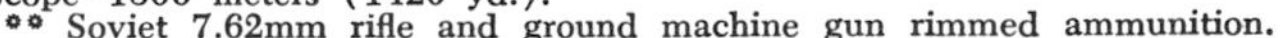
** Soviet 7.62mm rifle and ground machine gun rimmed ammunition.

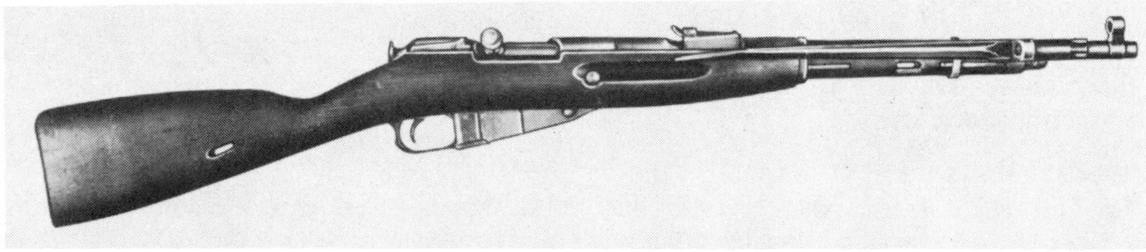

M1944 Carbine.

The carbine M1944, introduced during the latter part of World War II, was the last of the Mosin-Nagants. The permanently fixed bayonet folds down along the right side of the carbine stock when not in use. Except for a slightly longer barrel and the addition of the bayonet, the carbine M1944 is identical to the M1938. It is still in use in various Soviet satellites.

How to Load and Fire the Bolt Action Rifles and Carbines

The Rifle M1891. To set the safety, draw back the cocking piece and turn it to the left. This prevents the bolt from opening. To put off SAFE, pull the cocking piece back, turn it to the right, and allow it to move forward.

The rifle M1891 is loaded in the same manner as the United States Springfield or any Mauser rifle. Open the bolt, place a clip of cartridges in the clip guides, and press the rounds down into the magazine. Close the bolt; the clip will then fall out of the clip guides onto the ground. The weapon is now ready to fire.

To unload the rifle M1891, open the magazine floor plate and remove the cartridges. The magazine floor plate catch is located on the lower rear part of the magazine, forward of the triggerguard. Press the catch rearward; the follower and floor plate will swing down and forward on a pivot pin, and the cartridges will spill out. Open the bolt and extract the round from the chamber.

The M1891 bayonet is attached by a locking ring; if the M1891/30 bayonet is used, a spring-loaded catch holds the bayonet in place.

The Dragoon Rifle M1891. Operating instructions for Dragoon M1891 are the same as for rifle M1891.

The bayonet of the rifle M1891 or M1891/30 is attached to the Dragoon M1891 in the same manner as described for the rifle M1891.

The Rifle M1891/30. Operating instructions for the rifle M1891/30 are the same as those for the rifle M1891.

The bayonet is attached by a spring-loaded catch.

The Sniper rifle M1891/30. Operating instructions for this rifle are the same as those for the rifle M1891. The bayonet for the rifle M1891/30 is attached to the sniper rifle by means of a spring-loaded catch.

The Carbine M1910. Operating instructions for the carbine M1910 are the same as those for the rifle M1891; however, bayonets are not provided for this carbine.

The Carbine M1938. Operating instructions for the carbine M1938 are the same as those for the rifle M1891; bayonets are not provided for this carbine.

The Carbine M1944. Operating instructions for the carbine M1944 are the same as those for the rifle M1891; however, this carbine has a nondetachable bayonet which may be folded or extended by forcing the spring-loaded bayonet tube away from the pivot pin, and then swinging the bayonet to either folded or fixed position.

SOVIET AUTOMATIC and SEMI-AUTOMATIC RIFLES and CARBINES (Pre-WORLD WAR II)

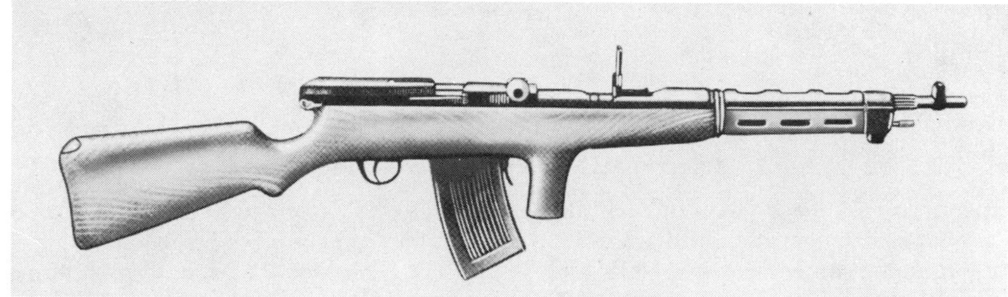

Federov Model 1916 "Avtomat."

The Federov Model 1916 "Avtomat" was made in limited quantity during World War I. It was a selective fire rifle chambered for the 6.5mm Japanese cartridge. It could be considered one of the first assault rifles.

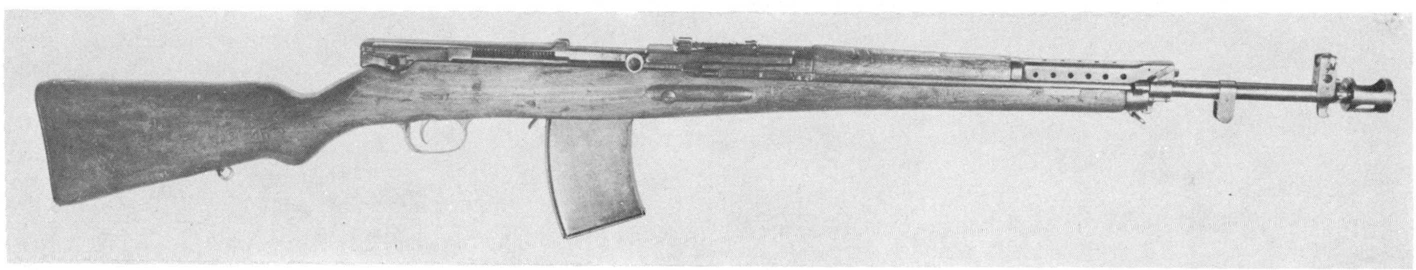

Simonov Model 1936 (AVS).

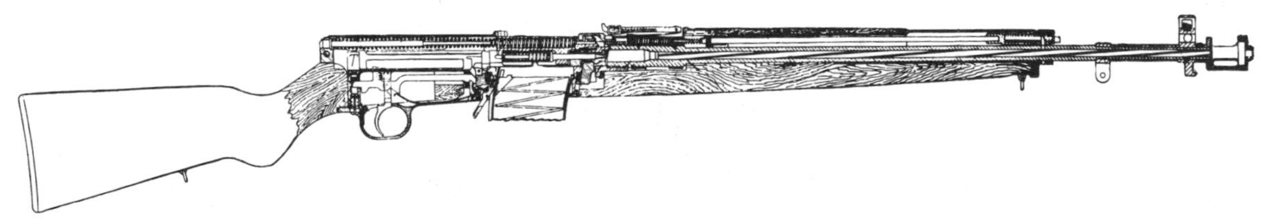

Section View of Simonov.

The Simonov automatic rifle M1936 (AVS) was one of the first automatic and semi-automatic rifles produced by the U.S.S.R. in 7.62mm caliber. Imperial Russia had previously produced the Federov automatic rifle M1916 in 6.5mm caliber, but the weapon did not prove successful and very few were manufactured. The Simonov rifle M1936 evidently did not meet requirements either for it is no longer used in the Soviet Army.

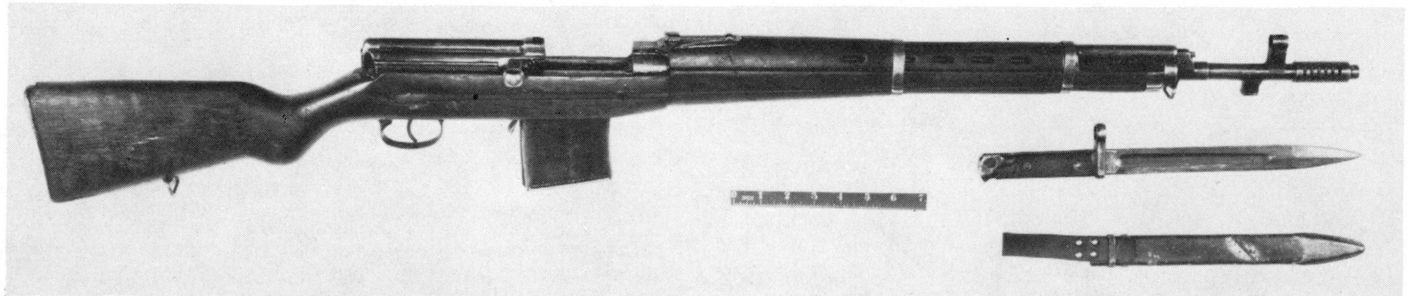

M1938 7.62mm Tokarev Rifle (SVT). Action open.

The Tokarev 7.62mm semi-automatic rifle M1938 (SVT) was the second of a series of Tokarev rifles. This model has a two-piece stock and is very lightly built.

The Tokarev 7.62mm semi-automatic rifle M1940 (SVT), as well as the **7.62mm automatic and semi-automatic rifle M1940 (AVT),** while considerably sturdier than the M1938, still proved rather flimsy for military use. Considerable difficulty was experienced

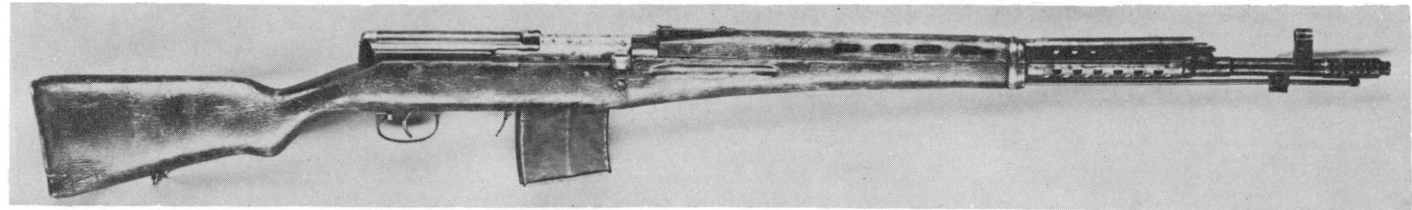

Tokarev M1940 Semi-Automatic Rifle.

in repair and maintenance of these weapons during World War II, and they are no longer standard weapons.

The Tokarev semi-automatic sniper rifles M1938 and M1940, because of their flimsy construction and the difficulties experienced in their repair and maintenance, are no longer standard weapons. These sniper rifles are merely Tokarev semi-automatic rifles M1938 (SVT) and M1940 (SVT) which have been specially selected for accuracy and adapted for mounting telescopic sights.

The Tokarev 7.62mm semi-automatic carbine M1932 was made only in small numbers. Its weaknesses, with regard to durability, repair, and maintenance, were apparently the same as those of the Tokarev rifles. This carbine is not a standard weapon.

Field Stripping Tokarev M1940

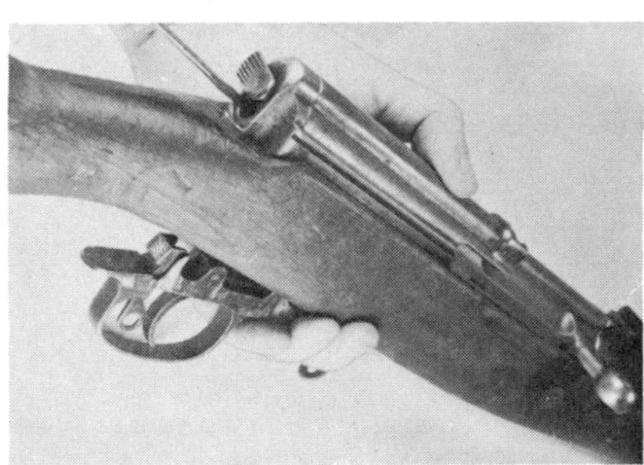

Remove Trigger Assembly. First turn the thumb latch at the extreme rear of the receiver up to the left as far as it will go. This will expose a cylindrical hole in which the triggerguard locking collar rests. With a screwdriver or a bullet point, push this spring-loaded locking collar in. This will pivot the locking bar in the rear of the receiver and will free the rear end of the triggerguard assembly which may then be removed from the receiver. (Note: When replacing this unit, it is necessary that the bolt be back far enough from the chamber so the disconnector is able to rise. Otherwise the front end of the triggerguard unit will not seat in the receiver notches.)

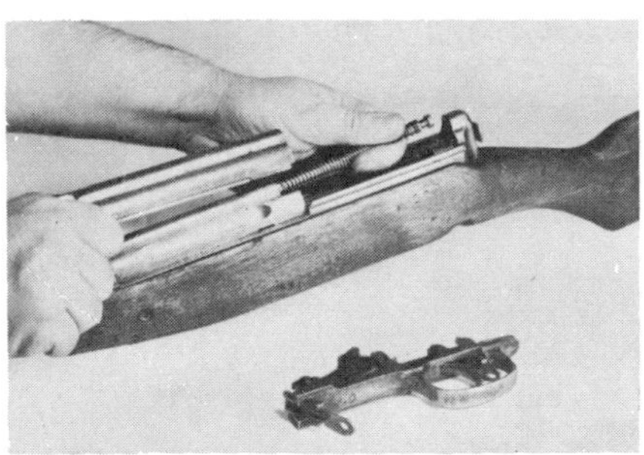

Remove Operating Spring Dust Cover. First rest the muzzle of the rifle on the floor, as considerable force must be applied. Then pull the steel cover to the rear of the bolt straight down toward the muzzle. This action will force the buffer and operating springs down inside the bolt, as the buffer guide rod is seated in a groove machined for it at the extreme rear of the cover. When the cover has been pulled down as far as it will go in its guides in the receiver, grasp it firmly with the left hand and squeeze it tightly against the bolt. While retaining this grasp with the left hand, with the thumb of the right hand push the buffer rod down far enough to free its head from the seating in the cover; then push it carefully out away from the cover and ease it and the springs up out of the bolt hole. The cover is free to come off at this point.

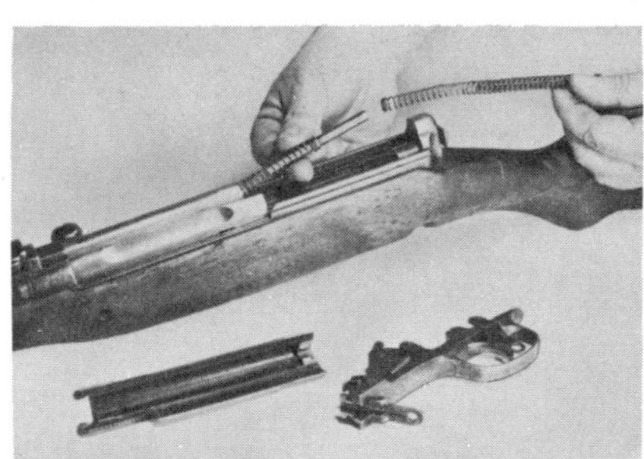

Remove Operating and Buffer Spring Assemblies. Holding the protruding buffer spring and rod close to the bolt hole, ease them up and to your right so the rod will clear the rear of the receiver. When all tension is off the springs, the buffer spring and its guide rod may be lifted out of engagement with the hollow operating spring rod. The operating spring and its rod may now be removed from the bolt hole.

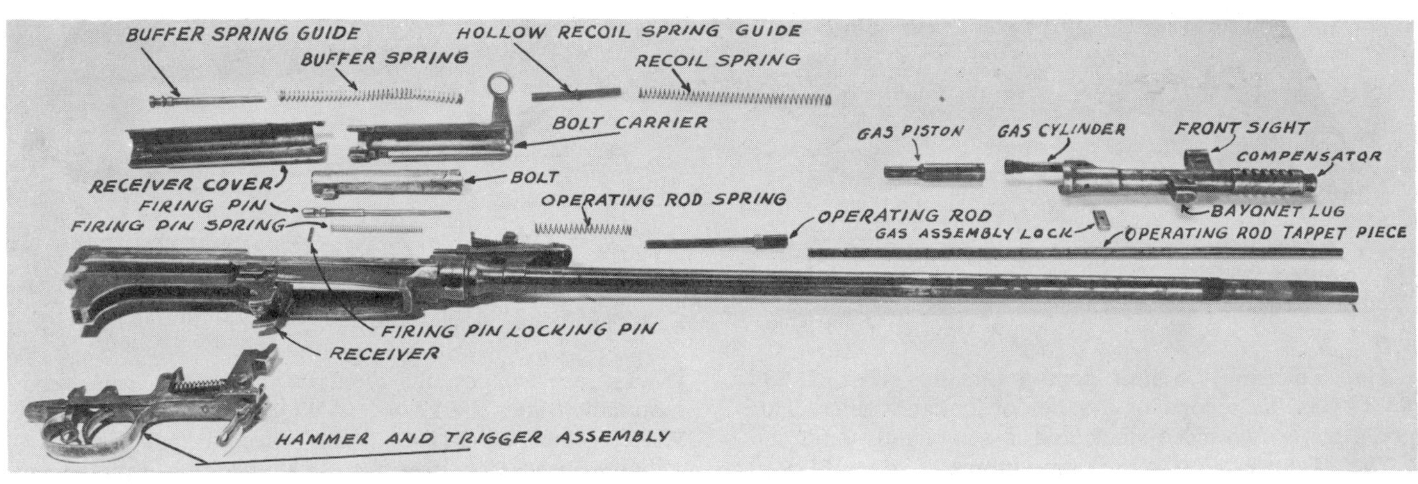

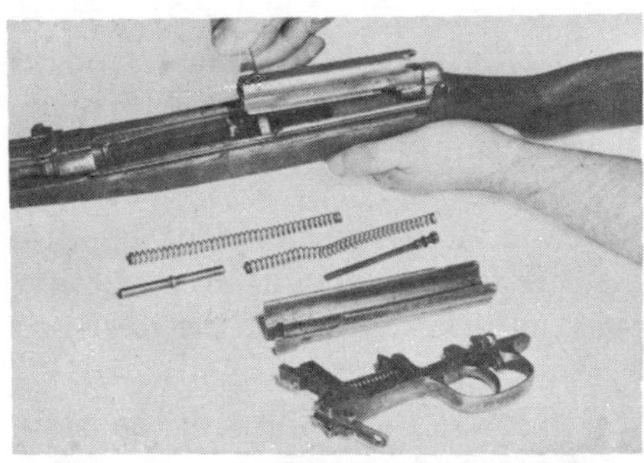

Remove the Bolt Assembly. Pull the bolt handle back slowly until the bolt carrier and the bolt have cleared the magazine well. Then lift up on the bolt handle and continue to pull back and up. At this point the bolt assembly is free of its receiver guides and may be tilted and lifted up out of the receiver. (Note: When re-assembling this unit, the assembly will drop into its receiver tracks at just the one proper point. Do not exert force, but "feel" for this point if you cannot locate it immediately.)

Remove the Bolt from its Carrier. Hold the assembly in the palm of the left hand upside down. Place the forefinger over the firing pin hole and the thumb (of the right hand) over the rear of the firing pin and push the bolt slowly ahead inside the carrier. At the proper point the cam faces on the bolt will mate with the proper surfaces on the bolt carrier and the bolt may then be lifted up out of the carrier.

Remove the Gas Piston. Press in the lock on the front band and push the band forward. This will permit the perforated metal upper cover to be lifted off.

The pierced wooden forearm covering the gas piston may then be lifted off. (Note: If it is necessary to remove the stock, unscrew the bolt from the right side of the receiver below the firing chamber and pull it out. The lower metal fore-end piece may then be removed and the receiver and barrel assemblies lifted out of the stock complete.)

Pull the piston back until it clears the face of the gas cylinder over which it is mounted. Holding the piston at this point, pull the operating rod in which the piston seats back far enough to permit the piston to be lifted off. Then ease the rod forward against the tension of its spring, and remove the rod and its spring from their seating in the receiver below the line of the rear sight.

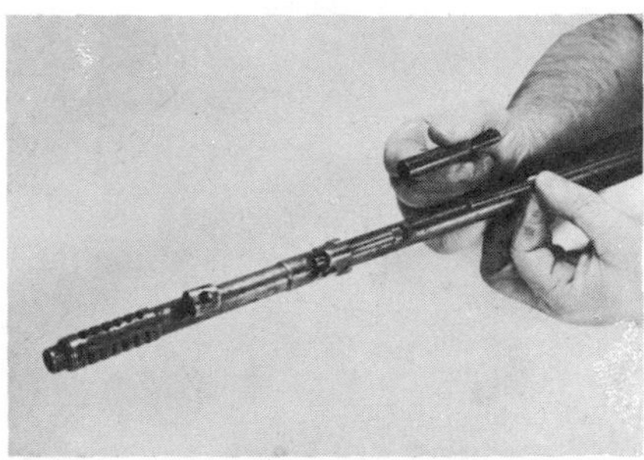

Remove Compensator and Gas Cylinder Assembly. Drift the retainer out preferably from the right. The compensator and assembly may then be unscrewed from the barrel and removed.

How the Rifle Works

A loaded magazine is inserted in the bottom of the receiver until its catch locks it. The bolt handle is drawn back and released to cock the hammer and strip a cartridge into the firing chamber.

The rear end of the bolt is forced down by the bolt carrier into locking position. The carrier proceeds to ride over projections on the bolt to hold it in the locked position.

When the trigger is pressed, it forces a bar forward to rotate the sear. The sear is fitted vertically in the trigger-guard. It now engages a bent in the head of the hammer. The hammer is rotated forward to strike the firing pin and explode the cartridge.

As the bullet passes down the barrel, a portion of the gas escapes through a port drilled in the top of the barrel under the upper section of the wooden fore-end. (The gas regulator has five positions for adjustment.) The expanding gas impinges on the head of the piston rod (which is positioned on top of the barrel) driving it backward for a stroke of about 1½ inches.

The thrust is transmitted to the operating rod which passes it on to the bolt carrier.

The operating rod is mounted above the barrel; its

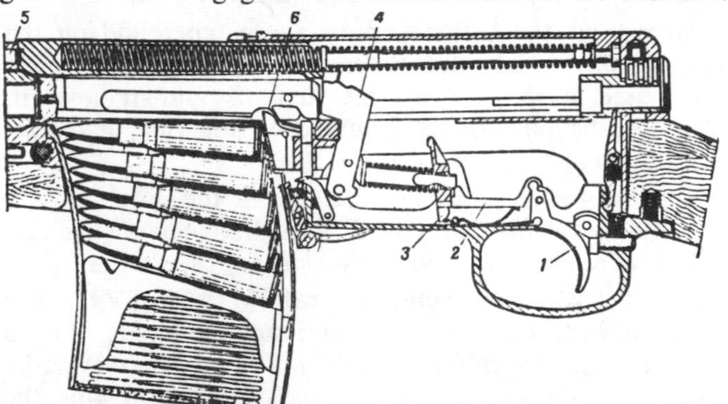

Action closed. Magazine loaded, hammer forward. Details of recoil spring shown.

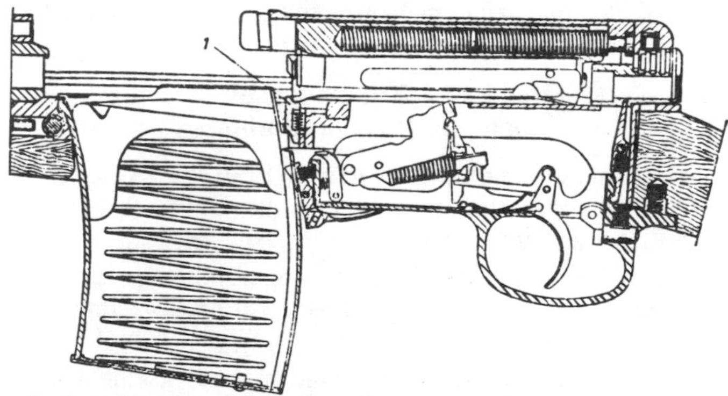

Action open on firing last shot. Recoil spring compressed, hammer cocked, ready for reloading.

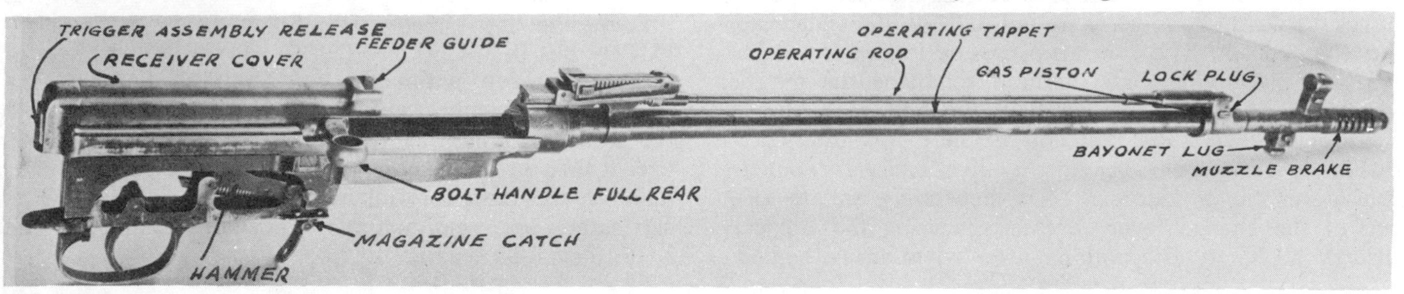

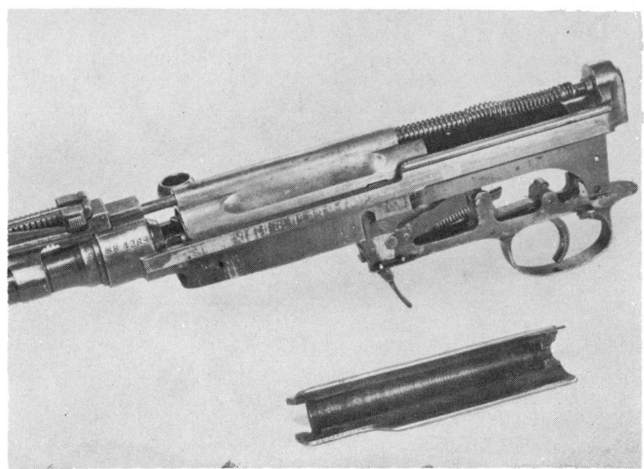

Metal parts removed from stock to show operation of mechanism and dust cover removed. Operating rod is being driven back through hole in the receiver and has pushed bolt carrier back until carrier has unlocked bolt and is carrying it back with it.

rear end passing through a hole in the receiver directly above the forward face of the locked bolt, and in line with the bolt carrier which rides on top of the bolt. The operating rod return spring is mounted around the rod itself.

The carrier travels back about ¼ of an inch before unlocking. The bolt travels on back carrying with it the empty cartridge case which is ejected to the right. It also compresses the dual springs mounted in the top of the receiver to store up energy for the return motion. At the same time it forces the hammer to rotate on its axis until it is caught and held by the sear.

When the last shot has been fired, a catch in the bottom center of the bolt way is operated by a projection of the magazine platform and holds the bolt open.

How To Load and Fire The Automatic and Semi-Automatic Rifles and Carbines

The Simonov automatic rifle M1936 (AVS). Set the safety with the thumb of the right hand. Rotate the safety forward until it rests against the trigger.

Place the change lever in the upper position for semiautomatic fire, or in the lower position for automatic fire.

This rifle is loaded in the same manner as the United States carbine M2. Insert the loaded magazine from the bottom; pull the bolt back and release it. As the bolt moves forward, it slides a round out of the magazine and chambers it. The rifle also may be loaded from the top, with five-round clips, without removing the magazine. To load in this manner, pull the bolt back, insert the rounds, then allow the bolt to slide forward. Turn the safety rearward. The rifle is then ready for either semi-automatic or automatic fire, depending on the setting of the change lever. Before squeezing the trigger, observe all safety precautions used when firing United States rifles. After the last shot, the bolt remains open.

NOTE 1: Care should be taken in loading the magazine to make certain that the rim of each round is placed forward of the preceding round.

NOTE 2. A loaded weapon may be accidentally discharged by a jolt. This is due to the peculiar construction of the sear and sear spring, and the failure of the designer to provide the necessary safety features.

Unload the weapon as follows: Place the rifle on safe. Press the magazine release forward and remove the magazine. Open the bolt and extract the cartridge from the chamber. After inspecting the chamber, release the bolt.

To remove the bayonet, place the rifle stock on the ground. Grasping the area of the gas cylinder with one hand and the bayonet with the other hand, pull the bayonet up until it stops; then force the bayonet outward, swing it downward to the stop, pull the handle forward, and remove the bayonet from the rifle.

Remove the cleaning rod by pulling the head of the cleaning rod away from the rifle, and withdrawing the rod with a forward motion.

The Tokarev semi-automatic rifle M1938 (SVT). The safety is set by rotating it downward into a vertical position behind the trigger.

The rifle is loaded in the same manner as the M1936 Simonov. After the magazine has been inserted, swing the safety to the left; pull the bolt back and release it. The weapon is now ready to fire. Before squeezing the trigger, observe all safety precautions used in firing United States rifles. The bolt will remain open after the last round has been fired.

To unload the rifle, place it on safe (swing the safety into vertical position in line with the trigger); press the magazine catch forward and at the same time remove the magazine; pull the bolt back and extract the cartridge. After inspecting the chamber, release the bolt.

To remove the bayonet, press the catch found on the left side of the bayonet handle to the right, and at the same time push the bayonet forward and remove it. When the bayonet is not mounted on the rifle, it is carried in a scabbard.

To remove the cleaning rod, press the catch at the rear end, and push it forward. Pull the catch to the side and then remove the rod with a rearward motion.

The Tokarev semi-automatic rifle M1940 (SVT). The operating instructions for the semi-automatic rifle M1940 are the same as those for the M1938 semi-automatic, except that the cleaning rod is removed by pressing the cleaning rod catch (located on the right side of the bayonet lug) to the left and, at the same time, pulling the cleaning rod forward. The attachments for the cleaning rod are carried in a separate canvas pouch.

The Tokarev automatic rifle M1940 (AVT). The operating instructions for the automatic rifle M1940 are the same as those for the semi-automatic rifle M1940 except that the safety is so constructed as to permit movement to the right for full automatic fire, in addition to the safety and semi-automatic positions found on the M1940 semi-automatic.

Characteristics of Soviet Pre-World War II 7.62mm Automatic and Semi-Automatic Rifles

Characteristics	Automatic rifle M1936	Semi-automatic rifle M1938	Semi-automatic rifle M1940	Automatic rifle M1940	Semi-automatic sniper rifle M1938	Semi-automatic sniper rifle M1940
Weight—						
w/o bayonet & magazine	8.93 lb.	8.70 lb.	8.59 lb.	8.35 lb.	9.52 lb.	9.18 lb.
w/bayonet & magazine	....	10.8 lb.	9.48 lb.	9.24 lb.	....	....
Length—						
w/o bayonet	48.6 in.	48.1 in.	48.1 in.	48.1 in.	48.1 in.	48.1 in.
w/bayonet	59.3 in.	60.84 in.	57.1 in.	57.1 in.	60.84 in.	57.1 in.
Barrel length	24.16 in.	25 in.	24.6 in.	24.6 in.	25 in.	24.6 in.
Magazine capacity	15 rounds	10 rounds	10 rounds	10 rounds	10 rounds	10 rounds
Instrumental velocity at 78 ft. w/hvy ball	2519 f.p.s.	2519 f.p.s.	2519 f.p.s.	2519 f.p.s.	2519 f.p.s.	2519 f.p.s.
Rate of fire (semi-automatic)	30-40 r.p.m.	25 r.p.m.	25 r.p.m.	30-40 r.p.m.	25 r.p.m.	25 r.p.m.
Maximum sighting range	1500 meters	1500 meters	1500 meters	1500 meters	Iron sights: 600 m. (660 yd.) Telescope: 1300 m (1430 yd.)	Iron sights: 600 m. (660 yd.) Telescope: 1300 m. (1430 yd.)
Front sight	Open guard blade	Hooded post	Hooded post	Hooded post	Hooded post	Hooded post
Rear sight	Tangent	Tangent	Tangent	Tangent	Tangent and telescope	Tangent and telescope
Principle of operation	Gas	Gas	Gas	Gas	Gas	Gas
Ammunition	*	*	*	*	*	*

* 7.62mm U.S.S.R. rifle and ground machine gun rimmed ammunition.

NEW SOVIET SHOULDER WEAPONS

The Soviets have two new shoulder weapons: The Avtomat Kalashnikov, which is commonly called the AK; and the Simonov carbine, commonly called the SKS. Both are chambered for a new 7.62mm "intermediate-sized" cartridge, i.e., a cartridge intermediate in size between the U. S. cal. .30 carbine cartridge and the U. S. cal. .30 rifle cartridge. This cartridge (which is considerably smaller and has considerably less power than the 7.62mm NATO cartridge or the older Soviet 7.62mm rimmed cartridge) is now used in all Soviet squad-level small arms except the Stechkin pistol. The official Soviet nomenclature for the cartridge is Cartridge, 7.62mm, M1943. There are five types of this cartridge in use:

- Ball Type PS (PS indicates the use of a mild steel core)
- Tracer Type T-45
- Armor-Piercing Incendiary Type BZ
- Incendiary Tracer Type Z
- Blank (has rosette-type crimp)

The Soviet M1943 cartridge appears to be a further development of the German 7.92mm Kurz, or "short," of World War II. The German cartridge, whose official German nomenclature was Pistolen Patrone 43, was used in the Mkb 42, MP 43, MP 44, and StG 44 series of weapons. Essentially, cartridges of the size of the German 7.92mm short and the Soviet 7.62mm M1943 are cut-down versions of full-size rifle cartridges, and are limited in effective range and penetration; they do, however, have certain advantages over the full-size cartridges.

M1943 7.62mm Intermediate-Size Cartridge.

They are considerably lighter, and therefore the soldier can carry more cartridges on his person. The lightness is also a logistical advantage in shipping and handling.

They require less material in manufacture.

Since they are shorter than full-size cartridges, the weapons made for them can be shorter and lighter than those made for full-size cartridges—although this is not always true in practice.

They have considerably less recoil than do full-size cartridges.

It is significant, however, that the Soviets still use their old full-size 7.62mm rimmed cartridge in their heavy machine guns, which may be used for fire over the heads of their own troops or for long-range interdictory fire. It should also be borne in mind that the Russians who have competed in international rifle matches in recent years do not use the new intermediate-sized M1943 cartridge; they use a 7.62mm Match Cartridge which has the same case as the old 7.62mm rimmed cartridge. In other words, where first-rate accuracy is a requirement, the Soviets still use the full-size rifle cartridge.

7.62mm Assault Rifle AK (Avtomat Kalashnikov) (Left Side).

AK Assault Rifle (Right Side).

Caliber: 7.62mm (1943 cartridge).
System of Operation: Gas, selective fire.
Weight: 10.58 lb.
Overall Length: 34.25 in.
Barrel Length: 16.34 in.
Feed Device: 30-rd., curved, staggered-row, detachable box magazine.
Sights, Front: Protected post.
Rear: Tangent leaf with open V-notch, graduated from 1 to 8 (100m to 800m) with battle-sight.
Muzzle Velocity: 2329 f.p.s.
Cyclic Rate of Fire: 600 r.p.m.

The AK has frequently been called a submachine gun. It is true that the AK has replaced the PPSh M1941 and PPS M1943 submachine guns in the Soviet service, but it is not entirely practical to class the AK, which fires rifle-type cartridges, with submachine guns, which fire pistol cartridges. The AK is much more accurate over a longer range than any of the normal run of submachine guns such as the British Sten, U. S. M3A1, or Israeli Uzi, all of which use pistol ammunition. The average submachine gun firing single shots will produce a group from 12 to 18 inches in diameter at 100 yards. The AK will group into 6 inches at 100 yards; this is about average for a military rifle at that range. The AK is outwardly quite similar to the German MP 43 and MP 44 series of weapons, but internally is quite different. The weapon is made almost completely from milled steel components, few stampings being utilized. Surprisingly enough, this is a characteristic of all of the Soviet postwar small arms, and is in sharp contrast with their extremely large-scale use of stampings during World War II. The AK is made in two versions, one using a wooden stock and the other using a folding metal stock. Originally the AK did not have a bayonet, but now has a knife-type bayonet. The bayonet has a blade of approximately 8 inches. The AK is replacing the SKS carbine as the principal shoulder weapon of the Soviet Army. AK is now frequently called AK-47.

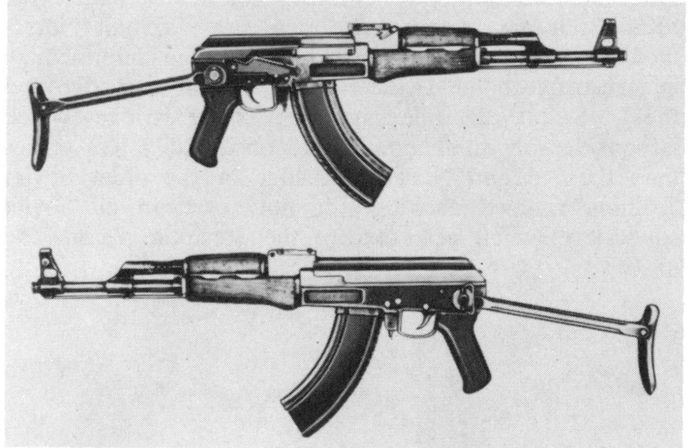

AK Rifle with Folding Stock.

AK Assault Rifle with bayonet.

North Korean Copy of Soviet 7.62mm Assault Rifle, AK.

Loading and Firing the AK

The thirty-round magazine is loaded by hand by pressing the cartridges down into the mouth of the magazine

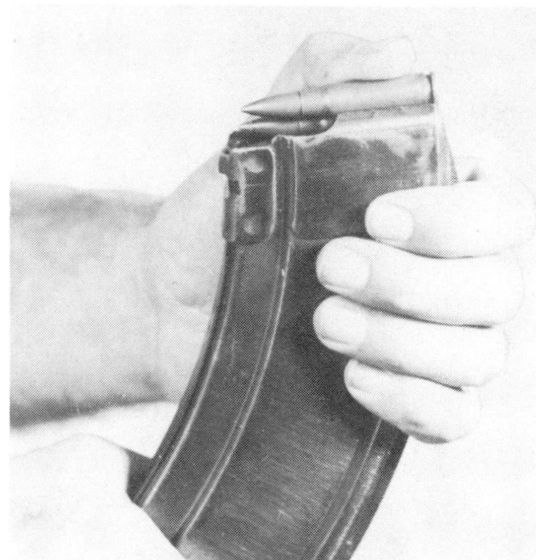

Loading AK Magazine.

with the thumb. Insert the magazine into the underside of the receiver, forward end first; then draw up the rear end of the magazine until a click is heard or until the magazine catch is felt to engage its slot at the rear of the magazine. Pull the operating handle (which pro-

Inserting AK Magazine.

trudes from the right side of the receiver) smartly to the rear and release it. The bolt and bolt carrier will go forward under the pressure of the recoil spring and will chamber a cartridge. To put the weapon on safe, push the safety selector catch (mounted on the right side of the receiver) as far up as it will go. When on safe, the safety selector blocks rearward movement of the operating handle and covers a gap to the rear of the bolt carrier. For semi-automatic fire, push the end of the safety selector lever all the way down (so that its forward end is opposite the bottom two Cyrillic letters), aim, and squeeze (do not pull) the trigger. For full automatic fire, push the safety selector lever to the middle position marked by the two Cyrillic letters "AB" (which stand for "automatic"). Although the AK is quite heavy, it climbs rapidly in automatic fire; it is therefore necessary to get a good grip on the weapon before squeezing the trigger for automatic fire.

Field Stripping the AK

Remove the magazine and pull the operating handle to the rear to clear weapon of any live ammunition. At the rear of the stamped receiver cover, a serrated catch protrudes; this is the rear end of the recoil spring guide

Removing AK Receiver Cover.

rod. Push the catch in with the finger and at the same time pull the receiver cover upward and backward from the receiver. After removing the receiver cover, push the recoil spring guide forward, so that the bottom rear lug section of the guide clears the dovetail slot at the rear

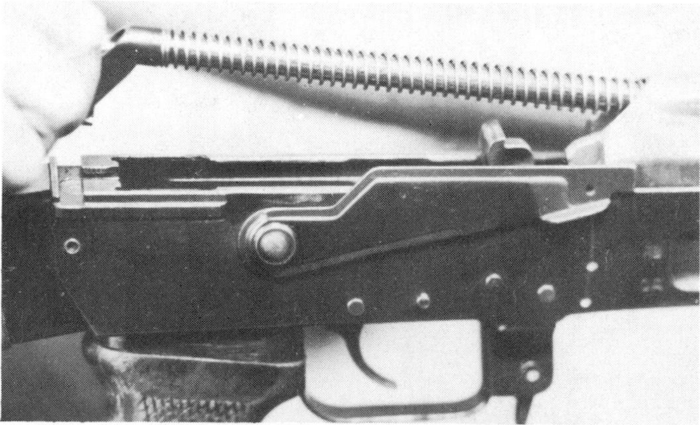

Removing Recoil Spring Assembly.

of the receiver. Remove recoil spring. Note that the recoil spring and its guide rod are a packaged unit; i.e., they are held together as one piece by a collar fitted to the end of the guide rod. This is similar to the recoil spring used on the cal. .50 Browning machine gun. The bolt carrier, piston, and bolt can now be removed as a unit by pulling them back to the cutout section in the

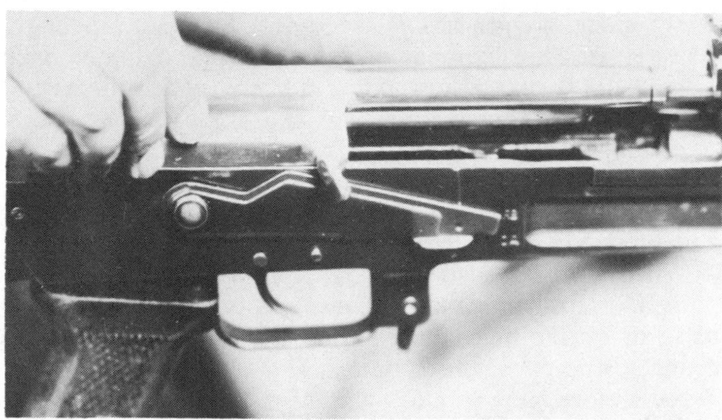

Removing Bolt Carrier Assembly.

receiver track and lifting them upward and rearward. To remove the bolt from the bolt carrier, turn its head so that the guide lug aligns with the cam surface of the bolt carrier, move the bolt as far to rear as possible,

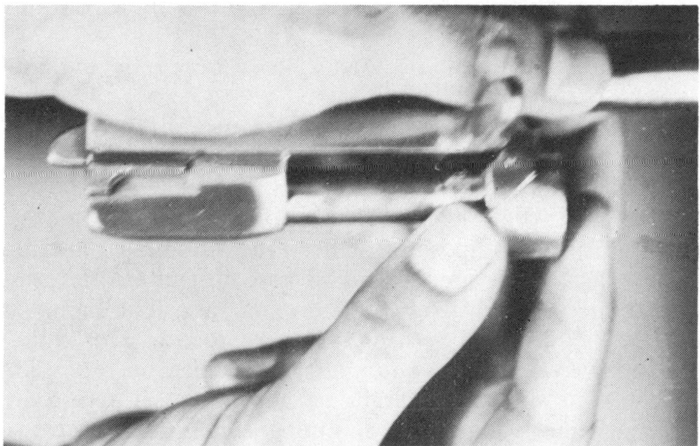

Removing Bolt.

rotate the bolt so that the guide lug leaves the camway of the bolt carrier, and pull the bolt forward and out of the bolt carrier. This operation is not as complicated as it seems; the bolt can actually be shaken out of the bolt carrier. Rotate the handguard lock lever (on the forward right side of the rear sight base) upward, and the handguard-piston tube assembly can be lifted out. No further disassembly is recommended.

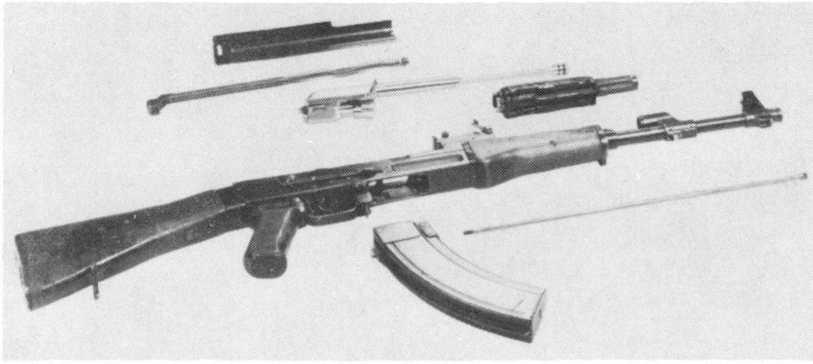

AK Field Stripped.

To assemble the weapon, carry out in reverse the steps outlined above.

How the AK Works

Full automatic fire. With the safety selector set on full automatic fire, a cartridge in the chamber (to chamber a cartridge initially, since the AK fires from a closed bolt, it is necessary to pull the operating handle to the rear and release it), and a loaded magazine in the weapon, the following actions occur when the trigger is pulled. The safety selector lug is far enough to the rear to release the rear end of the trigger, but stays directly above the rear end of the disconnector. Thus, while the trigger is free to rotate, the safety selector lug prevents the disconnector from rotating. One large multi-stranded spring is used as both hammer spring and trigger spring in the AK.

Semi-automatic fire. To fire a single round from the rifle, set the weapon for semi-automatic fire by rotating the safety selector as far downward as possible, and then press the trigger.

When the trigger is pressed, the semi-automatic sear and disconnector rotate. The rear end of the sear (which is actually part of the trigger) raises the ends of the hammer-and-trigger spring. As the trigger rotates, the semi-automatic sear releases the hammer cock notch.

The hammer-and-trigger spring rotates the hammer forward, and the hammer strikes the rear end of the firing pin, pushing it forward so that it strikes the primer of the cartridge. The cartridge fires, and gases from the cartridge flow through the gas port in the barrel into the gas cylinder and force the piston and bolt carrier assembly to the rear. As the piston and bolt carrier assembly move to the rear, the recoil spring is compressed. The bevel in the bolt carrier cam acts on the bolt guide lug, rotating the bolt to the left and thereby unlocking the bolt.

After the bolt is unlocked, the bolt carrier and bolt move to the rear together. The bolt carrier rotates the hammer to the rear, compressing the hammer-and-trigger spring. As the hammer rotates, it rotates the disconnector. When the head of the hammer has passed the notch in the disconnector, the disconnector spring forces the disconnector to engage the disconnector notch in the hammer. This holds the hammer at full cock.

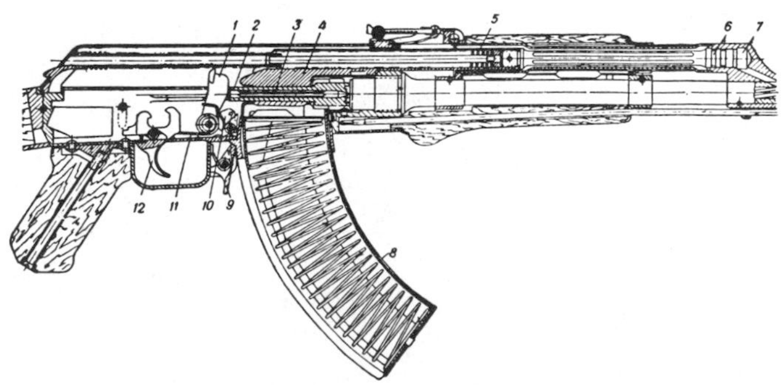

Section View of AK.

1. Hammer
2. Bolt
3. Firing pin
4. Operating rod
5. Recoil spring
6. Gas piston
7. Gas cylinder
8. Magazine
9. Magazine catch
10. Full automatic sear
11. Trigger and hammer spring
12. Trigger

The full automatic sear spring rotates the full automatic sear into engagement with the full automatic sear notch in the hammer. The full automatic sear, however, does not hold the hammer in the cocked position, since the disconnector is already performing this function. As the full automatic sear rotates, the upper end of the sear rises to obstruct the passage of the full automatic disconnector.

As the bolt moves to the rear, the extractor pulls the cartridge case from the chamber. When the case strikes the ejector, it is ejected from the receiver.

The top round in the magazine is forced upward by the follower until it is arrested by the magazine flange.

The rearward movement of the bolt carrier and bolt is arrested by the rear wall of the receiver. Forward movement of these parts is caused by the decompression of the recoil spring.

As the bolt carrier moves forward, the top cartridge in the magazine is stripped from the magazine and forced into the chamber.

As the bolt approaches the barrel face, the first stage in the rotation of the bolt to the right takes place. At the same time, the extractor engages the extractor groove of the cartridge case. As the bolt carrier moves to the extreme forward position, it produces the final rotation of the bolt to the right, locking the bolt.

After the bolt is locked, but while the bolt carrier is still a short distance from the extreme forward position, the full automatic disconnector (which is integral with the bolt carrier) strikes the upper end of the full automatic sear, and rotates the sear forward. This action moves the full automatic sear away from the hammer, so that the hammer will not be prevented from rotating.

The next round is fired by releasing the trigger, and then pressing it again. When the trigger is released, the hammer-and-trigger spring rotates the disconnector and semi-automatic sear to the rear, disengaging the disconnector from the disconnector notch in the hammer. The trigger-and-hammer spring rotates the hammer until the hammer cock notch engages the semi-automatic sear. This is accompanied by an audible click.

When the trigger is again pressed, the semi-automatic sear releases the hammer cock notch. The hammer once again strikes the firing pin, and the entire operating cycle of the automatic mechanism is repeated.

Automatic fire. To fire the rifle automatically, set the selector at full automatic fire by rotating the indicator until it is opposite the Cyrillic letters AB on the receiver, and press the trigger.

When the trigger is pressed, it rotates on the trigger pin. The disconnector, because it is prevented from rotating by the selector lever, does not engage the disconnector notch in the hammer.

As the trigger rotates, the semi-automatic sear releases the hammer cock notch. The hammer-and-trigger spring rotates the hammer, which strikes the firing pin forcibly. The round is fired. The powder gases act on the gas piston, thrusting the operating rod to the rear, opening the bolt, extracting and ejecting the cartridge case, and cocking the hammer.

The full automatic sear engages the full automatic sear notch in the hammer, holding the hammer at full cock.

The top round in the magazine is raised by the follower.

As the bolt carrier and bolt are moved forward by the recoil spring, the round is fed into the chamber and the bolt is locked.

When the bolt carrier is a short distance from the extreme forward position, the full automatic disconnector strikes the upper end of the full automatic sear and rotates the sear, releasing the hammer. The hammer strikes the firing pin, firing the next round. The entire operating cycle of the automatic mechanism is repeated.

The rifle will continue firing until the last round in the magazine is expended or until the firer releases pressure on the trigger. In the first case, the bolt carrier and bolt will remain in the forward position and the hammer will not be cocked (the AK has no bolt-holding-open device to hold the bolt to the rear after the last round is fired). In the second case, the rifle will be loaded and ready to fire again if the rifleman ceases fire before expending all the rounds in the magazine.

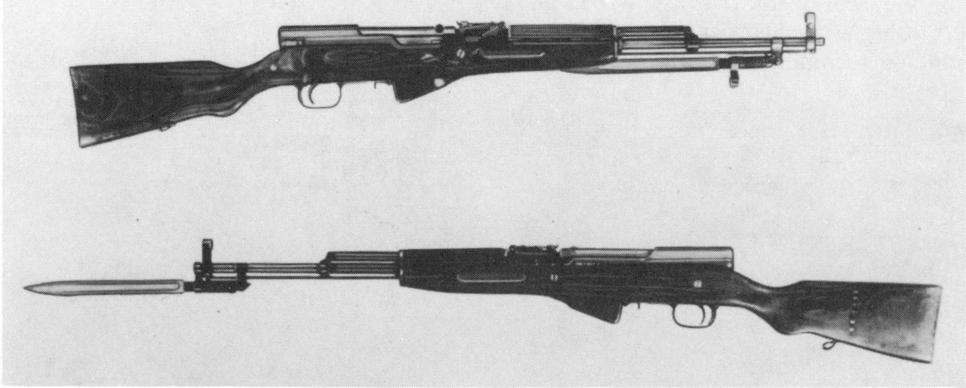

Soviet 7.62mm Simonov Semi-Automatic Carbine (SKS).

The SKS, like the AK automatic rifle and RPD machine gun, is chambered for the new Soviet "intermediate-sized" M1943 cartridge previously described. The action of the SKS is basically a scaled-down version of the action of the obsolete 14.5mm PTRS antitank rifle. The SKS is a well-designed gun and is very easy to use. Its disassembly is not quite as simple as is the AK's, but is still relatively easy. The SKS is distinguished by its folding bayonet, which—unlike earlier Soviet folding bayonets—is of blade section and folds under the weapon rather than to the side of the weapon.

Caliber: 7.62mm (M1943 cartridge).
System of Operation: Gas, semi-automatic only.
Weight, Loaded: 8.84 lb.
Overall Length: 40.16 in.
Barrel Length: 20.47 in.
Feed Device: 10-rd., fixed, staggered double-row box magazine.
Sights, Front: Hooded post.
Rear: Tangent leaf, graduated from 100 m to 1000 m.
Muzzle Velocity: 2411 f.p.s.

NOTE: The Soviets call the SKS a carbine because of its short barrel length. It is not intended to be nor is it used as a replacement for the pistol (as the U. S. carbine was designed to be). The SKS was intended to be used as the tactical equivalent to the U. S. M1 rifle or the new U. S. M14 rifle.

Field Stripping the SKS

Turn off the safety by rotating it downward. Swing the bayonet upward so that it projects at a 90-degree angle from the muzzle of the rifle. Remove the cleaning rod by disengaging its head from the lugs on the underside of the barrel and pulling the rod forward. Rotate the bayonet downward until it locks in its folded position.

Hold the small of the stock with the left hand and, with the right hand, rotate the receiver cover retaining pin arm (located at the right rear of the receiver) upward; then, pressing on the receiver cover with the thumb of the left hand, move the pin to the right as far as possible, and remove the cover from the receiver. Remove the recoil spring assembly from the bolt carrier. Note that the recoil spring assembly is, like that of the AK, a packaged unit.

To remove the bolt and bolt carrier from the receiver,

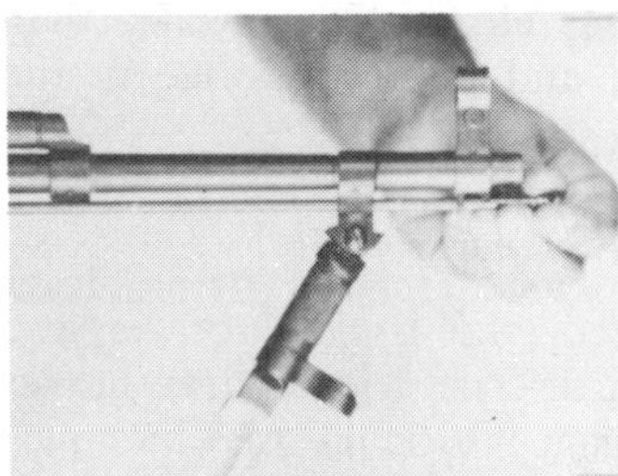

Removing Cleaning Rod.

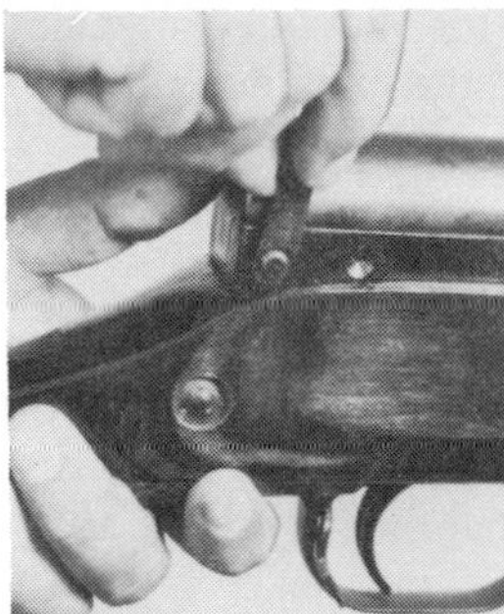

Loosening Receiver Cover Retaining Pin.

Removing Receiver Cover.

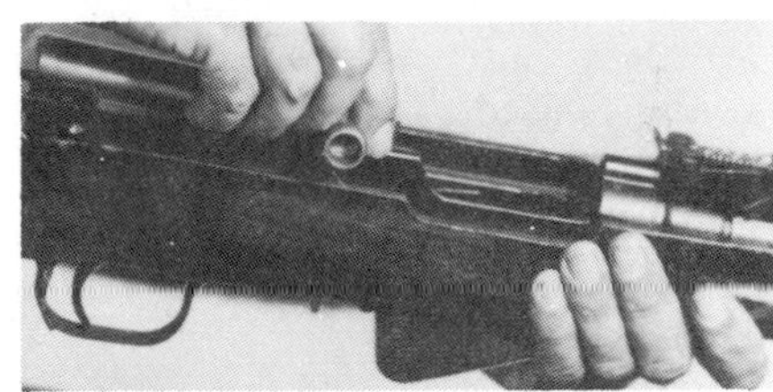

Removing Bolt and Bolt Carrier.

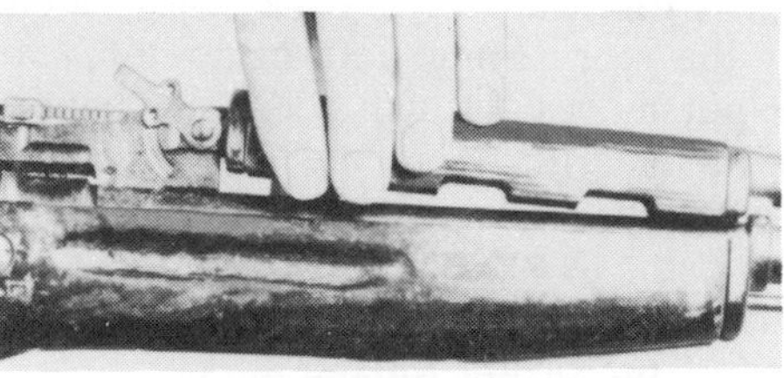

Removing Handguard and Gas Piston Assembly.

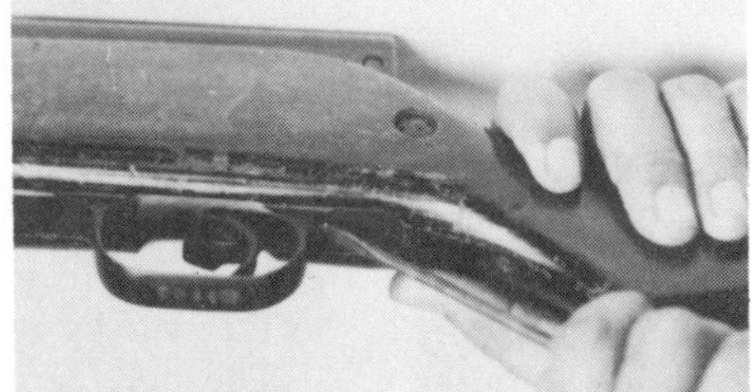

Unlocking Triggerguard.

Removing Trigger Group.

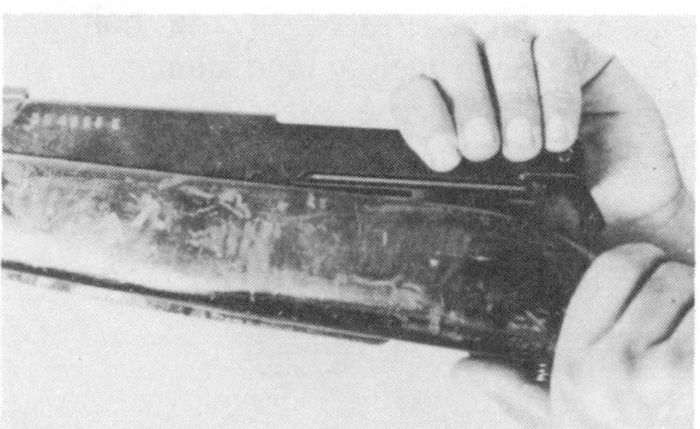

Removing Barrel and Receiver.

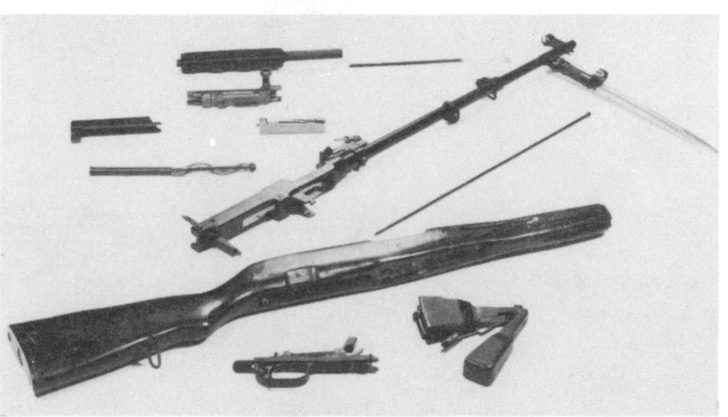

SKS Field Stripped.

pull back on the operating handle; the whole assembly will lift out, and the bolt can be removed from the bolt carrier.

Hold the fore-end of the carbine with the left hand and, with the right hand, rotate the gas cylinder tube lock lever upward (the lock is at the right front side of the rear sight base) until the lock lever lug is stopped by the upper wall of the cutout in the rear sight base. Then the gas cylinder tube and handguard assembly can be slightly raised and pulled rearward off the weapon. The gas piston will slide out of the gas cylinder tube.

To assemble the weapon, follow the above steps in reverse order.

Loading and Firing the SKS

Set the weapon on "SAFE" by turning the safety lever up as far as it will go. The safety lever is at the rear of the triggerguard. Pull the operating handle to the rear as far as it will go; the bolt and bolt carrier will be held to the rear by the bolt-holding-open device. If the cartridges are assembled in the ten-round charger normally used, insert one end of the charger in the charger guide which is machined into the top forward end of the bolt carrier. Push down on the cartridges with the thumb until all the cartridges are loaded into the magazine; then remove the empty charger guide. Pull back on the operating handle and release it; the bolt and bolt carrier will now go forward and chamber a cartridge. Disengage the safety by turning it down as far as it will go. The rifle is now ready to fire.

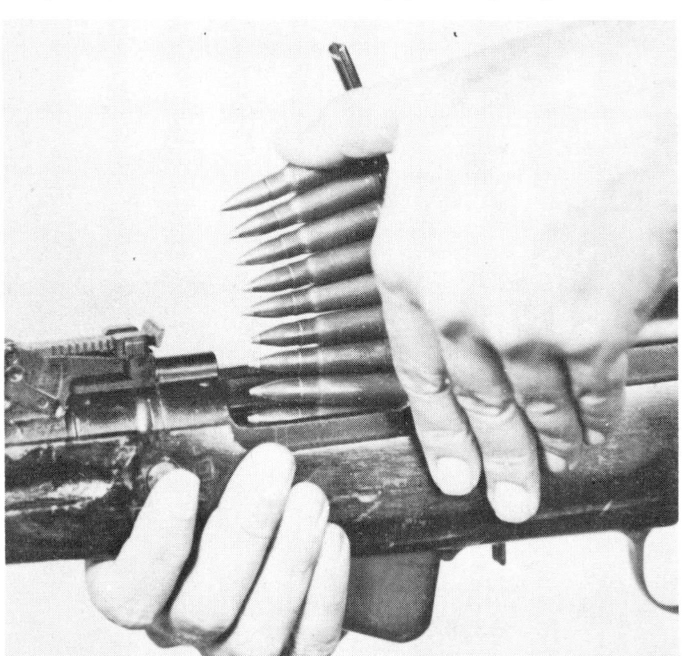

Loading the SKS.

If all ten rounds are fired, the bolt and bolt carrier will stay to the rear, leaving the action open for reloading. If only a few rounds are fired, and it is desired to unload the weapon, the following procedure should be observed. To the rear of the magazine, on the underside of the weapon, is a catch; pull this catch rearward. The magazine body will now swing downward and the rounds in the magazine will spill out. The round in the chamber is removed by pulling the operating handle to the rear.

To Fix the Bayonet

To fix the bayonet, the bayonet handle is pulled to the rear, and the bayonet is rotated upward until the bayonet muzzle ring snaps over the muzzle of the weapon. To fold the bayonet, pull the bayonet handle upward until the bayonet muzzle ring clears the muzzle; then swing the bayonet downward and into its groove in the stock.

How the SKS Works

When the trigger is pressed, the trigger rotates and moves the trigger arm forward. The trigger arm moves the sear forward and disengages it from the hammer. The hammer spring, now being free to expand, rotates the hammer, which strikes the firing pin and drives it through the bolt channel. When the hammer is rotated, the hammer heel lowers the forward end of the disconnector and the forward end of the trigger arm. At this time, the trigger arm is disengaged from the sear, which, under the action of the sear spring, returns to the rear position. The firing pin moves through the bolt channel until the firing pin tip emerges from the bolt face and strikes the primer. After the bullet passes the gas port in the wall of the barrel, the gases enter the gas cylinder, exert pressure on the piston, and move the bolt carrier to the rear by means of the piston rod.

The bolt carrier, after traveling a path of eight mm, raises the rear end of the bolt, disengages the bolt locking surface from the receiver lug and brings the bolt to the rear. As the bolt moves to the rear, it extracts the empty cartridge case, which is held in the bolt face by the extractor lug. After traveling a distance of 70 mm, the base of the cartridge case meets the ejector, and the case is ejected from the weapon. In moving to the rear,

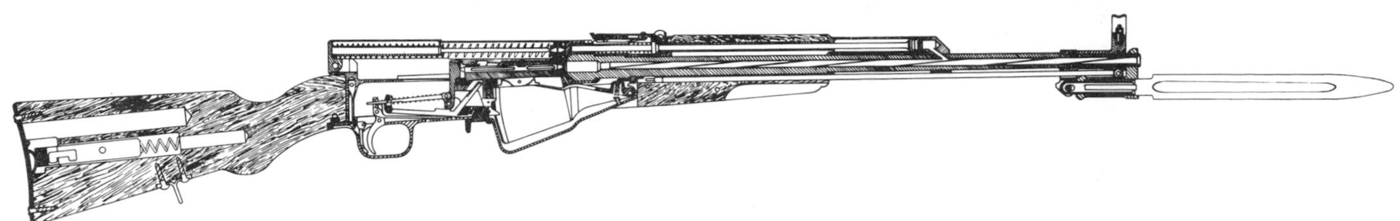

Section View of SKS.

the bolt carrier, and then the bolt, cocks the hammer. The forward end of the disconnector, under the action of the hammer spring, is raised upward, and the hammer is positioned on the disconnector notch at the same time. The forward end of the trigger arm is located between the base of the triggerguard and the sear. Under the action of the sear spring, the sear, which is in the extreme rear position, is positioned under the hammer cock notch. Under the action of the follower lever spring, the follower positions the next round for the feed rib. The piston, together with the piston rod, pushes the bolt a distance of 20 mm. The bolt thereafter continues by inertia to the extreme rear position, at the same time compressing the recoil spring, and the piston and piston rod return to the forward position under the action of the piston rod spring.

Under the action of the expanding recoil spring, the bolt moves forward, and the bolt feed rib grasps the next round in the magazine and sends it into the chamber. The bolt carrier lowers the rear end of the bolt upon approaching the barrel face, and the bolt locking surface is positioned in front of the receiver locking lug to seal the bore. The bolt, in lowering, depresses the protruding front end of the disconnector, at which time the hammer is disengaged from the disconnector and is then cocked. As it approaches the barrel face, the extractor, which is now sliding along the base of the cartridge case, is forced to the right to grasp the cartridge case rim. The extractor spring is compressed at this time. Under the action of the follower lever spring, the follower raises the next round until it meets the bolt. Before the next round is fired, it is necessary to release the trigger; under the action of the trigger spring, the trigger returns to the forward position, and the front end of the trigger lever is disengaged from the sear and is positioned opposite the sear shoulders.

To fire the next round, it is necessary to press the trigger. The hammer can be released from the cocked position only when the bolt is in the extreme forward position and the bore is completely sealed. If the bolt is in the rear position (on the stop), or if the bore is not completely sealed (bolt in extreme forward position), the forward end of the disconnector is not depressed, the forward end of the trigger lever presses against the guide lugs for the sear in the triggerguard groove, and the hammer cannot be released. If the bolt travels past the locking lug and depresses the forward end of the disconnector, and the bolt carrier has not attained the extreme forward position, the weapon still cannot be fired. In this event, the hammer, in moving forward will not strike the firing pin, but will strike the vertical surface of the bolt carrier which cocks the hammer.

SOVIET SUBMACHINE GUNS

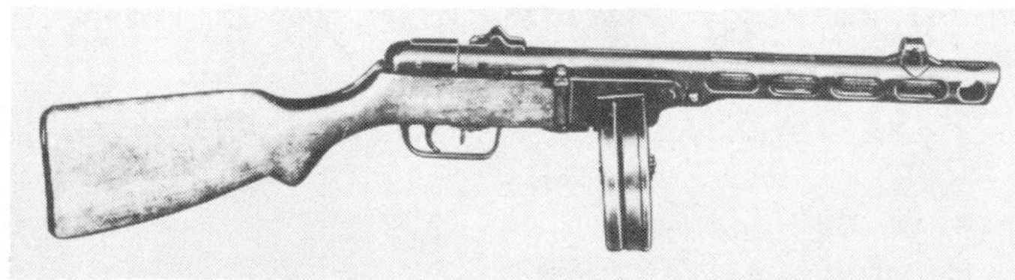

PPSH M1941 with 71-rd. Drum Magazine.

All pre-World War II and World War II Soviet submachine guns were chambered for the Soviet 7.62mm pistol cartridge Type P. Although the two latest types, the PPSh M1941 and the PPS M1943, are still in use in some of the satellites, all of these guns are obsolete in the U. S. S. R.

	PPD Model 1934/38	PPD Model 1940	PPSH Model 1941	PPS Model 1943
Caliber:	7.62mm	7.62mm	7.62mm	7.62mm
System of Operation:	Blowback Selective fire	Blowback Selective fire	Blowback Selective fire	Blowback Automatic fire only
Weight: w/loaded drum magazine:	11.5 lb.	11.90 lb.	11.99 lb.	
Weight: w/loaded box magazine:	8.25 lb.		9.26 lb.	7.98 lb.
Length Overall:	30.63 in.	30.63 in.	33.15 in.	Stock extended—32.72 in. Stock folded—24.25 in.
Barrel Length:	10.63 in.	10.63 in.	10.63 in.	9.45 in.
Feed Device:	71-rd. drum or 25-rd. box	71-rd. drum	71-rd. drum or 35-rd. box	35-rd. box
Sights, Front:	Blade	Hooded blade	Hooded post	Post w/ears
Rear:	Tangent leaf	Tangent leaf	Tangent leaf or L-type	L-type
Cylic Rate:	900 r.p.m.	900-1100 r.p.m.	700-900 r.p.m.	650 r.p.m.
Muzzle Velocity:	1640 f.p.s.	1640 f.p.s.	1640 f.p.s.	1608 f.p.s.

NOTE: A 1942 version of the PPS M1943 also exists, but differs only in minor details from the Model 1943.

Pre-World War II and World War II Soviet Submachine Guns.

Note that the bolt is a very simple machined piece. The recoil spring guide is resting in a hole in the rear of the bolt, with the spring around it; and a plastic buffer at its rear end. This spring arrangement also serves to spring-lock the receiver when the weapon is assembled.

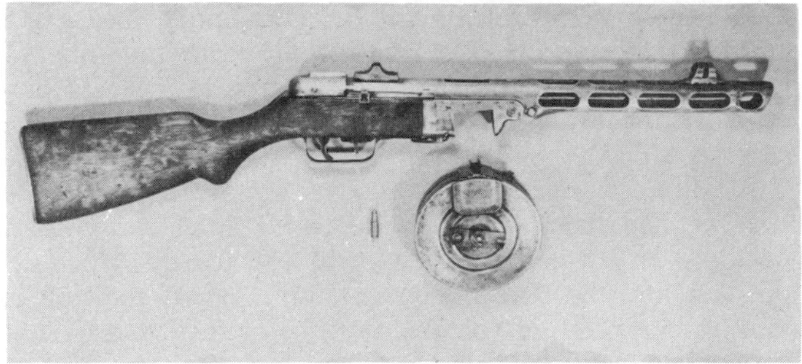

PPSh M1941 (right side). Magazine detached. Cocking handle in rear position.

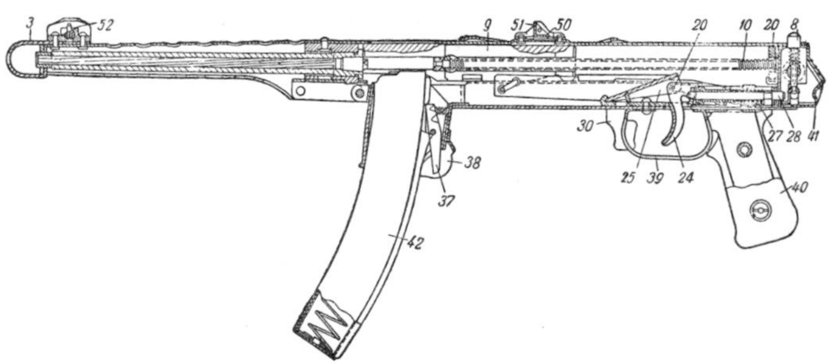

Section View of PPS M1943.

3 Muzzle brake (compensator)
52 Front sight post
42 Magazine
37 Magazine latch
38 Magazine guide
9 Bolt
51 "L" type flip sight
50 Rear sight guard
30 Safety
25 Sear
26 Sear pin
24 Trigger
39 Triggerguard
10 Recoil spring
20 Buffer
8 Stock release catch
27 Trigger spring
28 Trigger spring guide
41 Take down latch
40 Plastic grip

Field Stripping PPSh M1941

Push forward on receiver catch and hinge barrel and barrel casing down.

Draw straight back on bolt handle a short distance, meanwhile exerting an upward pull. The bolt may be lifted out.

Remove recoil spring and buffer.

Barrel is removable from casing. Further dismounting is seldom necessary.

M34/38, PPD M1940, PPSH M1941, and PPS M1943 (top to bottom).

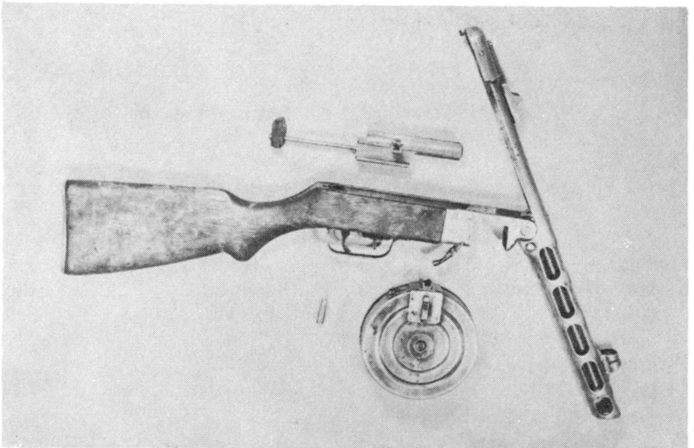

PPSh M1941 Field Stripped.

SOVIET MACHINE GUNS

The weapons listed in the chart below are, with the exception of the DT and DTM, no longer used in the U. S. S. R., although they may be encountered in Soviet satellites. The M1943 Goryunov is covered later in this section, since it is still used in quantity by the Soviets. All these weapons are chambered for the Soviet 7.62mm rimmed cartridge.

DT, the Tank Gun Version of the DP.

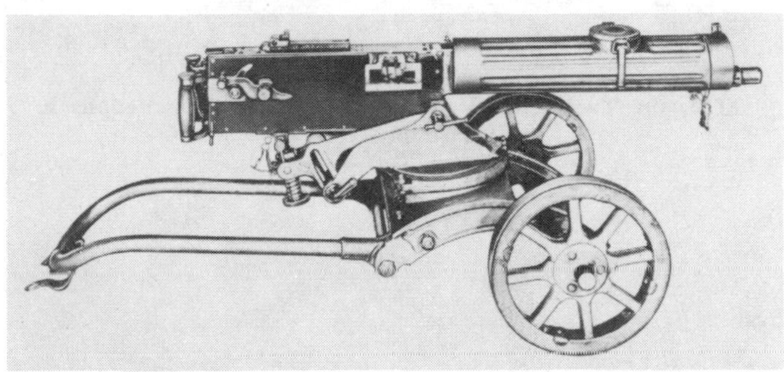

Maxim M1910 Heavy Machine Gun (SPM).

DS M1939 Heavy Machine Gun.

	Model 1910 Maxim (SPM)	Model 1939 DS	DP	DPM	DT	DTM
Caliber:	7.62mm	7.62mm	7.62mm	7.62mm	7.62mm	7.62mm
Type of gun:	Heavy ground gun	Heavy ground gun	Squad automatic	Squad automatic	Tank gun	Tank gun
System of Operation:	Recoil, automatic only	Gas	Gas, automatic only	Gas, automatic only	Gas, automatic only	Gas, automatic only
Weight:	52.47 lb. w/water	26.4 lb.	26.23 lb. loaded	26.9 lb.	27.91 lb.	28.46 lb.
Mount weight:	99.71 lb. w/shield	Approx. 45 lb. w/shield				
Length Overall:	43.6 in.	46 in.	50 in.	50 in.	Stock extended 46.46 in. Stock retracted 39.76 in.	Stock extended 46.44 in. Stock retracted 39.76 in.
Barrel length:	28.4 in.	28.4 in.	23.8 in.	23.8 in.	23.5 in.	23.5 in.
Feed Device:	250 rd.	250-rd. web belt or 50-rd. link belt	47-rd. drum	47-rd. drum	60-rd. drum	60-rd. drum
Sights:						
Front	Blade	Post w/ears	Post w/ears	Post w/ears	None on Tanks On bipod: Post w/ears	None on tanks On bipod: Post w/ears
Rear	Leaf	Leaf	Tangent leaf	Tangent leaf	Aperture	Aperture
Cycle Rate of Fire:	500-600	2 Rates: 500-600 1000-1200	500-600	500-600	600	600
Muzzle Velocity w/light ball:	2822 f.p.s.	2832 f.p.s.	2756 f.p.s.	2756 f.p.s.	2756 f.p.s.	2756 f.p.s.
Cooling:	Water	Air	Air	Air	Air	Air

NOTE: An aircraft version of the Degtyarev, the 7.62mm DA, was also used. It has been obsolete for some time.

Pre-World War II and World War II Soviet 7.62mm Ground Machine Guns.

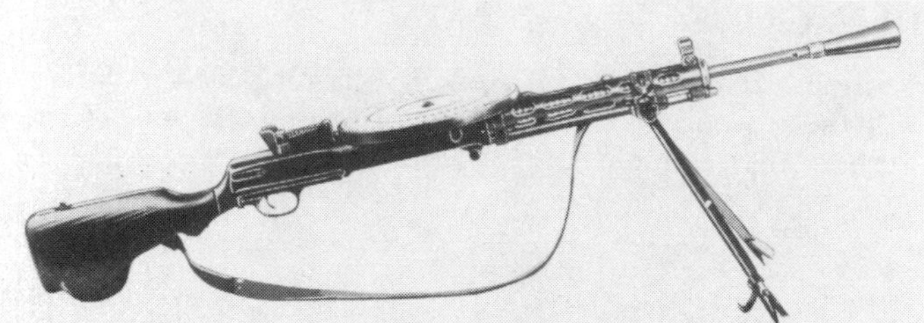

DP Light Machine Gun.

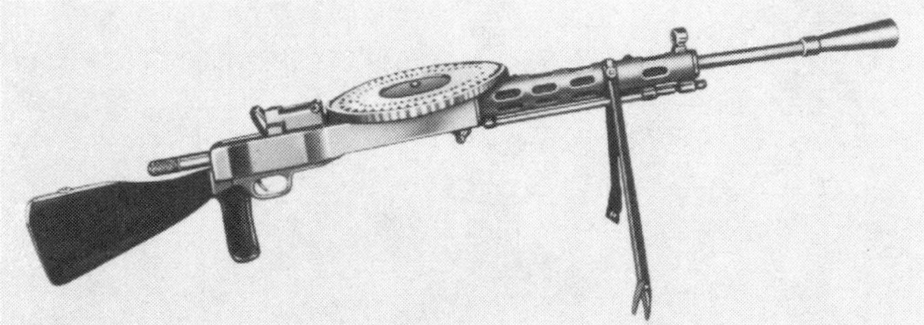

DPM Light Machine Gun, a Modified DP.

DTM, the Tank Gun Version of the DPM. Instructions in Chinese on Receiver.

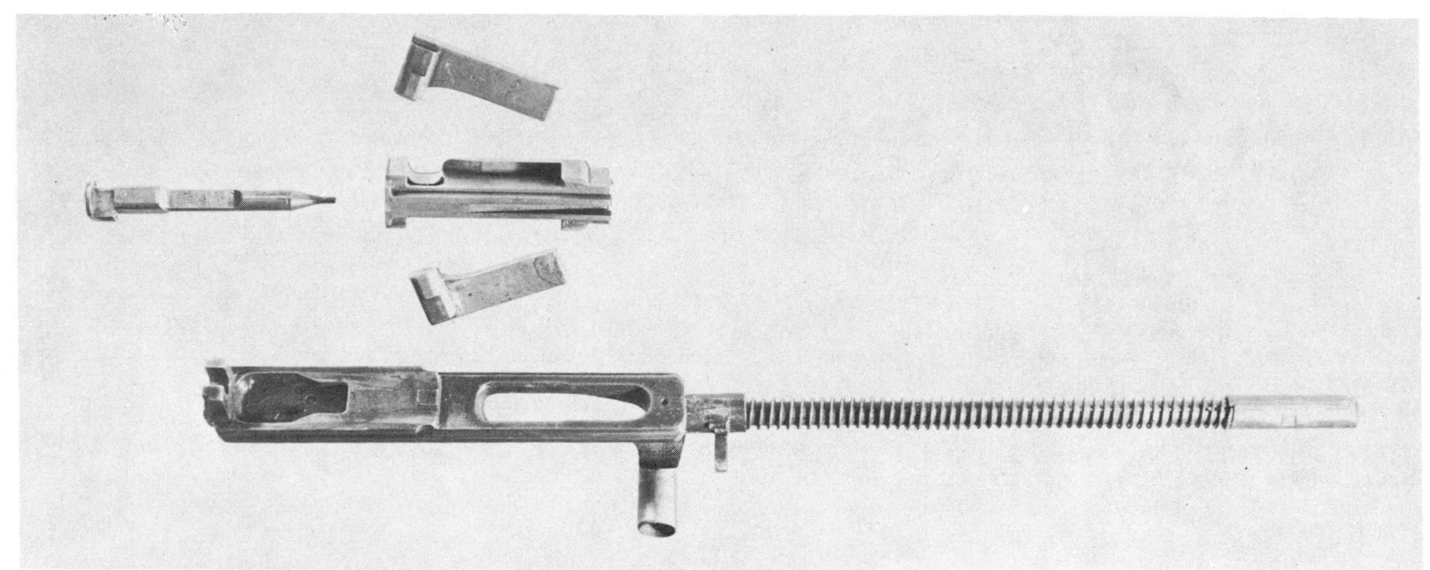

DP Bolt or Breechblock Mechanism.

Top view of the bolt (or breechblock) is seen, showing feed. The right and left bolt locks are mounted in the sides of the bolt. Their camming faces are the means by which their rear ends are forced out into receiver wall cuts to lock the action as the arm fires.

The heavy firing pin is assembled with its flanged head held between the prongs at the end of the slide. When the slide moves forward it carries the bolt assembly along to chamber a cartridge. When the bolt is fully forward, the slide can still go ahead a short distance, and as it does so it carries the firing pin still farther ahead inside the bolt. The cam faces on the firing pin force the rear sections of the bolt locks into locking cuts in the receiver. Only when the locking action is completed can the firing pin point emerge to hit the primer of the cartridge in the chamber.

When the slide starts back, it pulls the firing pin back to remove it from the path of the bolt locks before camming action begins to force the locks flush into the side walls of the bolt. From there on the assembly moves back as a unit.

The operating assembly is the heart of the weapon. The gas piston at the forward end receives the blast of the gas escaping from the barrel port into the gas cylinder as the bullet passes over. The piston drives the operating rod back and compresses the spring around the rod. The bolt assembly is carried on top of the slide which is to the rear of the operating rod.

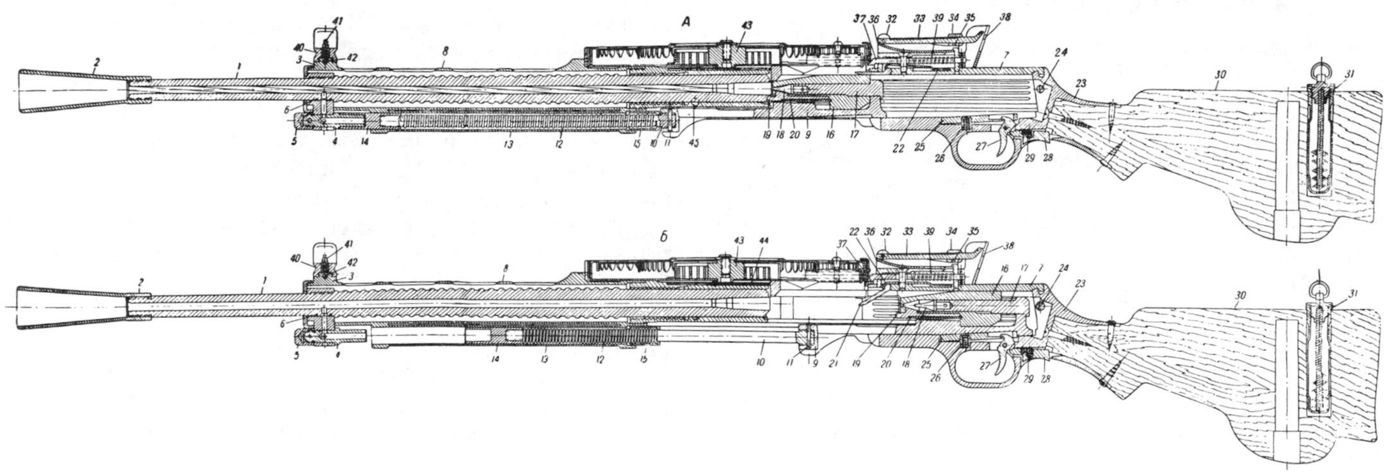

Section View of the DP Light Machine Gun.

Field Stripping The DP

To remove the barrel, pull the cocking handle to the rear to cock the weapon. The barrel locking stud is on the left side near the front of the receiver. Press this stud in, which will release the barrel, then twist the barrel up one quarter turn to the right. Now slide the barrel straight forward out of the receiver.

Both sights are carried on casing. Rear sight base serves as magazine catch.

Flash hider is screwed to barrel. Gas cylinder is just forward of barrel cooling rings. Bolt is shown with right and left side locks and firing pin removed.

Gas piston with operating rod and spring shown attached to bolt carrying slide.

Bipod is easily detachable. Bottom view of magazine to show cartridge feed system. A squeezer-type safety is positioned in the rear of the triggerguard; and is automatically pressed in as the firing fingers tighten around the grip.

Press the trigger and ease the cocking handle forward. Pull out the bolt at the rear of the triggerguard, which leaves the stock and triggerguard free to be turned until the rear of the triggerguard is clear of the receiver. Pull the stock and triggerguard assembly back and out of the receiver.

A small sleeve fits behind the recoil spring at the rear of the gas cylinder tube. Press this forward and twist it to the left; this will free the bolt together with the slide and the gas piston attached to it to be withdrawn at the rear of the receiver.

The bolt may now be lifted from the top of the slide. The firing pin may now be slid out of the rear of the bolt. The bolt locks on each side of the bolt may now be lifted out; and the front of the extractor spring raised and pulled forward to permit removal of it and the extractor.

This completes field stripping. Assembling the gun is equally simple and merely calls for reversing the stripping procedure.

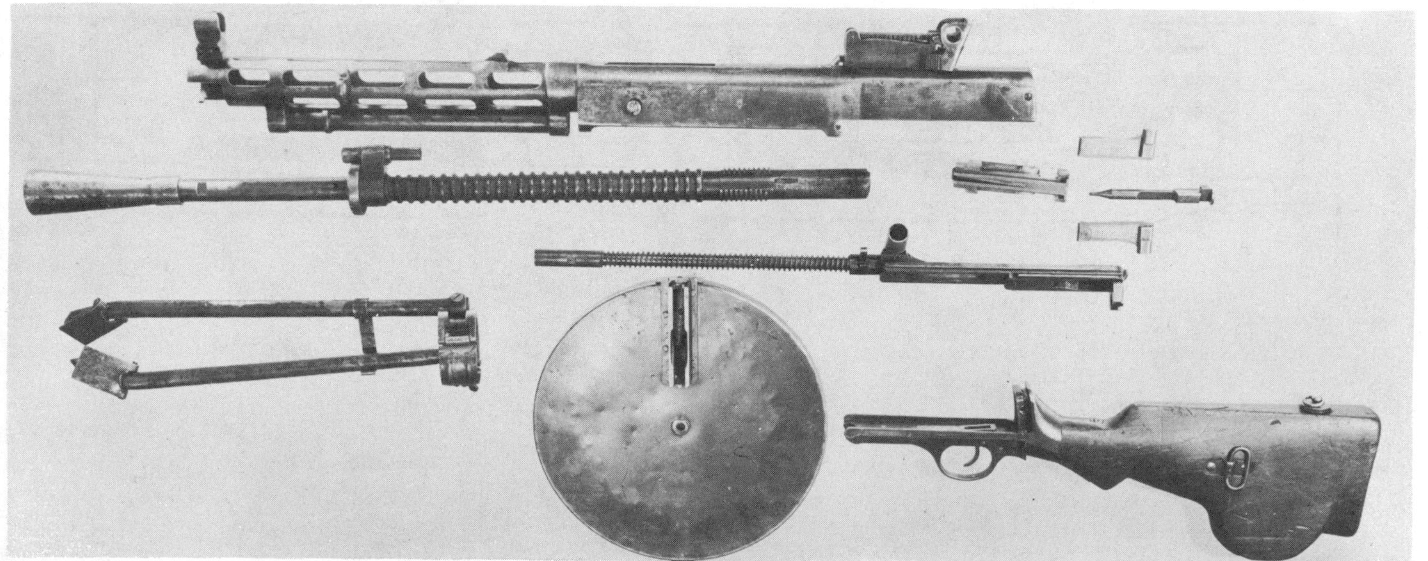

DP Field Stripped.

Loading and Firing The DP and DPM

The Magazine. This type drum differs radically from the Lewis type. The inner center rotates, while the outer rim is fastened securely to the gun. The cartridges lie in single line around the inside of the pan.

To prepare for firing. Mount a loaded magazine on top of the receiver and press firmly down until it is caught by the magazine catch. (The magazine catch is mounted in the front end of the rear sight base.)

Now pull back the cocking handle as far as it will go. It will stay open. Pressing the trigger will now fire the gun. Full automatic fire will ensue as long as the trigger is held down and there are cartridges in the magazine.

Note: A safety catch to the rear of the triggerguard is automatically pressed in as the rifle is gripped ready to fire.

How the DP and DPM Work

A loaded pan magazine is placed on top of the receiver where it engages with a hook on the barrel jacket and is held at the rear by a spring catch, the handle of which forms a guard for the rear sight. The handle on the right side of the gun is drawn back to its full length. This compresses the recoil spring which is positioned below the barrel and which travels with a rod connecting the gas cup to the slide. This spring is compressed against its lock by a gas cup. The rod moves backwards through the center of this spring and lock.

During this opening movement unlocking also takes place and the bolt is held open when it is caught by the sear.

Pressing the trigger rotates the sear down and out of its notch in the bottom of the slide. The bolt is carried on top of the slide. The operating rod is attached to the front end of the slide. The compressed spring is now free to pull the moving members forward.

A moving plate inside the fixed magazine pan has brought a cartridge through the medium of a rotor spring into the feed lips in line with the bolt. The bolt strikes this cartridge and drives it ahead into the firing chamber. On each side of the bolt is a loose plate. These plates are flush with the bolt when it is cocked. As the bolt brings up against the face of the cartridge in the chamber and its forward action is stopped, the firing pin is carried still farther ahead by the operating slide on which it is mounted; and cams on it force the loose locking plates out into recesses machined into the receiver to accommodate them. The firing pin now discharges the cartridge, with the bolt locked securely to the receiver.

Return Movement of the Action

A small quantity of gas passes through the port in the barrel as the bullet goes over it. This passes into a nozzle attached to the barrel which directs the expanding gas against the head of a cup which serves in lieu of a piston. The cup walls extend forward about an inch around this nozzle.

The energy from the expanding gas is transmitted through the gas cup at the end of the rod to the attached slide which it starts backward. The first movement of the slide withdraws the firing pin and from thereon a projection on the bottom of each loose lock plate rides in a cam groove in the slide, camming the projections toward the center. This pulls the locks out of their recesses in the receiver. The slide is then able to carry the bolt straight back extracting and ejecting the empty cartridge case.

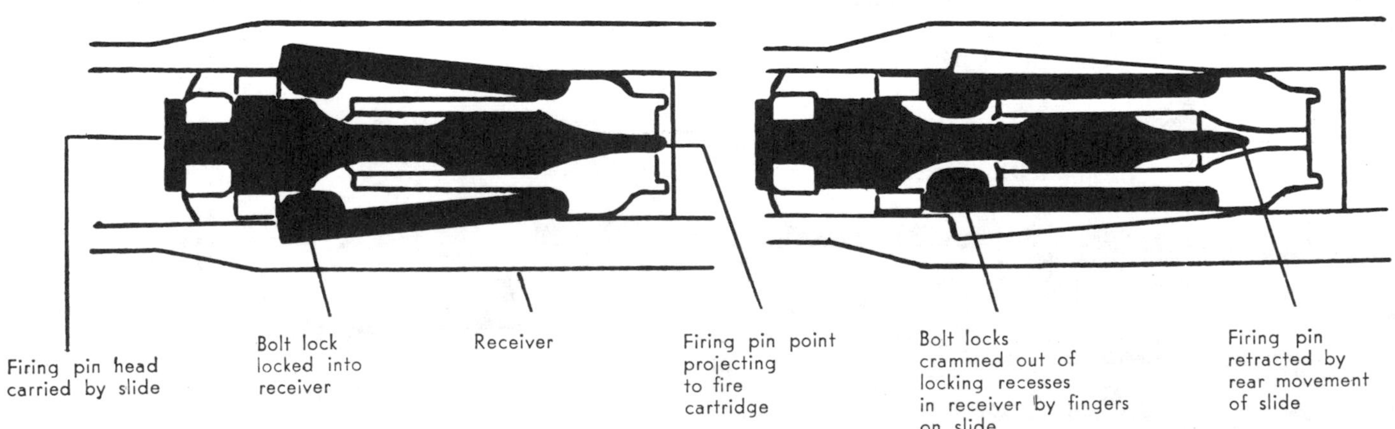

Locking and Firing Movement of the Action.

Unlocking Action.

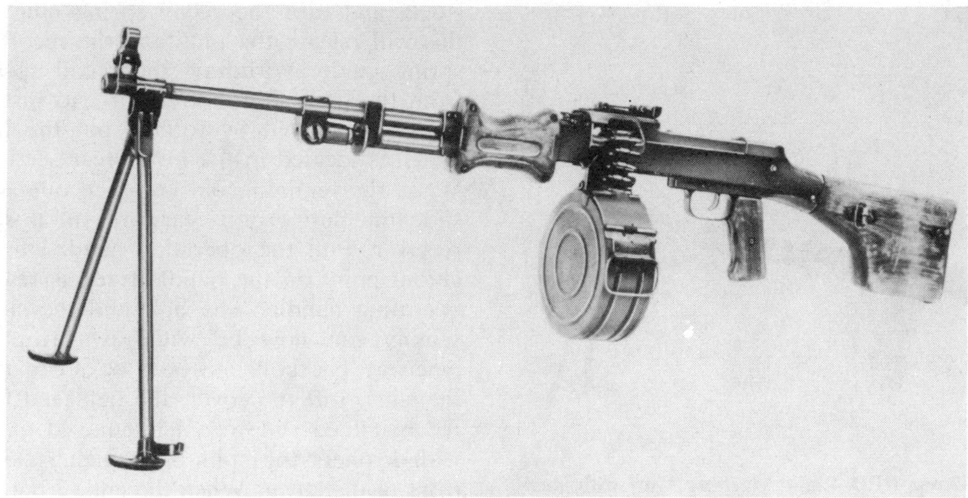

Soviet 7.62mm Degtyarev Light Machine Gun. (RPD) (Left Side).

Caliber: 7.62mm (1943 cartridge).
System of Operation: Gas.
Weight, Loaded: 19.4 lb.
Overall Length: 40.83 in.
Barrel Length: 20.6 in.
Feed Device: 100-rd. metallic link belt, housed in a drum magazine attached below the receiver.
Sights, Front: Protected post.
Rear: Tangent leaf, open notch.
Muzzle Velocity: 2411 f.p.s.
Cyclic Rate of Fire: 650 r.p.m.

The Ruchnoi Pulemet Degtyarev, or RPD, as it is commonly called by the Soviets, is the standard squad automatic weapon in the Soviet Army. It has replaced the DP light machine gun and is chambered for the same "intermediate-sized" cartridge as are the AK and the SKS. The RPD is the tactical equivalent to the U. S. Browning automatic rifle or the British Bren gun. It is designed only for use on a bipod and is not designed for, or capable of, long periods of sustained fire. The RPD is a very simple weapon in design and should be relatively easy to service in the field. Its basic operating mechanism is a modification of that of the earlier DP, but the RPD is belt fed, while the DP is fed from a pan-type magazine. The RPD is the lightest belt-fed gun in service in the world today. It should be kept in mind, however, that the RPD is not chambered for a full-size rifle cartridge; if it were, it probably would be several pounds heavier.

Loading and Firing the RPD

The link belt of the RPD is loaded by pushing the individual rounds into the belt so that the bottom hook-like section of the link snaps into place in the cartridge extractor groove. The two fifty-round sections are joined together by slipping the tongue of the end link on one belt section through the slots of the starting link on the other belt section. A cartridge is then inserted, locking the two belt sections together.

The belt is then rolled into a tight circle and fitted into the stamped metal drum. The drum is fitted on the weapon by sliding its top dovetail on the mating surfaces which protrude under the forward part of the receiver. The belt loading tab should be protruding from the spring-loaded trap door of the drum, so that it can be inserted

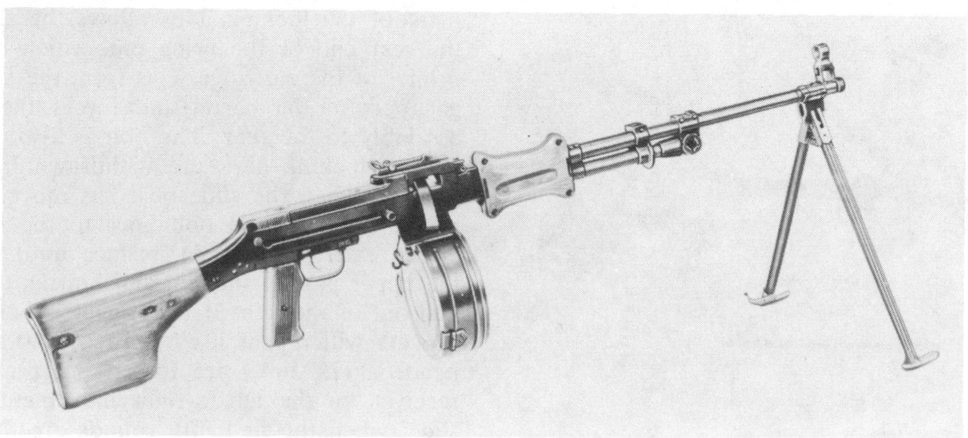

RPD Light Machine Gun (Right Side).

Late Model Soviet 7.62mm RPD Light Machine Gun with dust covers on feed and link ejection ports and new type operating handle.

in the receiver. The drum is locked in place by pulling down the lock on the underside of the receiver; this lock keeps the drum from moving backwards off the gun during fire.

Cock the gun by pulling operating handle to the rear. On older guns, which have the non-folding operating handle, the handle will remain to the rear. On the newer type guns, which have the folding type operating handle, the handle should be pushed forward after pulling to the rear.

Open the cover by pushing forward on cover latch and lifting the cover. Lay belt on feedway so that the leading cartridge lies beside the cartridge stop. Close cover.

If the trigger is squeezed, the weapon will now fire. The safety catch is located on the right side of the pistol grip butt group, immediately above the trigger. When the catch is forward of the trigger the gun is on safe; to put the gun on fire, rotate the catch to the rear position.

To unload the gun, lift the cover by pushing forward on the cover catch located at the rear of the cover. Lift the link belt out and snap the cover shut.

Field Stripping the RPD

Turn the butt trap cover so that it is at right angles to the butt stock. Place a screwdriver in the top hole in the stock, and turn the recoil spring plug one quarter turn; this will release the plug and the recoil spring and recoil spring guide. Withdraw the recoil spring and its guide from the gun. The entire butt and pistol grip group can then be removed by forcing out the butt retaining pin, which is located in the lower rear section of the receiver. When the retaining pin is pulled out as far as it will go, slide the butt group rearward till it separates from the receiver. Pull the operating handle to the rear until the cutout point on the handle track is reached. Pull out the operating handle. The bolt and the slide and piston assembly can now be withdrawn from the rear of the receiver. The bolt and bolt locks can now be lifted from the slide. Lift the cover; the belt feed lever assembly and the belt feed slide can be removed by pinching together with a pliers the split pin which is located at the right front of the cover. When the end of the pin is compressed, its locking collar can be removed, and all the belt feed components can be removed. Like many other gas-operated weapons, such as the U. S. and FN Browning automatic rifles and the British Bren guns, the gas cylinder of the RPD can be easily adjusted. To adjust the gas cylinder of the RPD to obtain a different size of orifice, a special wrench is used.

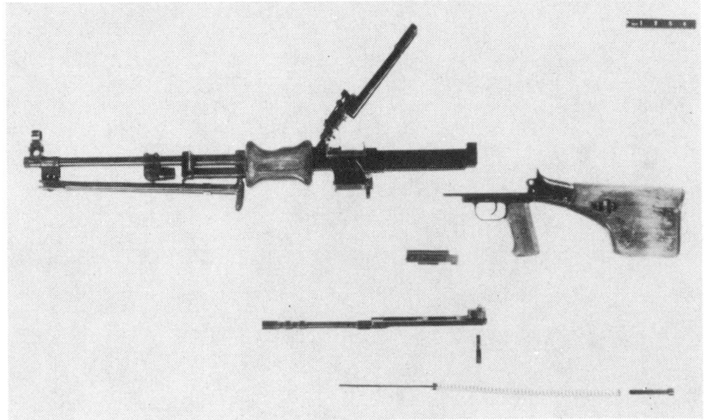

RPD Field Stripped.

To reassemble the weapon, perform the above steps in reverse order.

How the RPD Works

With the belt loaded in the gun and the bolt group to the rear, the trigger is pulled. The trigger pulls the sear down from its engagement in the sear notch on the underside of the slide. The slide piston assembly with the bolt goes forward under the pressure of the decompressing recoil spring. The slide post stud, which operates in the track of the belt feed lever, moves the belt feed lever, which in turn moves the belt feed slide over, indexing the cartridge so that the top of the bolt can engage the cartridge and strip it forward out of the link and downward into the chamber. The locking flaps mounted on the sides of the bolt are cammed out into their locking surfaces in the receiver by the rearward movement of the bolt on the slide, when the bolt abuts the barrel. The outward movement of the locking flaps allows the slide post to strike the rear end of the firing pin, which in turn strikes the primer of the cartridge. Gas from the cartridge enters the gas port in the barrel and forces the piston and slide assembly to the rear. The bolt is also drawn to the rear, and its locking flaps are withdrawn into their unlocked position when the slide post has moved a slight distance to the rear. As the bolt goes to the rear it carries the empty cartridge case in its face until the ejector strikes the upper part of the rim and knocks the case downward and out of the gun. If the trigger is held to the rear, this process will repeat itself until the 100-round belt is expended. The links are forced out the right side of the receiver by the left-to-right movement of the belt feed slide; when the first fifty rounds are fired, the first fifty-round link belt section falls out of the gun.

Special Note on the RPD

Although there is nothing new in the design of the RPD, the weapon is rather remarkable for its simplicity. There are some indications that the weapon/cartridge combination has only marginal operating power, but it does not appear that there would be too much that could go wrong with the RPD in the field, at least from a mechanical point of view. There have been some changes in the RPD since its first issue. The original weapons had a male type of gas cylinder and a female type of piston head; later weapons have a male-type piston head and a female-type gas cylinder. When the weapon is cocked, there is an air space between the piston head and the gas cylinder; thus, in operation, much of the operating gas is absorbed in the surrounding air rather than forming carbon in the gas cylinder and on the piston.

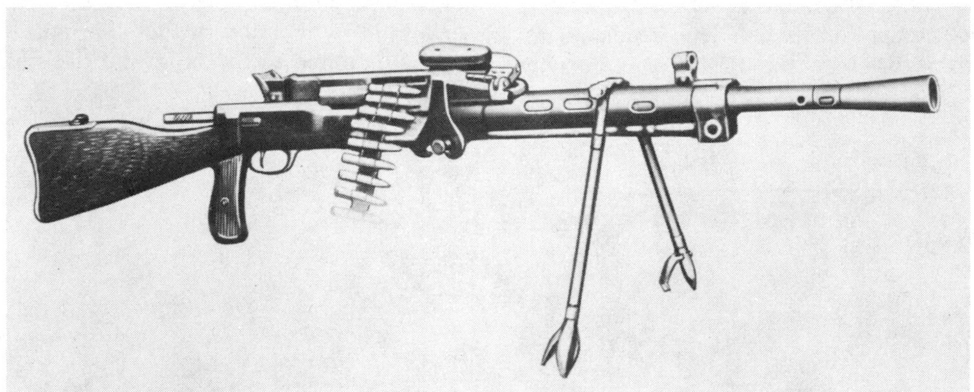

Soviet 7.62mm Company Light Machine Gun M1946 (RP-46).

Caliber: 7.62mm.
System of Operation: Gas, automatic only.
Weight: 28.7 lb.
Overall Length: 50 in.
Barrel Length: 24 in. (approx.).
Feed Device: 250-round nondisintegrating metal link belt.
Sights, Front: Post with protecting ears.
Rear: Tangent leaf.
Muzzle Velocity: 2756 f.p.s.
Cyclic Rate of Fire: 600-650 r.p.m.

The RP-46 is basically a modification of the 7.62mm DPM light machine gun, which appeared during World War II. The DPM itself was a modification of the DP. While both the DP and DPM were fed by pan-type magazines, the RP-46 can be fed either by a pan or by the same 250-round nondisintegrating link belt that is used with the 7.62mm Goryunov heavy machine gun. As its name implies, the RP-46 is a company-level weapon. It is therefore much heavier than the RPD, and is capable of a higher level of sustained fire since it has a quick-change barrel and the RPD does not. The RP-46 is chambered for the old Soviet 7.62mm rimmed cartridge, which is quite similar in performance to the U. S. cal. .30 rifle and machine gun cartridge (the .30-06). It therefore has a much higher muzzle velocity and range than does the RPD, and it can be used for engagement of targets far beyond the range of the Soviet squad-level weapons. The RP-46 is the tactical equivalent of the U. S. M1919A4 or A6 machine guns, or to the new U. S. M60 machine gun when it is used as a light gun on a bipod. The RP-46 is apparently always used on a bipod.

How to Load and Fire the RP-46

Cock gun by pulling operating handle to the rear. Pull rear sight base to the rear and lift cover. Lay belt, open side up, on the feed plate so that the leading round contacts the cartridge stop and close cover. Pull trigger and gun will fire. An alternate method of loading is to cock gun, insert the long tab end of the link belt into the feed from the right and pull through from the left. Pull trigger, releasing bolt, cock gun again and fire. To unload the gun, pull the rear sight guard to the rear, lift cover, remove belt. If the gun has been fired, there will still be one round in the feed way—remove round. The safety is on when the lever is pointing toward the muzzle.

Field Stripping the RP-46

Field stripping of the RP-46 is similar to that of the RPD, except that the recoil spring is mounted in a tube

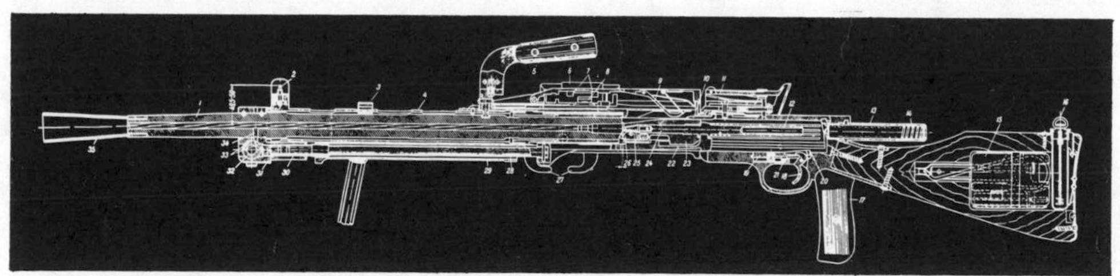

Section View of RP-46.

which projects out from the right rear side of the receiver. The tube and spring are dismounted by pushing in on the tube lock and turning it to the right, then withdrawing the tube and spring from the receiver. The barrel can be removed by pushing in the latch on the left forward side of the receiver and pulling the barrel out.

How the RP-46 Works

The RP-46 has the same basic operating system as the other Degtyarev guns (DP, DPM, and RPD) and operates the same as they do except for its belt feed mechanism. An ingenious system is used on the RP-46 to translate the forward and backward movement of the operating handle into a side-to-side movement of the belt feed lever. The operating handle on its forward and backward travel operates a double-arm type of feed lever which transmits this movement to parts in the feed mechanism; these parts in turn transmit the movement to the belt feed slide. This system is also used on the Soviet 12.7mm DShK M1938/46 machine gun. Insofar as the bolt parts of the Degtyarev weapons are concerned, there is only one major difference among the lot. In DP, DPM, and RP-46 the firing pin is mounted in the slide post; in RPD, the firing pin is mounted in the bolt, and the slide post itself serves as a hammer.

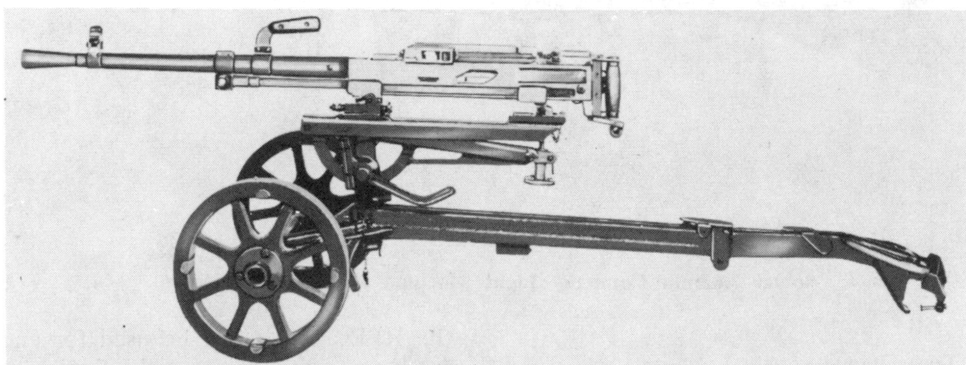

Soviet 7.62mm Goryunov Heavy Machine Gun M1943 (SG-43).

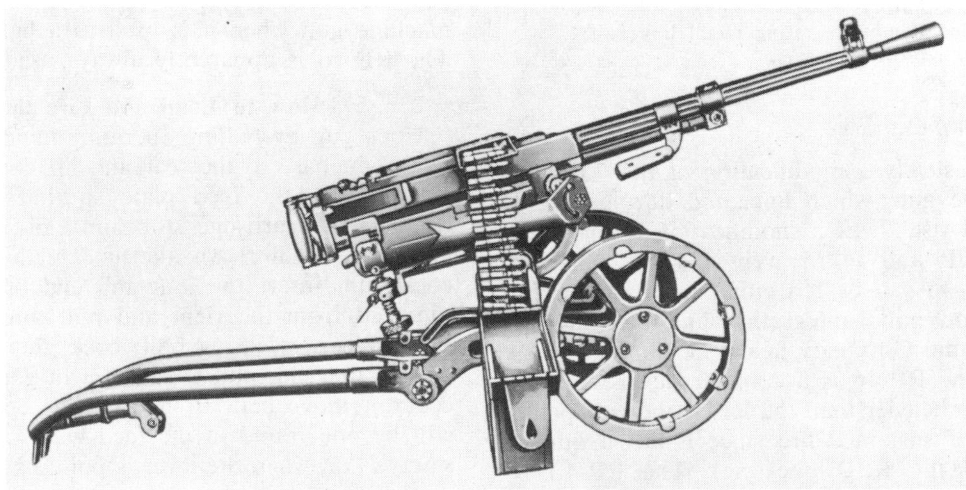

Modernized Goryunov (SGM) on Wheeled Mount.

System of Operation: Gas, full automatic fire only.
Weight, Gun Only: SG-43, 30.42 lb.; SGM, 29.76 lb.
Wheeled Mounts: Old type w/shield, 59.3 lb.; new type 50.9 lb.
Tripod Mount: 30.6 lb.
Overall Length (Gun Only): 44.09 in.
Barrel Length: 28.3 in.
Sights, Front: Blade, adjustable for windage (for zeroing only).
Rear: Tangent leaf, open U-notch.
Muzzle Velocity: 2625 f.p.s., with heavy ball.
Feed Mechanism: 250-rd. non-disintegrating link belt.
Rate of Fire, Practical: 250 r.p.m.
Cyclic: 600-700 r.p.m.

The Goryunov appeared during World War II and has replaced the Maxim M1910 watercooled gun in the Soviet Army. The Goryunov has itself been modified since World War II, and its modification is called the SGM or Heavy Modernized Goryunov. Both the older and the new Goryunov are apparently in service in the U.S.S.R. The Goryunov is used as a battalion-level gun and is also used on armored personnel carriers. The original Goryunov had a wheeled mount which could be fitted with a shield. The newer gun appeared with two mounts: a wheeled mount somewhat similar to the Sokolov mount used with the Maxim and a light tripod mount. Both the old and new guns, however, can be used on any of the three mounts. As a matter of passing interest it should be noted that the Soviets use the term "Ruchnoi,"

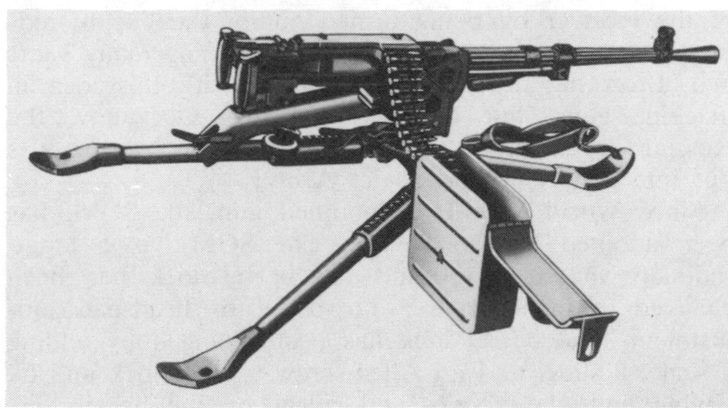

SGM on Tripod.

which means hand, for light machine guns (i.e., a machine gun which is carried in the hand). They use the term "Stankovy" for heavy rifle-caliber machine guns; "Stankovy" means mounted, i.e., a gun on a mount.

How to Load and Fire the Goryunov

To load the Goryunov, open the top cover by pushing forward the cover latch. Insert the link belt on the feedway, placing the rim of the cartridge in the jaws of the feed carrier. Close the cover and pull the operating handle to the rear as far as it will go. The operating handle of the SG-43 is at the rear underside of the gun, under the spade grips. After the operating handle has been retracted, it should be pushed forward again; the bolt remains to the rear since the Goryunov fires from an open bolt. Raise the safety lock with the left thumb and press the upper end of the trigger with the right thumb. The weapon will now fire, and will continue to fire until the trigger is released. The weapon can be unloaded by raising the top cover and lifting out the link belt. NOTE: On the SGM, the operating handle projects from the right underside of the gun.

Field Stripping the Goryunov

Open the top cover by pushing the cover catch forward; then lift the feed cover slightly and remove the feed carrier. Move the cover and feed cover to the vertical position. On the SGM, lift the rear sight leaf and with a punch, push out the backplate catch pin and move the catch backward; turn the backplate one quarter-turn to the right, and remove it from the receiver; remove the recoil spring and recoil spring guide. Remove the trigger mechanism from the receiver. Move the slide rearward with the operating handle until the bolt emerges from the receiver; grasp the bolt and slide and remove them from the receiver. Lift the bolt up and out of the slide. Move the operating handle rearward until it rests against the rear clamp of the receiver, and, turning it upward, separate it from the receiver. Move the plate covering the lower opening of the receiver to the rear and remove it from the receiver. Move the belt feed slide to the right and withdraw it from the receiver. To remove the barrel, press on the barrel lock with the thumb, moving the lock as far to the left as it will go; then, grasping the barrel handle, pull the barrel forward and remove it from the receiver.

No further disassembly is recommended. To reassemble the weapon, reverse the above procedure.

The field stripping of the SG-43 differs in that the backplate is removed by pulling out its retaining pin, which is located at the bottom rear of the receiver.

How the Goryunov Works

In loading, the belt is positioned in the feedway with the cover raised, so that the spring-loaded holders of the feed carrier engage the rim of the first round. The cover is closed and the operating parts retracted by means of the handle provided. The gun is then ready for firing. The feed carrier, which reciprocates in the feed tray (feed cover), operates in a notch in the top of the bolt. As the bolt is retracted, the feed carrier withdraws the cartridge from the belt. A belt holding pawl is located in the cover. The belt feed slide, reciprocating in a cut in the receiver, operates on a cam of the operating slide.

The gun fires from the open bolt position. The bolt is held to the rear by the sear, which is a part of the backplate assembly. The trigger operates through a connector to disengage the sear from the bolt. When the bolt is released, it is driven forward under the energy of the compressed driving spring which operates against the operating slide. As the round is pushed forward by the bolt, it is forced downward, out of the carrier, and into the feeding tray. From the feeding tray, the round enters the chamber. As the bolt approaches its forward position, a cam on the operating slide forces the rear of the bolt 3/16 of an inch to the right and into a recess in the receiver. The head of the bolt is recessed at an angle with the center of the bolt to give normal support to the base of the round in firing. As the round is chambered, the spring-loaded extractor, which is located in the left side of the bolt and is pivoted on a pin on the right side of its center, is forced over the rim of the round. After the bolt has been forced into the locked position, the slide moves forward to contact the firing pin. The firing pin strikes the primer, causing ignition of the round.

As the bullet is forced from the barrel by the expanding powder gas, some gas passes through the gas port in the

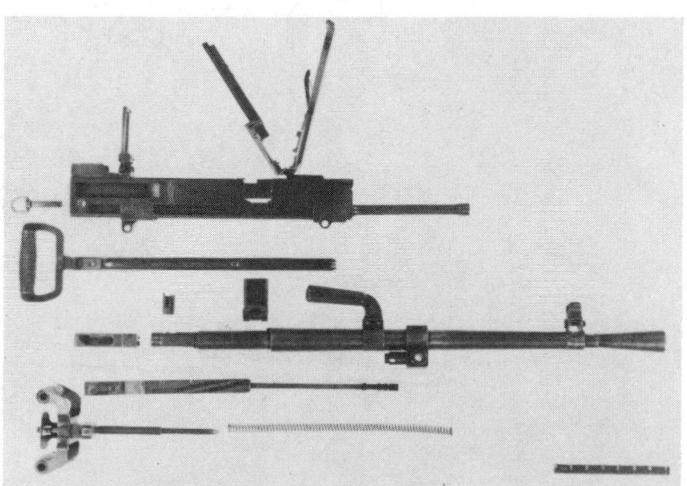

SG-43 Field Stripped.

barrel and impinges upon the piston attached to the slide, forcing it to the rear. The slide assembly moves independently of the bolt for a fraction of an inch. At this point, the bolt is forced out of engagement in the receiver and is drawn to the rear.

The extractor withdraws the fired case from the chamber. As the operating parts approach the rearward position, the ejector, a pin placed at an angle through the right side of the bolt to contact the base of the cartridge case, contacts the locking recess of the receiver. The ejector and the cartridge case are forced forward. The case, pivoted on the extractor, is ejected through the ejection port in the left side of the receiver.

If the trigger continues to be depressed, the firing cycle will be repeated. However, should the trigger be released, the sear will engage the bolt and hold it to the rear.

Notes on the Goryunov Machine Guns

The idea of a bolt whose rear end locked into the side of the receiver by being turned out of the line of axis of the bore was patented by John Browning many years ago. Browning never did very much with this idea in machine guns, but the Russians did. Goryunov, the Russian developer of this gun, died before his gun was put into service in the Soviet Army.

Since World War II a modified gun, the SGM, has been adopted by the Soviets. The SGM has a longitudinally fluted barrel and the barrel lock has been changed to incorporate a provision for headspace adjustment. The barrel lock has been changed by adding a scale, a slide, and an Allen-screw type of lock and by having multiple grooves and ridges on the barrel lock and barrel. Thus, as the barrel and/or receiver wears, it is possible to unlock the slide, tighten it in the desired position (which can be determined from the scale), and relock it. This, of course, is not done with every barrel change, but only after the components have had enough wear to make a significant difference in headspace.

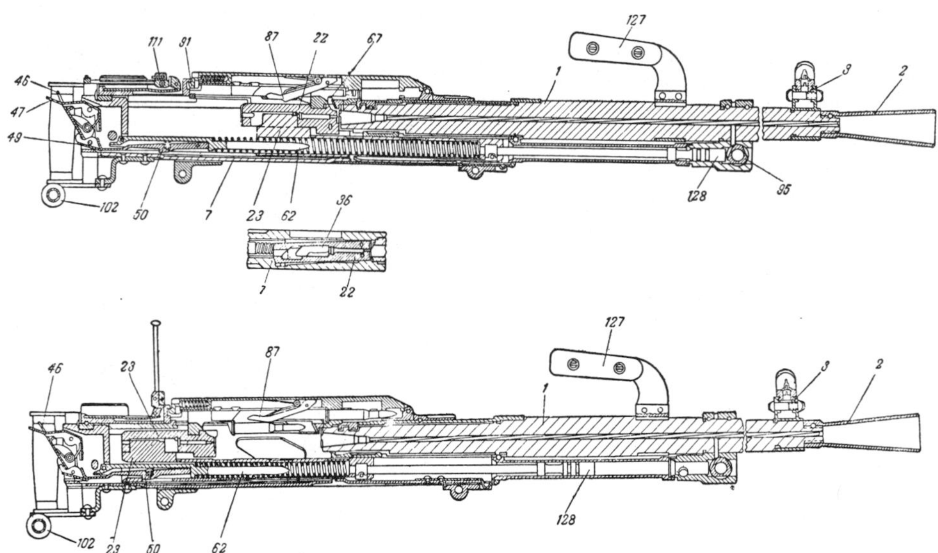

Section Views of the SG-43.

Soviet 12.7mm DShK M1938 Heavy Machine Gun.

Soviet 12.7mm DShK M1938 Heavy Machine Gun.

Caliber: 12.7mm (rimless).
System of Operation: Gas, automatic fire only.
Weight of Complete Gun: 75 lb.
Weight of Mount, w/Shield and Shoulder Stock: 269 lb.
Length of Gun Overall: 62.74 in.
Length of Barrel: 39.37 in.
Feed Device: 50-round metallic link belt (push-out type, non-disintegrating link).
Cyclic Rate of Fire: 550-600 r.p.m.
Muzzle Velocity: 2822 f.p.s w/AP cartridge.
Sights, Front: Blade, adjustable for windage; AA ring-type also provided for mounting on barrel jacket.
Rear: Leaf, open U-notch graduated from 0 to 35, (0 to 3500 meters), aperture sight attached to leaf for AA fire.

The DShK is another of the Degtyarev series of weapons; its basic system of operation is similar to the other Degtyarev guns. The original DShK had a rotating block type of feed; the M1938/46 has a belt feed lever type similar to the RP-46's. These guns are chambered for the Soviet 12.7mm cartridge, which is almost identical in performance to (although not interchangeable with) the U. S. cal. .50 cartridge. The M1938 was the primary Soviet heavy ground gun; in Korea it was frequently used by the North Koreans against aircraft. The weapon has been replaced in the Soviet Army in this role by the 14.5mm ZPU series of weapons. It is still used as antiaircraft armament on tanks and armored personnel carriers, and is beginning to be used as co-axial armament on tanks. The ground mount for the DShK weapons is a wheeled mount, which can be converted into a tripod mount for AA fire.

DShK 12.7mm M1938/46 Heavy Machine Gun.

How to Load and Fire the DShK M1938

Push forward the feed cover latch located at the top rear of the feed cover. Lift the feed cover and place the feed belt on the revolving feed block so that the first round can be put in the upper recess of the feed block. Hold the free end of the ammunition belt with the right hand and press the feed belt against the revolving block. Rapidly rotate the block with belt as far to the right as it can go (the upper recess should rotate 120°). Close the feed cover. Pull reloading handle to the rear until the slide is engaged by the sear. Hold spade grips with both hands and press the trigger slowly with the index fingers of both hands; the weapon will fire. To put the weapon on safe, rotate the safety catch forward.

How to Load and Fire the DShK M1938/46

Loading and firing of the DShK M1938/46 are the same as for the 7.62mm RP-46.

Field Stripping the DShK M1938

Set the safety on fire and loosen (one turn) the latch of the machine gun mounting studs on the gun mount. If the bolt is to the rear, move it forward by pulling the trigger. Stand with back to the muzzle in front of the mount axle with the left foot resting on the axle. Grasp the gas piston tube with both hands and pull it as far forward as it will move. Then turn the tube clockwise with both hands until the support of the tube comes out of its grooves in the barrel. Push all the moving parts (bolt and slide group) to the rear until the recoil stop roller emerges from its recess in the receiver.

Unscrew the connecting screw of the rear machine gun locking bracket. Remove the backplate pin and tap the

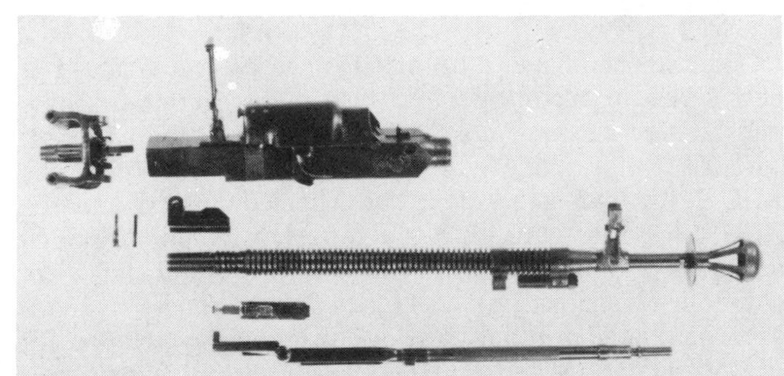

DShK Field Stripped.

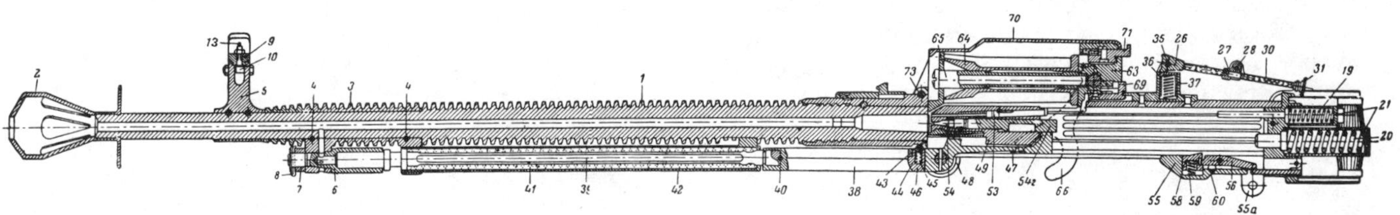

Section View of DShK M1938.

backplate lightly with a wooden mallet or a copper hammer to separate it from the receiver, meanwhile supporting it with one hand. Remove the trigger housing and then withdraw the bolt and slide group from the rear of the receiver. Remove the firing pin and the bolt and bolt locking flaps. To reassemble the weapon, perform the above steps in reverse order.

How the DShK's Work

In general, both of the 12.7mm Degtyarev guns operate the same as the 7.62mm guns of this series. The M1938 has a circular type of feed mechanism which operates somewhat like the cylinder of a revolver. The feed lever, which is operated back and forth by the slide, turns the feed drum which carries the cartridges in its recesses. As the cartridges are turned, their links are stripped, and in the final feed step the cartridge is alined with the bolt, which rams it into the chamber. The feed system on the M1938/46 is basically the same as that on the RP-46.

ZPU-2 14.5mm Machine Gun.

ZPU-4 14.5mm Machine Gun.

The Soviets have introduced since World War II a new series of recoil-operated heavy antiaircraft machine guns. These weapons are the ZPU-1, ZPU-2, and ZPU-4. The ZPU-1 has one gun on a two-wheeled mount, the ZPU-2 has two guns on a two-wheeled mount, and the ZPU-4 has four guns on a four-wheeled mount. Although designed primarily for use against low-level air attack, all can be used against ground targets as well. These weapons are chambered for the cartridge originally developed for the Soviet PTRS and PTRD AT rifles. This cartridge is comparable in performance to the experimental U. S. cal. .60 cartridge which was developed for use in U. S. aircraft machine guns some time ago.

The basic machine gun used on these mounts has a strong resemblance to the German MG 151 series of weapons, insofar as its receiver configuration is concerned. The weapon has a quick-change barrel and is fed by a nondisintegrating metallic link belt.

Special Note on Soviet Machine Guns

It is of interest to note that all modern Soviet automatic weapons have chromed barrels, and that all current Soviet ground machine guns, with the exception of the RPD and the 12.7mm DShK, have quick-change barrels. Soviet machine guns as a group are characterized by ruggedness and simplicity of maintenance. This is not, however, synonymous with simplicity of manufacture. It may be necessary to use very complicated and expensive machine work to manufacture an item which is simple to maintain in the field. The Soviets are apparently moving away from easily made stamped weapons judging by their post-World War II models.

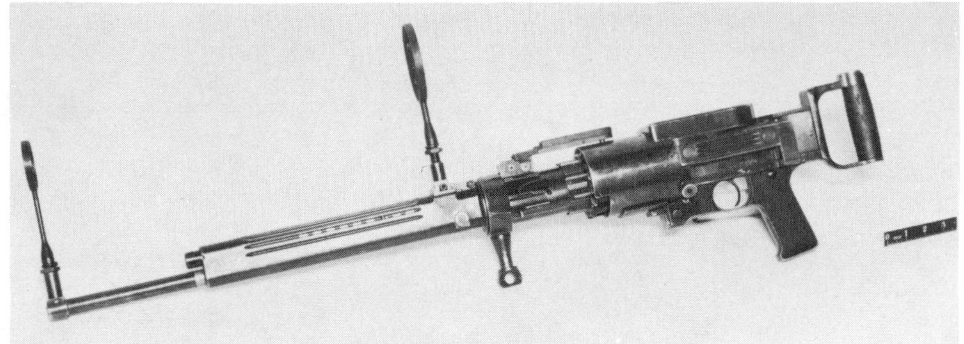

ShKAS 7.62mm Aircraft Machine Gun.

The Soviets have aircraft machine guns in 7.62mm, 12.7mm, 20mm, 23mm, and 37mm calibers. The two larger caliber weapons are the only ones used on the latest aircraft. The 7.62mm ShKAS first appeared in service during the Spanish Civil War, at which time it was supplied with Soviet aircraft to the Spanish Loyalist forces. The ShKAS was distinguished by a very high rate of fire for its time (well over 1000 rounds per minute), and a very complicated squirrel-cage type of feed mechanism. The ShKAS is a toolmaker's nightmare, insofar as complexity of manufacture is concerned, and was probably handmade to a large extent. The ShKAS served as the model for the 20mm ShVAKs which saw extensive service in World War II. The 12.7mm UB was also introduced during World War II; it was a much less complicated weapon than the ShKAS and the ShVAK. The 23mm VYa was essentially a scale-up of the UB, and was mounted in the wings of the famed IL-2 Stormovik "tank killer." All the foregoing aircraft guns were gas operated; the later NS, NR, and N series of weapons are recoil operated.

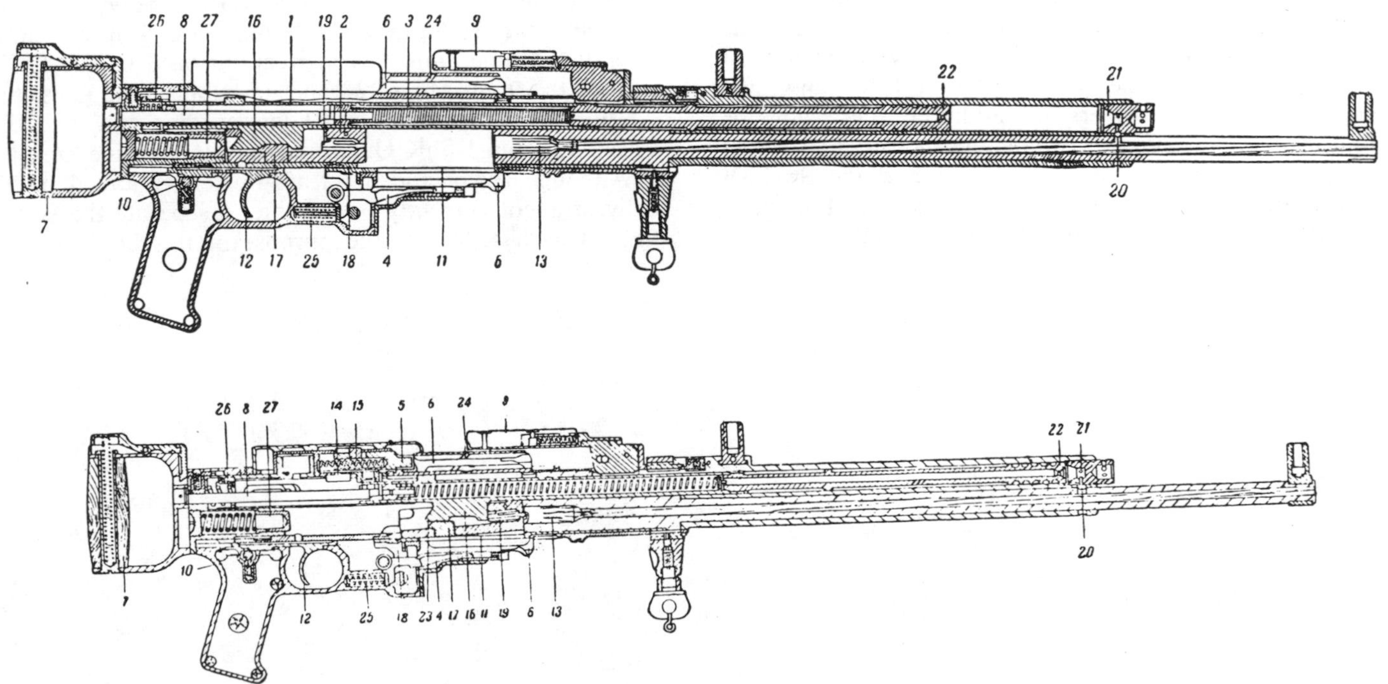

Section Views of the ShKAS.

Chapter 44. (Former) United Arab Republic (Egypt and Syria)

The UAR was composed of Egypt and Syria, and was dissolved in 1961. Because of various political and economic circumstances, the UAR has made extensive arms purchases from the Soviet bloc since 1954. Originally Egypt, the larger member, was equipped for the most part with British weapons of World War I origin. Since the end of World War II, however, Egypt had begun to purchase and, in a few cases, manufacture weapons of non-British origin. Egypt purchased 7.92mm FN semi-automatic rifles (the prewar design commonly known as the M1949, ABL, or SAFN) prior to the end of the Egyptian monarchy. Some of these rifles, captured by the Israelis during the Sinai campaign of 1956, are now in circulation in the U. S. They can be identified by the Egyptian crown stamped on their receivers. In addition, the Egyptians had arms plants set up to manufacture the Swedish Model 42 Ljungman rifle in 7.92mm caliber and the Swedish 9mm Model 45 (Carl Gustaf) submachine gun. Purchases were also made, from Spain, of the 7.92mm Alfa heavy machine gun.

Syria was originally a French Mandate, and received her independence at the end of World War II. The Syrian Army was therefore originally equipped mainly with French weapons, including the 8mm Lebel and Mannlicher Berthier rifles and carbines, the 7.5mm Model 1924 M29 (Chatellerault) light machine gun, and the 7.5mm M1936 rifle.

Soviet weapons seen in the hands of UAR troops include the 7.62mm AK assault rifle, the SKS carbine, the RPD light machine gun, the Goryunov SG-43 heavy machine gun, the 12.7mm DShK M1938 heavy machine gun, and the 14.5mm ZPU-2 and ZPU-4 heavy antiaircraft machine guns. Czech weapons used by the UAR include the 9mm Model 23 and 25 submachine guns, the 7.62mm Model 52 rifle and light machine gun, and the Czech 12.7mm DShK Quad antiaircraft machine gun.

Although Egypt and Syria are no longer joined politically, it is not currently practicable to separate the coverage on each so far as the purpose of this book is concerned.

Chapter 45. The United States

THE NEW FAMILY OF SMALL ARMS

The United States has adopted a new family of small arms, and now has these weapons in production. All fire the 7.62mm NATO cartridge (its cartridge case was formerly known as the cal. .30 T65E3), which is now standard and will replace the familiar cal. .30 that has been the service cartridge since 1906. One of the principal advantages of the new family of weapons, from a logistical point of view, is that a few weapons are to replace a large number of weapons. The new M14 rifle will replace the M3A1 submachine gun, the M2 carbine, the M1 rifle, and the Browning automatic rifle M1918A2 (the BAR). The M60 general purpose machine gun will replace the Browning M1919A4, M1919A6, and M1917A1 machine guns.

Two new tank machine guns, the 7.62mm M73 and the cal. .50 M85, have also been adopted. An interim tank machine gun, the cal. .30 M37, is given rather perfunctory treatment in this chapter, since it will be replaced by the M73. A 40mm grenade launcher, the M79, has also been adopted.

The 7.62mm NATO Cartridge

The 7.62mm NATO cartridge was adopted as standard by the United States in 1954, although weapons chambered for the cartridge were not adopted as standard until 1957. The 7.62mm NATO design is the result of approximately nine years of experiment and testing. Its ballistics are essentially the same as those of the larger cal. .30 round, and its lethality equals the cal. .30. The standard U. S. 7.62mm ball cartridge, the M59, has a 150-grain bullet with a mild steel core. This bullet, because of its boat-tailed configuration, gives better ballistic performance at the longer ranges than does the cal. .30 M2 bullet.

The 7.62mm NATO cartridge also is standard for new weapons adopted by Canada, Great Britain, West Germany, Israel, Australia, New Zealand, Belgium, Luxembourg, and many other nations. It is becoming the standard cartridge of the larger part of the Western world.

U.S. PISTOLS AND REVOLVERS

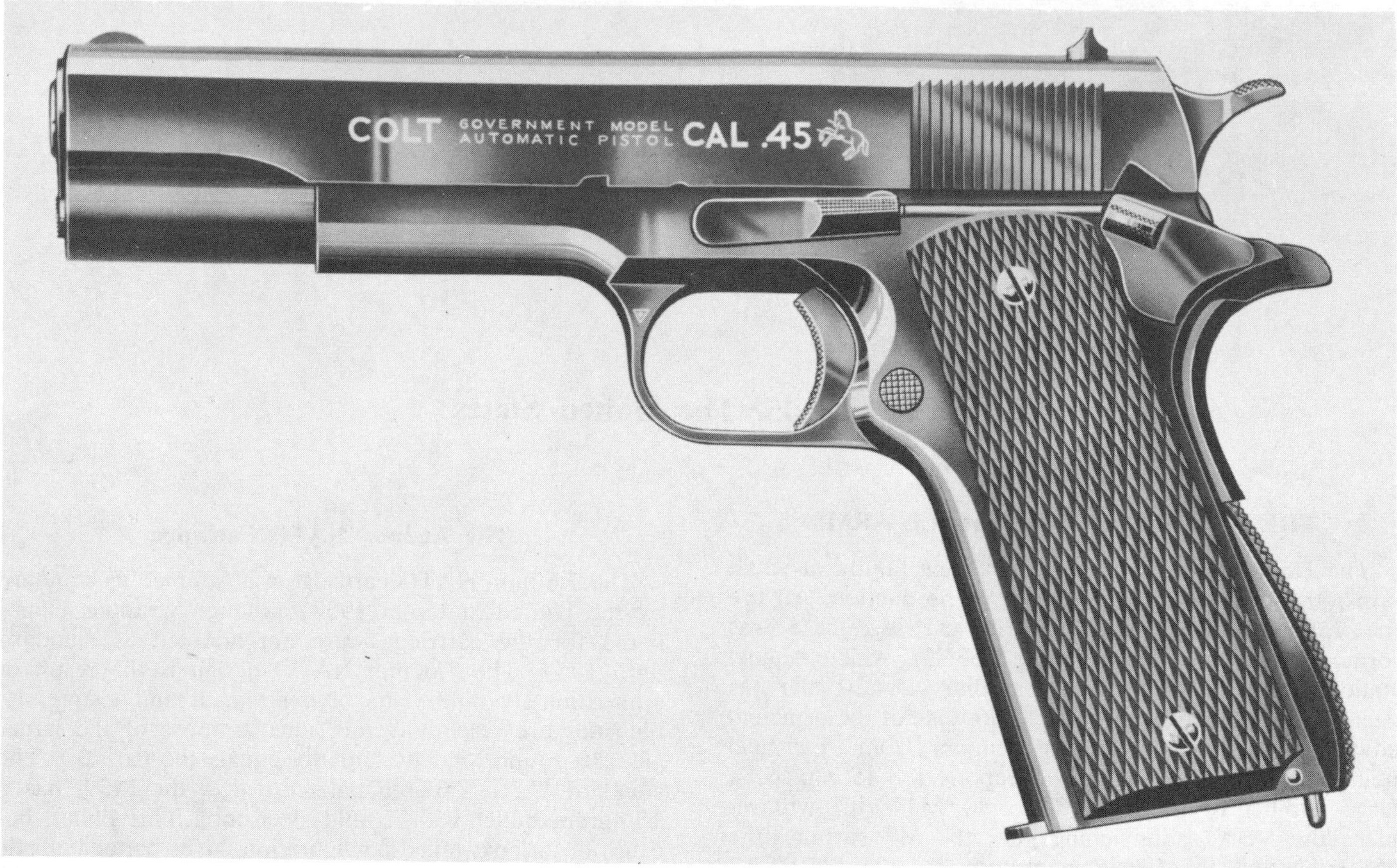

M1911A1 Automatic Pistol.

Caliber: .45 M1911 cartridge, ball ammunition.
Magazine: Box type, single line. Capacity 7 cartridges. (Note: Capacity of pistol is 8 cartridges, 1 in firing chamber and 7 in magazine.)
Muzzle Velocity of Government Cartridge: 830 feet per second.
Muzzle Velocity of Commercial Cartridge: 860 feet per second.
Weight of Bullet: 230 grains, lead with metal jacket.
Muzzle Striking Energy, Government Cartridge: 340 foot pounds.
Muzzle Striking Energy, Commercial Cartridge: 378 foot pounds.
Barrel Length: 5 inches.
Overall Length of Pistol: 8½ inches.
Weight of Pistol: 39 ounces.
Sights: Partridge type, fixed.
Accurate Range: 50 yards.
Maximum Range: About 1600 yards elevating pistol to 30°.
Pistol Operated by: Recoil.
Locked: Ribs on top of barrel lock in slots on underside of slide near breech until period of dangerous breech pressure is passed.
Type of Fire: Single shot only. One squeeze of trigger is necessary to fire each shot. Should more than one be fired by a single squeeze, pistol is dangerous and disconnector needs replacing.
Magazine Release Catch: Button on left side near trigger. Pressing it will eject magazine from handle.

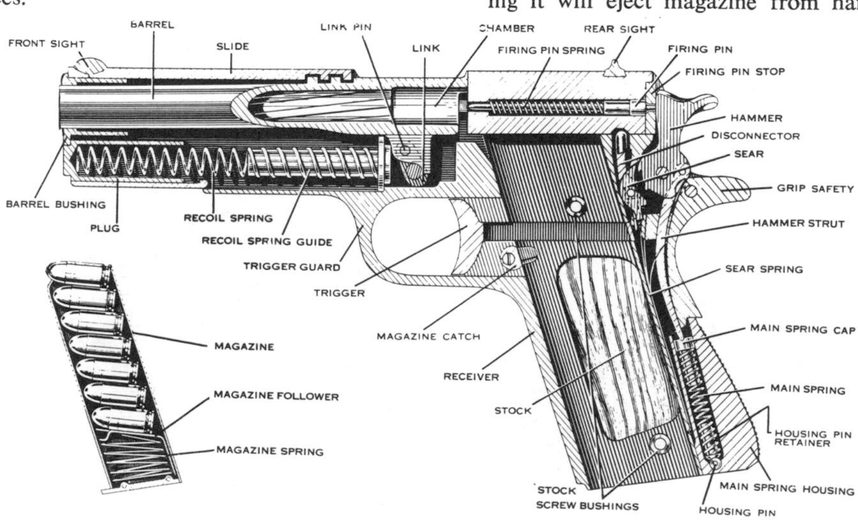

Position of Slide When Last Shot is Fired: Open.

Safeties: (a) **Grip Safety** prevents weapon from being fired until pistol is held firmly in hand. This safety is purely mechanical.
(b) **Thumb safety** at rear left end on receiver. When hammer is cocked, this safety may be pushed up into its slot in the slide; it locks hammer, sear, and slide. This is an applied safety.
(c) **Disconnector.** Postively prevents pistol being fired until slide and barrel are locked. This is an automatic safety.

Differences Between Models 1911 and 1911A1: These pistols are identical except for the following improvements in the 1911A1 model: (a) Tang on grip safety is longer to protect hand better. (b) Receiver is cut back on left side where trigger finger rests to allow more natural finger position. (c) Trigger face is cut back and ridged to afford better trigger pressure. (d) Mainspring housing at bottom of handle is arched and knurled to provide better grip. (e) Top of front sight is wider to help in quicker aiming.

Note: Model 1911A1 is illustrated above. Model 1911 is shown in following photographs.

Instructions for Loading and Firing

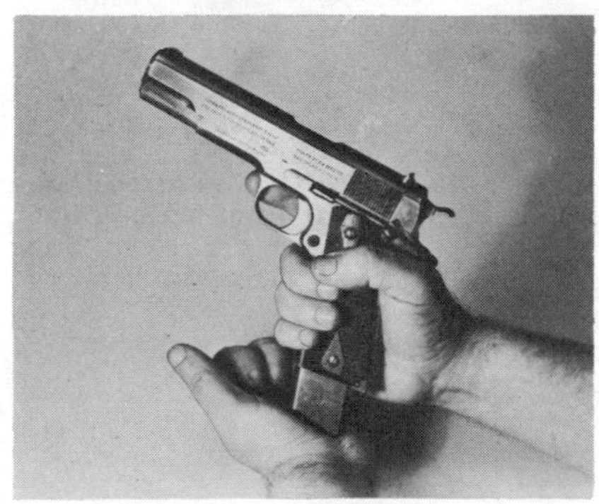

To extract magazine: Press magazine catch (button). Magazine will normally be ejected and should be caught with left hand. If spring is weak, it may come only part way; withdraw it from handle.

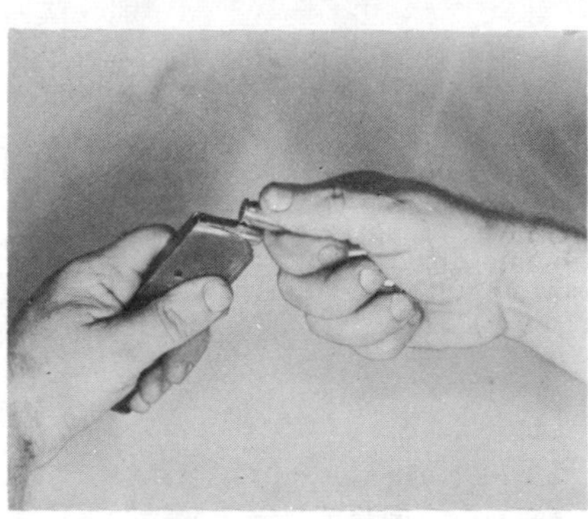

Load magazine: Holding firmly in left hand, press cartridge down in forward end of magazine follower (platform) and slide in under the curved lips of the magazine. Press following cartridges down as illustrated. Any number from 1 to 7 may be inserted.

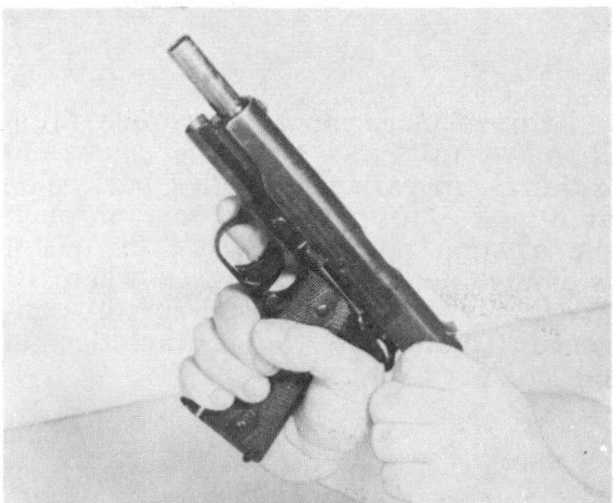

To load firing chamber: (a) Holding pistol at height of right shoulder and pistol 6 inches from shoulder, insert loaded magazine and press home until it locks with a click. (b) Grasp slide with thumb and fingers of the left hand, thumb on right side of slide pointing upwards and pull back slide as far as it will go. This compresses the recoil spring, cocks the hammer and permits the magazine spring to push the top cartridge into line with the breech block. (c) Release slide.. The recoil spring will drive it forward and feed a cartridge into the firing chamber; barrel will be forced up on its link and will lock into slide; firing mechanism will engage ready for first shot.

To engage thumb safety: Unless pistol is to be fired at once, always push safety lock up into place as soon as firing chamber is loaded. A stud on the inner face of the thumb safety locks the hammer and sear when the safety is pushed up into the slide. It can be released by simply pushing down on the thumbpiece.

Slide stop: When the last shot has been fired, a section of the front end of the magazine follower, pushed up by the magazine spring, presses against the underside of the slide stop. This forces the stop up into a niche cut in the slide and holds the slide open as an indication that the pistol is empty.

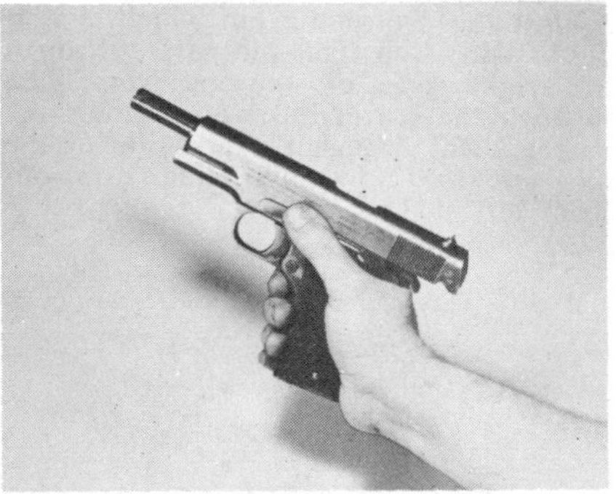

Reloading from open slide: (a) Press magazine catch and extract empty magazine. (b) Insert loaded magazine. (c) Push down on slide stop with right thumb. This will release the slide to drive forward and load the firing chamber.

Note: Slide stop cannot be released while an empty magazine is in the pistol. Slide will go forward only on a loaded magazine or when the magazine has been pulled part way out.

Field Stripping

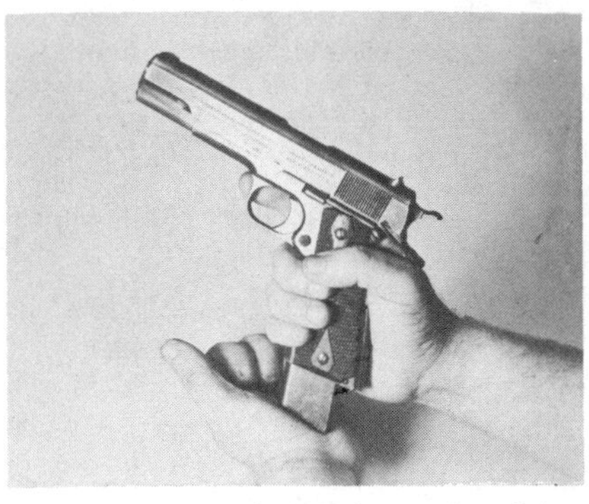

Remove magazine and examine firing chamber: (a) Press magazine catch and withdraw magazine. (b) Draw back slide and look into firing chamber through the ejection port to be sure the pistol is empty. Remember that even when the magazine is out, the pistol is still dangerous: there may be a cartridge in the chamber.

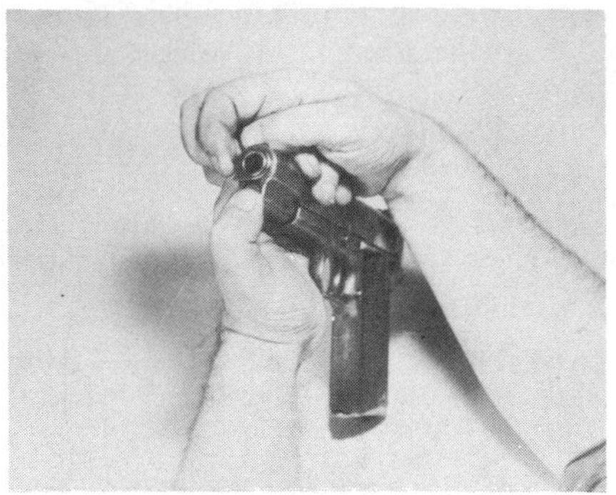

Release tension of recoil spring: (a) Press in on plug which covers end of recoil spring, using thumb or butt of magazine if it is too stiff. (b) Barrel bushing, freed from spring tension, may now be turned to the right side of the pistol.

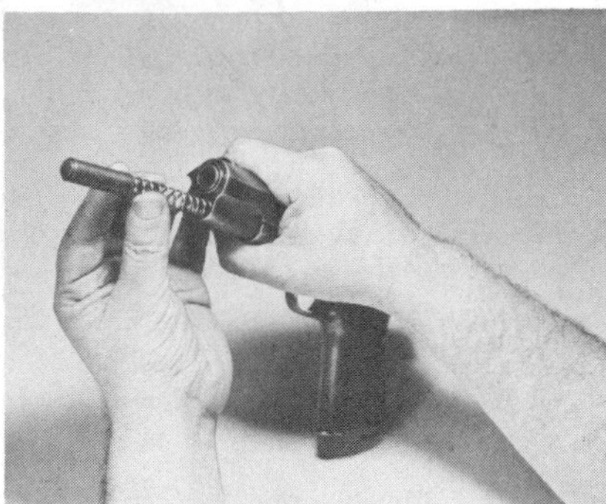

Ease out plug and recoil spring: The spring is very powerful. Take care not to let it fly out of the pistol. Do not withdraw these parts from the pistol yet, as they serve to keep the recoil spring guide in place and make the next step easy.

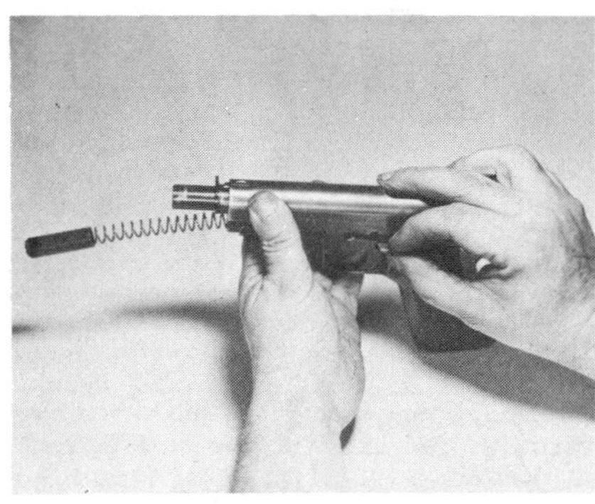

Remove slide stop. (a) Push slide back until the rear edge of the smaller recess in the lower edge of the slide is even with the rear end of the slide stop. (b) Now press from the right side against the protruding pin which is part of the slide stop. This pin passes through the right side of the receiver, then through the barrel link which holds the barrel, then through the left side of the receiver. (c) Now pull slide stop out from left side of pistol.

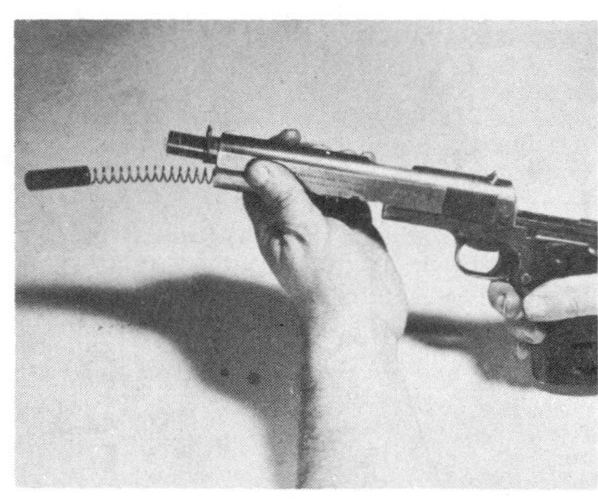

Remove slide and components: Pull slide forward on its guides in the receiver and remove. With the slide will come the barrel, barrel link, barrel bushing, recoil spring and recoil spring guide.

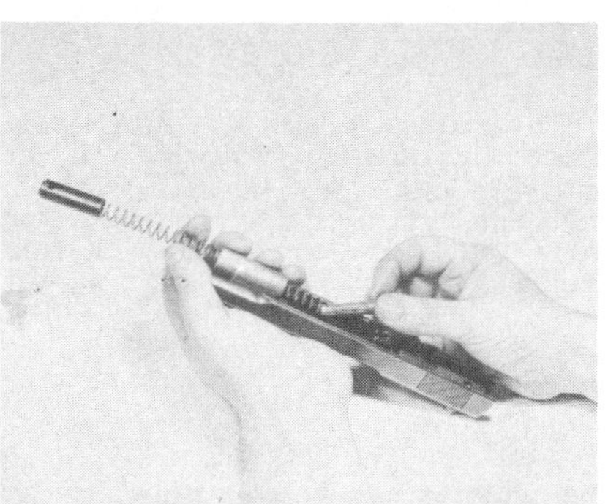

Remove recoil spring guide: (a) The recoil spring guide (on which the recoil spring compresses) may now be lifted out to the rear. (b) The recoil spring and plug are pulled out from the front. (c) The barrel bushing is turned to the left which unlocks it so it can be withdrawn.

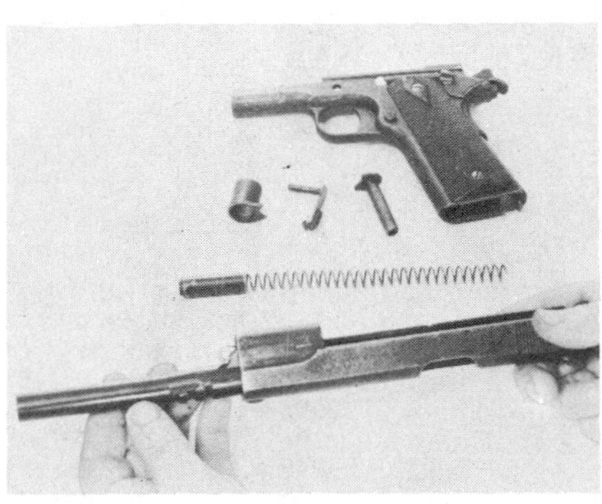

Remove barrel: Turn barrel link forward on its pin and withdraw from the front of the slide.

Note: Normally no further stripping of this pistol is required.

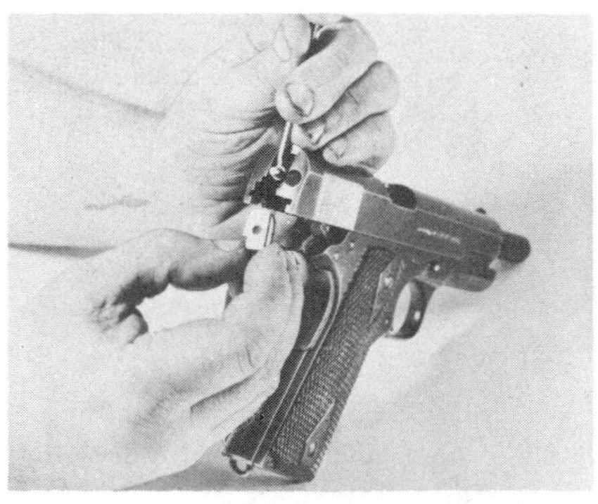

To remove firing pin: (a) Should it be necessary, the firing pin may be easily removed by pressing the pin in against the tension of its spring, at the same time pushing down on the firing pin stop which holds the firing pin in place. This may be done with a nail, match, or similar object. (b) Slide the stop down out of its grooves and ease out the firing pin and spring.

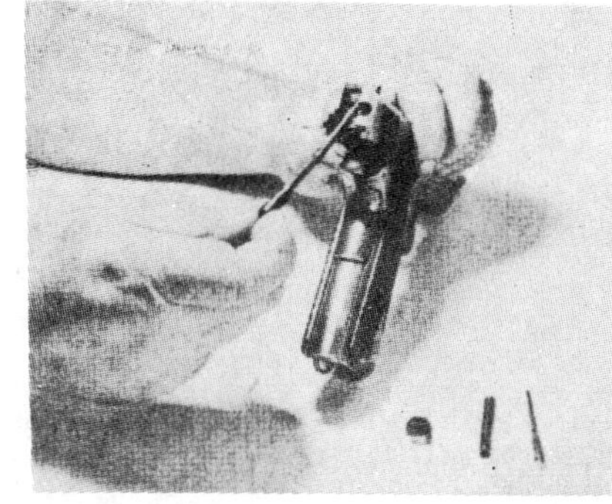

To remove extractor: When the firing pin has been removed the extractor, which is a long piece of spring steel inserted in a hole to the left of the firing pin, may be pried up and pulled out to the rear as illustrated.

While no stripping beyond that illustrated is ever necessary to clean and properly care for this pistol, the following instructions will be helpful to those who wish to master every detail.

To Remove Safety Lock. (a) Cock hammer. (b) Grasp thumbpiece of safety lock between thumb and index finger, pull steadily outward and at same time move back and forth.

Remove Hammer. (a) Lower hammer—do not snap it. (b) Use safety lock to push out hammer pin, removing from left side. (c) Lift out hammer and hammer strut.

Remove Mainspring Housing. (a) Using hammer strut, push mainspring housing pin out from right side of receiver. (b) Slide housing and its contained spring down out of its guides. (c) Pushing in on mainspring cap, at same time push out mainspring cap pin.

Remove Sear and Disconnector. Using hammer strut, push out sear pin from left side of receiver and remove sear and disconnector.

Remove Magazine Catch. Press in checkered left end to permit turning catch lock a quarter turn to left out of its seat in receiver, using long leaf of sear spring. Catch, its lock and spring may now be removed. Be careful not to let spring jump away when released.

Remove Trigger. Pull straight to the rear.

Remove Slide Stop Plunger, Safety Lock Plunger, and Plunger Spring. Draw straight to rear.

Notes on Assembling

Barrel link must be tilted forward and link pin properly in place before it will slide into place in the slide.

Put sear and disconnector together, hold by their lower ends, place them in the receiver, and replace sear pin.

Sear spring should be replaced after sear and disconnector are in place, care being taken that lower end is in its place in the cut in the receiver; upper end of left hand leaf resting on sear.

Insert mainspring housing until lower end projects about one-eighth inch below frame. Then (a) Replace hammer and pin; (b) Grip safety; (c) Cock hammer and replace safety lock; (d) Lower hammer and push mainspring housing home, and insert pin.

Cock hammer. Insert end of magazine follower to press safety lock plunger home.

When inserting slide stop, make sure that its upper rear end stops on the receiver just below the small slide stop plunger. Then push stop upward and inward with the one motion. This will enable the upper round part of the stop to push the plunger back and let the stop snap into place.

In replacing sear and disconnector, hold the receiver as when firing, then tilt front end down. Insert the sear and the disconnector using the trigger bar as a guide to align the holes in these two parts with the receiver holes. Slight pressure may be applied on the trigger until the holes are properly lined up. When replacing the mainspring housing, it is important that the rear end of the hammer strut be in its place in the mainspring cap.

Description of Mechanism

The pistol has three main parts: receiver, barrel, and slide. The receiver is fitted with guides in which the slide runs. Its handle is hollow to permit insertion of the box magazine which is locked by the magazine catch.

The receiver also holds the trigger whose front end projects through the triggerguard. The firing mechanism, made up of the hammer, sear, automatic disconnector, grip safety, and safety lock, are at the rear of the receiver. Here too are the mainspring and sear spring. The mainspring is a coiled spring seated within the mainspring housing which is held by the mainspring cap pin. The mainspring cap and housing pin retainer are also in this housing.

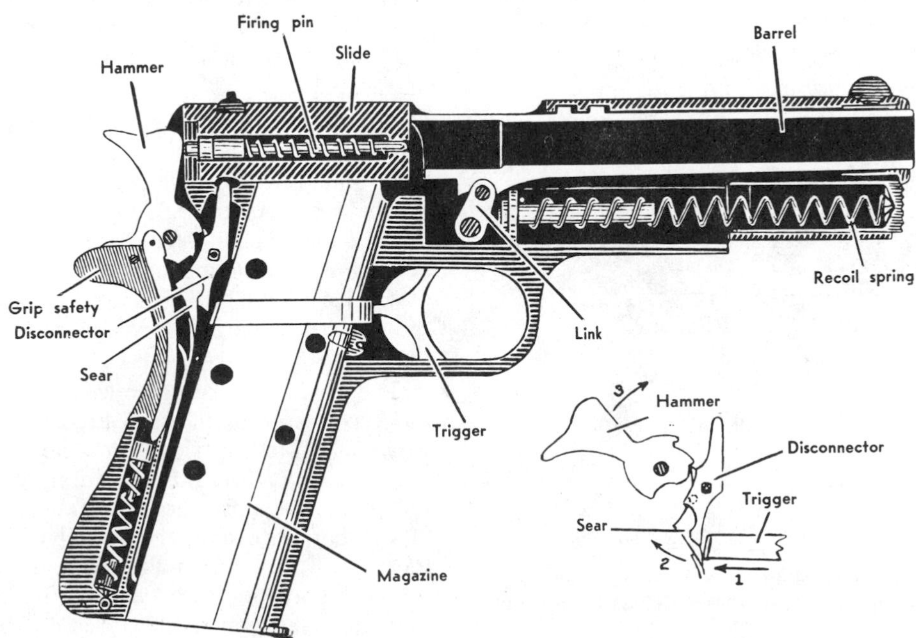

The sear spring is a flat spring with a rib fitting into a slot in the rear wall of the receiver to prevent the spring from moving vertically. The mainspring housing bears against the rear of the spring and locks it into position to give it the required tension.

A bent metal piece called the hammer strut is fastened to the hammer by a pin in rear of its pivot, while its end rests in the mainspring cap. In a tube above the handle are the slide stop and safety lock plungers whose ends protrude from front and rear of the tube respectively, as well as the spiral spring plunger seated between the two which holds them in position.

The ejector, a solid piece of metal against which the head of the withdrawn cartridge case strikes, is fastened to the top of the receiver near the rear end.

The top of the receiver extending forward above the triggerguard forms a semi-tubular extension to provide a seat for the rear section of the recoil spring.

The barrel has two transverse locking ribs on its rear upper surface. They positively lock into corresponding slots on the inside of the slide when in firing position. The lower rear end of the barrel is attached to the receiver by a swinging link and pin. It can thus move a limited distance lengthwise and downwards.

The heavy slide mounts on the receiver from the front end and the distance of its rearward movement is controlled by a tubular abutment which absolutely prevents it being thrown rearward from the receiver.

In this abutment at the front end of the slide rests the forward portion of the recoil spring and the plug which fits over its end; while the rear end of this spring is fitted over a removable guide which is supported by the shoulder at the front of the receiver.

A barrel bushing is inserted in the front of the slide over the barrel and locks when turned down into place. It serves to retain the recoil spring and the plug and also supports the muzzle end of the barrel.

When the barrel and slide together are mounted on the receiver, the slide stop is in place, its pin passing through the receiver from side to side and through the barrel link, thereby positively locking slide, barrel, and receiver together.

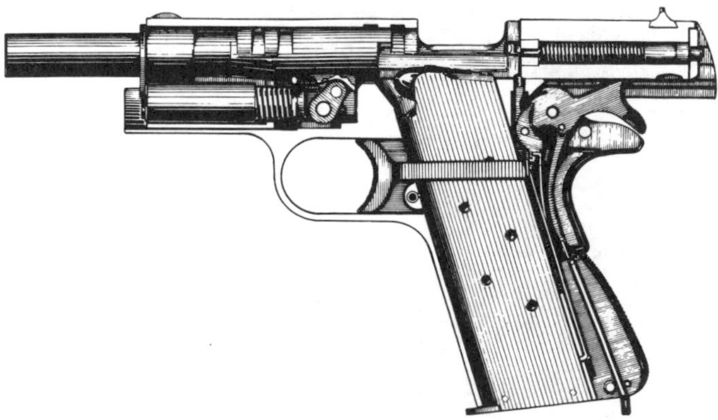

Action open and cutaway to show barrel swung back and down on link for unlocking. Lockwork shows details of cocking and firing mechanism.

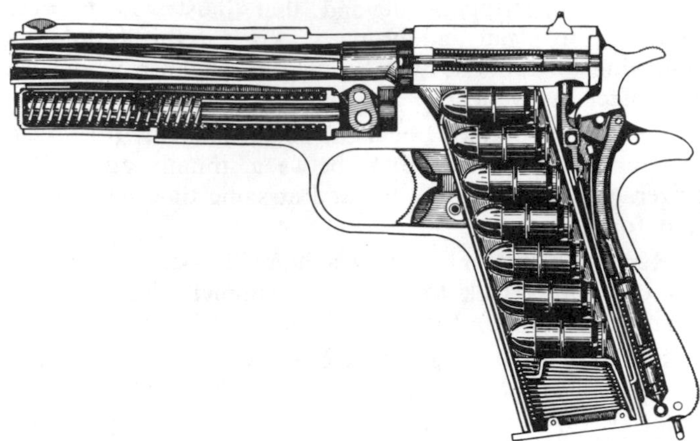

Action cutaway to show details of swinging link barrel lock and lockwork at rest.

The exterior of the slide stop is provided with a checkered thumb piece to be pressed for releasing slide from the open position. When the safety lock is pushed into the upward position, it enters a recess on the slide and a stud on the inner face at the same time locks the sear and hammer when in the full cocked position. This safety can only be applied when the pistol is cocked.

The grip safety is a curved metal piece pivoted in the upper part of the receiver. It acts automatically to lock and release the firing mechanism without any attention on the part of the shooter.

The disconnector is a small lever which when pressed down prevents the trigger mechanism from engaging with the sear and hammer in all positions except when breech is fully closed. This also prevents more than one shot following each pull of trigger.

How the Pistol Works

A magazine holding any number of cartridges from 1 to 7 is inserted in the handle and pushed in until it locks. This locking is produced by the thumb catch lock snapping into a notch cut in the upper front end of the magazine.

As slide is drawn back for the opening movement, it compresses a recoil spring, and forces the hammer back and down to full cock. Here it is held in position by the sear. As the slide goes back the disconnector is pressed back, positively preventing the trigger from connecting the firing mechanism. When slide is to the rear as far as it will go, it clears head of the magazine, and the magazine spring feeds a cartridge up in line with the breech.

The slide on being released is forced forward by the recoil spring and the breech bolt face of the slide carries the first cartridge into the barrel chamber. As the slide nears its foremost position, the face of the breech bolt comes against the rear extension of the upper part of the barrel forcing the barrel forward and upward on the barrel link. When the slide and barrel reach the full forward position, the locking ribs are positively locked into the corresponding grooves on the inside of the slide.

The firing pin spring, firing pin, and the extractor are located in the breech bolt section of the slide. As the cartridge is seated in the barrel chamber, the extractor, which is made of heavy spring steel, springs over the head and into the cannelure of the cartridge, thus preparing it to be drawn back during the rearward motion of the pistol for extraction.

The firing pin is a "flying" one. It is seated in the breechblock surrounded by its spring. It is shorter than the breechblock itself. Thus if the hammer is lowered all the way down on the firing pin, it will push the pin inside the breechblock but cannot push it far enough to make it rest against the primer in the cartridge. The one way in which the firing pin can touch the primer is when it is struck a sharp blow by the hammer itself. As the hammer falls, it drives the firing pin ahead to strike the primer and is stopped itself by the face of the breechblock. The inertia of the firing pin causes it to fly ahead and strike the primer, then its compressed coil spring pulls it back into the breechblock.

The pressure of the powder gases driving the bullet down the barrel also drives the empty case back against the base of the breechblock pushing the slide and barrel together rearward, until the bullet is safely out of the barrel. At that point the barrel swings downward on its pivoted link leaving the slide free to continue direct rearward motion in its guide in the receiver, extracting and ejecting the empty shell, cocking the hammer, and compressing the recoil spring for the next forward movement.

Breech Pressure. When the .45 automatic pistol is fired, a pressure of 16,000 lbs. per sq. inch is generated in the firing chamber. Since the base of the bullet has an area of .159 sq. inches, a total pressure of 2,225 pounds is exerted against the base of the bullet, driving it forward down the barrel. The same total pressure is exerted back against the face of the breechblock driving it backwards.

The bullet, weighing only a fraction as much as the moving section of the pistol, gets under way much more quickly and utilizes most of the pressure as it travels down the barrel. The pistol's motion as compared to that of the bullet is inversely proportional to the weights of the pistol and the bullet.

Thus the bullet is well out of the barrel before the pistol has recoiled sufficiently to permit the locking mechanism to open. The pressure, of course, lasts only for a very small fraction of a second. However, in high powered military pistols of comparatively low weight, it is necessary that the breech be positively locked until the bullet has left the barrel. The locking principle on the .45 automatic pistol, model 1911, is among the best ever designed.

How the Slide Stop Works. The forward end of the magazine follower is split in two longitudinally for a short length. The left hand section is bent down below the level of the follower.

When the last cartridge has been stripped from the magazine, the follower rises under the influence of the magazine spring, and the bent section presses against the rear of the inside of the slide stop, thus forcing the projection on the top of the stop up into line with the large notch in the base of the slide into which it locks.

The slide will not go forward while the magazine is empty. If the empty magazine is extracted, pressing on the slide stop will permit the slide to run forward by pulling the stop down out of its locking notch. If a loaded magazine is inserted in the handle, then the magazine follower with its bent arm is in position below the cartridges on the inside of the magazine. Hence, if the slide stop is pushed down when a loaded magazine is in the handle, it will release the slide to run forward and load the chamber.

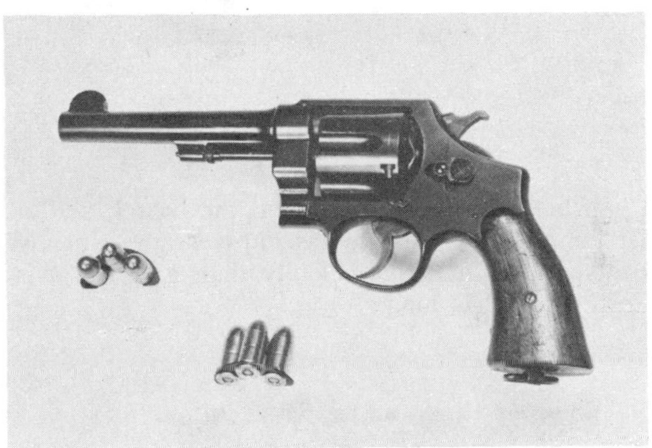

Smith and Wesson Cal. .45 M1917 Revolver.

Caliber: .45 M1911 cartridge with clips.
Cylinder: 6 chambers.
Muzzle Velocity: About 810 feet per second.
Weight of Bullet: 230 grains, lead with metal jackets.
Striking Energy: 340 foot pounds.
Barrel Length: 5½".
Overall Length of Revolver: 10¾".
Weight: 36¼ ozs.
Sights: Service type front, square notch rear. Fixed.
Accurate Range: 75 yards.
Maximum Range: About 1600 yards.
Lock: Cylinder is locked in rear and the arm of the crane has a latch to lock it to the front end of the frame. The ejector rod latches into place at extreme front end of housing below barrel.
Safety: Hammer rebounds automatically after striking cartridge, and can strike at primer only when the trigger is deliberately pulled.

Note on Ammunition

A cartridge known as the .45 Auto-Rim is commercially manufactured in the United States for use in this revolver without the use of a clip. Cartridge is similar to the automatic pistol cartridge except that it has a revolver-type rim. This converts it to a typical revolver cartridge. Ballistics are practically the same as for standard .45 Automatic Pistol cartridge when it is fitted with a metal-jacketed bullet. This cartridge may also be obtained with a lead bullet. The velocity obtained will be rather lower than that obtained in the automatic pistols, because in the automatic the firing chamber is a part of the barrel and no gas escapes. In the revolver there

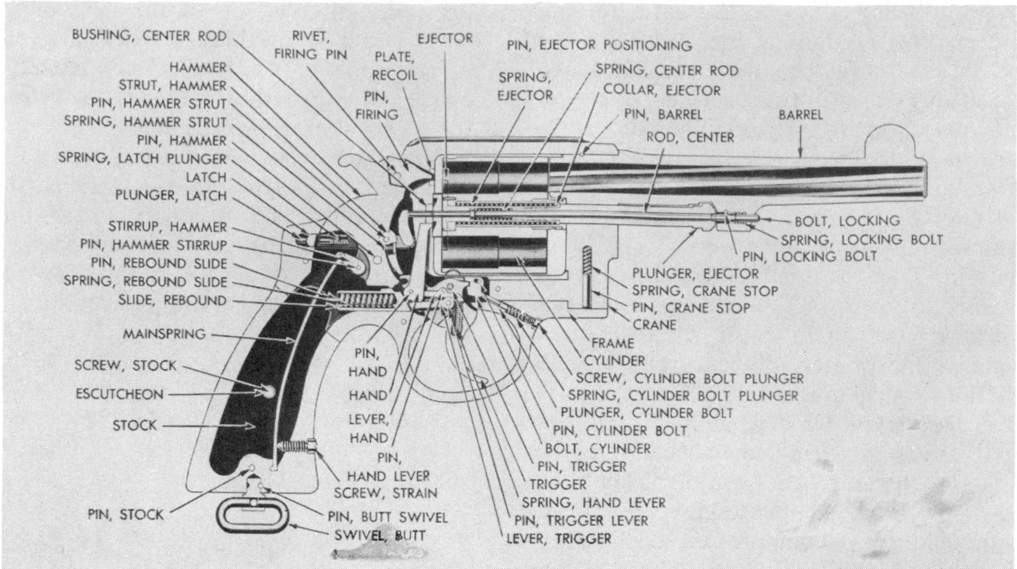

is a gap between the cylinder and the barrel; and as the bullet jumps this gap some gas must escape. Note: When a revolver gives a better velocity than a pistol, it is because the barrel is longer.

How the Swing-Out Cylinder Works

Swinging out the cylinder gives access to the cylinder and barrel for all normal cleaning purposes. Actual takedown of any revolver is ordinarily unnecessary and is a job for a skilled armorer. The spring and lever system is so complex that attempts at stripping should be discouraged.

When the thumb latch is pushed it forces forward the locking pin which passes down the center of the ejector rod. Thus simultaneously the locking pins at the rear of the cylinder and at the extreme end of the ejector rod are both released, permitting the cylinder to be swung out on its crane to the left of the revolver.

Loading and Firing

This revolver was designed to use the rimless .45 Government Automatic Pistol cartridge. Revolver cartridges must have rims to catch on the cylinder and over the head of the extractor to permit extraction. Automatic pistol cartridges, on the other hand, should be rimless, so they will lie properly in place on top of each other in the magazine and will feed in and out of the action with a minimum of difficulty.

To make it unnecessary for the Army to use special cartridges for revolvers, Smith & Wesson developed steel half-moon clips, into which three automatic pistol cartridges can be placed. These clips slip into the cannelures of three cartridges and lock them securely. Thus it is possible to load the six chambers of the cylinder with two motions.

Smith & Wesson cylinders are constructed with a shoulder at the lower end of each chamber as is customary in the automatic pistol, and if one has automatic pistol cartridges but no clips, the cartridges may be individually loaded into the chambers and will rest on these shoulders. The revolver may now be fired in the ordinary way. However, since there are no rims on these individually loaded cartridges for the extractor to catch on, pushing back on the ejector rod will not take them out of the chambers as they are not held by the extractor. Sometimes they may be shaken out, but normally they will have to be dug out with a knife or punched out with a pencil or some similar instrument.

Ejection of Empty Cartridge Cases. The cylinder being swung out to the left, pressure on the ejector rod will compress the spring, force out the star-type extractor

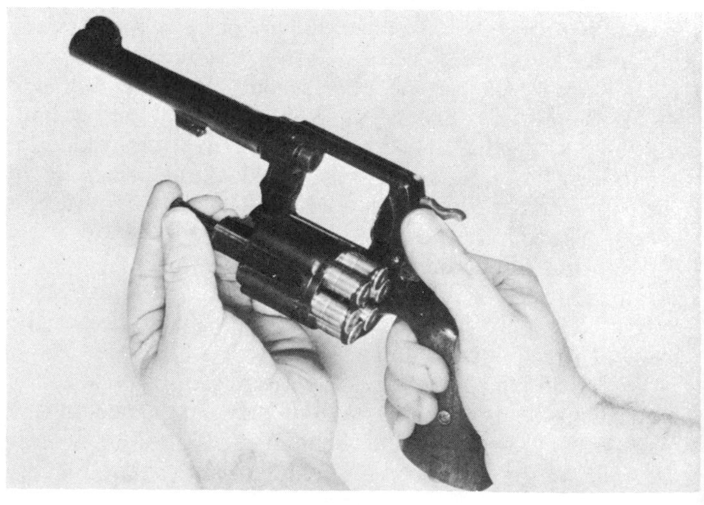

which fits around the rim of each cartridge, and which is attached to the ejector rod mounted in the center of the cylinder, and will push empty shells completely out of the revolver. The compressed ejector spring will force the ejector and extractor back into place in the cylinder when pressure on the rod is released.

How the Revolver Works

As hammer is drawn back by thumb or by action of trigger, its underside catches below the trigger nose and draws the rear end of the trigger up and back. When the hammer reaches full cock, it will be held there by the trigger nose. As the hammer goes backwards, it compresses the flat mainspring in the grip. During the rearward motion of the hammer, the attached hand or pawl pushes up against the ratchet on the face of the extractor and revolves the cylinder the full distance of one firing chamber. This movement is made possible by the hammer moving a rebound lever which depresses the cylinder stud freeing the cylinder to move. The cylinder is locked securely to the frame by the cylinder catch stud positioned in the center of the extractor and supported by a strong spring. This stud enters a locking recess in the frame and is held in position there under the influence of the spring until the thumb latch is pushed forward to relieve the tension and permit cylinder to be swung out. This cannot be done while the hammer is at full cock.

When the trigger is squeezed, the hammer is released, to go forward and strike the cartridge in the chamber lined up with the barrel. As the finger is loosened for the next shot, a spring pushes the trigger back into position and the hammer immediately rebounds against the top of the rebound stop and is prevented from going forward again except on complete pull of the trigger. The forward end of the rebound stop and the rebound arm on the hammer are so shaped that the forward motion of the stop pushes the lower part of the hammer forward and takes the nose of the hammer to the rear.

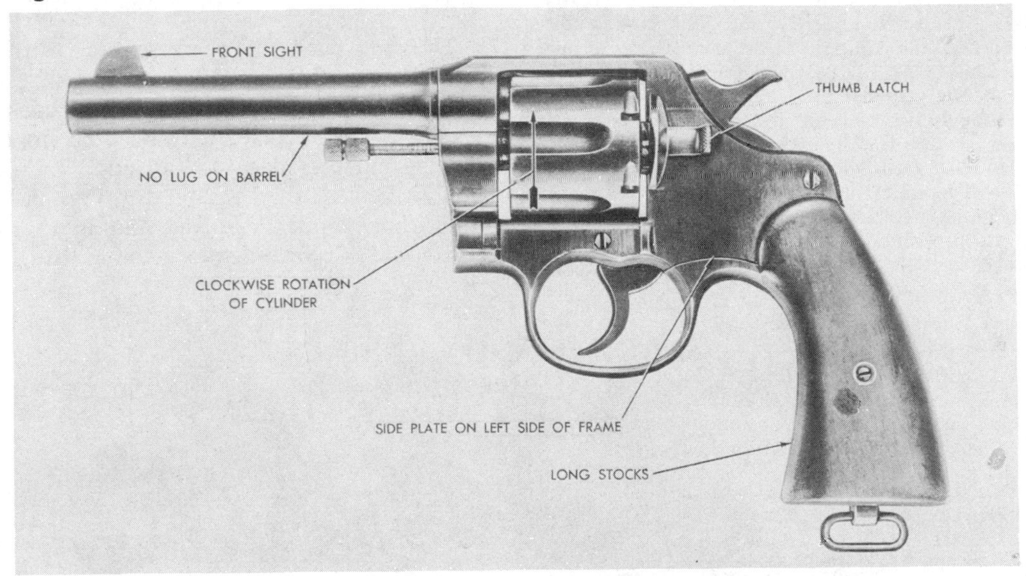

U. S. Colt Cal. .45 M1917 Revolver.

Caliber: .45 Model 1911 cartridge, used with half-moon clip.
Cylinder: 6 chambers.
Ballistics: About same as for automatic pistols.
Barrel Length: 5½".

Overall Length: 10¾".
Weight: 40 ozs.
Sights: Fixed.
Type of Fire: Single action or double action.

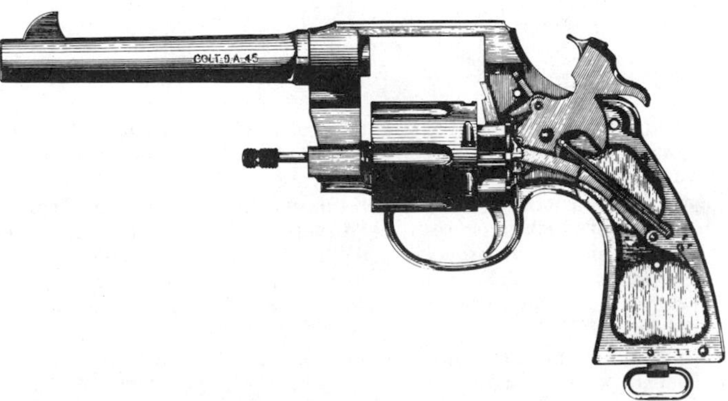

Cylinder swung out, ejection started and hammer at full cock. Side cutaway to show action of mainspring.

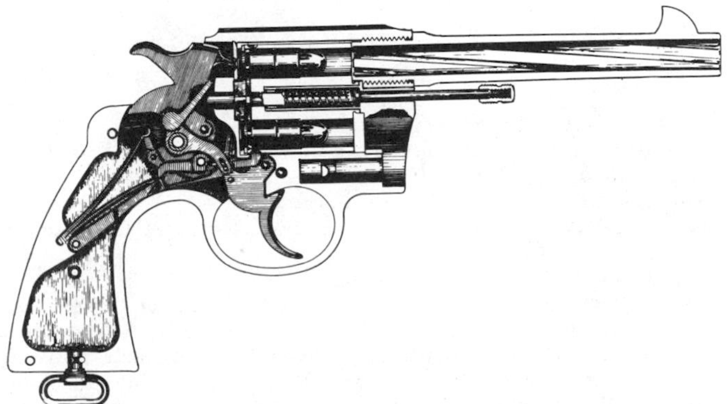

All parts at rest. Action cutaway to show details of cylinder construction and lockwork.

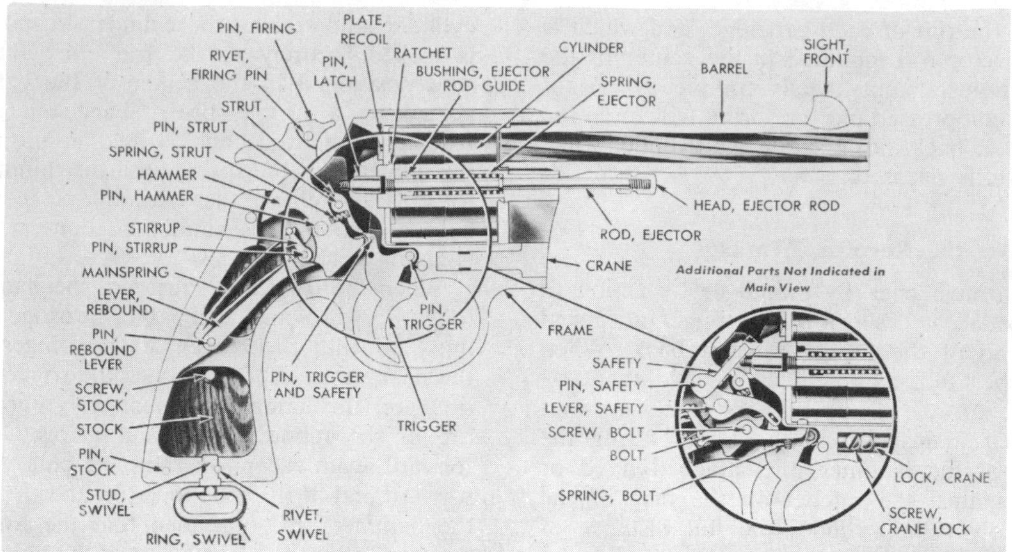

Cylinder Latch on Left Side Plate: Must be drawn back to release cylinder.

Safety: Fitted with Colt positive safety lock. This is a small intercepting slide inside the frame on the right side terminating in a block. This block is entirely automatic, and unless the trigger is deliberately pulled the face of the hammer cannot come far enough forward for the firing pin to reach the cartridge in the chamber. This revolver cannot be fired unless the hammer has gone to full cock, the trigger has been pulled, and the hammer driven forward by the main spring. If the swing-out system is not fully home and locked by the latch pin, its projection into the lock chamber interferes with the movement of the safety lock and the weapon can be neither cocked nor fired.

Loading and Firing

Drawing back the cylinder latch with the thumb permits the cylinder to be swung out to the left on its crane. The cylinder is loaded, then swung back into place until it clicks. The revolver may be fired now either by drawing the hammer back to full cock (single action) or by double action, that is, by drawing back on the trigger until the cylinder revolves and locks and the hammer cocks and is released to fire the cartridge.

U. S. RIFLES AND CARBINES

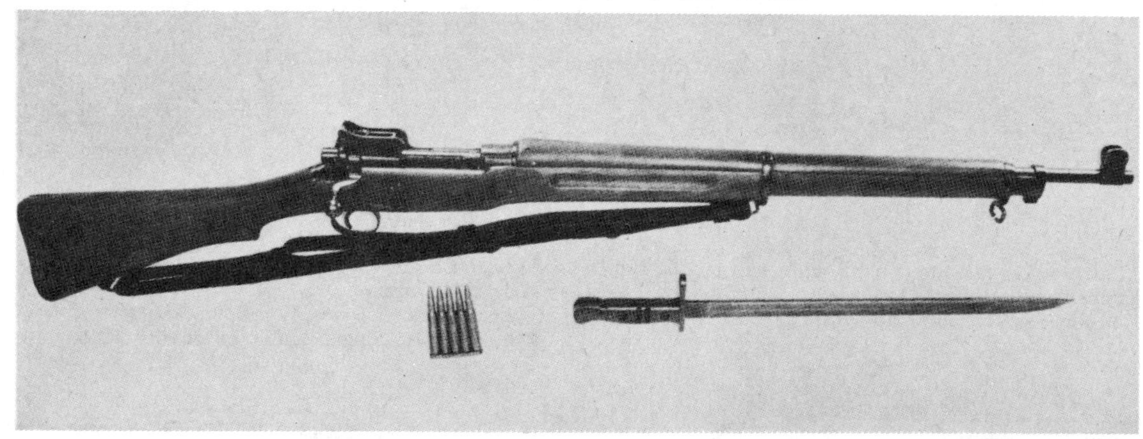

U. S. Enfield Caliber .30 M1917 Rifle.

Caliber: .30-06, M1 or M2 ammunition.

Magazine: Vertical box directly below the bolt. Loaded from top with a 5-cartridge clip, same as Springfield.

General Ballistics: Same as for Springfield.

Barrel Length: 26″ from base of bolt to muzzle, including chamber.

Overall Length of Rifle: 46.3″.

Sights. Blade front, mounted in protective carrier. Peep rear sight mounted on receiver directly above bolt handle. Has a peep battle sight. When sight leaf is raised, slide may be raised vertically on the leaf and held in place by slide stop screw. The base of the slide is checked to prevent light reflection which might interfere with aiming. Numbers on leaf indicate 100-yard units, notches being at 100-yard intervals from 200 to 900 yards. Notches on right edge of sight leaf are at 100-yard intervals from 200 to 900 yards; and at 50 yard intervals thereafter to 1600-yard range.

Locked: By rotating bolt. Lugs on end of bolt as in Springfield; they lock into recesses directly ahead of the cartridge to give maximum support at the instant of firing. This is very important, as the breech pressure runs from 47,000 to 50,000 pounds per square inch in the chamber at the moment of discharge.

Cutoff: No magazine cutoff is provided on this rifle. It may be loaded singly directly into the chamber, but the magazine follower must be pushed down by the thumb of the left hand and the bolt started forward over the follower. This weapon is intended strictly for magazine use. When rifle is empty, magazine follower rises in path of bolt, preventing it being closed. The follower is the metal strip under which lies the magazine spring, and on top of which the cartridges rest.

Safety: A safety lock is provided on the right side of the rifle to the rear and below the rear sight mounting. It has a heavy, swiveled thumb-piece which when rocked back to the rear makes it impossible to fire the rifle. The forward position is the fire position. There is also a built-in safety device which prevents the trigger being pulled unless the bolt handle is down and fully locked.

Bolt Stop: On the left side of the receiver just below the rear sight mounting in a spring held thumb-piece; when pulled out against the spring tension, the bolt can be removed to the rear.

Magazine Capacity: While the capacity of the magazine is only five cartridges, as in the case of the Springfield, if the cartridges in the loaded magazine are pressed down and the bolt pushed forward over the head of the top cartridge, a sixth cartridge may then be loaded directly into the firing chamber.

This rifle is often called the "American Enfield" in this country. During World War I, Springfield rifles were standard equipment in our forces; but we did not have facilities for producing them fast enough. Machinery which had been turning out British service rifles—popularly called "Enfield"—was converted to manufacturing a modified version of the Enfield which would take our standard rimless cartridge as used in the Springfield and permit magazine loading with the usual service cartridge clip. Huge numbers of these very fine weapons were in use through the world, particularly by British units. In Great Britain this weapon is often erroneously called "Springfield."

Loading and Firing

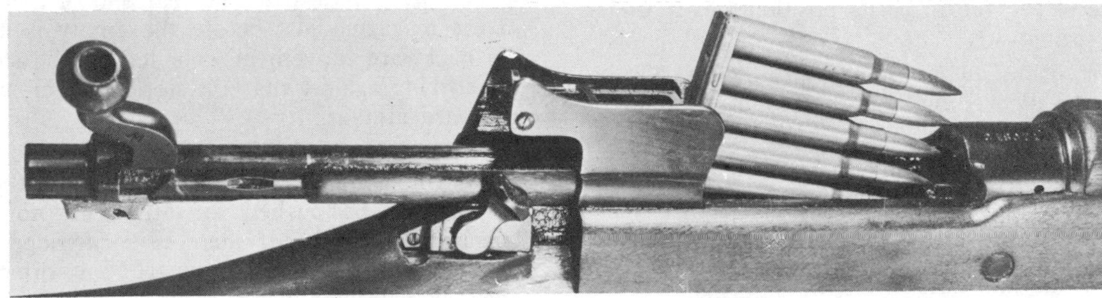

Raise bolt handle as far up as it will go and draw straight back to the rear as far as possible. Now place a loaded clip in the clip slots in the receiver (clip may be inserted by either end), and with thumb of right hand push cartridges down into magazine until the top cartridge is caught and held by the right edge of the receiver. Clip may be pulled out, or the forward motion of the bolt will knock it out of the rifle as the bolt is pushed forward to load the topmost cartridge into the firing chamber. The rifle is now ready to fire; it cocks as the bolt is thrust forward.

Field Stripping

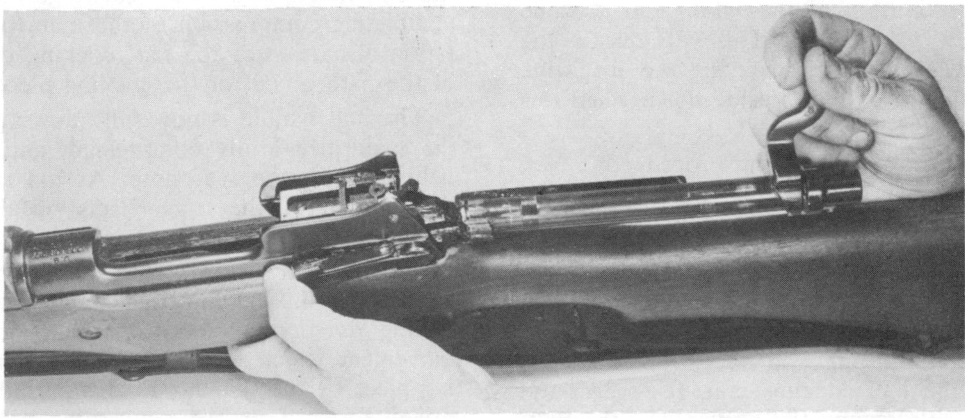

Pull out thumb-piece at forward end of the bolt stop against tension of the spring. While holding this out, pull the bolt straight out to the rear.

To Dismount Bolt. Hook a loop of string over dismounting hook on cocking piece lug; hold bolt firmly in left hand and draw cocking piece out until lug clears end of bolt.

Turn with right hand from right to left to unscrew sleeve from bolt; this permits withdrawal of sleeve, cocking piece, and striker.

Hold sleeve with left hand and rest point of striker against a wooden surface (this is necessary so striker point will not be injured). Force sleeve toward the point of striker, thus compressing the mainspring until the cocking piece lug clears the lug slot in the sleeve. With right hand, twist cocking piece a quarter turn right or left which will disengage it from the striker and permit it to be drawn off to the rear.

Relieve spring tension slowly as it is removed, being careful that parts do not fly from the hand. Now turn extractor to cover the gas escape holes in the bolt, and push it forward with thumb until it is free of the ears on the collar.

To Assemble Bolt. With mainspring sleeve over the striker, press point of striker against wooden surface and, placing the sleeve against the end of the spring (see that the flats in its bore register with the flats on the striker), compress spring by forcing sleeve toward the point of the striker.

Hold sleeve with spring fully compressed and put cocking piece back on end of striker, locking it by a quarter turn so its lug will line up with the lug slot in the sleeve.

Now let the sleeve return to its position slowly under action of the spring.

Holding bolt firmly in left hand start the threads on the barrel of the sleeve into the threads at the end of the bolt.

With right hand holding string looped around dismounting hook on cocking piece, draw cocking piece out. Again moving right hand in a circular path, this time from left to right, screw the sleeve home into the bolt. Place the lug in the half cocked notch.

Now slide the extractor in place in line with the gas escape holes, being sure the undercut lug on the extractor engages with the sears on the ring. Lift the hook so its tongue will slide over end of bolt. Turn the extractor so it lies over the solid lug and replace bolt in the receiver. Push down magazine follower, force bolt home and turn it down into its locking place.

Stripping Magazine Mechanism. The same as the Springfield rifle. Press bullet end of cartridge through hole in floor plate at bottom of magazine, and at same time draw floor plate to the rear. This will release the floor plate which will come out carrying the magazine follower. The rifle should be held upside down when this is done.

To Assemble. Reverse the foregoing procedure.

How the U. S. Rifle Model 1917 Works

Starting with the rifle just fired: The bolt handle is raised which turns the bolt to the left. The lug at the rear of the bolt rests against the cocking piece groove and is prevented from turning and so is forced to the rear in the bolt by the half cocking cam. It engages the half cocked notch, withdrawing the striker into the bolt.

When the bolt has been turned up far enough for its locking lugs to be turned out of their locking recesses, the locking cams and safety lug on bolt handle clear the receiver safety lug; the extracting cams on the bolt and receiver engage and act together during the continued rotation of the bolt to draw back the bolt a short distance and start the extraction of the empty case from the chamber. During this period of bolt rotation, the guide in the receiver prevents the extractor from turning, while the sleeve is held against rotation by engaging with the receiver. When the bolt has gone up as far as it will, the locking lugs are in a horizontal position. The bolt may now be drawn back straight to the rear, with the extractor pulling out the empty case.

During the first stage of backward travel of the bolt, the cocking piece passes over and depresses the nose of the sear; and the safety stud rises into the clearance provided for it on the bolt. As the cocking piece clears the nose of the sear, the sear is raised to normal position by its spring.

As the rear face of the slotted locking lug reaches the ejector, the ejector is forced into its slot in the lug and protrudes through it. As the rearward movement continues, the empty case strikes against the ejector and is hurled out to the right.

The bolt passes over the rear end of the top cartridge in the magazine just before the empty is ejected. Then the backward movement is halted by the slotted locking lug striking against the bolt stop lug. This completes the rearward motion.

Forward Motion of the Bolt. If magazine is empty, the spring forces the follower up in line with the bolt so the bolt cannot be pushed forward. This notifies you the magazine is empty. If there is a cartridge in the magazine, the forward stroke of the bolt drives it forward and the extractor head snaps over the groove in the cartridge case.

During the first stage of the closing movement, the ejector is thrust outward by the side of the bolt, then the sear notch in the cocking-piece connects with the sear nose and is held; the bolt then slides forward over the striker to further compress the mainspring.

As the bolt handle is turned down into locking position, its locking lugs engage the locking cams, forcing the bolt home, seating the cartridge in the chamber, and completing compression of the mainspring. This bolt rotation also restores the half cocking cam, turning it out of the path of fall of the cocking piece lug.

The bolt handle is now fully down, the bolt is locked, the mainspring fully compressed, and the cocking-piece held back by the sear nose. As the trigger is squeezed, the bearing of the trigger acts on the bearing of the receiver, slowly depressing sear nose and providing the first (or slack) trigger pull.

Next the heel of the trigger engages the receiver completing the depression of the sear nose and the creep movement which terminates in the release of the cocking piece by the sear nose. This permits the striker to be driven forward by the mainspring, to strike the primer of the cartridge, and fire it. As the sear nose is being depressed, the safety stud rises through its hole in the bottom of the well to enter the interlock slot in the bolt. Hence, if the bolt is not fully locked, the interlock slot does not register with the safety stud and the trigger is prevented from being pulled.

As pressure on the trigger is relaxed, the sear spring returns the sear and the trigger to their normal positions.

Note on Operation of Bolt Action Rifles

The foregoing description of the functioning essentially covers all bolt action rifles of the Mauser type. While various models throughout the world differ in details, the general magazine and locking principles are much the same. A knowledge of the rifle just described enables you to grasp very easily the operating detail of most of the bolt action rifles in use.

The British Enfield System differs in that the locking lugs are at the rear of the bolt. This does not give enough bolt support to permit the superlative accuracy of the Springfield. On the other hand, the British system permits easier cleaning of the locking recesses and faster action under all conditions. Aimed rate of fire with the British type is about one-third faster than with the Mauser type.

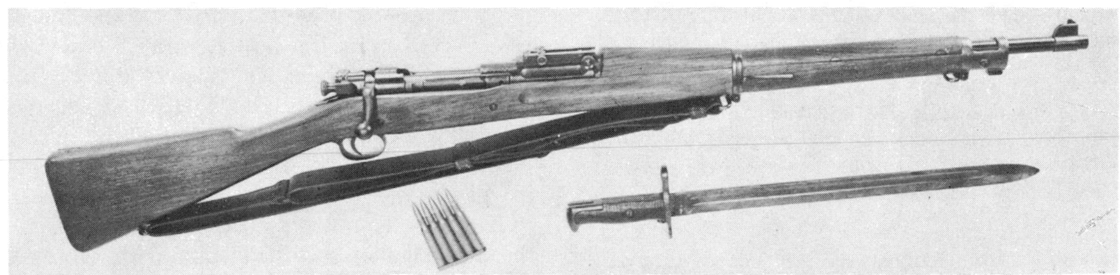

U. S. Springfield Cal. .30-06 M1903 Rifle.

Caliber: .30-06, M1 and M2.
Magazine: Staggered box type in receiver, capacity 5 cartridges. When magazine is loaded, pressing down on cartridge with left thumb will permit pushing bolt handle slightly forward over top cartridge. Magazine cut-off may now be turned to "off." An extra cartridge may now be fed by hand directly into the firing chamber.
Cartridge Clip: Holds 5 cartridges.
Muzzle Velocity: 2800 feet per second with M2 ammunition.
Striking Energy: About 2680 foot pounds.
Barrel Length: 24".
Overall Length of Rifle: 3' 7¼". With M1 bayonet, 10" longer.
Weight of Rifle: 8.69 lbs. With bayonet, about 9 lbs. 8 ozs.
Front Sight: Blade type, fixed.

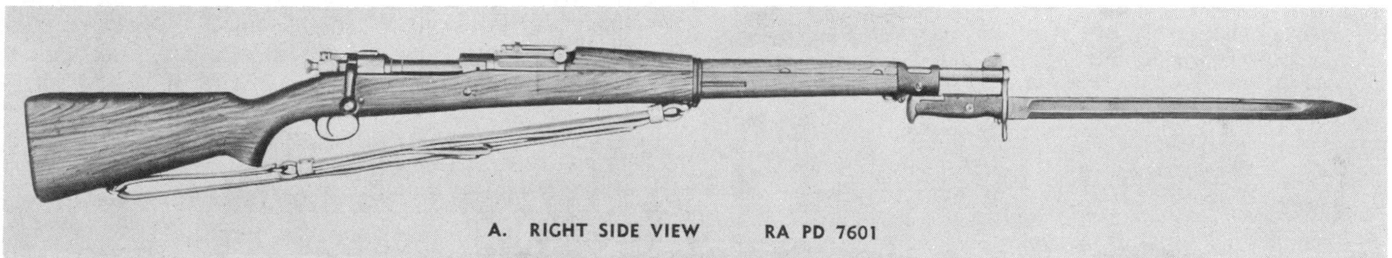

M 1903A1 with M1905 Bayonet.

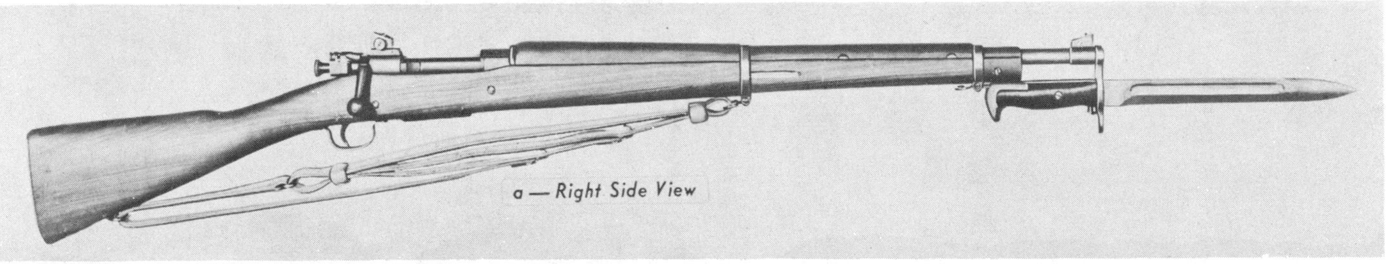

M 1903A3 with M1 Bayonet.

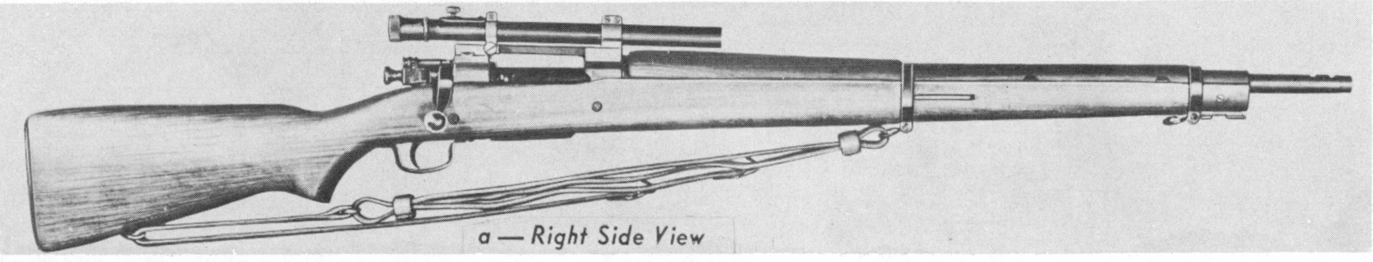

M 1903A4.

Rear Sight: When leaf is down, a rear "U" is on top. This is the battle sight, set for 530 yards range. When leaf is snapped up, a screw-adjusted slide can be set in stages of 100 yards from 100 to 2350. Near the base of the slide is a small aperture, then an open triangle with open sight notch, and on top another sighting notch, in upper edge of leaf. As sight is elevated, it is moved to the left by a drift slide, which automatically compensates for drift of the bullet. The sight leaf has lines across it for setting sights in stages of 100 yards; while in between these stages are shorter lines for 50-yard and for 25-yard divisions. Ranges of 100 to 2450 yards can be obtained through the open notch at the bottom of triangle; Ranges from 1400 to 2750 through open sighting notch in upper edge. The maximum sight range of 2850 yards can be obtained by using the open notch in the upper end of the leaf.

Most Effective Ranges: Up to 600 yards.

Penetration: At close distances, this rifle will send a bullet through 70 or more pine boards ⅞″ thick. At 600 yards it will penetrate 15″ of board.

Trajectory: Extremely flat, only ½″ at 100 yards, and 6″ at 300 yards.

Locked: By turning bolt. Mauser type.

Cutoff: A thumb cutoff is provided on the left side of receiver. When this is turned down, single cartridges may be inserted in the firing chamber. When cutoff is up, cartridges will feed from magazine and magazine follower will hold bolt open when last cartridge has been ejected.

Safety: Thumb piece on rear end of bolt. When rifle is cocked, it can be switched over to the right, in which position it is safe. When in normal position on the left, the rifle is ready to fire.

Automatic Safety: A special mechanical design makes it impossible to fire the cartridge unless the bolt is fully locked. If bolt is not fully home, a cam on the cocking piece strikes the cocking cam on the bolt itself and the mainspring energy will be expended in forcing the bolt shut, not in striking the primer. A misfire occurs when this happens.

Loading and Firing

As a Single Shot Rifle. Check the magazine cutoff on the left side of the receiver, making sure that it is down and the word "Off" can be seen. Turn the bolt handle up as far as it will go. This will release the locking lugs from their recesses in the receiver, and permit the bolt to be drawn straight back. Now place a cartridge in the firing chamber, thrust home the bolt to seat the cartridge properly and permit the extractor to snap over the cannelure of the cartridge case, and turn the bolt handle down as far as it will go to lock the piece. Note: This rifle is cocked as the bolt is rotated clockwise. The knob on the cocking piece will project out of its casing when the weapon is at full cock. If desired, the safety lock may now be applied, by turning the safety lock thumb piece at the rear of the bolt over to the right as far as it will go, when the word "Safe" will be seen on its face.

If safety is not set, pressing the trigger will explode the cartridge in the firing chamber, which then may be extracted and ejected by turning up and pulling back sharply on the bolt handle.

To Load Magazine. Turn cutoff up as far as it will go and the word "On" will appear. Now lift up and pull back on the bolt handle as far as it will go, and since the cutoff is in the position of magazine loading, the bolt will be permitted to travel farther back than when single shot firing is to be done with the cutoff in the "Off" position. When the cutoff is set for magazine loading, the bolt can be drawn back far enough to permit the magazine follower to rise in front of it.

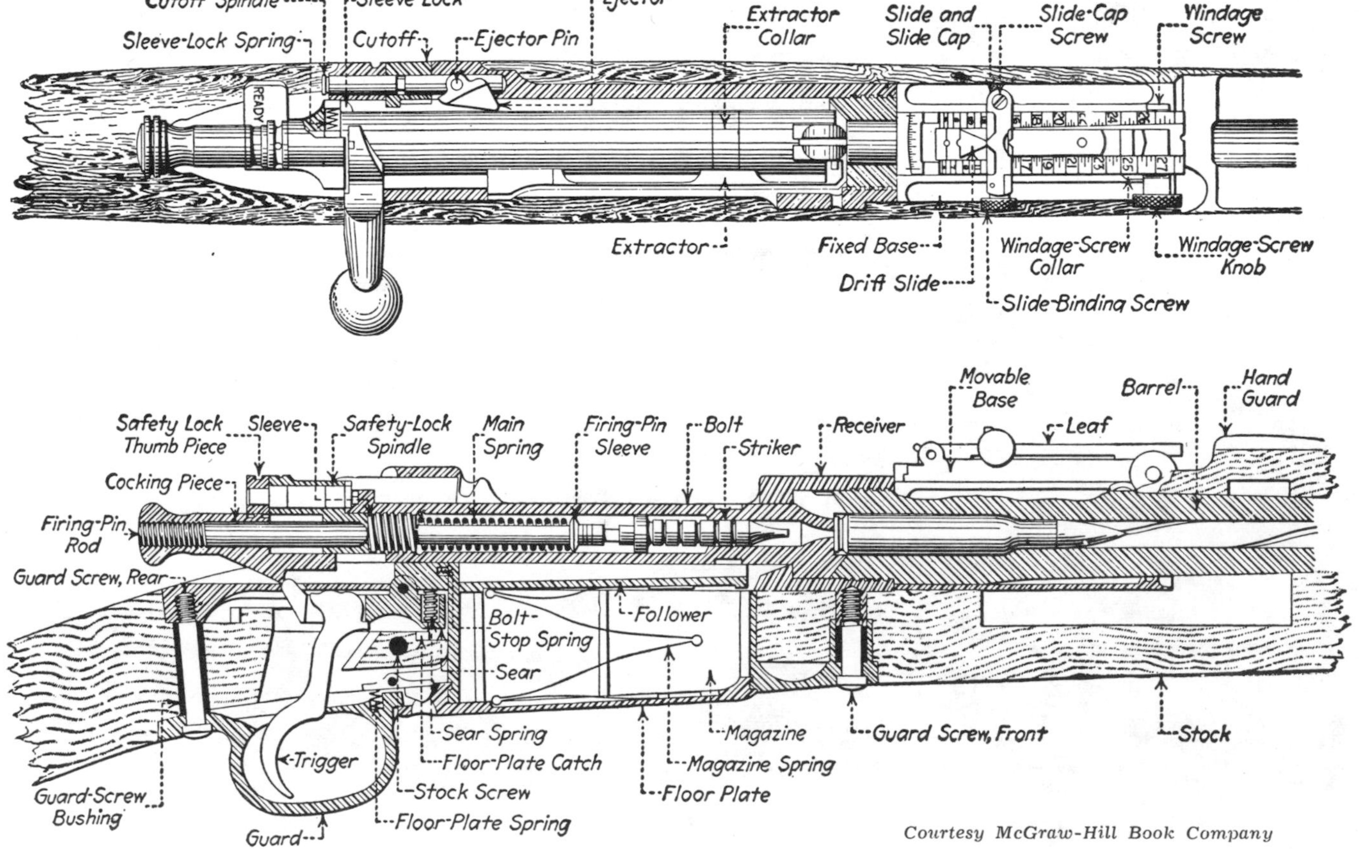

Courtesy McGraw-Hill Book Company

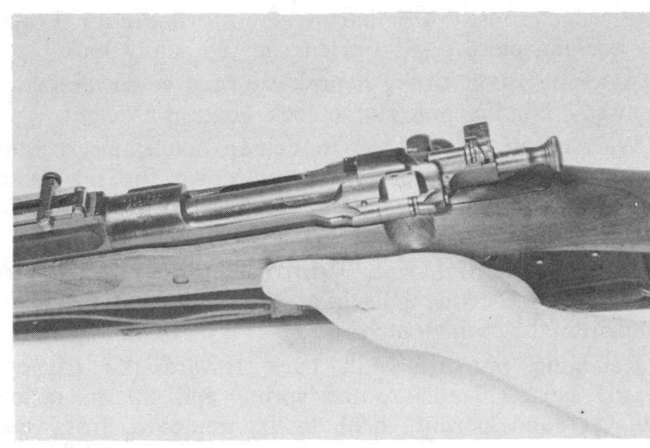

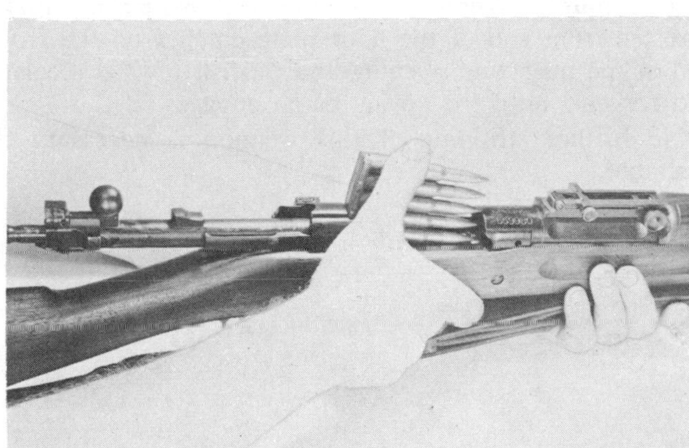

With muzzle pointed up in the air at an angle of 45°, insert a loaded clip in the clip slots; place thumb of right hand over powder space on top cartridge, extend fingers around the rifle with tips resting on magazine floor plate, and with thumb force the five cartridges down into the magazine. Now pull out the empty cartridge clip. Push the bolt home and turn down the locking handle. Set the safety lock on the "Safe" position unless weapon is to be used at once.

To load rifle with six cartridges, proceed as follows: With cutoff set in the "On" position, raise and draw bolt handle back as far as it will go. Load magazine with full clip as above. With left thumb push down on top cartridge, forcing it down below the line of the bolt; and push the bolt slightly over it. Now insert a cartridge in the firing chamber, and push the bolt all the way home, turning and locking it.

Magazine cutoff may now be turned to the "Off" position and the rifle used as a single loader, with the full magazine in reserve. Magazine may be brought into play at any time by merely turning up cutoff.

Setting the Sights on This Rifle

The elaborate sighting system of the Springfield rifle has a great deal to do with its reputation as the most accurate military rifle ever developed. To set the sight, the binding screw on the right hand side of the sight leaf is unscrewed so as to permit the slide to be raised or lowered on the leaf. The index line near the peep is lined up with the range line on the sight leaf which is directly under the number giving the yard range.

Some sights do not have 25- and 50-yard graduation lines, and in such case you must estimate the distance between the 100 yard graduations on the sights. Binding screw must be screwed up tight when the index line is properly aligned for the range at which you wish to shoot.

Wind Gauge. A wind gauge is provided on this sight to compensate for the drift of the bullet caused by wind. The windage screw knob is at the forward end of the sight base on the right hand side. The graduated windage indicator is at the rear end of the base. Turning the windage screw knob will turn the sighting line to right or left, one point of windage for each calibrated line. If the sight leaf moves to the right, the bullet will strike to the right; if sight leaf moves to the left, bullet will be directed to the left.

Field Stripping

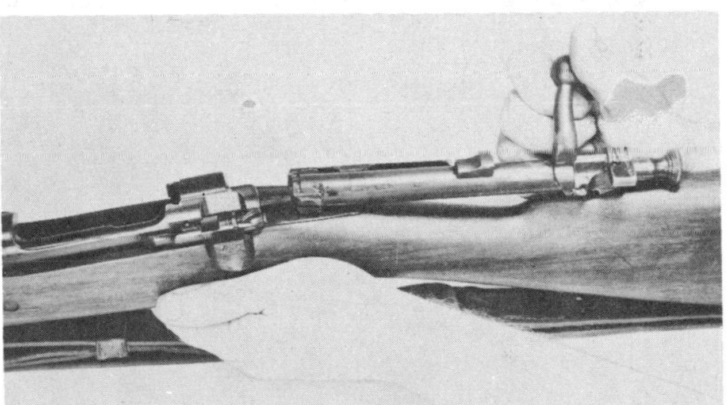

Turn the magazine cutoff to the center of the position midway between "off" and "on." Draw the cocking piece back to full cock. Turn the safety lock up to the vertical position, midway between "off" and "on." Now raise the bolt handle and draw the bolt straight back to the rear out of the receiver.

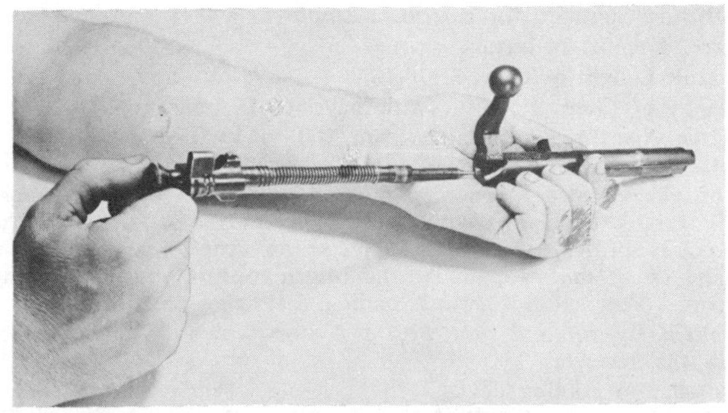

To Dismount Bolt. Holding bolt firmly in left hand, press in bolt sleeve lock with right thumb and unscrew, turning to the left. Bolt sleeve assembly can now be drawn back out of bolt.

Holding firing pin sleeve with left forefinger and thumb, pull back on the cocking piece with the right middle finger and right thumb, and turn the safety lock to the left with the right forefinger to release it. This will relieve part of the tension of the mainspring.

Resting the head of the cocking piece on a firm surface, pull back the firing pin sleeve and remove the striker. Firing pin sleeve, mainspring, and firing pin rod may then be withdrawn.

Extractor is removed by turning it to the right and pushing forward.

Assembling Bolt. Holding bolt handle up in left hand, make sure that the extractor collar lug is in line with the safety lock on the bolt, and insert the extractor collar lug in its undercut in the extractor, then push extractor until tongue comes in contact with bolt face. Now press extractor hook against a rigid surface to spring it into its groove in the bolt.

See that the safety is down and to the left, and assemble firing pin rod and bolt sleeve. Place the cocking piece against a solid surface, draw back the firing pin sleeve and attach the striker. The firing pin must be cocked before the bolt can be screwed on. This is done by pressing the striker point against a wooden surface (which must not be hard enough to injure it). Force the cocking piece back and engage the safety lock.

Assembled bolt sleeve is now replaced in the bolt and screwed until the bolt sleeve lock engages.

With cutoff still turned to center notch, insert bolt in its guide in the receiver, push down the magazine follower and push the bolt home. Now turn safety lock and cutoff down to the left, and press the trigger.

Stripping the Magazine. Turn rifle upside down, insert nose of bullet in the hole in the rear of the floor plate to depress the spring catch.

Retaining pressure, pull back toward the triggerguard. This will release the spring and the magazine follower, and permit them to be removed from the weapon.

Assembling. When assembling the magazine, make sure the front end of the floor plate catches on the front end of the magazine opening and push it toward receiver and forward until the spring catch engages.

No further stripping of this weapon is necessary or desirable.

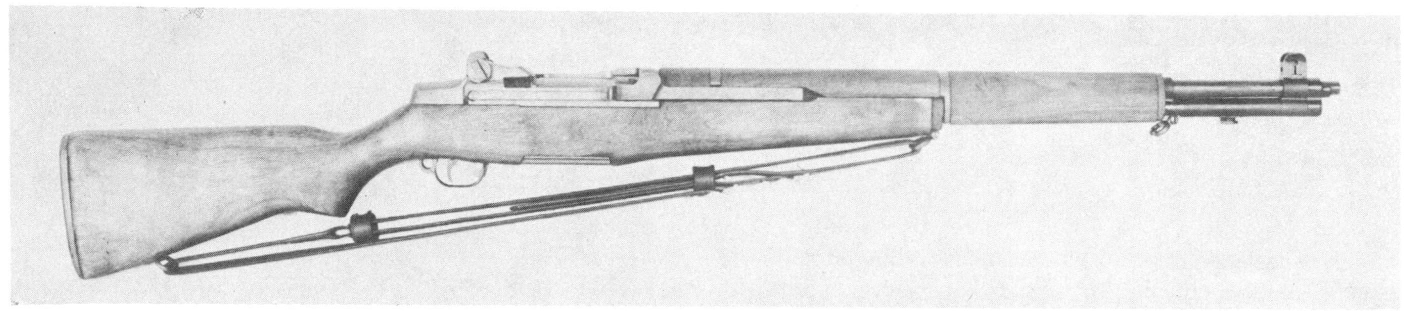

U. S. Rifle Cal. .30 M1 (Garand Semi-Automatic Rifle).

Caliber: .30 U. S.

Magazine: Fixed box type in receiver loaded with clip.

Cartridge Clip: Capacity 8 rounds. Note that this is not the Springfield type. The Garand clip is inserted in the rifle with the cartridges.

When Last Shot Has Been Fired: Empty cartridge clip is expelled through top of the rifle.

Ballistics: Standard for cartridges employed.

Barrel Length: 24 inches.

Overall Length of Gun: 3′ 7″.

Weight of Gun: 9½ lbs. (with bayonet 1 lb. more).

Sights: Aperture. Adjustable from 100 to 1200 yards.

Rifle Operated by: Gas. As bullet leaves barrel, a small quantity of gas escapes through a port into the gas cylinder where it forces back a piston under the barrel, compresses the recoil spring, extracts and ejects the empty cartridge case, and cocks the weapon. As the return motion ends, the spring forces the action forward loading the firing chamber.

Locked: By rotating bolt with two lugs which fit into recesses in the receiver.

Cooled: No cooling device.

Position of Operating Rod Handle When Weapon is Ready To Fire: Fully forward. This gun fires from a closed bolt.

Type of Fire: Single shot only. This is a semi-automatic rifle. It is impossible to fire more than one shot for each pull of the trigger.

Ejection: Empty cartridge cases are ejected on the right upwards and to the front. When rifle is empty, bolt will stay open. This serves notice that the weapon is empty and permits immediate insertion of a fully loaded clip, so that firing may be speedily resumed.

Gas Ports: In early models, port is in a sleeve in front of the barrel muzzle. In later models, the port is bored in the barrel.

Loading and Firing

Pull operating rod straight to the rear. It will be caught and held open by the operating rod catch.

Place the loaded clip on top of the magazine follower; with right side of right hand against the operating rod handle press down with right thumb on the clip until it is caught in the receiver by the clip latch.

Remove the right thumb from the line of the bolt and let go of the operating rod handle which will run forward under the compression of the spring. Push operating rod handle with heel of right hand to be certain that bolt is fully home and locked.

Pressing the trigger will now fire one cartridge. Weapon will be ready for the next pull of the trigger.

If weapon is not to be used at once, set the safety. The safety is in front of the triggerguard. Pulling it back toward the trigger sets it on safe; pushing it forward is the fire position.

Note that the cartridge clip is reversible and may be fed into the rifle from either end.

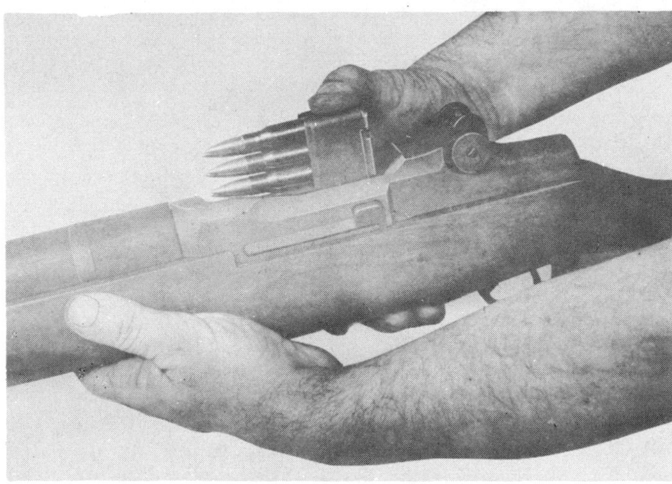

Unloading the Garand Rifle

First check to be sure that the safety is off.

Pull the operating rod back sharply and hold it in rear position. This will eject the cartridge that was in the firing chamber. With the left hand grasp the rifle in front of triggerguard. Hold the butt against the right hip to support it. With the left thumb release the clip latch.

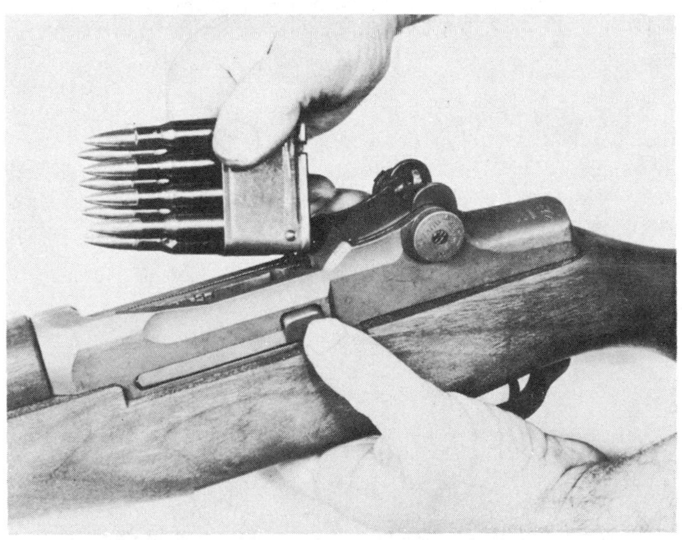

The clip and whatever cartridges remain in it will now pop up into the right hand.

With the right side of the right hand held against the operating rod handle, force the operating rod slightly to the rear. With the right thumb now push down the magazine follower and permit the bolt to move forward about an inch over the end of the follower.

Remove the thumb smartly from the follower and let go of the operating rod. The action will close under the tension of the spring. Now press the trigger.

If you wish to unload the firing chamber but leave the magazine loaded, pull the operating rod back as described above to eject the cartridge from the firing chamber; then pull the operating rod handle back past its normal rear position, force the clip down, ease the rod far enough forward to let the bolt handle ride over the top of the clip, then let operating rod go forward.

Field Stripping

A thorough knowledge of field stripping is necessary in order to give the rifle the care essential to its correct operation.

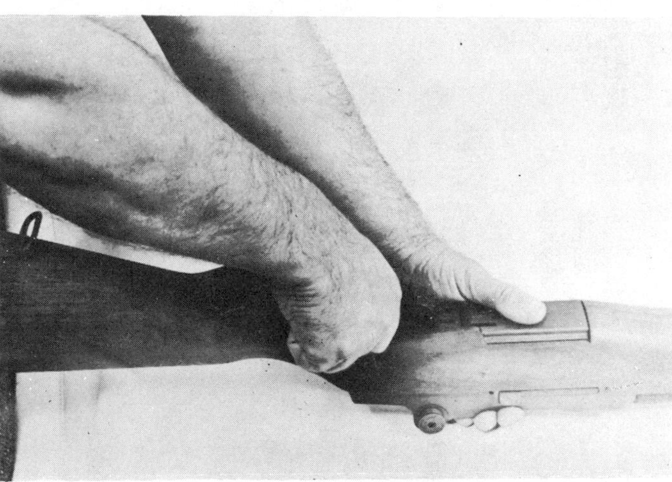

Start by placing the rifle upside down on a firm surface. Holding the rifle with left hand, rest the butt against the left thigh.

With thumb and forefinger unlatch the triggerguard by pulling back on it.

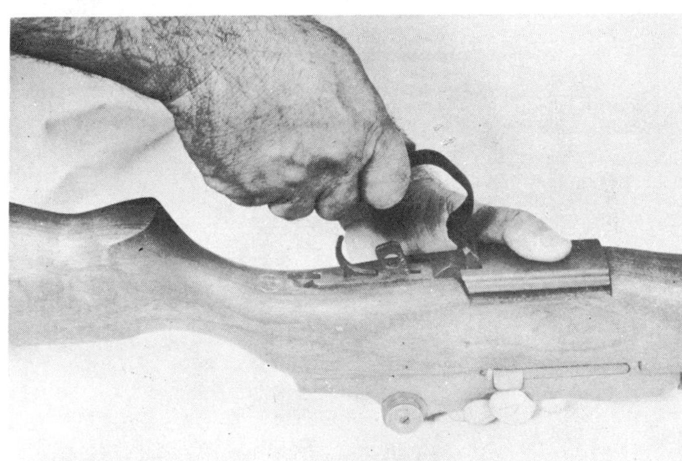

Continue the pressure and pull out the trigger housing group.

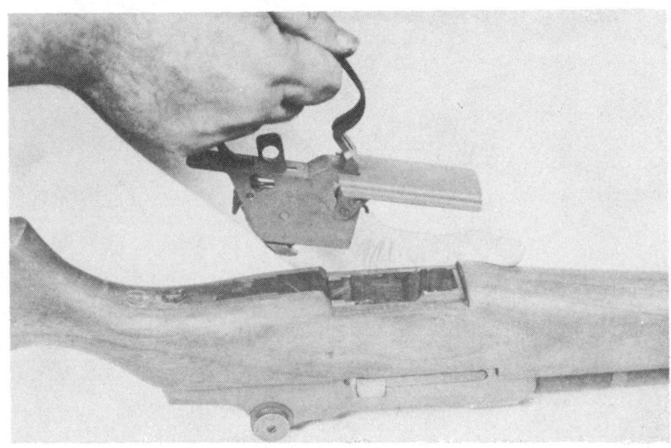

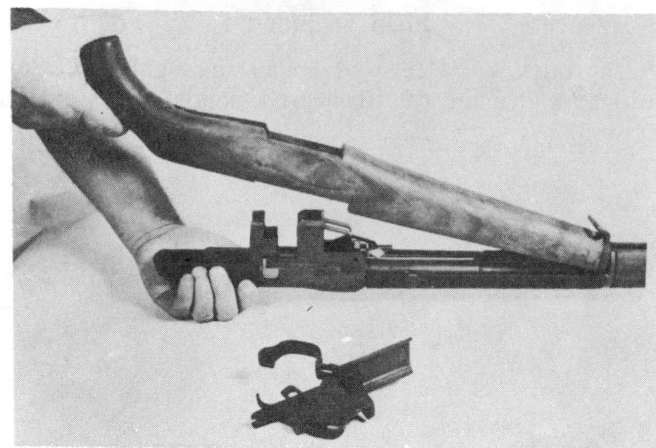

With left hand grasp rifle over rear sight. With right hand strike up against the small of the stock, firmly grasping it at the same time. This will separate the barrel and receiver group from the stock group.

To Dismount Barrel and Receiver Group

With the barrel down, grasp the follower rod at the knurled portion with thumb and forefinger and press it toward the muzzle to free it from the follower arm.

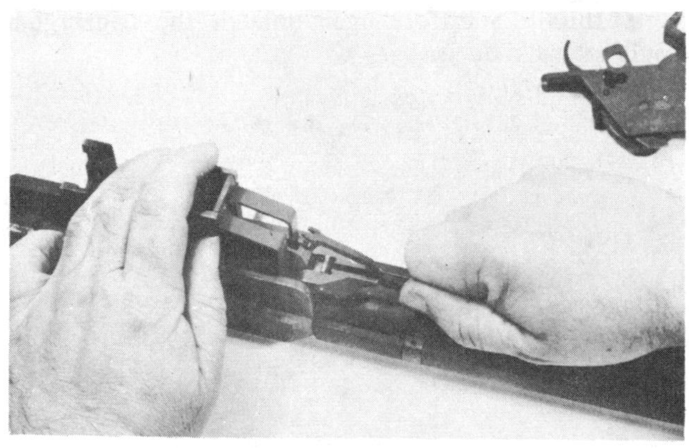

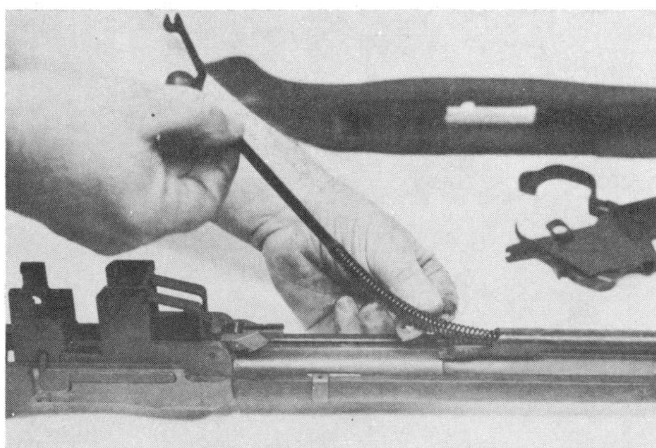

The follower rod and its compensating spring which is attached may now be withdrawn to the right. The compensating spring is removed from the follower rod by holding spring with left hand and twisting rod toward the body with the right hand and pulling slightly to the right.

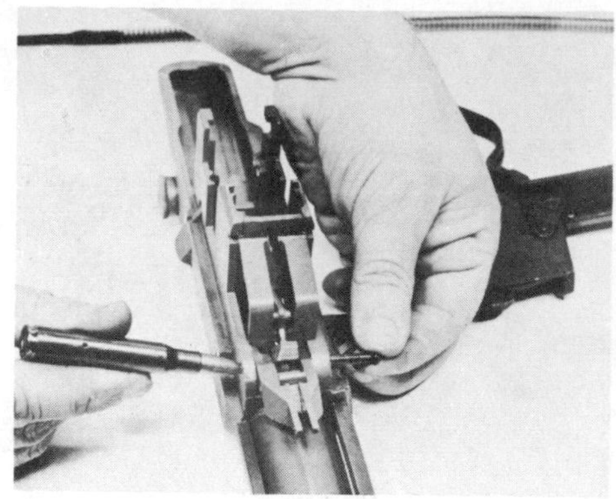

With the point of a bullet, push the follower arm pin from its seat and pull it out with the left hand.

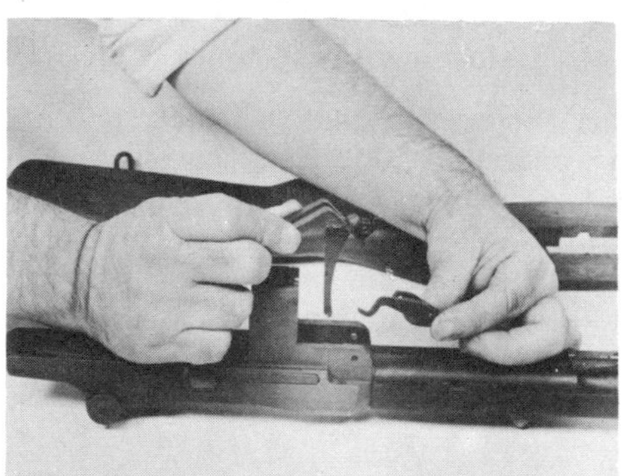

Seize the bullet guide, follower arm, and operating rod catch assembly; draw these to the left until they disengage. The three separate parts may now be lifted out. Accelerator pin is riveted in its seat, so do not attempt to remove accelerator from operating catch assembly.

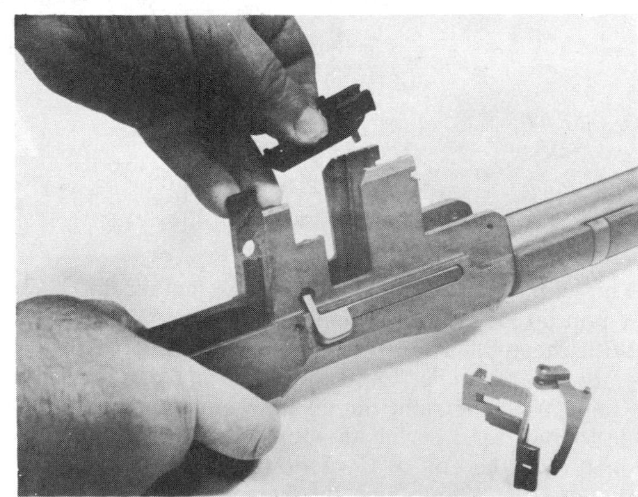

Lift out follower with its slide attached (do not separate follower from slide).

Holding barrel and receiver assembly with left hand, grasp the operating rod handle with right hand and move it slowly to the rear, meanwhile pulling the rod handle up and away from the receiver. (This disengages operating rod from bolt, when the lug on the operating rod slides into the dismount notch of the operating rod guide groove.) When operating rod is disengaged pull

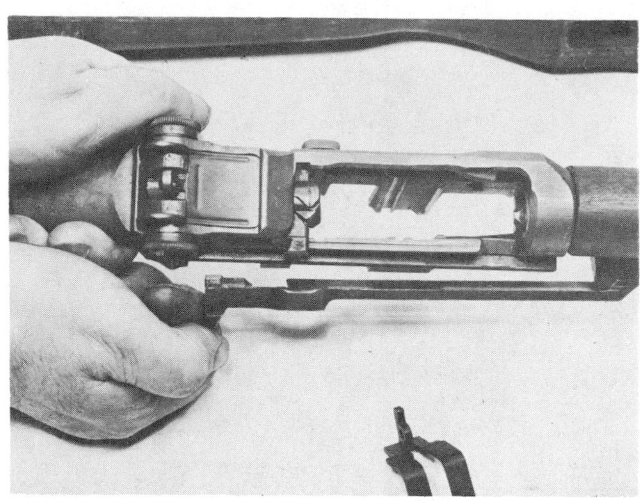

it down and back and withdraw it. (Note that the operating rod is bent. This is intentional. Do not attempt to straighten it.)

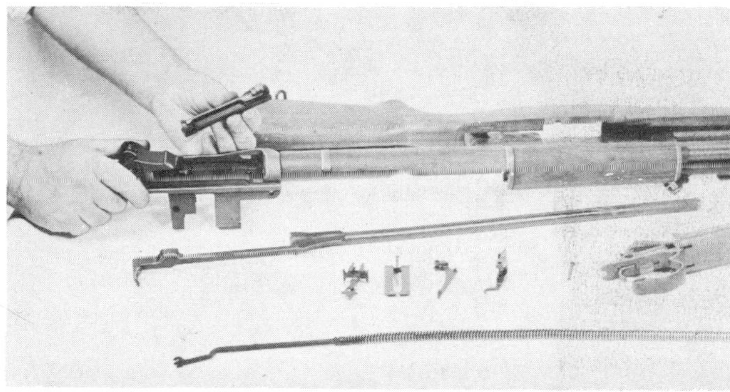

Slide the bolt from the rear to the front by pushing the operating lug on it, and lift it out to the right front with a slight twisting motion.

Note on Gas Cylinder

A spline-type gas cylinder is used in which the barrel protrudes beyond the cylinder. The front sight screw is entered from the rear of the sight and is sealed to prevent unscrewing. The combination tool must be used to unscrew the gas cylinder lock screw.

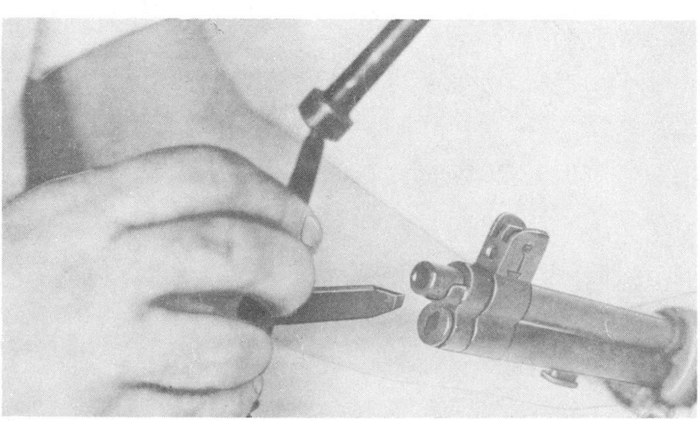

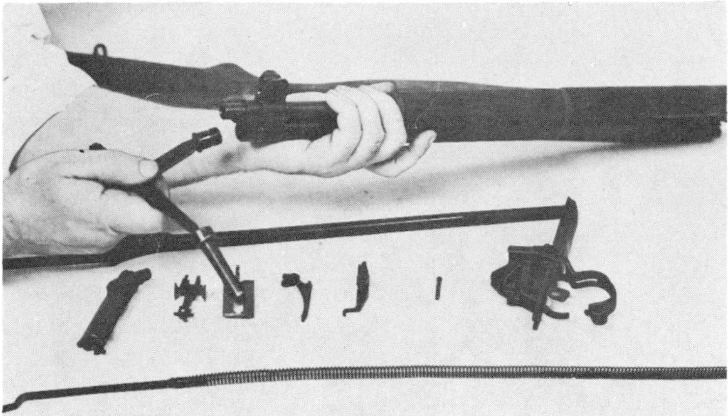

Unscrew the gas cylinder lock.

The gas cylinder is tapped toward the muzzle and removed from the barrel.

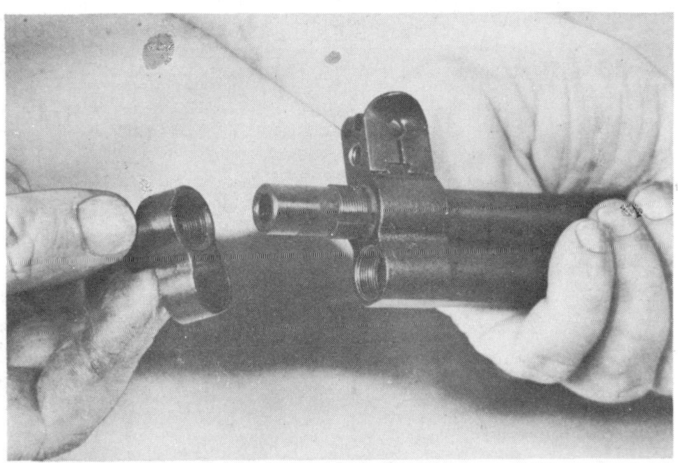

Gas cylinder assembly should never be removed except when necessary to replace the front handguard assembly.

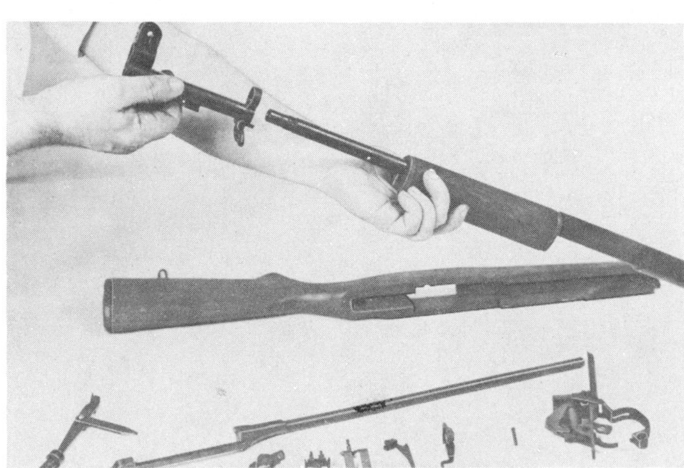

Assembling the M1 Rifle

Replacing gas cylinder, if it has been dismounted, is done by merely reversing the dismounting procedure.

To assemble barrel and receiver group, tilt the barrel and receiver assembly, sight up and muzzle to the front to an angle of about 45°.

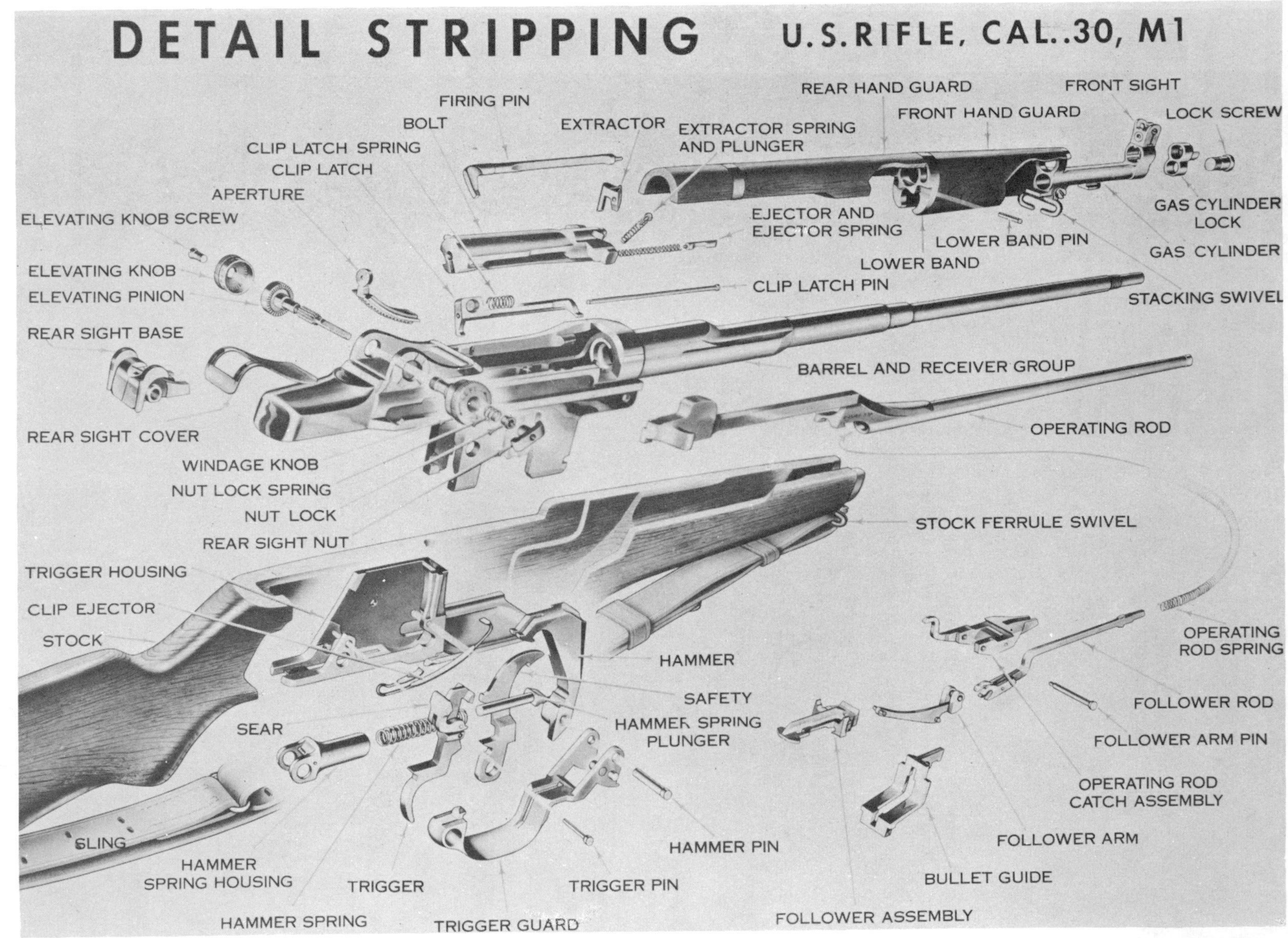
DETAIL STRIPPING
U.S. RIFLE, CAL. .30, M1
FIRING PIN
BOLT
EXTRACTOR
EXTRACTOR SPRING AND PLUNGER
REAR HAND GUARD
FRONT HAND GUARD
FRONT SIGHT
LOCK SCREW
CLIP LATCH SPRING
CLIP LATCH
APERTURE
ELEVATING KNOB SCREW
EJECTOR AND EJECTOR SPRING
LOWER BAND PIN
LOWER BAND
GAS CYLINDER LOCK
GAS CYLINDER
ELEVATING KNOB
ELEVATING PINION
CLIP LATCH PIN
STACKING SWIVEL
REAR SIGHT BASE
BARREL AND RECEIVER GROUP
REAR SIGHT COVER
OPERATING ROD
WINDAGE KNOB
NUT LOCK SPRING
NUT LOCK
REAR SIGHT NUT
STOCK FERRULE SWIVEL
TRIGGER HOUSING
CLIP EJECTOR
STOCK
OPERATING ROD SPRING
HAMMER
SAFETY
HAMMER SPRING PLUNGER
FOLLOWER ROD
SEAR
FOLLOWER ARM PIN
OPERATING ROD CATCH ASSEMBLY
FOLLOWER ARM
SLING
HAMMER PIN
HAMMER SPRING HOUSING
TRIGGER
TRIGGER PIN
BULLET GUIDE
HAMMER SPRING
TRIGGER GUARD
FOLLOWER ASSEMBLY

Holding the bolt by the right locking lug so the front end of the bolt is somewhat above and to the right of its extreme forward position in the receiver, insert the rear end in its bearing on the bridge of the receiver. Switch it from right to left far enough to let tang of the firing pin clear the top of the bridge. Next guide the left locking lug of the bolt into its groove just to the rear of the lug on the left side of the receiver, and start right locking lug into its bearing in the receiver. Now slide bolt back to its extreme rear position.

Turn barrel and receiver assembly in left hand until barrel is down.

Grasp operating rod at the handle and holding it handle up, insert piston head into gas cylinder about 3⁄8″. Be sure that operating rod handle is to the left of the receiver.

Hold barrel and receiver assembly in left hand and twist to the right until barrel is uppermost.

Adjust operating rod with right hand so that camming recess on its rear end fits over operating lug on bolt. Now press operating rod forward and downward until bolt is seated in its forward position.

With barrel and receiver assembly held barrel down and muzzle to your left, replace the follower with its attached slide so that its guide ribs fit into their grooves in the receiver. (The square hole in the follower must be to the right.) The follower slide rests on the bottom surface of the bolt when the follower is in the correct position.

With left hand replace bullet guide, fitting the shoulders of the guide into their slots in the receiver and the hole in the projecting lug in line with the hole in the receiver.

With left hand replace follower arm passing stud end through bullet guide slot and inserting stud in proper grooves in front end of follower.

Place the forked end of the follower arm in position across the projecting lug on the bullet guide, with pin holes properly alined.

Insert rear arm of operating rod catch into clearance cut in the bullet guide (be sure its rear end is below the forward stud of the clip latch which projects into the receiver mouth). Line up the holes in the operating rod catch, the follower arm, and the bullet guide with those in the receiver; and insert the follower arm pin in the side of the receiver toward your body and press the pin home.

Insert operating rod spring into operating rod; assemble follower rod by grasping the spring in left hand and inserting follower rod with right hand, twisting the two together until the spring is fully seated.

Seize the knurled portion of follower rod with thumb and forefinger of left hand with hump down and forked end to the right.

Place front end of follower rod into operating rod spring and push to the left, seating the forked end against the follower arm.

Insert U-shaped flange of stock ferrule in its seat in the lower band.

Pivoting about this group, guide chamber and receiver group and press into position in the stock.

Replace trigger housing group with triggerguard in open position into the stock opening.

Press into position, close and latch triggerguard. This completes reassembly.

How the U. S. Rifle M1 Works

Starting with the rifle loaded and cocked the action is as follows: The trigger being pressed, the hammer strikes the firing pin, exploding the cartridge in the chamber. As the bullet passes over the gas port drilled in the under side of the barrel, some of the gas escapes into the cylinder and blasts back against the piston and

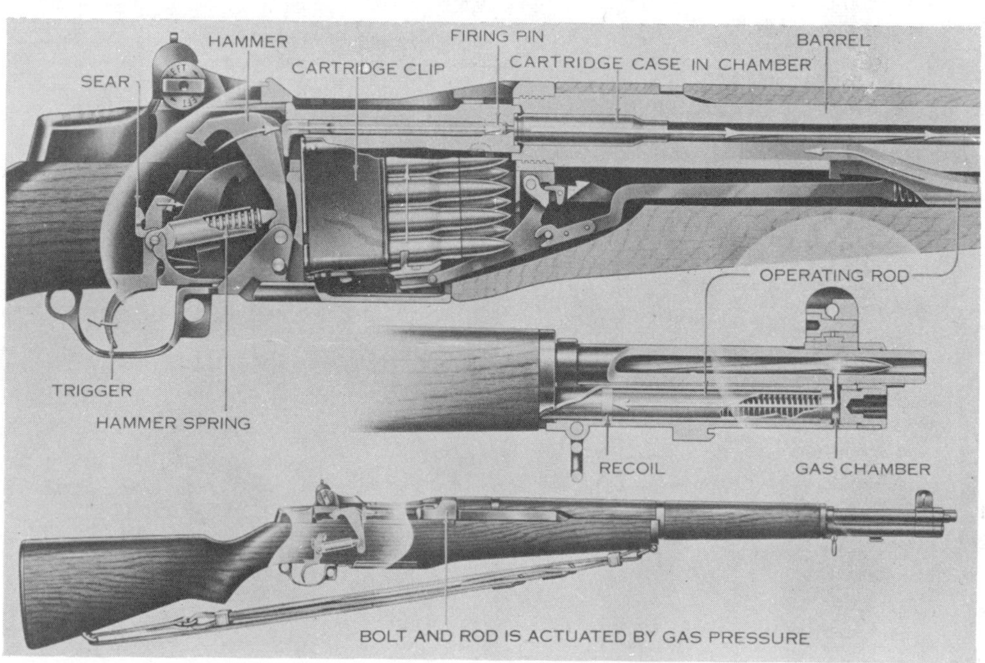

Basic Functioning of the Garand.

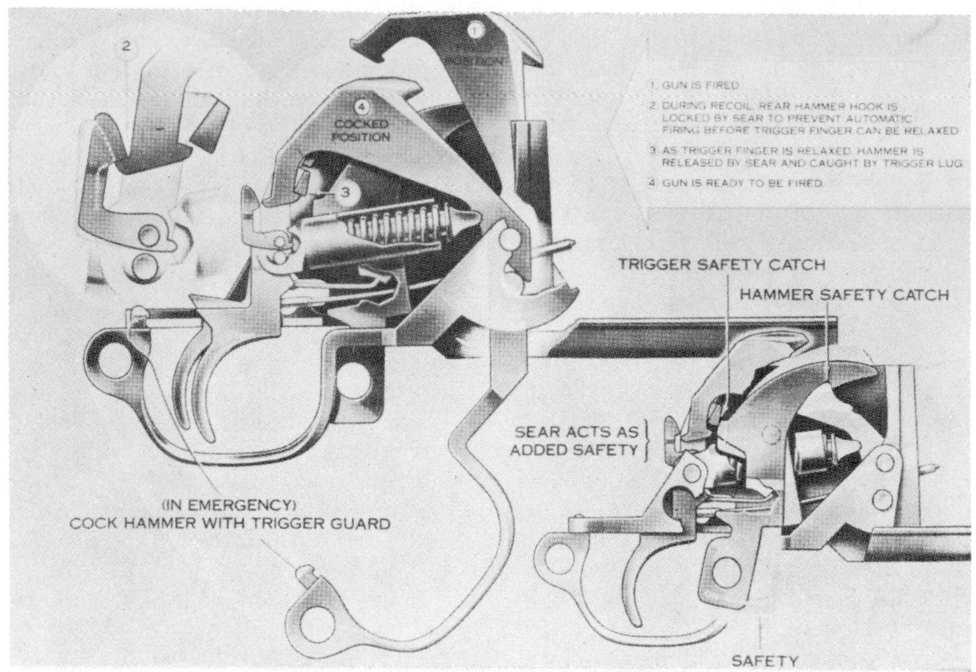

Trigger and Safety Functioning.

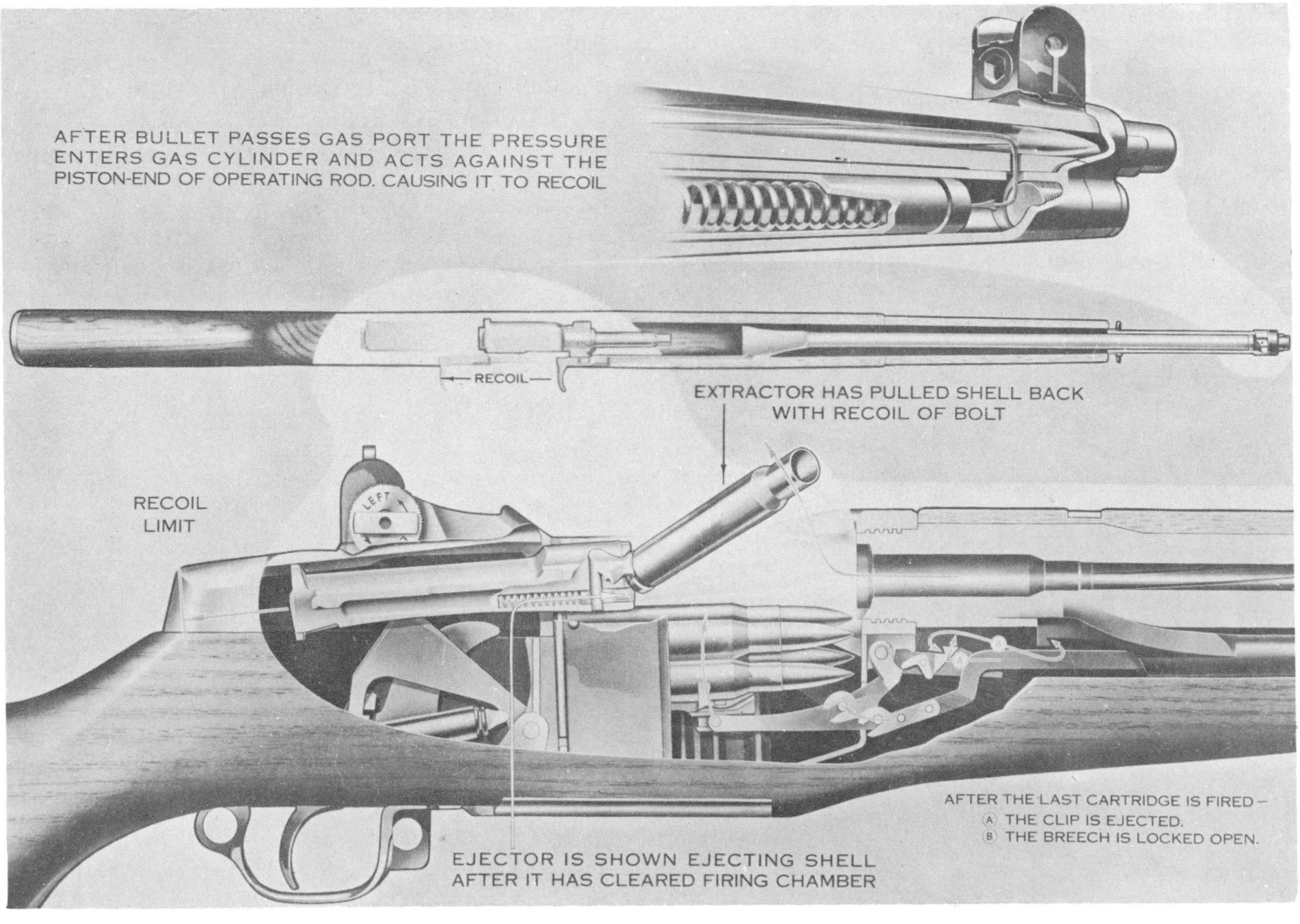

Bolt and Gas Cylinder Functioning.

operating rod with force enough to drive the rod to rear and compress the spring.

During the first 5/16″ of rearward travel the operating lug slides in a straight section of the recess on the operating rod; after which the cam surface of this recess is brought in contact with the operating lug which it cams up, thereby rotating the bolt from right to left to unlock its two lugs from their recesses in the receiver.

During the moment of delayed action, the bullet leaves the barrel and the breech pressure drops to a safe point. The further rotation of the bolt then cams the hammer away from the firing pin and pulls the firing pin back from the bolt. The operating rod continues its backward movement carrying the bolt with it as the lug on the bolt has reached the end of its recess.

During this rearward motion of the bolt, the empty case is withdrawn from the chamber by the extractor positioned in the bolt until it is clear of the breech; at which point the ejector, exerting a steady pressure on the base of the cartridge case, throws it to the right front by the action of its compressed spring.

The rear end of the bolt at this point forces the hammer back, rides over it, and compresses the hammer spring; and finally stops in the rear end of the receiver.

As the bolt has now cleared the clip, the follower spring forces the cartridges up until the topmost one is in line with the bolt.

The operating rod spring comes into play at this point to pull the action forward.

Forward Movement of the Action. As the bolt moves forward, its lower front base strikes the base of the cartridge case and pushes it into the firing chamber. The hammer, pressed by its spring, rides on the bottom of the bolt. While it tends to rise, it is caught and held by the trigger lugs engaging the hammer hook, if trigger pressure has not been released. Otherwise the trigger engages the rear hammer hook until letting go the trigger disengages the sear from the hammer. The hammer then slides into engagement with the trigger lugs.

When the bolt nears its forward position, the extractor engages near the rim of the cartridge and the base of the cartridge forces the ejector into the bolt, compressing the ejector spring.

The rear surface of the cam recess in the operating rod now cams the operating lug down and thereby twists the bolt from left to right until the two lugs lock into their places in the receiver.

The operating rod drives ahead for another 5/16″. The rear end of the straight section of the operating rod recess reaches the operating lug on the bolt, which completes the forward movement and leaves the rifle ready to fire when the trigger is pressed.

This cycle continues as long as there are cartridges in the magazine and the trigger is squeezed.

Care of the M1 Rifle

The rifle must be kept clean and properly lubricated. Failure to do so may result in stoppages at a critical moment. The rifle should be inspected daily.

To Clean the Bore. A clean patch saturated with bore cleaner should be run through the bore a number of times. Plain water, hot or cold may be used if bore cleaner is lacking. While the bore is still wet, your metal brush should be run through several times to loosen up any material which has not been dissolved by the water. Dry patches should then be pushed through the bore until thoroughly dry. The bore should then be coated with light issue gun oil. Also use the chamber cleaning tool to give the chamber the same attention. Remember that primer fouling in the bore contains a salt which rusts the steel.

To Clean Gas Cylinder. The carbon forming in the gas cylinder varies in amount in different weapons. When the deposit is heavy, the rifle is sluggish in action and may fail to feed. The carbon must be scraped from the exposed surface of the front of the cylinder and the gas cylinder plug and piston head after extensive firing. A knife or similar sharp bladed instrument should be used for this scraping process.

Gas cylinder plugs and grooves in the gas cylinder should be cleaned so they will feed correctly in the plug.

The gas cylinder lock should be removed, and the lock screw inserted in the cylinder far enough to break loose any carbon. Inside the cylinder must be thoroughly wiped clean and oiled at the conclusion of any extensive firing.

When firing is expected to be resumed the next day, tilt the muzzle down and place a few drops of oil into the cylinder between the piston and the walls of the cylinder. Then operate the rod by hand a few times to distribute the oil thoroughly.

Wipe the outside of the gas cylinder and the operating rod and then oil lightly. Should no firing be expected for a week or two, remove the rod and gas cylinder lock screw (or plug) so that the cylinder is open at both ends. Then clean cylinder with rod and patches exactly as the bore of the rifle is cleaned.

Hold the weapon so that no water gets into the gas port. Do not remove the gas cylinder for cleaning.

Piston head and rod should be cleaned with cleaner or with water and dried thoroughly, while the rod and cylinder should be oiled before assembling. Any carbon present should be removed. Do not use abrasive cloth if it is possible to avoid doing so; and should it be used, take proper care that the corners of the plug or lock screw and piston head are not rounded.

Attention to Other Parts of Rifles. Graphite cup grease is used for lubricating bolt lugs, bolt guides, bolt cocking cams, compensating spring, contact surfaces of barrel and operating rod, operating rod cams and springs, and operating rod groove in the receiver.

All other metal parts should be cleaned and covered with a uniform light coat of oil.

Wooden parts must be treated with light coat of raw linseed oil about once a month.

The leather sling should be washed, dried with a clean rag, and lightly oiled with neatsfoot oil while it is still damp, whenever the sling shows signs of stiffening or drying. Rust should be removed from the metal parts with a piece of soft wood and oil, never with abrasive. Screw heads must be kept clean to prevent rusting.

Be careful not to use too much oil as any heavy coat will collect dirt and interfere with operation.

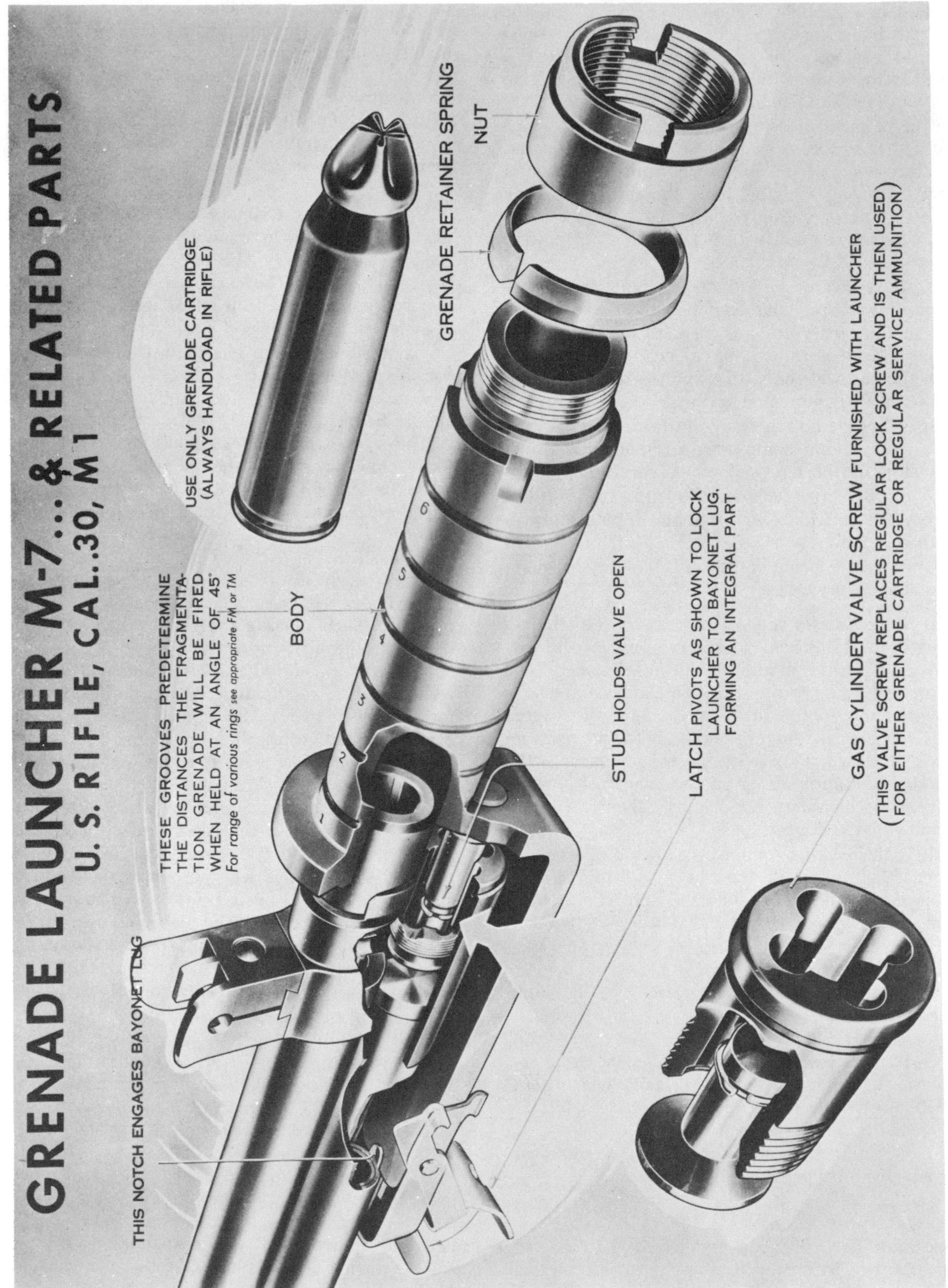

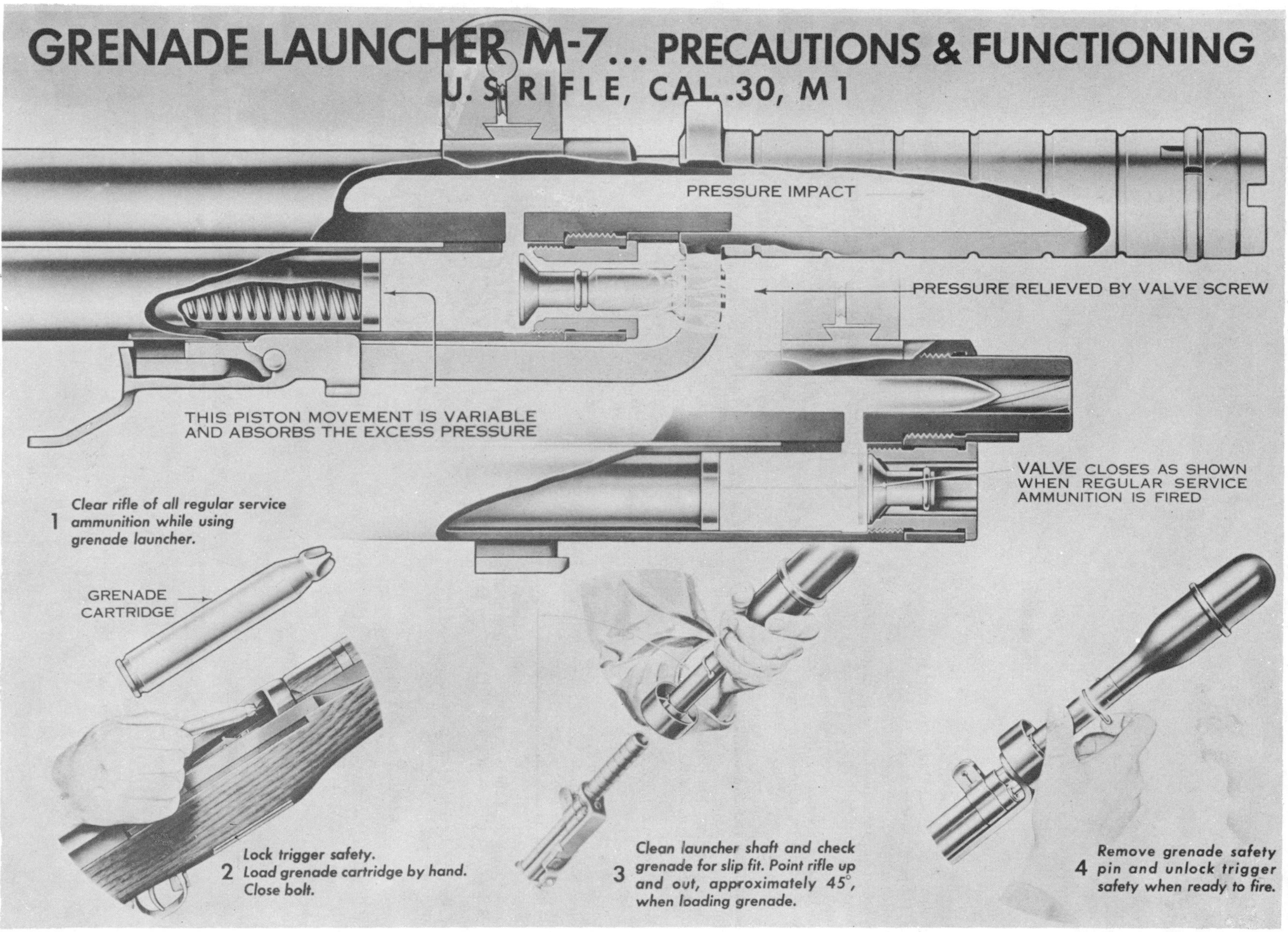
GRENADE LAUNCHER M-7... PRECAUTIONS & FUNCTIONING
U. S. RIFLE, CAL .30, M1
PRESSURE IMPACT
PRESSURE RELIEVED BY VALVE SCREW
THIS PISTON MOVEMENT IS VARIABLE AND ABSORBS THE EXCESS PRESSURE
VALVE CLOSES AS SHOWN WHEN REGULAR SERVICE AMMUNITION IS FIRED
1 Clear rifle of all regular service ammunition while using grenade launcher.
GRENADE CARTRIDGE
2 Lock trigger safety. Load grenade cartridge by hand. Close bolt.
3 Clean launcher shaft and check grenade for slip fit. Point rifle up and out, approximately 45°, when loading grenade.
4 Remove grenade safety pin and unlock trigger safety when ready to fire.

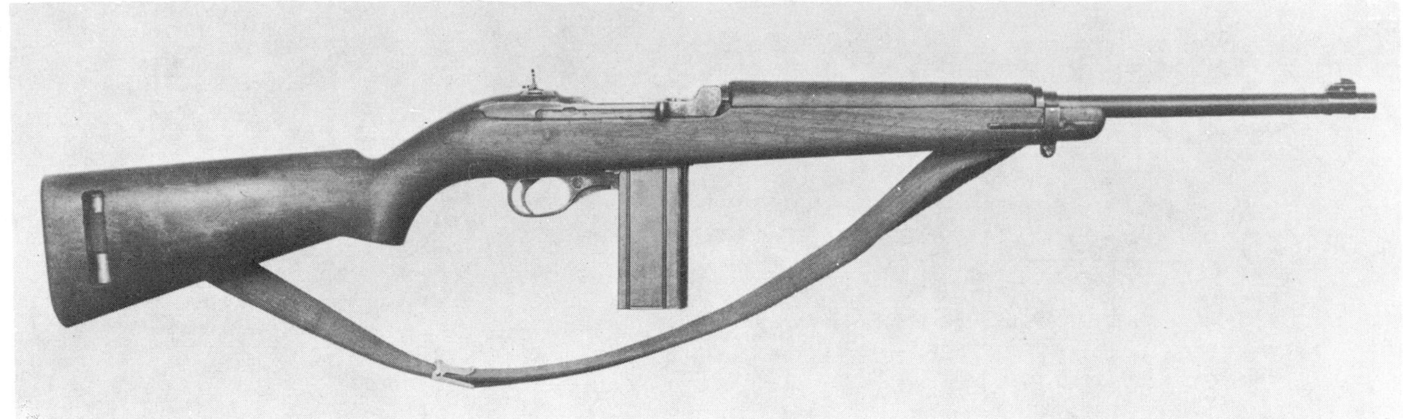

U. S. Carbine Cal. .30 M1.

Magazine: Box type, detachable, capacity 15 rounds. Positioned directly under receiver.
Muzzle Velocity: 1900 feet per second.
Weight of Bullet: 110 grains, lead with metal jacket.
Striking Energy: About 900 foot pounds.
Barrel Length: 18″.
Overall Length of Carbine: 35.58″.
Weight: About 5½ lbs. with sling strap, oiler, and empty magazine.
Sights: Blade front protected by wings; L-type rear with apertures set for 100 and 300 yards on first models. Ramp sight with adjustable windage is now supplied with this weapon.
Accurate Range: About 300 yards.
Maximum Range: About 2,000 yards.
Carbine Operated By: Gas. As bullet passes a small hole in the barrel, gas is drawn into a gas cylinder below the barrel. This expands and drives back a piston which operates the action.
Locked: By rotating bolt as in Garand rifle.
Type of Fire: Single shot only on M1 and M1A1. Pressing the trigger fires the cartridge, ejects the empty case, loads in a new cartridge and leaves the weapon cocked and ready for next pull of trigger. The M2 modification adds a selector and other parts to make carbine capable of automatic fire.
Magazine Release Catch: Button on right side to rear of magazine housing.
Position of Bolt When last Shot is Fired: Closed.
Safety: Cross lock type forward of trigger.

Loading and Firing

Load magazine exactly as for automatic pistol with 15 cartridges.

Thrust up into position in the trigger housing until it locks.

Pull back handle of operating slide on right side of gun as far as it will go, opening the action and allowing a cartridge to rise in the magazine in the path of the bolt, and cocking the weapon and compressing the return spring.

Remove hand and permit operating slide to go forward, loading the firing chamber. With heel of hand push operating slide handle forward to be sure it is fully locked. The weapon is now ready to fire.

Push the button safety in the front end of the trigger-guard all the way through to the right. This is the safe position. Pushing the button through to the left side as far as it will go releases the safety.

How the Carbine Works

Starting with the gun loaded and cocked, the action is as follows: The trigger being pressed, the hammer is released to strike the firing pin and discharge the cartridge. As the bullet passes down the barrel, a minute quantity of gas behind it flows down through a very fine hole bored in the under side of the barrel and escapes into a sealed cylinder where it expands against the head of the piston-like operating slide. This operating slide moves back a short distance until a cam recess engages

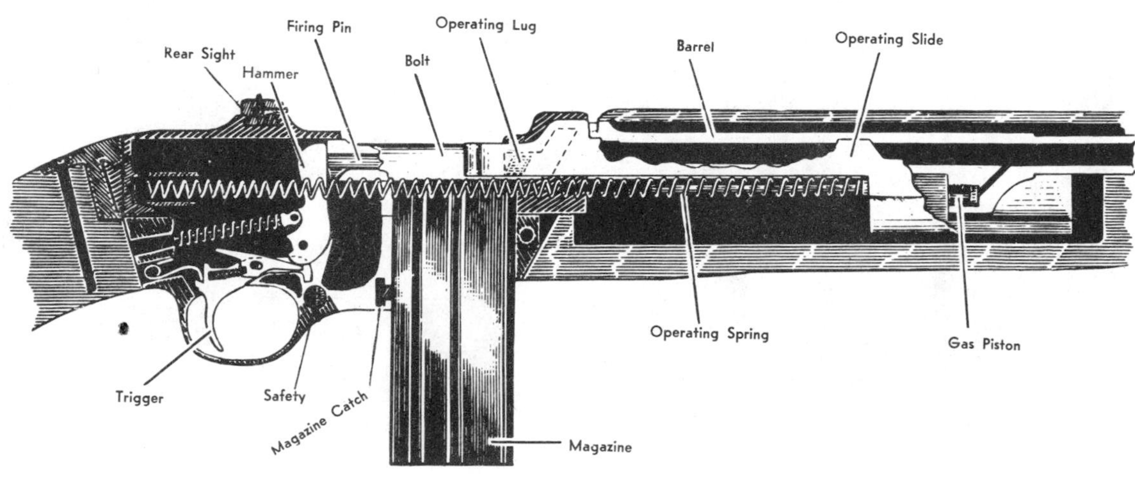

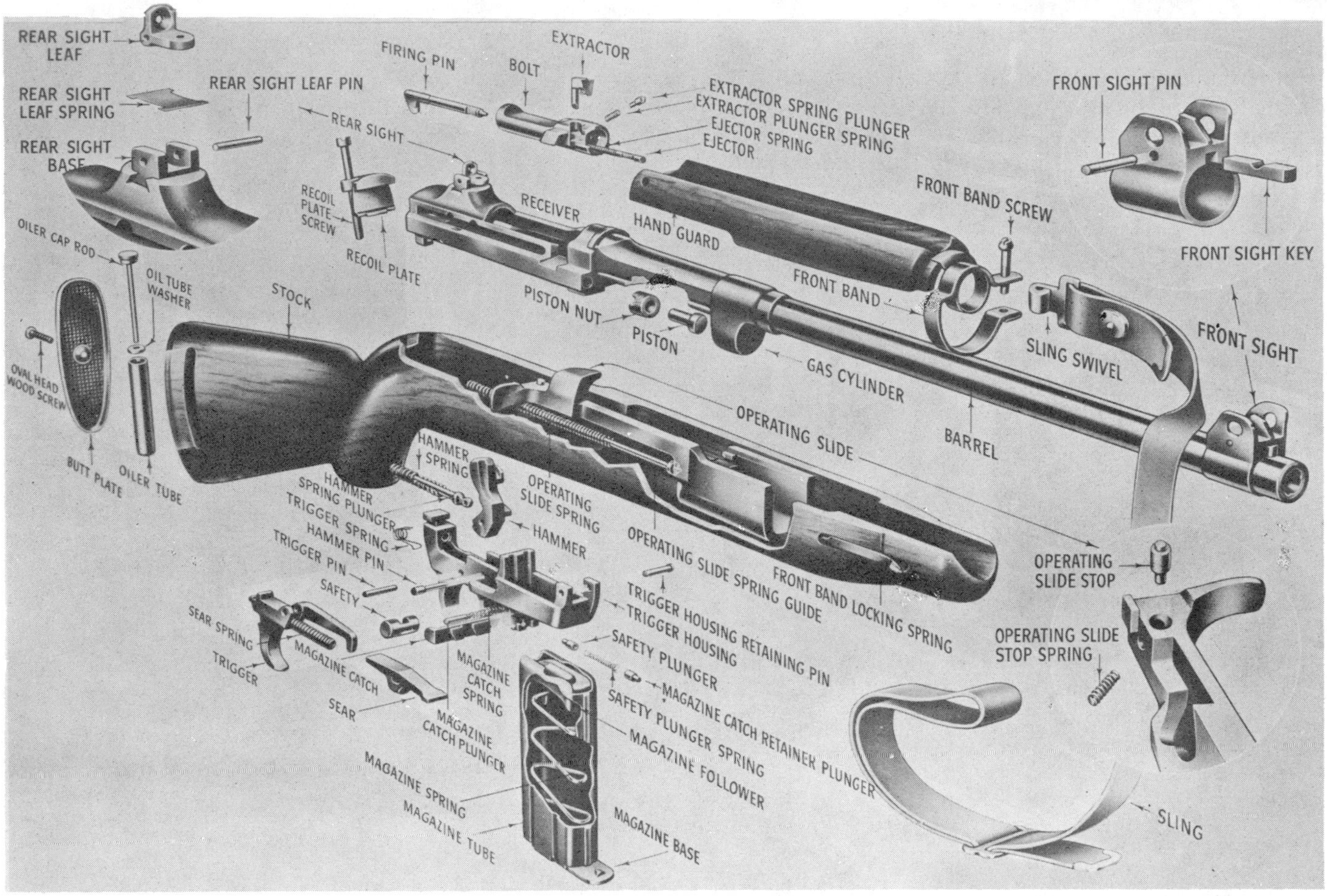

Parts of the M1 Carbine.

an operating lug on the bolt. During this time the bullet has had sufficient time to leave the barrel and it is safe for the action to open. The extractor fastened in the bolt draws the empty cartridge back to strike the spring-actuated ejector which hurls it out to the right front of the weapon. The bolt is rotated out of its locking recess, simultaneously turning the hammer away from the rear of the firing pin and forcing the firing pin point to draw back inside the bolt. This compresses the hammer spring. The rearward motion of operating slide is completed when rear end of its inertia block strikes against forward end of receiver. Bolt stops when it reaches the end of bolt hole in rear receiver. Boltway is now clear permitting the next round to rise in the magazine in line with the bolt. During this motion the powerful operating slide spring has been compressed. It now drives the bolt forward loading the chamber. The cam recess in the operating slide again comes into play. Pressing against the bolt operating lug, it rotates it from left to right into its locking recess.

Forward movement of operating slide continues until the rear of its inertia block lodges against the piston in the cylinder. This action continues each time the trigger is squeezed until the last cartridge has been fired.

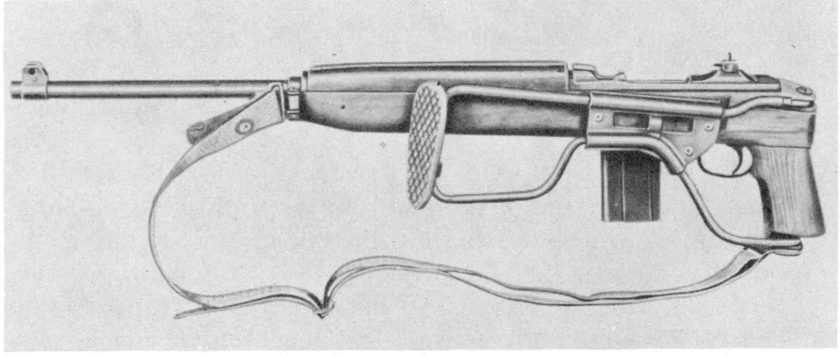

U. S. Carbine Caliber .30 M1A1.

This is a special model designed for use by paratroopers. It is in every way identical with the regular carbine M1 except in the detail of its folding stock.

As the picture shows quite clearly, a separate pistol grip is attached to the stock. To this is hinged a metal folding skeleton stock with necessary sling attachment.

Length of this weapon when the stock is folded over for carrying is 25.51 inches. When the stock is extended the length is practically the same as that of M1—about 35.63 inches.

Weight is 6.19 pounds.

Field Stripping

Push the magazine catch to the left (it is positioned just in front of the triggerguard on the right side), and withdraw magazine from below.

Draw back bolt to examine chamber and make sure that the weapon is unloaded.

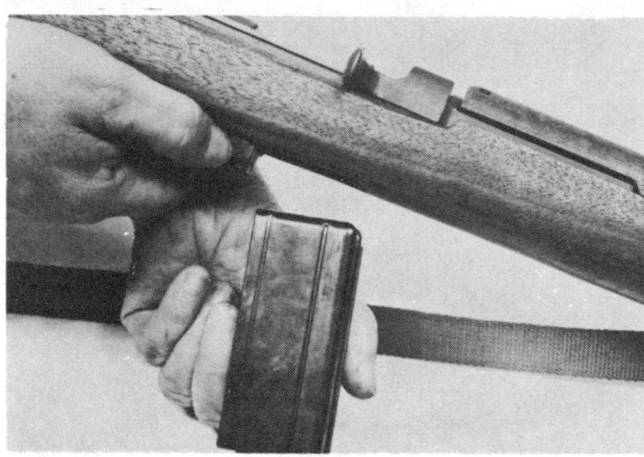

At the end of the wooden fore-end is a sling swivel. Push this back against the fore-end and loosen it by unscrewing the front band screw. A cartridge may be used as a screwdriver.

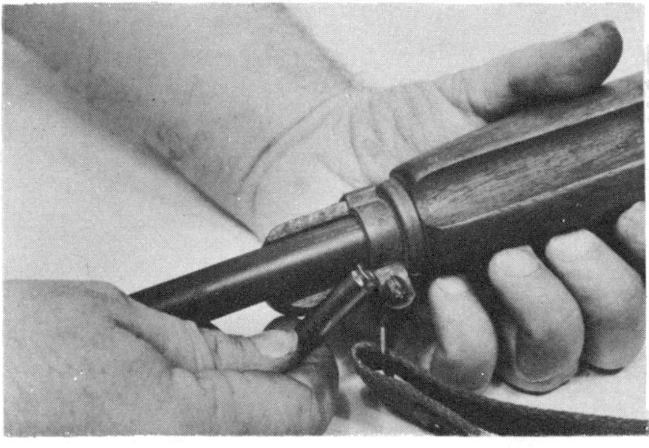

Press the front end of the lock spring toward the rear and slip the front band forward over its locking spring; it will not slip off the barrel unless the front sight is removed.

Now slide the wooden handguard on top of the barrel forward until its liner disengages from the undercut in the forward face of the receiver; it can then be lifted from the barrel.

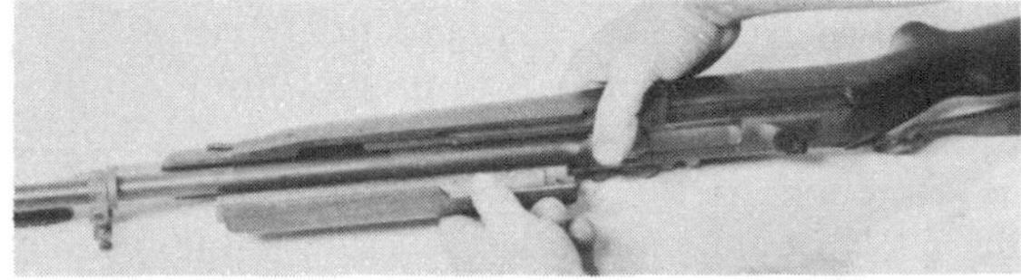

Holding the stock firmly with the right hand, grasp the barrel near the front end with the left hand and raise it until the lug at the rear of the receiver clears the retaining notch on the face of the recoil plate (the

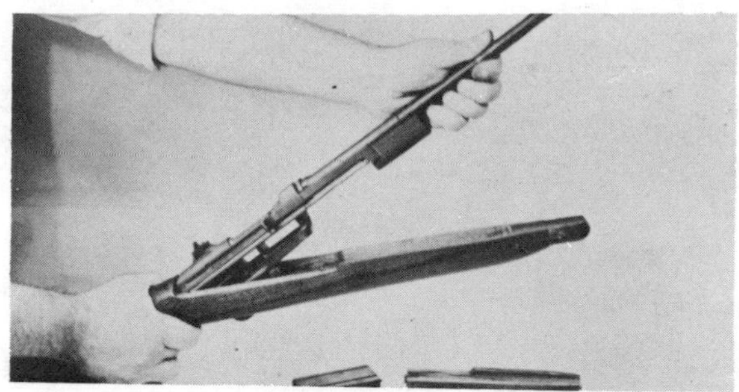

plate just above the pistol grip). The barrel and receiver can now be pulled forward and lifted out of the stock; carrying the trigger housing group with them.

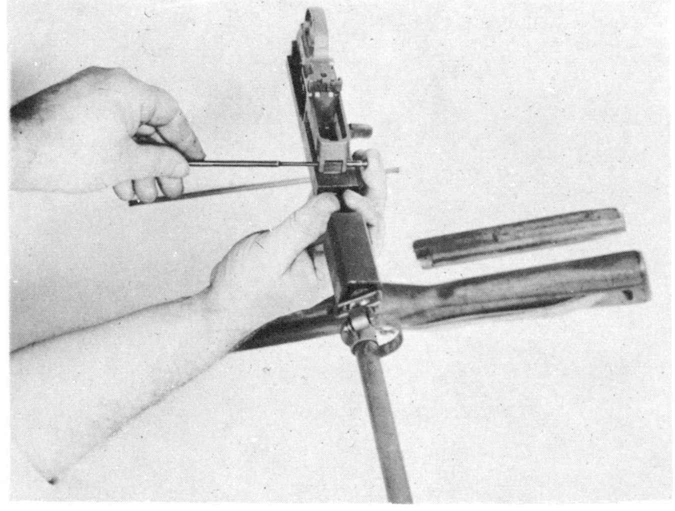

At forward end of triggerguard is the trigger housing retaining pin. Push it out until it clears the lug in the receiver.

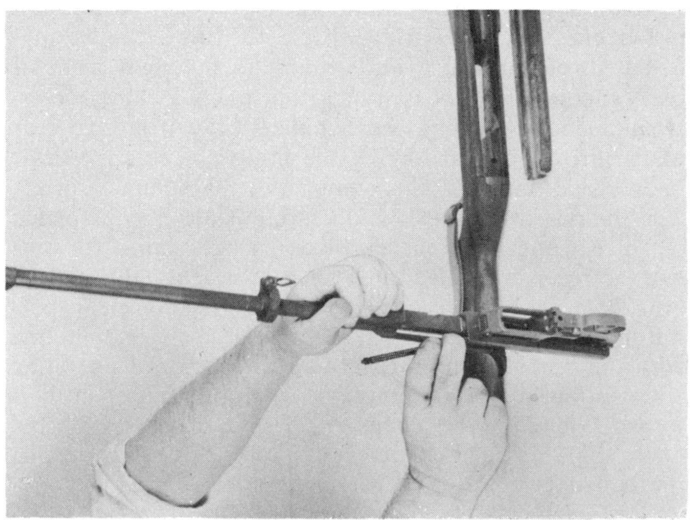

Pull back the operating slide spring guide a short distance until it is free of the operating slide. Pulling it forward and to the right permits it and its spring to be withdrawn.

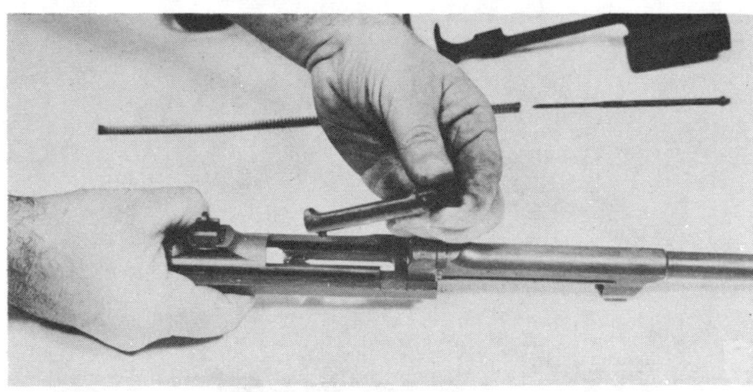

Take hold of the bolt and slide it to the rear until its face is behind the locking shoulder in the receiver. Twist the bolt from right to left, lift it to an angle of 45° and turn it bottom up. It may now be drawn forward and up out of the receiver.

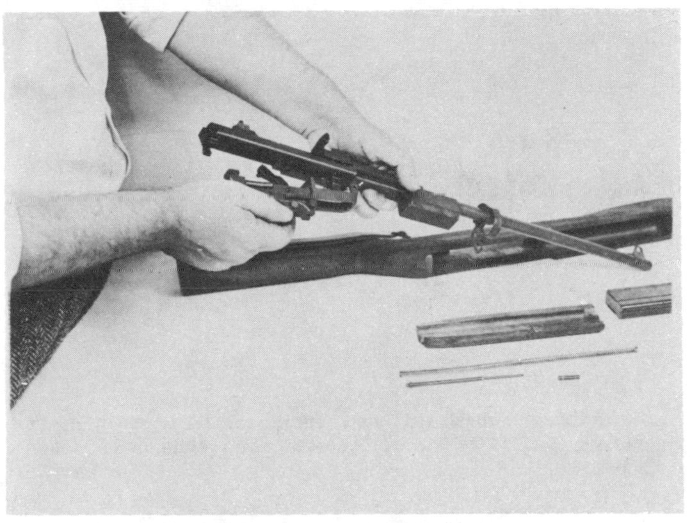

Pull the housing forward until it clears the grooves in the receiver, when it may be lifted out.

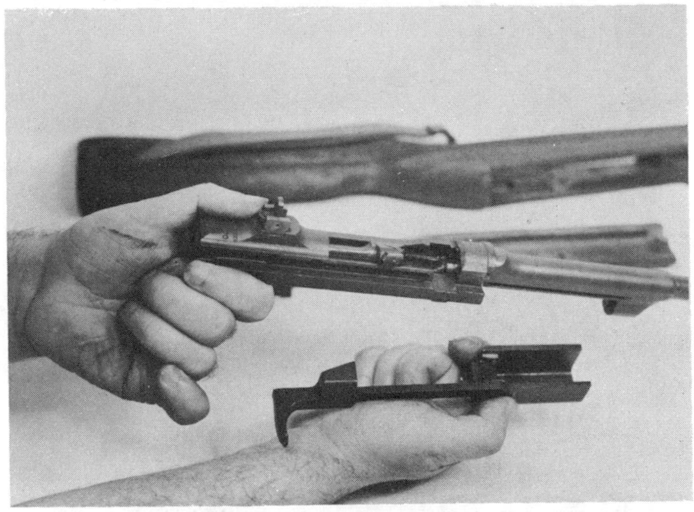

Pull the operating slide back until the guide lug at bottom of handle end alines with dismounting cut in receiver. Lift handle up and to right until the guide lug clears the retaining cut in receiver and also disengages from the bolt lug. Then push slide forward until the left barrel guide lip alines with clearance cut on bottom of left barrel guide groove. Rotating the slide body so as to free the left guide lip of the slide from its barrel guide groove will permit removing the slide from barrel.

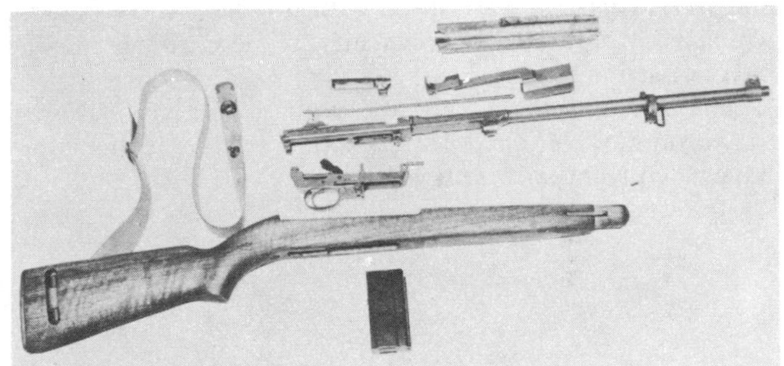

This completes field stripping. To assemble, reverse the procedure.

Caliber .30 M2 Carbine

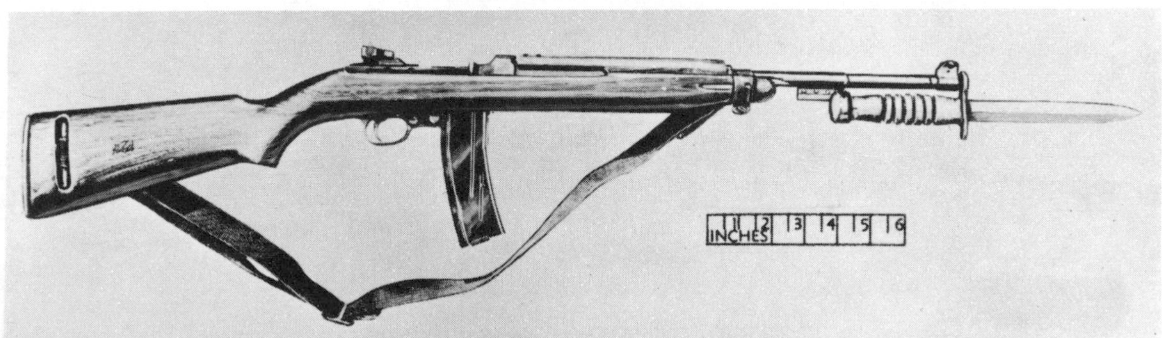

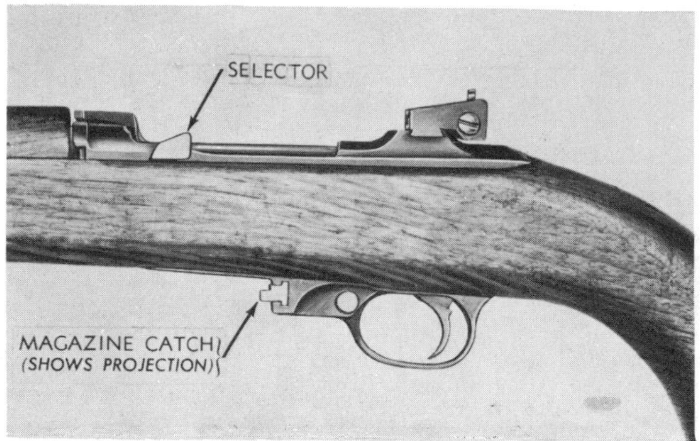

Identifying Points of the M2 Carbine.

Following are characteristics of the M2 carbine which differ from those of M1: Weight w/loaded 30-round magazine: 6.60 lbs. Cyclic rate of fire: 750-775 r.p.m.

The M2 carbine is the selective fire version of the M1. Parts which differ from those of the M1 carbine are as follows: hammer, sear, trigger housing, operating slide, magazine catch, and stock. Added parts are as follows: disconnector group, disconnector lever assembly, and selector group. All M2 and M3 carbines and many M1 and M1A1 carbines are fitted with a front band assembly which incorporates a bayonet lug. These carbines use the bayonet-knife M4.

The M3 carbine is an M2 with a receiver designed to accommodate an infrared sniperscope. It does not have a conventional rear sight.

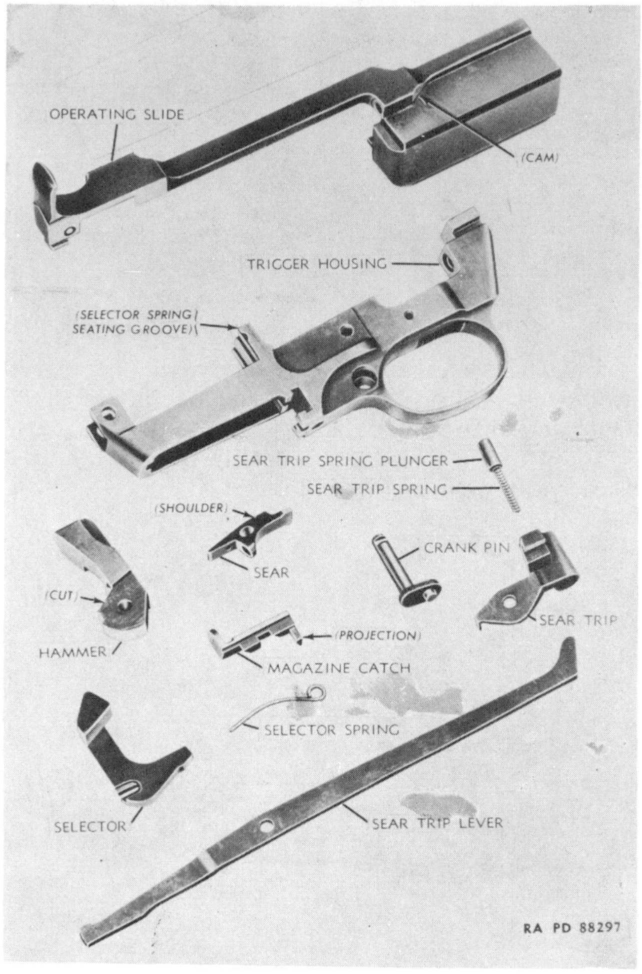

Modified, redesigned, and additional parts used in converting the M1 to the M2. Arrows show changes to standard parts.

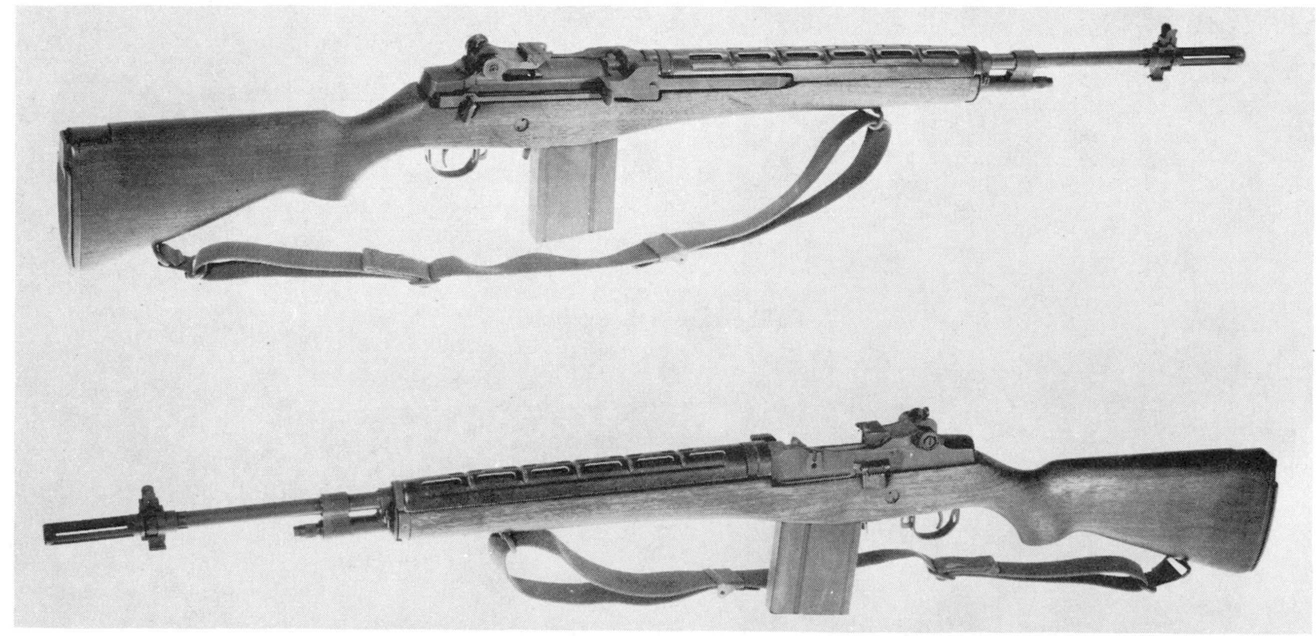

7.62mm Rifle M14, production version.

Caliber: 7.62mm NATO.
Weight of basic rifle (with empty magazine, less sling): 8.7 lb.
Weight of rifle, ready to fire (fully loaded with sling): 10.0 lb.
Length of rifle: With flash suppressor: 44.14 in.
With bayonet-knife: 50.71 in.
Length of barrel: 22.0 in.
Rifling: Four grooves, right-hand twist, 1 turn in 12.0 in.
Sight radius (at 100 yd.): 26.75 in.
Type of mechanism: Rotating bolt.
System of operation: Gas-operated (cut off and expansion system) selective fire.
Trigger pull: Maximum: 7.5 lb.
Minimum: 5.5 lb.
Loading device: 5-round charger.
Feed device: 20-rd detachable, staggered row box magazine.
Cyclic rate: 750 r.p.m.
Cooling: Air.
Muzzle velocity: 2800 f.p.s.
Range, maximum: 3500 yd.
Chamber pressure, maximum: 50,000 p.s.i.
Ammunition types: Ball, AP, tracer.
Designation of ball cartridge: Caliber 7.62mm M59.
Sights: Front: Blade with protecting ears.
Rear: Aperture with adjustment for windage and elevation.

The M14 is the current standard rifle of the United States Army. It is in production at Harrington and Richardson Arms Co., Thompson Products, and at the New Haven (Winchester) plant of the Winchester-Western Arms Division of Olin Mathieson Corp. It also is in limited production at Springfield Armory. As stated previously, the M14 will replace the M1 rifle, M3A1 submachine gun, M2 carbine, and the Browning automatic rifle (BAR). A companion piece to the M14—the M15, a heavier barreled weapon—was originally intended to replace the BAR as the squad automatic weapon, but has since been dropped from the program. The M14 is capable of automatic as well as semi-automatic fire, and a certain proportion will be fitted with bipods to serve as squad automatic weapons.

The model designation of the M14 when it was in experimental status was T44E4. The M14 is an evolution of the M1 rifle; in the design of the M14 many of the shortcomings of the M1 have been eradicated. The basic action of the M1 remains, but the troublesome eight-round en bloc clip has gone. The hanging of the gas cylinder on the end of the M1 rifle's barrel gave some accuracy difficulties; these have been overcome, in the M14, by moving the gas port and gas cylinder back about eight inches from the muzzle. The gas cutoff and expansion system used on the M14 lends itself to better accuracy because its action is not as abrupt as that of the M1. Various other changes have been made to give the Army a basically better weapon than the M1.

There has been much fuss in the public press recently about various foreign countries having rifles in service superior to those of the United States. One very important factor is overlooked in much of this comment: the fact that at the conclusion of World War II the United States was the only power whose army was completely equipped with semi-automatic rifles. There was no urgent need for the United States to go into a crash program on rifles since we had in service the best rifle in the world at the time. The British, by contrast, were equipped with a bolt action design that traced its ancestry back to 1889; and the Soviets were mainly equipped with the bolt action Mosin Nagant which originated, in its basic form, in 1891. It was only to be expected that these and other countries, being considerably behind the United States in rifles, would push rifle development very hard. It is worthy of note, too, that United States troops equipped with semi-automatic M1's met communist troops equipped with bolt action rifles in Korea five years after World War II. Had the Soviets possessed their new small arms in adequate quantity at that time, they would surely have been delighted to field-test them on American targets in Korea. Each nation, at the conclusion of a major conflict, will spend most of its usually limited research and development money on those items proved most seriously in need of replacement. Our experiences in both World War II and Korea did not indicate that the rifle should have the highest priority for replacement. One can't give every item highest priority!

How to Load and Fire the M14

Application of Safety. Place the safety in the SAFE position by cocking the hammer and snapping the safety rearward.

Loading of Rifle. Place the safety in the SAFE position.

Insert a loaded magazine into the magazine well, front end leading, until the front catch snaps into engagement; then pull backward and upward until the magazine latch snaps into position.

Pull the operating rod handle to its rearmost position and release; this allows the top round to rise and the bolt to move forward, thus stripping and chambering a round from the magazine.

Semi-automatic Fire with Selector Lock. With the selector lock in the rifle, it cannot be fired automatically. Load the rifle and release the safety. The rifle will now fire one round upon each pull of the trigger.

Semi-automatic Fire with Selector. Press in and turn the selector until it snaps into position with its blank face to the rear and its projection downward. The connector assembly is inoperative in this position since the connector is held forward and out of engagement with the operating rod.

Load the rifle and release the safety. The rifle will now fire one round upon each pull of the trigger.

Full Automatic Fire with Selector. Press in and turn the selector until it snaps into position with the face marked "A" to the rear and the projection upward. This rotation of the eccentric selector shaft moves the sear release to the rear into contact with the sear and moves the connector assembly rearward into contact with the operating rod.

Load the rifle and release the safety.

Pull and hold the trigger. The rifle will fire automatically as long as the trigger is squeezed and there is ammunition in the magazine. To cease firing, release the trigger.

Bolt Lock. When the last round of ammunition is fired, the magazine follower engages the bolt lock and raises it into the path of the retracted bolt; this holds the bolt in the open position.

Unloading of Rifle. Place the safety in the SAFE position.

Grasp the magazine, placing the thumb on the magazine latch, and squeeze the latch. Push the magazine forward and downward to disengage it from the front catch and remove the magazine from the magazine well.

Pull the operating handle rearward to extract and eject a chambered round, and to inspect the chamber. The rifle is now clear.

Gas Shutoff Valve. For semi-automatic and full automatic firing, turn the valve to the open position by pressing in and rotating. The valve is open when the slot in the head of the valve spindle is perpendicular to the barrel. The shutoff valve in the gas cylinder opens and closes the port in the cylinder between the barrel and the gas piston.

Disassembly of the M14

General Disassembly (Field Stripping). Unload the rifle, remove the magazine, and place the safety in the SAFE position.

Turn the rifle upside down with the muzzle pointing to the left.

Insert the nose of a cartridge into the hole in the triggerguard and pry upward to unlatch the triggerguard.

Swing the triggerguard upward and lift the trigger group from the stock.

Separate the stock from the rifle by cradling the receiver firmly in one hand and by striking upward sharply on the stock butt with the palm of the other hand.

Turn the barrel and receiver group on its side with the connector assembly upward. Press in and turn the selector until the face marked "A" is toward the rear sight knob and the projection forward (this step applies to rifles modified for selective firing). Press forward on the connector with the right thumb until the forward end can be lifted off the connector lock. Rotate the connector clockwise, until the slot at the rear end is aligned with the elongated stud on the rear release. Lower slightly the front end of the connector and lift it from the sear release. **Note:** The connector assembly is a semipermanent assembly and it should not be disassembled.

With the barrel and receiver group upside down, pull forward on the operating rod spring, relieving pressure on the connector lock. Pull the lock outward, disconnect the operating rod spring guide, and remove the spring guide and spring. Turn the barrel and receiver group right side up.

Retract the operating rod until the key on its lower surface coincides with the dismount notch in the receiver. Lift the operating rod free and pull to the rear, disengaging it from the operating rod guide.

Grasp the bolt group by the roller and, while sliding it forward, lift it upward and outward to the right front with a slight rotating motion. The rifle is now field stripped, and basic assemblies such as the bolt and the trigger groups may be disassembled, if required.

Bolt Group. With the bolt in the left hand and the thumb over the ejector, insert the blade of a screwdriver between the extractor and the lower cartridge seat flange. Pry the extractor upward to unseat it. The ejector will snap out against the thumb. Lift out the ejector assembly, and the extractor plunger and spring. Remove the firing pin from the rear of the bolt. **Note:** No attempt should be made to disassemble the roller from the bolt stud.

Barrel and Receiver Group. Disassemble the rear sight as follows: Run the aperture all the way down and record the reading for use in reassembling the sight. Hold the elevating knob and unscrew the nut in the center of the windage knob. Withdraw the elevating knob. Unscrew and remove the windage knob. Pull the aperture up about one-half inch. Place the thumb under the aperture and push upward and forward to remove the aperture, cover, and base. Separate the rear sight cover from the rear sight base.

Loosen the setscrew in the base of the front sight lug on the flash suppressor. Unscrew the flash suppressor nut and slide the flash suppressor forward off the barrel.

Loosen and remove the gas plug, using the gas cylinder plug wrench. Tilt the muzzle down and remove the gas piston from the gas cylinder. Unscrew the gas cylinder lock and slide the lock and the gas cylinder off the barrel.

Slip the front band off the barrel. Push the handguard forward and lift it from the barrel.

Trigger Group. To disassemble the trigger group, close and latch the triggerguard. Squeeze the trigger, allowing the hammer to go forward. Hold the trigger housing group with the first finger of the right hand on the trigger and the thumb against the sear. Place the front of the trigger housing against a firm surface. Squeeze the trigger with the finger and push forward on the sear with the thumb. At the same time, using the tip of a cartridge, push out the trigger pin from left to right. Slowly release the pressure with the finger and thumb; this allows the hammer spring to expand.

Lift out the trigger assembly. Remove and separate the hammer spring plunger, hammer spring, and the hammer spring housing.

Push out the hammer pin from left to right, using the tip of a cartridge. Move the hammer slightly to the rear and lift out.

Unlatch the triggerguard. Push out the stud of the safety from its hole. Remove the safety and safety spring. Slide the triggerguard to the rear until the wings of the triggerguard are aligned with the safety stud hole. Rotate the triggerguard to the right and upward until the hammer stop clears the base of the housing. Remove the triggerguard.

Drive out the magazine latch spring pin with a suitable drift to remove the semipermanently assembled magazine latch and spring.

To assemble the rifle, reverse the disassembly procedure. However, the following instructions are provided to facilitate and to insure satisfactory assembly:

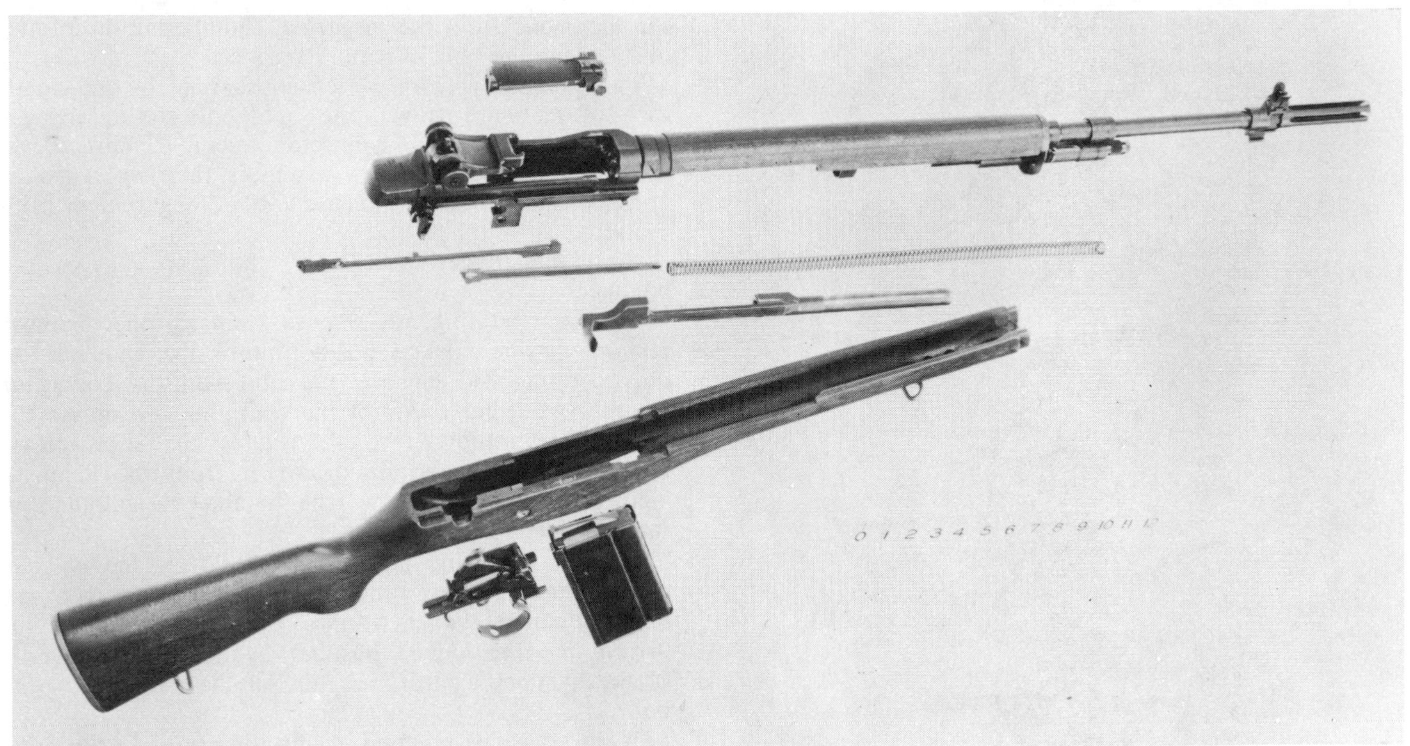

M14 Rifle Field Stripped.

Handguard. To assemble the handguard, when the gas cylinder and related components are in place, position the front end of the guard in the front band and snap the rear band of the handguard assembly into the barrel grooves. **Note:** The handguard need not be reassembled prior to assembly of the gas cylinder and related components.

Trigger Group. To assemble the trigger group to the stock and receiver, cock the hammer and swing the triggerguard to the open position. Insert the assembly into the receiver, and close the triggerguard.

Gas System. To assemble the gas system, replace front band, gas cylinder, and gas cylinder lock. Tighten the lock by hand to its full assembled position and then "back off" until the loop is alined with the gas cylinder. Assemble the piston and the gas cylinder plug.

Special Note on the M14 Rifle

Although the M14 is a selective-fire weapon, most weapons in the hands of troops will have their selectors locked in the semi-automatic position. When desired, these weapons can be made to deliver selective fire by the removal of the selector lock. This feature has been added to the weapon since combat experience with the M2 carbine and troop tests with earlier prototypes of the M14 indicate that troops keep selective fire weapons set on full automatic as a matter of course. This limits the effectiveness of the weapon at long ranges, since it is effective in off-hand automatic fire only at ranges up to about 100 yards. It also results in a great expenditure of ammunition with little in the way of results to show for this expenditure. Those weapons equipped with bipods for use as squad automatic weapons will not have their selectors locked, and will be capable of selective fire at all times. Production M14's have aluminum butt plates with shoulder support and plastic hand guards.

How the M14 Works

Operational System. Operational power is derived from a gas cutoff and expansion system. In this system, gas is bled from the barrel through a port in its underside which registers with a port in the rear loop of the gas cylinder and a port in the wall of the hollow gas piston. Propellent gases released by firing enter these ports and are trapped in the hollow chambers in the gas piston and gas cylinder. The piston, in contact with the operating rod, is driven rearward a complete stroke (one and one-half inches). The resultant force is of sufficient magnitude to drive the operating rod and the bolt to their rearmost positions, and to compress the operating rod spring. The exhaust port in the bottom of the gas cylinder is uncovered as the gas piston nears the end of its stroke; this allows the expanded gases to escape.

The reaction of the operating rod spring now returns the bolt and operating rod to their original positions.

The gas system functions in the same manner for all firing cycles unless the port in the gas cylinder is closed by the shutoff valve. When the valve is closed, the gas system becomes inoperative, thus necessitating manual operation of the operating rod.

Semi-automatic Fire. During its rearward travel, the operating rod unlocks and carries the bolt assembly rearward; this action extracts and ejects the fired cartridge case and cocks the hammer. Ammunition is lifted

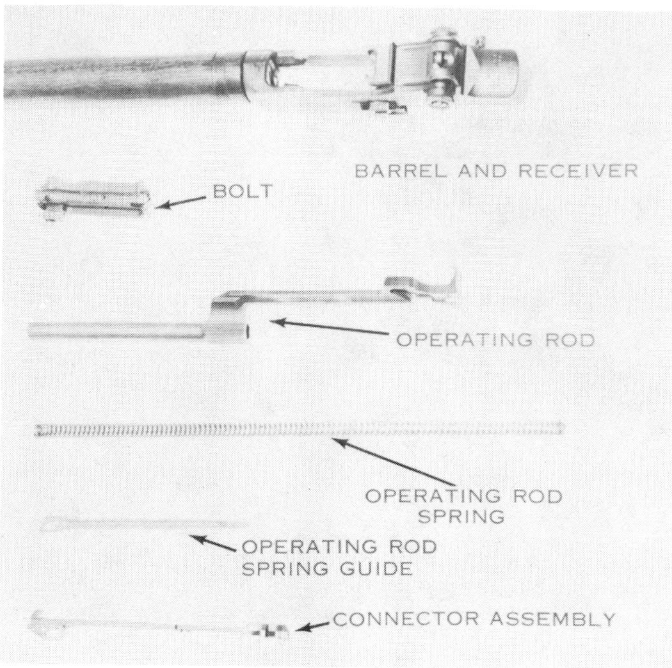

Parts of the M14 Rifle.

into the path of the retracted bolt by action of the magazine spring and follower.

The operating rod moves forward under spring pressure; this carries the bolt assembly forward, stripping the top round from the magazine, chambering the round, and locking the bolt in battery position.

Full Automatic Fire. After approximately one-eighth inch of rearward travel, the operating rod disengages from the hook on the connector assembly. This allows the spring-loaded connector assembly to move rearward and to rotate the sear release out of engagement with the sear.

With the trigger held back, the sear engages the hammer.

As the operating rod moves forward, the hammer remains in the cocked position until the shoulder on the operating rod engages the hook on the connector assembly. Further travel of the operating rod moves the connector assembly forward, rotates the sear release against the sear, and disengages it from the hammer. This disengagement allows the hammer to fall and to fire the chambered cartridge.

Because the firing pin is prevented from moving forward prematurely by the bridge in the receiver, the weapon cannot be fired until the bolt is locked (or driven into the locked position by action of the nose of the hammer against the cam on the rear end of the bolt).

If the trigger is released at any time prior to the firing of the last round, the hammer will be held in the cocked position by the trigger lugs (secondary sear) and automatic actuation of the sear release by the connector assembly will not release the hammer to fire the chambered cartridge.

7.62mm Rifle M14, fitted with bipod for use as a squad automatic weapon.

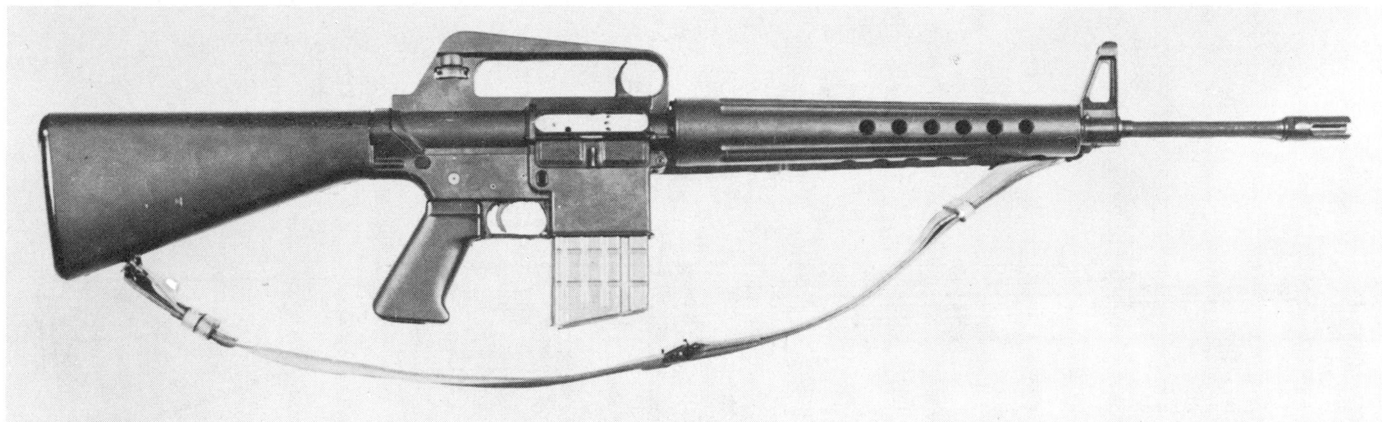

Armalite 7.62mm NATO AR-10 Rifle As Made at Hembrug.

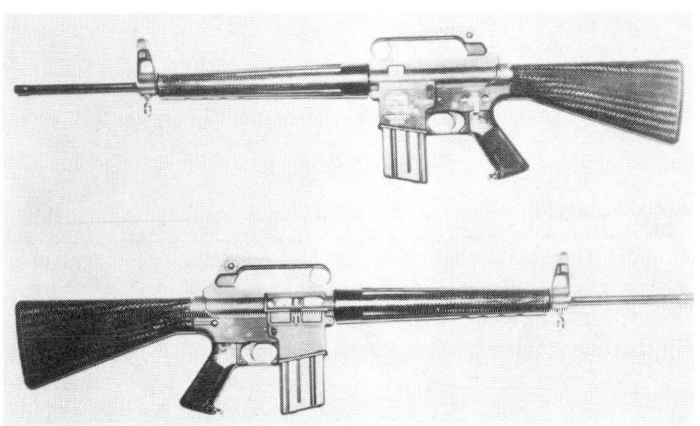

Armalite Caliber .222 AR-15 Rifle.

	AR-10	AR-15
Caliber:	7.62mm NATO.	Cal. .222 Remington or cal. .224 Winchester.

System of operation: Gas, selective fire, for both AR-10 and AR-15.

	AR-10	AR-15
Weight, loaded:	8.4 lb. (approx.).	6 lb. w/20-rd. magazine. 6.12 lb. w/25 rd. magazine.
Length, overall:	41.25 in.	37.5 in.
Barrel length:	21.4 in.	20 in.

Feed device: 20-round, detachable, staggered-row box magazine for both AR-10 and AR-15; 25-round magazine also has been used with AR-15.

Sights: Front: Blade w/protecting ears, for both AR-10 and AR-15.

Rear: Peep, adjustable for elevation, graduated from 200 to 600 yd.

	AR-10	AR-15
Muzzle velocity:	2723 f.p.s.	3300 f.p.s.
Cyclic rate:	700 r.p.m. (approx.).	750 r.p.m.

The AR-10 and AR-15 rifles are developments of the Armalite Division of the Fairchild Engine and Airplane Co. They have recently been tested in quite a few countries, and there is apparently a possibility that some countries may adopt one or the other of the weapons.

Fairchild has done some work for the U. S. Air Force on survival weapons. Presumably, this work aroused the company's interest in the use of lightweight materials in gun construction. The AR-10 and AR-15 make extensive use of aluminum and foamed plastics in their construction.

A late version of the AR-15 has a cocking handle at the rear of the receiver, rather than on top of the receiver as shown in the photo. The cocking handle at the rear of the receiver does not reciprocate with the action. A three-power scope is made for the AR-10, and can be attached to the carrying handle without alteration to the weapon. This scope is graduated for ranges up to 700 meters.

The AR-10 has been produced in quantity at Artillerie Inrichtingen, Hembrug Zaandam, The Netherlands. Although this is a Dutch government arsenal, the weapons were not being produced for the Dutch government. The AR-10 is chambered for the 7.62mm NATO cartridge. The AR-15 is a later version of the AR-10; it is chambered for the cal. .222 or .224 cartridge, and is produced by Colt's Patent Firearms Manufacturing Co. of Hartford, Conn.

How to Load and Fire the AR-10 and AR-15 Rifles

Insert loaded magazine. Pull charging handle all the way back, and release it. Put selective-fire lever on "Safe," "Semi," or "Auto." The weapon will fire when the trigger is pulled (unless set on "Safe"). Upon firing the last round in the magazine, the bolt remains open; then, after inserting a new loaded magazine, pushing the bolt stop lever allows the bolt to close, feeding a new round into the chamber.

Field Stripping of the AR-10

No special tools are required for field stripping and assembling the AR-10. Clear the weapon. With the bolt in forward position, press out rear pin, and open the rifle. Withdraw bolt and bolt carrier assembly from upper receiver. Withdraw firing pin retaining pin. Withdraw

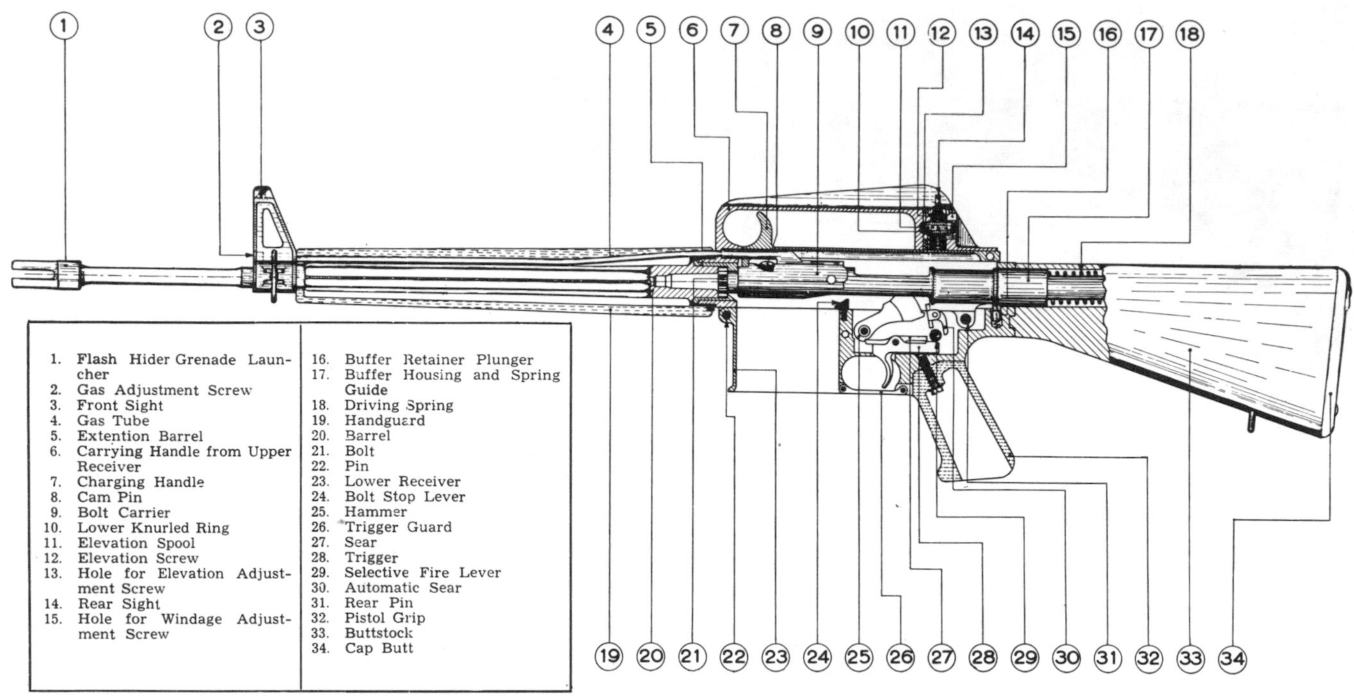

Section View of AR-10 Rifle.

firing pin. Withdraw cam pin. Withdraw bolt from bolt carrier.

Using firing pin to start it, pull out extractor pin, and remove extractor and extractor spring. Spring will remain with extractor.

After cocking the hammer by hand, use bullet point to depress buffer retainer plunger.

Remove buffer assembly and drive spring.

For assembling the weapon, proceed in the reverse order.

Further stripping is unnecessary under normal field conditions. If necessary, the trigger group may be stripped for cleaning without the use of tools. The hammer pin should be removed first, using the firing pin to start it. All pins in the trigger group are spring retained, and may be removed and replaced from either side of the receiver. Hammer and trigger pins are interchangeable. Before closing the weapon, insure that the hammer is in cocked position.

How the AR-10 Works

With the weapon loaded and the selective-fire lever on "Semi," pulling the trigger causes the hammer to strike the firing pin, which detonates the primer.

When the bullet passes beyond the gas port, gas passes through the gas tube and into a chamber formed by the bolt carrier and bolt. At this time, the bolt is in the locked position, acting as a stationary piston. The entering gas pressure causes the bolt carrier to move to the rear. In moving rearward, the bolt carrier rotates the bolt, unlocking it and carrying it rearward. As the bolt assembly travels to the rear, the gas is exhausted through a port in the side of the bolt carrier. The cartridge case is then extracted and ejected in the usual manner.

When the selective-fire lever is on "Auto," the automatic sear holds the hammer in cocked position. Upon locking of the bolt, with the trigger held to the rear, the bolt carrier trips the automatic sear, firing the weapon.

When the selective-fire lever is on "Semi," the sear holds the hammer in cocked position. The hammer is released by pulling the trigger.

The firing pin can strike the primer only when the bolt is completely locked.

Special Note on the AR-10 and AR-15 Rifles

The gas system of these weapons is similar to that of the Swedish Ljungman M42 and the French Model 49 and 49/56 rifles, in that no piston rod is used. The gas blows back directly into the bolt (in the other rifles mentioned, it blows back into the bolt carrier). The bolt system, itself, appears to be unique. The use of a fixed carrying handle which acts as a rear sight base and guard is very similar to the combined rear sight/carrying handle of the British cal. .280 EM-2 rifle, which appeared in the late forties. Originally the AR-10 appeared with an aluminum barrel, inside which was a rifled steel insert. Apparently it was soon realized that steel barrels could be made light enough to compare favorably with the composite barrel. The prong-type flash suppressor can be used as a grenade launcher. Lightweight alloy magazines with a waffle-type gridding are advertised for these weapons. The weight of the empty magazine for the AR-10 is four ounces.

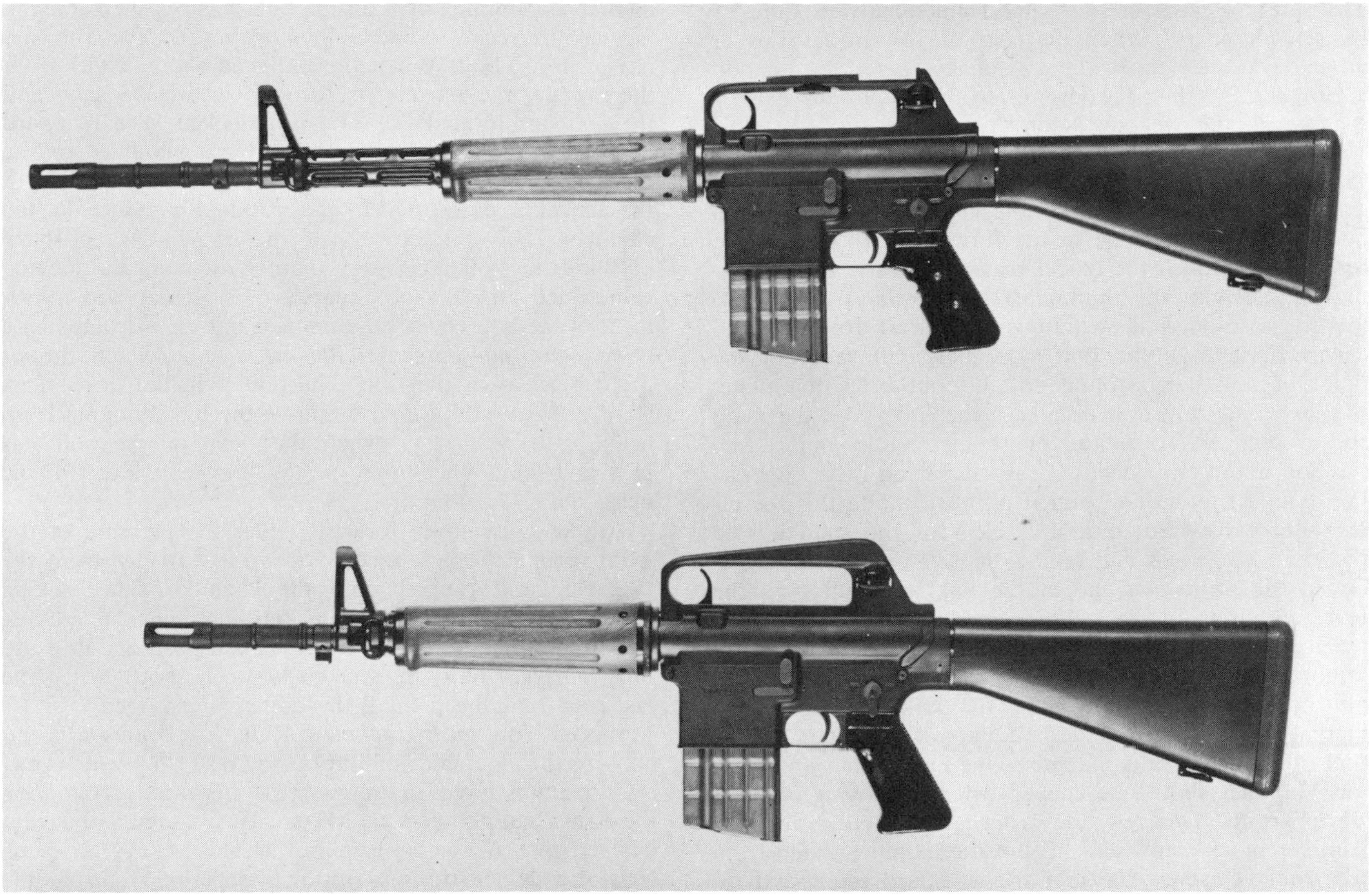

Experimental models of AR-10 Rifle made at Hembrug. Note the built-in grenade launchers.

The Johnson Caliber .30 Semi-automatic Rifle M1941

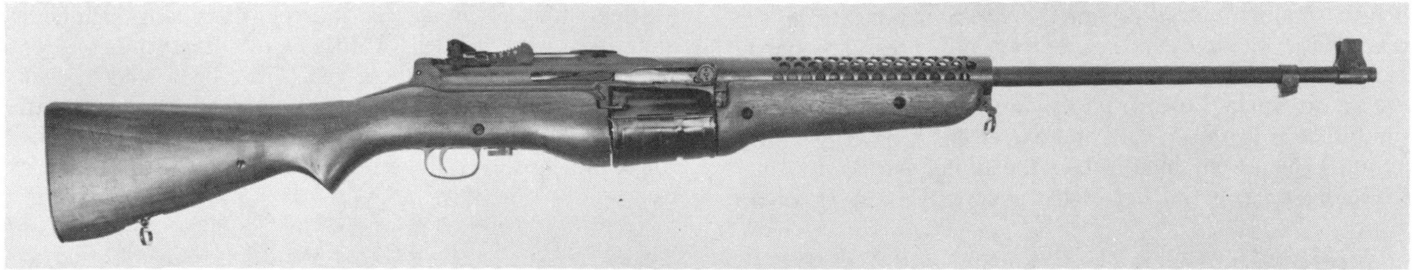

Caliber: .30 U. S.
System of Operation: Recoil.
Weight: 9.5 lbs.
Length, Overall: 45.87 in.
Barrel Length: 22 in.
Feed Device: 10-round rotary type non-detachable magazine, can be loaded with 5-round chargers or single rounds, also made with vertical magazine.
Sights: Front—Protected post.
Rear—Aperture with micrometer type adjustment for range and windage.
Muzzle Velocity: Approx. 2700 f.p.s.

How to Load and Fire the Johnson Rifle. Lift magazine cover, on right side of receiver below and parallel to ejection port, insert five rounds either on a Springfield type charger (stripper clip) or singly. If using a charger, insert horizontally into charger guides in charging port. When last round is stripped or fed singly into magazine, magazine cover will close automatically. Raise the operating handle 20° and pull completely to rear; bolt will run forward, chambering a round. The rifle is now loaded and will fire if the trigger is pulled. When the last round is fired, the bolt will remain to the rear; load as directed above and pull bolt handle slightly to the rear and release it—the bolt will run home chambering a cartridge and the weapon is loaded. The Johnson can be loaded with single rounds or chargers with the bolt home on a loaded chamber. It is therefore easy to replenish the magazine at any time. The magazine can be emptied by depressing the magazine cover with the thumb of the right hand.

The safety lock lever is located immediately in front of the trigger guard. When the free end of the lever is at an angle to the right of the axis of the barrel, the weapon is on "safe." When the lever is to the left of the axis of the barrel, the weapon is on "fire."

How to Field Strip the Johnson. Check rifle to insure that it is empty. With the point of a bulleted round (or a drift), push on the latch plunger of the hinged barrel latch found in the hole in the forward right side of the fore-end and push the barrel rearward. Raise the operating handle with the thumb of the left hand to the unlocked position and withdraw the barrel from the receiver. Disengage the bolt stop plate plunger with the point of a bulleted round and lift out bolt stop plate. Remove bolt stop and disengage the link from the main spring plunger. Raise the operating handle and retract the bolt about two inches. Grasp the knob of the operating handle spindle and pull it outward. Slide the operating handle forward until it is clear of the shoulders in the extractor recess and remove it. Lift out the extractor. Grasp the projecting end of the link and pull it to the rear, withdrawing the bolt through the rear end of the receiver. Rotate the locking cam counterclockwise and remove it from the bolt, remove the firing pin, and push out the link pin and remove the link. Disengage the hammer block pin and push it out with point of bullet; pull off the butt stock. Remove the ejector pin and ejector. Hammer should be cocked before removing the butt stock group. Unscrew the front guard screw and the hammer block screw and lift out the hammer group from the stock. Unscrew the rear trigger guard screw and remove the trigger guard and safety assembly. No further disassembly is recommended. To reassemble, follow the above directions in reverse order.

How the Johnson Works. When the trigger is pressed, the sear disengages from the hammer. The hammer is driven against the firing pin which protrudes from the rear of the locking cam and the weapon fires. The barrel recoils against the tension of the barrel recoil spring and the main spring (transmitted through the bolt.) When the bullet is at the muzzle the barrel has moved rearward about 1/64 of an inch; when the bullet is about 2 feet from the muzzle the barrel has recoiled about ⅛ of an inch. The camming arm on the bolt engages the camming face in the receiver and unlocking begins. The Johnson has an 8-lug bolt. When the bullet is about 5 feet from the muzzle, the barrel has recoiled its full ⅝ inch and the bolt has rotated 20° and is unlocked. The rearward motion of the barrel is stopped by a shoulder in the receiver. The bolt moves to the rear independently of the barrel due to inertia and residual pressure in the chamber. The extractor gives the empty case a sharp pull and the bolt receives a sharp blow from the locking cam which taps the bolt rearward. The rearward movement of the bolt cocks the hammer and the extracted case is brought into contact with the ejector which throws the case clear of the rifle. The bolt is halted in its rearward travel by the forward end of the link bringing it up against the bolt stop, when the head of the bolt has passed behind the base of the top cartridge in the magazine.

As the bolt moves forward under the pressure of the main spring, the bolt face picks up a cartridge from the magazine and rams it into the chamber. The locking lugs enter the barrel locking bushing and the locking cam rotates the bolt 20° to the locked position. Pressure on the trigger must be relaxed between shots. When the last round has been fired, the bolt remains open.

Special Note on the Johnson Rifle. The Johnson is the only recoil operated military shoulder rifle which has been manufactured in quantity. It appeared soon after the Army had adopted the M1 and at the time its backers claimed that it was far superior to the M1. A series of tests and demonstrations during the period 1939-40 indicated that the Johnson was not superior to the M1 and Springfield Armory was already tooled up to produce the M1. Therefore the M1 continued to be the basic U.S. shoulder weapon.

Quantities of the 1941 Johnson were used by the U.S. Marines for a limited period of time and significant quantities were made for the Dutch East Indies. Considerable quantities of these rifles have been sold by arms dealers in the United States within the past several years. The rotary magazine is the common version of the Johnson Rifle, however a vertical feed version was made as well.

40mm Grenade Launcher M79

Caliber: 40mm.
System of Operation: Single-shot, break-open type.
Weight of Launcher (loaded): 6.45 lbs.
Length of Launcher: 28.78 in.
Length of Barrel: 14 in.
Muzzle Velocity: 250 f.p.s.
Sights: Front—Protected blade.
Rear—Leaf, adjustable for windage.

The M79 grenade launcher is a shotgun type weapon designed to fire a high explosive grenade considerably more accurately than a grenade can be fired from a rifle grenade launcher.

How to Load and Fire the M79. Move barrel locking latch *fully* to the right and break open breech. Moving latch fully to right automatically puts the weapon on "safe." Insert cartridge in chamber until the extractor contacts the rim of the cartridge case. Close the breech, push safety to forward position exposing the letter "F." Pressure on the trigger will now fire the weapon.

How to Field Strip the M79. Under normal conditions it should not be necessary (for maintenance purposes) to do more than break the weapon using the barrel locking latch. The firing pin retainer in the face of the standing breech can be tightened up from time to time by use of the lugs on the combination wrench supplied with the weapon. If the weapon has been immersed in water or snow the following procedure should be followed: Re-

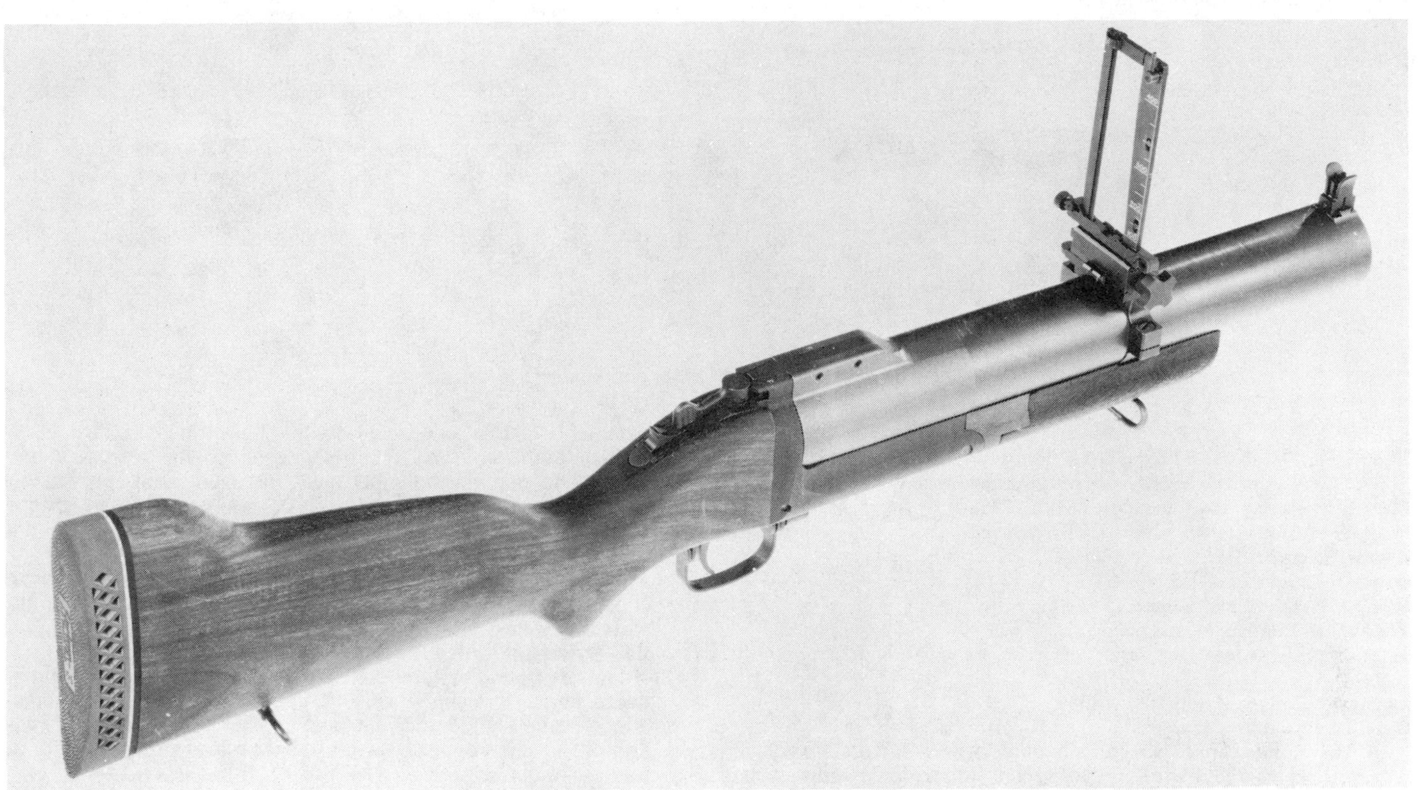

40mm Grenade Launcher M79.

move the fore-end assembly by taking out screw which passes through the rear mounting hole of the front sling swivel. Pull front end of fore end away from barrel until lug on the rear sight base is clear of the hole in upper surface of fore-end bracket. Keeping lug clear of hole, pull forward on fore end assembly until it is free of receiver assembly. Operate barrel locking latch and open breech, holding the stock and receiver stationary, move the barrel rearward in the receiver until it is disengaged from the fulcrum pin. Separate barrel from receiver group. From bottom of stock, near front end, remove machine screw, lock washer, and flat washer which secure stock to receiver. Separate stock from receiver. To reassemble, perform the steps listed above in reverse.

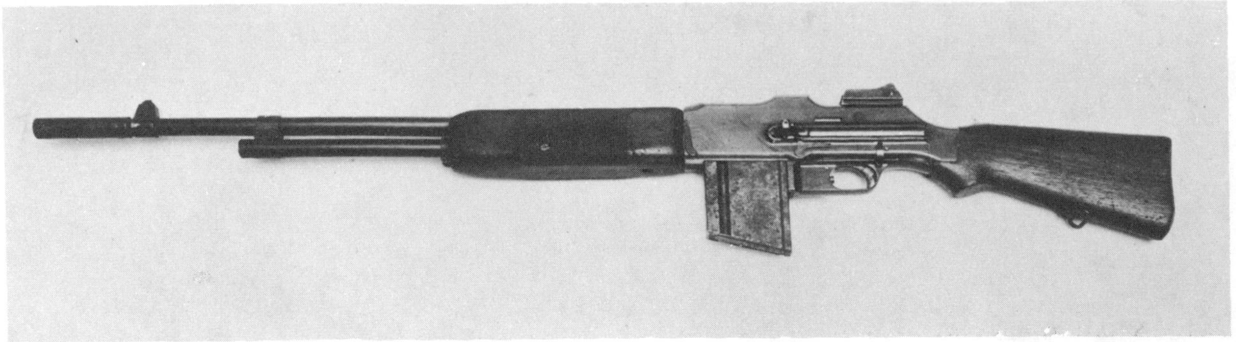

Browning Cal. .30 M1918 Automatic Rifle.

Caliber .30.
Magazine: Detachable box type, holding 20 cartridges in staggered line. Magazine positioned directly under receiver.
Muzzle Velocity of Cartridge: About 2680 feet per second.
Weight of Bullet: 150 grains, full jacketed.
Barrel Length: 24″.
Overall Length of Gun: 47″.
Weight Without Magazine: 15½ lbs.
Weight of Loaded Magazine: 1 lb. 7 ozs.
Sights: Blade front sight; aperture rear sight, graduated to 1600 yds.
Accurate Range: About 800 yds.
Rifle Operated By: Gas escaping through small hole in underside of barrel into an expansion chamber where it forces back a piston under the barrel operating the action and compressing the recoil spring.
Locked: By rising bolt lock which locks into recesses in the top of the receiver. A slide screwed to the piston contains the hammer which is connected to the link which in turn is attached to the bolt. As the slide moves to the rear, it causes the link to pull the bolt lock and bolt from their recesses.
Cooled: Air cooled. Bolt remains open between shots permitting air circulation through breech end down barrel.
Cyclic Rate of Fire: About 500 per minute.
Normal Rate of Fire: 40 to 60 shots per minute, semi-automatic. It is possible to deliver 150 shots per minute semi-automatic with this weapon.
Note: Maximum full automatic rate is 600 per minute.
Position of Operating Handle: On left side of receiver above triggerguard. Drawing this back cocks the hammer; the operating handle should then be pushed back to its forward position. It is not connected with the cocking mechanism in its forward motion.
Flash Hider: This is a metal tube extending beyond the muzzle of the weapon, to hide the flash caused by powder burning after it leaves the muzzle.

Fire Control

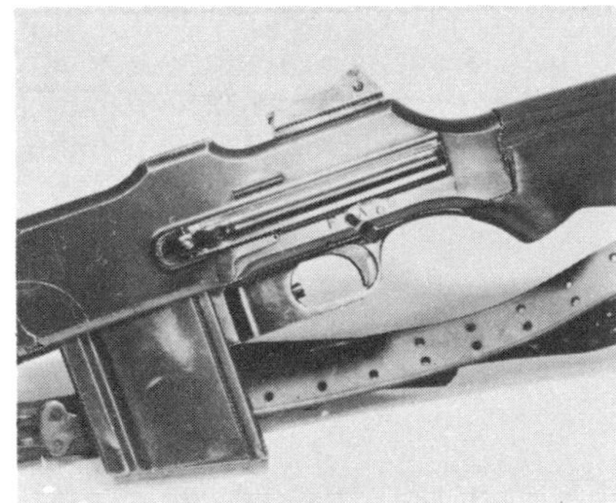

The change lever is directly above the trigger. Push this lever all the way forward to the direction of the letter "F," and the rifle will fire one shot each time you pull the trigger. Set this lever in the vertical position covering the letter "A" for full automatic fire. (Note: On the 1918A2 Model, no single shot fire. The "F" gives slow rate; while "A" gives high rate.) Push in the small change lever stop, and push the change lever back and over the stop as far as it will go in the direction of the letter "S" and the weapon is safe and cannot be fired. This change lever stop prevents the weapon being set on "safe" without the knowledge of the firer; and it permits a quick change to the full automatic or single shot position.

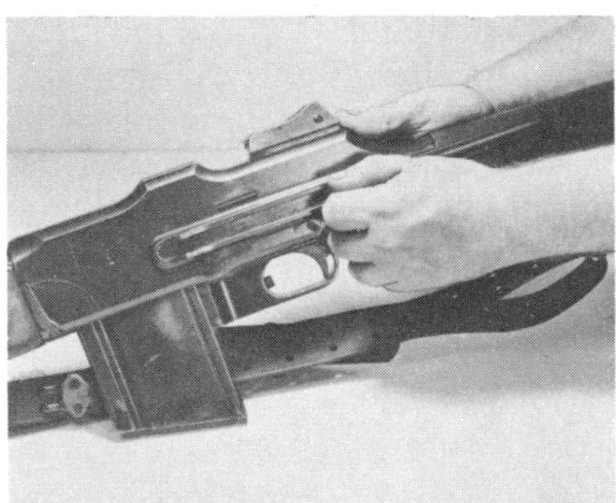

Drawing back the operating handle as far as it will go cocks the weapon and compresses the recoil spring. Pushing it forward makes it unnecessary for the action to carry the handle to the closed position on the forward stroke during firing.

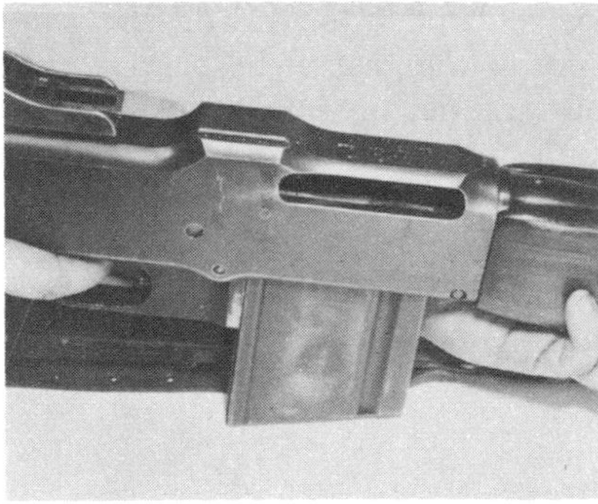

When last shot is fired, bolt stays open and trigger cannot be pulled. Pushing in the stud in the forward end of the triggerguard will release the magazine, and permit it to be withdrawn and a new magazine inserted in its place.

Instructions for Loading and Firing

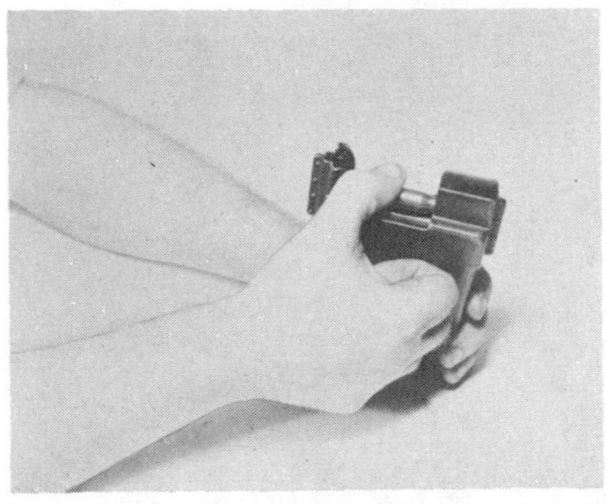

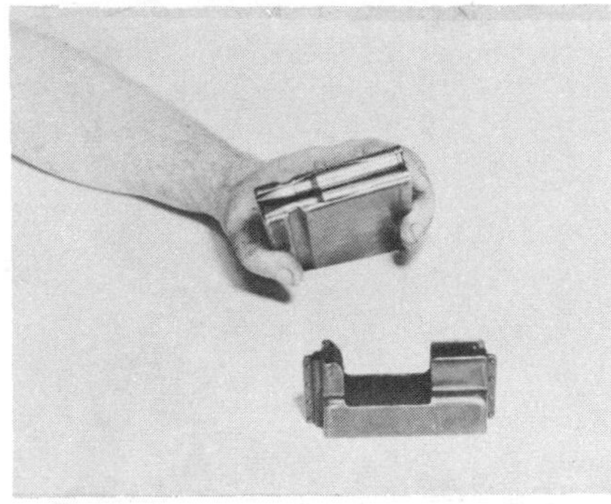

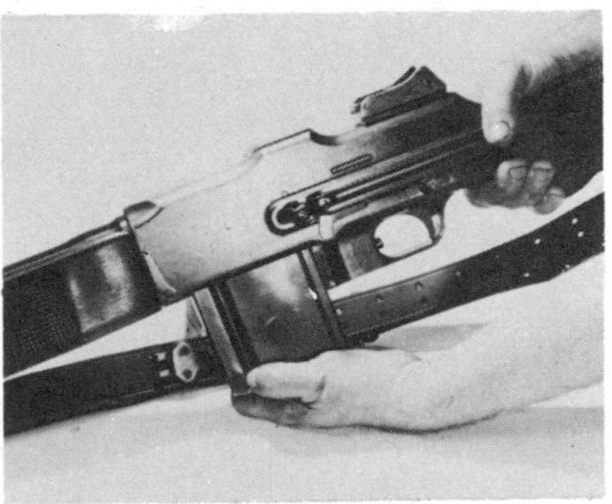

If a magazine filler is available, place the wide end over the top of the magazine so the grooves fit over the magazine catch rib. Insert a clip of cartridges in the filler and with the right thumb strip the cartridges into the magazine exactly as though they were being fed into a bolt action rifle. Single cartridges may be so loaded. If no filler is available, cartridges may be loaded singly into the magazine as for automatic pistol.

Insert magazine between sides of receiver in front of the triggerguard and push home until it locks. This will normally be done with the right hand. While the magazine may be inserted with the weapon uncocked, it will ordinarily be done after the rifle has been cocked and set on "safe."

Field Stripping

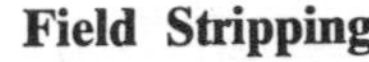

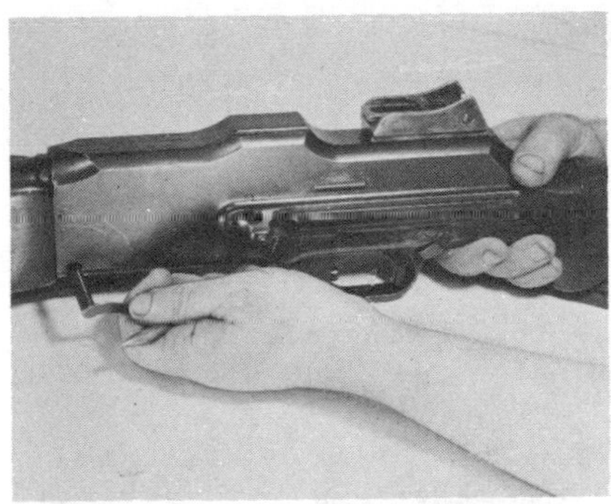

If weapon is equipped with a mount, remove it. Pull the operating handle back to cock the weapon. Then thrust it fully forward.

Rotate the gas cylinder retaining pin (at forward left end of the receiver) and withdraw it from its socket.

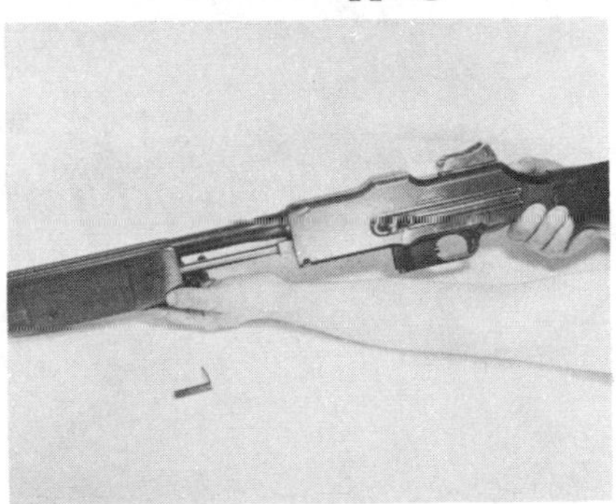

Now pull forward the forearm and gas cylinder tube and remove from the rifle. Ease the mechanism forward.

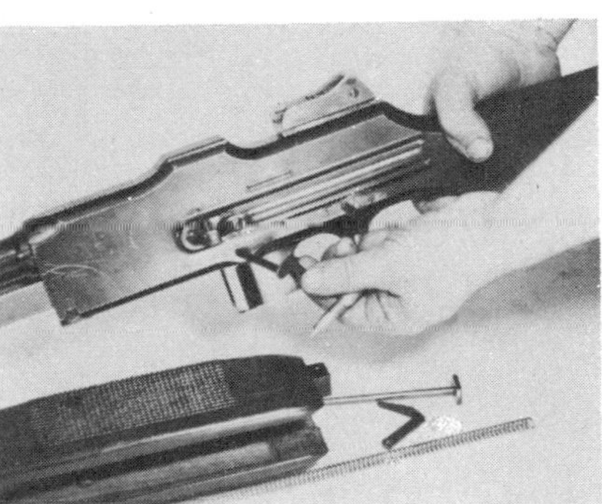

Rotate the retaining pin at forward end of triggerguard and withdraw it.

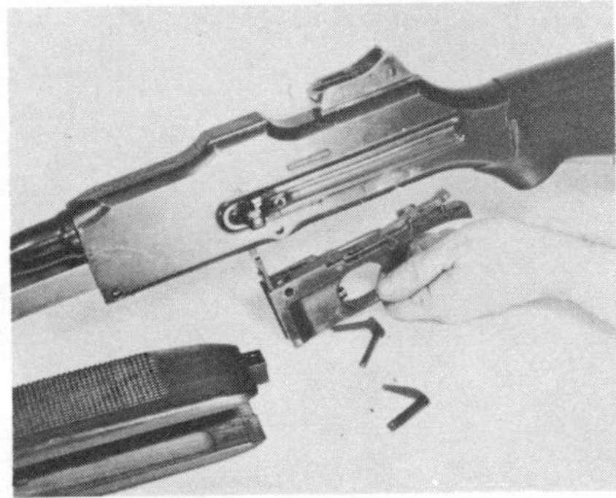

The entire trigger mechanism may now be withdrawn from the bottom of the rifle.

Remove the recoil spring guide. Press in the checkered surface on its head and turn it until the ends clear the retaining shoulders; ease out the guide and the recoil spring and withdraw. Withdraw the handle by lining up the hammer pin holes on the side of the receiver and on the right side of the operating handle. Insert the point of a bullet in the hole in the operating handle with the right hand. Press back against the hammer pin while pushing the slide backward with the left hand.

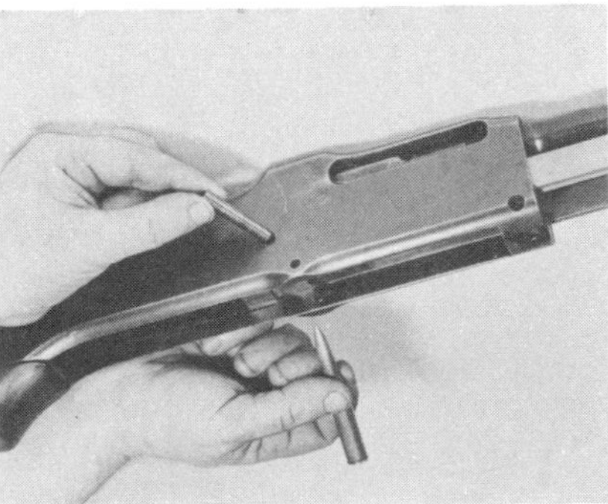

As the two holes register, the pressure of the bullet will force the hammer pin out of the large hole on the left side of the receiver and it may be withdrawn. This will permit the operating handle to be pulled straight to the rear and out of its guide.

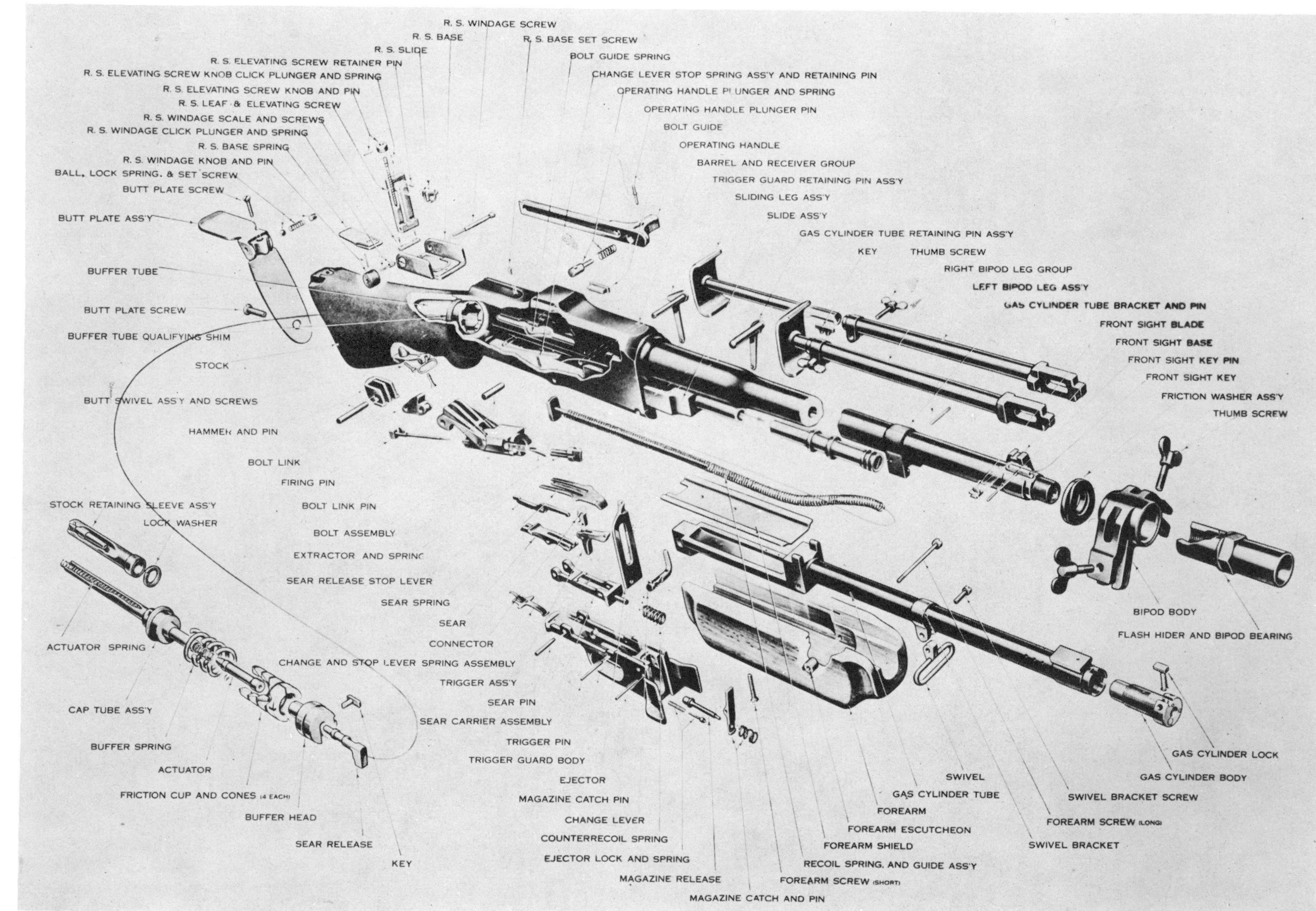
R. S. WINDAGE SCREW
R. S. BASE
R. S. BASE SET SCREW
R. S. SLIDE
R. S. ELEVATING SCREW RETAINER PIN
BOLT GUIDE SPRING
R. S. ELEVATING SCREW KNOB CLICK PLUNGER AND SPRING
CHANGE LEVER STOP SPRING ASS'Y AND RETAINING PIN
R. S. ELEVATING SCREW KNOB AND PIN
OPERATING HANDLE PLUNGER AND SPRING
R. S. LEAF & ELEVATING SCREW
OPERATING HANDLE PLUNGER PIN
R. S. WINDAGE SCALE AND SCREWS
R. S. WINDAGE CLICK PLUNGER AND SPRING
BOLT GUIDE
R. S. BASE SPRING
OPERATING HANDLE
R. S. WINDAGE KNOB AND PIN
BARREL AND RECEIVER GROUP
BALL, LOCK SPRING, & SET SCREW
TRIGGER GUARD RETAINING PIN ASS'Y
BUTT PLATE SCREW
SLIDING LEG ASS'Y
BUTT PLATE ASS'Y
SLIDE ASS'Y
GAS CYLINDER TUBE RETAINING PIN ASS'Y
KEY
THUMB SCREW
BUFFER TUBE
RIGHT BIPOD LEG GROUP
LEFT BIPOD LEG ASS'Y
BUTT PLATE SCREW
GAS CYLINDER TUBE BRACKET AND PIN
FRONT SIGHT BLADE
BUFFER TUBE QUALIFYING SHIM
FRONT SIGHT BASE
STOCK
FRONT SIGHT KEY PIN
FRONT SIGHT KEY
FRICTION WASHER ASS'Y
BUTT SWIVEL ASS'Y AND SCREWS
THUMB SCREW
HAMMER AND PIN
BOLT LINK
FIRING PIN
STOCK RETAINING SLEEVE ASS'Y
BOLT LINK PIN
LOCK WASHER
BOLT ASSEMBLY
EXTRACTOR AND SPRING
SEAR RELEASE STOP LEVER
SEAR SPRING
BIPOD BODY
SEAR
FLASH HIDER AND BIPOD BEARING
ACTUATOR SPRING
CONNECTOR
CHANGE AND STOP LEVER SPRING ASSEMBLY
TRIGGER ASS'Y
SEAR PIN
CAP TUBE ASS'Y
SEAR CARRIER ASSEMBLY
TRIGGER PIN
BUFFER SPRING
GAS CYLINDER LOCK
TRIGGER GUARD BODY
ACTUATOR
SWIVEL
GAS CYLINDER BODY
EJECTOR
FRICTION CUP AND CONES (4 EACH)
GAS CYLINDER TUBE
SWIVEL BRACKET SCREW
MAGAZINE CATCH PIN
FOREARM
BUFFER HEAD
CHANGE LEVER
FOREARM SCREW (LONG)
FOREARM ESCUTCHEON
COUNTERRECOIL SPRING
SEAR RELEASE
FOREARM SHIELD
SWIVEL BRACKET
EJECTOR LOCK AND SPRING
RECOIL SPRING, AND GUIDE ASS'Y
KEY
MAGAZINE RELEASE
FOREARM SCREW (SHORT)
MAGAZINE CATCH AND PIN

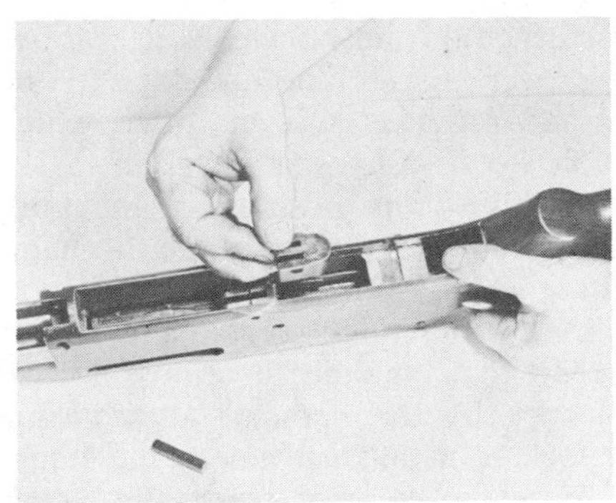

Push the hammer forward out of its seat in the slide and lift it out of the weapon.

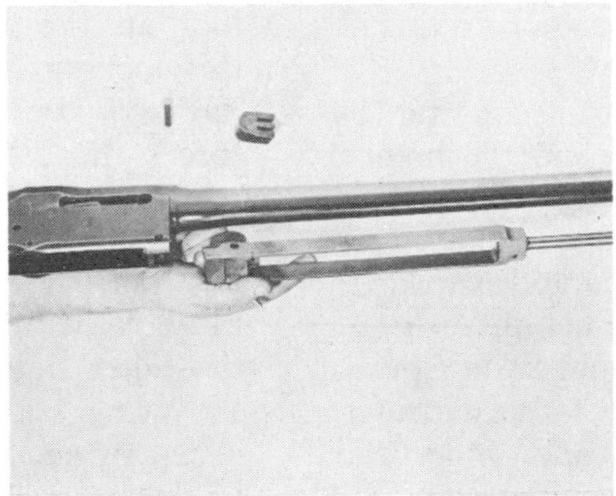

Pull the slide directly forward out of the receiver, taking care that the link is pushed well down so that slide can clear it. Remove the slide carefully to avoid striking the gas piston or its rings against the gas cylinder tube bracket female.

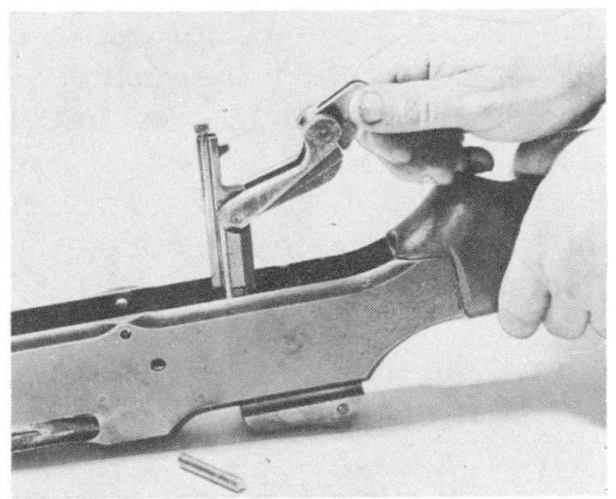

With the point of a bullet force out the spring bolt guide from inside the receiver, then lift the bolt, bolt lock, and link by pulling slowly to the rear end of the receiver and then lifting them out. The firing pin may now be lifted out of the bolt and the extractor removed by pressing the small end of the cartridge against the claw and exerting upward and frontal pressure. No further stripping is normally necessary or recommended.

How the Browning Automatic Rifle Works

Starting with the gun loaded and cocked, the action is as follows: Pressing the trigger pulls down the nose of the sear, disengaging it and permitting the slide to move forward under the action of the recoil spring. The rear end of the slide contains the hammer which is connected by a link to the bolt. The slide is pulled forward by the compressed recoil spring. During the first quarter inch of travel of the slide, the front end of its feed rib strikes

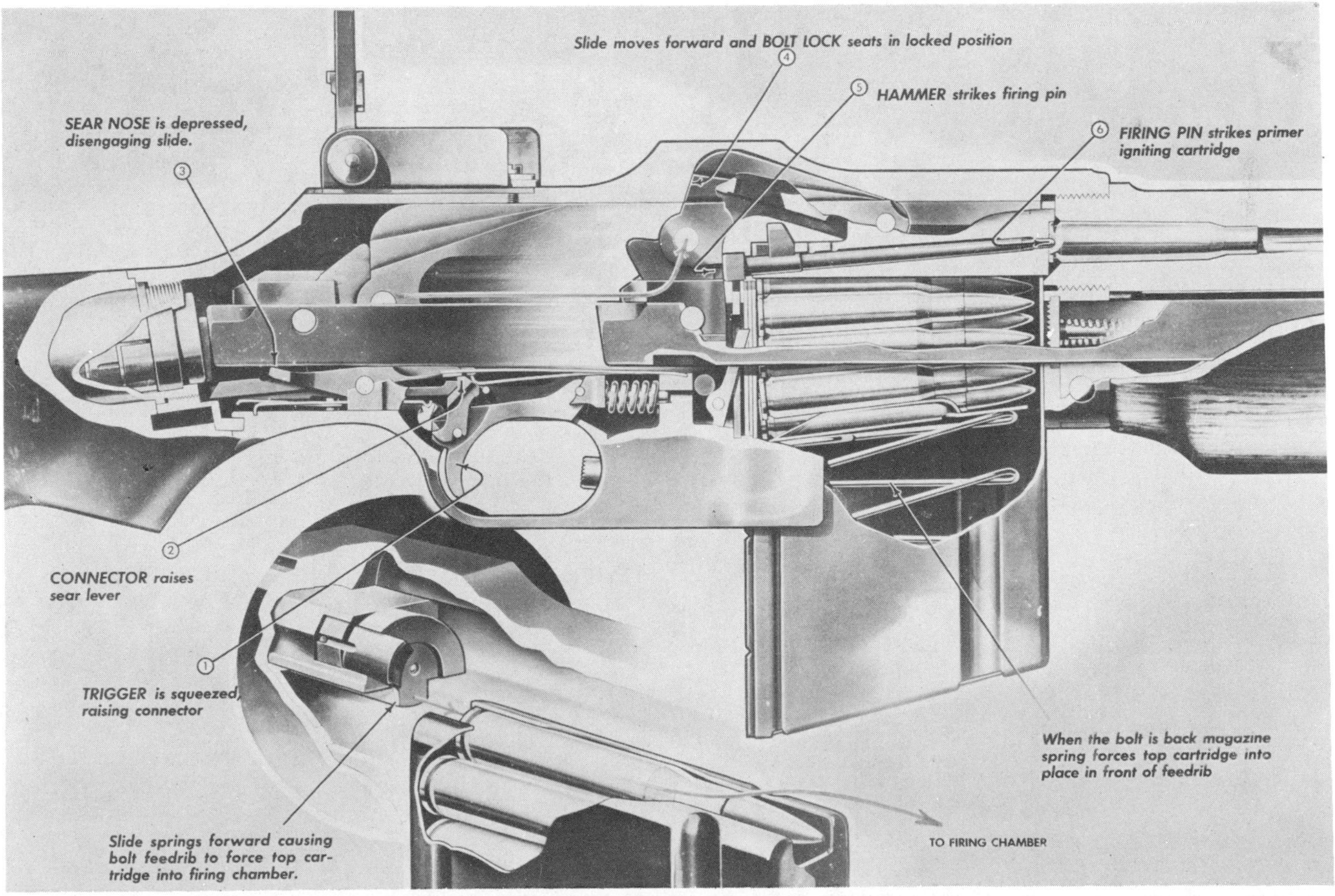

Details of firing action of the Browning Automatic Rifle as trigger is pressed. Follow numbers to study the sequence of action.

the base of the top cartridge in the magazine, driving it ahead toward the firing chamber.

When the cartridge has traveled about a quarter of an inch, the bullet strikes the bullet guide on the breech and is deflected upward toward the chamber. This action also guides the front end of the cartridge from under the magazine lip. When the head of the cartridge reaches the part of the magazine where the locking lips are cut away and the opening enlarged, the magazine spring forces it out of the magazine. The base of the cartridge now slides across the face of the bolt and under the extractor; and if it fails to position correctly the extractor will still snap over its head as the bolt reaches its forward position. At the time the cartridge leaves the magazine, the bullet nose is so far in the chamber that it is guided from that point on.

When the slide is within two inches of its complete forward position, a circular cam surface on the bottom of the bolt lock starts to ride over the rear shoulders of the bolt support, camming up the rear end of the bolt lock. The link pin rises above the line joining the bolt pin and the hammer pin, so that its joint has a tendency to buckle upwards. As the attached bolt is now opposite its locking recess in the receiver it pivots upward about the bolt lock pin. The link whose lower edge is attached to the hammer pin revolves upward and forces the bolt lock up; the rounded surface on the bolt lock, just above this locking face, slips over the locking shoulder in the hump of the receiver and provides a lever thrust which forces the attached bolt home into final position.

The bolt lock is now above the position of the bolt, and locks firmly in the hump in the receiver as the hammer pin passes beneath the link pin. The firing pin is in the bolt, with a lug on its rear end buried in the slot at the other side of the bolt lock, making it impossible for the firing pin to be struck by the hammer at any time except when the bolt lock is in its recesses in the hump of the receiver. Thus when the hammer pin passes under the link pin, the head of the firing pin is exposed to the center rib of the hammer; and as the slide still continues forward, the hammer drives the firing pin ahead and explodes the cartridge in the chamber.

The forward motion is now halted when the front end of the slide strikes against a shoulder at the rear end of the gas cylinder tube.

Return Movement of the Action. About 6″ from the muzzle, a small port is bored in the bottom of the barrel. As the bullet passes over this port, a small amount of gas, still under high pressure, escapes through it and passes through similar ports in the gas cylinder tube bracket, the gas cylinder tube, and the gas cylinder. The gas cylinder port is the smallest of these and acts as a

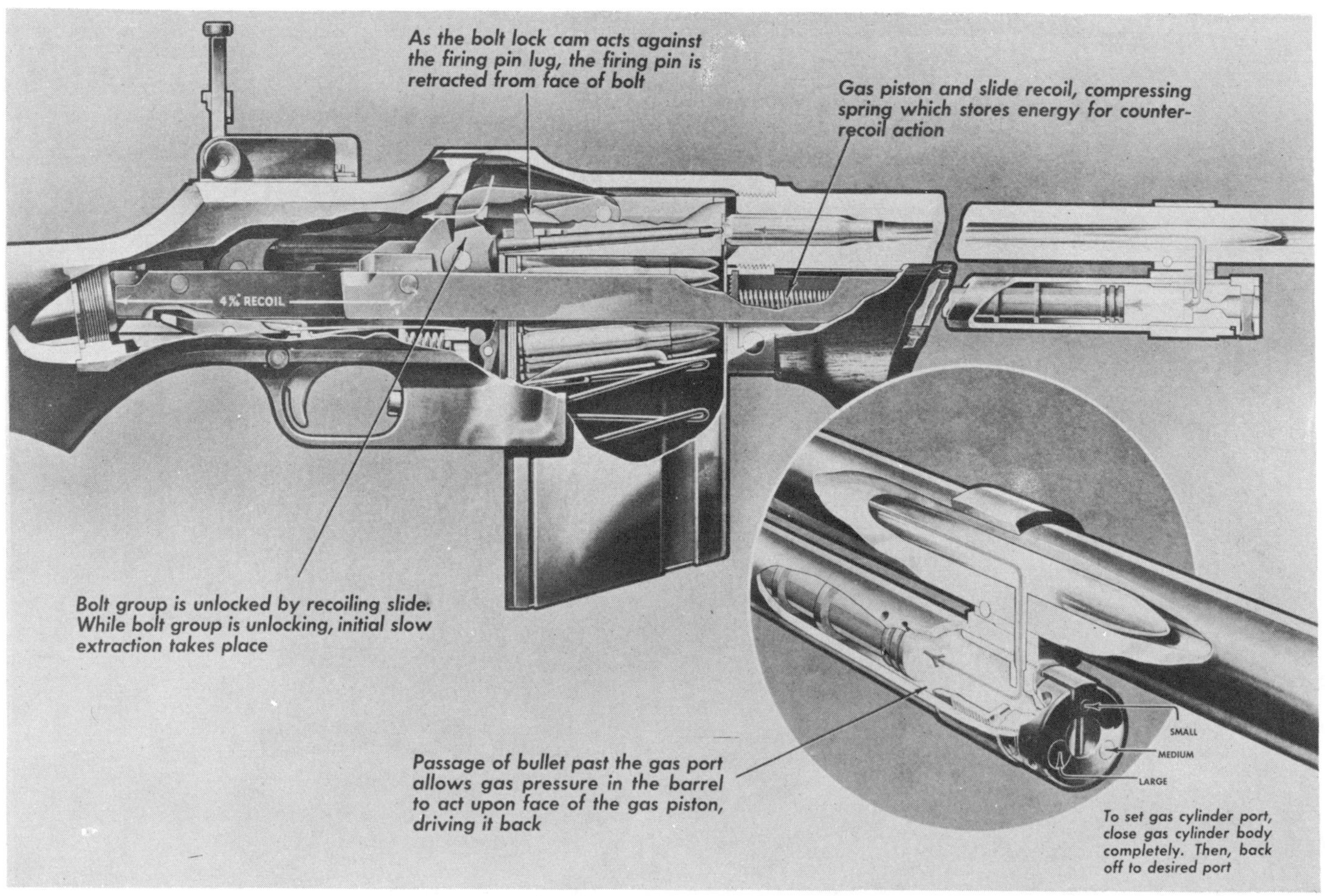

Recoil and unlocking action of the Browning Automatic Rifle showing action beginning as bullet passes over gas port and gas escaping into cylinder starts the rearward action.

throttle on the barrel pressure. The ports in the gas cylinder lead radially into a small well situated in the head of the gas cylinder. Through this well the pressure is conducted to the gas system plug, through which it acts on the piston for the length of time the bullet is traveling the 6″ distance from barrel port to muzzle. This results in a sudden, hard blow, backward against the piston plug.

The gas piston is assembled to the slide, and the sudden blow as it drives the gas piston back also forces back the slide and the parts attached to it and compresses the recoil spring which is seated in the slide.

After the piston has traveled back a little over ½″, bearing rings on its rear and corresponding ones in the gas piston plug pass out of the gas cylinder. The gas now expands around the gas piston head into the gas cylinder tube where it is exhausted into six portholes in the tube placed just at the rear of the gas cylinder tube brackets.

Two rings on the piston about 1¼″ from the head prevent most of the gas from traveling back through the gas cylinder tube; and also act as bearings to maintain the front end of the piston in the center of the gas cylinder tube after the piston has passed out of the cylinder.

Unlocking Action. As the hammer pin is slightly in advance of the connecting link pin, the initial backward movement of the slide carries the hammer back without moving either the attached bolt lock or bolt; and when the movement has progressed far enough (about 1/5″) and the high breech pressure has dropped to safe limits the unlocking action starts. The link is compelled to revolve forward about the hammer pin, and so to draw the bolt lock down out of a hump in the receiver and start it to the rear. The motion of the bolt and bolt lock is now accelerated as the lock is drawn completely out of its locking recess, locking the shoulders in the receiver.

As the bolt lock is prevented from revolving from below the line of backward travel of the bolt, further rearward travel of all moving parts is in a straight line. Meanwhile, however, during the unlocking motion, a cam surface on the slot in the bottom side of the bolt lock has come in contact with a cam surface on the firing pin lug, and has drawn the firing pin away from the base of the bolt.

Also during the backward action, the circular cam surface on the lower part of the bolt lock, operating on the rear shoulders of the bolt support, has produced a lever action tending to loosen the cartridge case in the firing chamber. From that point, the slide and all its moving parts are traveling to the rear at the same speed, carrying along the empty cartridge case held in its seat in the face of the bolt by the extractor (the extractor is positioned in the upper right side of the bolt near the ejection port). Thus as the slide nears the end of its travel and the base of the empty cartridge case strikes the ejector on the left side of the bolt feed rib, the empty case is pivoted about the extractor and through the ejection port. As the front end of the cartridge case passes out of the receiver, it is so pivoted that it strikes the outside of the receiver about an inch to the rear of the ejection port; and hence rebounds toward the right front.

The rearward motion is now completed as the end of the slide strikes against the end of the buffer, and the sear nose catches in the notch at the underside of the slide and holds the weapon open and ready for the next pull of the trigger. (If the weapon is set for full automatic fire, the sear nose is held depressed, so that it does not stop the slide which continues forward, firing the weapon in the full automatic cycle.)

The buffer is a tube in the butt of the rifle in which are placed a buffer head against which the slide stops, a friction cup slit to allow for expansion, a steel cone to fit into the cup, and four more cups and cones in series. Behind these is the coil buffer spring and the buffer nut which is screwed into the end of the tube to form a seat for the spring.

As the rear end of the slide strikes the buffer head, it moves it to the rear, forcing the cups over the cones causing them to expand tightly against the tube, thus producing friction as the cups move back and the buffer spring is compressed. The rearward motion of the slide is therefore checked gradually, and practically no unpleasant rebound occurs. The friction mechanism is returned to its original place by the compression of its spring.

Notes on the BAR

A very important feature of this rifle is that the bolt, bolt lock, and link mechanism start back comparatively slowly and do not attain the speed of the slide itself until after the period of high breech pressure passes. This feature is also important in that it does not subject the mechanism to undue strain as the gas pushes the piston back.

There are three different gas ports. The weapon will normally be set to operate on the smallest port. It is properly alined by screwing in the gas cylinder with combination tool until the shoulder of the cylinder is one turn from the corresponding shoulder of the gas cylinder tube, and the smallest circle on the cylinder head is toward the barrel. (To permit setting the regulator, the split pin must be pushed out sufficiently to permit the regulator to be turned.)

If the rifle is sluggish from insufficient gas, the cylinder should be set one complete turn on each side of the original setting. However, it is to be noted that the larger ports are provided only for emergency use. They should be utilized only when through lack of oil or accumulation of dirt or carbon, the rifle is sluggish and conditions make it impossible to properly correct these troubles. It is therefore essential that the threads should be kept cleaned and oiled and cylinder free to turn at all times.

In field service, at the first sign of insufficient gas, unscrew the cylinder a third of a turn, and line up the medium circle and port with the gas opening.

When gas is insufficient, the weapon may fail to recoil because the port is not properly alined or is unusually dirty. A very dirty mechanism may also cause such a stoppage. Or the weapon may not recoil far enough to permit complete ejection or the ejection may be weak. Under some conditions, although this is unusual, it may result in uncontrolled automatic fire.

On the other hand if the gas pressure is too high, the rifle will be speeded up too much causing a pounding which will interfere with accuracy. This may also generate excessive heat in the gas operating mechanism.

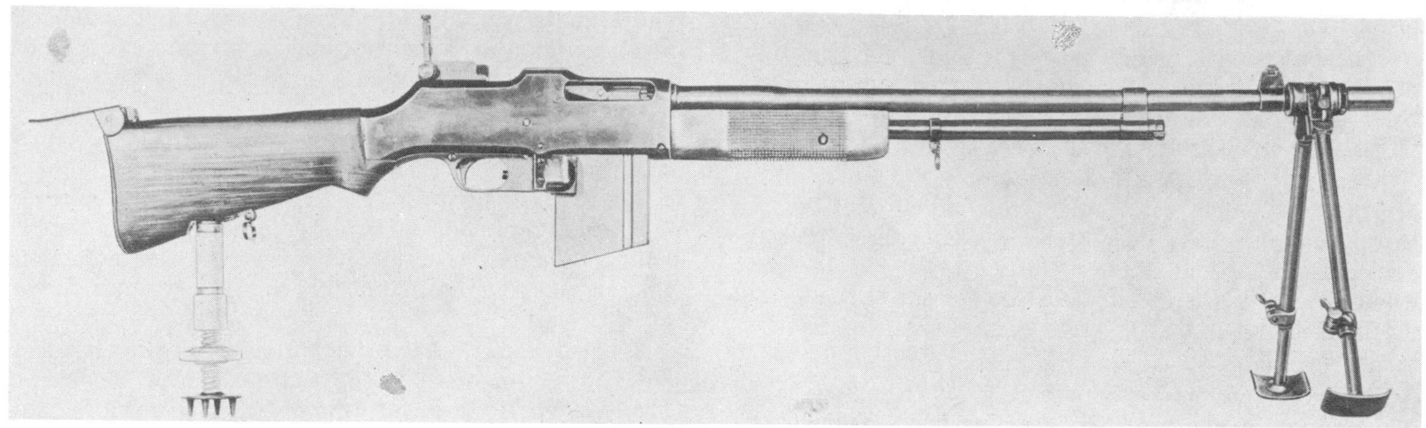

Browning Automatic Rifle M1918A2.

This is a modification of the famous Browning Automatic Rifle. The change lever spring and the carrier have been modified. Several new components have been added. These include a sear release stop lever, a sear, key and head buffers, sear release actuator and actuator spring, actuator stop, and buffer head. The bipod is attached to the flash hider. A stock rest has been added and the forearm made lighter. A trap plate has been added between the barrel and the gas cylinder tube.

This gun has been modified to replace the single shot mechanism. Single shots can be fired in this modified version only by pressing and releasing the trigger rapidly.

However, as a compensating factor, the gun has been designed to fire at a low and a high rate of speed somewhat in the manner of the British Besa Machine Guns.

Setting the change lever at "S" renders the gun safe as in earlier models. Setting the change lever at "A" permits full automatic fire at the regular rate as in the earlier models.

Setting the change lever at "F," however, brings into play a rate-reducing mechanism, which slows the rifle down to a rate of about 340 shots per minute.

When the change lever is at "F," the rifle is cocked in normal fashion and the sear engages in a notch in the slide. Pressing the trigger in the usual manner results in controlled automatic fire at a reduced rate which will be delivered as long as the trigger is held back. There is a distinct difference noticeable when handling the gun when the mechanism is in operation and when it is firing full automatic without it. There is no provision made for semi-automatic fire in this model.

On pressing the trigger the slide goes forward in normal B.A.R. fashion firing the cartridge; then the slide starts on its rearward movement in the usual manner, driven back by gas expanding into the gas cylinder, but it picks up the sear release and strikes it on the front end. This forces the sear release to the rear until the slide reaches the face of the buffer head while during this movement it also meets the front end of the actuator. The actuator tube is forced to the rear, meeting the actuator stop. At this point the actuator reverses its direction of travel moving forward under the tension of the actuator spring and the slide engages on the sear. The slide remains in engagement with the sear until the actuator reaches its extreme forward position. At that point the actuator forces the sear release forward forcing it to move through the buffer head, while the foot of the sear release is in contact with the angle surface of the rear of the sear. This cams the sear out of engagement with the slide forcing the slide to go forward at this point to fire the cartridge.

The result of this action is to fire the gun full automatic but with a distinct halt between shots. This characteristic has been particularly valuable in jungle warfare, where the B.A.R. has more than proven its worth. While the regular full automatic rate is of value for burst firing or against low flying planes, its normal rate is too high for ordinary land operation without wasting ammunition. With the lower rate, the B.A.R. with its powerful cal. .30 cartridge provides an ideal weapon for firing in forests and jungles where greater penetration than is normal in the submachine bullet is desirable; and where targets are not always visible and hence are not susceptible to individual aimed shots. The M1918A2 was the standard squad automatic weapon of World War II and Korea.

U.S. SUBMACHINE GUNS

Reising Cal. .45 Model 50 Submachine Gun.

Caliber: .45 M1911 cartridge, ball or tracer ammunition.

Magazine: Box type, holding 12 cartridges in single line box or 20 cartridges in double line box. Magazine positioned under receiver.

Muzzle Velocity of Cartridge: About 920 feet per second with this barrel length.

Weight of Bullet: 234 grains, lead with metal jacket.

Muzzle Striking Energy of Bullet: 431 foot pounds.

Barrel Length: 11 inches.

Overall Length of Gun: 34⅗ inches (including compensator).

Weight without Mazagine: 6¾ lbs.

Weight of Loaded 20-Round Magazine: 1.4 lbs.

Front Sight: Patridge type, can be adjusted to right or left.

Rear Sight: Aperture. By raising rear sight and sliding sight elevator, it can be adjusted for 50, 100, 200, and 300 yards range.

Accurate Range: About 100 yards shooting against men.

Gun Operated By: Rearward pressure of gas in firing chamber pressing back on fired cartridge case and supporting bolt.

Locked: By retarded blowback during period of high pressure. Friction of cammed surfaces on bolt and receiver and resistance of action bar spring keep the weapon locked until bullet has left the barrel.

Cooled: By cooling fins which radiate heat from barrel during firing.

Cyclic Rate of Fire: 450 to 600 shots per minute.

Position of Action Bar (which is pulled back to cock gun): In slot cut in bottom of stock in front of magazine.

Type of Fire: By pressing down and setting selector (on right side of gun just below the rear sight elevator) gun may be set for either semi-automatic fire (S.A.), one shot being fired for each pull of the trigger, or for full automatic (F.A.), the gun firing as long as the trigger is held and there are cartridges in magazine. Selector may also be used to make gun safe by setting on (S).

Compensator: This is a metal tube fastened on the end of the gun barrel. It is solid on the bottom. The top is cut back somewhat, and has slots cut in it. When the bullet leaves the barrel, the powder gases expand in the compensator. By deflecting these gases the compensator assists the gunner in controlling upward climb of the muzzle in full automatic fire.

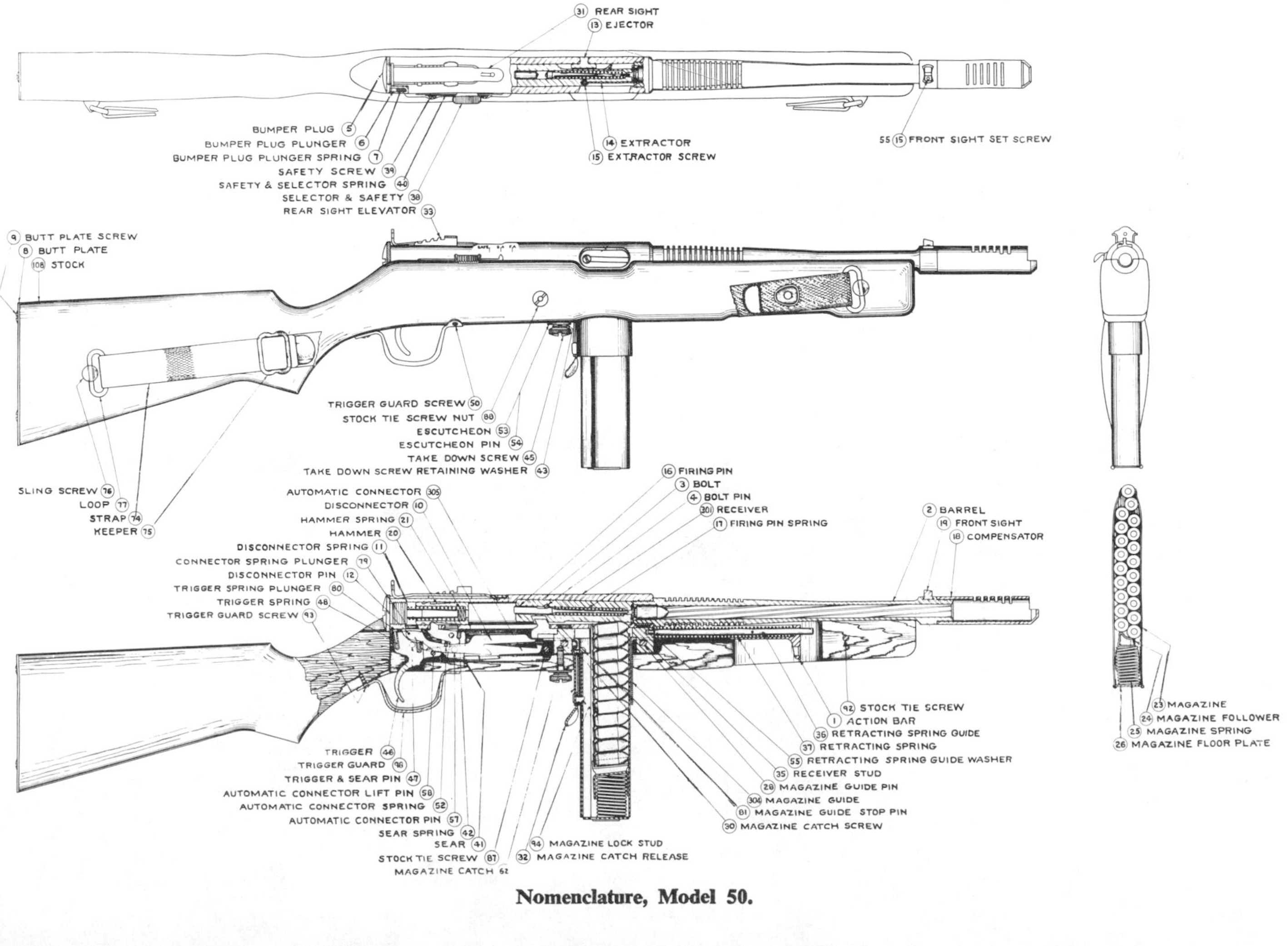

(31) REAR SIGHT
(13) EJECTOR
BUMPER PLUG (5)
BUMPER PLUG PLUNGER (6)
BUMPER PLUG PLUNGER SPRING (7)
SAFETY SCREW (39)
SAFETY & SELECTOR SPRING (40)
SELECTOR & SAFETY (38)
REAR SIGHT ELEVATOR (33)
(14) EXTRACTOR
(15) EXTRACTOR SCREW
55 (15) FRONT SIGHT SET SCREW
(9) BUTT PLATE SCREW
(8) BUTT PLATE
(108) STOCK
TRIGGER GUARD SCREW (50)
STOCK TIE SCREW NUT (88)
ESCUTCHEON (53)
ESCUTCHEON PIN (54)
TAKE DOWN SCREW (45)
TAKE DOWN SCREW RETAINING WASHER (43)
SLING SCREW (76)
LOOP (77)
STRAP (74)
KEEPER (75)
AUTOMATIC CONNECTOR (305)
DISCONNECTOR (10)
HAMMER SPRING (21)
HAMMER (20)
DISCONNECTOR SPRING (11)
CONNECTOR SPRING PLUNGER (79)
DISCONNECTOR PIN (12)
TRIGGER SPRING PLUNGER (80)
TRIGGER SPRING (48)
TRIGGER GUARD SCREW (93)
(16) FIRING PIN
(3) BOLT
(4) BOLT PIN
(301) RECEIVER
(17) FIRING PIN SPRING
(2) BARREL
(19) FRONT SIGHT
(18) COMPENSATOR
TRIGGER (46)
TRIGGER GUARD (96)
TRIGGER & SEAR PIN (47)
AUTOMATIC CONNECTOR LIFT PIN (58)
AUTOMATIC CONNECTOR SPRING (52)
AUTOMATIC CONNECTOR PIN (57)
SEAR SPRING (42)
SEAR (41)
STOCK TIE SCREW (87)
MAGAZINE CATCH 62
(94) MAGAZINE LOCK STUD
(32) MAGAZINE CATCH RELEASE
(92) STOCK TIE SCREW
(1) ACTION BAR
(36) RETRACTING SPRING GUIDE
(37) RETRACTING SPRING
(55) RETRACTING SPRING GUIDE WASHER
(35) RECEIVER STUD
(29) MAGAZINE GUIDE PIN
(304) MAGAZINE GUIDE
(81) MAGAZINE GUIDE STOP PIN
(30) MAGAZINE CATCH SCREW
(23) MAGAZINE
(24) MAGAZINE FOLLOWER
(25) MAGAZINE SPRING
(26) MAGAZINE FLOOR PLATE

Nomenclature, Model 50.

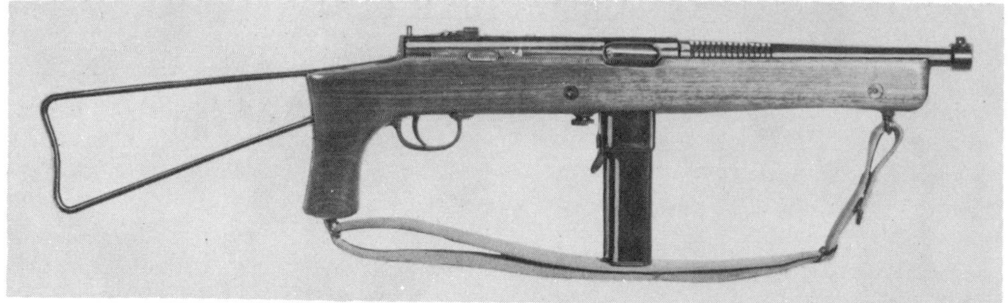

Reising Cal. .45 Model 55 Submachine Gun.

Barrel Length: 10½ inches.
Overall Length of Gun: 22½ inches (without compensator and with steel folding stock folded forward).
Weight without Magazine: 6¼ lbs.

Note: All other data same as for Model 50. This gun was developed at the request of Marine Corps experts for use with either one or two hands. Extensively used by Parachute Troopers, Mechanized Troops, and Vehicle Operators during World War II.

How the Reising Gun Works

Starting with the gun loaded and cocked the action is as follows: The trigger is pressed. This results in the hammer being released to be driven forward by the compressed hammer spring. The hammer drives the firing pin against the primer in the head of the cartridge. The primer explodes the powder in the cartridge.

The bullet is driven forward and out of the barrel.

The rearward thrust of the gases formed by the combustion of the powder pushes the empty cartridge case (or shell) back against the bolt. The heavy action bar spring, together with friction of cammed surfaces of the bolt and receiver, keeps the action closed until the bullet has left the barrel, and the pressure has dropped to safe limits.

The blow-back of the gases now drives the bolt and action bar to the rear in a straight line, compressing the action bar spring. As the bolt moves to the rear, the extractor set in the bolt face and hooked over the now empty shell pulls the shell out of the firing chamber. The pressure still in the barrel is called residual pressure. It works with the extractor by pushing the empty shell back into the receiver. This shell now strikes against the ejector and is cammed up and out of the gun through the ejection port on the right side of the gun.

As the bolt passes to the rear over the top of the magazine, the magazine spring forces a cartridge up into line.

The backward movement of the action compresses the hammer spring over the guide of the bumper plug. The rearward motion of the recoiling parts is stopped by the bolt and hammer striking against the bumper plug.

Return Movement of the Action. The energy stored up by the compression of the action bar spring now drives the action forward. The feed rib on the bottom of the bolt strips the top cartridge from the magazine.

The bolt as it nears its foremost position is cammed up into the locking shoulders of the receiver by the camming lug on the action bar working in the camming recess in the bolt.

As the bolt drives the cartridge into the firing chamber, the extractor snaps over the head of the cartridge.

When the bolt locks, the firing pin is moved into position to be engaged by the hammer.

The trigger mechanism engages. The piece is now ready for the next shot.

If the selector is set for "S.A.," pressing the trigger is necessary to fire. If the selector is set on "F.A.," the trigger mechanism permits the hammer to go forward if the trigger is held back.

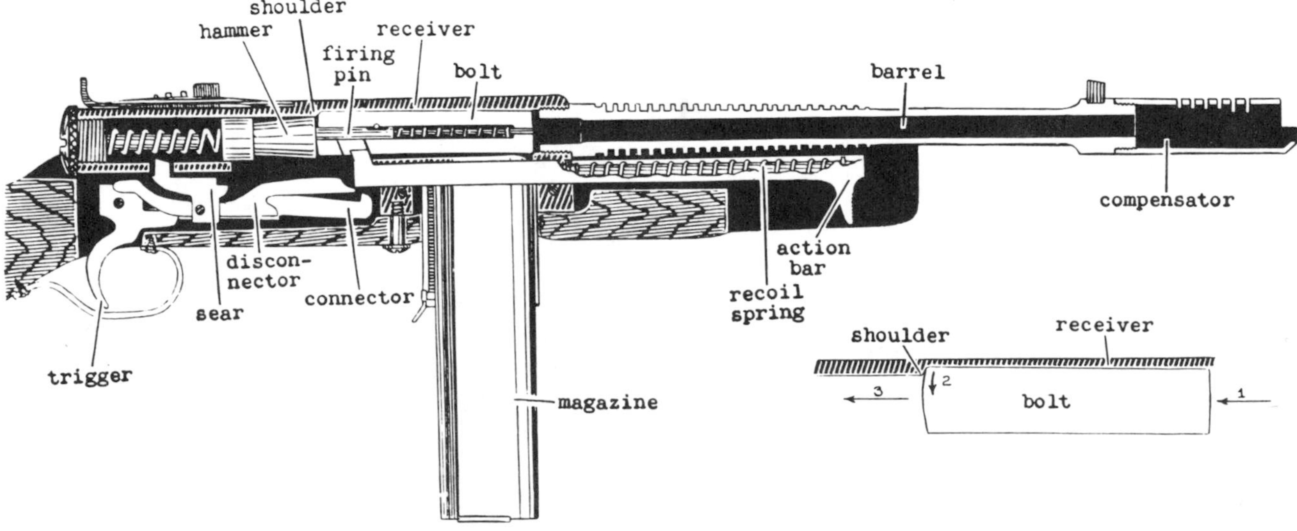

Stoppages and "Immediate Action"

This weapon is so simple and rugged in construction that very few stoppages are likely to be encountered if the weapon is given reasonable care and cleaning.

If the weapon has been kept clean and lightly oiled (too much oil slows down the mechanism), stoppages are likely to be caused by either faulty ammunition or defective magazines.

If the magazine spring has been weakened or the lips of the magazine damaged, the weapon may fail to feed.

If the ammunition is defective, it may fail to fire after being chambered or may stick in the action.

Immediate Action. This is the action taken automatically as the probable remedy. (1) Retract action bar with a quick motion to eject the cartridge in the chamber. (2) Resume fire.

If the Gun Still Fails to Fire. (1) Set selector on "Safe." (2) Remove magazine. (3) Pull back action bar and look through ejection port to see if gun is cleared. (4) Insert new magazine. (5) Reset selector and resume firing.

Note: When applying "Immediate Action" always keep gun trained on the target. Put your finger on the trigger only while the gun is pointing at the target. Use "F.A." only in case of emergency. Then fire in bursts of 3 to 5 shots. One body hit with a .45 bullet will stop almost any enemy.

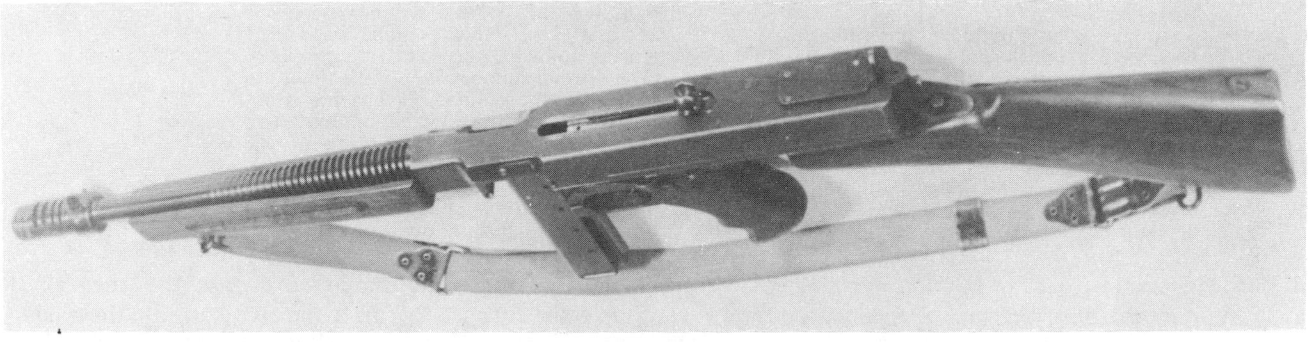

Thompson Cal. .45 M1928A1 Submachine Gun.

Caliber: .45 M 1911 cartridge, ball and tracer ammunition.

Magazines: (a) Type XX staggered box 20-shot capacity. (b) Type L, Drum, 50 rounds capacity. (c) Drum 100-round capacity, now obsolete.

Muzzle Velocity, Cartridge: With this barrel about 920 feet per second.

Muzzle Striking Energy: About 440 foot pounds.

Barrel Length: 10½" (With compensator on muzzle, 2" longer).

Overall Length of Gun: With stock and compensator about 33".

Overall Length Without Stock: 25¼".

Weight Without Magazine: 9 lbs. 13 ozs.

Weight of Loaded 20-Round Magazine: About 1¼ lbs.

Weight of Loaded 50-Round Magazine: About 4¾ lbs.

Front Sight: Fixed blade.

Rear Sight: Aperture, graduated to 600 yards with lateral adjustment to allow for windage and drift. A 50-yard open sight is provided for close quarters work with sight lever down. (Note: Gun may also be fitted with operative battle sight without adjustment.)

Accurate Range: About 100 yards.

Operated By: Rearward pressure of gas in firing chamber pressing back on fired cartridge case and its supporting bolt. This is a blowback system.

Locked: Claimed semi-locked by adhesion. Delayed locking system is claimed for this weapon. However, the weapon functions equally well with or without the alleged locking device. (Note: Later and cheaper models of this gun eliminate the so-called "Blish Principle" of adhesion of slipping inclined faces.)

Cooled: Cooling fins on barrel. Bolt stays open between shots, permitting circulation of air through breech opening and barrel.

Cyclic Rate of Fire: 600 to 700 per minute. (In some commercial models it is much higher.)

Actuator Knob: This is commonly known as a cocking handle. It is mounted on top of the receiver in the line of sight; and is slotted down the center to permit proper sight alignment.

Type of Fire: Single shot or full automatic. When weapon is cocked, the fire control lever positioned on the left side above the pistol grip may be pushed to either "Single" or "Auto." Also on the left side above the pistol grip is the thumb safety. It can be pushed to positions stamped "Safe" or "Fire." Note that the gun must be cocked before either of these levers can be set.

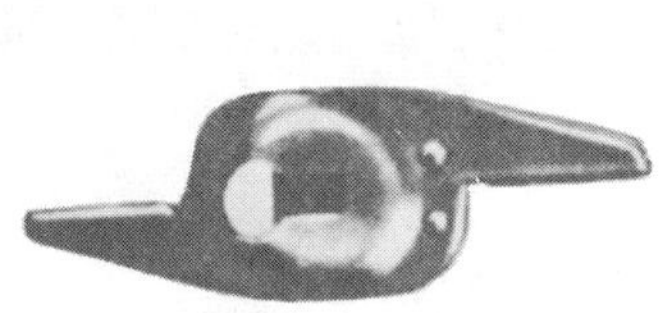

To load drum magazine: Raise the flat magazine key spring to disengage its stud and slide the key off via its slot.

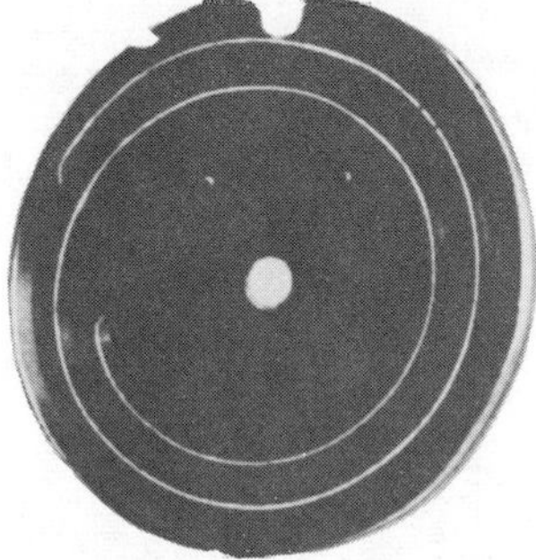

Lift off the magazine cover. Insert 5 cartridges base down in that section of the rotor in which the magazine feed opening is cut. Loading from right to left, place 5 cartridges in each section of the spiral track, taking care to load all outer spirals first.

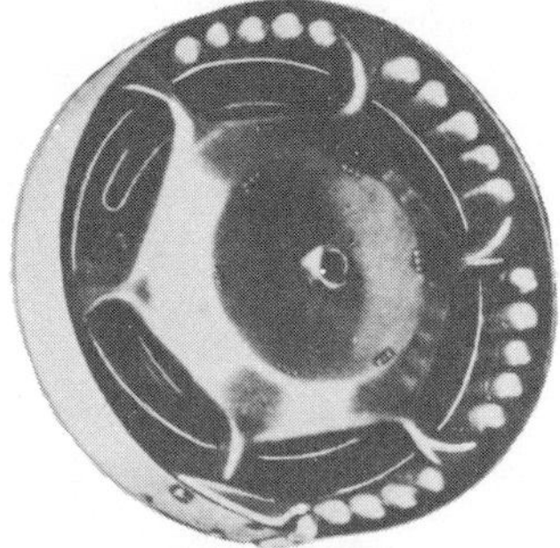

When correctly loaded, the first four sectors starting left from the magazine opening will contain 10 cartridges each, while the last two will have 5 each. Warning: Be careful not to insert any cartridges near the loops opposite the two sectors which hold five cartridges each; any cartridges so placed will jam the magazine when the rotor revolves. Now replace the magazine cover. Make sure that the large slot cut in it engages properly with the cover positioning stud. Slide the magazine key into place. Check to be sure that the stud on the spring correctly engages the center piece. Now wind the key from left to right. As it turns you will hear a distinct click. Count the number of clicks. Stamped on the magazine cover you will find the correct number of clicks necessary to indicate sufficient spring tension to work the magazine properly. (The normal number is 9 or 10 for a 50-shot magazine.) Note: If magazine is not to be used at once, wind up only two clicks to assure proper locking of the magazine and prevent straining spring. Caution: Never rewind a partially empty magazine. This is unnecessary and may break the magazine mainspring.

To Load Box Magazine. Load as for automatic pistol magazine, but support base of magazine against body or a solid surface if heavy spring tension makes it difficult to force cartridges down.

To Insert Box Magazine. Cock the gun, set the fire control lever for the type of fire desired. Put the safety on "safe." Insert rib at back of magazine in its recess at the front of the triggerguard and push in until the magazine catch engages with a click.

Warning: Remember that when the bolt goes forward in this weapon a cartridge is fired. Hence, if the weapon is not to be fired and you wish to move the bolt forward to prevent straining the recoil spring, first press down the magazine catch and remove the magazine from the gun. **Note:** While it is possible to insert the box type magazine in this gun with the action forward (that is, uncocked) this procedure is not recommended. In so inserting the magazine, make sure that the magazine catch is fully engaged because the overhang of the magazine spring must be taken up before the engagement is securely locked.

Inserting a Drum Magazine. Cock the gun. Set fire control lever for "single" or "full auto" fire. Put safety on "Safe." Hold magazine so that key spring is facing forward. Now insert the two ribs on the magazine into their horizontal grooves in the receiver and slide the magazine into the gun from the left side. Push in until the magazine catch clicks into place.

Warning: While this magazine may be inserted from the right side, it is unwise to do so as this may injure the magazine catch. Also, do not try to insert the magazine when the bolt is in forward position. The bottom of the bolt will strike against the mouth of the magazine and may injure it.

Field Stripping

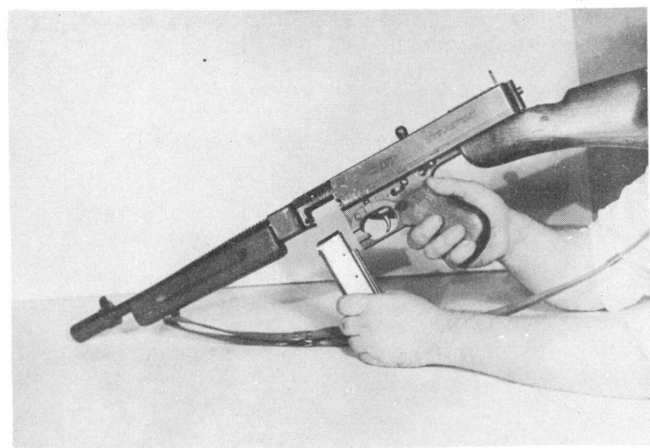

Remove magazine by pressing magazine catch up with the thumb and pulling 20-shot magazine straight down; or sliding 50-shot magazine out to the left.

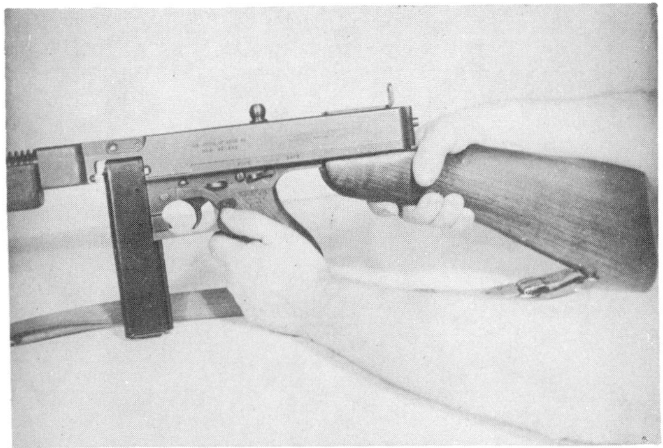

Set safety on "Fire" and set fire control lever on "Full Auto." Remember this can only be done when the weapon is cocked.

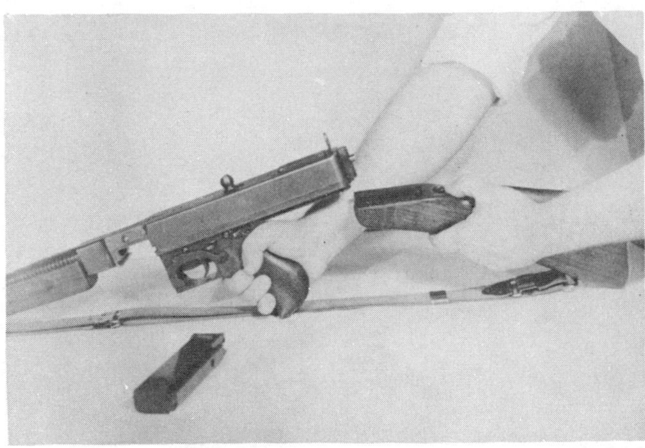

Remove buttstock by pressing its slide catch down and pulling stock straight to the rear out of its guide.

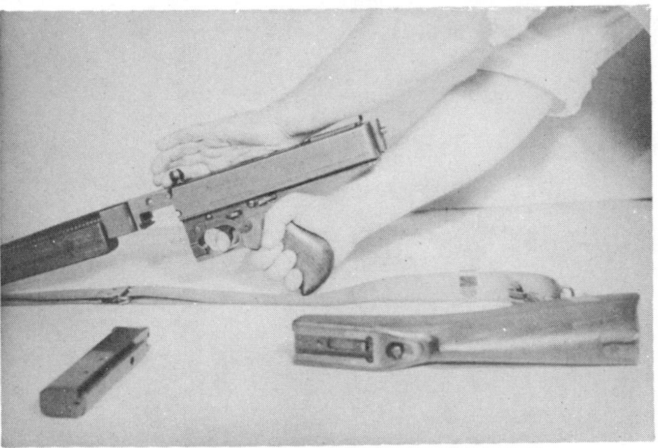

Hold firmly to actuator knob with left hand, pull trigger with right forefinger and ease bolt forward.

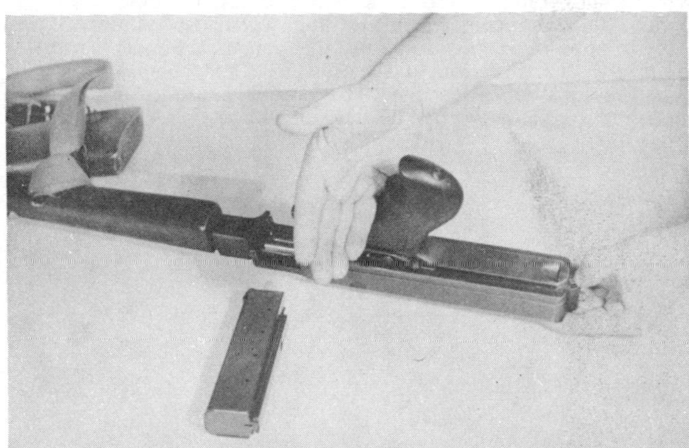

Turn gun upside down on table or knee. Push in the frame latch (the spring plunger on under side of frame behind pistol grip), and tap frame with right hand until it slides back a short distance.

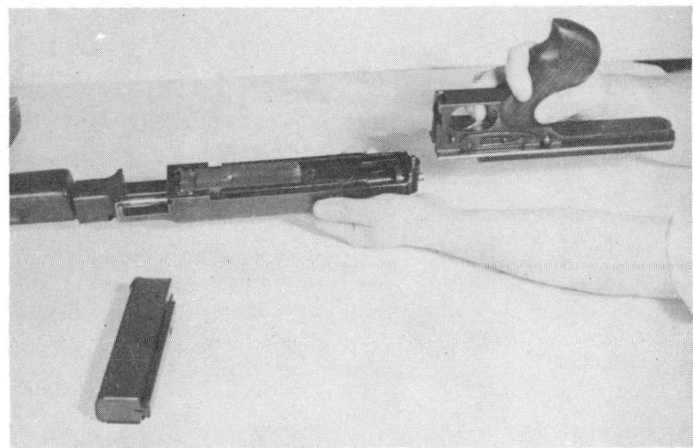

Grasp the rear grip with the right hand and pull the trigger holding the receiver firmly in the left hand, and slide the pistol grip group off out of its grooves.

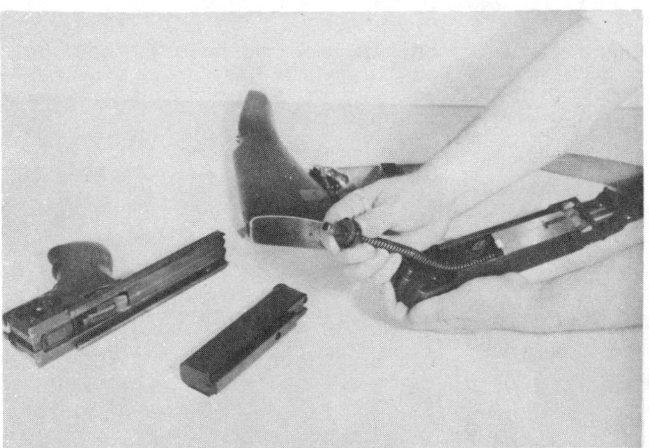

Remove recoil spring, as follows: With gun held firmly, turned upside down, grasp buffer flange with first and second fingers of right hand and pull out with upward and forward motion.

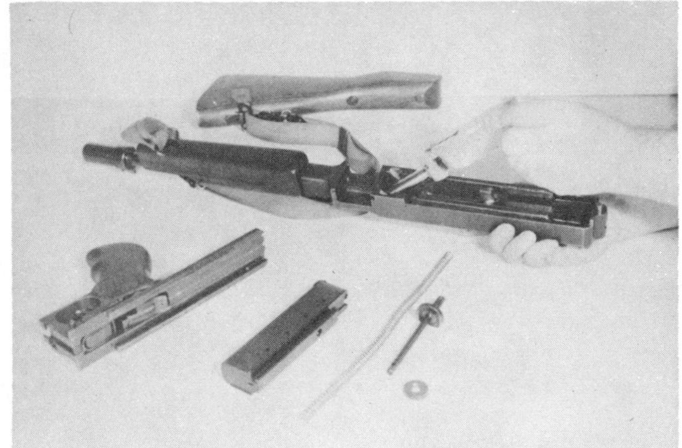

By pulling back on actuator knob, bolt is drawn back and can be removed to the rear.

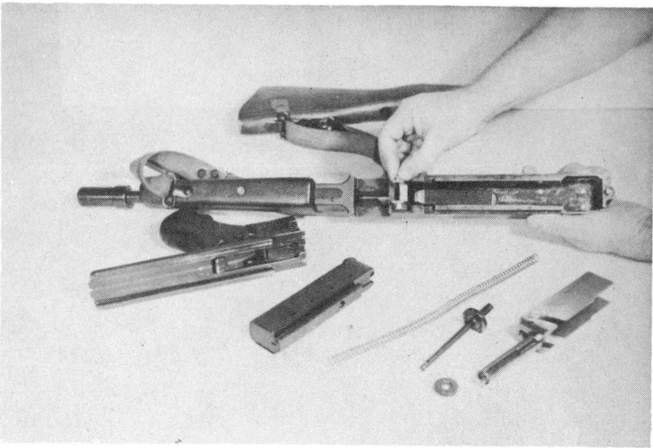

Actuator is then slipped forward with lock, and lock removed through its grooves in the receiver.

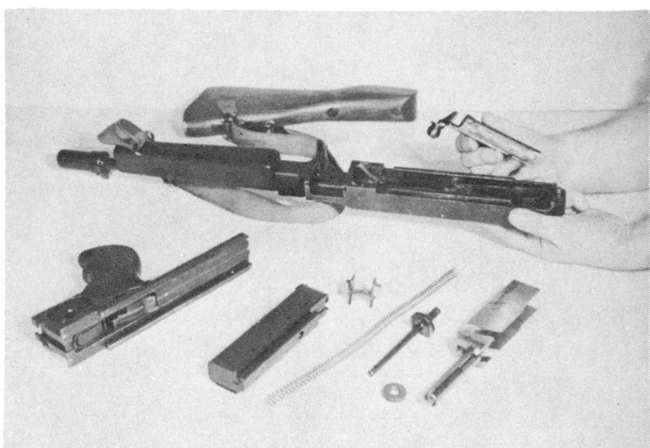

Then actuator itself is removed by sliding it to the rear. This completes field stripping, no further dismounting is necessary.

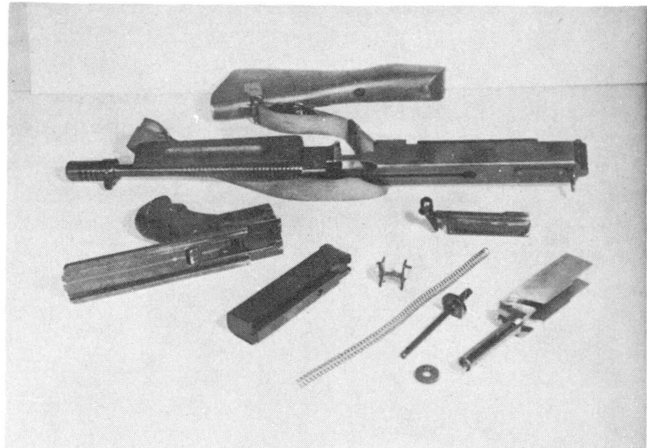

Note: On earlier models of this gun a special tool is required to remove the recoil spring. In this type, the stripping tool is inserted into its hole in the front end of the buffer rod. Then it is pushed in as far as it will go in the direction of the bolt. The rear end of the buffer rod is thus withdrawn from its hole at the rear end of the receiver. By tilting this stripping tool, the buffer may be grasped by the hand, and the recoil spring, fiber buffer disc, and rod will come out with the stripping tool. Buffer rod and spring are to be securely held so they do not fly apart.

Assembling

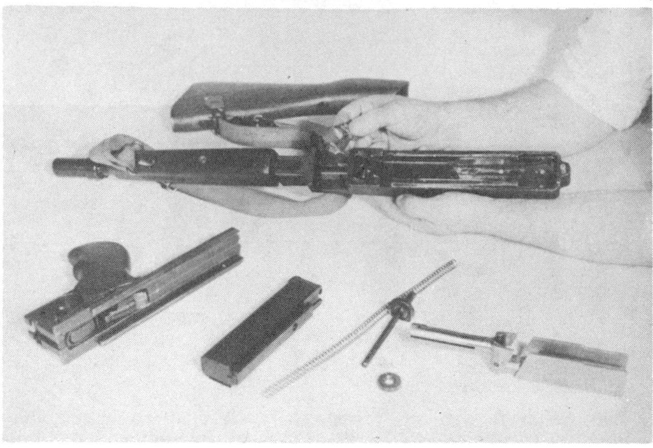

Inserting the actuator knob at its rear position, pull it forward and replace the lock which must be placed in its recesses in the receiver, so that the word "up" stamped on it is in uppermost position and the arrow stamped on it is pointing in the direction of the muzzle. The crosspiece of the lock (the lock is called the "H-Piece" because of its shape) must fit into the jaws of the actuator knob.

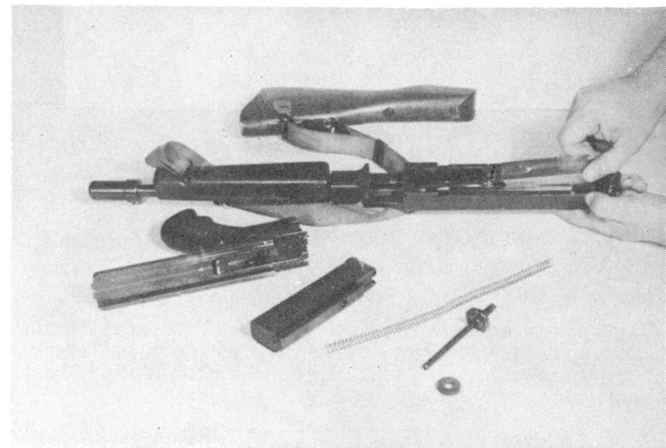

Pull the actuator and lock back and insert the bolt. Be sure and insert its bolt-end first so that the inclined cuts line up with the side members of the lock. (Now push the assembly forward as far it will go.)

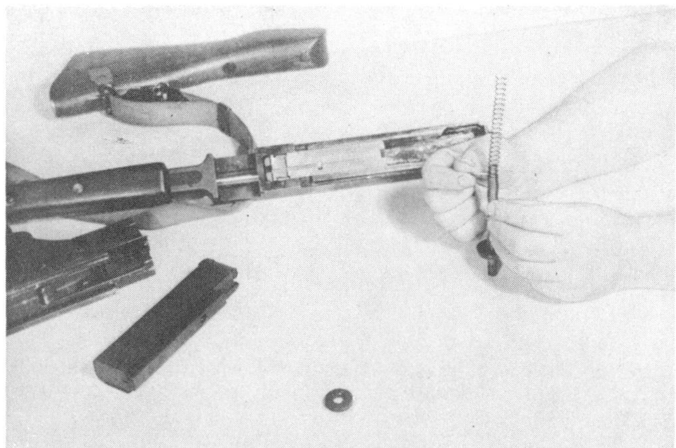

Compress the recoil spring over its rod, push it forward and down and push a nail or clip between the coils and through the hole in the rod.

Insert end of spring in hole in bolt; press rod forward until head of rod will slip into receiver and protrude through its hole to the rear; then withdraw nail.

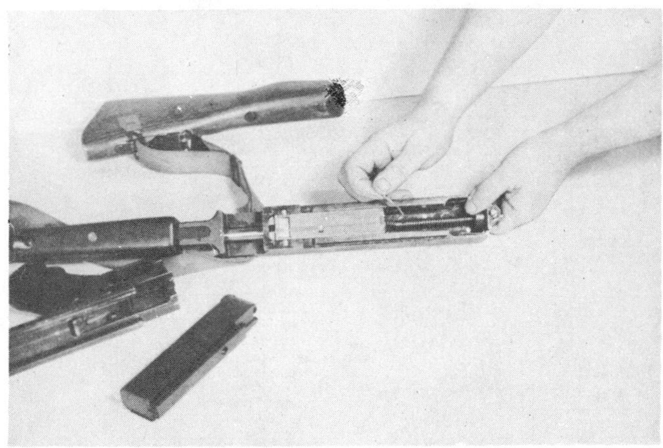

Note: If the gun is the earlier model, put the recoil spring over its rod and push front end of spring into housing and rear of breech block. Compress recoil spring on buffer rod a little at a time. While partly compressed, hold spring on rod with left hand and insert stripping tool into hole and buffer rod to retain spring in position. Replace fiber buffer disc and insert loose end of recoil spring in its hole in the actuator knob. Now place rear end of the buffer rod in its hole at the rear end under receiver. Draw back actuator knob until rear of bolt touches stripping tool. Recoil spring will now enter proper holes. Withdraw stripping tool.

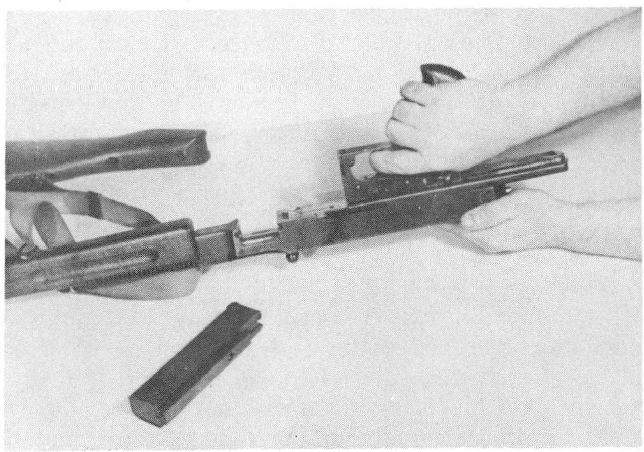

Holding the frame by rear grip pull the trigger and slide the frame forward in its guide in the receiver. Remember that safety must be at "Fire" position and fire control lever at "Full Auto."

Insert undercut of the frame in the buttstock and slide the butt forward until it locks in place.

How the Thompson Gun Works

Starting with the gun loaded and cocked the action is as follows: When the trigger is pressed, it moves the disconnector up to lift the sear lever. The sear lever raises the forward portion of sear, thus depressing the rear section and disengaging it from the notch on the bolt. The bolt is now free to be driven forward by the coiled recoil spring. If the fire control lever is set for semi-automatic fire, the rocker will act on the disconnector and sear lever to leave the sear free to lodge in the bolt on backward motion.

In its forward motion the bolt strips the top cartridge from the magazine, forces it into the firing chamber and drives the lock downward into locked position. The forward end of the bolt is round to fit in the bolt wall of the receiver, and the rear portion is rectangular to fit into the receiver cavity.

The forward motion of the bolt is halted by the rectangular end abutting against the receiver. The lock is an H-shaped piece of steel with lugs on each side whose center is engaged by the actuator.

The hammer is pivoted in the bolt between the H-piece and the receiver bottom, and as the action closes the lower end of this hammer strikes the abutment somewhat in advance of the bolt so that as the cartridge is seated, the upper end of the hammer strikes the firing pin. (The hammer is made so it can strike the firing pin only when the bolt is completely closed.) The extractor snaps over the cannelure of the cartridge case, and the firing pin strikes the primer.

Return Movement of the Action. The residual breech pressure forces the empty cartridge case back against the bolt, which in turn transmits the pressure to the H-piece locking device. This in turn transmits it to the locking surface of the receiver.

How the Lock Works

The lock, or H-piece, is situated in a 70° inclined slot in the bolt, with its lugs engaged in short 45° grooves recessed in the receiver. When engaged in the short 45° inclined slot with the H-piece offering resistance to the backward motion of the bolt, resistance to this lifting action is offered by the forward inclined base of the H-piece meeting the rear face of the 70° inclined slot in the bolt itself. The rising of this H-shaped lock is further resisted because its bridge is thrust up into the slot in the actuator knob, which is set at an angle of 10° from the vertical, pointed to the rear.

The general direction of movement of the locking piece, as a result of the movement of these several components, is upward and backward. Thus the bolt is prevented from moving to the rear while the chamber pressure is dangerous.

Because of the rapidity with which the pressure in the bore rises to its maximum on firing, the bolt is said to be supported by adhesion of the inclined surfaces until the pressure has again dropped materially, which acts as a breech locking factor.

For this adhesion lock to work, it is essential that the engaging surfaces remain constantly lubricated by the oil pads in the receiver.

Note: Engineers disagree as to the actual value of this locking system. The necessity for constant oiling, incidentally, is a source of jams. Regardless of the real or theoretical value of the locking device, the fact remains that the weight of the parts themselves and the inertia of the recoil spring are sufficient to work the weapon safely and satisfactorily when the locking device is removed from the gun.

The forward end of the recoil spring is housed in a cavity in the actuator. The buffer forms a guide for the rear end of the recoil spring, permitting it to compress in a straight line as the action goes backward. A fiber washer is provided to absorb the shock of recoil, and oil pads in the receiver lubricate the locking lugs and bolt sides during the passage of those pieces.

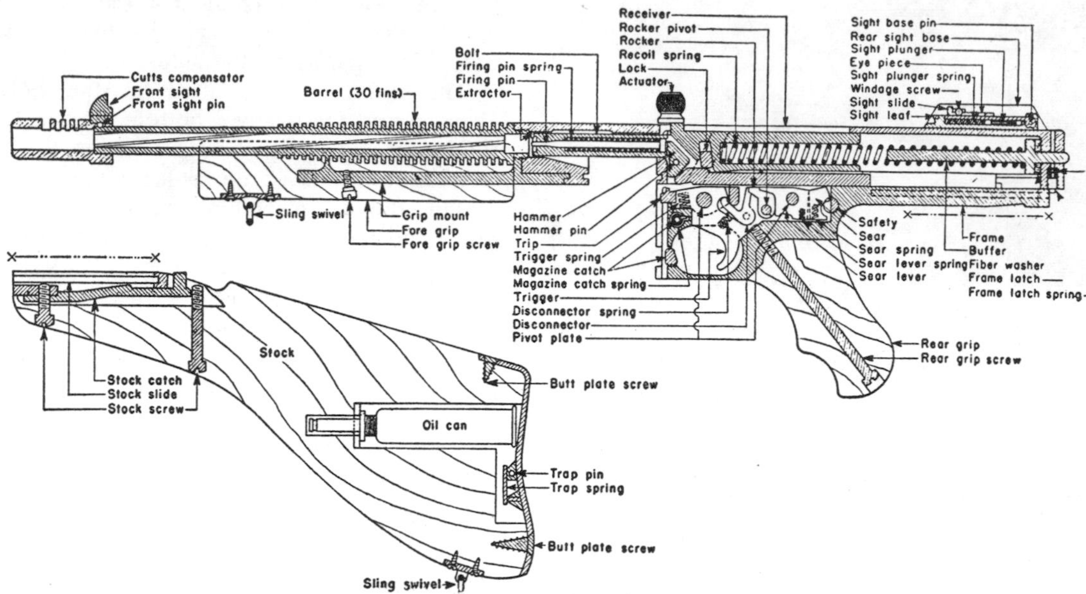

The extractor, which is positioned on the right forward end of the bolt, draws the empty case out of the firing chamber until it strikes the ejector which moves into a clearance cut in the bolt path and hurls it out of the ejection port.

If a box type magazine is in the weapon, the magazine spring forces cartridges up in line bringing the next cartridge into position for the forward movement of the bolt. If the drum magazine is being used, springs inside the drum twist the spiral and feed a cartridge into line.

Stoppages and Immediate Action

It is essential that this weapon be kept properly oiled. When considerable dust is present, care must be taken that the supply of oil is very low. All surfaces of the receiver, bolt extractor and ejector having contact with powder gases should be cleaned as soon after firing as possible in a solution of a quarter-pound sal soda to a pint of very hot water. Boiling water will suffice if there is no sal soda available. Parts must then be thoroughly dried and well oiled. Give special attention to cleaning the compensator attached to the muzzle. Firing will fill the escape slots in the compensator with burnt powder residue which will interfere with the efficiency of the compensator. This will radically affect the sighting of the weapon as well as increase the recoil.

Considerably more attention must be paid to oiling the working surfaces of this gun than to the average blowback-type of submachine gun. Since the cartridge cases are lubricated as they are fed into the firing chamber, there is a tendency for oil and residue to cake there; and the breech cleaning bristol brush supplied with the gun should be used to clear the firing chamber, whenever possible.

Failure to Extract. Failure to extract or eject will usually indicate a weak or broken extractor, or poor ammunition. If the extractor is broken, the bolt traveling forward will feed another cartridge, jamming the weapon. To clear such a condition, draw the bolt to the rear, and remove the magazine, allowing the live cartridge to slide out of the receiver. Empty case may then be punched out or pried out. It will be necessary to remove the bolt and replace the extractor to correct the condition.

If the ammunition is weak, usually indicating old ammunition, the feed of the forward motion of the bolt will be slowed and the cartridge will not feed from magazine into the firing chamber. In this case, the bolt should be drawn rapidly to the rear to throw out the misfire.

If cartridge fails to fire due to defective primer (a condition often caused by oil seeping in around the primer seat), rapidly pull the bolt back as far as it will go to let the next round rise in line.

Magazine Trouble. If mouth of magazine has been damaged, round will not feed up correctly. It is necessary to insert a perfect magazine. If cartridge fails to feed because it has not been properly positioned in the magazine, slip it out of the magazine, allow the next one to go into place and return magazine to firing position. Should this type of stoppage continue, replace with new magazine and oil weapon at first opportunity.

Dent in Magazine. Mishandling the magazines will often dent the walls. In such a case the rising magazine spring may be interfered with, or the follower may be stopped by the dent and cause poor feeding. The remedy here is to replace the magazine.

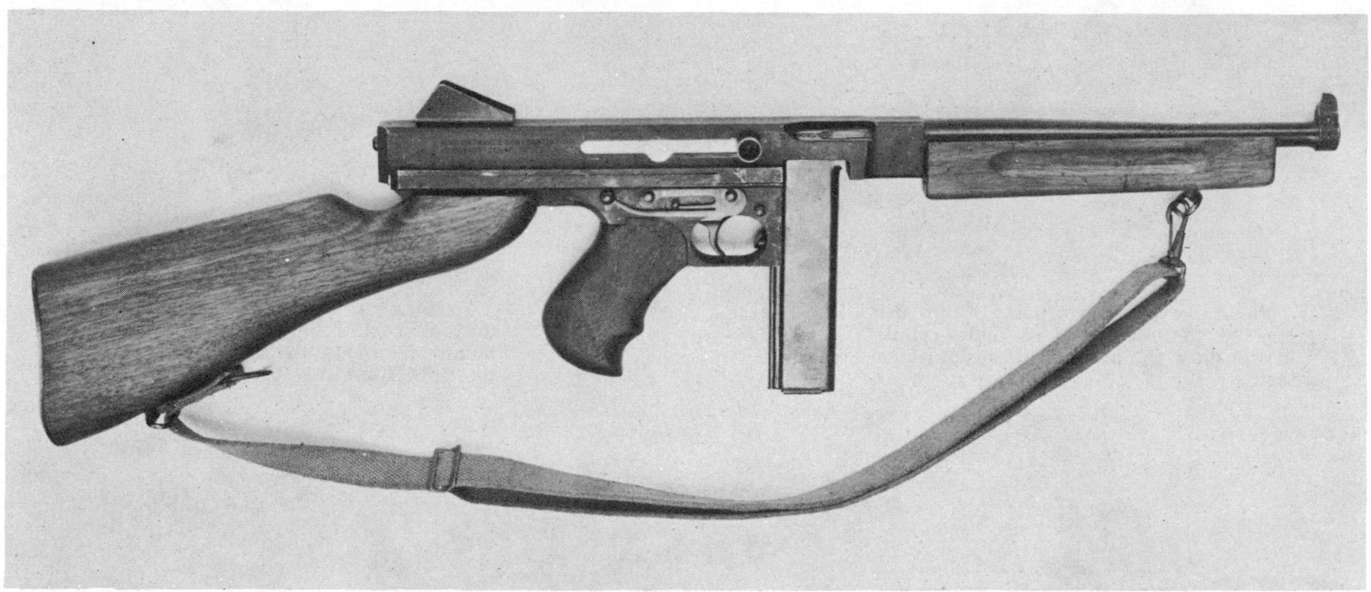

Cal. .45 Submachine Gun M1.

This was one of the last models of the Thompson Submachine Gun manufactured for the United States Army. While it looks very much like the Thompson 1928 A1, actually it is a very much simpler, sturdier, and cheaper weapon. The bolt in the M1 model is heavier than the bolt in the earlier type.

This model eliminates the useless lock, actuator, and breech oiler of the earlier models. This design is further simplified by eliminating the cooling fins on the barrel. No compensator is issued with this gun.

While many of the parts are interchangeable in these two guns, it must be noted that the earlier models use the complicated Blish system which theoretically locks the weapon by adhesion at the moment of firing. The M1 type, which is simpler in all respects, makes no pretensions to being anything more than the safe, sturdy, blowback weapon that it is. The bolt handle travels in a slot cut on the right hand side of the receiver.

While the frame looks like the 1928A1 model, it differs in that the buttstock is permanently attached by screws and cannot be slid off as can the one in the Model 1928A1.

While the design of the safety and the rocket pivot have been changed, they perform the same functions as the corresponding parts in the earlier model.

This gun will take straight line box magazines holding 20 or 30 cartridges. The drum magazine cannot be used on this gun.

The M1A1, the last production Thompson, has a firing pin machined into the face of the bolt and thereby does away with the firing pin, firing pin spring, and firing pin retaining pin of earlier models.

Field Stripping

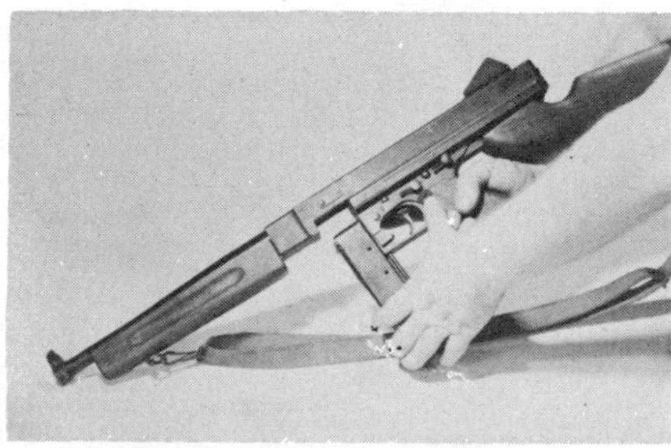

Remove magazine by pressing magazine catch up with the thumb and pulling the box magazine straight down and out of its guide.

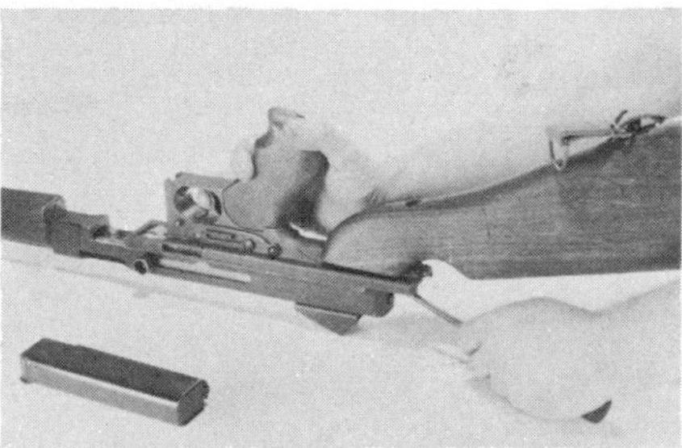

With bolt forward, push in on receiver locking catch.

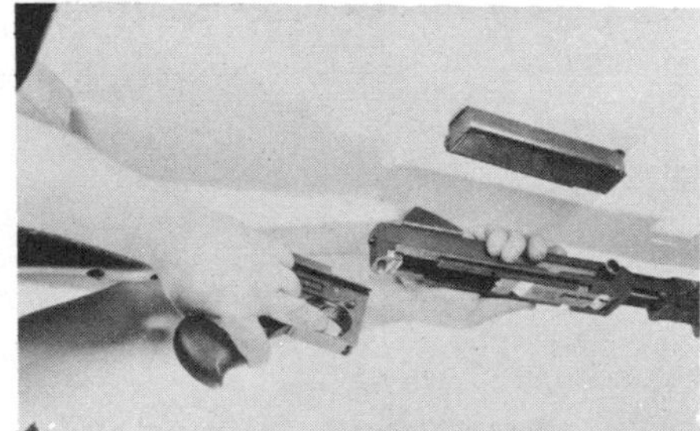

Pressing trigger, draw frame straight back out of its guides in the receiver.

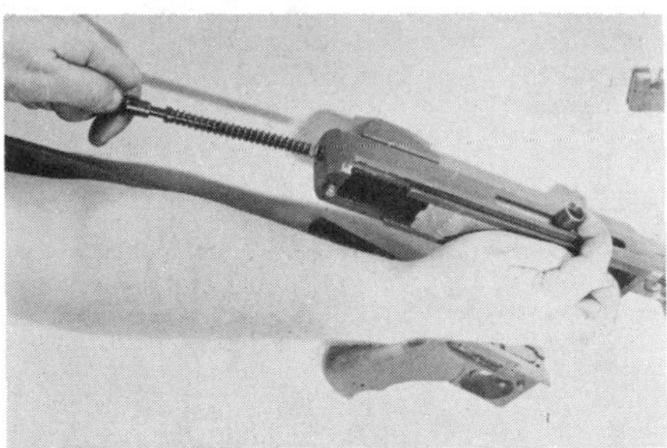

Push the plug protruding from the rear of the receiver (the buffer pilot) in and draw the buffer pad up out of its seat.

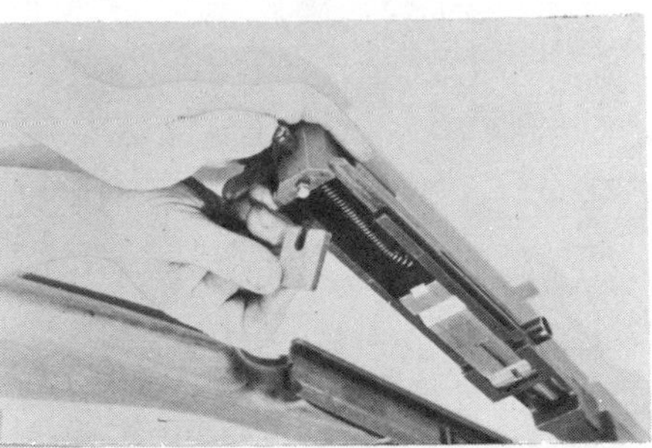

Holding on to the buffer pilot, pull the bolt back about half way. This will permit removing the recoil spring and the pilot from the rear of the receiver.

Still holding the weapon upside down, lift the rear end of the bolt when the bolt handle is opposite the low cut in the center of its slot in the receiver. Pull the bolt handle out.

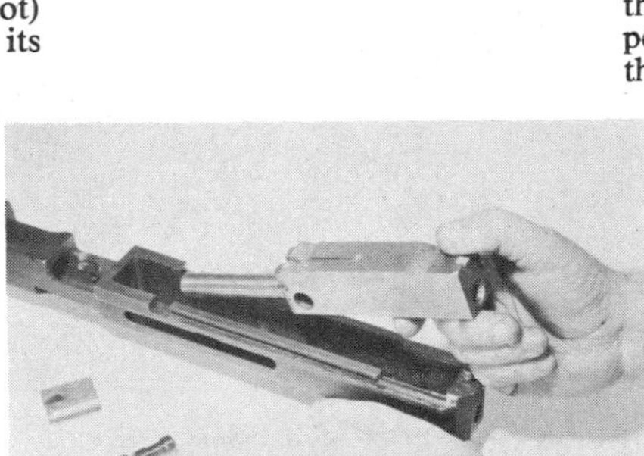

Lift the bolt back and up out of the receiver.

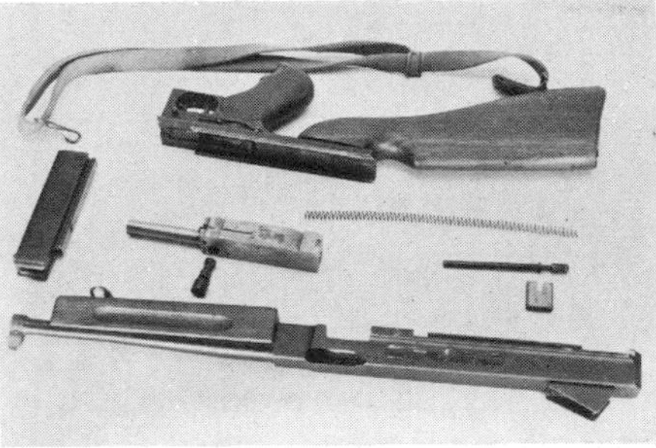

This completes field stripping. No further dismounting is normally necessary.

Field Assembling

Assemble the buffer pilot to the recoil spring and holding the gun on the knee insert the recoil spring through the buffer pilot hole in the receiver from the outside, permitting the recoil spring to slide into the hole in the bolt.

Replace the bolt in the receiver so the bolt handle hole is in the center of the half circle in the receiver slot. Push the back end of the bolt up slightly out of the receiver. Push the hammer back against the shoulder of the bolt and the bolt handle can then be inserted. Then slide the bolt forward.

Now move the bolt halfway in the middle of the receiver, and assemble the buffer pilot with the recoil spring into the receiver and bolt.

When the end of the buffer pilot is flush with the outside of the receiver, the buffer pad can be placed over the buffer.

Cal. .45 M3 Submachine Gun.

This weapon was developed by our Ordnance Department to fill the need for a submachine gun low in cost and simple to manufacture. It is the United States' answer to the British Sten gun and the German Schmeisser Machine Pistol 38. It is crude in appearance, because its cost is less than that of a good automatic pistol.

Caliber: 45 M 1911 cartridge, ball and tracer ammunition.
Magazine: Box magazine positioned under receiver, capacity 30 cartridges.
Muzzle Velocity, Cartridge: About 920 feet per second.
Ballistic Data: About same for other submachine weapons using this cartridge.
Barrel Length: 8".
Overall Length of Gun: About 30".
Weight: 8 lb. 1 oz.
Sights: Fixed. Aperture rear sight.
Range: Standard for this type of weapon and cartridge. About 100 yards.
Gun Operated By: Backward pressure of gases against fired cartridge case in chamber.
Locked: Simple blowback, unlocked. Heavy bolt and return spring delay opening of breech until bullet has left barrel. An added factor in this weapon is a fixed firing pin in the bolt, so constructed that excess energy from its forward movement is expended simultaneously with the explosion of the powder. This feature also gives greatly improved accuracy, because it is largely responsible for the fact that the gun does not climb, as do other weapons of this type, during rapid fire.
Cooled: Bolt remains open between shots permitting air to circulate through breech and barrel.
Position of Cocking Handle: A rocker arm on right side of gun just behind magazine housing. Pulling this back draws bolt back to full cock.
Special Feature: This rocker arm, when pushed forward while bolt is back, stays in forward position while firing. Cocking handles in most other submachine guns travel back and forth with each movement of the bolt. This is often a disturbing factor for firer.
Type of Fire: Full automatic only.
Rate of Fire: 450 rounds per minute. This is very nearly the ideal rate for submachine use in full automatic fire. Gun was deliberately slowed down to this figure.
Breech Cover: Another special feature on this weapon is a hinged breech cover which springs open when the rocker arm is pulled back to cock the bolt. This provides added protection for the working mechanism, and keeps dirt out of the action. This cover, as explained later, is also a safety.
Stock: A skeleton stock is provided. This skeleton is of heavy wire and slides into tubes on the side of the frame when not in use. In this position it is exceptionally compact and the gun may be used as a machine pistol. Pulling out these heavy wires provides a shoulder stock, converting the weapon to a full submachine gun.

Loading and Firing

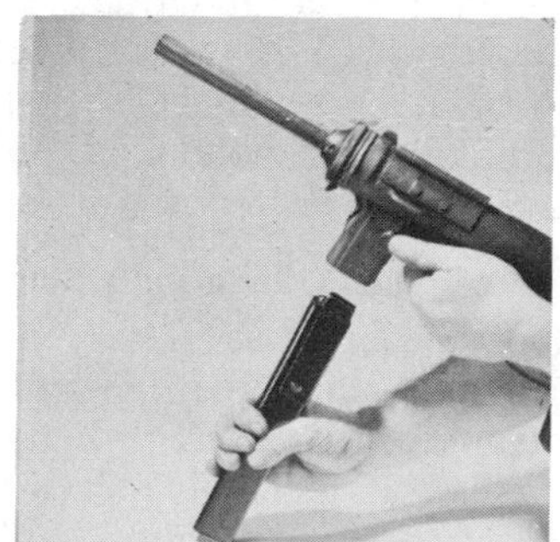

A loaded magazine is inserted in the magazine housing from below until it locks.

Pull the cocking handle back as far as it will go to open the ejection port cover to its full extent and draw the bolt back until it is caught and held by the sear. Release the handle and let it fly forward.

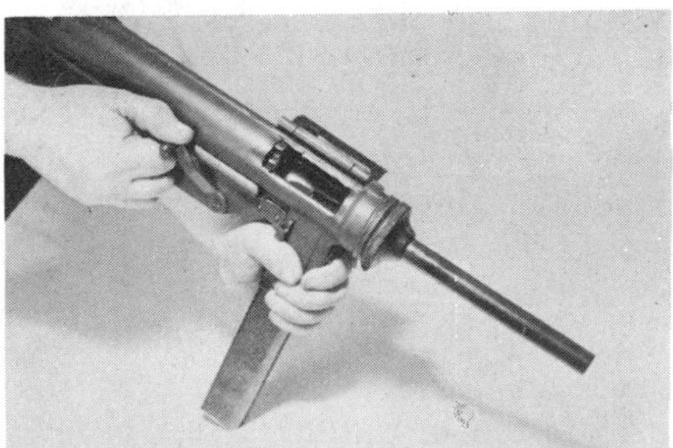

If it is desired to carry the gun ready for use but on safety, push the cover down into place. Otherwise the gun is ready to fire on a pull of the trigger.

Field Stripping

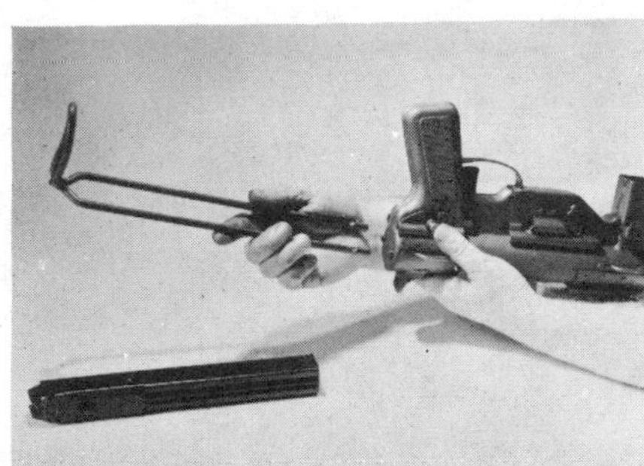

With the magazine out of the weapon, push in the stock catch on the left side of the receiver above the pistol grip with the left thumb and pull the wire stock out of its grooves.

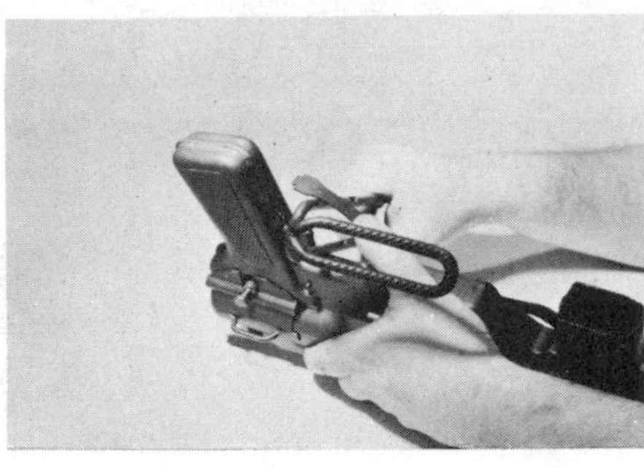

Insert the shoulder end of the wire stock inside the triggerguard to provide a pressure point. Then press down on the lower end of the triggerguard until it springs out of its slot in the pistol grip. Handle this triggerguard carefully as it is of light gauge spring steel. Rotate it toward the muzzle of the gun. This will unhook it so it can be lifted out.

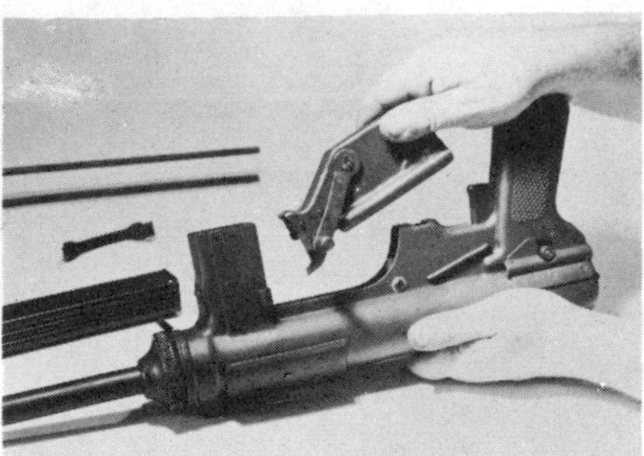

Push down on the housing assembly unit a short distance, and then lift it to the rear until it can be lifted off. This should be done with care to prevent injury to the metal.

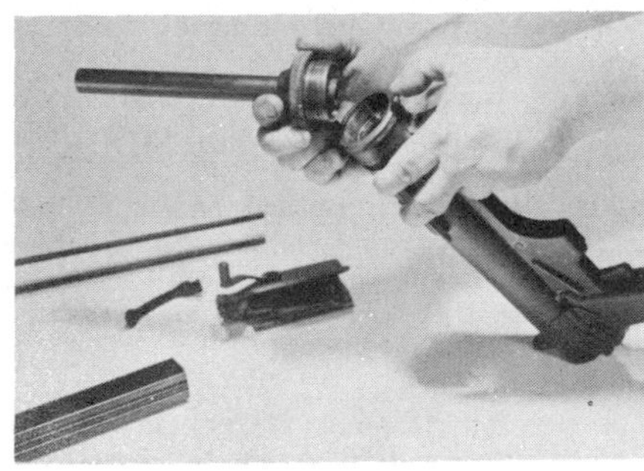

Pull the ratchet catch back with the left thumb and unscrew the barrel assembly from left to right. The barrel and its collar will come out.

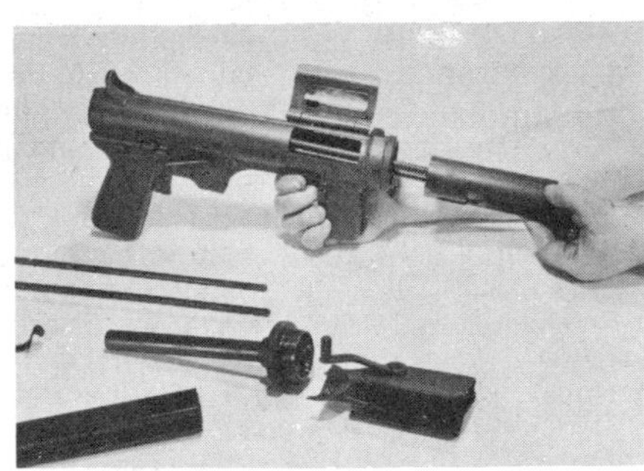

Open the bolt cover and tilt the gun forward. The bolt and the two guide rods and their springs will come forward out the front of the receiver.

No further stripping is normally necessary.

How the M3 Submachine Gun Works

When a loaded magazine is inserted into the magazine housing and pushed upward until it locks, the cocking handle on the right side of the gun is drawn back to its full extent. This movement raises the bolt cover (which must be opened full to permit proper ejection) and also cocks the bolt against the tension of two recoil springs mounted in the receiver and extending one on each side into the bolt itself.

When the trigger is pressed the sear releases the bolt. The driving springs force the bolt forward and the feed guides machined into the bolt strike the rear of the topmost cartridge in the magazine and drive it ahead into the firing chamber.

As the cartridge enters the chamber the bolt continues forward and its extractor snaps over the head of the cartridge to fasten in the extracting groove.

The firing pin can now strike the primer and discharge the cartridge.

As the bullet moves out the barrel, the back pressure pushes the empty cartridge case out of the chamber and transmits its force to the bolt face pushing it to the rear.

The bolt assembly as it goes back takes the empty cartridge case with it. The case strikes against the ejector and is thrown out the ejection port.

The driving springs are compressed around their guide rods and the bolt travels back on tracks in the receiver until the energy is absorbed and the bolt is caught by the sear.

The gun will fire as long as the trigger is held back and there are any cartridges in the magazine. If the bolt cover is pushed down in place when the bolt is back, it acts as a safety by holding the bolt off the sear and also interfering with forward travel. It is also a dust cover.

Special Note on the M3 Submachine Gun

This weapon was developed as a low cost mass production submachine gun along the lines of the British Sten and the German Schmeisser MP 40. Its readily dismountable barrel and bolt assembly permitted it to be adapted, by replacing those units, to handle the 9mm German Parabellum cartridge.

As the Parabellum is the most widely used pistol and submachine gun cartridge in the world, this feature was valuable in making the weapon available to underground groups in Europe. The later model of this gun, the M3A1, is still used.

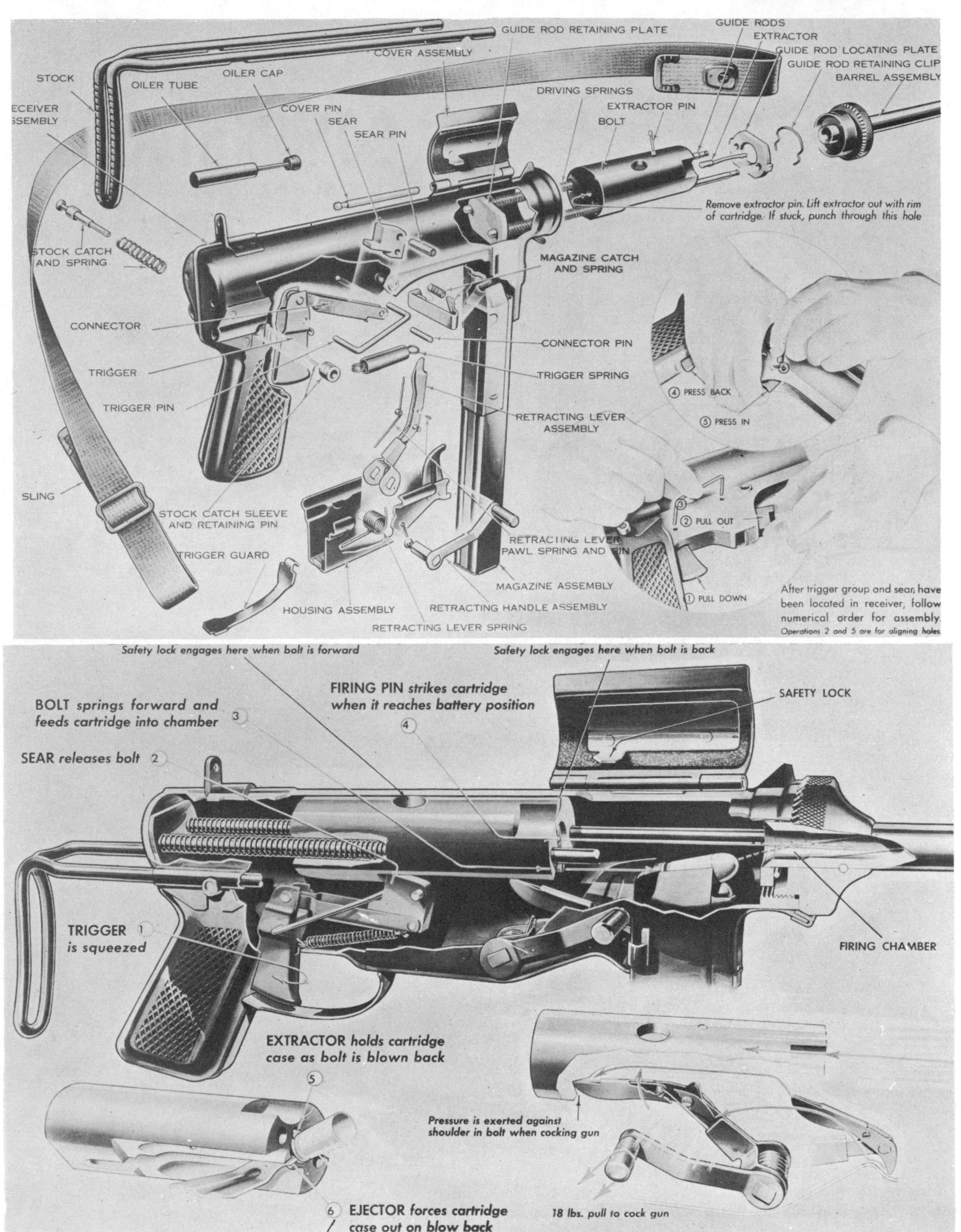
GUIDE ROD RETAINING PLATE
GUIDE RODS
EXTRACTOR
GUIDE ROD LOCATING PLATE
GUIDE ROD RETAINING CLIP
BARREL ASSEMBLY
COVER ASSEMBLY
STOCK
OILER CAP
OILER TUBE
RECEIVER ASSEMBLY
COVER PIN
SEAR
SEAR PIN
DRIVING SPRINGS
EXTRACTOR PIN
BOLT
Remove extractor pin. Lift extractor out with rim of cartridge. If stuck, punch through this hole
STOCK CATCH AND SPRING
MAGAZINE CATCH AND SPRING
CONNECTOR
CONNECTOR PIN
TRIGGER
TRIGGER SPRING
TRIGGER PIN
④ PRESS BACK
⑤ PRESS IN
RETRACTING LEVER ASSEMBLY
SLING
STOCK CATCH SLEEVE AND RETAINING PIN
② PULL OUT
RETRACTING LEVER PAWL SPRING AND PIN
TRIGGER GUARD
MAGAZINE ASSEMBLY
① PULL DOWN
HOUSING ASSEMBLY
RETRACTING HANDLE ASSEMBLY
RETRACTING LEVER SPRING
After trigger group and sear, have been located in receiver, follow numerical order for assembly.
Operations 2 and 5 are for aligning holes.
Safety lock engages here when bolt is forward
Safety lock engages here when bolt is back
FIRING PIN strikes cartridge when it reaches battery position 4
BOLT springs forward and feeds cartridge into chamber 3
SAFETY LOCK
SEAR releases bolt 2
TRIGGER 1 is squeezed
FIRING CHAMBER
EXTRACTOR holds cartridge case as bolt is blown back 5
Pressure is exerted against shoulder in bolt when cocking gun
6 EJECTOR forces cartridge case out on blow back
18 lbs. pull to cock gun

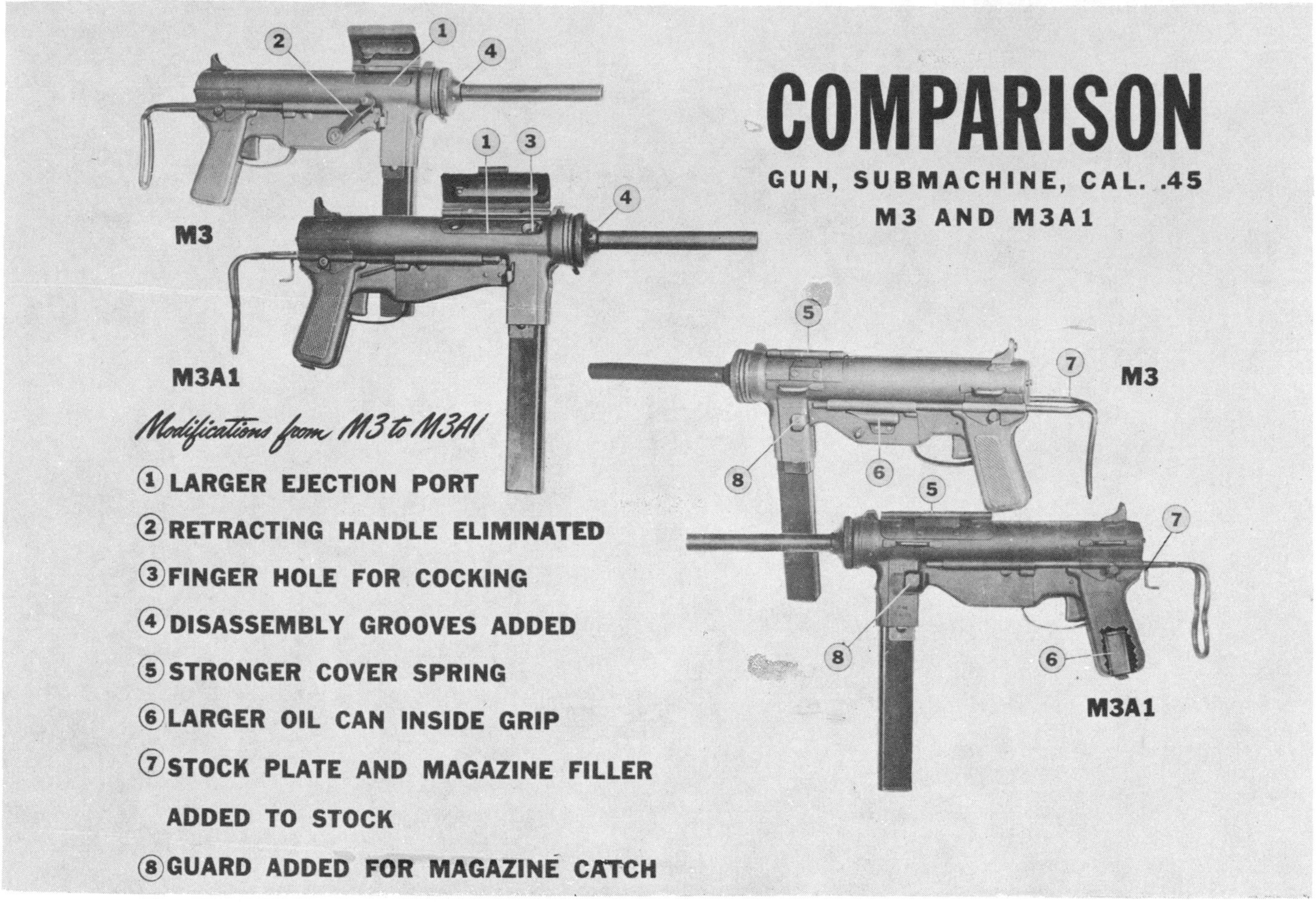

COMPARISON

GUN, SUBMACHINE, CAL. .45

M3 AND M3A1

M3

M3A1

Modifications from M3 to M3A1

1. LARGER EJECTION PORT
2. RETRACTING HANDLE ELIMINATED
3. FINGER HOLE FOR COCKING
4. DISASSEMBLY GROOVES ADDED
5. STRONGER COVER SPRING
6. LARGER OIL CAN INSIDE GRIP
7. STOCK PLATE AND MAGAZINE FILLER ADDED TO STOCK
8. GUARD ADDED FOR MAGAZINE CATCH

M3

M3A1

U.S. MACHINE GUNS

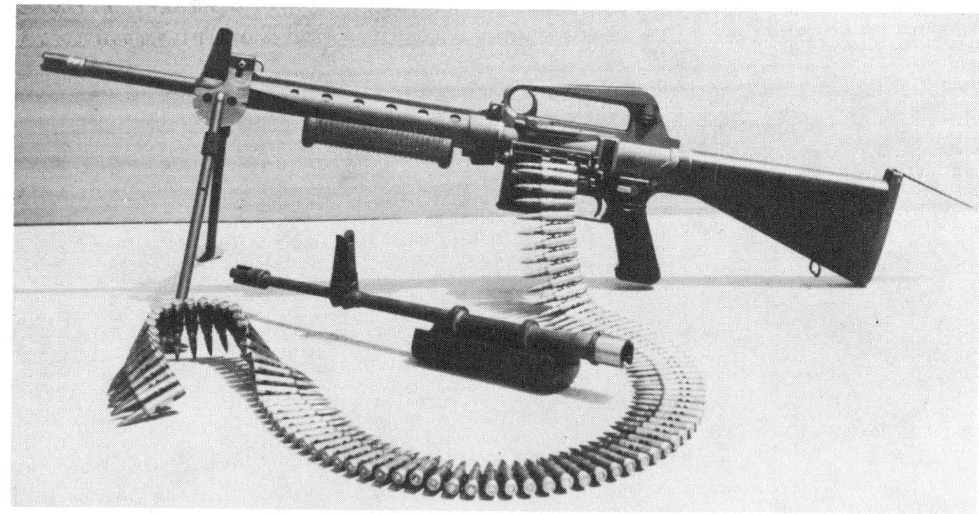

AR-10 7.62mm Light Machine Gun.

This is the machine gun version of the Armalite rifle with a heavy barrel. The light barrel shown in photo may also be used. This weapon uses a conventional metallic link belt.

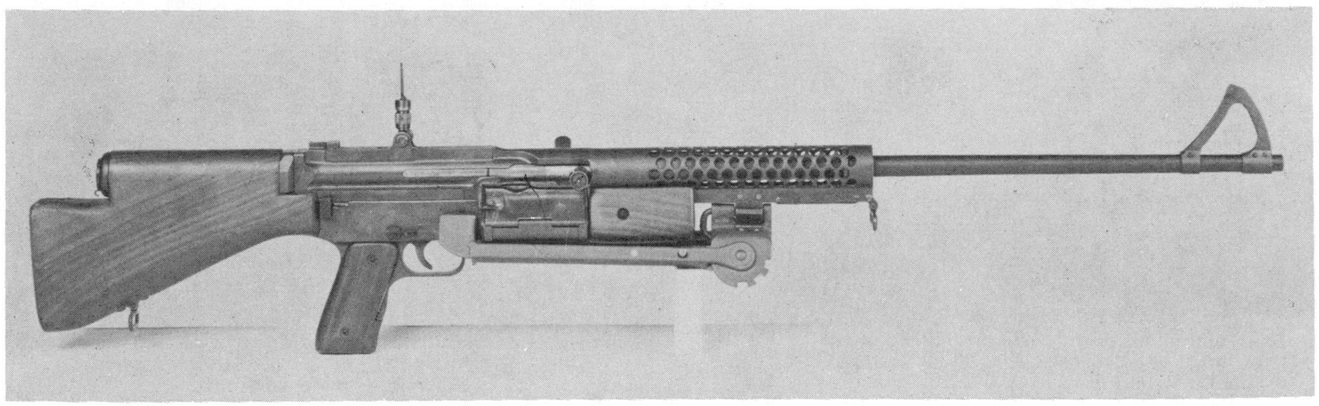

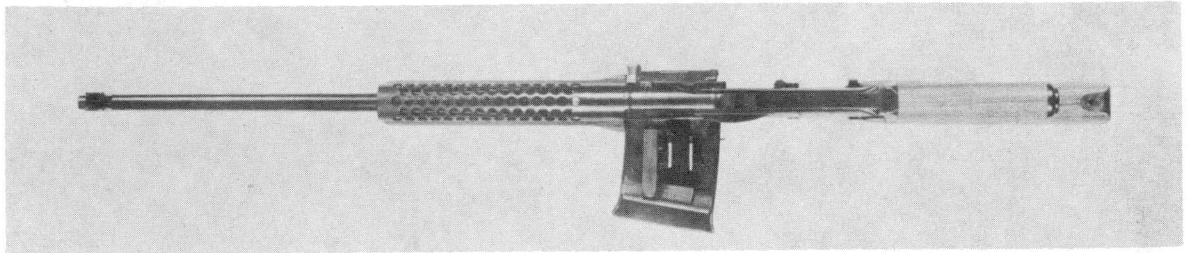

Johnson Light Machine Gun 1941 (Used by U.S. Marines in World War II).

Caliber: .30 U. S.
Magazine: Detachable box.
Capacity: 20 cartridges. Single column feed.
Positioned: On left side of gun. When empty it may be removed and replaced or may be loaded from right side of gun through loading gate with single cartridges or Springfield 5-shot clip.
Ballistics: Standard for cartridges employed.
Barrel Length: 22" standard.
Overall Length of Gun: 42".
Weight Without Magazine: 12½ lbs.
Sights: Special Lyman-Johnson rear peep sight with two automatic fire apertures set for long or average battle range. Adj. in ½ minute clicks.
Gun Operated By: Recoil. Barrel recoils ½" during which time the unlocking takes place. Straight line mainspring behind bolt is compressed by rearward action to provide energy for forward motion of the gun.
Locked: By rotary bolt with 8 lugs.
Cooled: Air. Gun has perforated cooling jacket about rear section of barrel. Also gun is fitted with a device to permit keeping the bolt open between shots, thus permitting circulation of air through breech and barrel.
Position of Cocking Handle: Right side of receiver.
Type of Fire: Single shot or full automatic. Change lever is on right side of gun above trigger. In center it is safe; pushed to the rear it is automatic; pushed to the front it will fire single shots.
Cyclic Rate: 400 to 450 rounds per minute with normal buffer tension. May be adjusted within limits of 300 to 900 r.p.m.

Loading and Firing

This is the only weapon made which may be fired from either a closed or an open bolt. Used as a semi-automatic weapon for accurate fire, the bolt is closed to prevent disturbing the aim by movement of the heavy parts going forward. Turning the change lever on the Johnson to the forward or semi-automatic position, allows the bolt to go forward and lock without firing a cartridge. When the trigger is pulled, one cartridge is fired and the gun is cocked and the bolt is closed ready for the next shot.

When firing automatically, bolt should be open to permit air circulation and prevent a cartridge in the firing chamber being cooked off by barrel heat during suspension of fire. This is achieved in the Johnson by setting the change lever back at the automatic position. The bolt will stay open in this position and will go forward to fire the cartridge when the trigger is pressed. The gun will continue to function until trigger is released or the magazine is empty.

Loaded magazine is inserted in the housing on left side of gun. If the weapon is to be fired single shot, set change lever at forward position for semi-automatic. If weapon is to be used full automatic, set change lever at rear position for full auto.

Pull bolt back as far as it will go. If set for semi-automatic, bolt will run forward and drive cartridge into firing chamber ready for full press of the trigger. If change lever is set for full auto, bolt will stay open and will go forward when trigger is pressed to fire cartridge and continue firing cycle as long as trigger is held.

Magazine release catch is on top of magazine housing. Pressing it down releases magazine to be withdrawn from the gun when empty.

A loading gate is provided on the right side of the gun. Single cartridges or Springfield clips may be inserted into the gate from the right hand side and forced through into the magazine. This permits reloading magazine while partly empty.

Field Stripping

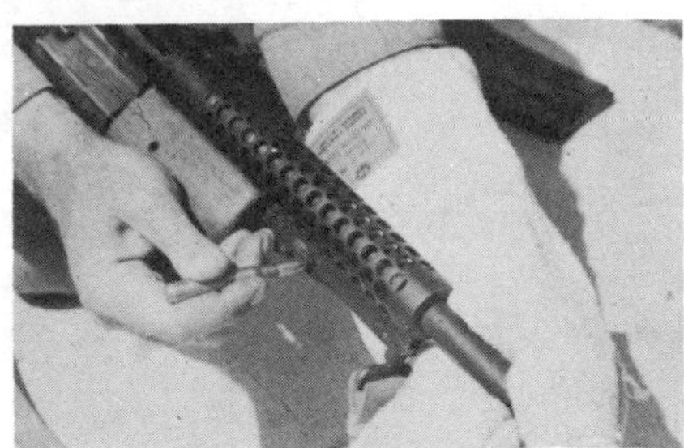

Push in barrel latch with point of bullet to disengage the latch and pull out the barrel.

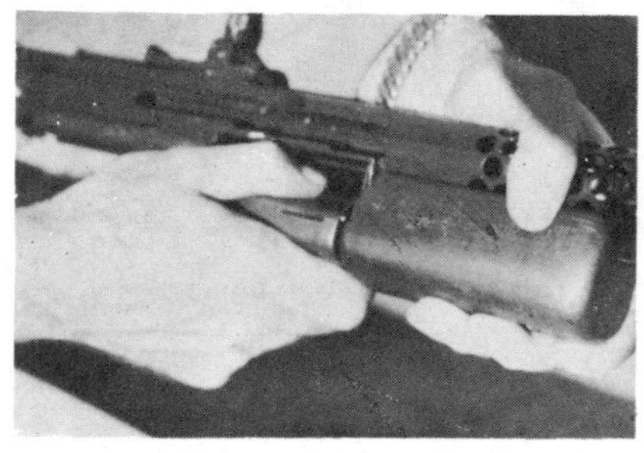

Press cover of magazine support and slide the support to the rear withdrawing it.

Buttstock is held by a thumb latch which may be pushed to permit buttstock to be removed.

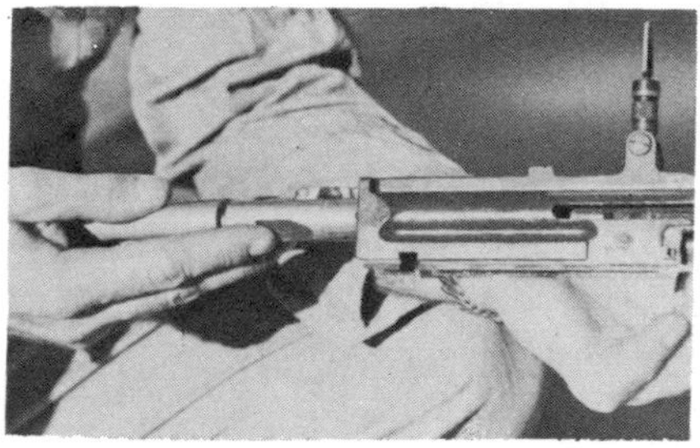

Bolt assembly may be withdrawn after sliding off the operating handle which is locked by a spindle.

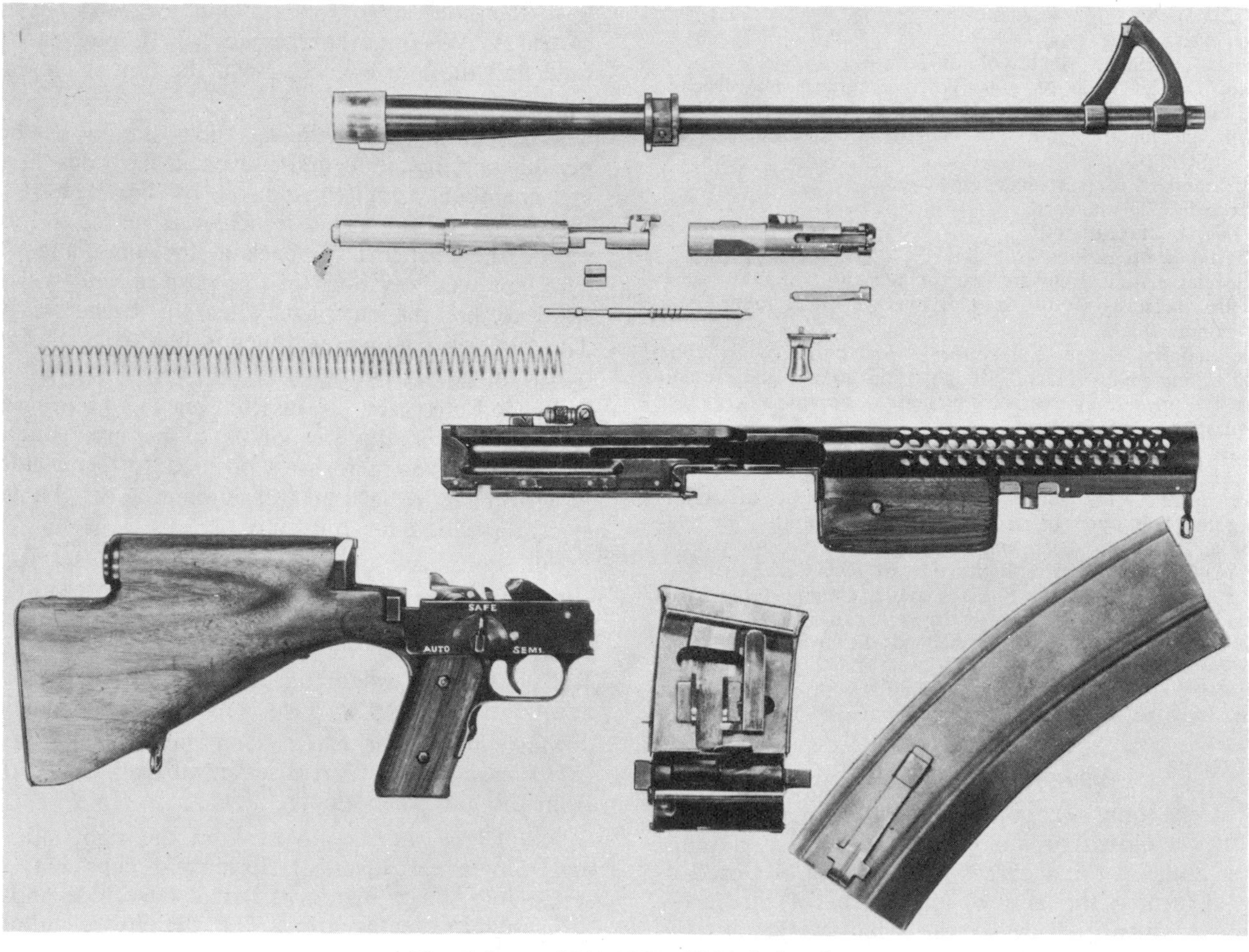

The Johnson M41 Fully Field Stripped.

How the Johnson Light Machine Gun Works

Starting with the weapon loaded and the gun cocked, the action is as follows:

The trigger being pressed the connecting sear is released from the bolt letting the bolt be driven forward by the recoil spring in the butt. The bolt picks up the cartridge from the magazine and drives it toward the chamber, the extractor snapping into the cannelure at the proper moment.

When the bolt goes forward a locking cam at the rear end of the bolt group causes rotation and locking of the bolt as the bolt reaches its fully closed position. This rotary action pushes the bolt through an arc of 20° bringing the 8 locking lugs distributed around the bolt head into their corresponding recesses on abutments in the barrel locking bushings.

This locking cam also carries the firing pin which now goes forward to fire the cartridge.

Rearward Movement of the Action. When the cartridge is fired, and the bullet travels down the barrel, the barrel and the bolt recoil together about ⅛ of an inch until the angular face of the operating cam comes against the corresponding face in the receiver. This imparts a twisting motion which causes the bolt to rotate far enough to free the 8 lugs from their recesses, which happens during the next ⅜" of travel.

After a recoil of about 7/16 of an inch, the barrel is stopped and the bolt continues on to the rear carrying the empty cartridge case by the extractor in its face.

At this point there still remains sufficient pressure in the chamber working back against the inside of the cartridge case to help extraction. As this weapon is fitted with a straight line buttstock as in the case of the German MG34 and MG42, the coil mainspring is in direct line behind the bolt and is compressed as the bolt travels to the rear.

When the bolt passes the end of the magazine, a buffer plunger at the rear of the locking cam is compressed when it touches the base of the mainspring tube in the buttstock. At this point the rearward motion of the weapon is stopped and the bolt starts its forward motion.

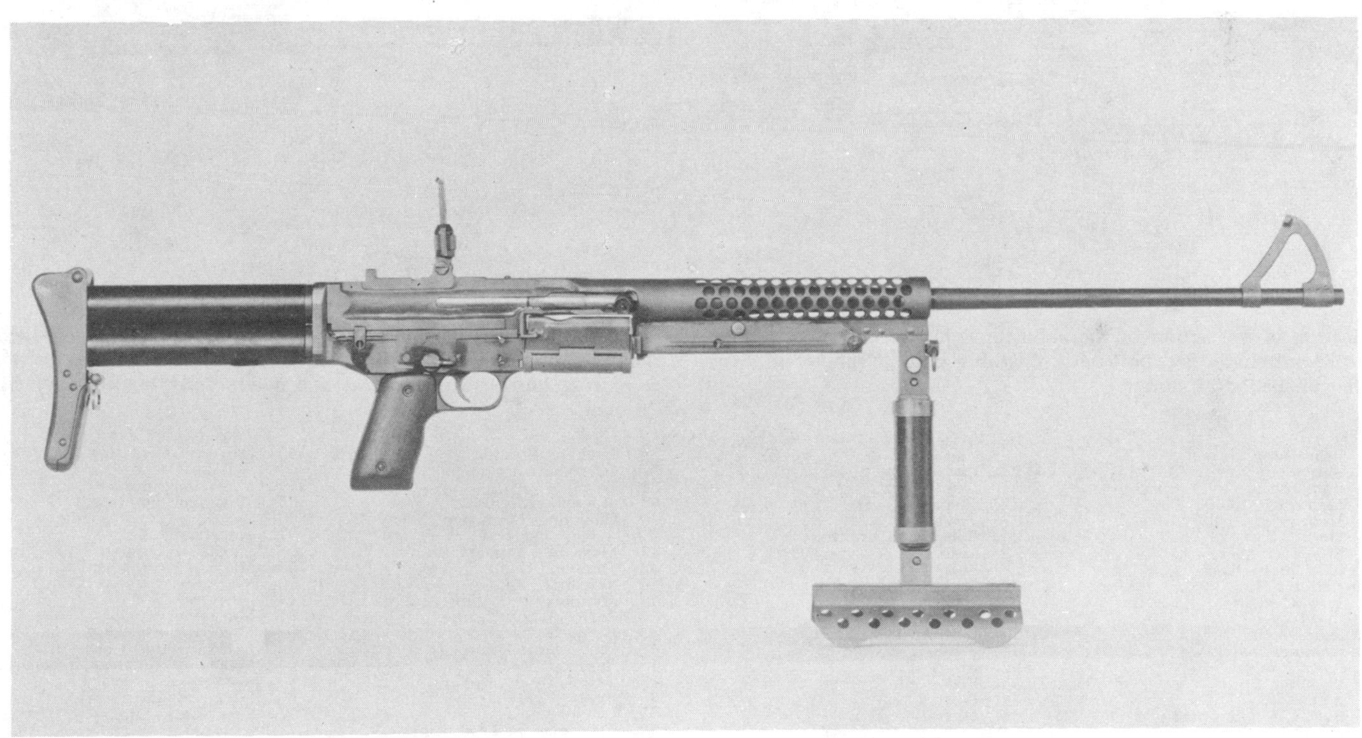

Johnson Light Machine Gun Model 1944 Caliber .30-06.

Caliber: .30-06.
Magazine: Detachable box.
Capacity: 20 cartridges, single column feed. Note: Five additional cartridges may be carried in the weapon, giving a total capacity of 25.
Ballistics: Standard for cartridges employed.
Barrel Length: 22 inches—barrel is quickly detachable.
Overall Length: 42.5 inches with this barrel.
Weight: 14.7 pounds with monopod. 13 pounds without monopod.
Sights: Folding leaf rear peep sight. Square post front sight.
Gun Operated By: Recoil. Johnson system.
Locked: By rotary bolt.
Cooled: Air. Has special heat radiating metal handguard.
Cocking Handle: On right side.
Type of Fire: Single shot per pull from closed bolt. Full automatic from open bolt.
Change Lever: Has three positions, full automatic when to the rear and with bolt open; semi-automatic when forward and bolt closed; safety when upright with bolt in open or closed position.
Cyclic Rate of Fire: 450 to 750 per minute (different types of ammunition and buffer springs account for this wide fluctuation).
Maximum Deliverable Rate of Fire: About 350 per minute.
Stock: Plastic. Two pieces of Micarta tubing ending in a fitting for the trap butt assembly. Pistol grip is also plastic. Its side plates may be plastic or black walnut.

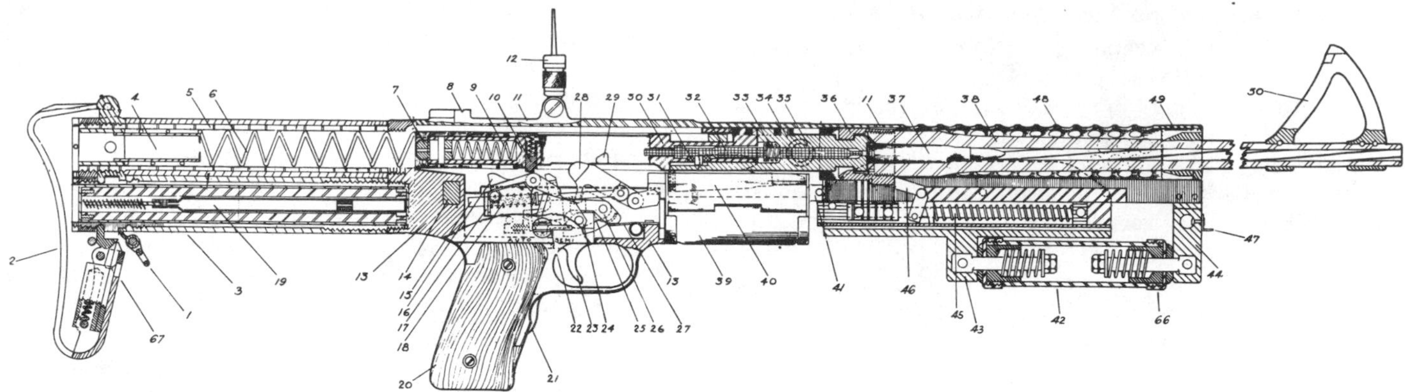

Section of the Johnson light machine gun with the parts in position for semi-automatic firing, hammer cocked, chamber loaded.

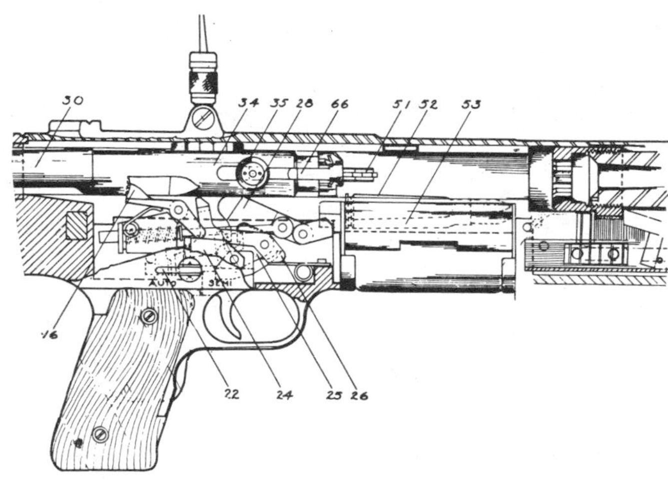

Section of the action of the Johnson light machine gun cocked for full automatic fire, bolt back, chamber clear. (Numbered parts have changed position.)

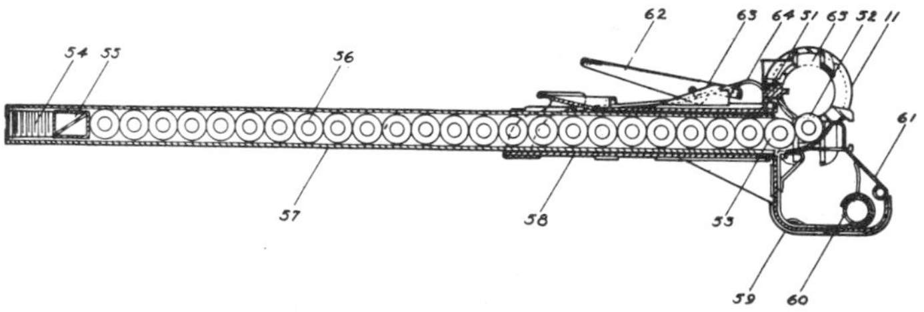

Section of the magazine of the Johnson light machine gun with the magazine support in its normal position in relation to the receiver—shown with magazine and action fully loaded—capacity 25 shots.

1. Rear Sling Swivel
2. Butt Plate
3. Butt tubes
4. Mainspring Tube Plug
5. Mainspring Tube
6. Mainspring
7. Buffer Plunger
8. Rear Sight Rest
9. Buffer Spring
10. Trip Plunger
11. Receiver
12. Rear Sight
13. Hammer Block
14. Lock Plunger
15. Hammer Strut
16. Bolt Catch
17. Bolt Catch Support
18. Hammer Spring
19. Cleaning Kit
20. Pistol Grip
21. Grip Filler
22. Change Lever
23. Trigger
24. Bolt Catch Control
25. Sear
26. Sear Trip
27. Sear Spring
28. Hammer
29. Platform Lug
30. Locking Cam Unit
31. Firing Pin Stop
32. Firing Pin
33. Firing Pin Spring
34. Bolt
35. Operating Handle
36. Locking Bushing
37. Cartridge in Chamber
38. Barrel
39. Magazine Support
40. Cartridge Positioned below feed lips
41. Magazine Support Pin
42. Monopod Tube
43. Monopod Foot
44. Monopod Mounting Lug
45. Barrel Latch Spring
46. Barrel Latch
47. Front Sling Swivel
48. Radiator Sleeve
49. Barrel Guide Collar
50. Front Sight
51. Ejector
52. Cartridge in Feed Lips
53. Cartridge Entering Cover Ramp
54. Magazine Spring
55. Magazine Follower
56. Cartridge in Magazine
57. Magazine
58. Magazine Support Guide Lips
59. Magazine Support Body
60. Magazine Support Cover Spring
61. Magazine Support Cover
62. Magazine Release Lever
63. Retainer Spring Ramp
64. Magazine Retainer Spring
65. Receiver
66. Monopod Pivot
67. Butt Plate Latch

Loading and Firing

Magazines may be loaded by single insertion or by stripping in from Springfield clips.

Insert magazine into housing from left side. Be sure to thrust it in smartly. The spring is cammed upward releasing the cartridges into the action as the magazine is inserted; this requires quick insertion to prevent spilling some cartridges.

To withdraw magazine, press down on the release lever above the magazine housing and withdraw quickly.

For single shot fire move the change lever to forward position ("semi"). Lift bolt handle slightly to permit it to be pulled straight back to its full length. Release it and a round will be stripped into the chamber. Pulling the trigger will now fire and eject and reload with the bolt closed. When magazine is empty the bolt will stay closed.

For full automatic rifle, move the change lever to the rear position ("auto"). Raise and pull back the bolt which will now stay open. Pressing the trigger will move the bolt forward to load and fire as long as cartridges are in the magazine.

To set safe, move the change lever to the horizontal position.

Firing without magazine may be accomplished by inserting single round directly into the chamber and allowing bolt to close as in semi-automatic fire.

With standard loaded Johnson magazine in place, and bolt closed, single rounds may be inserted directly into the action from the left side of the receiver. Clips of Springfield design may be seated in the clip guides on the right side of the gun and cartridges pushed in with the thumb.

How the Johnson 1944 Model LMG Works

When the cartridge is fired the barrel and bolt recoil locked together about ½ inch. While this is happening the rotary bolt is turned 20 degrees by the action of a camming arm on the bolt acting against a corresponding face in the receiver.

The bullet is out of the weapon before the unlocking action starts.

When the lugs are completely out of their seats, the barrel is halted in its rearward motion. The momentum and the remaining pressure transmitted to the bolt by the empty case forces it to continue its rearward travel and to extract and eject the empty shell at the same time that it compresses the recoil spring in the buttstock and cocks the hammer.

If the weapon is being fired semi-automatic, the force of the mainspring returns the bolt to closed position pushing a cartridge ahead of it into the firing chamber, revolving the rotary bolt, and securely locking the weapon. The bolt lock lever positions behind the roller of the locking cam and holds the locking and bolt cams in position. When the last shot has been fired the bolt stays closed.

When firing full auto, the bolt is held open by the bolt catch which is released when the trigger is pulled. The bolt goes forward to close and lock, and when the locking is completed the automatic sear is tripped allowing the hammer to fire the cartridge. The gun will fire as long as the trigger is held back.

Browning Cal. .30 M1917A1 Machine Gun.

This is the famous Browning Water Cooled Machine Gun, formerly the standard United States machine gun in its class. It is also very widely used throughout the world, having been manufactured and sold by the Fabrique Nationale de Guerre at Herstal, Belgium. This is the plant that controlled the Browning patents for sale in Europe.

Caliber: .30 M1 or M2 ammunition.
Method of Feed: Fabric belt holding 250 cartridges or metal link belt.
Direction of Feed: From left side of gun through to right.
Muzzle Velocity: M2 ammunition, 2800 feet per second.
Weight of Bullet: 150 Grains. Full jacketed.
Barrel Length: 24″.
Overall Length of Gun: About 38″.
Weight of Gun and Pintle: 32.8 lbs.
Capacity of Water Jacket: 7 pints, adding about 7¼ lbs. to the weight of the gun and pintle.
Weight of Tripod Mounting: 53.2 lbs. (M1917A1)
Weight of Loaded Belt and Carrying Chest: 19 lbs.; belt and ammunition alone about 14 lbs.
Front Sight: Blade type with cover mounted near muzzle.
Rear Sight: Adjustable leaf sight with apertures and open U sights. Has windage screw to adjust in mils and provide a deflection from zero to 20 right or left. Also fitted with an adjustment for drift as in the Springfield rifle sight. If gun is sighted for M1 ammunition, the graduations will be from zero to 3400 yards. If for M2 or 06 ammunition, they will be from zero to 2600 yards. On weapons for European use they may be from zero to 2800 meters.

Effective Range with Tripod, M1 Ammunition: About 2500 yards.

Maximum Usable Range: M1 ammunition, several guns firing in battery, about 4,000 yards.

Gun Operated By: Short recoil. As the powder gas drives the bullet down the barrel, that portion of the gas thrusting back against the base of the cartridge transmits the recoil to the face of the bolt and the moving parts.

Barrel, Barrel Extension, and Bolt: Recoil locked together about ⅝". The bolt is then automatically unlocked from the barrel extension and continues to the rear independently, compressing the driving rod spring, to furnish energy for the return motion. The barrel recoil not only unlocks the bolt, but also operates the accelerating mechanism which speeds the bolt farther to the rear against the action of the driving spring.

Locked: By a solid steel block capable of moving vertically, fitted with a projecting guide pin, which when the bolt has rejoined the barrel in forward movement is brought in contact with and rides up on a locking cam on the bottom plate. This steel block engages rigidly behind the shoulder in the bottom of the bolt, locking it against the face of the barrel extension.

Cooled: By water in jacket absorbing heat. In the top of the water jacket are steam escape tubes—a fixed inner tube with a hole in each end and a shorter outer tube which slides on the inner. When gun is depressed, this sliding tube closes the forward hole and the steam escapes from the rear and vice versa. A rubber hose runs from its outlet on the water jacket to a water chest where it condenses the steam to use again.

Cycle Rate of Fire: 50 to 600 rounds per minute.

Type of Fire: Full automatic only. It is possible by tapping trigger expertly to fire one or two shots, but in general any fire except full automatic can be achieved only by gaps in belt loading.

Loading

Check the following: Tripod to see that there is no unusual play; that it is firmly seated, that all its jamming handles are tight, and that the splayed feet of the legs are pushed securely into the ground. Check the water jacket and condenser. Make sure that both are full. Then check to see there is no water leakage at the muzzle glands. See that rear barrel packing is water tight and oil or grease it heavily if it is not. Check head space adjustment. Remember that this is a most important adjustment on this gun; if it is too tight the gun will refuse to fire; too loose head space will result in bulged or ruptured cartridge cases which will jam the gun badly. Check that ammunition belts are loaded uniformly and correctly and that they are clean and dry. Check rear sight for vision and working order. See that all moving parts are lightly oiled and work smoothly by drawing the bolt handle back and permitting it to go forward. All mechanism should work smoothly and no unusual effort be required to withdraw barrel and recoiling mechanism to the rear. When bolt handle is released it should position in its fully forward place and bolt should lock home properly. Bore should be inspected to be sure that it is clean.

With ammunition box securely locked in place on the left side of the gun and cover closed, insert the tag of the belt through the feed block as far as it will go to the right and pull the belt sharply to the right.

Pull the bolt handle to the rear as far as it will go. This will compress the barrel plunger spring and the

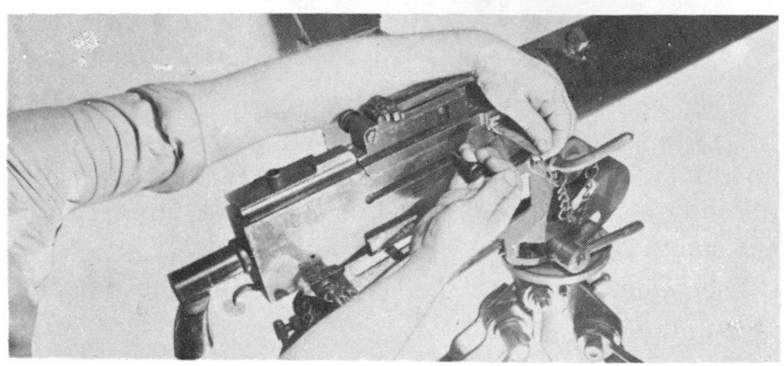

driving rod spring, and when the bolt handle is released, these two springs will drive the action forward, moving the recoiling parts to their forward locked position, and half load the gun.

Now pull the bolt handle back a second time as far as it will go. Release it and let it fly forward. This completes the loading, leaving a cartridge properly positioned in the firing chamber and the weapon cocked and ready for firing.

Unloading

Pull back the cover latch (this is the milled knob on top of the receiver to the rear of the rear sight). The spring controlled section will move backwards and permit you to raise the feed cover.

Lift the belt out to the left and replace it in its box.

Pull the bolt handle to the rear and look inside the bolt way to make sure there is no cartridge in the firing chamber or in the face of the breechblock.

Now push the extractor down to its seat in the front of the breechblock and let go of the cocking handle, permitting the breechblock to go forward.

Snap down the cover and press the trigger.

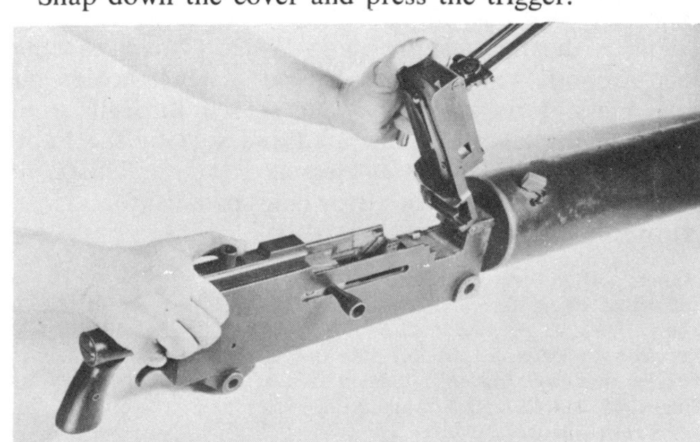

Stripping

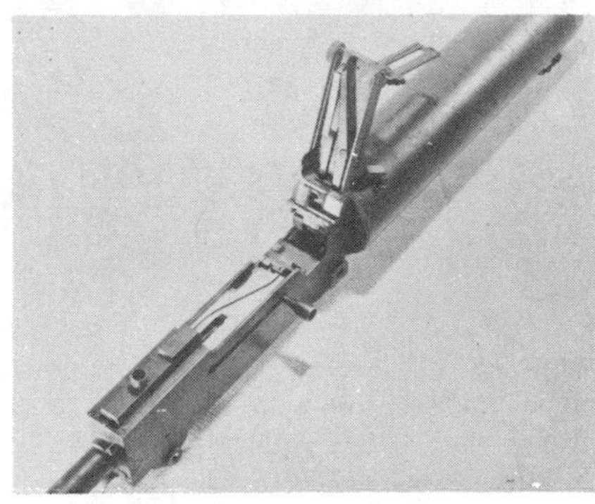

Raise the rear sight. Pull back the cover latch (the knob on top of the receiver behind the rear sight base) and raise the cover.

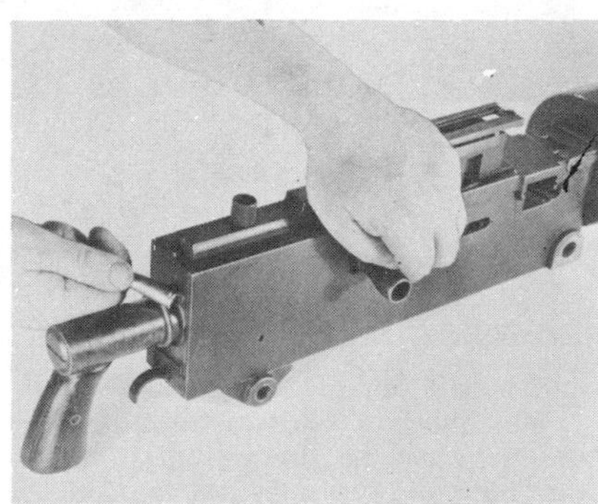

Draw bolt handle back as far as it will go and hold it firmly with the left hand. The driving spring rod protrudes through the back plate of the gun. Insert the base of a cartridge in the slot in the head of the rod. Push the rod in to compress the spring, and turn the rod to the right. This will lock the driving rod and its spring under compression inside the bolt.

Push the bolt handle forward a few inches to draw the driving rod out of the locking hole in the back plate. Then pushing the cover latch forward with the left thumb, raise the pistol grip up and out of its retaining slots in the rear of the receiver.

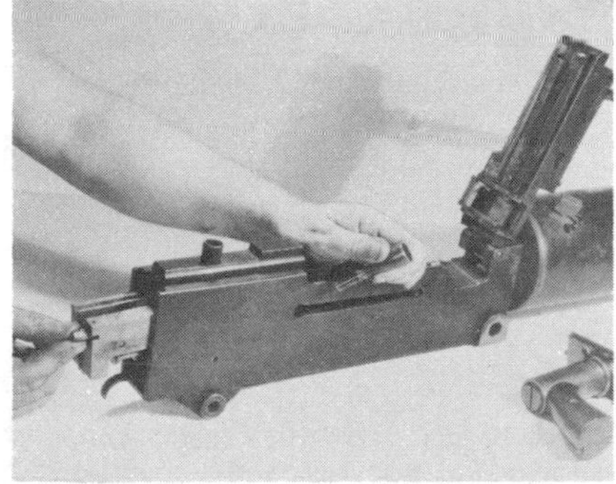

Pull the bolt handle as far as it will go to the rear, at which point it may be pulled to the right out of the bolt and receiver. Reach inside the receiver and grasp the driving rod; then pull the bolt directly to the rear and out of the receiver.

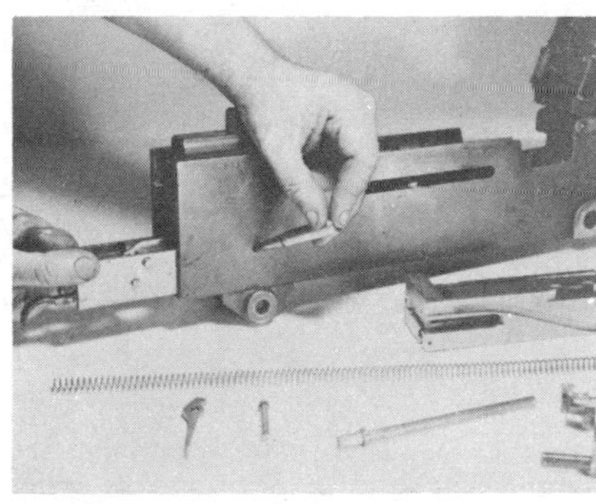

Insert the point of a bullet in the trigger pin locking hole in the lower right side of the receiver and push in the trigger pin against the tension of its spring. This frees the lock frame spacer and other recoiling parts and permits pulling them directly to the rear.

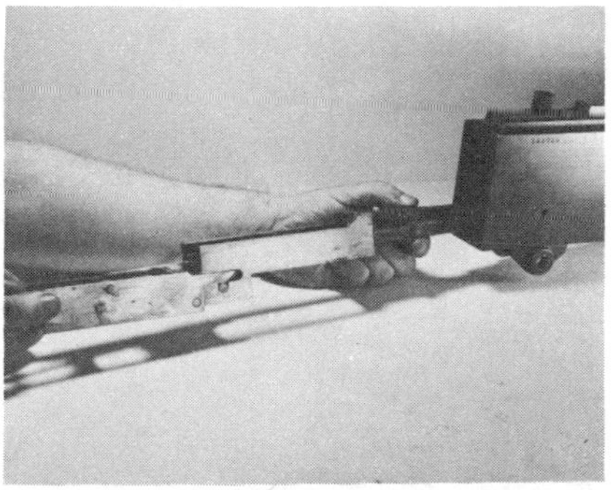

When the bottom projection at the rear of the barrel extension (the part screwed onto the barrel) drops below the bottom of the receiver, pull the combined lock frame spacer, barrel extension, and barrel directly to the rear out of the gun.

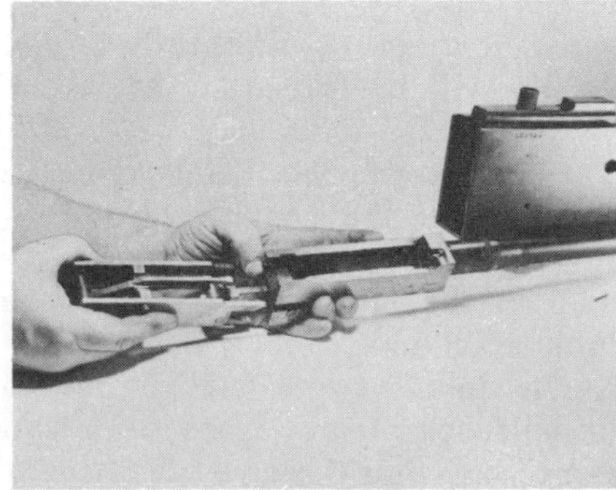

Grasp the lock frame spacer with the right hand, and with the left thumb, push forward on the turned up tips of the accelerator.

This will spring down and forward, separating the lock frame spacer (which

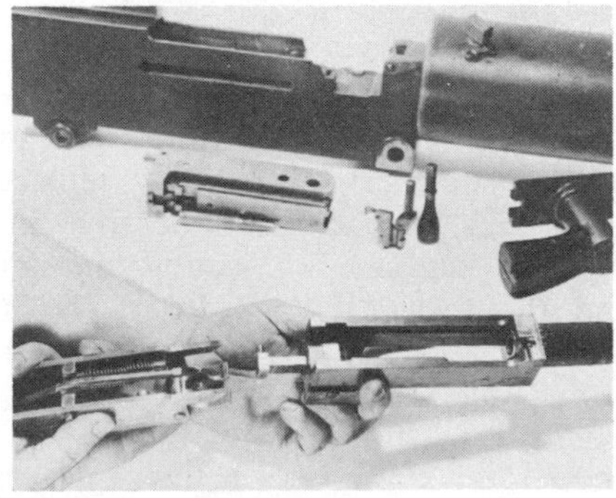

holds the trigger and accelerator mechanism) from the barrel extension.

Push the accelerator pin out of the lock frame spacer and remove the accelerator (this is the curved piece of metal with two claws).

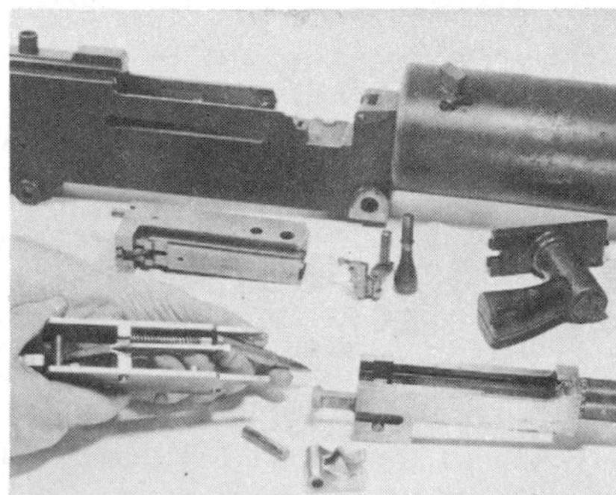

Insert head of cartridge in slit in head of barrel plunger at the left side of the lock frame. Twist it and ease it out. Remember that it is under strong spring tension (if necessary trigger pin may now be pushed out and spring and trigger removed).

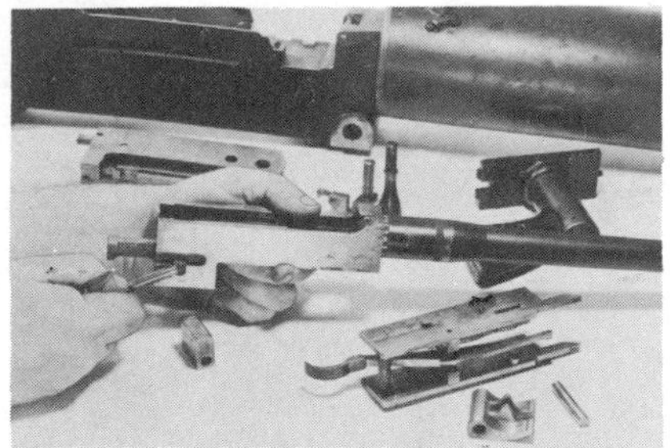

Holding the barrel extension with the left hand, use the point of a bullet to start the breechblock pin from left side and remove it from the right, permitting the breechblock (the heavy wedge whose lower front end is beveled) to drop down out of the barrel extension. (Barrel extension may now be unscrewed from the barrel if necessary.)

Turn the extractor (the swinging hook-shaped piece on the left forward end of the bolt) up as far as it will go

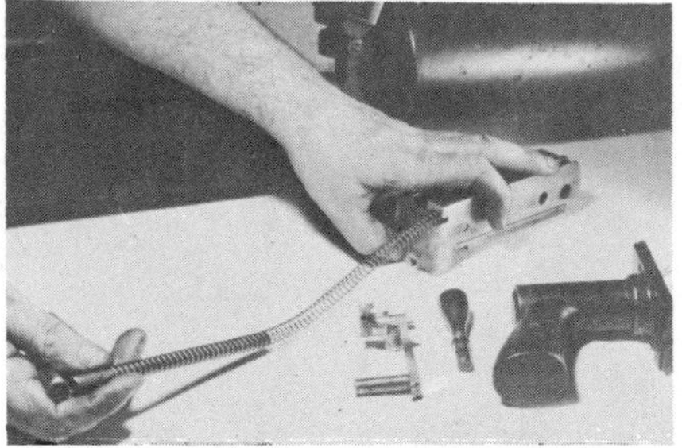

and pull it out of its hole in the bolt.

With the base of a cartridge, push in the head of the driving spring rod in the bolt and twist it to the left. Be careful of the very powerful driving spring which will now be free to fly out the back carrying the driving spring rod with it. Grip this firmly and ease it out gradually.

Push out the cocking lever pin from the upper front left side of the breechblock and lift out the cocking lever.

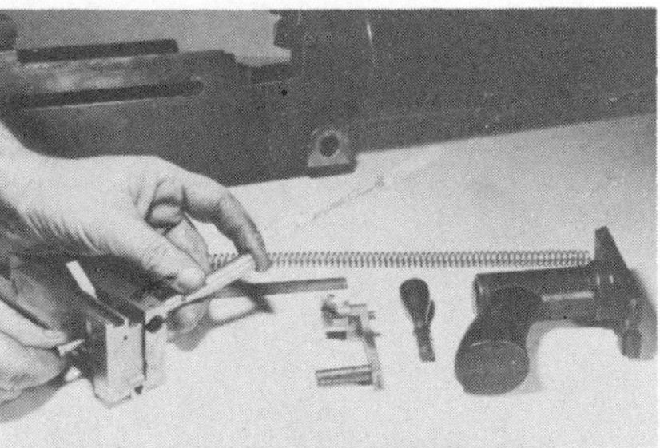

Turning the breechblock upside down, push the sear up with the bullet to release the firing pin spring; turn the breechblock the right way up again and insert the bullet into the slot of the sear spring. Push over to the left, pry the sear spring into a locking recess and the sear drops out. When sear spring is pushed back into normal position its pin may be pushed up and it and the spring removed. The firing pin and its spring may now be dropped out of the back of the breechblock.

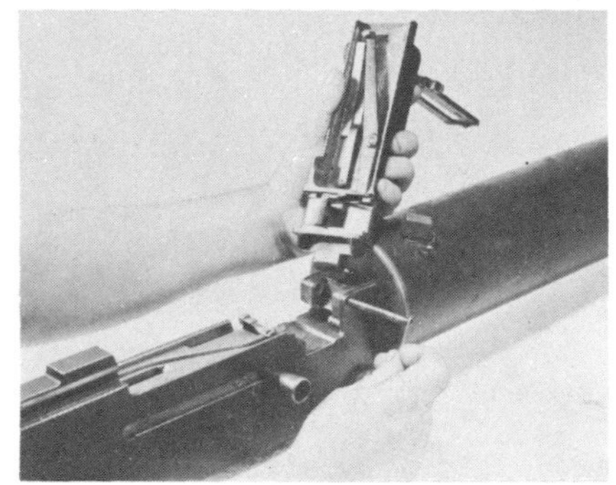

Use the point of a bullet to turn up the cover pin spring at the right side of the receiver just behind the water jacket. Pull the pin out to the right and lift the cover up out of the receiver.

Pushing back on the nose of the split pin on the left side of the feed block,

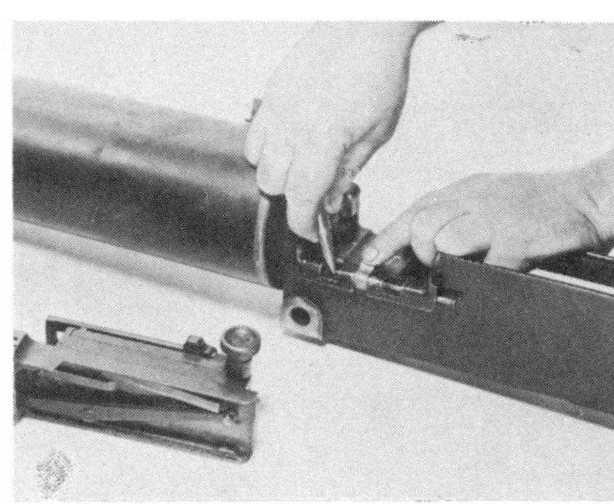

control the feed pawl with the left thumb and ease the pawl and its spring up out of the receiver as the locking pin is pulled out.

Insert point of bullet between the extractor cam and the long flat piece of metal on the side of the cover opposite

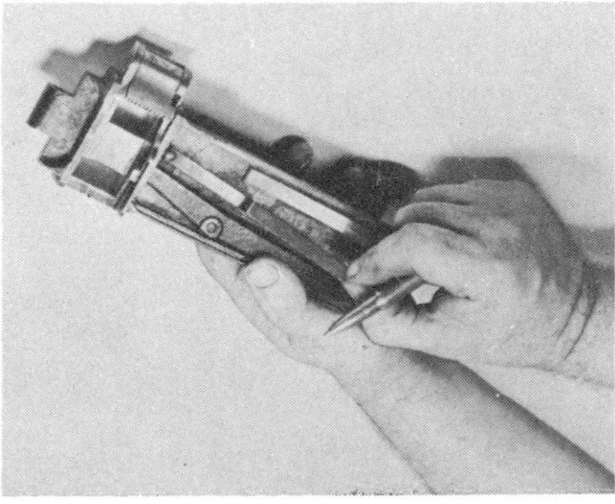

the belt feed lever (this is the extractor spring) and pry the extractor spring out of its seat in the cam, then lift it up and out. The feed lever and slide may be removed if necessary by turning feed lever pivot pin spring outwards. This completes stripping the Browning machine gun.

Assembling the Gun

Start by screwing the barrel into the barrel extension, then insert the barrel and barrel extension into receiver. Slide slowly forward until the lower projection of the barrel extension (which holds the bolt back) is against the bottom plate of the receiver. Holding the lock frame in the right hand, place the accelerator claws between the rear face of the barrel extension and the forward faces of the T-lug extension and at the same time insert the forward projections of the lock frame into their grooves in the barrel extension. Give a quick thrust forward to the lock frame to tip back the accelerator claws and compress the barrel plunger spring; this locks the lock frame to the barrel extension.

Now push the lock frame attached to the barrel extension and barrel farther ahead in the receiver until the trigger pin on the lower right side comes against the side of the receiver. Push in the trigger pin against its spring tension and the whole assembly can now be pushed fully home while the trigger pin will be forced by its spring into its slot in the right side of the receiver.

Now replace the bolt in the receiver being sure the extractor is in position and that the cocking lever projecting through the top is fully forward.

Insert the bolt handle in the end of the slot in the receiver and into its hole in the bolt, then push it forward far enough so that when the cover latch is pushed forward, the pistol grip and back plate may be slid down in their grooves in the receiver. Pull the cover latch back to lock the back plate in position; holding bolt handle back as far as it will go, insert the base of the cartridge into the slit in the driving rod, push in and turn to the left to release the driving rod spring. Now permit the bolt to run forward under the thrust of the driving rod spring.

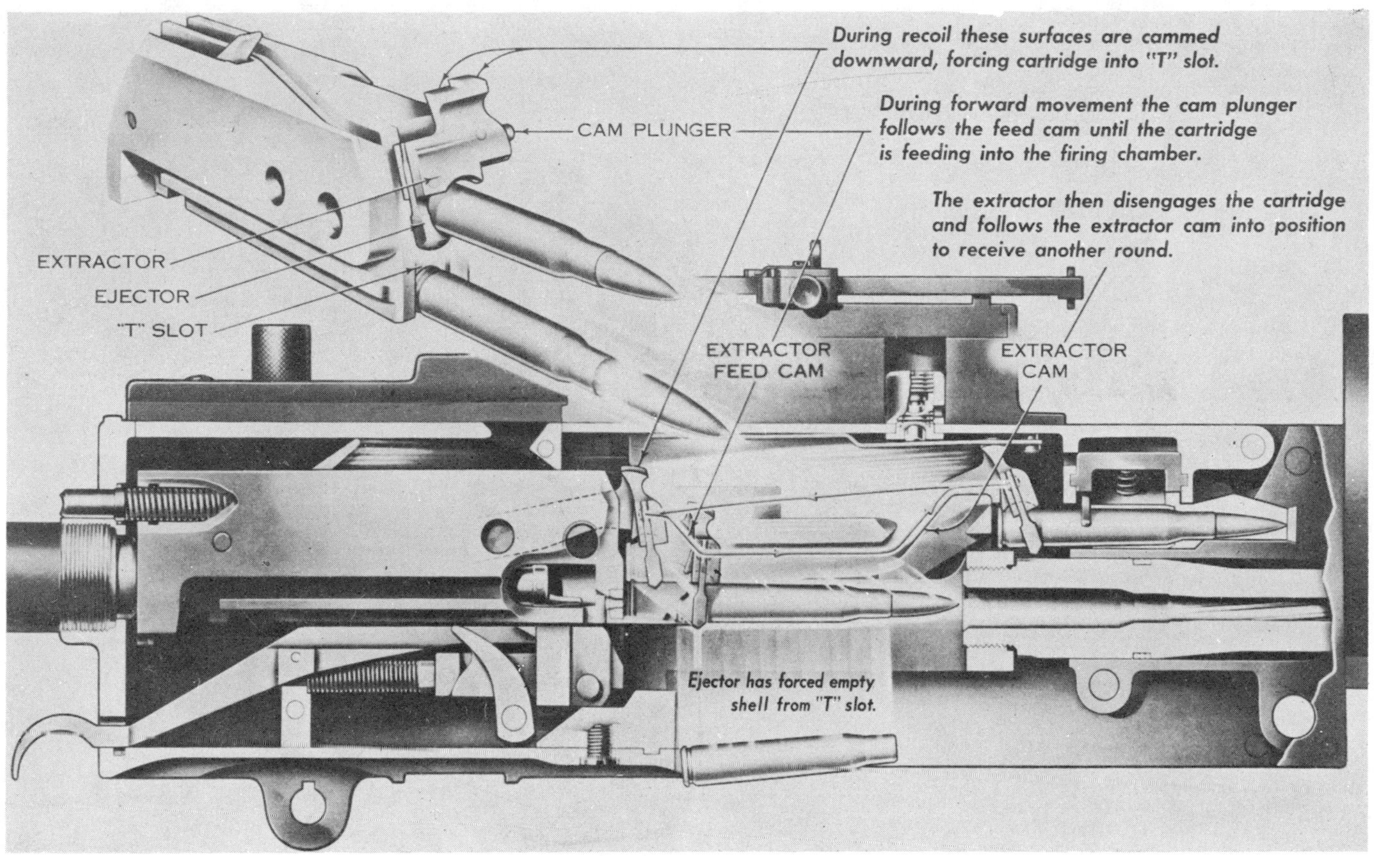

Cross-Section of Parts in Firing Position.

How the Browning Machine Gun Works

Starting with the weapon loaded and cocked the action is as follows: The trigger being pressed, the trigger bar disengages from the sear block and allows the striker to be driven forward by the spring in the bolt to fire the cartridge.

As the bullet goes down the barrel the recoil drives back against the base of the cartridge base which transmits the blow to the bolt face thereby starting the locked recoil action and barrel to the rear.

The barrel, barrel extension, and bolt recoil, locked together, about 5/8 of an inch. For the first half of this travel, during the period of high breech pressure, they are securely locked together, and then the front projections of the lock frame (which are set against the sides of the pin passing through the barrel extension and the breechblock) force the breechblock pin down, drawing the breechblock down out of its locking slot on the under side of the breechblock. The bolt is thus released from the barrel extension and so can continue straight to the rear. As the barrel extension itself travels to the

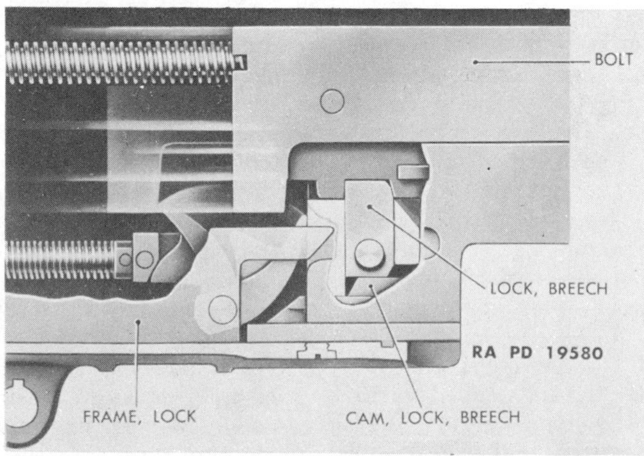

Breech Locked.

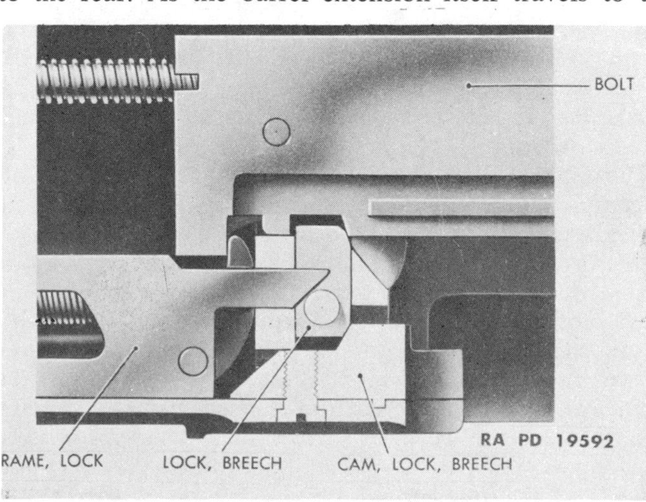

Breech Lock Beginning to Open.

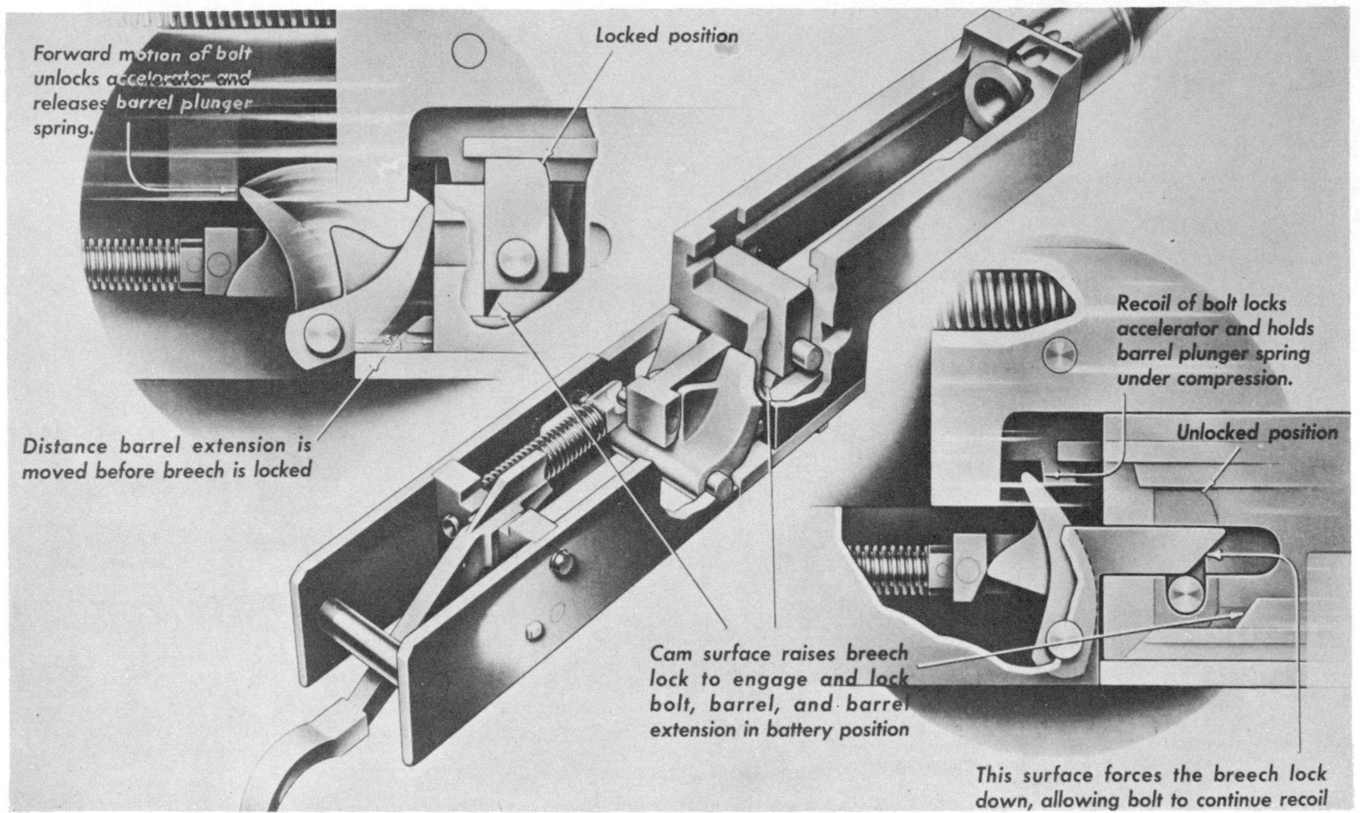

Operation of Accelerator Mechanism.

rear, the barrel plunger spring is compressed and the rear of the barrel extension drives the claws of the accelerator back sharply, flipping the accelerator up and backwards on its pin.

As the accelerator turns, the tips of its claws strike bottom projections on the bolt and thus accelerate the rearward motion of the bolt by transmitting to it the thrust absorbed from the barrel extension, which is now held in rearward position locked to the frame spacer slots. Speeding the rearward motion of the bolt, at the same time that the barrel is slowing up, permits the empty case to be extracted from the chamber without the sudden tug that would normally occur. (This makes special lubrication unnecessary.) The accelerator claws while engaging the shoulder of the T-lug firmly lock the barrel extension in the rearward position to the lock frame. A stop prevents the accelerator from going backwards too far and the barrel plunger spring is held compressed.

During backward motion of the bolt, the driving spring is compressed over the driving spring rod whose head is held securely in the back plate of the receiver. The extractor fitting over the top front of the bolt draws a loaded cartridge from the belt at the same time that the T-slot machined into the face of the bolt draws the empty cartridge case from the firing chamber. The extractor cam plunger (which rides along the top of the extractor cam and the extractor feed cam) is finally forced in by the beveled section of the extractor feed cam. The cover extractor cam thus forces the extractor down and the plunger spring out behind the extractor feed cam.

During the backward movement of the bolt, a stud on the belt feed lever (which is mounted in the front of the cover on a pivot) moves to the right in the cam groove cut in the top of the bolt. Thus the belt feed slide which is attached to the lever is moved to the left. The belt feed pawl (located on the under side of the cover above the belt) springs over the left of the first cartridge (which is being held in position by the belt holding pawl below the belt on the left side of the feed block) and supports the cartridge and the belt to prevent feeding trouble.

The cocking lever is fastened by a pivot pin inside the bolt and its top protrudes through the top of the bolt and rests inside the top cover of the receiver. Thus as the bolt starts backwards, pressure on the lower part of this lever drives it back revolving it on its axis and the firing pin spring is compressed drawing back the firing pin. The firing pin engages a notch in the sear (which has been pulled upward by the action of the sear spring).

The rear of the bolt strikes against the buffer plate mounted in the back plate at the upper part of the pistol grip and the remainder of its energy is absorbed in friction and by the buffer disc. (A brass buffer ring is forced over a plug and expands against the inner wall of the grip.)

The driving spring in the bolt which is now fully compressed reacts to drive the bolt forward. During this forward motion, the upper end of the cocking lever is forced to the rear, thus pulling the lower end away from the rear of the firing pin. The extractor feed cam

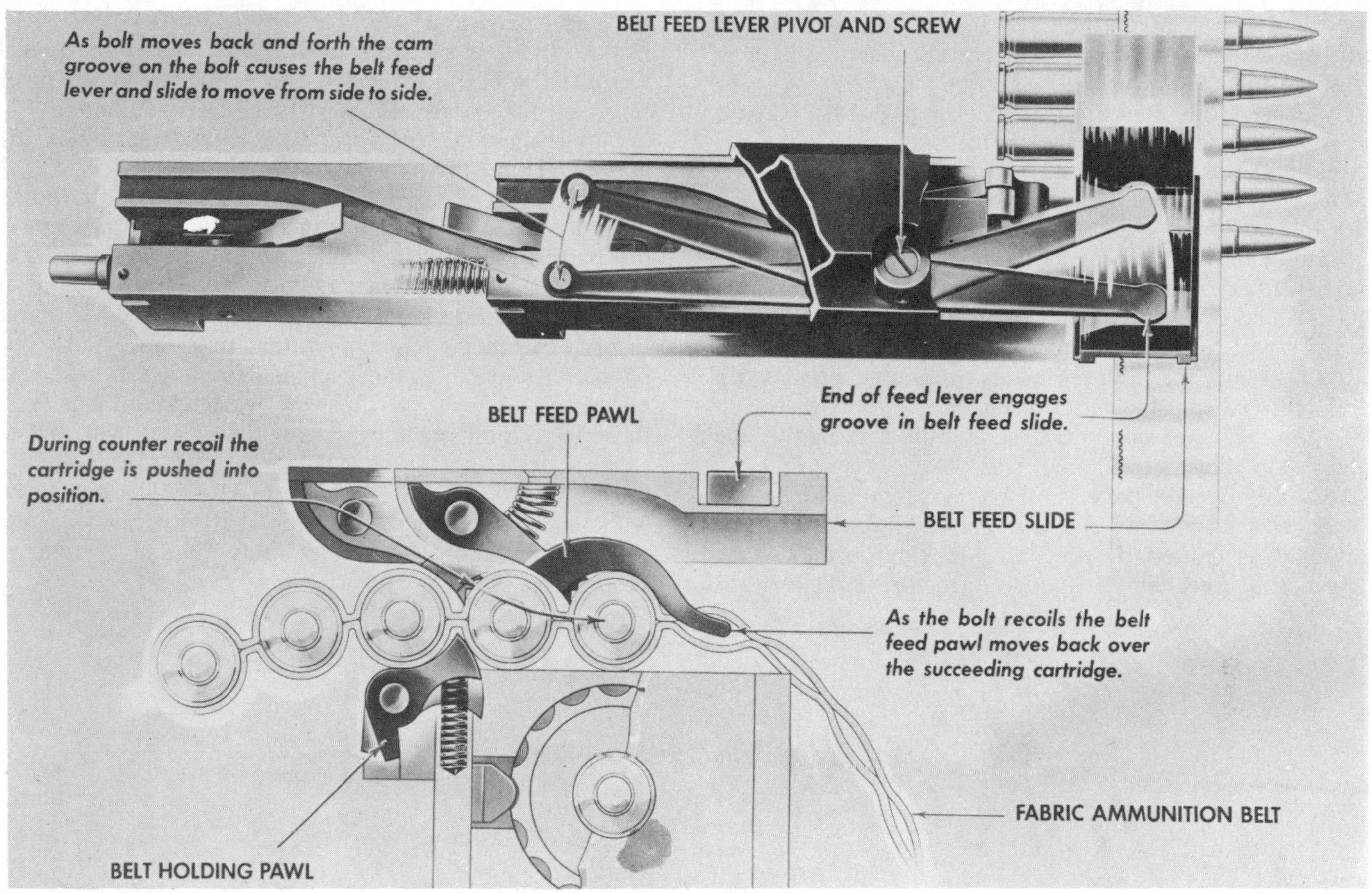

Belt-Feed Mechanism.

acts on the extractor cam plunger, forcing the extractor down so that the cartridge it is holding drops down the T-slot in the face of the bolt until it reaches a direct line with the firing chamber. The ejector strikes the empty case in the T-slot expelling it through the bottom of the gun and stopping the live cartridge when properly positioned.

Also during the forward motion of the bolt, the bottom projection strikes the top of the accelerator to swing it forward on its axis pin. This unlocks the barrel extension from the lock frame, permitting those two units to move forward as the bolt acts through the accelerator against the rear end of the barrel extension. The forward motion of the barrel extension and barrel is further assisted by a thrust from the barrel plunger spring as it uncoils. The force passed on by the accelerator from the bolt to the barrel extension is sufficient to guarantee proper timing of the locking action.

The actuating stud on the feed lever fits down in a cam groove in the bolt. Thus as the bolt goes forward, the stud rides in the cam and forces the lever on its pivot to the left; the forward end of the lever which carried the feed slide is thus pivoted to the right, bringing with it the belt feed pawl, the belt and the next cartridge. As the motion ends, the cartridge to be fed is held between the cartridge stops and the feedway. The next round to load is pulled over the belt holding pawl which rises behind it. It is in position to be engaged by the belt feed pawl on the next movement.

The final action of the extractor during forward motion of the bolt is to rise under the influence of its plunger riding along the top of the extractor cam. As the ejector pivots forward, the extractor releases its hold on the cartridge which is now well into the chamber. The extractor continues to ride upwards and over the base of the next cartridge in the belt in the feedway. Then the flat extractor spring in the top cover forces the extractor down and into the cannelure of this cartridge gripping it ready to pull it back on the next movement to the rear of the bolt.

The breechblock, mounted in the rear of the barrel extension, strikes a cam as the recoiling parts near the firing position and is forced up this cam and into a recess cut in the bottom of the bolt. Thus as the action comes to a complete close, the breechblock firmly locks the barrel extension (into which is screwed the barrel) to the breechblock.

Special Note on Adjustments

It is extremely important that the headspace on this gun be correctly adjusted before firing. To test the adjustment, pull the bolt handle back and let it run forward several times.

If the bolt does not go home fully and smoothly, it indicates too tight space between the face of the bolt and the face of the firing chamber. If the gun is put into use in this condition, it will fire sluggishly or it may refuse to fire at all.

To correct this condition, it will be necessary to strip the weapon and unscrew the barrel one notch, then assemble and test again.

To Test for Loose Head Space. Lift the cover and raise the extractor; then pull the bolt slightly to the rear. If the bolt moves back at all without carrying the barrel and barrel extension with it, then gun is too loose. Fired in this condition, the pressure of the gas in the firing chamber will bulge the head of the empty cartridge case (since it is not fully supported by the bolt), or may rip it off entirely, causing a serious jam.

To correct this condition, screw up the barrel one notch, then retest.

Adjusting Head Space. Screw the barrel into its extension and stop when the first clicking sound is heard (this click is caused by the barrel-locking spring).

Push the breechblock (minus extractor) fully forward on barrel extension.

Push the lock piece up from below to lock the breechblock to the barrel extension; and while holding it firmly, screw up the barrel until resistance is encountered.

Now check to see that barrel locking spring is in a notch and that the lock piece is solidly seated.

Now let go of the lock. If it drops freely, the adjustment is correct. This adjustment should be punched on the barrel, to save time when assembling in future.

Water Leakage. If water leaks from muzzle end, remove the muzzle gland. Wind packing around the barrel. Press it together with combination tool. Then push back on barrel and guide the packing into its seat. Screw the muzzle gland back on. Test by working bolt handle. If there is friction, packing is too tight. This will make a sluggish gun.

If water leaks from breech end, remove barrel and work oiled packing down into barrel cannelure with combination tool. Test as before for undue friction and head space.

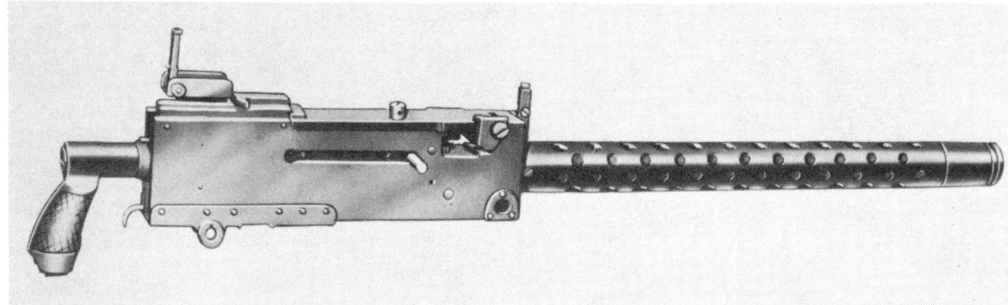

Browning Cal. .30 M1919A4 Machine Gun.

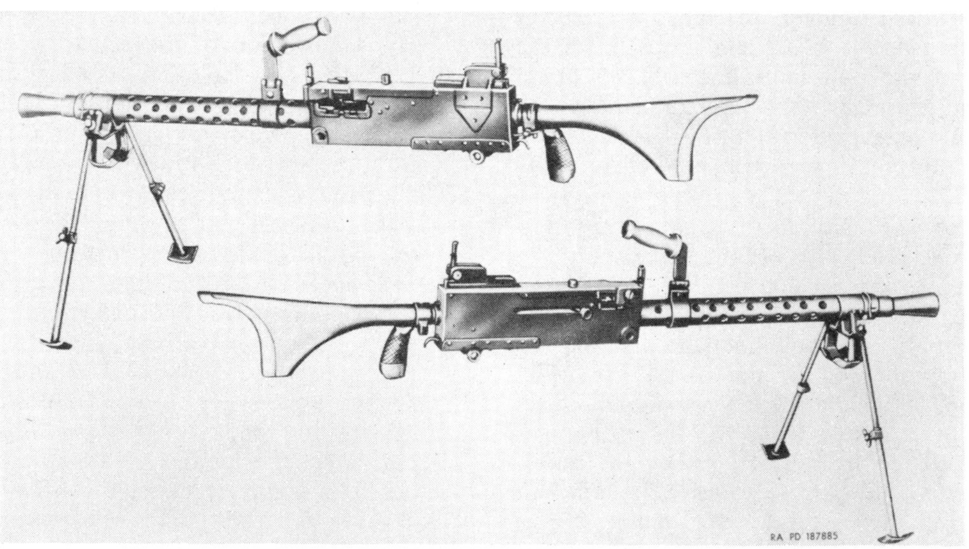

Browning Cal. .30 M1919A6 Machine Gun.

Although these weapons are now limited standard in the United States Army and are scheduled to be replaced by the 7.62mm M60 General Purpose Machine Gun, they are still in wide use in this country and abroad. The M1919A4 Browning was evolved from the 1919A2 which, through successive modifications, had been developed from the Browning Tank Gun M1919.

Two types of the M1919A4 have been issued—the fixed gun and the flexible gun. The fixed gun was widely used on World War II armored vehicles; the flexible gun was mainly used as the infantry company-level machine gun. The M1919A4 is used on the caliber .30 M2 mount as a ground gun. The mechanism of the M1919A4 is identical with that of the caliber .30

	M1919A4	M1919A6
Caliber:	.30	.30
System of Operation:	Recoil automatic fire only.	Recoil automatic fire only.
Length Overall:	40 in.	53 in.
Barrel Length:	24 in.	24 in.
Feed Device:	Disintegrating link belt (pullout type).	Disintegrating link belt (pullout type).
Sights, Front:	Folding blade.	Folding blade.
Rear:	Leaf adjustable for elevation and windage.	Leaf adjustable for elevation and windage.
Muzzle Velocity:	2800 f.p.s.	2800 f.p.s.
Weight:	31 lb.	32.5 lb.
Weight of barrel:	7 lb. 5 oz.	4 lb. 10 oz.
Weight of M2 tripod:	14 lb.	14 lb.

M1917A1 Browning gun which has been covered in detail. The principal differences between the M1919A4 and the M1917A1 are as follows:

The M1919A4 has a ventilated barrel jacket rather than a water jacket.

The M1919A4 is normally used on a light mount with limited terrain command and is classified as a light machine gun by the United States. The M1917A1 is normally used on a heavier mount with much greater terrain command and is classed as a heavy machine gun; it was the battalion-level gun.

The M1919A4 has a much heavier barrel than the M1917A1, but has a lower sustained rate of fire than the water-cooled gun.

The sights of the M1919A4 and the M1917A1 are different. There are other various minor differences between these guns. The M1919A5 is the same as the M1919A4, except that it has a bolt retracting slide and a different cover detent. These changes on the weapon were necessary to mount it in the World War II M3 light tank.

The M1919A6 was a wartime modification of the M1919A4 to give the weapon more tactical flexibility. A bipod, shoulder stock, and carrying handle were added to the basic Browning machine gun action to create a weapon which was easier to move and to get into action than the tripod-mounted M1919A4. The M1919A6 also has a lighter barrel and a different front barrel bearing than the M1919A4. The lighter barrel of the M1919A6 gives it a higher cyclic rate of fire than the M1919A4.

A post-World War II version of the M1919 Brownings (in addition to the M37) also exists; this is the M1919-A4E1. This weapon also has a retracting slide similar to the M1919A5.

The method of loading and firing and the method of field stripping the M1919 series of guns is, in all essentials, the same as that of the caliber .30 M1917A1 water-cooled Browning gun.

The M1919A4 and the M1919A6 may be used with the M1917A1, M2, or M74 tripods, but are normally used with the M2 tripod. The M1919A6 is also used on the bipod shown in the photo.

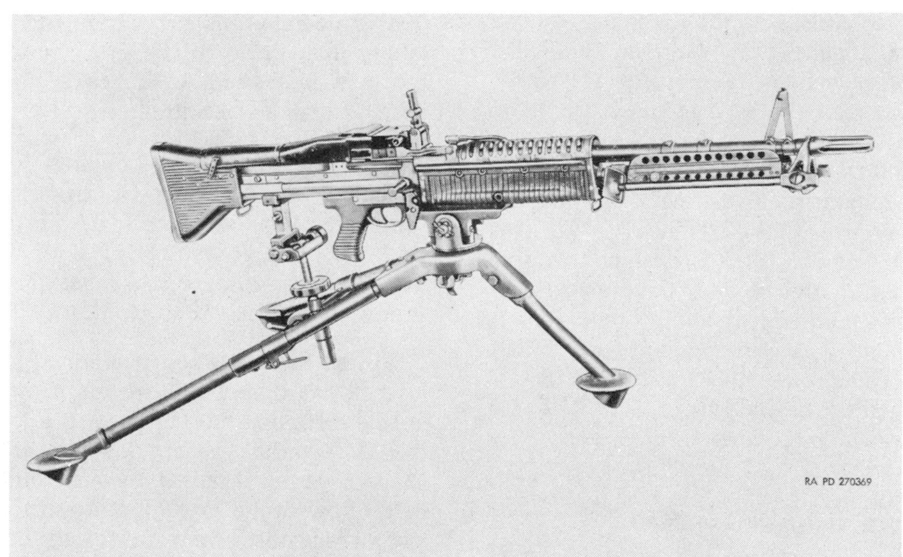

7.62mm Machine Gun M60 on M122 Mount. (This is the Caliber .30 M2 mount with an adaptor for the M60.)

Caliber: 7.62mm NATO.
System of Operation: Gas, cutoff and expansion, automatic fire only.
Weight of complete gun: 23.16 lb.
Weight of barrel assembly: 8.38 lb.
Length of gun overall: 43.5 in.
Length of Barrel: 22.0 in.
Feed Device: Disintegrating link belt (push-through type).
Cyclic Rate of Fire: 550 r.p.m.
Sustained Rate of Fire: 125 r.p.m. for 40 minutes, or 250 r.p.m. for 3 minutes, with one barrel. If two barrels are used and alternated every 500 rounds, the weapon will fire 125 r.p.m. for 60 minutes.
Muzzle Velocity: 2800 f.p.s.
Sights, Front: Blade.
Rear: Leaf, calibrated to 1200 yd.; adjustable for windage and elevation.
Sight Radius: 21.25 in.
Mount: Cal. .30 M2 mount with adapter or bipod.

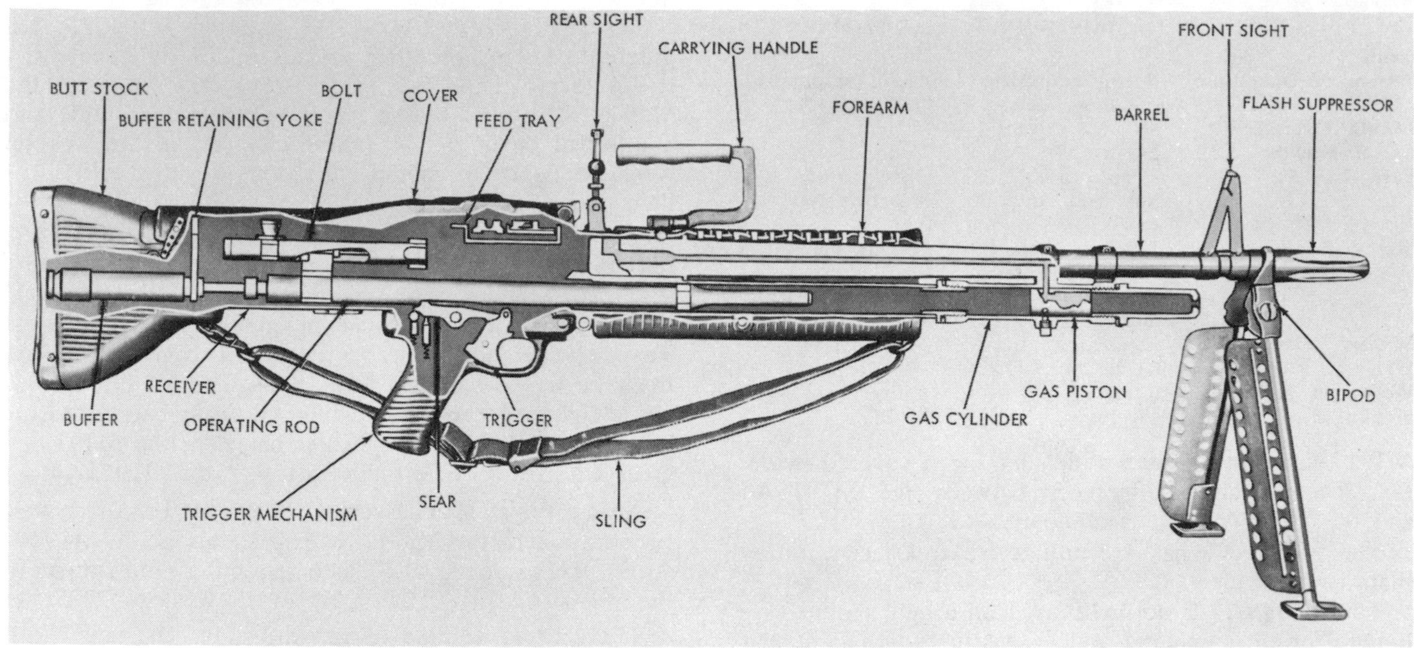

Section View of M60 Machine Gun with Bipod.

The M60 is called a general purpose gun because it replaces the cal. .30 Browning light and heavy machine guns. The M60 is used on a bipod as a light machine gun, and on a tripod as a heavy machine gun. The M60 (T-161E3) is the result of a series of designs started at approximately the end of World War II. The first of these was called the T44 and was essentially a combination of the belt feed mechanism of the German MG 42 with the operating mechanism of the German automatic rifle FG 42. A later design, which was considerably modified, was the T52; and from the T52 evolved the T161 series of guns.

The M60 therefore has, in a considerably modified form, the belt feed mechanism of the MG 42 and the operating mechanism of the FG 42. The FG 42 was capable of selective fire but the M60 is designed to give only full automatic fire, although it does have a low cyclic rate which allows the gunner to get off single rounds without too much difficulty. An interesting fact is that the basic FG 42 bolt system was itself a further development of the U.S.-designed Lewis gun of World War I fame, which in turn was a modification of a design by McLean, also an American.

How to Load and Fire the M60

Cocking. For all normal purposes this weapon, being fully automatic, should remain cocked at all times. The gun can be cocked only with the safety off or in "F" position. Pull the cocking lever handle, extending from right front of receiver, to its maximum rearward position, where the engagement click of the sear is heard. Return the cocking lever forward to engage its retaining latch. NOTE: Cocking lever will return to its latched position on the first shot, but this practice is not recommended, although it is not harmful if done occasionally. Return the safety lever to the "S" or safe position.

Loading. Rounds should be firmly assembled and positioned in their push-through links. Raise feed cover by lifting cover latch at right rear. Feed cover is retained vertically by a torsion spring and detent. The feed plate should remain in place on the receiver rails. Place the linked belt on the feed plate, links up, with the first round to be fired in the feed plate groove and held by the feed plate retaining pawl engaging the second round. An empty link ahead of the first round will help to position the belt, if desired. Close cover firmly, making sure the cover is latched securely.

Alternate Method of Loading. Enter lead tab followed by linked belt, links up, from the left. Pull firmly to right until two clicks are heard, or the first round has entered the feed plate groove. NOTE: A single round should be fired by raising cover and positioning round in feed plate groove. Close cover to hold round in place.

Firing. With weapon positioned and aimed, push safety lever forward and up, out of the way, with right thumb. Visual examination will show the lever is directed toward the "F" symbol. When down, near the right thumb, the safety lever is directed toward the "S" symbol. Because of the low cyclic rate (550 r.p.m.) of this weapon, single rounds or short bursts can easily be fired. It is important that the trigger be completely released after each shot, to fire single rounds, or to interrupt firing at any time.

Reloading. After firing, if the belt has been exhausted, the gun will be closed and must be cocked by hand to reload. The last link of the belt will remain in the feed plate. This link can be removed by the alternate method of loading described above; or, if a leading-link tab is provided, the link can be pushed through by utilizing the tab; or, finally, it can be removed when the cover is open for reloading.

Sights. The weapon as furnished is sighted in at 100 yards. A "quick adjustment" type of rear sight is provided. Barrels are zeroed-in by utilizing the lateral and elevating adjustments on the rear sight. For lateral adjustment, turn the knob at the lower left side of the rear sight. If additional lateral adjustment is required, the spring dove-tail (base) can be moved in its dove-tail on the receiver. The receiver should be restaked to retain the sight in the position permanently. For normal use, the spring action of the sight base is sufficient to hold the sight in place.

For elevating adjustment, a scale slide is provided on the rear sight. Zero the barrel to the aperture; then, after this zeroing is accomplished, the scale can be lined up with the aperture by loosening the lower screw, sliding the scale to its desired location, and tightening the screw securely.

Barrel Changes. Barrels are changed by raising the lever found at the extreme right front of the receiver to the vertical position and withdrawing the barrel. Use the bipod as a handle. Assemble the barrel by inserting from the front, aligning the gas cylinder pilot nut with the receiver extension tube. Press the lock lever down and rearward to the full limit of travel.

Disassembly of the M60

For ease in cleaning, oiling, and inspection, this weapon can be taken down as follows, using the cartridge as a tool. With gun in closed or fired position:

Unlatch and raise feed cover.

Remove butt stock by lifting shoulder rest and insert cartridge in exposed latch hole. Withdraw butt rearward.

Lift lock plate vertically for removal, holding the buffer to prevent drive spring from ejecting it. Withdraw buffer.

Pull operating rod drive spring guide and spring out of the rear opening. Withdraw operating rod and bolt assembly rearward with the cocking lever, pulling the bolt out of the receiver by hand the remaining distance. As the bolt rotating cam is exposed, insert lock plate in front of cam opening to hold firing pin back. The operating rod can then be withdrawn from the bolt.

CAUTION: Roller bearing and pin retainer are staked in place and should not be removed. These parts are normally also held in place by the firing pin; therefore, care should be exercised to prevent their loss.

Remove trigger housing assembly by pressing spring lock flat against the trigger housing at extreme front pin to unlock it from the pin. Rotate the spring lock down and away from the receiver to disengage it from the pin, and withdraw it. Remove the front pin from the left. Remove trigger housing by sliding it forward to disengage it from the receiver.

Feed cover removal is not necessary for field stripping but can be done if desired. With feed cover raised vertically, and feed plate in place on the receiver (at approximately 90° with cover), use bullet nose to remove cover pin spring, and withdraw cover pin spring and cover pin by hand, rocking cover slightly to aid disengagement. Cover and plate are free for removal. A torsional counterweight spring is also retained by the pin, and is removable when pin is removed.

Remove barrel by raising lock lever to its vertical position and pulling the barrel out in a forward direction.

Handguard removal is not necessary for field stripping, but can be done if desired. Grasp the handguard firmly. Insert a bullet nose in the hole provided at the bottom rear of the handguard. Push cartridge to disengage spring lock. Slide handguard off to front. It is helpful to position the receiver vertically, with the front extension tube resting on a flat hard surface when disengaging the lock. After unlocking and sliding the handguard forward to disengage it from the receiver, tip the handguard to clear the tripod clevis and remove.

The weapon can be reassembled by reversing the order of the above steps.

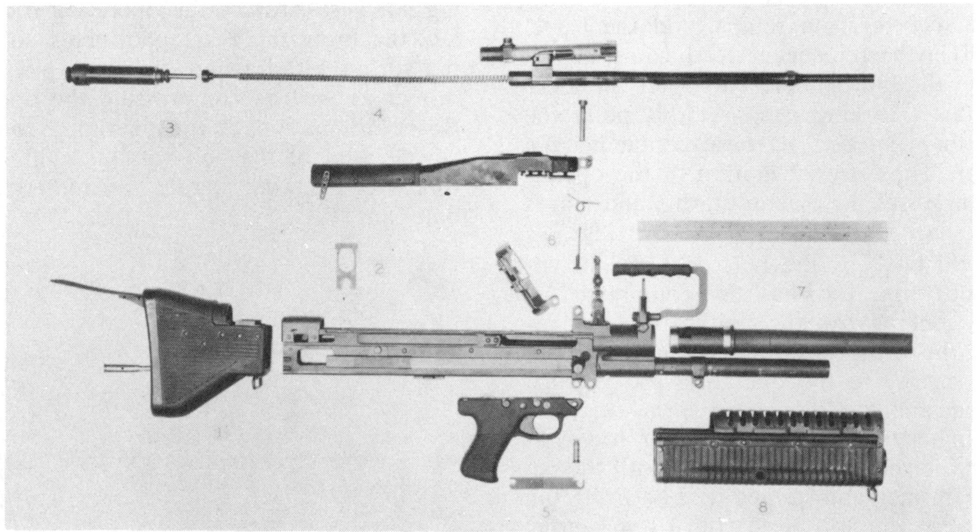

M60 Field Stripped.

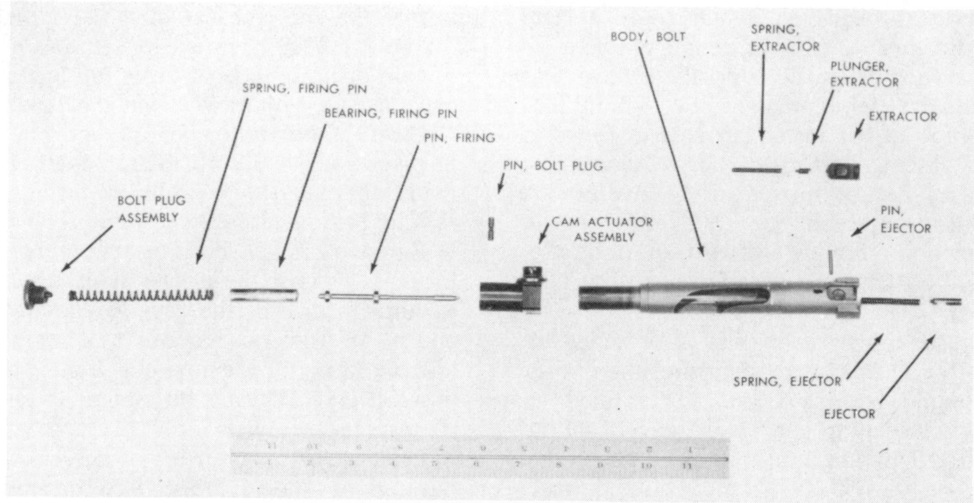

Bolt Assembly of the M60.

How the M60 Works

With the gun loaded, in the cocked position, the following is the sequence of operation:

Release the safety, and pull the trigger. The trigger raises the front of the sear, dropping the rear of the sear out of its engagement notch in the operating rod.

The operating rod, released by the sear, is propelled forward by the energy stored in the drive spring by the cocking operation. The bolt, engaged by the operating rod cam yoke is carried forward with the rod, as is the gas piston, should it be positioned to the rear.

The bolt top locking lug strikes the rear edge of cartridge in the feed plate groove, where the cartridge is positioned by the belt link and the feed cover guides and springs. The bolt strips the cartridge from its link, carrying the cartridge forward out of the feed plate. The empty link is retained in the feed plate by the cartridge guide and the next round.

As the bolt enters the barrel socket, the round has been deflected downward and into the chamber by the front cartridge guide, the receiver feed ramps, and the barrel socket feed ramp. The barrel socket lead cams impart clockwise rotation to the bolt sufficient to enter the locking lugs into the socket locking cam. At this point the round is seated in the chamber, its base contacting the extractor and ejector. The forward motion of the operating rod and bolt compresses the ejector spring, and moves the extractor out to snap over the rim of the cartridge.

The firing pin, held back by the bolt cam and its engagement with the operating rod, has also compressed its drive spring during cocking. As the bolt rotates, its rotating cam releases the firing pin. The firing pin spring now contributes its energy to the operating rod through the bolt rotating cam and aids the drive spring to complete the bolt locking rotation. The operating rod continues forward, carrying the firing pin with it until the pin strikes the cartridge primer and ignites it. The firing pin is stopped by its seat in the bolt at the pin front bearing spool, stopping the operating rod. The operating rod has also positioned the piston in its forward position.

After ignition of the powder charge by the primer, the bullet is forced down the bore by the gases released. At a point about 8 inches from the muzzle, the bullet passes the barrel gas port, allowing part of the gases under pressure to enter the gas cylinder and hollow piston through their respective ports, which are aligned with the barrel port.

Gas under pressure, bled from the bore by the gas port, fills the hollow piston until enough pressure is built up to overcome the mass of the piston and operating rod and the load of the operating rod spring. The piston begins its travel rearward, propelled by gas pressure against the forward end of the cylinder. After a very short travel rearward, the piston ports and collector ring are out of line with the barrel gas port, sealing off a measured charge of gas under pressure in the cylinder and hollow piston. By this time, the bullet is well out of the bore, and gas pressure in the bore rapidly falls to help provide easy extraction of the spent round.

The piston, propelled rearward by the trapped expanding hot gases, forces the operating rod rearward to contact the firing pin rear spool. This compresses the firing pin spring withdrawing the firing pin from the cartridge primer as well as compressing the operating rod spring. Rearward motion of the operating rod continues in the "dwell" slot of the bolt rotating cam, until the rod yoke rollers contact the spiral, or counterrotating part of the bolt cam.

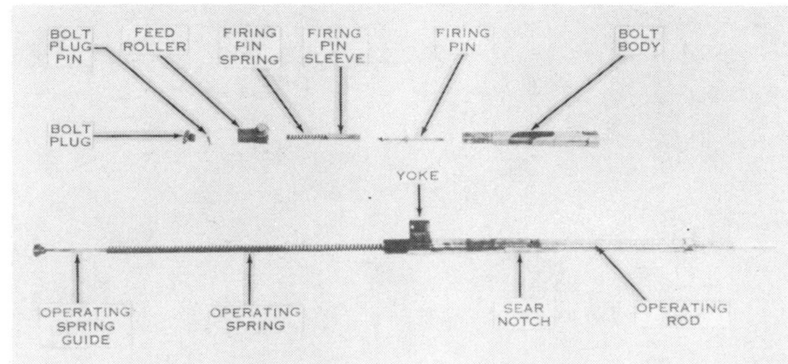

M60 Operating Group Disassembled.

The bolt now begins its counterclockwise rotation and unlocking, urged by the energy of the operating rod. At full unlock, the firing pin spring is fully cocked, the roller of the rod cam yoke contacting the rear of the bolt rotating cam.

Bolt and rod together continue to the rear, propelled by the energy of the expanding gas, withdrawing the spent cartridge from the barrel chamber. As the spent cartridge leaves the chamber it is moved sideward in the direction of the ejection port, the ejector spins the case sideward to pivot about the extractor lip and disengage, allowing the case to be ejected with force out of the port, and against the ejection deflector which propels it downward.

In this interval the piston has reached the limit of its travel. Spent gases are exhausted through ports provided in the gas cylinder, uncovered by the piston in its rearward travel.

Air behind the piston is exhausted through a set of ports near the rear of the gas cylinder, allowing escape of dirt and powder residue.

The bolt and operating rod continue rearward, propelled by stored energy and inertia, compressing the operating rod drive spring. As the drive spring is fully compressed, the operating rod contacts the buffer through the drive spring guide rod collar. Energy remaining in the rod and bolt is now transferred to the buffer. As the buffer plunger is forced rearward against its pads and preloaded springs, the rubber pads are compressed, acting as a high-rate spring. The rubber is forced to flow radially, to expand frictional surfaces tight against the buffer tube wall. Further rearward motion compresses the buffer return spring and the sliding friction of the pads on the tube wall absorbs the remaining energy of the rod and bolt. The moving parts now come to rest, and the counterrecoil cycle begins.

The energy stored in the drive spring now forces the operating rod and bolt forward. The frictionally damped buffer springs return the buffer plunger to its initial position. The firing pin spring also contributes some force until it is halted by the front of the rod yoke, which stops the firing pin in the "cocked" position in the bolt rotating cam. As the rod continues forward with the bolt, if the trigger has been released, the sear is held up against the bottom of the rod by the sear spring. As the sear engages the sear notch in the rod, forward motion stops, and the weapon is held in cocked position, ready for fire. If the trigger has not been released, the weapon continues to fire until interrupted by the sear, or until the ammunition is exhausted. If the last round is fired and the trigger held down, the gun will close on an empty chamber, and must be recocked manually.

Feed Cycle. For simplification of description, this portion of the operation is considered separately. As the bolt travels forward for firing, the feed cam mounted in the feed cover is engaged by the feed cam actuator roller attached to the rear of the bolt. Forward motion of the bolt and actuator causes the feed cam to swing to the right, forcing the front of the feed cam lever to the left. This carries the cartridge feed pawl plate assembly to the left where the pawls drop over and engage the next or second round for transport, and remain there until the round in the plate is stripped and fired.

As the bolt recoils, the actuator forces the feed cam to the left, and the feed pawl assembly transports the round to the right into the feed plate groove. The round is forced down into the groove by the cartridge guides and their springs. The empty link left on the plate is pushed out the port in the feed plate by the new round as it is fed. The feed plate contains a spring-loaded retaining pawl that retains the belt, holding the second round when the first round is in the plate groove. Two anti-friction rollers help guide the belt in place, and support the hanging belt. The weapon is provided with sufficient reserve power to lift a 100-round belt vertically under all normal operating conditions.

Special Note on the M60 Machine Gun

The M60 is the first United States machine gun to have a true quick-change barrel. It was specifically designed for light weight, and components design was simplified for manufacture. Stampings or fabrications were used wherever possible. The quick-change barrel, light weight, and adaptability for use as either a heavy or light machine gun, as well as relative ease of manufacture, make the M60 superior to the Browning guns it is replacing. The performance of the lined and plated barrel of the M60 in sustained fire is really exceptional. United States experience in the Korean war with the Chinese Communist "human wave" type of tactics indicated the need for a weapon capable of long periods of sustained fire. The old water-cooled Browning M1917A1 stood up fairly well, but it is far too heavy and bulky, and it lacks tactical flexibility. Moreover, it is not inconceivable that, at some time in the future, United States troops might be forced to fight in an area where water would be worth its weight in gold. An added factor of advantage in the case of the M60 versus the Brownings is that the M60, like most other weapons with a quick-change barrel, has no headspace adjustment problem. One of the principal causes of trouble with the Brownings in the field was error in headspace adjustment, which resulted in blown cases, with most of the case very thoroughly stuck in the barrel. The weapons were modified after World War II to make this occurrence less likely, but it is still a possibility with the Brownings.

The M60 was developed mainly by the Bridge Tool and Die Manufacturing Co. of Philadelphia and the Inland Manufacturing Division of General Motors.

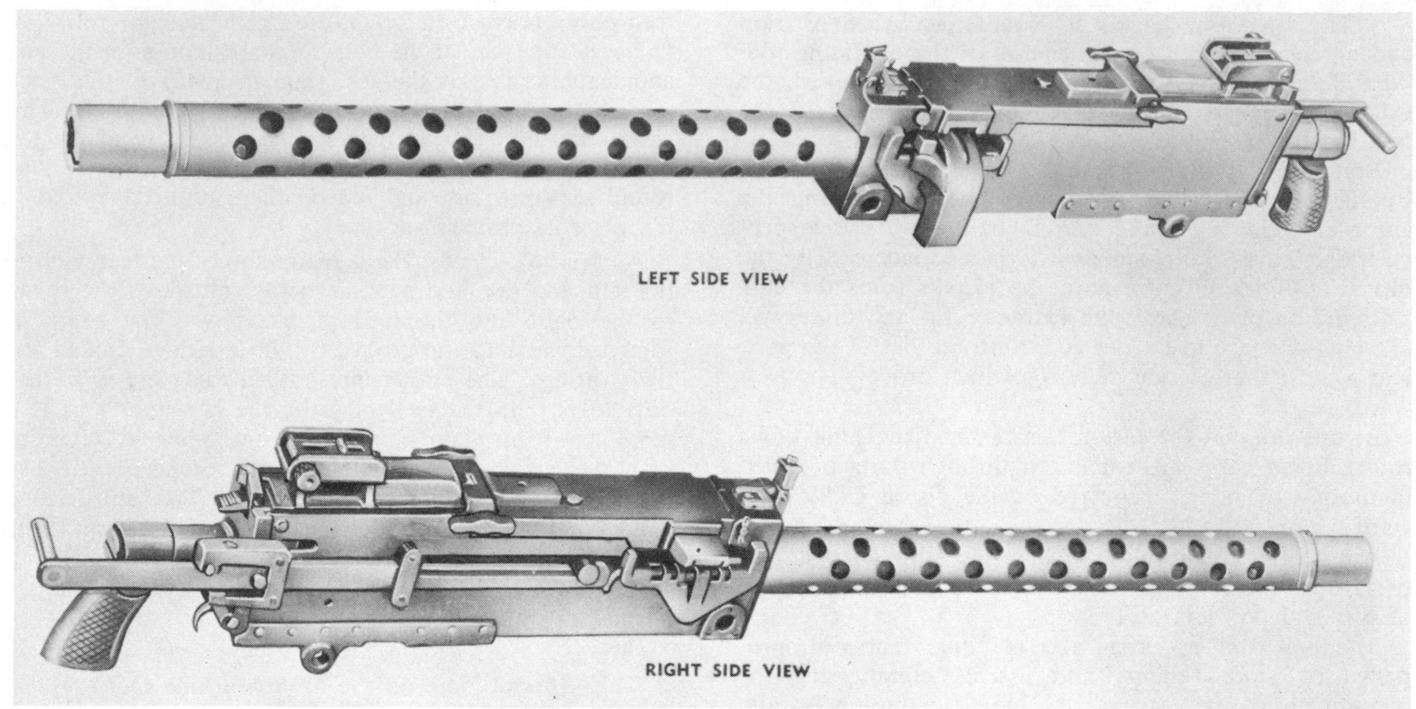

Cal. .30 Tank Machine Gun M37.

Caliber: .30.
System of Operation: Recoil operated, full automatic fire only.
Weight of Complete Gun: 31 lb.
Length of Gun, Overall: 41.75 in.
Length of Barrel: 24 in.
Feed Device: Disintegrating link belt, (pullout type).
Cyclic Rate of Fire: 400 to 550 r.p.m.
Muzzle Velocity: 2800 f.p.s. with M2 ball.
Sights, Front: Blade, mounted on folding base.
Rear: Leaf, adjustable for elevation and windage.

The M37 is basically a modification of the Browning M1919 series of weapons. It was designed to produce a weapon which would have more usefulness in tank mountings than did the Browning M1919A4 and A5. Since the M37 is an interim weapon and will be replaced by the 7.62mm M73 tank machine gun, it is not covered as thoroughly as the other United States post-World War II weapons.

Notes on the M37 Tank Machine Gun

The principal differences between the M37 and the Browning M1919 series of guns are given below:

The M37 can be fed from either the right or left side. The bolt has a dual track for the belt feed lever stud. By positioning two switches, the ejector, and various feed components, the weapon can be easily changed to feed from either side. This arrangement is generally similar to that found on the Browning cal. .30 M2 aircraft gun and the cal. .50 M2 and M3 aircraft guns.

The cover catch has been changed so that it can be opened easily from either side.

Backplate removal has been simplified by the addition of a new type of backplate latch.

The driving spring assembly has been made into a packaged unit similar to that used on the cal. .50 Browning gun, and a stranded wire spring is used.

A metal link ejection chute has been added; this component is changed from side to side when the feed components are changed.

The functioning of the M37, as well as its field stripping, loading, and firing, is essentially the same as for the earlier M1919-series guns. An earlier modification of the Browning M1919 series, the cal. .30 M1919A4E1, fed from only one side. It was fitted with a retracting bar, as is the M37, for ease of charging the gun in a tank coaxial mount. Both the M1919A4E1 and the M37 can be used as ground guns on the M1917A1, M2, or M74 mounts.

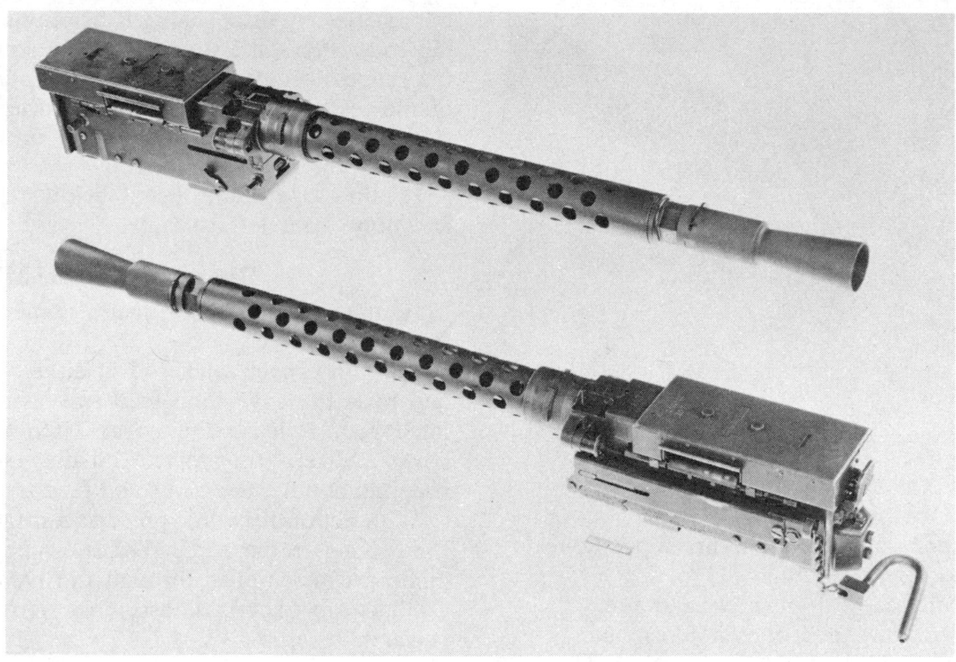

7.62mm Tank Machine Gun M73.

Caliber: 7.62mm NATO.
System of Operation: Recoil, with gas boost; automatic fire only.
Weight of Complete Gun: 28 lb.
Weight of Barrel: 5 lb. 10 oz.
Length of Gun, Overall: 34.75 in. (Note this is 7 in. shorter than the cal. .30 M37 tank machine gun.)
Length of Barrel: 22 in.
Feed Device: Disintegrating link belt (pushout type).
Cyclic Rate of Fire: 450-500 r.p.m.
Sights: None on weapon, sights mounted in vehicle.
Muzzle Velocity: 2800 f.p.s.

The development of the M73 (formerly known as the T197E2) was the result of the need for a rifle-caliber machine gun designed specifically for use in tanks. It had become evident that the use of the Browning-type guns was not as satisfactory as it could be. The outstanding shortcoming of the Brownings for use in tanks was their long receivers. Space is at a premium inside the turret and hull of a tank. There was a need for a much shorter gun which would at least equal the performance of the Brownings. The M73 fills this need. It also has a quick-change barrel, and can be fed from either side. The M73 uses the same link, the M13, that is used with the M60 general purpose machine gun. It can be charged and fired either by manual operation or solenoid. The barrel jacket of the M73 is to be attached to the tank in a semipermanent manner, and all the working components of the weapon, plus the barrel, can be removed from inside the tank for cleaning and repair.

How to Load and Fire the M73

Preparation for Firing. Open cover by pressing the cover latching rod on the side of the receiver from which the belt will be fed. Pivot the cover to an open position.

Retract the action to seared position, using the charging mechanism; make sure that the safety is at the "F" position. NOTE: Mount the charger on either left or right side of the receiver as determined by the mounting conditions of the weapon. Slide the charger connector to the proper side by pressing the retainer and sliding the connector manually.

Slide the safety to the SAFE position, exposing the letter "S" on the back plate.

Visually inspect the barrel chamber and inside of receiver for assurance against possible obstructions.

To load the weapon: Insert the cartridge belt with the first round in the slot of the feed tray (open side of link loops facing downward).

Press the cover latch rod, close the cover, and release the cover latch rod to the lock position.

Firing. Slide the safety in the back plate to the FIRE position, exposing the letter "F" on the back plate ("S" for SAFE).

Actuate the solenoid for remote firing.

Press the trigger on the back plate for manual firing.

Immediate Action Procedure (to resume fire after a stoppage). When a stoppage occurs BEFORE COMPLETING A 200-ROUND SERIES (starting from a cool gun), perform the operations listed below in the

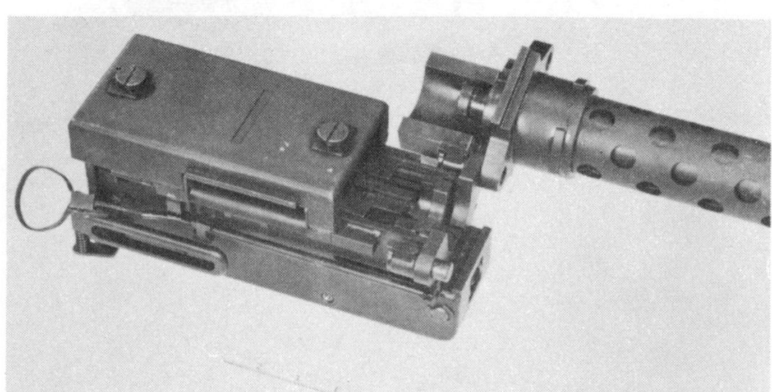

Quick-Change Barrel of M73.

M73 With Cover Open.

given order. (If weapon starts after the first operation, do not perform the next, etc.)

Charge weapon fully to sear position and fire.

Repeat above twice if weapon does not respond.

Charge weapon fully and hold back on charger. Then—

Open cover and remove belted ammunition.

Open feed tray and remove live or spent cartridges from the action.

Charge and hand-function weapon.

Load and fire.

If the weapon still does not fire, inspect for broken parts. NOTE: To prevent the possibility of an open-breech cook-off with the cover open, proceed as follows: When a stoppage occurs AFTER FIRING MORE THAN A 200-ROUND SERIES (starting from a cool gun), charge and fire three times. If weapon does not resume fire at this point, charge fully (do not open cover) and allow the gun to cool to near-ambient temperature before opening cover as above.

Feed Change. Observe the following instructions when changing from left-hand to right-hand feed:

Remove the cover assembly from the receiver.

Swing the feed tray to a vertical position relative to the receiver by disengaging it from one of the cover latching rods. Press the plunger of the round stop, and slide the round stop to engage the locating hole on the left side of the feed tray. In this position, the "R" on the round stop will be adjacent to the "R" on the feed tray ("L" and "L" for left-hand feed).

Follow operations listed below to convert the cover assembly from left to right.

Disassembly of the M73

Actuate the trigger to insure that the weapon is in the forward position.

Press the cover latch rod at either side of the receiver, and raise the cover and feed tray assemblies to clear the latch rod. Release the cover latch rod, and allow the cover and feed tray to rest on the rod. Press the second rod, and remove the cover and feed tray from the receiver.

With action forward, press and rotate counterclockwise the driving spring rods. Withdraw the driving spring and guide rod assemblies through the holes in the backplate.

Slide the backplate assembly vertically from the receiver housing.

Depress the buffer support lever at either side of the receiver, and slide the barrel extension with the barrel to the rear, by pulling the charger handle. Remove the barrel extension and the barrel from the rear of the receiver. NOTE: An alternate method of field stripping is to pull on either receiver disconnector and pivot the receiver down and about the opposite receiver disconnector. Remove the receiver from the mounting block by withdrawing the second receiver disconnector. Proceed as above, and withdraw barrel from mounting block assembly.

Assembly. Assemble the weapon by reversing the procedure given above.

Slide the feed support retainer away from the feed cam.

Slide the feed cam fully forward and lift it out, retaining it in hand.

Lift out the feed support and retain this in the same hand.

Remove the feed track and slide as a unit. Reassemble

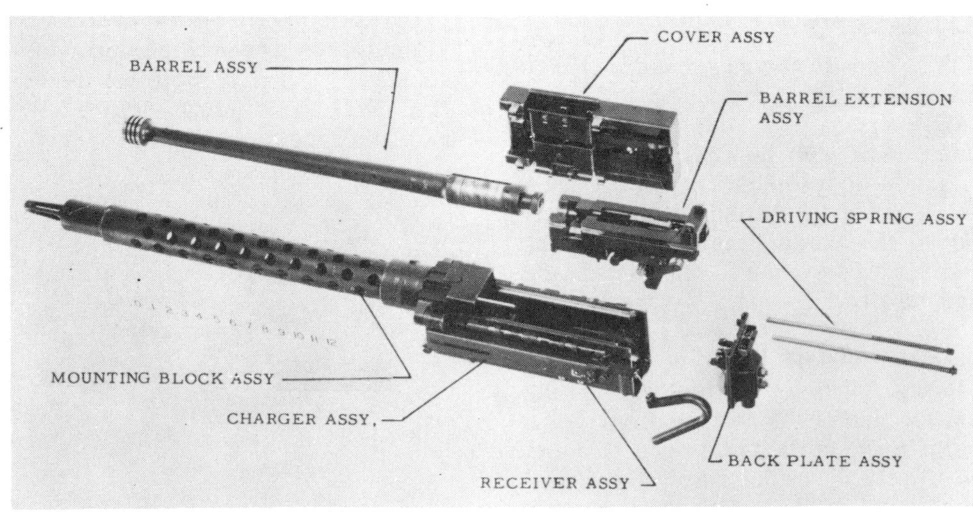

M73 Field Stripped.

this unit to the cover after turning it end for end (180°). This will align the "R" of the feed track with an "R" in the cover ("L" and "L" for left-hand feed).

Slide the feed support retainer fully to the opposite side of the cover.

Replace the feed support.

With the "R" side of the feed cam facing up, assemble to the cover in the fully forward position ("R" on cam adjacent to "R" on cover), picking up the feed slide roller during the operation. (Assembly notches prevent improper assembly.) Slide feed cam to rear of cover.

Slide the feed support retainer to the central lock position where it will secure the assembly. NOTE: In changing from right-hand to left-hand feed, reverse the foregoing procedure.

Reassemble the cover to the receiver by placing it in proper position and pressing the two cover latching rods.

How the M73 Works

Operational Power. The energy of recoil is supplied by the momentum of the recoiling parts and a muzzle booster driving the action rearward to buffer contact. Counterrecoil energy is supplied by the driving springs and the buffer spring that were compressed during the recoil cycle. The open-bolt action employs the driving springs alone and counterrecoil for the first shot from the sear position.

Recoil Movement. During the rearward movement of the barrel extension, the attached lever linkage actuates the rammer assembly by means of opening closing cams located in the sides of the receiver. The rearward movement of the barrel extension enables the sliding breechblock to move transversely to the right and away from the base of the chambered cartridge case. The extractor with the rammer grips the rim of the case and removes the spent round from the chamber, carrying it rearward to engage the round carrier grips. At this point, the spent case is transferred from the extractor to the round carrier grips. In the interim, the hammer which is assembled to the barrel extension is cocked by the cocking cam and is secured in the seared position by the sear assembly. At this stage of the recoil cycle, the ammunition will have been fed into the path of the retracted rammer assembly by the barrel extension and the connected feed cam in the cover assembly. The buffer assembly that is attached to the receiver trunnion block limits the rearward travel of the recoil mechanism.

Counterrecoil Movement. Energy of the driving springs and buffer return spring forces the barrel extension forward. During this movement, the rammer assembly strips and chambers the next round; the round carrier transports the empty case downward where it is dislodged by a fixed ejector; the breech assembly locks the next round in position; the rate control slide is released to actuate the hammer sear and allow the hammer to fall on the firing pin extension. The forward motion of the barrel extension is limited by the trunnion block in the receiver.

Firing will cease when the trigger is released and the barrel extension is engaged in the open-bolt position by the sear.

7.62mm Machine Gun M73C on XM132 Tripod

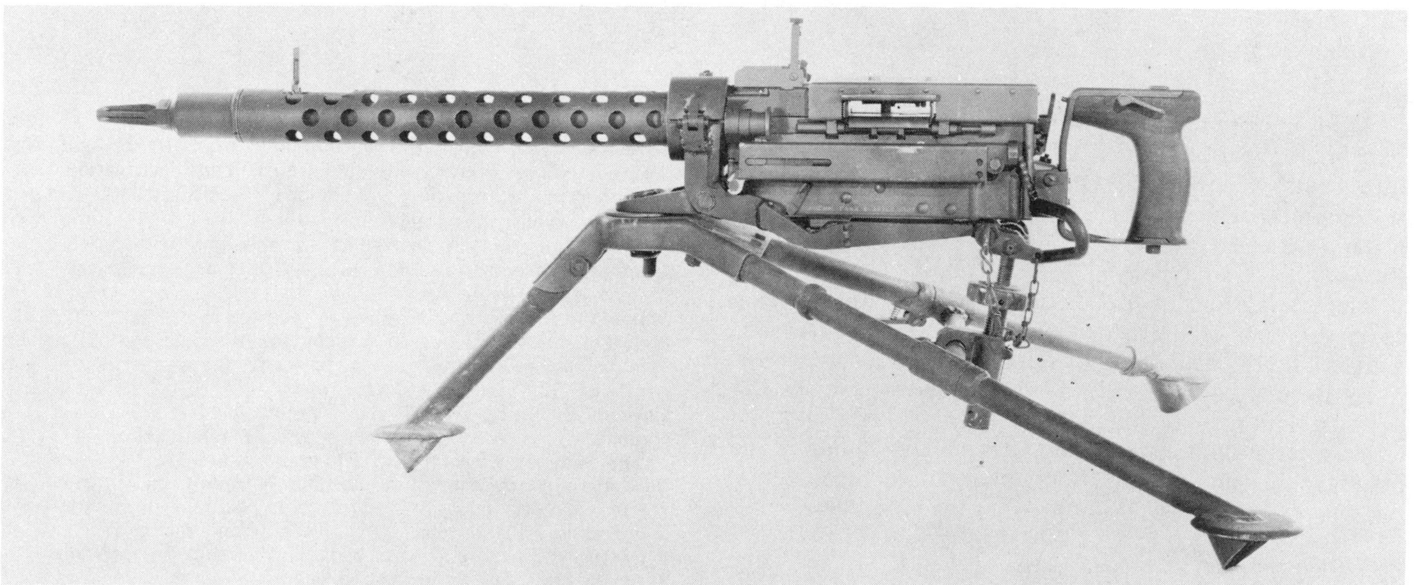

Caliber: 7.62mm NATO.
System of Operation: Recoil with gas boost.
Weight: 30.8 lbs.
Length, Overall: 40.25 in.
Barrel Length: 22 in.
Feed Device: M13 disintegrating metallic link belt.

Sights: Front—Folding post.
Rear—Leaf graduated from 100-1100 meters, adjustable for windage.
Cyclic Rate: 450-550 r.p.m.
Weight of XM132 Mount: 19.6 lbs.

This is the flexible version of the fixed M73 tank machine gun. It is basically the same gun as the M73, with sights and a pistol grip trigger added. The solenoid, which is normally used to fire the gun in a tank, is integral with the back plate and remains on the M73C. The weapon is loaded as the M73 and is fired as follows: Slide the safety in the back plate to the fire position—letter "F" exposed. Push down on trigger.

The XM132 tripod mount is the caliber .30 M2 mount with a special adaptor for the M73C. This weapon exists only in prototype form.

Browning Cal. .50 HB M2 Machine Gun

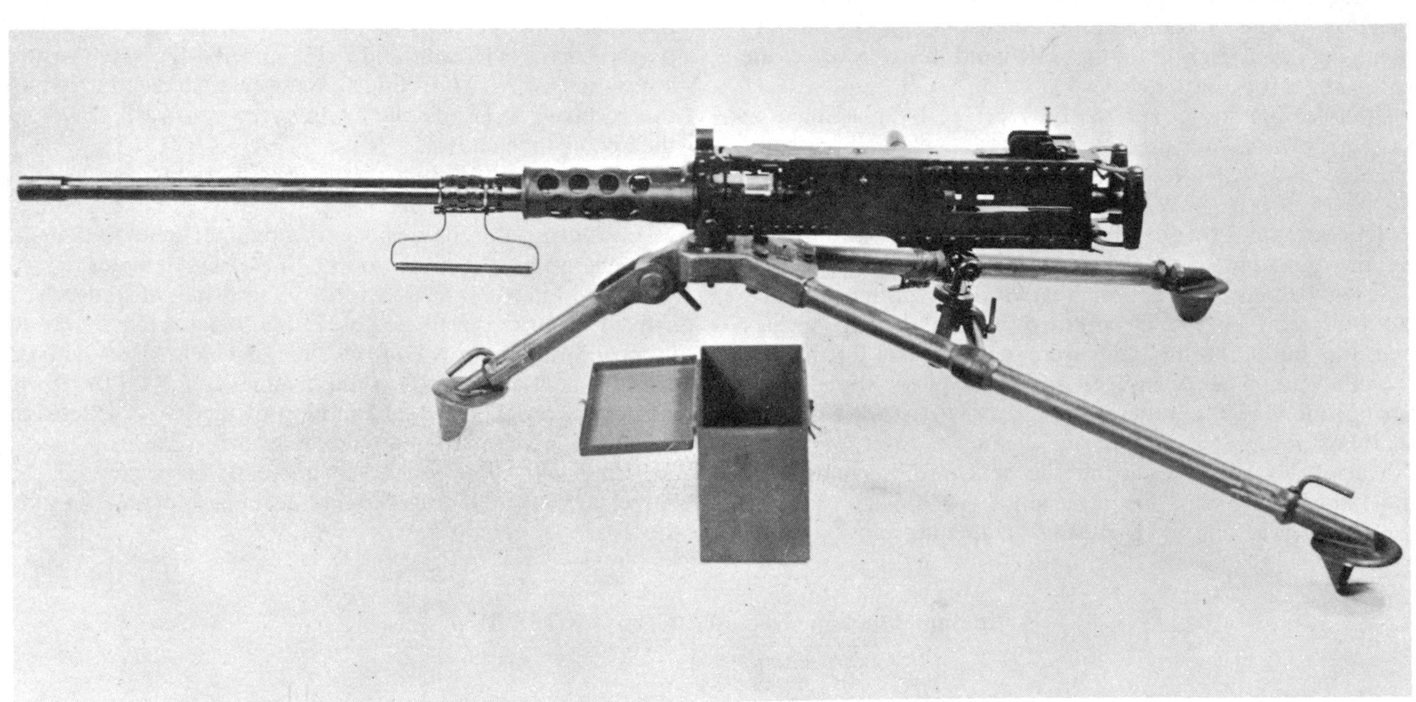

This gun is produced with three different types of barrels for various types of use. The aircraft model, fitted with a perforated barrel jacket or casing weighs 64 pounds. This is a fixed-type machine gun whose general design, except for firing mechanism, resembles that of the other types.

The antiaircraft model is fitted with a water jacket as in the case of the Browning .30, model 1917A1 and weighs 121½ pounds. The third type, the model HB, M2, Ground, fitted with a heavy barrel, weighs 84 pounds. This gun is designed for tank and field use and its description will serve for a better understanding of the other types, which are much less likely to be encountered.

Caliber: .50.

Feed: Belt fed with 100-round belts.

Muzzle Velocity: 2400 feet per second to 2660 feet per second.

Barrel Length: 45″.

Overall Length of Gun: 65″.

Weight: 84 pounds.

Barrel Weight: About 28 pounds.

Weight of Loaded 100 Round Belt: About 31 pounds, without ammunition chest. Chest adds about 4½ pounds to the weight.

Sight: Telescopic. Weighs 3 pounds.

Standard Sights: Customary front and rear. Rear sight leaf graduated in both yards and mils. Yard graduation corresponds to ammunition with muzzle velocity of 2400 feet per second; while mil graduation may be used with ammunition of any muzzle velocity, which in this gun with special ammunition may run as high as 3,000 feet per second. The rear sight is adjustable for windage.

Maximum Range: Approximately 7400 yards.

Gun Operated By: Recoil. Except for the addition of an oil buffer assembly, the gun is basically the same as the gun caliber .30, model 1917A1.

Locked: Browning system, rising breech block.

Cooled: Air cooled. Heavy barrel. Barrel removable.

Cyclic Rate of Fire: 400 to 500 per minute.

Position of Retracting Slide Handle: Normally on right side of gun. Handle remains in forward position throughout the operation of the gun. This differs from the caliber .30 in which bolt handle travels back and forth with the bolt.

Type of Fire: Full automatic only.

Special Feature: There is a bolt latch on this gun at the upper rear of the receiver. This securely latches the bolt in the recoil position. Instead of the pistol grip of the caliber .30, this weapon has a double spade-grip of the Vickers type attached to the back plate which carries a bolt latch release and lock as well as a thumb trigger.

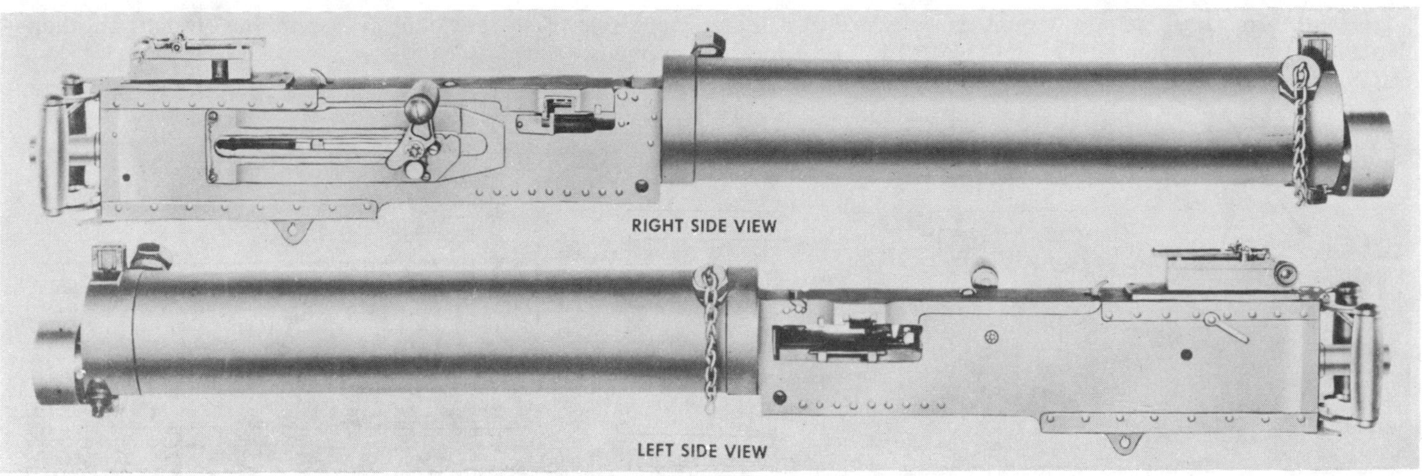

The M1921, watercooled.

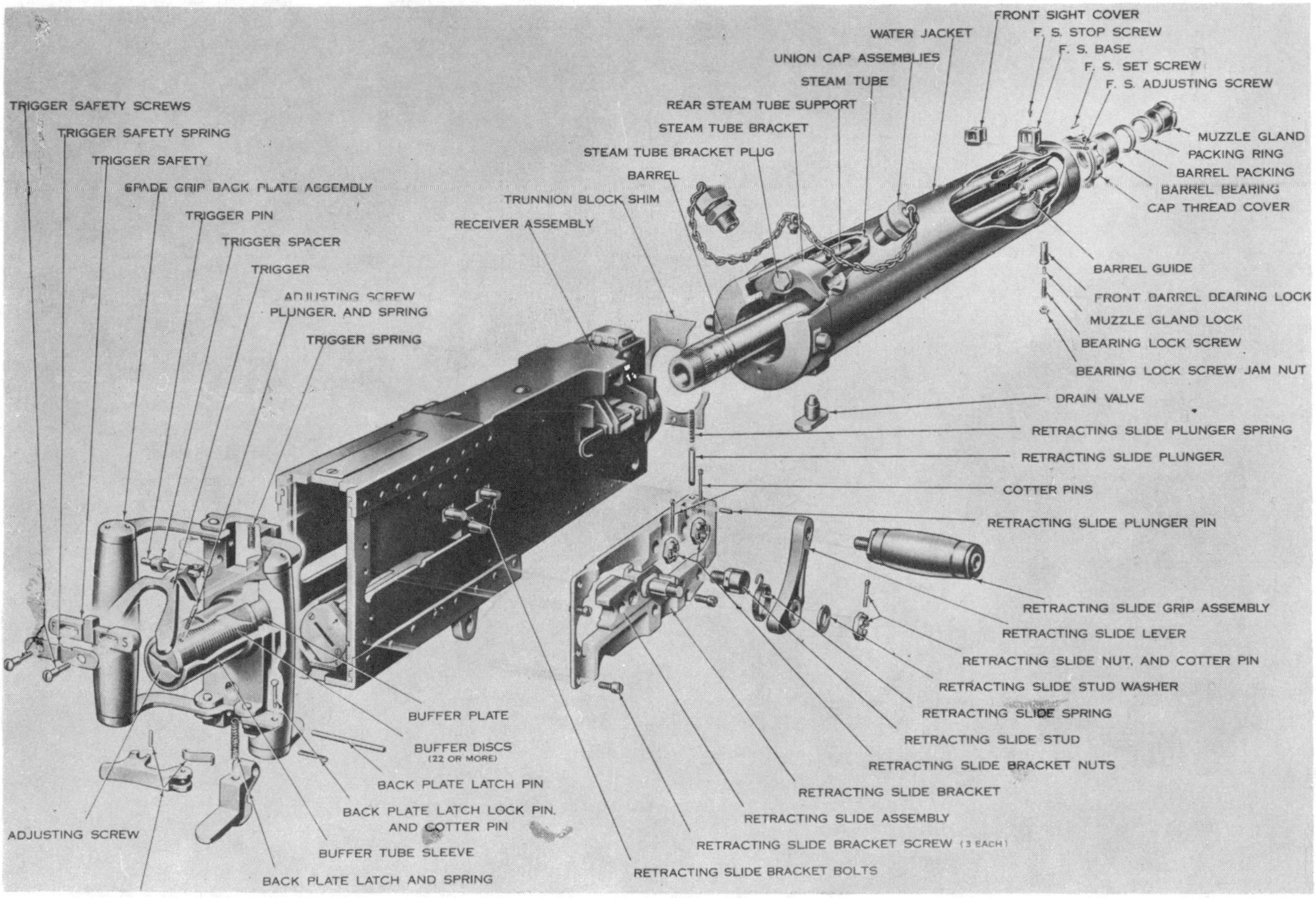

FRONT SIGHT COVER
WATER JACKET
F. S. STOP SCREW
F. S. BASE
UNION CAP ASSEMBLIES
F. S. SET SCREW
STEAM TUBE
F. S. ADJUSTING SCREW
TRIGGER SAFETY SCREWS
REAR STEAM TUBE SUPPORT
TRIGGER SAFETY SPRING
STEAM TUBE BRACKET
MUZZLE GLAND
STEAM TUBE BRACKET PLUG
PACKING RING
TRIGGER SAFETY
BARREL
BARREL PACKING
SPADE GRIP BACK PLATE ASSEMBLY
BARREL BEARING
TRUNNION BLOCK SHIM
CAP THREAD COVER
TRIGGER PIN
RECEIVER ASSEMBLY
TRIGGER SPACER
BARREL GUIDE
TRIGGER
ADJUSTING SCREW PLUNGER, AND SPRING
FRONT BARREL BEARING LOCK
MUZZLE GLAND LOCK
TRIGGER SPRING
BEARING LOCK SCREW
BEARING LOCK SCREW JAM NUT
DRAIN VALVE
RETRACTING SLIDE PLUNGER SPRING
RETRACTING SLIDE PLUNGER
COTTER PINS
RETRACTING SLIDE PLUNGER PIN
RETRACTING SLIDE GRIP ASSEMBLY
RETRACTING SLIDE LEVER
RETRACTING SLIDE NUT, AND COTTER PIN
RETRACTING SLIDE STUD WASHER
RETRACTING SLIDE SPRING
BUFFER PLATE
RETRACTING SLIDE STUD
BUFFER DISCS (22 OR MORE)
RETRACTING SLIDE BRACKET NUTS
BACK PLATE LATCH PIN
RETRACTING SLIDE BRACKET
BACK PLATE LATCH LOCK PIN, AND COTTER PIN
ADJUSTING SCREW
RETRACTING SLIDE ASSEMBLY
BUFFER TUBE SLEEVE
RETRACTING SLIDE BRACKET SCREW (3 EACH)
BACK PLATE LATCH AND SPRING
RETRACTING SLIDE BRACKET BOLTS

Watercooled adaption.

Tripod Mount. A tripod mount is provided for the Browning machine gun caliber .50 HB M2. The tripod assembly weighs about 40½ pounds, while the pintle and elevating mechanism assemblies weigh another 4 pounds.

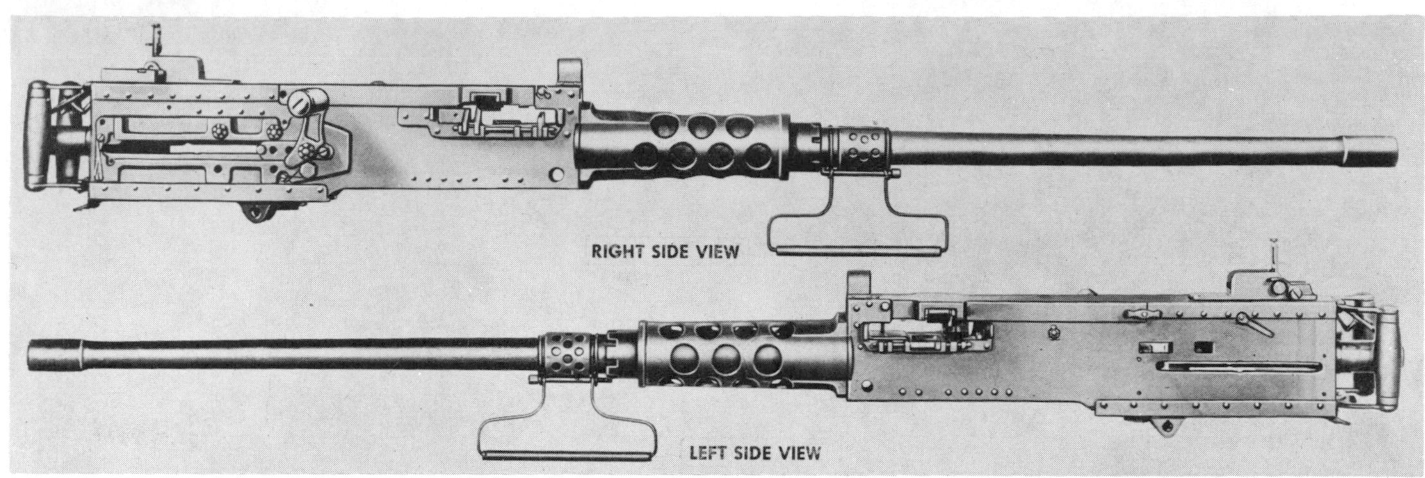

The M2, heavy barrel, flexible.

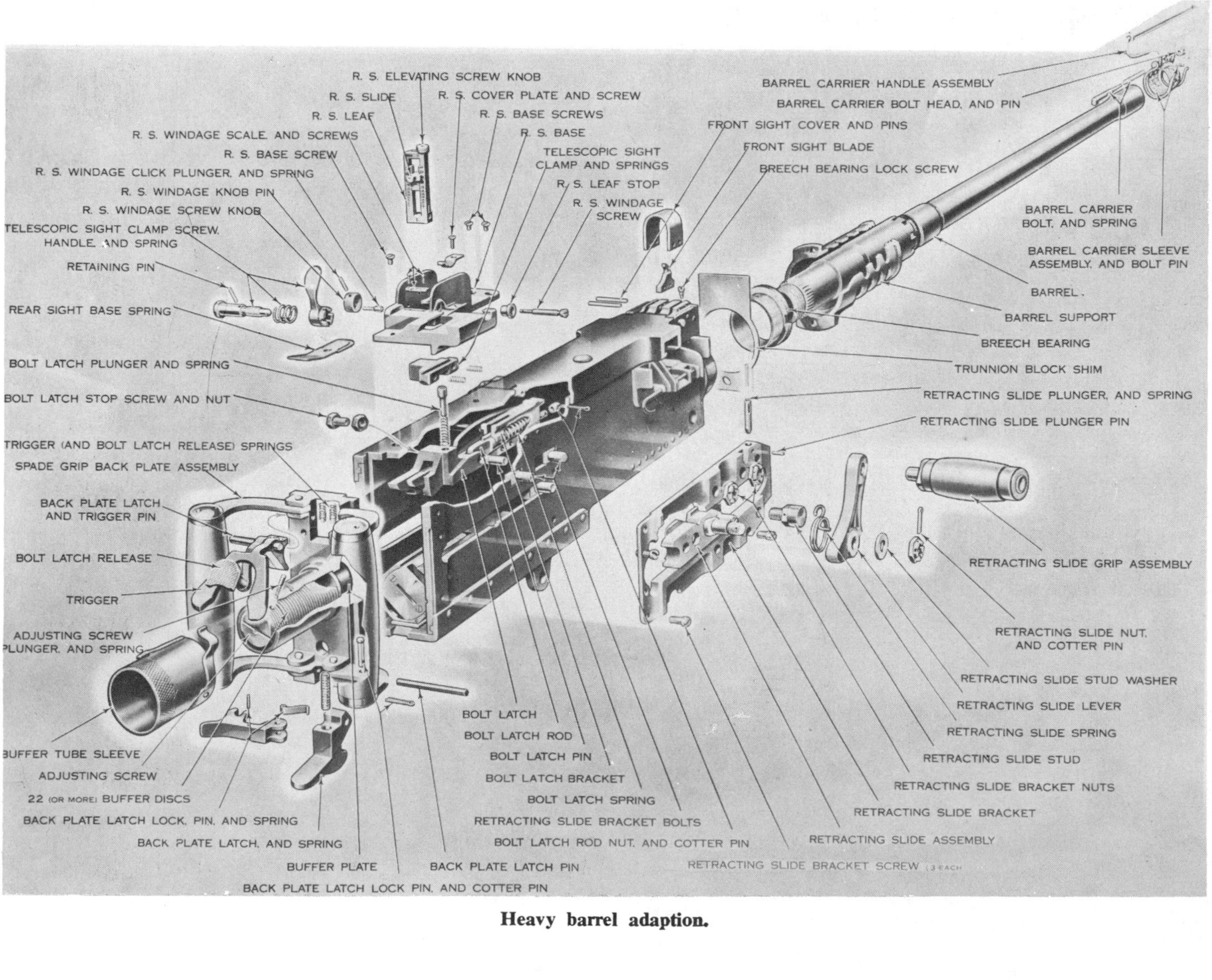

Heavy barrel adaption.

Loading and Firing

To provide for mounting in aircraft or in vehicles where position or space available require a right-hand feed, this gun is fitted with a receiver which is interchangeable for right or left hand feed. Normally ground guns will be fitted with the left hand feed as in the case of the caliber .30.

Ammunition box is mounted on the left side of the gun and belt fed through the feed block from the left side as for the caliber .30. Pull belt through as far as it will go, and while retaining grip pull back retracting slide handle as far as it will go and permit it to run forward. This half-loads the gun. Pull the retracting handle back again as far as it will go and release to complete loading.

Note that in this gun the bolt latch release must be locked down before bolt is retracted for loading the gun.

Unlock the bolt latch release by pressing down on it. Pressure on the thumb trigger will now fire the gun. It should be fired only in short bursts.

To Unload the Gun. Lift the cover and remove the belt. Pull back the retracting slide handle and look and feel in the feedway, the slot, and the chamber to be sure the gun is unloaded.

Release the bolt and let it go forward and then lower the cover.

Press the trigger. If the bolt latch release is unlocked, alternately pressing the trigger, then the bolt latch release will fire the single shots.

If the bolt latch is locked down and the trigger pressed and held, the gun fires until the trigger pressure is released.

Field Stripping

Grasp the barrel handle firmly and unscrew until the barrel is free from the barrel extension, then withdraw it to the front.

Release cover latch and raise cover as far as it will go.

Release back plate latch lock and also the back plate latch; this will permit the back plate to be lifted up out of the top of the receiver.

Push the protruding end of the driving spring rod forward and away from the slide plate and ease out the spring and the rod.

Pull the bolt back until the bolt stop lines up with the hole in the center of the slot in the side plate and then pull the bolt stud out to the right.

The complete bolt may now be removed from the rear of the casing. Driving spring unit need not be removed.

Insert the point of a bullet in the small hole at the rear of the right side plate to compress the oil buffer body spring lock. Oil buffer, barrel extension and the barrel assembly may now be taken back and out of the gun.

Pressing the accelerator forward permits the oil buffer assembly to be detached from the barrel extension.

This completes field stripping. Cover should not be removed or dismounted except for repairs, as considerable force is required to compress the pawl spring for reassembly, making this a difficult operation.

Field Assembly

Reverse the dismounting procedure.

Insert oil buffer into the oil buffer body from the rear, making sure that the cross groove in the piston is on the upper side where it can engage the shank of the barrel extension.

Assemble the buffer and buffer body to the extension. Holding the accelerator up under the barrel extension shank, start the breech lock depressors into their guideway in the barrel extension, and press forward permitting the shank of the barrel extension to engage the cross groove in the piston rod. Thrust sharply forward as far as oil buffer will go. The parts will now lock together and may be assembled into the receiver as a single unit. Press forward until the oil buffer spring locks in its recess in the right side plate.

Insert extractor in bolt and check that cocking lever is fully forward. Then insert bolt into rear of receiver. Press the rear end of the bolt down to elevate the front end just enough to clear the accelerator, otherwise the accelerator will be tripped and will not permit the bolt to be moved forward. When the accelerator has been cleared, raise the rear of the bolt to clear the buffer body. To do this it will be necessary to raise the bolt latch by reaching under the rear of the top plate with thumb or finger of one hand, while the other hand pushes the bolt forward. Bolt latch must be kept in raised position until rear of bolt passes in front of it. If this is not done, its spring will force it downward and engage the notch in the rear of the bolt preventing the bolt from going forward.

Push the bolt forward until the bolt stud hole lines up with the hole in the slot in the side plate; then insert the bolt stud until its shoulders are inside the side plate.

Insert the driving spring rod assembly and push the bolt all the way forward and keep the stud at the rear end of the driving spring rod at the recess in the right side plate.

Holding out the back plate latch lock, insert the back plate from the top. Press the trigger.

Make sure that the bolt is fully home, then close the cover. If the bolt is not fully forward, the feed lever will be forced down in front of the bolt which may result in malfunctioning.

Holding barrel by barrel handle, use both hands to insert it carefully in the front end of the barrel support. Guide the rear end over the breech bearing until it contacts the threads of the barrel extension, then screw it in until definite resistance is met. Now back off two notches to make headspace adjustment.

Headspace Adjustment

As in the case of the Browning cal. .30 machine gun, the headspace adjustment is the most important adjustment on this gun. It is not necessary to remove the barrel to make this adjustment on the caliber .50.

Remember that headspace means the space between the rear end of the barrel and the front face of the bolt; and that if this space is too wide the gun will function sluggishly or not at all and may pull the head away from the cartridge case causing serious jams; while if it is too tight, the recoiling parts will not go fully home and the gun may refuse to fire.

Screw the barrel up tight into the barrel extension, then pull back the slide and let bolt go forward to test the action.

If the action does not close fully, unscrew the barrel one notch. Then the test should be made again by pulling the bolt back and then letting it go forward.

The barrel may be unscrewed a notch at a time by pushing with the point of a bullet to rotate the barrel when the cover is raised and the bolt is in rearward position.

Work the bolt by hand several times and if the breech does not close without effort, unscrew the barrel one notch.

Raise the cover and lift the extractor, then pull the bolt slightly to the rear. If it moves independently of the barrel extension, the adjustment is too loose. Screw the bolt up one notch and then repeat the test. When a dummy cartridge is in the chamber, there must be no rearward motion of the bolt independent of that of the barrel extension before the unlocking action takes place.

Headspace test should be made whenever gun is prepared for firing.

How the Gun Works

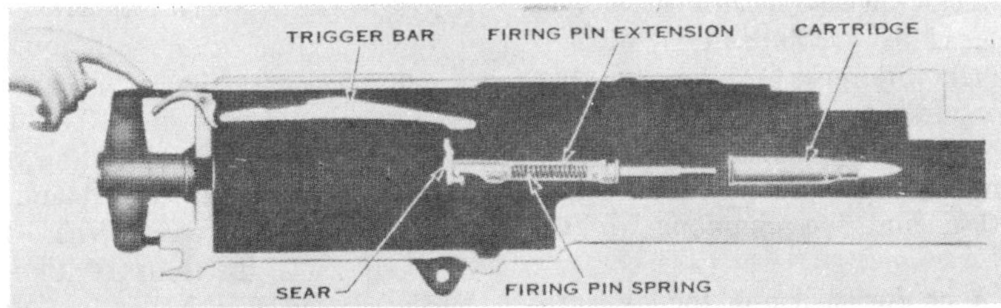

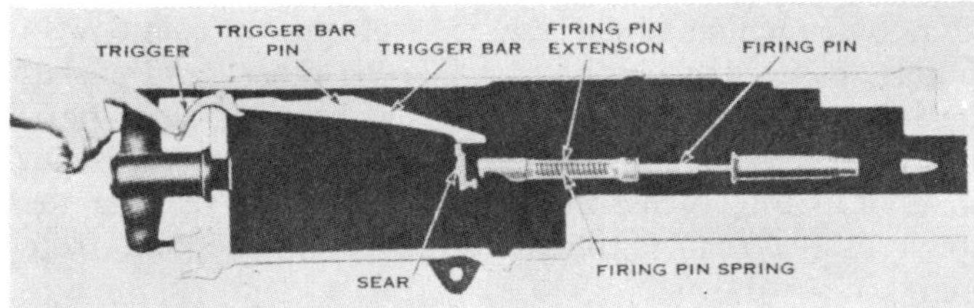

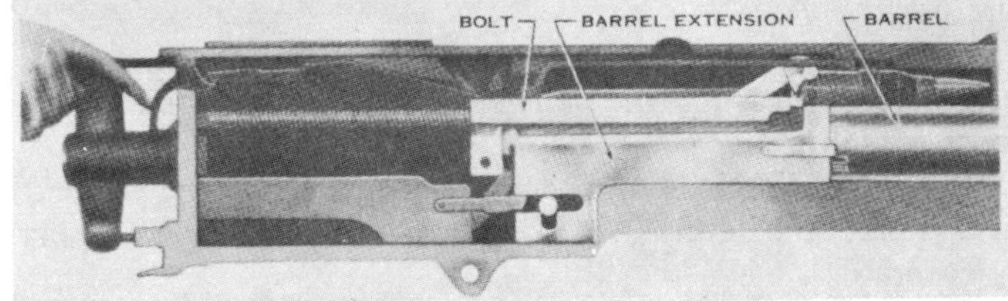

Starting with the gun loaded and cocked, the action is as follows: Pressing the trigger raises the back end of the trigger bar which pivots on the trigger bar pin and presses its front end down on the top of the sear. The sear is forced down until its notch disengages from the shoulder of the firing pin extension. This permits the firing pin extension and the firing pin to be driven forward by the coiled firing pin spring. The firing pin strikes the primer of the cartridge and explodes the powder.

Recoil Action. As the bullet starts down the barrel, the rearward force of the recoil drives the securely locked recoiling mechanism directly to the rear. During this initial motion, the bolt is supported securely against the base of the cartridge by the breech lock which rides up from the barrel extension into a notch in the underside of the bolt.

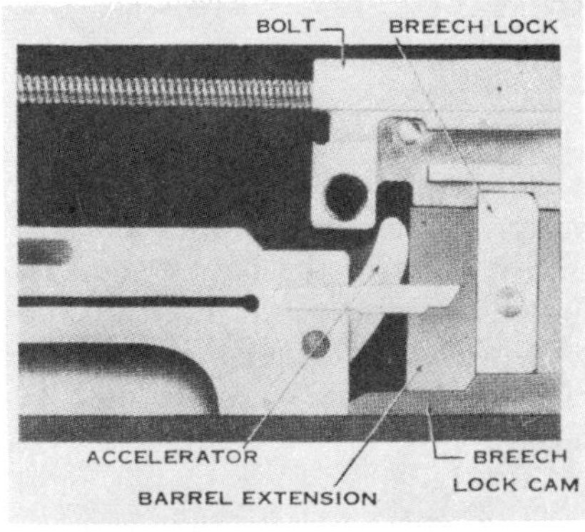

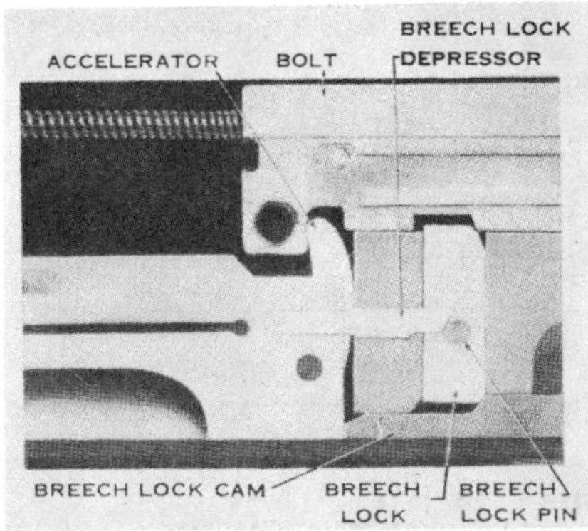

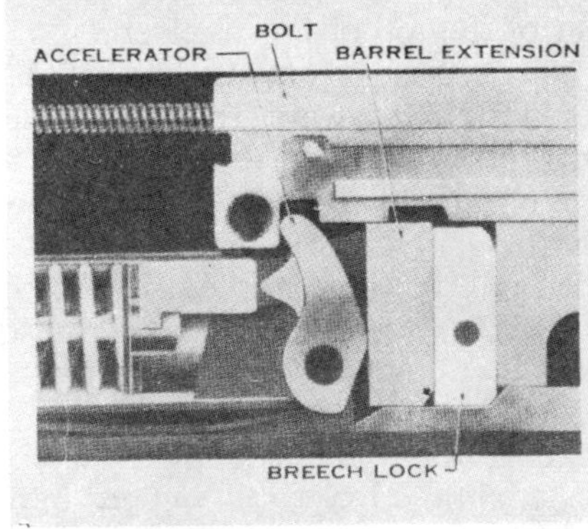

After a travel of about ¾″, during which time the bullet has left the barrel, the breech lock is pushed back off its cam. It is forced down out of its locking notch on the under side of the bolt by the breech lock depressors riding up and over the lock pin which passes through the breech lock and protrudes on either side. This action unlocks the bolt.

The barrel extension trips the accelerator up and to the rear of its pin. The tips of the accelerator striking the lower projection on the rear of the bolt accelerate

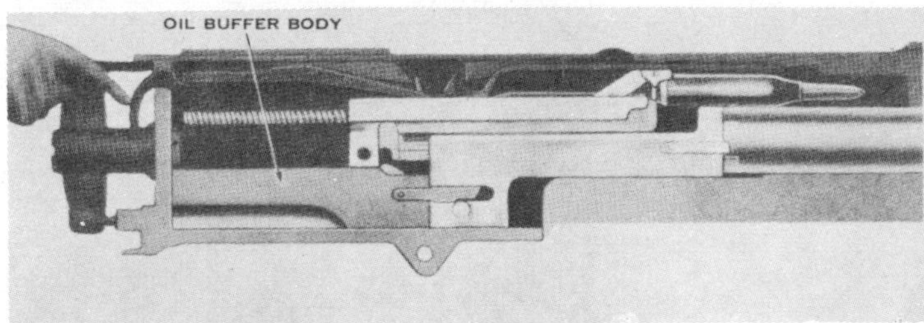

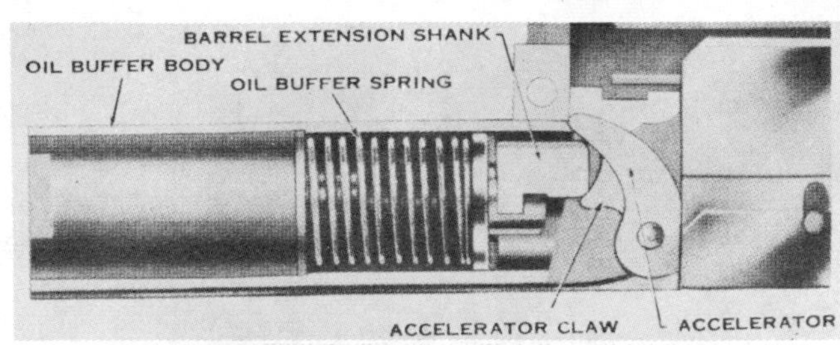

its rearward travel. After a travel of about 1⅛″, the barrel and barrel extension have completed their rearward travel. They are stopped by the oil buffer body assembly, whose oil buffer spring has been compressed in the oil buffer body by the shank in the barrel extension. The flipped-up claws of the accelerator lock the spring in compressed position as they are moved against the shoulders of the barrel extension shank.

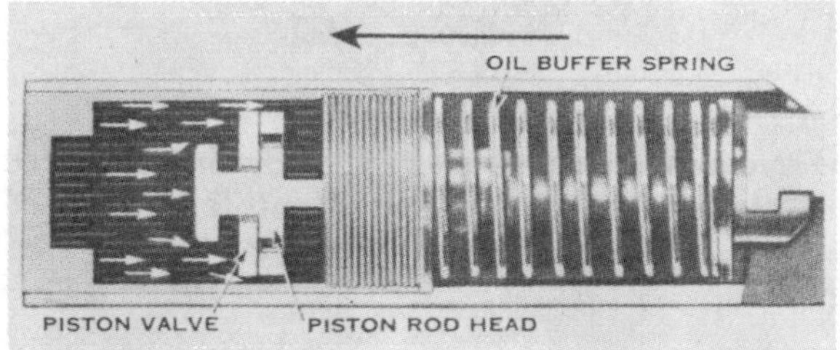

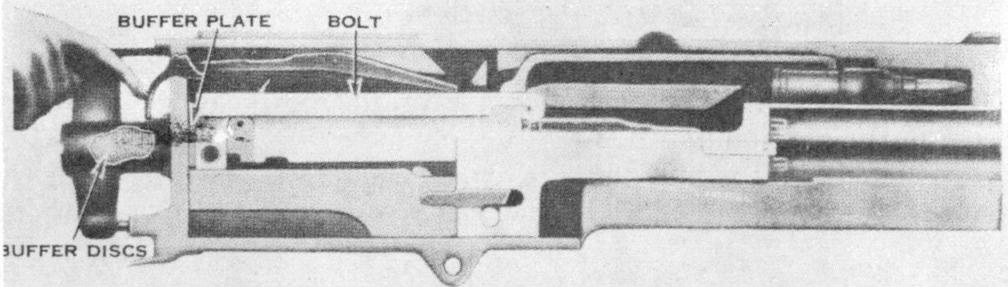

Meanwhile a piston rod head in the oil buffer assembly is forced from front to rear end of the oil buffer tube, and presses against oil in the tube to absorb the rearward shock of recoil until the oil escapes through the front side of the piston. This oil flow is through notches between the edge of the piston rod head and the oil buffer tube. This cushions the recoil and brings the rearward motion to a complete stop when the recoiling functions have been completed.

As the bolt travels to the rear, the driving springs inside it are compressed and its rearward motion is stopped when the rear of the bolt strikes the buffer plate.

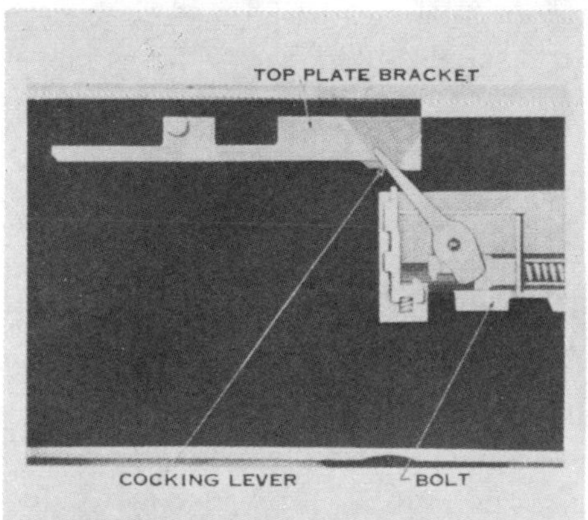

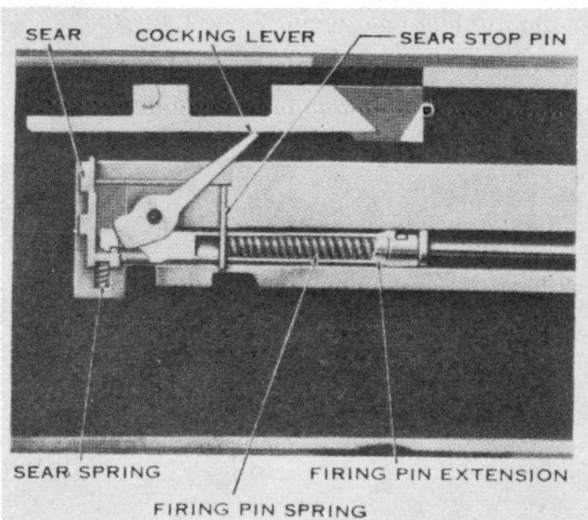

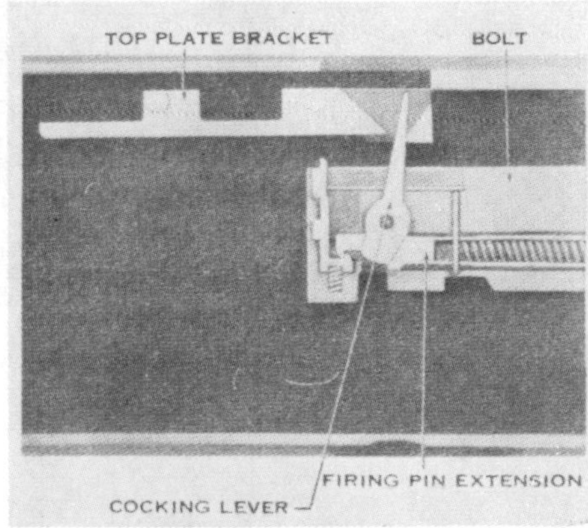

Cocking Action. The tip of the cocking lever protrudes through the top of the bolt where it lies in a V-slot in the top plate bracket. As the bolt starts to recoil, the tip of this cocking lever is pushed forward and its lower end is pivoted to force the firing extension rearward. This compresses the firing pin spring against the sear stop pin until the shoulder at the rear end of the firing pin extension hooks over the notch in the bottom of the sear under pressure of the sear spring.

When the bolt goes forward after the completion of the rearward motion, the tip of the cocking lever enters the V-slot in the top plate bracket, thus pivoting the bottom of the cocking lever out of the path of the firing pin extension to release the firing pin.

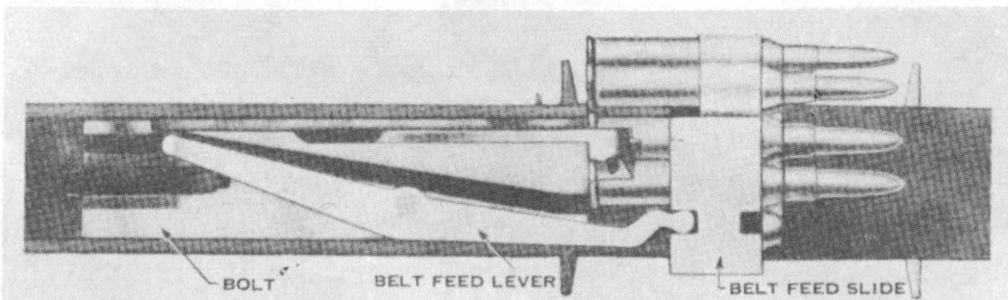

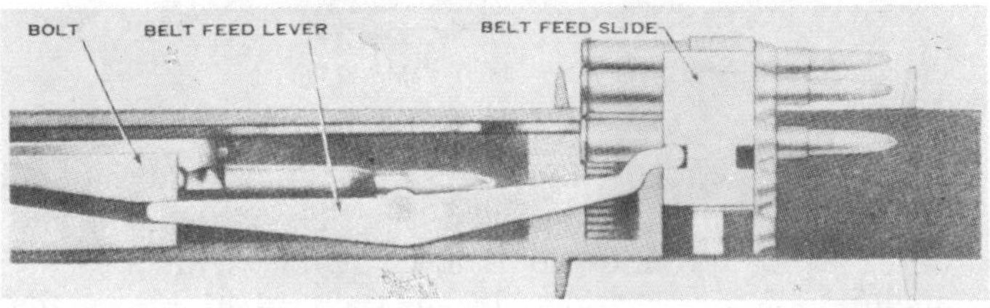

Feeding During the Rearward Motion. As the bolt moves to the rear, the stud at the rear of the belt feed lever is engaged in the diagonal groove on top of the bolt. This bolt stud thus serves to move the feed lever, which is pivoted near its center, and carry the belt feed slide at the front end of the lever out of the side of the

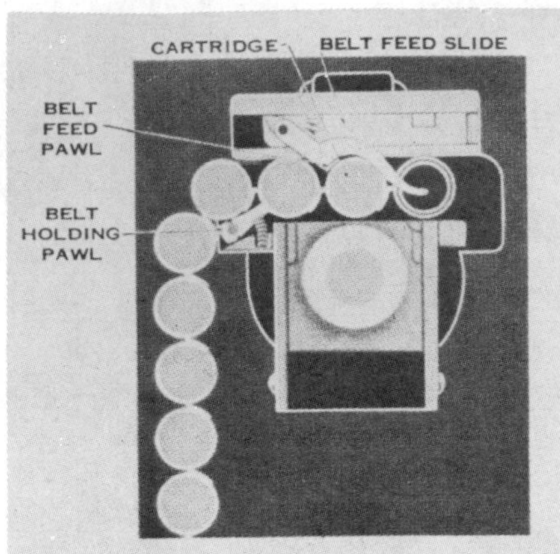

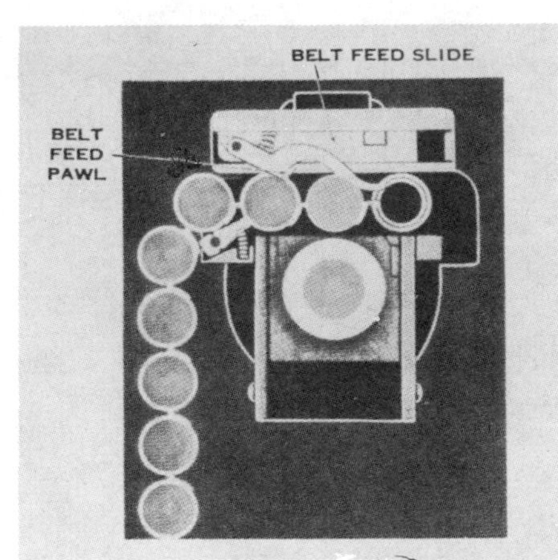

gun where its spring snaps it down over the next cartridge in the ammunition belt.

The belt is pulled into the gun by the belt feed pawl attached to the belt feed slide and ridges over the next cartridge.

As the recoiling motion is completed, the belt feed slide has traveled far enough to permit the belt feed pawl to be snapped down by its spring behind the next

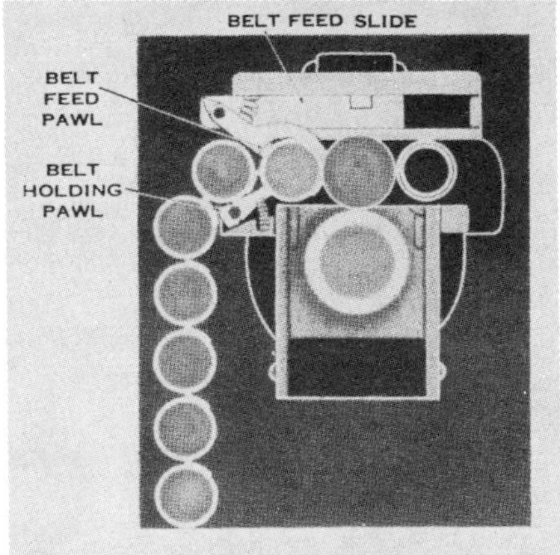

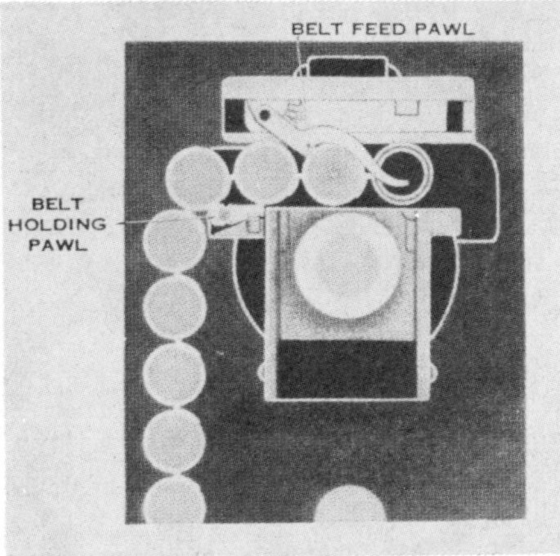

cartridge, ready to pull the belt forward into the gun on the next motion.

Forward Feeding Motion. As the bolt moves forward, the stud riding in its top pulls on the pivotal belt feed lever. The belt holding pawl is forced downwards as the cartridge is pulled over it and the belt holding pawl snaps up behind the next cartridge.

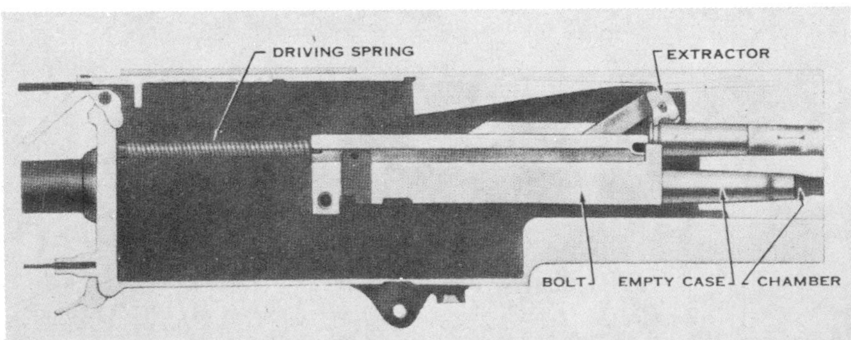

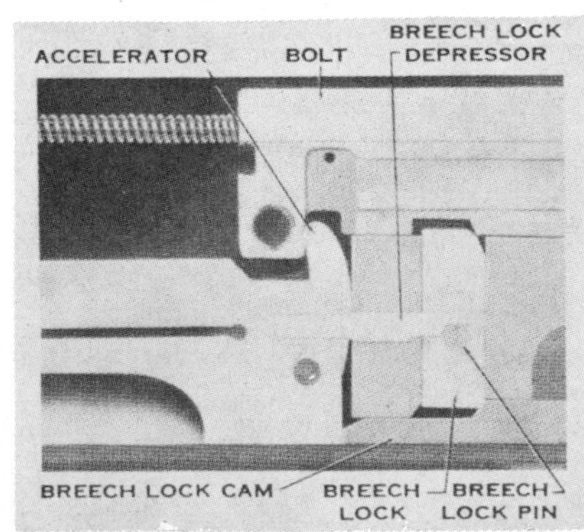

Extraction and Ejection. When the rearward motion starts, the extractor mounted in the side of the bolt and with its head above the bolt level snaps down into the cannelure of the cartridge in the belt, then draws the cartridge back out of the ammunition belt. The empty cartridge case is held in the T-slot in the front face of the bolt and the bolt withdraws it from the firing chamber.

The top front edge of the breech lock and the front side of the notch in the bolt are beveled to start withdrawals of the empty cartridge case slowly to prevent the case from being torn apart by the sudden jerking motion. As the breech lock is unlatched, the bolt pulls away from the barrel and barrel extension easily enough to prevent rupturing the cartridge case.

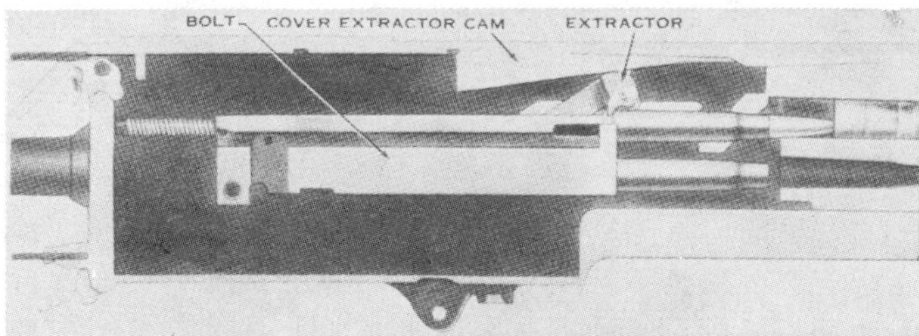

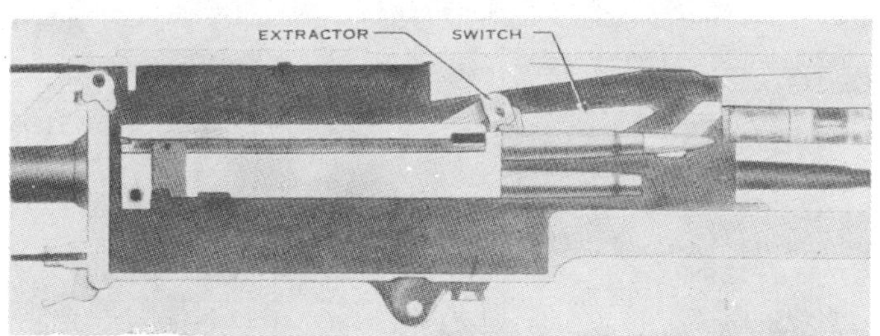

The cam on the inside of the cover forces the head of the extractor down, pushing the loaded cartridge into the mouth of the T-slot in the bolt. A lug on the side of the extractor rides against the top of the switch causing it to pivot downward at the rear; and as the recoiling motion comes to an end the lug on the extractor overrides the end of this switch, permitting it to snap up into normal position.

During this movement the empty cartridge case drops down out of the T-slot and is expelled through the bottom of the gun.

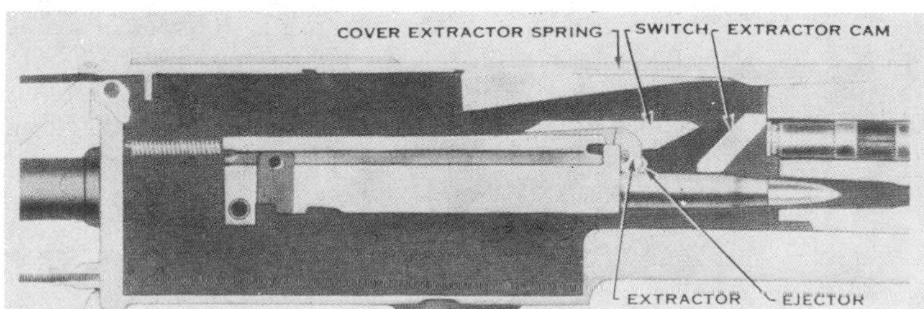

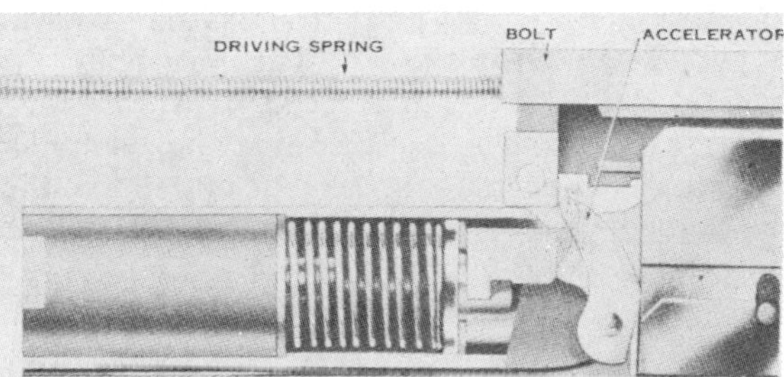

Forward Motion of the Extractor. As the bolt goes forward, the extractor lug riding under the switch forces the extractor farther down, thus forcing out the empty cartridge case if it has not already dropped out of the gun. A pin in the bolt limits the travel of the extractor and the cartridge, assisted by the ejector, is fed directly into the firing chamber.

When the cartridge is nearly chambered, the extractor rides up its cam compressing the cover extractor spring and is snapped into the cannelure of the next cartridge.

Further Action During Forward Movement. After the recoiling motion has been completed, the compressed driving spring and the compressed buffer disc force the bolt forward. The bolt travels about 5″, when the projection on its bottom strikes the tips of the accelerator, rolling the accelerator forward on its pin.

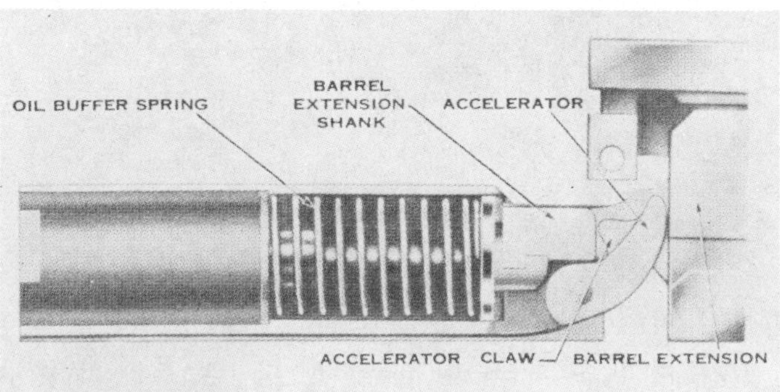

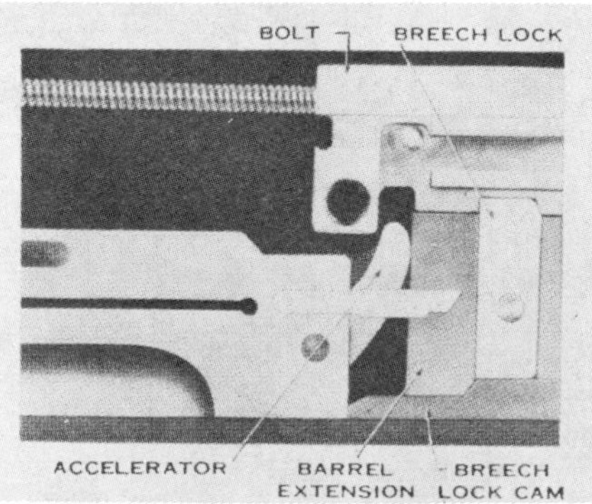

The accelerator claws are pulled away from the shoulder of the barrel extension shank, releasing the oil buffer spring. This spring now shoves the barrel extension on the barrel forward.

As the barrel extension goes forward, the breech lock strikes its cam and is forced upward on its pin. At that moment the bolt has reached the position where the notch on its underside is directly above the breech lock; and the breech lock rides up its cam and engages in this slot in the underside of the bolt. The bolt is locked to the breech end of the barrel just before the recoiling section reaches firing position.

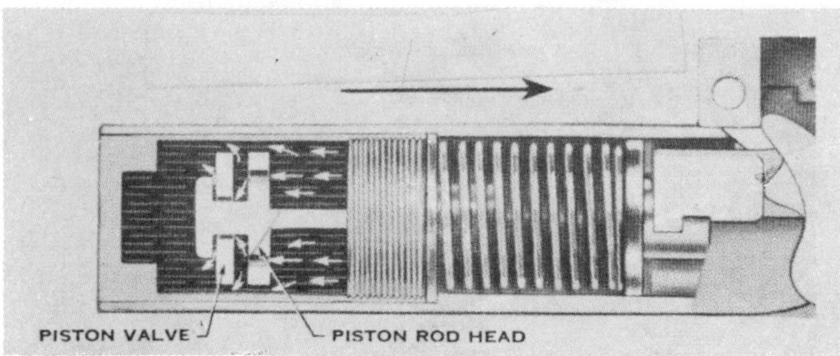

Oil Buffer. As the action moves forward additional openings for oil flow are provided in the piston rod head of the oil buffer assembly. The piston valve is forced away from the rod head as the parts move forward to uncover these openings. Thus the oil is permitted to escape freely from the opening in the center of the piston valve as well as at the edge of the valve near the tube wall, and so prepare it for the rearward motion.

Oil Buffer Adjustment. The oil buffer provides a method of regulating the speed of fire of this gun. Fire rate may be regulated by turning the oil buffer tube the required number of clicks. Turning the buffer tube to the left opens the oil buffer and permits oil to pass through the large ports, increasing the rate of fire. Turning the buffer tube to the right tightens up the oil buffer allowing it to absorb more recoil and reduce the rate of fire. This tube may be turned by inserting a screwdriver in the slot in the rear of the buffer tube.

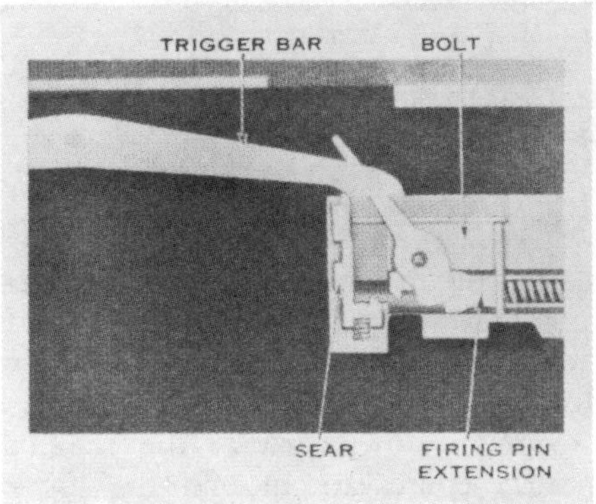

Automatic Fire. If the trigger is pressed and held down, the sear is depressed as its tip is pressed against the cam surface of the trigger bar by the forward motion of the bolt just before it completes its forward motion. The notch in the bottom of the sear releases the firing pin extension and firing pin, automatically firing the cartridge as the forward motion is completed and continuing the action as long as the trigger is held and cartridges are fed into the gun.

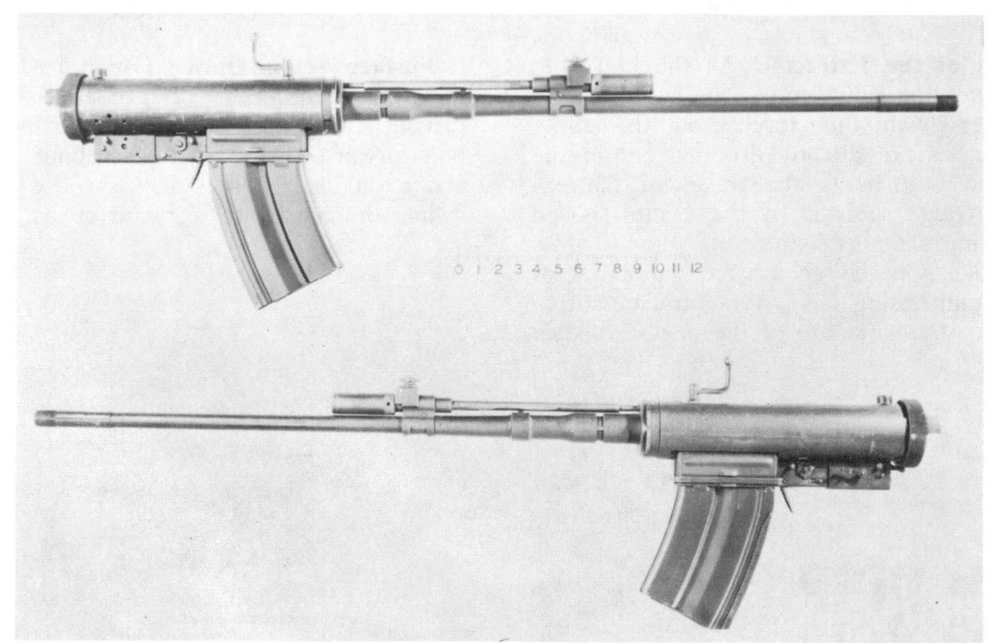

Cal. .50 Spotting Rifle M8C (Modified).

Caliber: .50.
System of Operation: Gas, semi-automatic only.
Weight w/20-rd. Magazine (Empty): 26.10 lbs.
Overall Length of Weapon: 44.9 in.
Length of Barrel: 32 in.
Feed Device: 20-rd. detachable box magazine.
Sights: None on spotting rifle (optical sights are mounted on the major weapon).
Muzzle Velocity: 1760 f.p.s. with cal. .50 M48 spotting cartridge.

The M8C spotting rifle is a special purpose type of weapon; it is not an antipersonnel weapon like most other small arms. It is mounted on the 106mm BAT (battalion antitank) recoilless rifle, and serves as a ranging rifle for that weapon. The cal. .50 cartridge used with the M8C is a considerably smaller cartridge than the cal. .50 used with the Browning guns. Its ballistics are matched with those of the 106mm high-explosive antitank (HEAT) projectile and the bullet contains a spotting charge which on impact gives off a bright flash and a cloud of smoke. By using the spotting rifle to get on target, and then firing the recoilless rifle at the same range and azimuth setting, the first-round hit probability with the recoilless weapon is considerably increased. A high first-round hit probability with recoilless weapons is of very great importance, because recoilless weapons are comparatively easy to spot during firing. Their great back-blast throws up clouds of dust and causes considerable movement in trees, brush, etc.

How to Load and Fire the M8C (Modified)

Loading. Ammunition for the spotting rifle is contained in a box-type (10-round or 20-round) magazine which fits into a well at the front of the firing mechanism housing and is retained by a pair of catches. The catches support the magazine at front and rear. The front catch is brazed to a rectangular yoke that surrounds the magazine well in the housing and is linked to and operated by the rear catch assembly. This arrangement is similar to that used in the M8 spotting rifle, except that the rear catch for the M8C (Modified) can be folded against the underside of the firing mechanism housing to prevent accidental release of the magazine or damage to the catch.

Charging. With a full magazine inserted, the spotting rifle is placed in readiness to fire by pulling the charging handle all the way to the rear and releasing. This automatically cocks the weapon and chambers the top cartridge in the magazine. The charging for the M8C (Modified) rifle is offset to clear the ejection path and provides a better grip than that of the M8 rifle. A plunger is incorporated in the handle to engage it with the slide and prevent accidental disassembly. The M8C (Modified) rifle is also provided with a bolt and slide retainer assembly. This assembly consists of a spring-loaded plunger operated by a knob on the top rear of the receiver. The retainer relieves the gunner of the necessity of holding the charging handle to the rear to inspect the chamber or clear the bore. When the charging handle is pulled to the rear and the retainer knob depressed, the plunger seats in a slot in the rear of the slide and prevents the weapon from going into battery when the charging handle is released. The slide is released by pulling the charging handle to the rear until the retainer plunger disengages. The weapon will then go into battery when the charging handle is released.

Firing. The weapon is normally used with a firing cable or lanyard arrangement which is attached to a trigger-type mechanism on the major weapon mount or inside the Ontos vehicle.

Disassembly of the M8C (Modified)

Magazine Assembly. Push forward on the rear magazine catch assembly and pull the magazine straight out of housing.

Disassemble magazine by sliding base off the tube. The magazine spring and follower can then be removed from the tube.

Guide Rods and Driving Springs. Press forward on rear of guide rods and turn them counterclockwise to disengage from bayonet slots in buffer bushings.

Draw rods and springs from the receiver.

Buffer Assembly. Press the buffer catch away from the buffer.

Rotate buffer counterclockwise and remove from receiver.

Charging Handle Assembly. Lift the charging handle plunger knob and slide the handle assembly forward out of its slot in the slide.

Slide and Bolt Assembly. Push the bolt and slide to the rear by pressing at the front of the slide.

Remove bolt and slide from rear of receiver.

Remove bolt assembly from slide by pushing bolt assembly rearward and pushing rear end of bolt away from the slide.

Removal of Firing Pin and Retractor from Bolt. Turn the bolt so the wide end of the retractor is down. The retractor will fall out, and the firing pin can then be removed from the end of the bolt.

Removal of Extractor from Bolt. Drive out the extractor plunger stop pin with a ⅛-inch drift.

With the drift, slide the extractor out of its slot. Use caution to avoid losing extractor plunger and spring.

Remove the plunger and spring.

Removal of Firing Mechanism Housing Assembly. Using a ⅛-inch drift, drive out the front and rear mounting pins.

Remove the buffer catch assembly and the buffer catch spring by pulling the assembly rearward.

Invert the weapon, lift the firing mechanism housing at the rear, and disengage it from the receiver.

Firing Mechanism Assembly. Release the hammer by pressing back on the connector block.

Remove the hammer pin cotter pin and drive out the hammer pin. Remove the hammer and hammer spring.

Remove cotter pins from the front retaining pin, firing cable housing retaining pin, and safety shaft. Drive out the front retaining pin, the safety shaft, and the firing cable housing retaining pin.

Lift the safety from the top of the channel and slide the channel out of the rear of the housing.

Push out the front stop pin, and slide the firing cable housing, connector block, and sear block out of the rear of the channel.

Release the ball of the firing cable from the connector block, and separate the sear connector from the sear block, releasing the connector spring.

Push out the sear pin to release the sear from its block. Push out the connector pin to release the connector from the connector block.

Disassembly of Gas Operating System. Unscrew the gas regulator lock ring bushing, turning it counterclockwise until the gas regulator components can be removed as a unit.

Using a spanner wrench, rotate the gas cylinder 180 degrees counterclockwise and pull it forward out of the gas cylinder body.

Pull the operating rod assembly forward and disengage its rear end from the hole in the receiver. The rod can then be pulled rearward and outward, away from the gas cylinder body and the barrel.

How the M8C (Modified) Works

Bolt and Slide Action. The reciprocating bolt and slide action of the spotting rifle is contained in the cylindrical receiver to which the barrel is threaded. The slide moves in keyways in the sides of the receiver, and the bolt is suspended in the underside of the slide by a pair of bolt guides. These guides are rectangular at one end and cylindrical at the other. The rectangular ends fit into keyways at the front end of the bolt, and the cylindrical ends fit into transverse holes at the front of the slide. The rectangular ends permit a relative sliding motion between the bolt and the slide, and the cylindrical ends permit a small amount of bolt rotation relative to the slide. Locking action of the bolt is based on this relative bolt and slide motion. As the slide moves forward in the receiver, it cams the rear of the bolt down into a locking recess (bolt lock) in the bottom of the receiver; after firing, the slide cams the bolt up out of the recess and carries the bolt rearward in the recoil.

Gas Cylinder and Operating Rod Action. The slide is driven in recoil by an operating rod assembly, which derives its energy from a gas cylinder group located on the barrel. When a cartridge is fired, a small amount of the propellent gas is drawn through a port in the side of the barrel and into the gas cylinder. Gas pressure in the cylinder drives the piston to the rear, transmitting energy through a spring-loaded operating rod which drives the slide.

Driving Springs and Buffer Assembly. The rear of the receiver is enclosed by a buffer assembly. On the inner face of the buffer is a plastic disc that absorbs residual slide recoil energy. The main force of slide recoil is stored in a pair of driving springs. These springs are seated over a pair of guide rods supported at the rear in a pair of buffer bushings and at the front in a pair of longitudinal holes through the slide. The springs bottom in the slide holes and are compressed when the slide recoils, storing energy for counter-recoil. When the bolt and slide stop against the buffer disc, the energy stored in the compressed drive springs forces the slide and bolt forward into battery, chambering a fresh cartridge.

Feeding. Feeding takes place as the bolt approaches the magazine. The lower front end of the bolt contacts the rear (or base) of the top cartridge, driving it forward out of the magazine and into the barrel chamber.

Firing Mechanism. The firing mechanism and its housing are pinned to the underside of the receiver. The mechanism is controlled by a cable connected to a firing knob on the elevation handwheel of the 106mm rifle system. When the knob is pulled, the following action takes place:

The cable draws the connector block, connector, sear block, and sear to the rear as a unit, releasing the hammer.

As the hammer rotates upward and forward to strike the firing pin, it first contacts the long leg of the connector, rotating the connector rearward and disengaging it from the sear block.

The sear block, released by the connector, is pushed forward by a spring, placing the sear into position to re-engage the hammer during recoil.

The hammer rotates the connector to the rear, insuring that the short leg of the connector is free of the sear block.

The hammer contacts and rotates the sear rearward, compressing the connector spring slightly; then, as the hammer rotates below the sear, the spring snaps the sear back into position, blocking forward movement of the hammer. When the firing knob is released, the sear block retainer spring moves the connector block forward and the sear connector reengages the sear block. The firing knob may now be pulled again to fire the next round.

Safety Action. The safety is operated by a lever on the side of the housing and consists of a block which is rotated to permit or prevent movement of the connector block.

Firing Pin and Retractor Action. The firing pin is contained in the bolt and is actuated by the hammer, as described above, and also by the firing pin retractor. The retractor is a flat, key-like component with rounded ends. The retractor fits through a slot in the firing pin and extends through the sides of the bolt. Its rounded ends are acted upon by cam surfaces on the inner sides of the slide. On recoil, the retractor is cammed to withdraw the firing pin from the cartridge primer; on counter-recoil, the retractor is held to the side to prevent forward movement of the firing pin until the bolt enters the battery position. This delayed camming prevents firing unless the bolt is safely locked in battery position.

Extraction. The extractor is seated in a T-slot in the top front of the bolt. A small amount of outward travel in the slot is opposed by a spring-loaded plunger arrangement. This outward travel permits the extractor claw to cam outward and past the rim of a chambered cartridge, whereupon the spring-loaded plunger draws the extractor inward to seat on the cartridge rim.

Ejection. The ejector is pinned to the front of the bolt lock in the bottom of the receiver. As the bolt travels rearward in recoil, the extractor draws the empty cartridge case against the ejector, which rotates the case free of the extractor claw and flips it through the opening in the top of the receiver.

Special Note on the M8 Series of Spotting Rifles

An earlier weapon, the M8 is also in extensive use. It differs from the M8C in the following:

It has a ten-round magazine rather than a twenty-round magazine.

Its firing mechanism housing cannot be used with the remote-controlled safety mechanism as can that of the M8C.

The M8C (Modified) rifle differs from the M8C in the following:

It has a large number of new components which are not interchangeable with those of the M8 and M8C.

It has an entirely new firing mechanism.

The M8C and M8C (Modified) were developed for use in the Ontos vehicle, which is used by the Marine Corps.

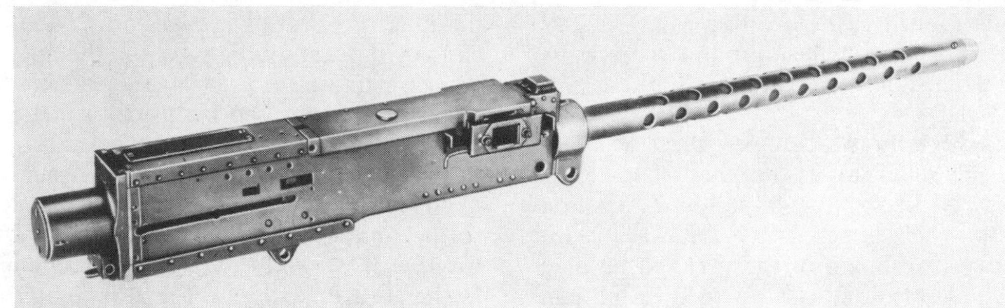

Cal. .50 Aircraft Machine Gun AN-M3.

Caliber: .50.
System of Operation: Recoil, automatic fire only.
Weight of Gun, with Recoil Adapter: 68.75 lb.
Weight of barrel: 11 lb.
Length of Gun: 57.25 in.
Length of Barrel: 36 in.
Feed Device: Disintegrating link belt (pullout type).
Cyclic Rate of Fire: 1150-1250 r.p.m.
Muzzle Velocity: 2840 f.p.s. with M2 ball.
Sights: None on gun (sights are mounted in aircraft).

This weapon was developed toward the end of World War II and during the period immediately afterward. It is a modification of the famed cal. .50 M2 Browning aircraft gun of World War II fame. The M3 gun saw extensive service in Korea, since most of the United States F-86 fighters were equipped with it. It is still in limited service in the Air Force, but has for the most part been replaced by heavier caliber guns and/or guided missiles.

The main modifications on the M2 were made to produce a higher rate of fire. The basic system of operation is the same as for the other Browning cal. .50 guns, and many, but not all, of the components of the M3 are interchangeable with those of the M2.

Notes on the AN-M3 Machine Gun

No backplates with spade-type grips are used with this gun, since it is always used in fixed or turret-type aircraft mounts. It can be used in the cal. .50 AA machine gun mounts M3 or M63, but will rarely ever be found so mounted, since it is basically an aircraft weapon.

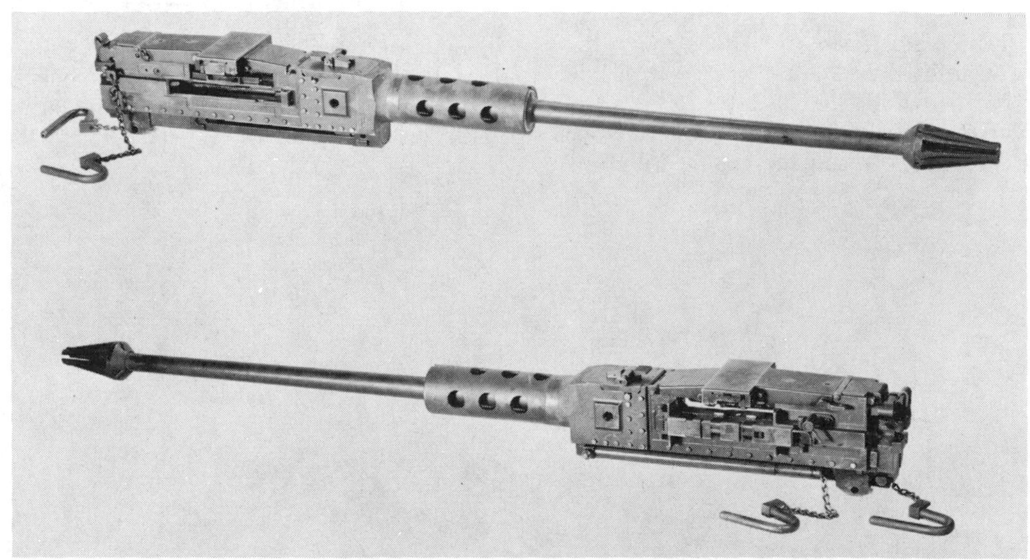

Cal. .50 Tank Machine Gun M85.

Caliber: .50.
System of Operation: Recoil; dual rate of automatic fire.
Weight of Complete Gun: 61.5 lb.
Weight of Barrel: 14.40 lb.
Length of Gun, Overall: 54.50 in. (with Flash Suppressor).
Length of Barrel: 36 in.
Feed Device: Disintegrating link belt (pushout type).
Cyclic Rate of Fire:
  Low Rate: 400 ± 50 r.p.m.
  High Rate: 1050 ± 50 r.p.m.
Muzzle Velocity: 2840 to 3450 f.p.s. (depending on type of cal. .50 cartridge used).

The M85 was developed by the Aircraft Armaments Corp. of Cockeysville, Md. as the T175E2 machine gun. It fills a requirement of the Armored Forces for a cal. .50 weapon suitable for co-axial or cupola mounting, having a dual rate of fire and quick-change barrel and being shorter and lighter than the cal. .50 Browning. This weapon is not yet in service, but will be mounted on a forthcoming United States tank.

The requirement for a dual rate of fire originated from the desire to have a high rate of fire for use against low-flying aircraft, and a low rate of fire for use against ground targets. While the cal. .50 Browning M2, HB, has an almost ideal rate for use against ground targets, its rate of fire for use against modern attack aircraft leaves something to be desired.

How to Load and Fire the M85. Open the cover and visually inspect the chamber to assure that chamber is clear. The bolt must be in the battery (closed) position before the ammunition belt is set in the feedway. Place the first round in the belt inboard of the two belt holding pawls. The belted ammunition must be placed in the gun with the open side of the links downward. Close the cover; the gun can be loaded without opening the cover if necessary. Pull bolt to the rear with the hand charger. Place safety on "safe" position. Set the rate selector lever to the proper position for the desired rate of fire. For high rate of fire, turn the lever completely to the left. For low rate of fire, turn the lever completely to the right. Do not change rate selector while firing a burst. Release the safety and fire the gun electrically by depressing the electrical trigger switch or manually by pushing forward on the manual trigger.

How to Field Strip the M85. Check to see that gun is not loaded. With hand charger control, allow the driving spring to slowly return the bolt to battery as follows:

1. Pull back and hold hand charger.
2. Depress trigger.
3. Allow the driving spring to slowly return the charging handle to the original position.

Remove the barrel. Transversely depress the lock on the barrel latch, fully depress the barrel latch, rotate the barrel 90° until the head of the "unlock" arrow is in line with the head of the arrow on the barrel support, and pull the barrel forward out of the barrel support. Remove the cover and tray assemblies. Open the cover, withdraw the quick release pins by inserting the rim of a cartridge case in the annular groove at the top of the pin; using the cartridge case as a lever, pry out the pin; withdraw the tray. Depress the latch lock on the lower left side of the back plate, then depress the back plate latch and lift the back plate straight up off the receiver. Remove back plate slowly for the first inch as the preload on the driving spring may cause the buffer assembly to jump out. *Caution:* Do NOT attempt to disassemble gun with bolt in the REAR position. The driving spring is then heavily loaded and may cause injuries. Remove the bolt buffer assembly from the rear of the receiver. Depress the sear block detent, visible through the right side of the receiver, with the nose of a cartridge and withdraw the sear assembly out of the rear of the receiver. Remove the feed and ejector assembly; withdraw the front and rear quick-release pins which fasten the feed and ejector assembly to the receiver. Remove the feed assembly by first pulling its front end out from the side of the receiver, then pull the assembly forward out of the receiver. Pull the barrel extension assembly, with the bolt in it, out through the rear of the receiver. Withdraw the quick release pin from the side of the receiver and lift the accelerator assembly straight up out of the receiver. Disengage the detent from the receiver by pulling on the knurled knob at the front end, and slide the hand charger forward. To reassemble, reverse the procedure given above.

Cyclic Operation—High Rate of Fire

Charging the Gun. To begin the cycle, the loaded gun must be hand charged. During the charging stroke, the feed mechanism is actuated by the bolt, positioning a round on the center line of the gun, in the forward path of the bolt.

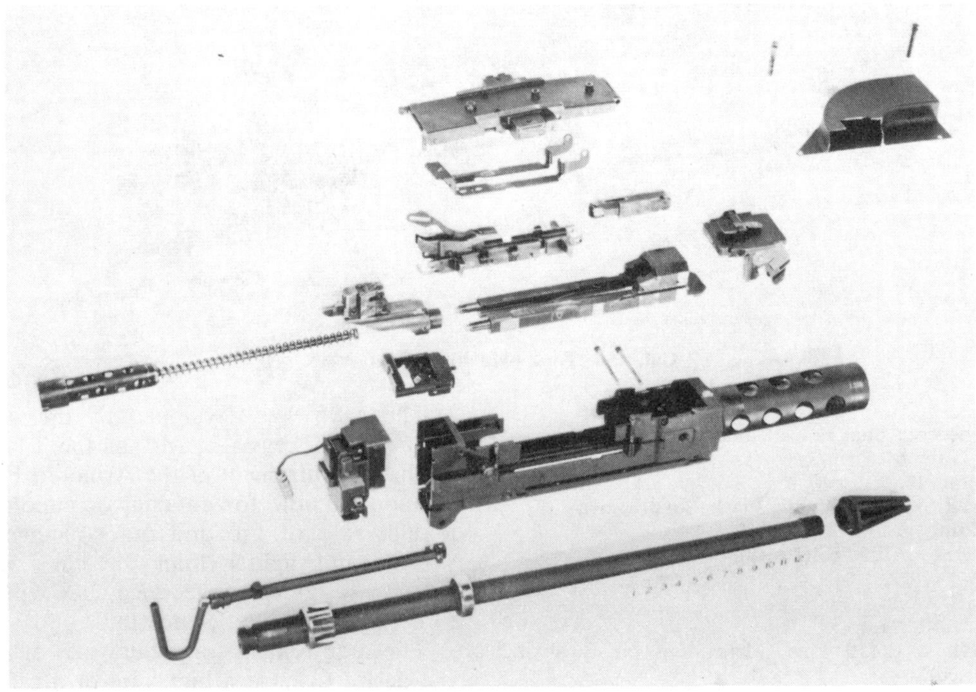

M85 Field Stripped.

The bolt is held in the open-bolt position by the sear, with the bolt-driving spring compressed.

Stripping and Chambering of Round. When the firing switch is depressed, or the hand trigger is pressed, the solenoid plunger pushes the sear actuator forward about its pivot, camming the sear up and out of the bolt notch.

The bolt is driven toward battery position by the compressed bolt-driving spring.

The round in the feedway is picked up by the stripper on the bolt, is stripped through the belt link by the action of the bolt, and is deflected downward into the chamber by the chambering ramp.

Locking and Firing. The forward motion of the bolt block is arrested by the base of the chambered round, and the bottom extractor engages the extraction groove at the rim of the cartridge.

The bolt slide continues forward, wedging the bolt locks in place.

As the bolt slide completes its forward motion, the firing pin protrudes through the bolt block and strikes the cartridge primer, firing the round and initiating the recoil stroke.

Recoil Stroke. The feed mechanism, operated by the recoiling barrel extension through a feed spring and a feed cam, is actuated at the beginning of the recoil stroke.

As the barrel and the barrel extension begin to recoil, the barrel actuates the accelerator, thereby driving the bolt slide rearward at an accelerated speed.

As the bolt slide starts to move rearward, it cams the bolt locks inward, releasing the bolt block which moves toward the rear, pulling the spent cartridge case out of the chamber and compressing the bolt-driving spring.

Ejection. The ejector mechanism is actuated by the action of the recoiling bolt on the ejector lever.

Just before cartridge ejection, the bottom extractor is disengaged from the extraction groove of the cartridge by the cam grooves in the barrel extension.

As the bolt continues rearward motion, the spring-loaded stripper is depressed by the incoming round.

The barrel group and the accelerator now start their return to battery position, driven by the barrel return springs and accelerator return springs.

As the ejector strikes the cartridge case, the case rotates about the side extractor and is thrown clear of the gun.

Bolt Buffing and Counterrecoil. As the bolt nears the end of its recoil stroke, it compresses the bolt buffer spring, which stops the rearward motion of the bolt.

By this time, the barrel group and the accelerator have returned to their battery position.

The compressed bolt buffer spring reverses the direction of the bolt, starting the counterrecoil stroke, and the cycle is repeated.

Firing will continue as long as the solenoid plunger remains forward, holding the bolt sear up, providing that ammunition is supplied.

The velocity of the counterrecoil stroke of the bolt is much higher on those cycles following the initial cycle because the force of the buffer spring adds to the force of the bolt-driving spring.

Cyclic Operation—Low Rate of Fire

Initial Action and Bolt Recoil. The rate selector lever is set for the low rate of fire, positioning the striker in the path of the bolt so that it is ready to actuate the time-delay drum.

The gun is loaded, hand charged, and initially fired, and the bolt recoils at the same velocity as during the high rate of fire.

Bolt Actuation of Time-Delay Drum. Near the end of the bolt recoil stroke, the bolt block extension contacts the striker, causing the time-delay drum to start rotating.

The drum rotation cams the yoke rearward, retracting the solenoid plunger.

The retraction of the solenoid plunger releases the sear actuator and the sear is forced down to locking position by its return spring. Drum rotation continues, winding up a torsion spring.

Bolt Searing and Time Delay. The bolt starts its counterrecoil stroke because of the action of the bolt buffer and driving springs, but is stopped by the sear.

During this time, the time-delay drum continues to rotate until it strikes a stop. Drum rotation is then reversed by the action of the wound torsion spring.

Bolt Release. The drum returns to its original position, driving the striker forward in preparation for the next bolt recoil stroke.

The yoke cam rollers fall into notches on the periphery of the drum, releasing the solenoid plunger.

The solenoid plunger moves forward, operating the sear by means of the sear actuator, and thus releasing the bolt. The bolt is driven forward on the counterrecoil stroke only by the driving force of the bolt-return spring.

This cycle is repeated as each round is fired.

Caliber .50 Machine Gun M85C

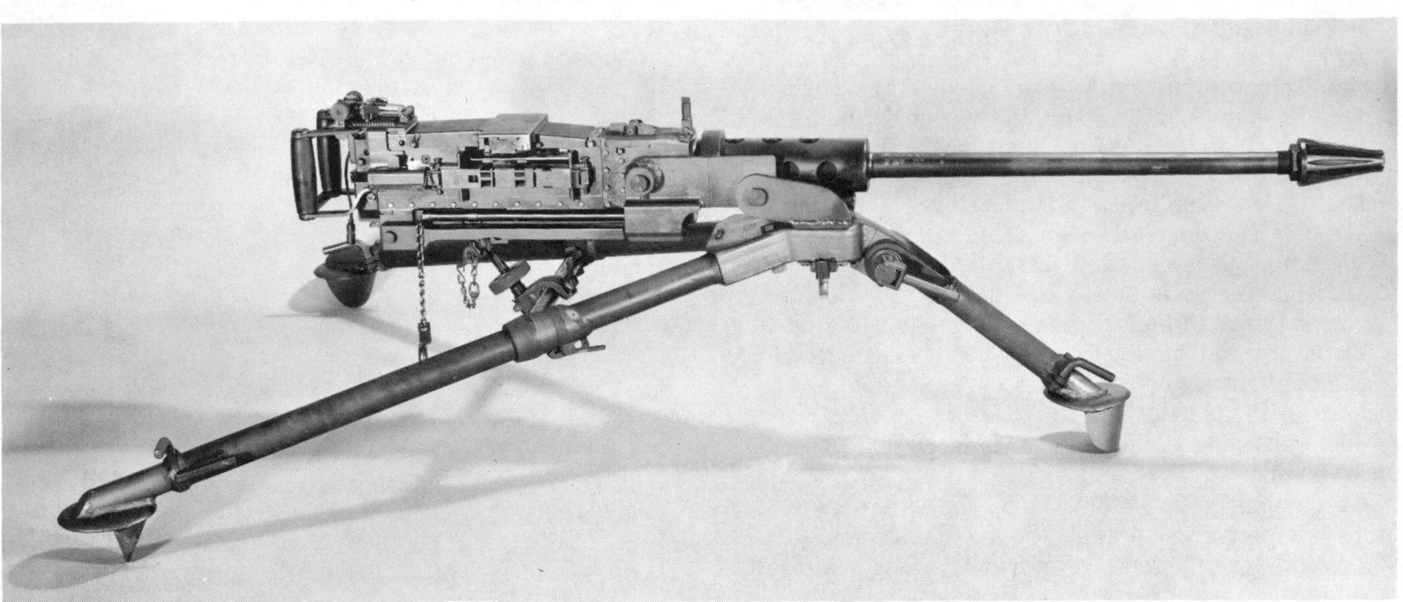

Caliber: .50.
System of Operation: Recoil.
Weight of Gun: 68 lbs.
Length of Gun: 57.25 in.
Length of Barrel: 40.125 in.
Feed Device: Disintegrating metallic link belt M15A1.
Sights: Front—Fold down post.
Rear—Tangent, graduated from 100 to 2500 meters; 750 meter battle sight setting. Adjustable for windage.
Cyclic Rate:
High Rate: 950 r.p.m.
Low Rate: 450 r.p.m.

The M85C is the flexible version of the fixed M85 tank machine gun. Like the M73C, it has a built-in solenoid type firing mechanism. It is the same as M85 except for sights, a feed adaptor, and spade-type grips with trigger. Firing is done by pressure on the thumb trigger. Loading, functioning, and field stripping are the same with the following exception: to remove back plate, rotate the locks 180° to the rear and withdraw the assembly rearward. This weapon exists only in prototype form.

Chapter 46. Yugoslavia

Yugoslavia, which of late has taken an independent political course, was almost completely stripped of weapons by the Germans in World War II. In the days prior to the split between Belgrade and Moscow, the Yugoslav Army received a good many Soviet World War II small arms. They already held a fair quantity of German weapons and some Italian weapons, seized from the defeated Axis troops. Yugoslavia decided to standardize on the Soviet 7.62mm pistol cartridge for pistols and submachine guns, and on the 7.92mm cartridge for rifles and machine guns. Yugoslavia manufactures both of these cartridges in quantity.

The Yugoslavs manufacture a submachine gun for the 7.62mm cartridge; they call the gun the Model 49. This weapon is somewhat similar in appearance to the Soviet PPD M1940 submachine gun. They also manufacture a 7.92mm Mauser similar to the Kar. 98k, and call it the Model 48. They are quite proud of the fact that they manufacture a copy of the German MG42 which they have nicknamed the SARAC. Considering the fact that Yugoslavia was basically an agricultural nation prior to World War II, and that the MG42 requires the use of powerful stamping presses for its manufacture, they have considerable justification for their pride.

YUGOSLAV PISTOLS

F.N. Browning M1922 Cal. .380 (9mm short) made for Yugoslavia prior to World War II.

YUGOSLAV RIFLES

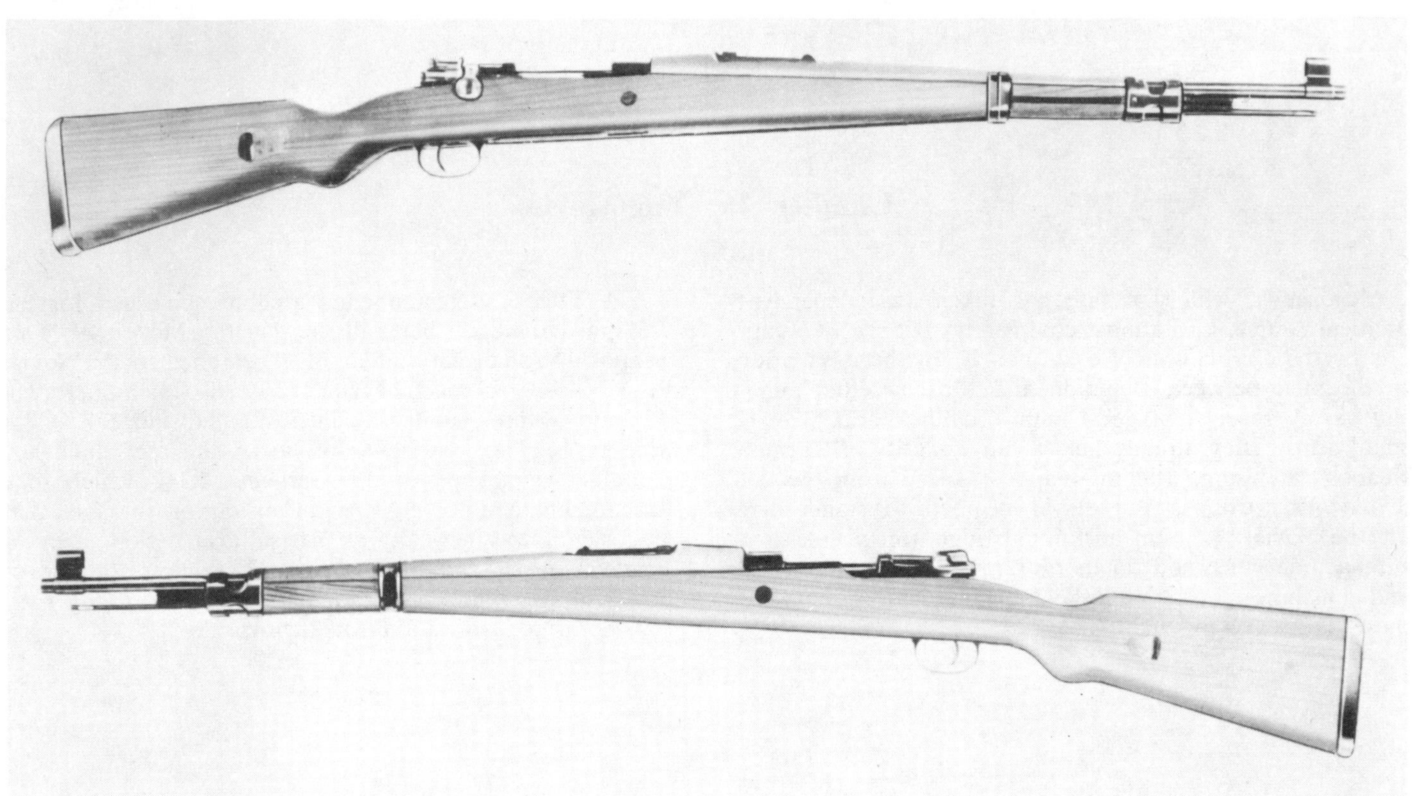

M1948 7.92mm Rifle.

Caliber: 7.92mm.
System of Operation: Manually operated bolt.
Weight: 8.62 lb.
Length, Overall: 42.9 in.
Barrel Length: 23.3 in.
Feed Device: 5-round, integral, staggered-row box magazine.
Sights, Front: Hooded blade.
Rear: Tangent w/ramp.
Muzzle Velocity: 2600 f.p.s. (approx.).

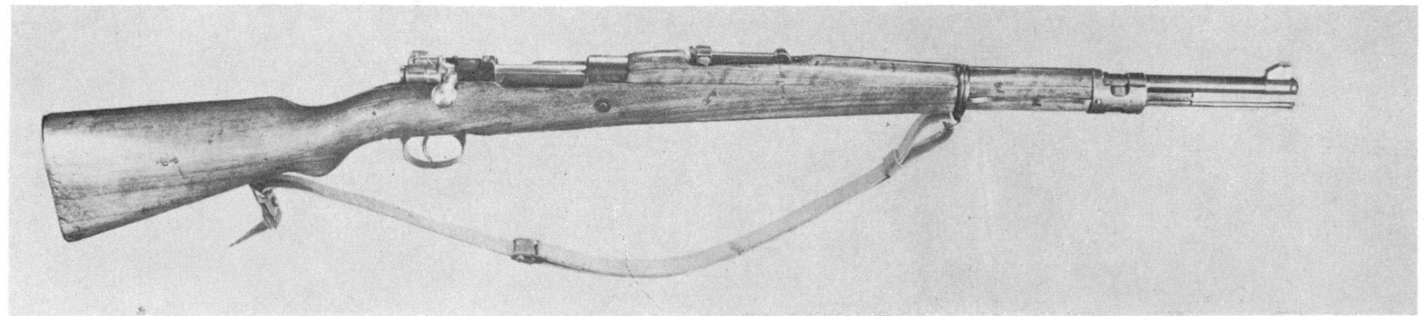

M1924 as made in Yugoslavia—7.92mm.

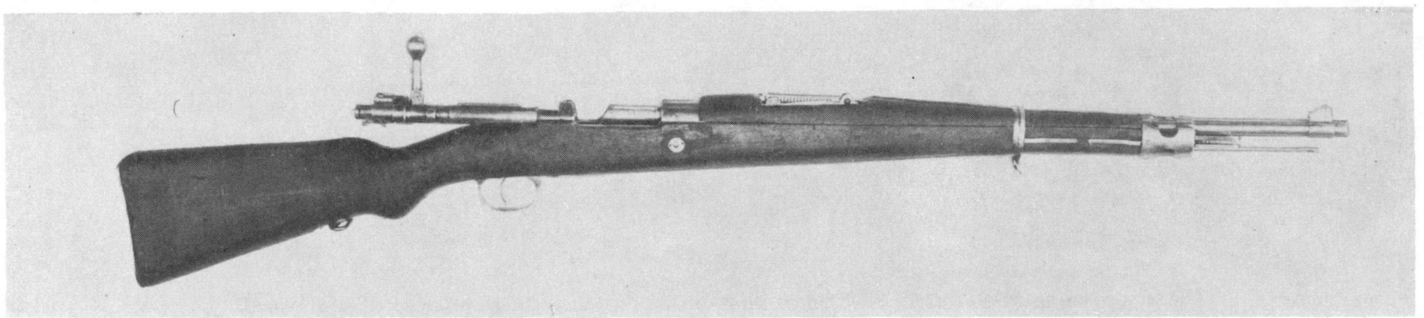

M1924 Made by F.N. Same as German Kar. 98k except for Minor Details.

YUGOSLAV SUBMACHINE GUNS

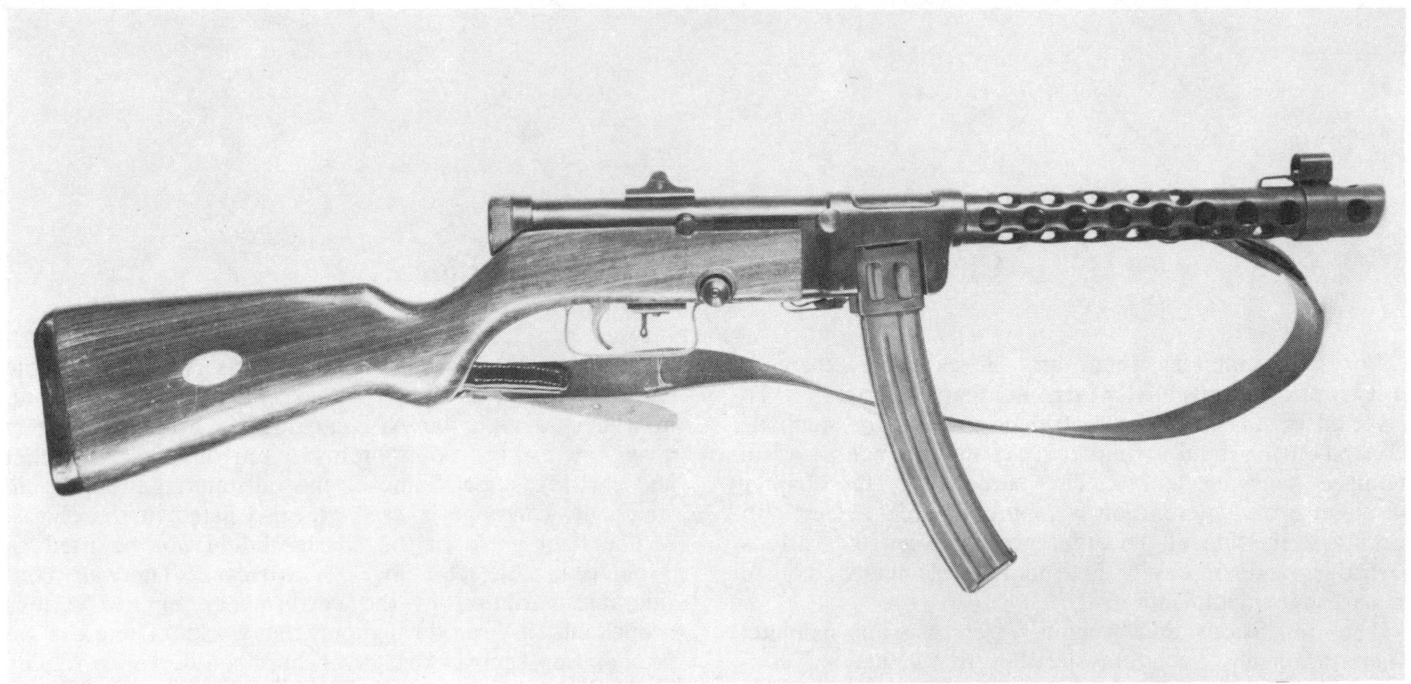

Yugoslavian machine pistol Cal. 7.62mm Model 49. Manufactured in Yugoslavia and presented to General Collins by Marshal Tito in October 1951. This is modified Russian blowback design. Full auto switch inside triggerguard.

Caliber: 7.62mm pistol ball.
System of Operation: Blowback, selective fire.
Weight: 9.44 lb.
Length, Overall: 34.4 in.
Barrel Length: 10.5 in.
Feed Device: 33-round detachable, staggered-row box magazine.
Sights, Front: Hooded blade.
Rear: L-type w/U-notch.
Muzzle Velocity: 1400 f.p.s. (approx.).

YUGOSLAV MACHINE GUN

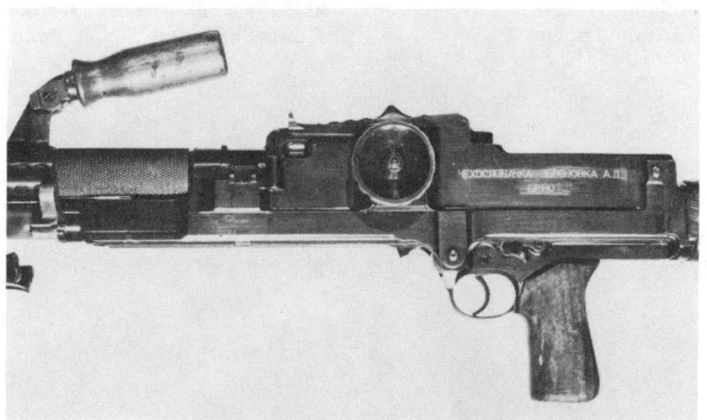

Czech Brno ZB made for Yugoslavia.

This gun is described in chapter 20.

Chapter 47. Small Arms Ammunition

For every military small arm in existence, there is at least one and, usually, a large number of cartridges. To cover in detail all of the cartridges used in the weapons covered in this book would require another book several hundred pages in length. The purpose of this chapter on small arms ammunition is to provide the reader with some appreciation of the differences between the various cartridges and thereby to give him an elementary course in cartridge identification.

The dimensions and weights given are approximate. There are many variations insofar as weights are concerned due to the different bullets used with type variations within a given caliber and the differing propellant weights among different types. Weights given are for the basic ball round in each type, except the Soviet 14.5mm, in which data on the API cartridge is given. Diameters given are for the point of maximum diameter of bullet and cartridge case. Some of the outstanding weapons in which the cartridge is used are also listed in the charts.

The data given in the charts should *not* be used as a guide in the reloading of cartridges. There is considerable variation in the performance of the various propellants in use throughout the world. Therefore no presentation such as that given here can serve as a guide to handloading unless the specific military or commercial model designation for the propellant is given.

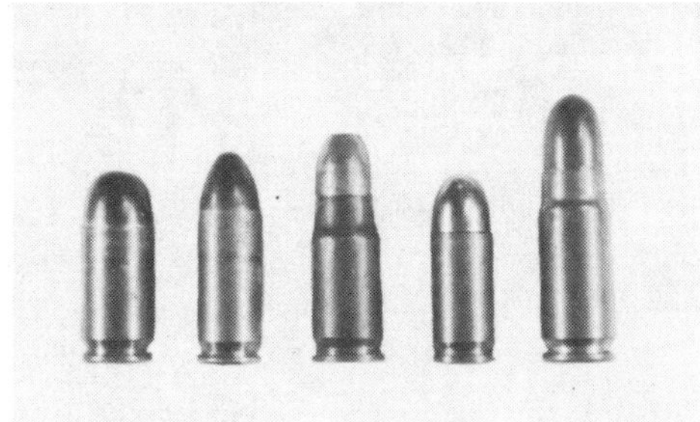

Left to Right—9mm Browning Short, 7.65mm French Long, 7.65mm Luger, 7.65mm Browning, and 7.62mm Soviet Pistol Type P.

Left to Right—Cal. .30 Carbine, Cal. .455 Webley, Cal. .45 Auto M1911, 8mm French Revolver, Cal. .38 S&W Revolver, 9mm Parabellum, and Soviet 9mm Makarov Pistol.

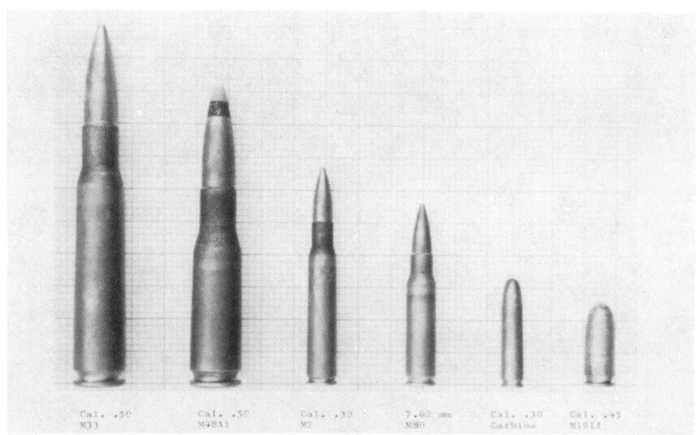

Current U.S. Service Ammunition.

M48A1 is for Cal. .50 Spotting Rifle.

PISTOL CARTRIDGES

Cartridge and Case Type	Complete Round Weight	Bullet Weight	Propellant Weight	Complete Round Length	Case Length	Bullet Diameter	Case Diameter	Some Common Synonyms	Best Known Weapons in Which Used
7.62mm Pistol Rimless Bottlenecked	167 gr.	87 gr.	7.71 gr.	1.36 in.	.97 in.	.307 in.	.39 in.	7.62 mm Type P (Soviet) 7.62mm M48 (Czech)	TT M1933 Pistol, M34/38 SMG, PPD 40 SMG, PPSh 41 SMG, PPS 43 SMG (All Soviet) SMG and M52 Pistol (Czech) and various satellite copies of Soviet pistol and SMG's, can also be used in weapons chambered for 7.63mm Mauser cartridge.—Note that Czech cartridge has a heavier charge.
7.65mm Browning Straight Semi-rim	121.0 gr.	73 gr.	2.47 gr.	.98 in.	.68 in.	.308-.311 in.	.354 in.	.32 A.C.P., 7.65mm Browning short	Colt Automatic, Walther PP & PPK, (German & various copies), Browning M1910 & M1922, large numbers of pocket automatic pistols throughout the world.
7.65mm Long Rimless Straight	132 gr.	85-88 gr.	5.0 gr.	1.19 in.	.78 in.	.309 in.	.335 in.	7.65 Longue Pour Pistole et Pistolet Mitrailleur .30 cal. Pistol Cartridge M1918 (Pedersen Device Cartridge)	French M1935A and M1935S Pistols and M1938 SMG.
7.65 Luger Rimless Bottlenecked	160.0 gr.	93 gr.	5.2 gr.	1.17 in.	.85 in.	.308 in.	.392 in.	Cal. .30 Luger	Swiss M 06/29 Pistol, some Pre-W.W. II Bergmann and SIG SMG's.
8mm Jap Rimless Bottlenecked	177.5 gr.	102 gr.	5.0 gr.	1.23 in.	.83 in.	.320 in.	.411 in.	8mm Type 14	Japanese Type 14 and Type 94 pistols and Type 100 SMG.
8mm Lebel Rimmed Straight	194.5 gr.	120 gr.	14.0 gr. black powder 11.5 gr. smokeless	1.44 in.	1.07 in.	.323 in.	.408 in. (Rim)	8mm M1892	French M1892 Revolver.
9mm Short Rimless Straight	148.8 gr.	95 gr.	3.5 gr.	.98 in.	.68 in.	.356 in.	.372 in.	9mm Browning Short, 9mm Kurz, 9mm Corto, .380 A.C.P., 9mm Court	Colt automatic, Walther PP and PPK and various copies, Hungarian M37, Italian M34 Beretta.
9mm Parabellum Rimless Straight	164 gr.	115 gr.	5.6 gr.	1.17 in.	.76 in.	.356 in.	.457 in.	Pistolen Patrone 08, 9mm M1, 9mm Mk1, 9mm M38, 9mm M39, 9mm Luger	German P08, P38, MP38, MP40, British Browning No. 2 Pistol, Sten SMG's and L2A3 SMG. French M50 Pistol and M49 SMG. Belgian Browning HP Pistol and Vigneron SMG, Swedish and Finnish Lahti Pistol and Suomi SMG's. Swedish M45 SMG, Israeli Uzi SMG, Madsen SMG's. Beretta M38, 38/42, 38/49, 5 & 12 SMG, Beretta M951 Pistol.
9mm Largo Rimless Straight	192 gr.	124 gr.	6.6 gr.	1.32 in.	.91 in.	.354 in.	.385 in.	9mm Bergmann Bayard	Spanish Super Star Pistol and Star Model Z45 SMG.
9mm Makarov Rimless Straight	156 gr.	94 gr.	3.7 gr.	.97 in.	.71 in.	.363 in.	.389 in.		Soviet Makarov and Stechkin pistols.
.380 MK II Rimmed Straight	246.5 gr.	181 gr.	5.0 gr.	1.22 in.	.76 in.	.357 in.	.435 in.	.38 S & W and .38 Webley Scott	British Pistol No. 2 (Revolvers) in all Marks, Webley Mark IV Pistol, S & W .38/200.
.45 M1911 Rimless Straight	327 gr.	230 gr.	5 gr.	1.275 in.	.91 in.	.452 in.	.480 in.	.45 A.C.P., 11.43mm, 11.25mm, 11mm M40	U. S. Pistol M1911 and M1911A1, M1928 A1, M1, M1A1, M3, and M3A1 SMG's. Norway-Pistol M1914. Argentina-Ballester.
.455 Webley Rimless Straight	324.0 gr.	224 gr.	7 gr.	1.22 in.	.91 in.	.455 in.	.502 in.	.455 Webley auto.	Webley Automatic Pistol.
.455 Revolver Rimmed Straight	350 gr.	265 gr.	7.5 gr.	1.22 in. to 1.26 in.	.76 in.	.455 in.	.532 in.	.455 Webley revolver .455 in. Mark II	Pistol No. 1 Marks 4, 5, & 6.

Left to Right—7.5mm M1929 French, 7mm Mauser, 6.5mm Mauser, 6.5mm Dutch and Romanian Mannlicher, 6.5mm Italian Mannlicher Carcano, and 6.5mm Jap Type 38.

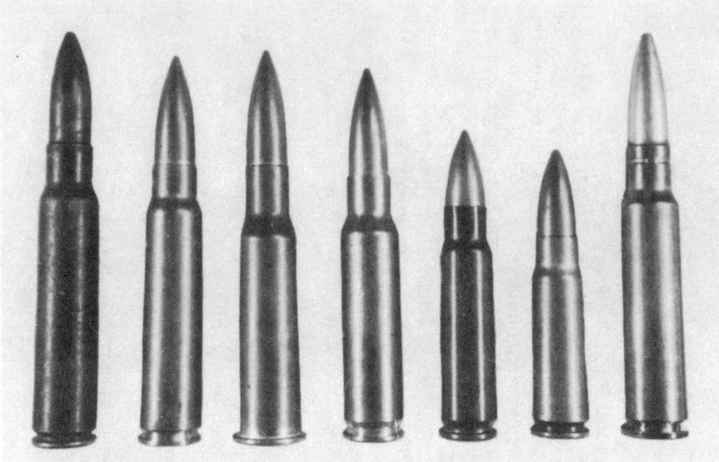

Left to Right—7.7mm Jap Type 99, 7.65mm Mauser, 7.62mm Russian Rimmed, 7.62mm NATO, 7.62mm Czech M52, 7.62mm Soviet M43 Rimless, and 7.5mm Swiss M11.

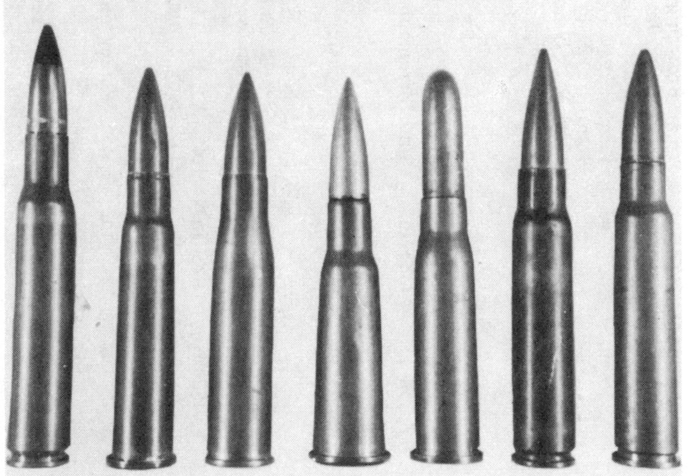

Left to Right—Cal. .30 AP, Cal. .303 British, 8mm Austrian M30S, 8mm Lebel, 8mm Austrian M90 (8 x 50mm), 7.92mm Mauser, and 7.7mm Jap Type 92.

Left to Right—Cal. .50, 13.2mm Jap Type 93, 14.5mm Soviet API, and 12.7mm Soviet API-T.

RIFLE CARTRIDGES

Cartridge and Case Type	Complete Round Weight	Bullet Weight	Propellant Weight	Complete Round Length	Case Length	Bullet Diameter	Case Diameter	Some Common Synonyms	Best Known Weapons in Which Used
6.5mm Dutch Rimmed Bottlenecked	356 gr.	156 gr.	37 gr.	3.03 in.	2.11 in.	.263 in.	.526 in.	6.5mm Romanian 6.5 mm M93 6.5 x 53mm R	Dutch M92, M95 rifles and M95 carbine, Romanian M92, M93 rifle & M93 carbine.
6.5mm Italian Rimless Bottlenecked	350 gr.	162 gr.	35 gr.	3.01 in.	2.06 in.	.2655 in.	.447 in.	6.5mm Mannlicher Carcano, 6.5mm M91-95	Italian M91 rifles and carbines Breda M30 MG.
6.5mm Jap Semi-rim Bottlenecked	326 gr.	139 gr.	33 gr.	2.98 in.	2.00 in.	.262 in.	.476 in.	6.5mm Type 38	Japanese Type 38 rifle, Type 38 and Type 44 carbine, Type 11 and Type 96 MG.
6.5mm Mauser Rimless Bottlenecked	363 gr.	139 gr.	36 gr.	3.15 in.	2.17 in.	.264 in.	.478 in.	6.5mm M94, 6.5mm Norwegian, 6.5mm Swedish, 6.5 x 55mm	Norwegian M94 rifle and M12 carbine, Swedish 94 carbine, M96, M38 and M42 rifles, M21 and M37 automatic rifles (used in some Swedish MG's as well).
7mm Mauser Rimless Bottlenecked	377 gr.	172 gr.	38 gr.	3.00 in.	2.24 in.	.284 in.	.474 in.	7 x 57mm	Spanish M93 rifle and M95 carbine.
7.5mm French Rimless Bottlenecked	363 gr.	139 gr.	44 gr.	2.99 in.	2.13 in.	.307 in.	.484 in.	7.5mm M1929	French M 07/15, M34, M36, M49, M49/56 rifles and M1924M29 automatic rifle. M31 and M52 MG.
7.5mm Swiss Rimless Bottlenecked	404 gr.	174 gr.	49.35 gr.	3.05 in.	2.18 in.	.308 in.	.496 in.	7.45mm Swiss 7.5mm M11 7.5mm Schmidt Rubin	Swiss M11 rifle and M11, M31, M31/42 and M31/43 carbines. M57 assault rifle, M11, M25, and M51 machine guns.
7.62mm NATO Rimless Bottlenecked	375 gr.	150 gr.	48 gr.	2.80 in.	2.01 in.	.308 in.	.469 in.	7.62mm Ball M59 7.62 x 51mm 7.62mm M1954 7.62mm OTAN .308 Winchester 7.62mm Ball M85	U. S. M14 rifle, M60 and M73 machine guns. British L2A1 rifle, Belgian FN FAL rifle and FN M.A.G. M.G. Canadian C1 rifle and C2 LMG. W. German FN and CETME rifles.
7.62mm Russian Rimmed Bottlenecked	348 gr.	148 gr.	50 gr.	3.03 in.	2.11 in.	.311 in.	.564 in.	7.62mm M1908 Type L. 7.62 x 54mm	Soviet Mosin Nagant rifles and carbines, Simonov M36 and Tokarev M32, M38, and M40 rifles and carbines. Maxim M1910, DP, DPM, DT, DTM, DA, ShKAS, SG-43, SGM, and RP-46 MG's. Soviet Satellite copies of these weapons.
7.62mm M43 Rimless Bottlenecked	253 gr.	122 gr.	25 gr.	2.20 in.	1.52 in.	.311 in.	.45 in.	7.62mm Russian Short 7.62mm M1943 Type PS 7.62 x 39mm	Soviet AK assault rifle, SKS carbine, RPD LMG.
7.62mm M52 Rimless Bottlenecked	293.7 gr.	132 gr.	27 gr.	2.35 in.	1.77 in.	.310 in.	.442 in.	7.62mm Czech Short	Czech M52 Rifle and LMG.
7.65mm Mauser Rimless Bottlenecked	390 gr.	174 gr.	38.6 gr.	2.95 in.	2.11 in.	.310 in.	.472 in.	7.65mm M30 7.65 x 54mm	Belgian M89 rifles and carbines, M35 and 36 rifles. Argentine M91 and M09 rifles. Turkish M91 and M03 rifles.
7.7mm Rimless Jap Rimless Bottlenecked	415 gr.	182 gr.	43.13 gr.	3.14 in.	2.25 in.	.310 in.	.47 in.	7.7mm Type 99	Japanese Type 99 rifle and LMG.
7.7mm Semi-rim Jap, Semi-rim Bottlenecked	429 gr.	200 gr.	44.18 gr.	3.14 in.	2.25 in.	.310 in.	.49 in.	7.7mm Type 92	Japanese Type 92 MG.

RIFLE CARTRIDGES

Cartridge and Case Type	Complete Round Weight	Bullet Weight	Propellant Weight	Complete Round Length	Case Length	Bullet Diameter	Case Diameter	Some Common Synonyms	Best Known Weapons in Which Used
7.92mm Mauser Rimless Bottlenecked	408 gr.	198 gr.	47 gr.	3.15 in.	2.24 in.	.323 in.	.468 in.	7.9mm SS 7.9 x 57mm 7.9 IS 7.9 JS 8mm Mauser .315 Mauser rimless 8 x 57mm M98.	German M98 rifles and carbines, M08, 08/15, 08/18, 15, 17, 34 and 42 MG's, FG-42. Czech M24, M33 rifles and carbines, M26, M30, M30J and M37 MG's. British BESA MG's, Chinese-Brens MK 2.
8mm Austrian Rimmed Bottlenecked	437 gr.	244 gr.	42 gr.	3.00 in.	1.99 in.	.323 in.	.554 in.	8mm M1893 8 x 50mm R	Austrian M90 rifles and carbines, M07/12 MG, M95 rifles and carbines.
8mm M31 Rimmed Bottlenecked	441 gr.	208 gr.	55 gr.	3.02 in.	2.21 in.	.330 in.	.55 in.	8mm M30S 8 x 56mm R	Hungarian M35 rifle and M31 MG. Austrian M30 MG, rebarrelled M95 Mannlichers.
8mm Lebel Rimmed Bottlenecked	429 gr.	198 gr.	43 gr.	2.95 in.	1.98 in.	.328 in.	.629 in.	8mm M1886 D(AM)	French M86M93, M1890, M92, M07, M07/15, M16, M17, M18 rifles and carbines. M14 and M15 MG's.
Cal. .30 Carbine Rimless Straight	195 gr.	110 gr.	14.5 gr.	1.67 in.	1.28 in.	.308 in.	.356 in.	Cal. .30 M1 Carbine	U.S. M1 and M2 carbines.
Cal. .30-06 Rimless Bottlenecked	396 gr.	150 gr.	50 gr.	3.33 in.	2.49 in.	.308 in.	.469 in.	Cal. .30 M2 Ball Cal. .300 Browning 7.62 x 63mm	U. S. M03, 03A1, 03A2, 03A3, 03A4 Springfield rifles, M17, M1, M1C, M1D rifles. Browning automatic rifle M18, M18A1, 18A2. Browning M17, 17A1, 19A4, 19A5, 19A6, M37 MG's.
Cal. .303 Rimmed Bottlenecked	384 gr.	174 gr.	37.5 gr.	3.04 in.	2.21 in.	.311 in.	.53 in.	.303 in. Mark 7 .303 British	British No. 1, MK's 1, 2, 3, 3*, 4, 5, 6, No 3, MK 1, 1*, No 4 MK 1, 1*, 2, No 5 MK 1, 1* rifles. Lewis MG, Hotchkiss MG, Bren MK's 1, 2, 3, and 4 MG's. Vickers MK 1 MG. Canadian Ross M05 and M10 rifles.

HEAVY MACHINE GUN CARTRIDGES

Cartridge and Case Type	Complete Round Weight	Bullet Weight	Propellant Weight	Complete Round Length	Case Length	Bullet Diameter	Case Diameter	Some Common Synonyms	Best Known Weapons in Which Used
Cal. .50 Rimless Bottlenecked	1800 gr.	709 gr.	240 gr.	5.45 in.	3.90 in.	.511 in.	.804 in.	Cal. .50 Ball M2 Cal. .50 Browning	U. S. M2, M2HB, M3 MGs.
12.7mm Soviet Rimless Bottlenecked	2160 gr.	788 gr.	271 gr.	5.76 in.	4.25 in.	.511 in.	.85 in.	12.7mm	Soviet DShK M38, DShK M38/46 and UB MG's.
13.2mm Rimless Bottlenecked	1836 gr.	805 gr.	232 gr.	5.35 in.	3.90 in.	.531 in.	.897 in.	13.2mm Hotchkiss 13.2mm Type 93	French M30 MG. Jap Type 93 MG.
14.5mm Rimless Bottlenecked	3089 gr.	979 gr.	.445 gr.	6.130 in.	4.48 in.	.585 in.	1.06 in.	14.5mm B-32	Soviet ZPU MG's.

Index

D

E

F

G

N

O

P